Physiology of the eye

Physiology
of
the eye

CLINICAL APPLICATION

Francis Heed Adler, M.A., M.D., F.A.C.S.

*William F. Norris and George E. de Schweinitz
Emeritus Professor of Ophthalmology,
University of Pennsylvania School of Medicine,
Philadelphia, Pa.; Consulting Surgeon,
Wills Eye Hospital, Philadelphia, Pa.*

With 437 illustrations, including 2 in color

Fourth edition

The C. V. Mosby Company
Saint Louis   1965

PREFACE TO FOURTH EDITION

This edition conforms to the general purpose of the previous three editions in that it strives to describe in simple terms the way the eye functions. Sometimes this can be done only at the expense of oversimplification, and I plead guilty to this in some places. However, since the book is intended primarily for students, I feel this is entirely justified.

Physiology is an ever-changing science. As soon as one question is answered, another is automatically posed. The farther we go down the road, the more side paths there are to explore. New editions are necessary to describe these untried and therefore beguiling vistas for research. One never reaches the end of the road. This is the discipline of physiology which makes it exciting. We must continually keep asking the questions How? and Why?

It would be impossible to list in this preface all the changes made in this edition. However, several chapters have been rewritten in order to organize the material better, and many new illustrations have been added.

Francis Heed Adler

PREFACE TO FIRST EDITION

Since the publication of the *Clinical Physiology of the Eye* twenty years ago the knowledge of this subject has so increased that an entirely new book, rather than a revision, is demanded. This is clearly indicated by the progress made in subjects such as the dynamics of aqueous humor formation, the photochemistry of the retina, and the application of electrophysiologic technics to retinal function. From the point of view of basic physiology the material to be covered requires fresh treatment.

The application of physiology to the study of disease has been richly rewarded in many fields of medicine and surgery. The time has come when knowledge of the function of the various parts of the eye can be likewise applied to ocular disorders. The ophthalmologist should know how the various portions of the eye normally function before he can adequately treat their diseases. The treatment of glaucoma, to be rational, should be based on an understanding of the formation and elimination of the aqueous humor, the permeability characteristics of the cornea, and the hemodynamics of the ocular circulation. The medical and surgical approach to strabismus should be through a comprehension of the neuromuscular mechanisms which normally maintain the two eyes in alignment.

A book is needed, therefore, which offers to the student and the practicing ophthalmologist the recent findings of the physiology of the eye gleaned from the experimental laboratory, and which applies these facts clinically. Such an undertaking has many pitfalls and obstacles. Many parts of ocular physiology are still unexplored, many are still controversial, and some facts have been determined in lower animals that have not yet been confirmed in the human subject. In many phases of ocular physiology the application to disease is still remote, and it will be some time before this knowledge can be applied to therapy.

For a comprehensive knowledge of each

9

of the basic subjects the original literature should be consulted. The bibliog-
raphy given at the end of each chapter
contains those books and papers which I
have found helpful; this list is by no
means complete. Wherever possible the
material has been correlated with clinical
experience. It is hoped that the reader
will discover other correlations, and may
be encouraged to make his own investigations in what are still fertile fields for research.

It would have been impossible for me
to have written the chapters on the aqueous humor, the lens, and portions of the
chapter on the cornea without the help
of Dr. V. Everett Kinsey, who has con-

tributed much to our present knowledge
of these fields. I spent many pleasant
weekends in Boston utilizing his time and
energy in an endeavor to portray correctly
the dynamics of the aqueous humor as
he conceives it.

The skill and ingenuity of my artist,
Miss Marie Wilson, have been of in-
estimable value in the preparation of the
illustrations, which I consider to be of
equal value with the text in any book.
There are others, too numerous to mention, whose advice and suggestions I have
followed with advantage. My particular
thanks go to all those authors whose published articles and illustrations have been
used.

Francis Heed Adler
Philadelphia

CONTENTS

FIGURES IN COLOR

Physiology of the eye

CHAPTER 1

THE EYELIDS

FUNCTION OF THE EYELIDS

The eyelids protect the eye from the entrance of foreign particles. Voluntary winking and reflex blinking aid in removing dust and foreign matter which may have gotten in while the eyes were open. The reflex blink also distributes a film of tears over the cornea, keeping it moist and maintaining an almost perfect optical surface. The closing of the lids also aids in the propulsion of tears in the direction of the lacrimal puncta and in the siphoning of the tears into the lacrimal sac. Relaxation of the tonus of the levator palpebrae muscle coupled with an increase of tonus in the orbicularis muscle keep the lids closed during sleep, thereby eliminating visual stimuli and constituting one of the most important factors in the sleep process.

The skin of the lids is the thinnest in the body and folds easily, permitting very rapid opening and closing of the palpebral fissures. The tarsal plates, held firmly by the medial and lateral palpebral ligaments and orbital septum, give support to the lids and offer some protection from trauma.

During a large part of embryonic life the eyeballs are exposed to the amniotic fluid since the lids do not grow out to meet each other until the third month of fetal life. During the period when the eyeballs are exposed to the amniotic fluid, the cornea is very thin since the mesodermal layers do not form until the third month of fetal life. Hence, both the cornea and lens are exposed to noxious influences circulating in the amniotic fluid during the first two months, which may account for some of the congenital anomalies of these structures. Once the lids have grown to meet each other, at the 37 mm. (8 weeks) stage, they fuse and do not separate again in man until the seventh month. In human beings, therefore, the lids are open at birth, whereas in most other mammals the lids do not separate until several weeks after birth.

During the act of blinking the lids come into apposition, but the closure can be made much more complete and tighter by the additional action of the muscles of the brow and face. In fact, the orbital opening can be closed and kept shut in such an effective manner that considerable force is required to open a patient's eyelids if he makes a determined effort to keep them shut.

THE CILIA

The cilia are hairs situated on the margins of the lids. There are about 100 to 150 cilia in the upper lid and half that number in the lower lid. In the upper lid the cilia are curved outward and upward. Those in the lower lid are curved outward and downward. Each cilium is a short stout cylindrical hair with a typical hair follicle at its base from which it grows. Each follicle is surrounded by a nerve plexus which has a very low threshold of excitation and fires off at the slightest deformation of the cilium. The cilia are, therefore, extremely sensitive hairs. A particle of dust touching a cilium is sufficient to excite the nerve plexus of the follicle and produce a reflex blink. The base of each cilium is surrounded by sebaceous glands opening into the follicle by short, wide ducts. Infection of these glands results in the common stye or hordeolum. Excessive and altered secretion of the glands produces various types of marginal blepharitis. Since the cilia are hairs, it is not surprising that they should be involved in the same disease processes which affect the hairs of the scalp, of which dandruff is the most frequent.

The cilia are normally deeply pigmented throughout adult life, but occasionally turn gray or white with advancing age, and in some disease conditions the newly formed lashes fail to become pigmented and stay white. This is known as poliosis. The average life of the cilia is three to five months, after which they fall out and new ones grow in to take their place. If a cilium is pulled out, the new one replacing it reaches full growth in about two months. If the cilia are cut, as is often done in operations on the eye, full growth usually occurs in two weeks.

In spite of their small size and seeming fragility, cilia have a way of penetrating structures which would almost seem impossible. It is not infrequent that a cilium will find its way into a punctum, upper or lower, and the protruding end will scratch the cornea, causing considerable pain. When patients complain of a foreign body in the eye and none is found, it is always wise to look for such cilia. They may easily be missed. Occasionally, a cilium becomes twisted and turned back toward the skin of the lid, which it then punctures, and grows into the skin. Cilia have often been reported in the anterior chamber following penetrating injuries.

THE EYEBROWS

The eyebrows protect the eyeballs from perspiration dripping into the eyes from the forehead. The eyebrows are moved by the frontalis muscle, which elevates them, and by the orbicularis muscle, which depresses them by closing the lids. The eyebrows are drawn together in the act of frowning by the corregator supercilii. The eyebrows are not moved in the ordinary act of blinking. The eyebrows can be voluntarily elevated without the eyeballs turning upward, but every forced upward gaze carries with it an elevation of the eyebrows. During the act of frowning the fissures are necessarily made narrower, and if this is carried to the extreme, a stenopeic slit is created, which may considerably improve visual acuity if a refractive error uncorrected by glasses is present. Hence, some people who have errors of refraction, especially astigmatism or myopia, continually frown when they do not wear glasses. This constant effort creates a pull on the galea aponeurotica and may cause headache. In young children the constant formation of a stenopeic slit leads to permanent narrowing of the fissures, a condition so often seen in adults with astigmatism.

In facial paralysis the eyebrow on the

paralyzed side is lower than that on the normal side, and in unilateral ptosis the eyebrow is frequently elevated due to the constant effort to keep the lid raised.

THE PALPEBRAL FISSURES

The palpebral opening or fissure is usually about 25 mm. long in adults. When the eyelids are open, the fissure at its widest part should measure 12 to 15 mm. The edge of the upper lid normally just covers the upper limbus from 10 to 2 o'clock, and the edge of the lower lid should come just above the lower limbus from 5 to 7 o'clock. The width of the fissure and the relative position of the lid margins to the limbus is important. If either the upper or the lower limbus is completely exposed, the fissures are wider than normal. When this is bilateral, it may have little significance. The eyeballs may be more prominent than usual, but equally so. Whenever the fissures are of unequal width, the condition is generally pathologic. The position of the globe in the orbit determines the width of the fissures to a large degree; the more prominent globe naturally leads to a wider fissure. Hence anything which causes one globe to protrude will lead to a wider fissure on that side. Similarly, if one globe is abnormally recessed in the orbit, the fissure on that side will be narrower. The globes are likely to be prominent if a high degree of myopia is present, so that the fissures are widened, whereas the small globe of the hyperope leads to narrower fissures. The shape and width of the fissure are racial characteristics, e.g., the almond or slit-shaped narrow fissure of the Mongolian race compared to the average width in the Caucasian race and the wide, round shape of the Negroid races (see p. 20 for a discussion of the differences in the upper skin fold). The psychic state changes the width of the fissures, e.g., the wide-open

eyes present during surprise and fright. The intensity of light striking the eyes and the presence of refractive errors, as just stated, also determine the width of the fissures. In children the fissures are not as long, but are relatively wider, and in infants the fissures may be nearly circular.

The width of the fissures also depends on the combined tonus of the muscles which lift the eyelids, i.e., the levator palpebrae and the smooth muscle and the orbicularis muscle which closes them. When a person is fatigued, the smooth muscle supplied by the sympathetics which elevate the lid loses its tonus, and the fissures become narrower. At this stage the levator palpebrae, supplied by the third cranial nerve, still retains full power to open the fissure at will, but the lids feel heavy since these muscles have to be activated by a willed effort. This causes the annoying sensation which one experiences in trying to stay awake that the upper lid is constantly dropping down. People remark that they are so tired that they can hardly keep their eyes open (see p. 26 for a discussion of the eyelids during sleep).

Under abnormal conditions the tonus of either the elevator muscles or the orbicularis muscle may be either too great or too weak. If the elevator muscles have excessive tonus or the orbicularis muscle has too little tonus, the fissure on that side will be wider than normal. Conversely, if the elevator muscles have insufficient tonus or the orbicularis muscle has excessive tonus, the fissure will be narrower.

By far the greater part of the apparent exophthalmos present in thyrotoxicosis is due to widening of the palpebral fissures caused by retraction of the upper eyelids and not to true exophthalmos.

The distribution curves of exophthalmometer measurements in normal persons and in a group of patients of the same age with diffuse toxic goiter are not too dissimilar. Normal persons measure from 12 to 21 mm., with a mean at 16 mm. Those with toxic goiter measure from 12 to 24 mm., with a mean at 18 mm. It is true that only 5% of normal persons have measurements greater than 19 mm., whereas the measurements in 32% of patients with toxic goiter are greater than this. But when one considers the fact that patients with diffuse toxic goiter are those in whom the greatest degree of exophthalmos is supposed to occur, it seems strikingly small by comparison with normal persons. Clinicians have been led to overestimate the degree of exophthalmos in these patients by virtue of the widened palpebral fissures, which gives them the appearance of marked exophthalmos when it does not really exist. The amount of exophthalmos should be determined only by measurements and should not be guessed at by the width of the palpebral fissure.

Widening of the palpebral fissure, known as Dalrymple's sign, is due to either excessive tonus of the sympathetically innervated Müller's muscle or excessive tonus of the levator palpebrae. Although most of the evidence supports the former, many still maintain that Müller's muscle is not concerned since there are no simultaneous pupillary signs of increased sympathetic tonus. It has been pointed out that not only the upper lid is retracted in thyrotoxicosis, but also the lower lid, so that both the upper and lower limbi are exposed. This would weigh heavily in favor of the sympathetically innervated Müller's muscle being primarily concerned. Von Graefe's sign—inability of the upper lid to follow the movement of the globe in downward gaze—is due to widening of the fissure or retraction of the eyelid. When marked

signs of thyrotoxicosis are present, the widening of the palpebral fissure and slowness of the eyelid to close cause the characteristic appearance of the patient— an expression of apprehension or fright. The eyes appear to be exophthalmic, and they *are* in the majority of patients, but not to the degree that they appear.

Unilateral retraction of the eyelid, or tucked lid as it has been called by Collier, can be caused by increased tonus of the levator and is a mark of an irritative lesion in the region of the superior colliculi. When a lesion is lower down in the brain stem, close to the third cranial nerve nuclei, ptosis instead of tucked lids is generally found.

Changes in position of the margins of the eyelids in respect to their apposition to the globe are important. Normally the margin of the eyelid remains fixed in apposition to the globe as the eyes move in various directions or the lids open and close. This is due to a combination of factors which when disturbed cause the eyelids to lose contact with the globe and to turn either in toward the globe, entropion, or out away from the globe, ectropion. The eyelids owe their form chiefly to the tarsal plates. If the form, position, or consistency of the tarsal plates is changed, this will have an influence on the form of the eyelids and, hence, on the position of the margin of the eyelid with respect to the globe. The lower lid, in which the tarsal plate is less developed than in the upper lid, is more easily disturbed from its position than the upper lid. The convex form of the tarsal plate is maintained by the pressure of the globe against the eyelids, which are held in place by the external and internal canthal ligaments (Fig. 1). If the globe shrinks or is taken out of the orbit or if there is a loss of the orbital contents so that the globe cannot exert its pressure against the eyelids, then,

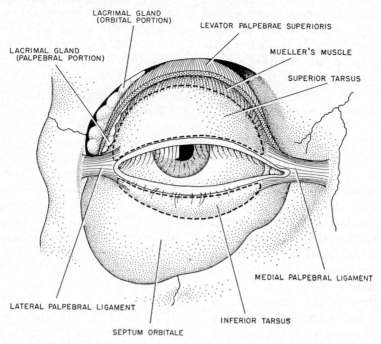

LACRIMAL GLAND
(ORBITAL PORTION)

LEVATOR PALPEBRAE SUPERIORIS

LACRIMAL GLAND
(PALPEBRAL PORTION)

MUELLER'S MUSCLE

SUPERIOR TARSUS

MEDIAL PALPEBRAL LIGAMENT

LATERAL PALPEBRAL LIGAMENT

INFERIOR TARSUS

SEPTUM ORBITALE

Fig. 1. Dissection of orbit from in front. Orbital septum has been removed. *Broken line,* extent of superior and inferior tarsi. Note that the entire front of the orbit is closed in by firm, resistant tissues except for the palpebral fissure, and this can be completely closed by the lid and accessory muscles. The palpebral ligaments reinforce this diaphragm. (Modified after Wolff.)

when the orbicularis muscle contracts to close the eyelids, it will exert too great a pull, and the margin of the lower lid will be carried backward. That part of the orbicularis muscle which is at the margin of the lower lid is called the muscle of Riolan and has a special influence on the position of the lower lid. The fibers which form the muscle of Riolan form an anatomic and functionally independent group of muscles. When the tonus of the orbicularis muscle is increased, as in inflammatory conditions of the eye accompanied by photophobia, this muscle may contract in such a forcible manner as to turn the margin of the lower lid in against the globe. This is called spastic entropion.

In addition to the spasm of this muscle, certain other conditions favor turning in of the margin of the eyelid. Spastic entropion very seldom occurs in young persons in spite of long-continued blepharospasm. Contraction of the orbicularis muscle produces a force which tends to narrow the palpebral fissure and to press the eyelid back against the globe. This latter force can produce inturning of the margin of the eyelid only if the free margin does not meet with its customary opposing force from the globe itself. Spastic entropion is favored, therefore, when the forces which keep the tarsus in its natural position are diminished, i.e., when the tarsus itself is small or poorly developed, when the supporting structures are thin or atrophic, or when the skin of the lid is very soft and easily put out of position. Hence, spastic entropion generally occurs in old people with hypertrophied thin wrinkled skin whenever there is chronic inflammation of the eyes or eyelids which produces blepharospasm. Scars in the skin may also cause a form of entropion, called cicatricial entropion. This is especially likely to happen if the tarsal plate has been injured.

Ectropion, or outward turning of the margin of the eyelid, occurs under a number of conditions, chiefly when there is paralysis of the orbicularis muscle. The tonus of this muscle being lax, the lid is no longer held in tight apposition to the globe, but falls away from it by gravity. Since the tears now spill over the margin of the lid onto the skin, chronic inflammation which causes shortening of the skin of the lid is set up. As a result, the lid is further turned outward, exposure of the conjunctiva added to the effects of drying leads to its thickening, and a vicious circle which tends to roll the eyelid further away from the globe is established. In many old people the relaxation of the skin of the lid, without any actual paralysis of the orbicularis muscle, may be sufficient to start this vicious circle and lead to marked and serious ectropion.

NORMAL MOVEMENTS OF THE EYELIDS
Elevation

When the eyelids are opened, the upper lid is raised against gravity approximately 10 mm. and is drawn back under the orbital rim at the fold of the lid. This action takes place by contraction of the levator palpebrae supplied by the third cranial nerve. The retraction of the lid under the orbital rim at the fold of the eyelid is caused by the insertion of part of the levator tendon into a broad area of the skin, from the free edge of the lid to the top of the tarsal plate (Fig. 2). Some of the fibers of the levator tendon insert into the top of the tarsal plate, but some pass in front of the tarsus to insert into the skin itself. In their passage these tendinous fibers run through the bundles of fibers of the orbicularis muscle.

The fold of the eyelid is formed by this retraction of the skin. This gets rid of the excess skin of the upper lid when the eyelid is raised and allows the palpebral fissure to open wide. In Oriental persons this fold is absent due, according to Sayoc,[1] to the fact that the terminal fibers of the levator palpebrae do not run forward to the skin, but insert only on the upper border of the tarsal plate.

In addition to the action of the levator, the upper lid is elevated by smooth muscle fibers which arise from the under surface of the levator and insert in the upper margin of the tarsus. These fibers are supplied by the sympathetic nerve and are called Müller's muscle of the eyelid. Because of the fascial expansions between the levator and the superior rectus muscles, Müller's muscle effects a pull between the tarsus and the point of insertion of the superior rectus. Hence, it produces both retraction of the eyelid and proptosis. The inferior palpebral muscle of Müller arises from a fascial expansion and breaks into two parts, one inserting in the conjunctiva of the lower fornix and the other entering the lower lid to insert in the tarsal plate. Contraction of these fibers exerts a direct pull between the tarsus and the under surface of the globe. This will produce depression of the lower lid and proptosis.

Another smooth muscle in the eyelids has been described by Landstrom. It consists of a number of unstriped fibers surrounding the front part of the globe, extending from the back of the orbital septum anteriorly to the equator of the globe. Here it is connected to fascial expansions derived from the ocular muscles near their points of attachment on the globe.

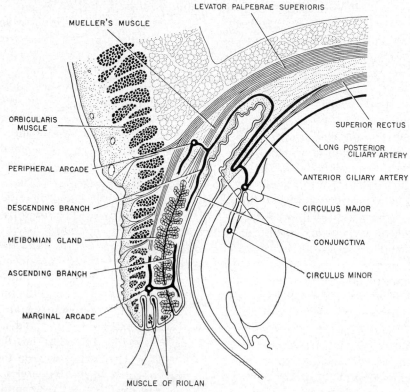

MUELLER'S MUSCLE

LEVATOR PALPEBRAE SUPERIORIS

ORBICULARIS MUSCLE

PERIPHERAL ARCADE

DESCENDING BRANCH

MEIBOMIAN GLAND

ASCENDING BRANCH

MARGINAL ARCADE

SUPERIOR RECTUS

LONG POSTERIOR CILIARY ARTERY

ANTERIOR CILIARY ARTERY

CIRCULUS MAJOR

CONJUNCTIVA

CIRCULUS MINOR

MUSCLE OF RIOLAN

Fig. 2. Section of the upper lid and anterior portion of the eye, showing fibers of the levator tendon passing between bundles of the orbicularis muscle to insert in the skin of the lids. (Modified after Wolff.)

This muscle is also supplied by the sympathetic nerve.

The combination of Müller and Landstrom's muscles effects a forward pull on the eye and according to some authors is capable of producing small degrees of exophthalmos, provided that there is coincidentally impairment of tonus of the rectus muscles.

The levator muscle is the chief muscle producing elevation of the upper lid, and its activity is always associated with contraction of the superior rectus to which it is attached by fascial bands. In extreme upward gaze the frontalis muscle aids the levator in further elevating the lid. When the gaze is directed upward, the lid follows the upward movement of the globe. This is a purposeful movement since, obviously, if the lid did not elevate when the globe turned up, the line of sight would be covered by the upper lid. The association of the levator and superior rectus muscles is due to the fact that both muscles are innervated by the same nerve, and both are differentiated from the same muscle mass in embryonic life. Further, the two muscles are connected by a common fascial sheath. These facts account for the frequent association of congenital ptosis and paralysis of the superior rectus.

Although the upper lid follows the globe on upward gaze during voluntary movements of the eyes, in the reflex act of blinking the globe moves in the opposite direction and turns upward as the eyelids close and downward as they open again. The upward movement of the globe during the act of blinking is not so marked as when the globe follows the upward movement of the eyelids in voluntary upward gaze. This probably is due to the short time allowed for the movement since the ordinary blink lasts less than one-half second. During this interval the visual line moves upward approximately 15 degrees from the horizontal.

The synergism between the superior rectus, frontalis, and levator is employed in operations for the relief of ptosis. In operations on the superior rectus, the fascial connections of this muscle with the levator must be kept in mind since a change in position of the insertion of the superior rectus alters the position of the upper lid. If the superior rectus is recessed to a position further back on the globe, the levator will be stretched so that the upper lid will be raised and the fissure will be widened. On the other hand, if the superior rectus is advanced or resected, the levator will be pulled forward and the eyelid will droop, creating ptosis.

When the levator is paralyzed, it might be supposed that the eyelid would be kept from drooping by the action of the smooth muscle innervated by the sympathetic nerve. This does not occur, however, due to the fact that the fibers of Müller's muscle take their origin from the under surface of the levator. When the latter is paralyzed, the smooth muscle fibers have no firm origin from which to pull, and their contraction becomes ineffective. The ptosis is, therefore, usually complete. If the sympathetic nerve is paralyzed, only a slight droop of the lid results. This is commonly seen in trachoma and is due to the action of toxins on the smooth muscle fibers which lie directly under the diseased conjunctiva in the upper retrotarsal fold.

Closure

Not only does the upper lid follow the upward movement of the eyeball, but it also follows the globe on downward movements. This is not due solely to gravity since it occurs when a person is placed on a tilted table with the head low.[2]

It has been suggested that the downward movement is caused by partial contraction of the orbicularis muscle or depression of sympathetic innervation to Müller's muscle. It has also been suggested that the third cranial nerve transmits fibers from the seventh cranial nerve.[3] The most likely explanation is relaxation of tonus in the levator muscle on the basis of reciprocal innervation. It does not seem likely that the orbicularis would be activated in downward gaze, and it has been clearly shown by Walsh[4] that downward movement of the upper lid occurs in patients with complete paralysis of the orbicularis muscle. As yet, however, no electromyographic studies have come to my attention which would prove this point.

The eyelids are closed by the action of the orbicularis oculi, supplied by the seventh cranial or facial nerve. Some evidence suggests that it may receive innervation also from the third cranial nerve,[2] but this concept is not generally accepted. There are two main portions of the orbicularis muscle—the palpebral and the orbital portions. The former is the main part of the muscle and is used in the acts of blinking and voluntary winking. When the eyelids are forced shut, such as occurs in blepharospasm, the orbital portion of the muscle is brought into play along with the muscles of the eyebrow. The two portions of the orbicularis are differentiated physiologically by their chronaxie.* The chronaxie of the palpebral portion is about half that of the orbital portion; this agrees well with the general rule that muscles designed for rapid movement have a lower chronaxie than those of slower but more forcible action.

Three distinct types of closure of the eyelid are affected by different combinations of fiber bundles of the orbicularis, working together with the muscles which control the eyebrows. These are blinking, voluntary winking, and blepharospasm.

Blinking. There are two types of blinking: (1) blinking of reflex origin and (2) spontaneous blinking, probably of central origin.

Reflex blinking. Many different stimuli cause reflex blinking. Strong lights, the sudden approach of an object toward the eyes, loud noises, and many other stimuli call forth rapid reflex closure of both eyes. It is possible, therefore, to divide reflex blinking into at least three different subtypes, depending upon the nature of the stimulus. The corneal reflex is an example of a tactile stimulus. Any object touching the unanesthetized cornea will produce a reflex blink. The dazzle reflex is produced by shining a bright light into the eye. Incidentally, this frequently calls forth a fit of sneezing in many persons, as an additional reflex. It is not uncommon for patients to complain that they always sneeze when they first go out of doors into bright sunlight, and I have occasionally seen patients who sneezed every time an ophthalmoscopic light was turned on the eye. The so-called menace reflex is produced by an unexpected or threatening

object coming suddenly into the near field of vision.

In the corneal reflex, the afferent pathway is the fifth cranial nerve and the efferent pathway the seventh cranial nerve. There is supposed to be a subcortical center, and the reflex persists in the thalamic animal. In man, the reflex has connections with the cortex, as is shown by the pain felt on touching the cornea and the strong spasm of the eyelids which occurs when such pain is produced. In man, this may be lost if there is a cortical lesion in the Rolandic area. The reflex is characteristically lost or impaired on the side of a tumor of the cerebellopontile angle. It is a diagnostic sign of great importance. The corneal reflex is lost before the other branches of the fifth nerve are affected.

In the other two reflex types of blinking, the afferent pathway is the optic nerve. The dazzle reflex appears to be subcortical, with the superior colliculi as the center and the efferent path by way of the association fibers to the facial nucleus. It may be lost in certain mesencephalic lesions which give no other external signs. The menace reflex is cortical and requires the presence not only of the occipital lobe, but also of its connections with the Rolandic area. This reflex may be lost when the corneal and dazzle reflexes persist.

Spontaneous blinking. This is the common form of blinking which occurs in a normal human being at frequent intervals during the waking hours and without any obvious stimuli, such as I have just described for the reflex blink. Each person seems to have his own individual rate of blinking which is maintained as long as the external environment is not changed. The rate may be altered by changes in the surroundings or in the mental state of the subject; if there is

---

*Chronaxie is the duration of time that a current of twice the rheobasic (galvanic threshold) intensity must flow in order to excite a tissue being tested. Chronaxie is related to irritability and is used as a measure of changes in irritability of a nerve or muscle.

any cause for excitement, the rate is usually increased considerably.

Spontaneous blinking does not occur during the first few months of life, and yet the delicate infantile cornea does not suffer from dryness. Although blinking occurs in all vertebrates possessing eyelids and living in air, its exact purpose is not understood. Its rate varies considerably in the animal kingdom. The lion blinks at a rate of less than one a minute, whereas some species of monkeys have a rate of forty-five blinks per minute. It has been suggested that the purpose of blinking was to distribute the tears over the cornea, and undoubtedly this does occur as a result of the movements of the eyelids, but, as pointed out, infants do not blink and yet show no lack of moisture of the entire cornea. Further, keeping a person in moist or dry air does not change the rate. The rate continues in persons who are blind so that retinal stimulation cannot be the cause. It has also been suggested that blinking provides rest for the ocular muscles, in that blinking allows a momentary upturning of the eyes, which is regarded as a position of rest. This is analogous to the position of the eyes during sleep. The act has also been regarded as a conditioned reflex[5] due to the frequently repeated association of indifferent sensory stimuli.

Motion pictures of blinking show that the lower lid remains almost stationary during the act. The upper lid begins to close as a shade would drop. The movement is completed by a narrowing of the palpebral fissures in a zipperlike action from the lateral canthus toward the medial canthus. This aids the displacement of the tear film toward the lacrimal puncta.[6] The duration of a full blink is approximately 0.3 to 0.4 second. The average period between blinks is about 2.8 seconds in men and just under 4 seconds in women. During the period of blinking vision must be in abeyance; therefore, if blinking is repeated frequently enough, it might have some practical bearing on occupations in which constant perception is a necessity, such as piloting a high-speed airplane. The percentage of time during which vision must be held in abeyance due to blinking has been called the blackout index. This is obtained by using the following formula:

$$\frac{\text{Duration of each blink}}{\text{Interblink period}} \times 100$$

Therefore, for the average person

$$\frac{0.3 \text{ sec.}}{2.8 \text{ sec.}} \times 100 = 10.7\%$$

A person with a very rapid rate of blinking might have a blackout index three times that; therefore, one third of the time he would not have visual perception. In supersonic speeds the result could, of course, be disastrous. An airplane traveling at 1000 mph covers 1466 feet every second. If a person loses 11% of 1 second by blinking, the plane will have traveled 133 feet during the blackout. The recent announcement by the army of a jet fighter plane with a speed of 2000 mph indicates that this factor may become serious.

By means of electromyographic studies it has been shown[7] that there are three main functional groups of motor units in the orbicularis oculi: (1) those responding in blinking and in the corneal reflex, (2) those responding in blinking and in sustained activity, and (3) those responding only in sustained activity. There is considerable anatomic overlap between the distributions of these three groups of motor units. Those in the first group lie mainly in the pretarsal region; those in the second group lie mainly in the preseptal region; whereas those in the third group extend from the preseptal region to the orbital region. During blinking, the units in the first group discharge brief bursts of impulses at very high impulse frequency—up to 182 per second in a single unit. This is of the order of the highest frequencies of discharge observed by Reid[8] in the extraocular muscle motor neurons of the cat under reflex drive. The extraocular muscles have a very brief contraction time (p. 402), and this may be true also of the white-fibered portions of the orbicularis, which are mainly in the pretarsal portion. This extremely rapid movement is capable of intermittence at very high frequencies since voluntary blinking in man has been recorded at a maximum frequency of 390 per minute. The maintenance of the narrowed position after a blink depends on the activity of units in other parts of the muscle and upon reciprocal innervation, i.e., relaxation of the levator. The first change to occur in a blink is partial relaxation of the levator, rather than contraction of the pretarsal part of the orbicularis. The preliminary partial relaxation of an antagonist is not a recognized feature of muscular contractions generally, but it may have significance in this unusual movement in that it allows the orbicularis to contract from the start against reduced resistance, and this would tend to shorten the time during which vision would be disturbed. (This same feature was hypothecated for the downward movement of the upper lid during downward gaze, p. 22.)

Voluntary winking. Voluntary winking is a voluntary contraction of the palpebral and orbital portions of the orbicularis muscle simultaneously. A wink is a forced closure of one eye. Many persons cannot wink until they are taught, and occasionally some never learn to close one eye at a time. Occasionally, a subject may learn to wink with one eye but not with the other. It has been noted that more people have difficulty in voluntarily winking with the right eye than with the left, and this has been attributed to the predominance of right-handedness, the theory being that there is greater development of the uncrossed fibers in the path of the facial nerve from the cortical centers to the subcortical centers on the left side in right-handed persons.[9] The act can be repeated at frequent intervals, but even at a maximum rate there must be a minimum period between winks of about 0.3 second.

Blepharospasm. Voluntarily squeezing the eyelids together entails contraction of both portions of the orbicularis as well as of the muscles of the brow. Since this invariably raises the intraocular pressure, it is dangerous to have a patient squeeze the eyelids shut during any surgical procedure in which the globe is opened, such as in a cataract extraction. Even the best devised speculum inserted during the operation to keep the eyelids apart will not prevent the pressure of squeezing the eyelids from being transmitted to the globe, thereby possibly forcibly expelling the vitreous. For this reason, during cataract surgery the branches of the seventh cranial nerve supplying the orbicularis muscle are usually temporarily paralyzed by injections of procaine. If the branches of the nerve are injected as they course into the eyelids, edema of the eyelids must occur to some extent from the injected fluid, and in order that this be eliminated, the nerve trunk may be injected instead. The trunk of the temporal, malar, and infraorbital branches is found by following the zygoma to a point just in front of and slightly below the external auditory meatus, where the procaine should be injected.

Blepharospasm is a frequent accompaniment of inflammatory diseases of the anterior segment of the globe and makes examination of the eye difficult. Many patients find it extremely hard to keep both eyes open when one is being examined, particularly if that eye is light sensitive, as most inflamed eyes are, and they invariably keep the other eye closed. The result is that both eyes turn upward (Bell's phenomenon, p. 27), making examination impossible. The patient should be told to keep the eye not being examined open at all times and if possible to fix his attention on some object in the room with this eye. When a patient is afforded a definite fixation point, he will find it easier to keep the unexamined eye open than if he just looks off into space.

Fibrillary twitching of the eyelids is a common complaint of some persons. The condition is transitory, but may be most annoying. Its reason is unknown, but it does not seem to be due to refractive errors or any pathologic condition in the eyes. When marked, it is called myokymia of the eyelids. The focus of irritation is thought to be in the nerve fibers of the orbicularis muscle.[10] Since quinine causes depression of the response of the motor end plates and ganglion cells both to nerve impulses and to acetylcholine liberated from the preganglionic nerve endings, the administration of small doses of quinine has been suggested in the treatment of this condition.

THE EYELIDS DURING SLEEP

During sleep closure of the eyelids is not a simple relaxation of the muscles which keeps the eyes open, but a tonic stimulation of the orbicularis, together with an inhibition of the levator—the converse of what occurs during the waking hours. With closure of the eyelids at the onset of sleep, the receptors for the dazzle and menace blinking reflexes cease to act, but the corneal reflex is not eliminated until the deeper stages of sleep have been reached. During deep sleep this reflex also disappears.

Closure of the eyelids which accompanies the onset of sleep is an inherited automatic act which takes place when cortical inhibition reaches a certain degree. It serves the purpose of protecting the eye from injury and allowing the ocular muscles to rest. Voluntary closure of the eyelids in preparation for sleep has been called the ritual of going to sleep. When sleep is desired under difficult circumstances, such as trying to sleep in the daytime, shutting the eyes is one of the few available acts of this ritual. It is not always successful in its purpose, but at least it does eliminate visual stimuli which would otherwise prevent or at least delay the onset of unconsciousness (for a fuller discussion of the position of the eyeballs during sleep, see p. 496).

CENTERS AND PATHWAYS FOR MOVEMENTS OF THE EYELIDS

In the frontal cortex close to the oculogyric centers is an area where stimulation produces raising of one eyelid or both, this movement being greater generally on the side opposite to that stimulated. Stimulation of the region of the motor cortex close to the representation for the thumb results in closure of the eyelid, usually bilaterally, but greater on the side opposite the stimulation (Fig. 3). In monkeys, lesions of this general region result in inability to close the eyes. The fact that closure of the eyes is not obtained from the same portion of the cortex which elicits movements of the eyeballs, but from that portion which causes movements of the face, is understandable when it is recalled that the extrinsic eye muscles are supplied by the third, fourth, and sixth cranial nerves, whereas the orbicularis muscle is supplied by the seventh cranial

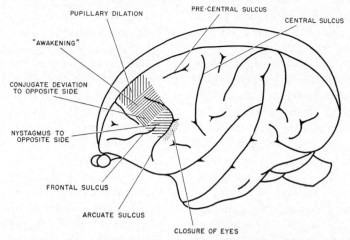

Fig. 3. Indicated subdivisions of the frontal eye field and the area yielding closure of the eyes in the monkey *(Macaca mulatta)*. (According to W. K. Smith.)

nerve, which also supplies the muscles of the face.

The pathway from the frontal cortex to the nuclei which control movements of the eyelids in the brainstem is not known. Lesions in the region of the colliculi frequently produce an association of paralysis of upward gaze and changes in motility of the eyelids—either ptosis or tucked lids. On the other hand, the paths for conjugate lateral or vertical movements of the eyes and those for the eyelids must be separate since lesions in the pons or tectum may abolish separately movements of either the eyelids or eyes. In the lower animals, when they have been conditioned after removal of the occipital lobes, centers may continue to function in response to visual stimuli. This has been demonstrated in dogs[11] and in monkeys.[12]

ASSOCIATED MOVEMENTS OF THE EYELIDS

Associated movements of the upper lid and the superior rectus muscle have been mentioned previously. Whenever the gaze is directed upward from the horizontal, the upper lid follows the movements of the globe. There is also an association between the movements of the eyelids and the globes when the eyes are closed. In the majority of persons the eyes are turned sharply upward when the eyelids are forcibly closed. This is a protective action that brings the cornea up under the covering eyelid away from impending danger. It is called Bell's phenomenon after the physician who first described it.

Many other movements of the eyelids and the simultaneous contraction of the ocular or facial muscles form associated movements under pathologic conditions. One of the most important of these is the so-called von Graefe sign, present in thyrotoxicosis. The lid fails to follow the downward movement of the globe during downward gaze so that the upper lid lags behind the eyeball. This results in exposure of the upper limbus so that sometimes several millimeters of white sclera remain visible. The lid eventually sinks down to its usual level, but the lack of synchronization between the movements of the globe and the lid is quite striking. The slowness of the eyelid to close is not caused by the exophthalmos since it may occur in the absence of any protrusion of the globe, but it seems as though the eyelids were prevented from moving down as rapidly as the globe because of spasm of either the levator or the smooth muscle muscle attached to it. In spite of the absence of pupillary changes, which seemingly should be present if the sympathetically innervated smooth muscle is hyperactive, most authors attribute the slowness of the lid to close to stimulation of the smooth muscle by thyroxin.

As stated, the widened fissure so produced gives rise to the appearance of exophthalmos and is largely the cause for the condition's being known as exophthalmic goiter. In the ophthalmopathic type of Graves' disease, in which there may be little evidence of thyrotoxicosis, infiltration of the ocular muscles and the orbital tissues with edema creates real protrusion of the globe, in addition to the apparent exophthalmos caused by the retraction of the eyelid.

Following recovery from paralysis of the third cranial nerve, occasionally an interesting phenomenon of the eyelid known as the pseudo-Graefe phenomenon occurs. In gaze straight ahead there is slight ptosis on the side of the previous palsy of the third cranial nerve. This ptosis persists when this eye is abducted, but disappears and is even replaced by excessive widening of the fissure when the eye is adducted. It is assumed that the cause of the pseudo-Graefe phenomenon is misdirection of nerve fibers intended for the medial rectus muscle into the third nerve bundle going to the levator muscle. The ptosis in the primary position and in the abducted position represents a residual weakness of the levator. In adduction, on the other hand, the medial rectus is innervated, and the misdirected fibers which have now reached the levator succeed in elevating the lid normally or even to an excessive degree.

Another abnormal phenomenon of the

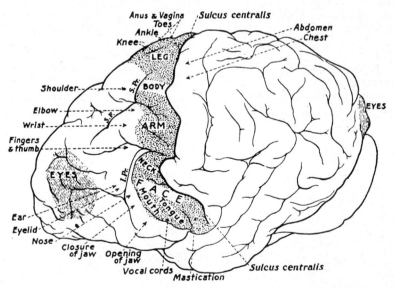

Fig. 4. Outer aspect of the brain of the chimpanzee, showing the position of the motor centers. Electric stimulation at the parts indicated causes coordinate movements of the corresponding muscle groups. (After Sherrington.)

eyelid is that known as jaw winking, or the Marcus-Gunn phenomenon, named after the men who first described cases of this peculiar action of the eyelid. It consists of rapid opening and shutting of the eyelids on one side during the act of chewing. The spontaneous movements of the eyelid are best produced by requesting the subject to move the lower jaw horizontally across the upper jaw. Apparently the pterygoid muscle which is involved in this motion is abnormally linked in some fashion with the levator muscle on that side so that, when the pterygoids are innervated, the surplus innervation flows to the levator and causes the winking. While it has usually been accepted that this associated movement is due to the misdirection of fibers intended for the pterygoid into the levator, it is difficult to see how this could occur. It may be of some significance that the cortical locus where stimulation produces elevation of the eyelid lies very close to the locus for jaw movements, and the fact that the condition is congenital may indicate that the defect is in the cortex and not further down in the pathways for innervation of these two areas (Fig. 4).

REFERENCES

1. Sayoc, B.: Absence of superior palpebral fold in slit eyes, Am. J. Ophth. **42:**298, 1956.
2. Walsh, F.: Clinical neuro-ophthalmology, Baltimore, 1947, Williams & Wilkins Co., p. 228.
3. Bender, M.: The nerve supply to the orbicularis muscle and the physiology of movements of the upper eyelid, Arch. Ophth. **15:**21, 1936.
4. Walsh, F.: Clinical neuro-ophthalmology, ed. 2, Baltimore, 1957, Williams & Wilkins Co., p. 187.
5. Martino, G.: The conditioned reflex of blinking, J. Neurophysiol. **2:**173, 1939.
6. Anantanarayana, A.: Note on the mechanism of eyelid closure in blinking, Proc. All India Ophthal. Soc. **10:**154, 1949.
7. Gordon, G.: Observations upon the movements of the eyelids, Brit. J. Ophth. **35:** 339, 1951.
8. Reid, G.: Rate of discharge of extraocular motoneurons, J. Physiol. **110:**217, 1949.
9. Suda, K., and Kitani, K.: Rinsho Ganka **9:**222, 1955; quoted from Ophthalmic Literature 9, no. 1, Item 672, p. 670, 1955.
10. Givner, I., and Jaffe, N.: Myokymia of the eyelids, Am. J. Ophth. **32:**51, 1949.
11. Marquis, D., and Hilgard, E.: Conditioned lid responses to light in dogs after removal of the visual cortex, J. Comp. Psychol. **22:**157, 1936.
12. Marquis, D., and Hilgard, E.: Conditioned responses to light in monkeys after removal of the occipital lobes, Brain **60:**1, 1937.

CHAPTER 2

THE LACRIMAL APPARATUS

SECRETION OF TEARS

The fluid normally found in the conjunctival cul-de-sac is a mixture of the secretion of the lacrimal gland and of the numerous glands of the conjunctiva—the so-called accessory lacrimal glands of Krause and Wolfring (Fig. 5). In addition, certain sebaceous glands, the glands of Zeis, and the meibomian glands (Fig. 2, p. 21) secrete an oily viscous fluid which covers the edges of the eyelids, preventing the lacrimal fluid from flowing over onto the cheek. The fluid which keeps the cornea moist under usual conditions is largely the secretion from these accessory glands, but any abnormal stimulus to the eye results in an excessive formation of tears from the lacrimal gland so that the cul-de-sac fills with true tear fluid. The secretion of the accessory glands is occasionally altered in character to such an extent that the lacrimal fluid in the cul-de-sac has an abnormal appearance, resembling seafoam or soapsuds.

It is difficult to determine the physical and chemical properties of normal lacrimal secretion since under ordinary conditions this is extremely scanty, and it is unwise to make any assumptions regarding the normal fluid from analyses derived from excessive formation of tears. For example, the fluid which has been analyzed to determine the properties of normal tear fluid is generally produced by subjecting a person to the fumes of ammonia or some similar stimulant to the production of tears. The fluid formed under these conditions can hardly represent normal secretion. Further, under normal conditions evaporation of the tear film takes place on the cornea, which must alter its physical properties considerably; therefore, no comparison can be made between normal lacrimal secretion and that produced by abnormal stimulation and collected immediately.

The precorneal film has a regulated composition, viscosity, and wetting potential, so balanced that it remains optically clear. It must be renewed continually to get rid of the constant contamination by desquamated cellular material. It is the medium through which gaseous exchange

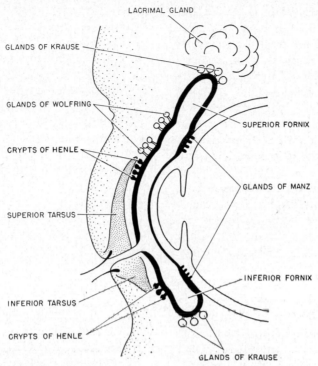

LACRIMAL GLAND

GLANDS OF KRAUSE

GLANDS OF WOLFRING

SUPERIOR FORNIX

CRYPTS OF HENLE

GLANDS OF MANZ

SUPERIOR TARSUS

INFERIOR FORNIX

INFERIOR TARSUS

CRYPTS OF HENLE

GLANDS OF KRAUSE

Fig. 5. Diagram of a sagittal section through the eyelids and eyeball to show the conjunctival sac and the position of its glands. (After Whitnall.)

between the air and the cornea occurs. Any physiochemical change in the component parts of the film influences the health of the epithelium and, if persistent, results in a disturbance of the underlying corneal stroma. For example, an increase of viscosity due to an inhibition of the secretion of lacrimal fluid, as in kerato-conjunctivitis sicca, results in a pathologic state of the epithelium. As will be shown, the precorneal film has both protein and mucoprotein components in such a delicate physiochemical balance that a stable viscous film with high wetting properties and optical clarity is maintained. The protein content is maintained by evaporation at a concentration higher than that of the lacrimal secretion as formed, but under normal conditions the film never becomes so viscous that bubbles are re-

tained which would obscure vision, probably because the evaporation stimulates an increased lacrimal flow. On the other hand, if the precorneal film is thinned with a free flow of lacrimal secretion, evaporation and loss of excess tears into the canaliculi soon re-establish a proper state of viscosity. Methyl cellulose in 0.5 to 1% solution, containing 0.9 per cent sodium chloride, acts as a conjunctival lubricant and substitute for tears. Vehicles containing methyl cellulose are better tolerated on the cornea than simple aqueous solutions because they do not reduce the normal emollient substances of the precorneal film.

Distribution of lacrimal fluid

Under normal conditions the tear fluid does not collect sufficiently to be visible to the naked eye. With magnification, such as with a loupe or better with a slit lamp, a strip of tear fluid can easily be made out at the margins of both the upper and lower lids. The strip measures approximately 1 mm., and in the lower strip it can easily be seen that the anterior surface exposed to the air is concave. When the lower lid is pulled away from the globe, the strip falls down into the cul-de-sac but immediately reappears when the lid is released to come in contact with the globe. A small amount of conjunctiva can also usually be seen in adults bulging into the tear strip. If the upper lid is elevated away from the globe, the tear strip rises into the upper cul-de-sac but reappears also as soon as the lid is let fall into place.

As stated, the lacrimal fluid is a combination of the fluid secreted by the lacrimal gland and that secreted by mucous cells and an oily substance secreted by the meibomian glands. The tear strips can usually be seen to contain the oily secretion on their concave surfaces, and presumably the mucous secretion remains concentrated on the back surface of each strip adjoining the corneal epithelium. Occasionally oily droplets can be seen on the surface of the strips, but usually the oil is distributed as a fine film, and its presence can be detected by the characteristic display of colors which oily substances show in films. The oily surface prevents the fluid from wetting the lid margin and flowing out of the cul-de-sac.

As the tears are formed by the lacrimal gland, they are conducted nasally along the upper tear strip from the upper temporal fornix. At the lateral canthus they fall by gravity to form the lower strip. Spreading nasally, the upper and lower strips reach the plica and caruncle, where they join. Tears do not flow over the cornea. The amount of fluid formed per minute is too small for any such flow. The movement across the cornea is due to the action of the lids, which spread a thin film of fluid up and down over the cornea with each blink.

The lacrimal gland

The lacrimal gland lies in the upper outer angle of the orbit just under the orbital rim. In many persons it can be exposed readily by turning the upper lid and pressing down on the temporal aspect of the everted lid. In Negroes especially, the gland can be herniated into the cul-de-sac very easily after everting the lid, probably because of the marked prominence of the eyes. The gland is divided into two portions by the fascia of the levator (Fig. 1, p. 19). These are the palpebral portion, lying under the aponeurosis of the levator, and the orbital portion, lying above it. The twelve ducts which collect the fluid from the tubules of the gland and empty into the upper cul-de-sac go through the palpebral portion of the gland. If this portion is excised, therefore, the whole gland becomes functionless. Each tubule of the gland is composed of a layer of cylindrical cells which line the central lumen and a layer of flat epithelial cells which form a basement membrane. These basal cells have contractile properties and may squeeze the fluid into the tubules and out into the ducts.

During the secretion of tears, the cells of the lacrimal gland show the usual granular changes in their cytoplasm which are interpreted as signs of secretory activity. In general, the gland cells resemble those of other secreting organs, and it is likely that they perform work in the sense of elaborating chemical products not found in the bloodstream. Their product, therefore, represents a true secretion.

The lacrimal gland has rich arterial and venous blood supplies. The nerves which have been traced into the gland are a branch of the ophthalmic division of the fifth cranial nerve, sympathetic fibers from the carotid plexus and possibly from the sphenopalatine ganglion, and fibers of the facial nerve (Fig. 6). It is not definitely known just what part of this innervation is concerned with the formation of tears.

The secretory fibers of the parasympathetic nerve supply arise in the pons above the superior salivary nucleus. They join the sensory root of the facial nerve (nervus intermedius) and emerge from the pons between the motor branch of the facial and the auditory nerve, having passed through the facial nucleus without forming a synapse (Fig. 6). Here they form part of the greater superficial petrosal nerve, which is a branch of the facial (sometimes called the geniculate) ganglion, and proceed as part of the vidian nerve to enter the sphenopalatine ganglion, where they form a synapse. From their origin in the pons up to this synapse is, therefore, the preganglionic part of the main secretory pathway for the lacrimal gland. The postganglionic fibers arise in the sphenopalatine ganglion and reach the lacrimal gland incorporated in the zygomatic nerve, which is a branch of the maxillary division of the fifth nerve.

The sympathetic supply arises in the hypothalamus and, descending in the cervical cord, leaves as white rami at the first, second, and third thoracic levels. The fibers then ascend in the cervical sympathetic chain as far as the superior cervical ganglion where they form a synapse. This constitutes the preganglionic pathway for the sympathetic fibers. The postganglionic fibers join the carotid plexus and reach the lacrimal gland by several routes. Some branches follow the carotid plexus and reach the gland along the lacrimal artery. Others go by the deep petrosal nerve, the vidian nerve, and passing through the sphenopalatine ganglion reach the gland with the parasympathetic nerve supply. Finally some branches from the cavernous plexus reach the gland by way of the lacrimal nerve, which is a branch of the ophthalmic division of the fifth.

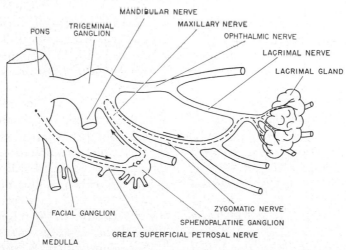

Fig. 6. Diagram showing the efferent pathway of the lacrimation reflex. (After Mutch.)

As stated, the lacrimal gland is innervated by the lacrimal, the facial, and the cervical sympathetic nerves. The evidence of which of these nerves is most concerned in tear formation is confusing due to the fact that experiments have been performed on many different species of animals, whose anatomy differs considerably from man, and from the fact that results after nerve sectioning are often misinterpreted due to the phenomenon of sensitization.

The best evidence now indicates that the lacrimal nerve is not concerned in any way with the secretory function but is purely the afferent pathway for the reflex arc. The facial nerve is primarily the secretory nerve, and the excessive flow of tears due to reflex stimulation is brought about by this nerve. On the other hand, the normal supply of tears found in the cul-de-sac without external stimulation is governed somewhat by the cervical sympathetics.[1, 2]

If the seventh nerve is interrupted above the facial ganglion, the denervated lacrimal gland becomes sensitized to the subcutaneous administration of parasympathicomimetic agents. The denervated gland fails to react, however, to neostigmine.[3]

The most commonly used clinical test for lacrimal secretion is the Schirmer test which gives the values for the sum of the normal lacrimal supply and that produced reflexly by the stimulus of a strip of filter paper inserted into the lower cul-de-sac.

The afferent pathways through which stimuli reach the parasympathetic and sympathetic nuclei are extremely numerous. Reflex lacrimation is easily produced by stimulation of the fifth and olfactory nerves. Any irritation of the endings of the fifth nerve, particularly those which supply the eye, results in tearing. Strong odor, particularly that from onions, produces marked tearing. But tearing may be produced centrally on an emotional basis, and the site of origin and pathways by which these impulses reach the nuclei for secretion are not known.

Lacrimation may accompany severe pain from any region of the body and often occurs in the acts of yawning, laughing, coughing, and vomiting.

Formation of tears

The normal amount of secretion in the cul-de-sac has been estimated to be about two thirds of a gram during the waking day (16 hours). Age seems to be a factor that influences the secretion of tears, and the decrease in flow of tears is roughly parallel to the increase in age.[4, 5] There is little difference in the rate of flow of tears between the two sexes, except among young persons (16 through 29 years of age). In this group, females exhibit a definitely greater flow of tears than males. Apart from the reflex influences just mentioned, the formation of tears may be accelerated by the administration of drugs such as pilocarpine and inhibited by the instillation of drugs in the atropine series. Maes[6] found that after degeneration of the postganglionic endings from the sympathetic supply the gland cells become much more responsive to drugs such as pilocarpine, acetylcholine, and epinephrine. In cats, removal of the superior cervical ganglion causes no change in the response of the denervated gland to the drugs until after the sympathetic nerve endings have degenerated, and then an increase in the normal response to the drugs is evident. Whereas this can be understood in the case of epinephrine, it is difficult to explain why the gland becomes sensitive to parasympathetic drugs after denervation of the sympathetic nerve. However, such sensitization has been observed in other organs. Rosenblueth[7] observed sensitization in the smooth muscle of the nictitating membrane, which showed an increased responsiveness after degenerative section of the cervical sympathetic nerve, not only to epinephrine, but also to acetylcholine, pilocarpine, physostigmine, and histamine. After section of the chorda tympani, the submaxillary gland also shows an increased sensitivity to pilocarpine. Maes adopts the theory proposed by Rosenblueth and Cannon[8] that these changes are caused by increased permeability of the cells of the gland following section of the sympathetic nerve.

If the stimulus be slight, the production of tears by reflex stimulation of the fifth cranial nerve is unilateral, but beyond a certain point it will involve both eyes. It is not unusual, therefore, that patients with corneal involvement in one eye have profuse bilateral tearing.

Certain lesions of the cornea are prone to produce tearing, whereas others, frequently with more widespread damage to the cornea, show little tearing. Foreign bodies, small blebs in the epithelium, and phlyctenules are particularly likely to be associated with profuse lacrimation, whereas large serpiginous ulcers or deep lesions of the cornea are less likely to produce such a flow. The lacrimation due to stimulation of the fifth cranial nerve can be inhibited by surface anesthesia or by paralysis of the ophthalmic division of the fifth cranial nerve.

If the sphenopalatine ganglion is blocked, no reflex or psychic lacrimation takes place, even though the ophthalmic division of the fifth cranial nerve is intact. Psychic stimulation still remains normal if the sensory root of the fifth cranial nerve is cut, provided that the greater superficial petrosal nerve is spared. Psychic weeping is always bilateral and cannot be inhibited by surface anesthesia or by paralysis of the fifth cranial nerve. Mutch[9] assumes that the fibers from the sphenopalatine ganglion which enter the maxillary nerve run to the gasserian ganglion before they pass along the zygomatic nerve. No interference with reflex or psychic lacrimation results from either unilateral or bilateral section of the cervical sympathetic chain in the neck. It seems unlikely, therefore, that the sympathetic nerve takes any part in reflex or psychic weeping.

Some authors, however, accept the view that the sympathetic nerve is concerned with the formation of tears. Duke-Elder states, "It seems more probable that the sympathetic governs normal secretion, while the facial is responsible for the occasional copious flow of weeping."* The fact that normal lacrimal secretion may continue or even be increased in the presence of total paralysis of the facial nerve (bulbar paralysis) makes it unlikely that the cell stations are to be found in the nuclei of the seventh cranial nerve. It has been suggested that these fibers originate somewhere in the neighborhood of the glossopharyngeal nucleus. The sphenopalatine ganglion probably forms a peripheral nerve center, for if this center is blocked, diminution in the secretion of the tears has been noted.[11]

Following lesions of the facial (geniculate) ganglion, regenerated nerve fibers destined for the salivary glands may enter the lacrimal gland rather than the maxillary or sublingual gland, resulting in the phenomenon of crocodile tears which occurs during eating. Mastication produces a flow of tears rather than, or in addition to, saliva.[12]

---

*From Duke-Elder, S.: Textbook of ophthalmology, vol. 1, St. Louis, 1932, The C. V. Mosby Co.

ELIMINATION OF TEARS

The secretion of the lacrimal glands is conducted over the surface of the eyeball in a thin layer by the action of the eyelids. Mixed with the secretion of the conjunctival glands, the fluid collects by gravity in the lower cul-de-sac. Since the surface of the cornea is constantly exposed to air during the waking hours, there is constant and rapid evaporation of the fluid from its surface which must lead to a considerable concentration of the tear fluid.

Between blinks some evaporation must be constantly taking place. In individuals who blink very little, especially in diseased states, the cornea runs the risk of becoming dried. In animals such as the rabbit, which blinks only a few times during the course of an hour, this could be serious. It has been found, however, that, at least as far as the rabbit is concerned, evaporation is partly prevented by a thin film of oil derived from the meibomian glands.[13]

I have frequently noted that some elderly patients complain during refraction that the line of letters blurs after a few minutes. This occurs when they are intently concerned with the resolution of the smaller letters. If they are instructed to blink several times, the letters clear up. These individuals become so intent that they fail to blink during the testing, and the evaporation of their scanty and often abnormal tear film fogs the cornea.

What fluid eventually collects in the lower cul-de-sac is gradually moved toward the lacrimal lake at the inner canthus. This is due partly to the motion imparted to it by the orbicularis muscle. The contraction of this muscle has the effect of a sphincter, and since its nasal attachment is fixed, the temporal part of the ring is pulled toward the nasal side. This moves the fluid effectively in this direction. It is prevented from running over the margins of the eyelids by the oily meibomian secretion, which keeps the fluid from wetting the margins, as already explained. If the outflow is prevented, it now collects in the lacrimal lake—for the first time in sufficient quantities to form drops.

Many different suggestions have been put forward to account for the passage of tear fluid down the lacrimal duct. It is thought that the fluid enters the two lacrimal puncta by capillary attraction and is then siphoned down through the canaliculi into the sac (Fig. 7). This is undoubtedly a factor and is a contraindication to slitting the canaliculi—an operation which used to be performed frequently in order to facilitate the passage of large probes into the duct. Although it is permissible to dilate the punctum and stretch the sphincter which surrounds it, permanent interference with its function is to be deprecated. Slitting the canaliculus does not increase the flow of tears down the duct, but tends to hinder it.

The flow of fluid into the nose is probably due to two other factors, in addition to capillarity produced by the puncta. On closure of the eyelids, the fluid is pushed towards the puncta by the orbicularis muscle, as just described, and the effects of gravity and capillarity of the duct cause the fluid to flow down into the nose.[14]

In addition, a lacrimal pump has been given credibility by the dissections of Jones,[15] which show that the fascia reflected from the periorbita converts the lacrimal fossa into a completely closed cavity. The fascia thus forms a diaphragm which creates alternate positive and negative pressures by its movements. These are brought about by contraction of the superficial and deep heads of the pretarsal portion of the orbicularis muscle and the deep head of the preseptal por-

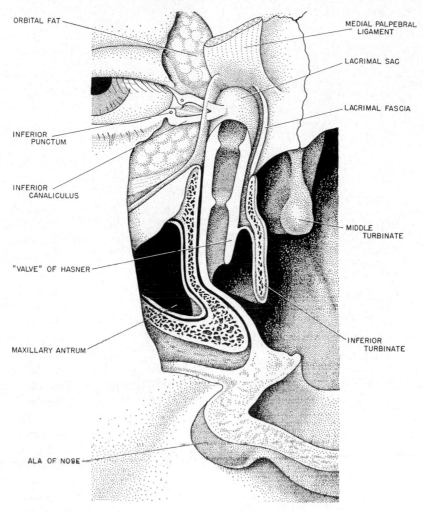

ORBITAL FAT

MEDIAL PALPEBRAL
LIGAMENT

LACRIMAL SAC

LACRIMAL FASCIA

INFERIOR
PUNCTUM

INFERIOR
CANALICULUS

MIDDLE
TURBINATE

"VALVE" OF HASNER

MAXILLARY ANTRUM

INFERIOR
TURBINATE

ALA OF NOSE

Fig. 7. Dissection to show the relations of the lacrimal sac and the nasolacrimal duct from in front. (Modified after Wolff.)

tion of this muscle (p. 22). Winking creates a constant pumplike mechanism which draws the tears into the lacrimal sac and expresses them into the nose. The emptying time of the lacrimal sac has been estimated variously from 10 to 30 minutes.[16, 17]

COMPOSITION OF TEARS

Table 1 shows the composition of tears as determined by Ridley.[18]

Perhaps the most striking feature in the chemical analysis of tears is the relatively high concentration of protein. Protein gives the tears a much lower surface tension and enables them to wet the epithelial surfaces more perfectly. It also enables them to produce a stable foam because of the absorption of the protein molecules at the interfaces between the air, the tears, and the cornea. This is of considerable importance since the trans-

Table 1. *Composition of tears**

Substance	Percentage
Total solids	1.8
Ash	1.05
Total protein	0.669
Albumin	0.394
Globulin	0.275
Nonprotein nitrogen	0.051
Total nitrogen	0.158
Urea	0.04
Sugar	0.065
Na_2O	0.6
K_2O	0.14
NH_3	0.003
Chlorine	0.394
NaCl	0.65

*From Ridley, F., and Sorsby, A., editors: Modern trends in ophthalmology, New York, 1940, Paul B. Hoeber, Inc.

parency of the cornea partly depends on it. The optical properties of the eye are greatly improved by this film since microscopic irregularities in the corneal epithelium are abolished thereby, thus producing a perfectly smooth and polished optical surface for the eye (p. 789). This further protects the eye from damage against small foreign bodies, such as dust and airborne bacteria, which are caught up and enclosed in the film. With the slit lamp, fine particles of dust are seen moving freely over the corneal surface. This would be impossible if the particles were in contact with the epithelium. The values for protein show considerable individual variation, ranging from 136 to 592 mg./100 ml., with an average of 360 mg./100 ml., according to Junnola.[19]

Various fractions of the proteins present in tears may be made by electrophoresis, but there is considerable difference in the fractions obtained, depending on the type of electrophoretic analysis made. Paper electrophoresis shows three fractions: albumin, globulin, and lysozyme; whereas agar microelectrophoresis shows four fractions having a mobility which exceeds that of albumin and one fraction which corresponds to lysozyme with an inverted direction of migration.

The tears produced by emotional stress contain appreciably more protein than those produced by irritation of the cornea.[20]

The urea content of tears is identical with that of plasma and follows changes in plasma urea. Potassium is present in greater concentration in tears than in plasma, which suggests that it is secreted by the lacrimal gland. This is also true, but to a less extent, for sodium and chloride, which are both in slightly higher concentration in tears than in plasma.[21]

Ridley[22] found that tears contain an active histamine-like substance which gives rise to a wheal and a flare (the triple response of Lewis) when tears are injected intradermally. Its significance is unknown. A similar substance has been described in the nasal mucus by Buhrmester and Wenner.[23]

Osmotic pressure. The osmotic pressure of the tears is important from both theoretical and practical points of view. The transparency of the cornea, so vital for the excellence of image formation on the retina, may be considerably affected by the physical properties of the fluids which bathe its surfaces. The transfer of substances into and out of the cornea necessary for its metabolism must depend to some degree on the osmotic concentration of the tear fluid as well as that of the aqueous humor. Finally, the osmotic pressure of the tears becomes a practical factor in the preparation of drugs, whose effectiveness depends upon their penetration of the cornea and whose tolerance by the patient depends upon the concentrations used.

Krogh[24] felt it was improbable that tears should be hypertonic and carried out a series of determinations of the osmotic pressure of human tears by means of the Boldes vapor-pressure method. In ten subjects he found the average concentration of tears equivalent to a 0.9% solution of sodium chloride. This would indicate that fluids used as medicaments in the conjunctival cul-de-sac should be made isotonic with blood. He found that fluids whose concentration was less than 0.6% and greater than 1.5% were disagreeable to most subjects. Others have confirmed these findings by other methods.[25] Some investigators have found the osmotic pressure of tears to be higher than this.[26] Recent studies by Mishima and others[27] indicate that the tears are either isotonic with blood plasma or slightly hypertonic; i.e., 1% sodium chloride solution.

pH of tears. When tears are collected with as little irritation as possible, their pH approximates that of blood, i.e., 7.35. An individual will exhibit variations in pH at different times and yet be free of any symptoms. In fifty normal persons the pH of the tears was found to vary from 5.2 to 8.35.[28] The largest number of these individuals had a pH between 7.0 and 7.4. Other workers have found a value of 7.4 for the pH of normal tears.[25] If the pH of the tears or of any solutions instilled into the cul-de-sac is above 7.8 or below 6.6, some unpleasant sensation usually arises. In conditions in which the reaction of the tears is highly alkaline, an acid buffer solution usually gives marked relief when used as an eyewash. Injuries to the cornea often produce a marked shift in pH of the tears to the alkaline side. In vernal catarrh the pH is also shifted to the alkaline side, but here it is customary to prescribe alkaline eyewashes to help dissolve and wash out the thick tenacious mucus so characteristic of this disease. No shift of

the pH to the alkaline side is said to occur in bacterial conjunctivitis.

Although the eye is usually made uncomfortable by instillation of any solution whose pH is under 6.6, the pH of a 4% solution of boric acid ordinarily employed in ophthalmology is 5.2. Boric acid is only slightly dissociated, however, and probably is washed out by the tears before the hydrogen ions can become active. Nevertheless, it seems illogical, as pointed out by Hosford and Hicks,[29] to put boric acid on an inflamed conjunctiva.

The alkaloids employed in ophthalmology are generally in the form of solutions of salts of the strong acids, e.g., sulfates, hydrochlorides, and nitrates. When these salts go into solution, and even when they are dissolved in a buffered solution of pH 7.6, the buffering capacity may be exhausted readily, and a fairly acid solution remains. The pH of the tears is of importance in the regeneration of the cornea after injuries. The optimal pH for the growth of fibroblasts is 7.6 to 7.8. Ideally, the tears should be kept at this pH after surgery in order to enhance healing of the wound.

The corneal epithelium is affected very little by changes in pH within a wide range. Solutions buffered from pH 4.0 to 10.0 do not affect the permeability of the epithelium.[30] It has been shown that corneal epithelium and endothelium are damaged by pure salt solution even if the pH and tonicity are within normal values. This is also true of cells from the human iris in tissue cultures. If the sodium chloride solution is balanced with other salts, these cell changes do not occur.

Lysozyme. Fleming, in 1922, found that tears contain lysozyme, an enzyme that dissolves many airborne saprophytes rapidly and completely. Lysozyme is found also in nasal mucus, sputum, various tissue extracts, vegetable juices, and egg white. The chemical action of this enzyme on the bacterial membrane has been studied by Meyer.[32] He found a marked increase in reducing sugars when lysozyme was acting on susceptible organisms, indicating that the enzyme had a specific action on the sugar linkages of certain aminocarbohydrates.

A number of factors influence the action of lysozyme, chief of which is the hydrogen ion concentration. The optimum pH for lysis varies with the solubility of the bacterial proteins but in general is somewhere between 6.0 and 7.4. Low salt concentrations (0.5%) favor lysis by increasing the solubility, whereas higher concentrations inhibit its action. Many factors favor the concentration of lysozyme in secretions such as tears. Tears of patients who have had epiphora over a period of time have a lower concentration of lysozyme than normal.[33, 34]

Tears also have the property of inhibiting the growth of many of the ordinary pyogenic cocci, such as *Staphylococcus* and hemolytic *Streptococcus, Diplococcus pneumoniae,* and *Vibrio cholerae.* In view of the fact that human tears contain a high concentration of lysozyme, it has been assumed that the inhibition of growth of these organisms might be due to lysozyme. However, Thompson and Gallardo[35] found that tears had a definite inhibiting effect on staphylococci, even after lysozyme is destroyed by heating acidified tears. Hence, lysozyme is not the sole agent responsible for inhibiting the growth of staphylococci. It is possible that lysozyme and some other as yet unidentified labile agent act together to this end.

Using the technique of electrophoresis, Smollens, Leopold, and Parker[36] analyzed human tears in order to determine the fraction which contained lysozyme. They found it possible to separate the nondialyzable material into at least four components. The three that migrated to the negative pole at pH 7.9 possessed all of the lysozyme activity. The mobilities of these components differed from those ascribed to crystallize lysozyme present in egg white. A specific antiserum prepared against this lysozyme failed to inhibit the lytic activity of tears. This demonstrates immunologic and chemical differences between lysozyme in egg white and lysozyme in tears.

REFERENCES

1. Whitwell, J.: Role of the sympathetic in lacrimal secretion, Brit. J. Ophth. **45:** 439, 1961.
2. Whitwell, J.: Denervation of the lacrimal gland, Brit. J. Ophth. **42:**518, 1958.
3. de Haas, E.: Lacrimal gland response to parasympathicomimetics after parasympathetic denervation, Arch. Ophth. **64:**34, 1960.
4. Henderson, J., and Prough, W.: Influence of age and sex on flow of tears, Arch. Ophth. **43:**224, 1950.
5. de Roetth, A., Sr.: Lacrimation in normal eyes, Arch. Ophth. **49:**185, 1953.
6. Maes, J.: The effect of removal of superior cervical ganglion on lachrymal secretion, Am. J. Physiol. **123:**359, 1938.
7. Rosenblueth, A.: Action of certain drugs on nictitating membrane, Am. J. Physiol. **100:**443, 1932.
8. Rosenblueth, A., and Cannon, W.: Adequacy of chemical theory of smooth muscle excitation, Am. J. Physiol. **116:**414, 1936.
9. Mutch, J. R.: The lacrimation reflex, Brit. J. Ophth. **28:**317, 1944.
10. Duke-Elder, S.: Textbook of ophthalmology, vol. 1, St. Louis, 1932, The C. V. Mosby Co.
11. Ruskin, S.: Control of tearing by blocking the nasal ganglion, Arch. Ophth. **4:**208, 1930.
12. Viallefont, H.: The oculoglandular syndrome, Ann. ocul. **187:**145, 1954.
13. Mishima, S., and Maurice, D.: The oily

layer of the tear film and evaporation from the corneal surface, Exper. Eye Res. **1**:39, 1961.

14. Gradle, H.: Capillarity as a factor in drainage of tears, Am. J. Ophth. **18**:69, 1935.

15. Jones, L.: Epiphora—its relation to the anatomic structures and surgery of the medial canthal region, Am. J. Ophth. **43**:203, 1957.

16. Hanney, F.: Diagnostic studies of the lacrimal system, Klin. Monatsbl. Augenh. **128**:336, 1956.

17. Demorest, B., and Milder, M.: Dacryocystography. II. The pathologic lacrimal apparatus, Arch. Ophth. **54**:410, 1955.

18. Ridley, F., and Sorsby, A., editors: Modern trends in ophthalmology, New York, 1940, Paul B. Hoeber, Inc.

19. François, g., and Rabaey, M.: Agar microelectrophoresis of human tears, Am. J. Ophth. **50**:793, 1960.

20. Brunish, R.: The protein components of human tears, Arch. Ophth. **57**:554, 1957.

21. Thaysen, J., and Thorn, N.: Secretion of urea, sodium, potassium and chloride in human tears, Am. J. Physiol. **178**:160, 1954.

22. Ridley, F.: "Active (histamine-like) substance" in tears, Tr. Ophth. Soc. U. Kingdom **58**: (pt. 2), 590, 1938.

23. Buhrmester, C., and Wenner, W.: Presence of histamine-like substance in nasal mucosa, nasal polypi and nasal secretion, Arch. Otolaryng. **24**:570, 1936.

24. Krogh, A., Lund, C., and Pedersen-Bjergaard, K.: The osmotic concentration of human lachrymal fluid, Acta physiol. scandinav. **10**:88, 1945.

25. Pedersen-Bjergaard, K., and Smidt, B.: Electrolytic conductivity, osmotic pressure and hydrogen ion concentration of human lacrimal fluid, Acta dermat.-venereol. **32** (supp. 29): 261, 1952.

26. Potts, A.: The nutritional supply of corneal regions in experimental animals, Am. J. Ophth. **36**:127, 1953.

27. Mishima, S., and Maurice, D.: The effect of normal evaporation on the eye, Exper. Eye Res. **1**:46, 1961.

28. Feldman, J.: pH and buffers in relation to ophthalmology, Arch. Ophth. **17**:797, 1937.

29. Hosford, G., and Hicks, A.: Hydrogen ion concentration of tears; its relation to certain ocular symptoms and to conjunctival and corneal lesions, Arch. Ophth. **13**:14, 1935.

30. Maurice, D.: Influence on corneal epithelium of bathing with solutions of differing reaction and tonicity, Brit. J. Ophth. **39**:463, 1955.

31. Harper, J., and Pomerat, C.: Effect of electrolyte mixtures on cells from the human iris, Am. J. Ophth. **49**:446, 1960.

32. Meyer, K., Palmer, J., Thompson, R., and Khorazo, D.: On mechanism of lysozyme action, J. Biol. Chem. **113**:479, 1936.

33. Hallauer, C.: Klinische und experimentelle Untersuchungen über den Lysozymgehalt im Bindehautsack und in der Tranenflussigkeit, Arch. Augenh. **103**:199, 1930.

34. James, W.: The lysozyme content of tears, Am. J. Ophth. **18**:1109, 1935.

35. Thompson, R., and Gallardo, E.: The antibacterial action of tears on staphylococci, Am. J. Ophth. **24**:635, 1941.

36. Smolens, J., Leopold, I., and Parker, J.: Studies of human tears, Am. J. Ophth. **32**:153, 1949.

CHAPTER 3

THE CORNEA

ANATOMY AND PHYSICAL PROPERTIES OF THE CORNEA

The cornea is the window through which the light rays pass on their way to the retina. In order to fulfill this function, the tissue must be transparent. It must also possess the proper curvature and the correct index of refraction so that rays of light, coming from objects at infinity, are imaged on the retina, for it is at the anterior corneal surface that the major portion of the refraction of light takes place.

The amount of bending of a ray of light at an optical surface depends upon two factors—the curvature of the surface and the difference in density of the two media through which the light ray is passing. The radius of curvature of the cornea and that of the anterior surface of the lens are nearly alike. The radius of the cornea in the optical zone is 7.8 mm. and that of the anterior surface of the lens 11 mm. A ray of light passing through the cornea comes from air, with a refractive index of 1.00, and strikes the cornea, a medium with a refractive index of 1.376, the difference between the two being 0.376. When this ray has traversed the cornea, it then enters the aqueous, which has a refractive index of 1.336.

From the aqueous it enters the lens, whose refractive index as a whole is approximately 1.42. The difference between the refractive index of the aqueous and of the lens is, therefore, 0.084. It is obvious that even if the curvatures of the cornea and the lens were alike there would be much more refraction at the corneal surface than at the surface of the lens. When the eye is in the resting state, the cornea is more deeply curved than the anterior surface of the lens. It follows, therefore, that the greatest amount of refraction by the eye takes place at the corneal surface. The total refractive power of the emmetropic eye is approximately 60 D. The power of the anterior surface of the cornea is 48.8 D. The power of the posterior surface, which is a concave meniscus, is minus 5.8 D. so that the total power of the cornea is 43.0 D, or 70% of the total refractive power of the eye.

The corneal curvature changes somewhat with age. It is more spherical in infancy and changes to astigmatism with the rule during childhood and adolescence, to become again more spherical in middle age and astigmatic against the rule in senility.[1]

The thickness of the cornea also changes somewhat with age. Normal corneas measure on an average 0.559 mm. in persons under 25 years of age, 0.565 mm. for persons between 25 and 65 years of age, and 0.571 mm. for persons over 65 years of age. In myopic persons with a defect greater than 5 D. the average thickness is 0.524 mm., and in hypermetropic persons with a defect greater than 3 D. it is 0.565 mm. The thickness of the cornea is largely determined by the degree of corneal hydration, which will be discussed more fully later on. In diseases of the anterior segment there may be a slight increase in corneal thickness without any clinical evidence of corneal edema or corneal scarring, however.[2]

The thickness of the cornea is greatest after the eyes have been closed for some time, as after sleeping. When the eyes are opened and exposed to the drying effect of the air, the thickness decreases slightly.[3]

The cornea is composed of five separate layers: epithelium, Bowman's membrane, substantia propria or stroma, Descemet's membrane, and endothelium.

The epithelium. The epithelium consists of five layers of cells. The most superficial cells are flat overlapping squamous cells, similar to the most superficial epithelial cells of the skin. Unlike these, however, the corneal squamous epithelium is never normally keratinized. The middle layers consist of cells becoming more columnar as the deeper layers are approached. The innermost layer is made up of columnar cells closely packed together. All of the cells are held together by a cement substance. Also, the surfaces of the cells form processes that are fitted into corresponding indentations of adjacent cells and connected in places by attachment bodies called desmosomes.[4]

Between the columnar epithelial cells and Bowman's membrane is a basement membrane from 10 to 30 mμ thick, consisting of tightly packed filaments. This membrane is adherent to the columnar cells in numerous places, and some filaments appear to run into the stroma of the cornea. The basement membrane has been examined histochemically[5] and was found to contain a lipoid layer. From the solubility and staining reactions it probably contains both a polysaccharide complex and a phospholipid, identified as plasmagen.

The epithelial cells form a layer of uniform thickness and great regularity. They possess a refractive index of 1.416, but since the anterior and posterior borders of this layer are parallel to each other, a lamina on a concentric plane is formed which does not of itself influence the passage of rays of light except at its surface. The surface epithelial cells are extremely smooth, forming a mirror, and are covered with a fine film, the lacrimal secretion, which increases their efficiency as an optical surface due partly to its high protein content and lipids.[6]

Bowman's membrane. This is a sheet of transparent tissue without structure as seen by light microscopy about 12μ thick. Under electron microscopy it appears to be made up of uniform fibrils running parallel to each other, probably of collagenous material.

The substantia propria or stroma. The substantia propria is composed of layers of lamellae, each of which runs the full length of the cornea, and although the bundles interlace with one another, they are nearly parallel to each other and to the surface. Their cell bodies, called corneal corpuscles, are flattened so that they too lie parallel to the surface, and their cell processes interlace with one another to form a syncytium. This arrangement of the fibers gives optical uniformity to the cornea. The stroma comprises about 90% of the whole cornea.

The layers of lamellae are made up of

bundles of fibrils of a collagenous-like material, separated from each other by a ground substance.

Descemet's membrane. This membranous sheet bounds the inner surface of the stroma. It is about 10 μ thick. It is considered to be the product of secretion of the endothelial cells.

The endothelium. This single layer of cells covers Descemet's membrane and is bathed on its inner surface by the aqueous humor. The cells contain nuclei and large numbers of mitochondria.

In the rabbit cornea, terminal bars or haptomeres are found in the endothelium.[7] In the frog cornea these terminal bars are missing, and in addition there is a complex interleaving of the lateral margins of the endothelial cells.[8] In these respects the human cornea more nearly resembles the frog.[4] The significance of these fine details of structure of the endothelium will be considered further in the section on transport of material through the cornea (p. 49).

The transparency of the cornea is assured by its anatomic construction as well as by its physiologic properties. Its transparency is further maintained by the absence of any blood vessels or lymphatics. Although there is a rich marginal blood supply, under normal conditions no vessels are found in the cornea any distance beyond the limbus.

The cornea is richly supplied with sensory nerves. These are derived from the ciliary nerves, which are the end branches of the ophthalmic division of the fifth cranial nerve. They enter the cornea in the middle and anterior layers from a plexus in the suprachoroidal space and run forward in a radial fashion toward the center of the cornea. They generally do not lose their myelin sheaths until they have traversed a millimeter or so of the cornea; so that in this location they can

frequently be seen as fairly thick fibrils. From this point on, they are more difficult to follow without using high magnification. As they run into the cornea, they divide dichotomously and, emerging from the deeper parts of the cornea, perforate Bowman's membrane and terminate by forming a plexus just underneath the epithelium. In their further course, the free nerve endings run between the epithelial cells. The cornea is one of the most sensitive tissues of the body, and this sensitivity serves to protect it and thus aids in maintaining its precious transparency. The corneal endothelium of rabbits has been found to contain nerve fibers ending within the cells, but this has not been confirmed in human beings.[9] The temperature of the cornea is relatively low. For example, in the rabbit the difference between the temperatures of the cornea and the iris amounts to 5° C.

The reactions of the cornea are quite important in disease processes since its tissue is avascular and therefore differs somewhat from those tissues which normally have a blood supply. The stratified epithelium and nerve fibers are of ectodermal origin; the remaining layers, including the endothelium, are of mesodermal origin. Bowman's membrane is merely a modified lamella of the stroma, whereas Descemet's membrane is a cuticular product from the endothelial cells. Bowman's membrane possesses little resistance to any pathologic process; therefore, it is easily destroyed and never regenerates. Descemet's membrane, on the other hand, is highly resistant and may remain in the form of a bulging balloon-like structure, called a descemetocele, after all the other layers of the cornea are destroyed. Even after it has been destroyed, it can regenerate. Ruptures are rare in Bowman's membrane, but they are common in Descemet's membrane.

Most diseases of the cornea result in its vascularization, and the type of vessels and their location in the cornea are often clues to the nature of the disease process. The diseases which commonly affect epithelial structures are accompanied by superficial vascularization, the vessels coming across the limbus from the conjunctiva; those diseases affecting parenchymatous tissues, on the other hand, are characterized by deep vessels, coming from the anastomosis of the long posterior ciliary arteries and the anterior ciliary arteries (Fig. 2, p. 21). Once the cornea has become vascularized, the vessels remain throughout life. They are frequently empty of blood, but their presence can always be detected with suitable magnification and is testimony to the fact that the cornea has been the seat of a previous inflammatory process.

There is considerable difference of opinion regarding the effect of corneal vascularization, i.e., whether it is beneficial or harmful. Some authors consider the blood vessels one of nature's methods of bringing further defensive mechanisms to the cornea to aid in its fight against noxious influences, whereas others consider the presence of the blood vessels only another harmful process which must be eliminated.

CHEMISTRY OF THE CORNEA

Most of the analyses of corneal tissue have been made on whole cornea, and although 90% of this is represented by the stroma, the cellular layers, epithelium, and endothelium differ in many respects from the stroma.

Table 2 gives a comparison of the chemical composition of the cornea and sclera. The most striking component of each is the protein content, which consists largely of collagen, 60% of the dry weight of the cornea, along with albumin and globulin. Some of the noncollagenous proteins are bound to mucopolysaccharide. Macroglobulins and β-lipoprotein are conspicuously absent.[10] The serum proteins present probably come into the cornea from the limbal blood vessels and move through the cornea by simple diffusion. However, there is a limiting size to the molecules which can diffuse through the cornea, and Maurice[11] has shown this to be around a molecular weight of 500,000, which probably accounts for the absence of macroglobulins.

Table 2. *Cornea**†

Constituent (%)	Sclera	Cornea	Corneal epithelium
Water	72.2	81.1	80.5
Solids	27.8	18.9	19.5
Inorganic matter	.70	.17	—
Organic matter	27.1	18.7	—
Mucoid	2.3	—	—
Collagen (gelatin)	22.1	18.4	—
Elastin (albuminoid)	1.5	—	—
Albumin and globulin	.6	.15	trace
Water-soluble extractives	.5	.13	—
Lipids (ether-soluble)	.1	.04	4.3 } Dry tissue
Nucleic acid	low	low	8.5 } (%)

*From Krause's figures on beef eyes.
†Fresh tissues, except where otherwise stated.

Small amounts of lipids are found in the cornea normally. The cholesterol content increases with age, and with increasing age many people develop the characteristic gray ring in the cornea just inside the limbus known as arcus or circulus senilis. This is not a true age change, however, as many geriatric patients show no signs of gerontoxon, and it is not infrequently found in young individuals. The ring is due to the deposition of cholesterol, phospholipids, and neutral fat, but its presence does not correlate well with the blood cholesterol. It is unquestionably associated with abnormal fat metabolism, as is demonstrated by the finding of hyperchlomicronemia of the large particle size in 100% of young individuals with gerontoxon. Impaired radioactive fat tolerance occurred in 70% of these individuals. Whether the excess fat in the blood inundates the tissues or whether the fat arises in the tissues primarily is at present unknown.[12]

A substance called mucoid was isolated from the cornea many years ago by Morner. The chemical nature of mucoid was first determined by Meyer and Chaffee,[13] who found it to be a monosulfuric acid ester of hyaluronic acid. According to Anseth and Laurent, this mucopolysaccharide occurs in two fractions as glucosaminoglycans and galactosaminoglycans.[14] At least three different polysaccharides exist in the cornea: keratan sulfate, chondroitin-4 sulfate, and chondroitin.

Glutathione, ascorbic acid, and riboflavin are present in the cornea.

The corneal epithelium has a high acetylcholine content. This is not affected by preganglionic section of the fifth nerve, but falls after postganglionic section. Acetylcholine probably is not directly concerned with the maintenance of the water content of the cornea, as inhibitors of cholinesterase and atropine are without effect on corneal hydration.[16]

Chemical differences between the stroma and the cellular layers. Some striking chemical differences of physiologic significance are found between the epithelium and endothelium, on the one hand, and the stroma. One of these is their lipid content, which is about one hundred times greater in the epithelium and endothelium than in the stroma. This probably accounts for the preferential permeability of the epithelium and endothelium to fat-soluble substances (p. 49). The corneal epithelium has a much higher content of reduced glutathione than the stroma[17] and a higher ascorbic acid content. Pierie believes that the high concentration of ascorbic acid in the epithelium is due to the fact that the ascorbic acid comes into the cornea from the aqueous humor through the endothelium and the stroma, but cannot pass through the epithelium where it is finally concentrated. It is not apparent why the ascorbic acid should remain concentrated in the epithelium instead of forming a steady state with the aqueous humor. The concentration of riboflavin is the same in the cornea as in the aqueous humor, and it has been suggested that the corneal epithelium may derive some of its riboflavin directly from the tears.[18]

Nucleoprotein is found in high concentration in the epithelium, while little is present in the stroma, which probably is due to the higher concentration of cells in this layer.

METABOLISM OF THE CORNEA

The term *metabolism* embraces all the chemical processes occurring in living tissues by means of which their growth, the replacement of new cells, and the production of energy for their activities takes place. This latter is chiefly accomplished in the cornea by the breakdown of glucose into carbon dioxide and water. In general two processes are involved: (1) the cleavage of glucose into pyruvic and lactic acid, called glycolysis and (2) the further oxidation of lactic acid into carbon dioxide and water by the process of respiration. Glycolysis may take place in either the presence of oxygen, known as aerobic glycolysis, or in the absence of oxygen, when it is called anaerobic glycolysis. The processes of respiration cannot be accomplished without oxygen, which takes an active part in the reactions.

Glycolysis takes place by means of the usual Embden-Meyerhof scheme, shown below. The rate of glycolysis in the excised cornea is about four times faster in

Glycogen
↓ ↑
Fructose monophosphate
↓ ↑
Fructose-1:6-diphosphate
↓ ↑
Dihydroxyacetone phosphate
+
3-Phosphoglyceraldehyde
↓ ↑
1:3-Diphosphoglyceraldehyde
↓ ↑
1:3-Diphosphoglyceric acid
↓ ↑
3-Phosphoglyceric acid
↓ ↑
2-Phosphoglyceric acid
↓ ↑
Phosphopyruvic acid

$$O$$
$$\|$$
Pyruvic acid $(CH_3-C-COOH)$

+2H   -2H

$$OH$$
$$|$$
Lactic acid $(CH_3-CH-COOH)$

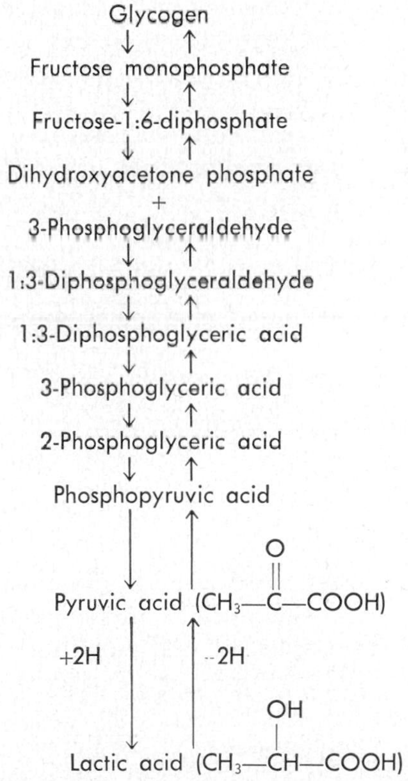

Glycolysis, showing the breakdown of glycogen to pyruvic acid and the reversible equilibrium between pyruvic acid and lactic acid.

the absence of oxygen (anaerobic glycolysis) than it is in its presence (aerobic glycolysis). This difference is probably due to the fact that the epithelium, which accounts for 95% of the glycolysis of the whole cornea, shows a marked reduction in its ability to form lactic acid in the presence of oxygen, whereas the stroma maintains the same glycolytic activity in either the presence or absence of oxygen. de Roetth found no aerobic activity of the epithelium,[19] while Langham found that in the presence of oxygen the production of lactic acid was halved.[20]

Respiration in the cornea, i.e., the oxidation of glucose, can occur by two routes: (1) the Krebs' or citric acid cycle and (2) the hexosemonophosphate shunt. Most of the respiration takes place in the epithelium.

Recent evidence suggests that the epithelium metabolizes 65% of the glucose by way of the glycolytic pathway and 35% by the hexosemonophosphate shunt. However, if only the oxidation of glucose is measured, the shunt mechanism is the more active; 70% of the total oxidation of glucose goes by this route.[21] Although the citric acid cycle is functioning in the epithelium, its role is probably a minor one.

It can be seen from the preceding discussion that the cornea can obtain its energy requirements from the metabolism of glucose by at least three routes, two of which require the presence of oxygen. It can convert glucose to pyruvic acid by anaerobic glycolysis through the Embden-Meyerhoff cycle, and it can oxidize glucose directly by the hexosemonophosphate shunt or oxidize pyruvic acid to carbon dioxide and water by the citric acid cycle.

The cornea presents certain structural peculiarities which must affect its metabolism. It is normally free of any blood vessels, except those at the limbus. It is bathed on its surfaces by fluids which are constantly being replaced and which normally differ considerably in their physical and chemical characteristics from blood serum. And on one side the cornea is subject to the effects of evaporation. Some of these factors will now be discussed as far as they bear on corneal metabolism.

Oxygen uptake of the cornea. The cornea has been shown experimentally to have a considerable uptake of oxygen.[22, 23] Most of the oxygen consumption by the cornea is due to the epithelium. The QO_2 of whole cornea is 5-6,[24] whereas that of the stroma alone is 0.23. Although it can be assumed that the cornea in air generally utilizes around 6 μl/hr. for each sq. cm. of surface, it can consume additional oxygen if it is exposed to an atmosphere of pure oxygen. The cornea can theoretically obtain oxygen from four sources: the aqueous humor, the capillaries at the limbus, the capillaries in the tarsal conjunctiva when the lids are closed, and the oxygen dissolved in the layer of tear film on the epithelial surface. It is quite possible that the corneal endothelium does get most of its required oxygen from the aqueous humor, but it is very doubtful if sufficient oxygen can diffuse through the stroma to supply the needs of the epithelium. The stroma offers resistance to the diffusion of molecules through it, and it has been calculated that the amount of oxygen that can diffuse across the cornea from the aqueous humor is insufficient to meet the needs of the epithelium. The amount of oxygen that will pass across the stroma in unit time is about one fortieth that of the normal oxygen uptake by the epithelial cells.[25]

Although the cornea offers some resistance to the diffusion of oxygen through it, this is not unidirectional as was claimed by older investigators, especially Fischer. It was believed that oxygen could diffuse from the air inward through the cornea into the aqueous humor but could not diffuse outward. The studies of Heald and Langham[25] show that oxygen can diffuse at the same rate through the cornea in either direction, and the diffusion rate is not altered by the absence of the epithelial and endothelial cells.

It is not likely that the cornea gets much of its oxygen from either the capillaries at the limbus or from those in the tarsal conjunctiva, although the latter may help offset the loss of oxygen in the air when the lids are closed, as at night during sleep. Everything points to the oxygen in the air as the chief source of oxygen for its respiratory needs. This is borne out in clinical experience with contact lenses. In the early form of contact lenses which were molded and completely covered the cornea, great difficulty was experienced in maintaining transparency of the cornea. After such lenses were worn for several hours, many corneas became steamy. Smelser was able to show that this was due to oxygen lack and not to osmotic factors.[26] Unless a constant supply of oxygen is permitted to reach the corneal epithelium from the air, the metabolism of the cornea will suffer, the processes of deturgescence will be interfered with, and the transparency of the cornea will be impaired as a result. This will be discussed more fully in a later section (p. 60). The use of the small corneal lens eliminates this factor to a large degree, as the lens can move about over the cornea and allow differing portions of it to be exposed to the atmosphere.

During sleep when the lids are normally closed the corneas are deprived of the supply of oxygen in the air. It has been shown that during such periods the cornea does suffer some interference with its normal metabolism, resulting in a slight turgescence of the cornea. As stated, it is probable that when the lids are closed some oxygen becomes available to the corneas from the blood in the tarsal capillaries. This concept has received support from the experiments of Langham.[24]

Most of the enzymes and coenzymes necessary for both glycolysis and respiration of the cornea have been found, chiefly in the cellular layers.

PERMEABILITY OF THE CORNEA

The permeability of the cornea is of importance from several aspects. We have seen that the nutrition of the cornea depends upon the diffusion of substances into it from the tear film covering its epithelial surface, from capillaries in the tarsal conjunctiva when the lids are closed, from the limbal capillaries, and from the aqueous humor bathing its endothelial surface. These are the sources from which the cornea can derive its supply of nutrients and into which it can discharge its waste products. The permeability of its surfaces and the rates of diffusion of substances through the stroma therefore determine the corneal metabolism to some extent. Likewise, the passage of drugs through the cornea depends largely upon their corneal permeability. Finally, it is conceivable that corneal permeability is a factor in the dynamics of intraocular pressure.

Three theories have been proposed to account for the permeability of cell membranes in general: the pore theory, the electrostatic theory, and the theory of solubility. The cornea may be regarded as a membrane with sievelike properties which determine the passage of substances through it only on the basis of their molecular or ionic size. It can also be regarded as a membrane with electrostatic properties which permit the passage of substances on the basis of the presence or absence of an electric charge. Finally, the cornea can be looked at as a membrane containing a solvent, or a series of sol-

vents, which permits the passage of any substance possessing appropriate solubilities.

It has been found that some substances, e.g., thiodiglycol which readily penetrate the epithelium-stroma combination are of considerably larger molecular size than those of many nonpenetrating substances, e.g., urea. Accordingly, the permeability of the whole cornea cannot be accounted for solely by the pore theory. On the other hand, the permeability of the isolated stroma must depend somewhat on particle size since various acid dyes penetrate the stroma inversely according to their approximate molecular size.

Electrolytes are uniformly retained by the epithelium, but so are many nonelectrolyes, and no exchange of ions occurs when different salts are present on each side of the cornea. Hence, charge or absence of charge cannot alone account for the differential permeability. The permeability of the cornea depends largely on the differential solubilities of the various substances tested. Substances which characteristically pass through the stroma but not through the epithelium are predominantly insoluble in fats. Those which pass equally well through the stroma and the epithelium-stroma combination are characteristically soluble in both water and fat. Finally, those which do not pass through either the stroma or the epithelium either have very large molecules, such as proteins and Congo red dye, or are insoluble in water.

It must be concluded from this that the transfer of substances through the intact cornea is largely a matter of phase solubility. Specifically, the epithelium is believed to be permeable to those substances possessing a fat-soluble phase and the stroma to substances possessing a water-soluble phase. It will be recalled that one of the major differences in the chemical makeup of the epithelium as compared

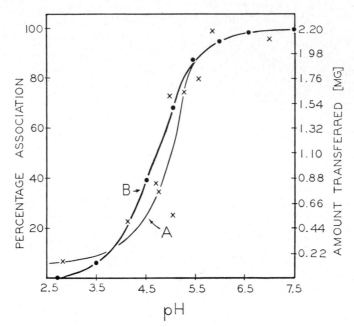

Fig. 8. The influence of pH on the permeability of the cornea to aniline. (From Cogan, D. G., and Hirsch, E.: Arch. Ophth. **32**:276, 1944.)

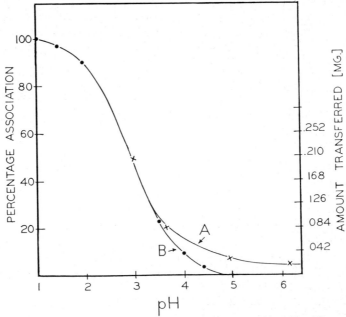

Fig. 9. Influence of pH on the permeability of the cornea to weak acids. (From Cogan, D. G., and Hirsch, E.: Arch. Ophth. **32**:276, 1944.)

to the stroma is its high lipid fraction. The epithelium contains a hundred times the amount of lipoid material present in the stroma (Table 2). Water itself is an exception for it passes through both the stroma and the epithelium. It is known that water can be transferred through other lipid membranes, however, and this fact has led to the development of the theory of the mosaic distribution of lipid elements on cell surfaces. For any substance to pass through the intact cornea, therefore, it is essential that it be soluble in both water and lipids.

The transfer of water across the intact cornea takes place equally well in either direction so that the earlier idea of the cornea's possessing a unidirectional permeability to water, as claimed by Fischer, appears to be erroneous.

Drugs instilled into the conjunctival cul-de-sac for their effect on the interior of the eye are subject to restraints in their passage across the cornea. The most important group of such substances are the alkaloids, which are weak electrolytes, and their solubilities in fats and water vary considerably, according to their dissociation. This is dependent upon the hydrogen ion concentration of the solution in which they are dissolved. Weak bases become progressively dissociated with *increasing* pH, i.e., lose their electric charge and gain in fat solubility. Weak acids become progressively dissociated with *decreasing* pH, i.e., gain an electric charge and gain in water solubility.

The influence of the state of dissociation on corneal permeability has been demonstrated by Cogan and Hirsch[27] in the transfer of aniline, a weak base, and salicylic acid, a weak acid, across the cornea. It may be seen in Fig. 8 that the amount of aniline transferred *increases* with pH; i.e., it increases when the aniline is in the associated (noncharged) state. Under these circumstances the aniline

possesses a greatly increased fat solubility. In the case of the weak acid (Fig. 9), permeability is increased with a *decrease* in pH. These experiments clearly indicate the dependence of corneal permeability upon phase solubility.

It has been found that the penetration of drugs through the excised cornea is also a function of the degree of their dissociation. Free bases penetrate the epithelium-stroma combination; whereas salts penetrate the stroma only. This effect of dissociation on the permeability is, likewise, attributed to the difference in solubility in fat and supports the previously stated thesis that substances penetrate the epithelium only in so far as they are soluble in fat. If the dissociation constant*

---

*When an electrolyte is dissolved in water, a certain proportion of the electrolyte becomes ionized. The portion of the electrolyte which is ionized varies, depending upon the concentration of the electrolyte and its nature. This can be expressed in an equation which involves the dissociation constant of the electrolyte. This is a physical characteristic of the electrolyte and is constant at any one temperature. Consider any weak acid, HA. This acid when dissolved, partially dissociates as follows:

$$HA \rightleftarrows H^+ + A^-$$

According to the law of mass action, this equilibrium may be expressed as follows:

$$\frac{[H^+]\ [A^-]}{[HA]} = K$$

The brackets represent the concentrations of the ions or molecules which they enclose in moles per liter, and K is the dissociation constant of HA. K for acetic acid is 1.86×10^{-5} or 0.0000186. A stronger acid which dissociates to a greater degree would have a larger K. For convenience, K may be expressed as ρK in order to avoid the use of very small numbers, in the same sense that ρH is used to express the hydrogen ion concentration. The ρK is the negative logarithm of K.

Thus $\rho K = -\log K = \dfrac{1}{\log K}$ since K for acetic acid $= 1.86 \times 10^{-5}$, $\rho K = 4.74$.

Stronger acids have a smaller ρK.

and solubility properties of an alkaloid are known, its permeability through the cornea may be predicted. The most important weak bases used in ophthalmic therapeutics are the various alkaloids and the majority of the local anesthetics. From the physiologic point of view, the important weak acids are metabolic products, such as carbonic, lactic, β-hydroxybutyric, and pyruvic acids.

The concept of the dependence of permeability on phase solubility is in accord with the findings of Swan and White[28] on the penetration of substances into the cornea. These authors studied the rate of penetration of various substances into the cornea. It had been generally assumed that the penetration of drugs into the cornea is in inverse relation to the size of their individual molecules, but Swan and White found that this is not so important as the solubilities of the penetrating substances.

They call attention to the importance of the relation and number of the polar groups in influencing the permeability of a compound. The term *polar* refers to the asymmetry of the molecular structure of a compound—a polar compound is asym-

metrical, whereas a nonpolar compound has a symmetrical structure. It has been found that the fat solubility of a substance depends, among other things, on its being nonpolar; e.g., carbon tetrachloride, CCl_4 (Fig. 10[*1*]), has an extremely symmetrical atomic structure; i.e., it is nonpolar. In the diagram, the chlorides are seen to be arranged symmetrically around the central carbon atom, and thus the CCl bonds cancel each other. Another example of a symmetrical compound, and the basic one used by Swan and White, is benzene (Fig. 10 [*2*]). Here again, the C-H bonds cancel each other. On the other hand, some compounds have an asymmetrical atomic structure, e.g., water, which is highly polar because of its asymmetry. It has the following configuration (Fig. 10[*3*]). The addition of so-called polar groups, such as NO_2, NH_2, and $NHSO_3$, in an asymmetrical pattern in the molecule increases the asymmetry of a compound and therefore increases its water solubility. For example, aniline (Fig. 10[*4*]) is formed by a replacement of one atom of hydrogen in the benzene ring by an NH_2 group, making the benzene ring polar.

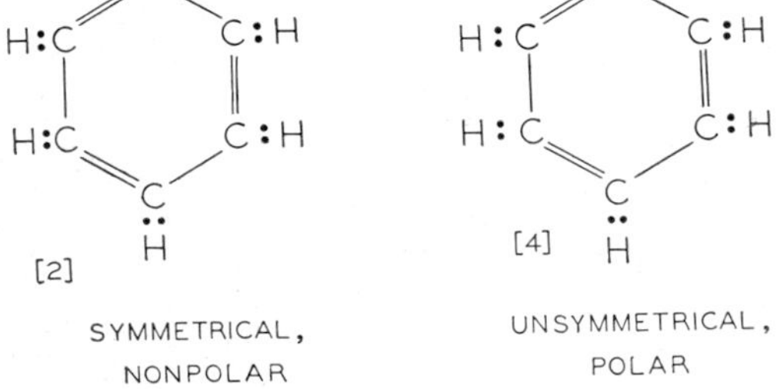

Nonpolar compounds are characteristically more soluble in organic solvents than in water and are spoken of as hydrophobic. The hydrocarbons are examples of this group of substances. The influence of polar and nonpolar structures on cell penetration seems to be related particularly to surface activity and, as stated, to solubility in water and lipids.

The studies of Swan and White are of considerable theoretical interest in any consideration of drugs which are to be exhibited by instillation into the conjunctival cul-de-sac because at least part of the drug must gain entrance into the eye through the cornea. The physical properties of the drug used, i.e., its

SYMMETRICAL, NONPOLAR

UNSYMMETRICAL, POLAR

Fig. 10. The polarity of chemical compounds.

phase solubilities, must be taken into account and also the physical properties of the vehicle in which the drug is administered, i.e., whether it is predominantly a fat or a water solvent. Polar compounds in water and nonpolar compounds in oil are retained in their respective vehicles and therefore must enter the cornea slowly. The partition of polar and nonpolar compounds between the cornea and vehicle simulates to a certain extent the distribution of a solute between two immiscible solvents. The hydrogen ion concentration, the osmotic pressure, and the presence of surface tension-reducing agents are other physical properties of vehicles which directly or indirectly affect the rate of penetration of drugs into the cornea.

We must give up the concept that the epithelium is a simple barrier to the penetration of substances into the cornea and that the endothelium prevents the escape of substances from the aqueous humor. As far as the epithelium is concerned, those substances which are nonpolar, i.e.,

fat-soluble, penetrate more readily into the cornea when the epithelium is intact than after it has been removed. Injuries to the epithelium, therefore, increase the penetration rate of polar and surface-inactive compounds, but may decrease the penetration of nonpolar and surface-active compounds.

From the studies of Cogan and Kinsey on permeability and those of Swan and White on penetration, Kinsey[29] has evolved the following concept of how a weak base, such as the alkaloid homatropine, may be transferred through the intact cornea (Fig. 11). As it is used clinically, a solution of homatropine hydrobromide consists of homatropine ions bearing a positive charge, R_3NH^+, bromide ions bearing a negative charge, Br^-, undissociated homatropine hydrobromide, and a small amount of undissociated homatropine (free base) R_3N. At a pH of 6.0, which is the approximate pH of the usual solution of homatropine, the ratio of the amount of homatropine existing in the dissociated state to the amount existing

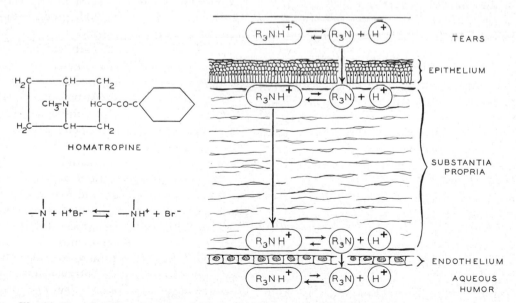

Fig. 11. Transfer of homatropine through the cornea, according to Kinsey.

in the undissociated state is approximately
1000:1. When a drop of this solution is
placed on the cornea, the undissociated
moiety penetrates the epithelium because
of its lipoid solubility, as previously explained. The dissociated remainder cannot
penetrate the epithelium since it is not
fat-soluble. Once inside the epithelium,
the undissociated moiety immediately re-
dissociates.

$$R_3N + H^+ \leftrightarrows R_3NH^+$$

The amount of this dissociation will
be the same as that in the bottle because
it depends on the pH, and that of the
cornea is presumably 7.3, but again the
homatropine will exist in both the dissociated and undissociated forms.

The next step is the penetration of the
substance from the epithelium into the
stroma. The dissociated moiety will penetrate the stroma because it is water-
soluble, whereas the undissociated fraction cannot. At the junction of the stroma
and endothelium, the same process must
again occur that took place at the surface
of the epithelium. Finally, the dissociated
homatorpine leaves the endothelium for
the aqueous humor.

In each of these four steps the substance is able to penetrate because of the
difference in solubility of the two forms
in which it exists. It must be remembered
that the process of transfer will not be
limited by exhaustion of the amount of
homatropine present in any one form
since, as soon as one molecule of either
form (dissociated or undissociated) leaves
the layer, redissociation takes place and
the process continues as before.

Agents which reduce the surface tension generally increase the permeability of
membranes. O'Brien and Swan[30] showed
that the use of a surface tension-reducing
agent increases the absorption of carbam-
inocholine (Doryl). Substances which re-

duce surface tension are called *wetting
agents*. The relative impermeability of the
corneal epithelium to Doryl is due to the
fact that this compound has a low lipoid
solubility; i.e., it is highly polar. It must
be remembered that wetting agents are in
themselves somewhat toxic to the epithelium. The concentration at which this
toxicity becomes manifest differs considerably among different wetting agents.

The rate at which a harmful substance
is able to penetrate the cornea is of considerable importance in determining the
total amount of corneal damage. The
barrier to the penetration of acids and
alkalies, presumably since they dissociate,
is the corneal epithelium. This has been
demonstrated[31] by comparing the effect
of irrigations of hydrochloric acid and
buffer solutions over the intact epithelium
with the effect of these same solutions
when injected intracorneally or when
used as irrigations after the mechanical
removal of the epithelium. The protective
influence of the epithelium is probably
due to the fact that the acid immediately
precipitates the protein which acts as a
barrier to the further penetration of the
acid. However, when the eye is exposed
to strong alkaline solutions, the first effect
is a swelling and then desquamation of the
epithelium. Hence, the preliminary removal of the epithelium has less effect on
the intensity of alkali burns, and even the
intact epithelium forms only a soft jellylike barrier to further passage of the
alkali.

The rate of penetration of substances
from the bloodstream into the cornea has
been studied[32] using tracer substances
such as Na^{24}, P^{32}, I^{131}, and CS^{134}. When
the rate of entry of these various ions
from the bloodstream into the various regions of the cornea was determined, it
was found that the more peripheral regions had a significantly higher concentra-

tion of the measured substances than the more central region. This would indicate that the limbal vascular plexus plays an important role in supplying such substances to the cornea. When this plexus is damaged, the concentration of injected ions is decreased materially in the cornea.

Substances injected subconjunctivally easily gain entrance to the eye. However, it has been shown that more atropine enters the eye after topical instillations, provided that the cornea is covered with the solution, than when similar amounts are administered subconjunctivally. The mode of entrance after subconjunctival injection is chiefly by diffusion, for complete stoppage of the circulation does not diminish the rate of penetration into the interior of the eye.[33]

The permeability of the epithelium is increased considerably if the tonicity of the solution of the test substance is hypotonic, i.e., below 0.9%. Potts[34] found the most favorable tonicity which does least damage to the corneal epithelium to be 1.35% sodium chloride, which he infers to be the tonicity of the tears (p. 38). However, increasing the tonicity of the solution from 0.9 to 10% caused no increase in corneal permeability.[35] The pH of the solution may be varied from 4.0 to 10.0 without affecting the permeability of the epithelium, but solutions outside this range increase the permeability.

Most of what has just been said relates to the permeability of the cornea as a whole, although occasionally either the stroma or the epithelial layer has been specifically mentioned. A comparison of the cellular layers with the stroma shows considerable differences in permeability. There is probably little difference between the cellular layers and the stroma as far as the permeability to water is concerned. Water can penetrate all the layers of the cornea from either direction, and the re-

sistance to diffusion is due chiefly to the stroma in accordance with its large share of the total thickness of the tissue. I have already called attention to the rapid penetration of the epithelium by fat-soluble substances. Since the epithelial cells contain a high proportion of lipids compared to the stroma, this is understandable. When it comes to the penetration of ionized substances, one finds a considerable resistance in the cellular layers compared to the stroma. In the early studies of Cogan and Kinsey[36-41] evidence was given that water can diffuse through the excised cornea in both directions, but that salt cannot diffuse through the cornea in appreciable quantities in either direction. Hydrostatic pressures up to 400 mm.Hg applied to balance the osmotic forces failed to force a 1% solution of sodium chloride through the cornea. Permeability to water was demonstrated by means of determination of the passage of heavy water, deuterium, across the cornea and the permeability to salt by direct chemical analysis. Their experiments indicated that the barriers to the passage of the salt were the epithelium and the endothelium. If the epithelium and endothelium were removed, salt could readily diffuse through the corneal stroma.

Further evidence of the impermeability of the epithelium and endothelium to salt was given by Holt and Cogan.[42] They determined the permeability of the cornea to ions by measuring the impedance of tissues to the passage of an electric current. They found that the stroma offered little resistance to the passage of ions, whereas the epithelium had relatively enormous resistance. They believed the epithelium was relatively impermeable to all ions. This is no longer accepted. It has subsequently been shown by many authors that although the epithelium and endothelium are less permeable to sodium and chloride than the stroma they do not act like semipermeable membranes, preventing the passage of ions and building up osmotic forces on one side. The importance of this fact will be enlarged on in the section on corneal turgescence.

While the epithelium and endothelium are permeable to both sodium and chloride, the resistance of the epithelium is considerable and probably many times that of the endothelium. However, as Maurice points out,[43] permeability measurements across the epithelium are confused by the presence of an active transport of the sodium ion and a resultant potential across this layer (p. 62), and if allowance is made for this, the resistance of both the epithelial and endothelial layers to all small ions is approximately the same.

Once a substance gains access to the corneal stroma through either the epithelium or endothelium, its passage through the stroma in either direction depends almost entirely on diffusion. There is no flow of water through the cornea in the strict sense. Whatever movement of water

does occur must be at a rate of less than 0.1 mm./hr., according to Maurice.[44] Previous experiments which indicated a flow of water out of the cornea through both the epithelial and endothelial surfaces, balanced in the latter case by the outward flow produced by the intraocular pressure, have not been confirmed.[45]

Table 3 shows the rates of diffusion of various substances in the corneal stroma. The values are expressed as the obstruction of the stroma to diffusion—how many times slower the substance diffuses in the stroma than it does in free solution. Diffusion takes place through the substance of the stroma and not through any preformed channels or canals. Water diffuses in either direction through the stroma at a rate of 0.4 ml./hr./sq. cm.[47]

In the endothelium, which is one hundred times more permeable to sodium than the epithelium, transport of ions is probably by way of a system of relatively large uncharged intercellular spaces.[48]

In the endothelial cells of the rabbit so-called terminal bars have been found between adjacent endothelial cells. These

Table 3. *Obstruction of corneal stroma to diffusion of various substances* *

Substance	Diameter (Å)	Obstruction[a]	
Cs[134]	⌐5	2.2 ± 0.05	
Br[82]	⌐5	2.7 ± 0.1	S.E.M.[e]
Na[24]	6.6	1.9 ± 0.2	
Fluorescein[b]	11	5	
Albumin[c]	74	8	
Mammalian hemoglobin[d]	64	10	
Planorbis hemoglobin[d]	185	∞	

*From Maurice, D.: The use of permeability studies in the investigation of submicroscopic structure. In Smelser, G., editor: The structure of the eye, New York, 1961, Academic Press, Inc., p. 385.

[a]Obstruction defined as how many times diffusion in tissue is slower than diffusion in saline at the same temperature. Small ionic diameters and diffusion coefficients from Robinson, R. A., and Stokes, R. H.: Electrolyte solutions, ed. 2, New York, 1959, Academic Press, Inc.

[b]Maurice, D.: Am. J. Ophth. 49:1011, 1960.

[c]Maurice, D. (1960): Unpublished data.

[d]Maurice, D.: J. Physiol. 136:263, 1957.

[e]S.E.M. = standard error of the mean.

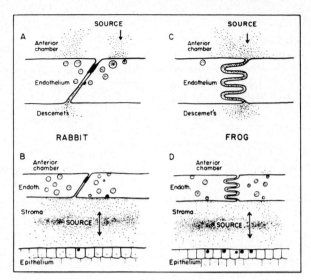

Fig. 12. Schematic summarization of the comparative aspects of the transport pathways described in the cornea of the rabbit and of the frog. In the rabbit colloidal markers are adsorbed at the apical surface of the endothelial cell and are transported around the terminal bar region by pinocytosis, **A.** They are subsequently expelled into the intercellular space from which they apparently flow into Descemet's membrane. Particles diffuse freely in Descemet's membrane and the stroma so that when marker is placed in the stroma, **B,** the particles accumulate at the margin of Descemet's membrane and endothelium. These pass out across the endothelium only within the membrane-bounded vacuoles, rarely appearing in the intercellular space. Some marker may pass across the basement membrane of the epithelium and be taken up by the basal epithelial cells. In the frog there is no terminal bar or other specialization of the apposing marginal membranes of endothelial cells, **C,** and marker passes freely down the intercellular space. Only an occasional pinocytotic vesicle is found in the cytoplasm of these cells. If marker is placed in the stroma, **D,** the pattern of particle transport is identical with that seen in the rabbit, **B,** except that more marker appears to cross the basement membrane of the corneal epithelium in the frog than in the rabbit. (From Kaye, G.: J. Cell. Biol. **15:**241, 1962.)

may alter the mode of uptake and transport of substances, particularly colloidal particles. These terminal bars are not found in the frog, according to Kaye.[49] In Fig. 12 is shown the mode of uptake and transport of colloidal markers in the rabbit with terminal bars and in the frog without these.

CORNEAL TURGESCENCE

The normal cornea during life maintains a fairly constant thickness. A slight increase in thickness occurs during sleep due to the absence of evaporation when the lids are closed. It normally keeps its water content at a steady level of about 75% of its weight. However, the corneal stroma has a marked affinity for water, and when excised pieces are immersed in solutions, they will absorb and hold water in large quantities. As a result, they become turgesced. The swelling takes place as an increase in the front-to-back thickness of the cornea, with slight contraction in tangential length. Pieces of cornea immersed in distilled water may increase their weight more than five times. Turgescence of the cornea is always accompanied by loss of transparency, the cornea eventually looking like ground glass. One might suppose that this turgescence was merely an osmotic effect, but this is not so as the excised cornea swells in physiologic salt solutions; in fact, it is greatest in NaCl solutions of about 1% concentration.

The hydration properties of excised pieces of cornea were studied by Kinsey and Cogan.[38, 39] They found that the amount of swelling is not dependent on the osmotic pressure of the solution per se since the degree of swelling is the same throughout a wide range of concentrations of glucose, urea, or glycerin. The cornea swells to the same extent and at the same rate in solutions of nonelectrolytes as in distilled water. In salt solutions, on the other hand, the amount and rate of swelling vary with the concentration and are distinctly different from those observed with distilled water. The degree of swelling cannot be correlated solely with the osmotic pressure of the solution or the valence of the ion. Each salt appears to have a specific effect on the rate and degree of corneal turgescence.

This swelling pressure, or thirst of the corneal stroma for water, can be measured by balancing it with a concentration of any solute whose osmotic pressure equals the swelling pressure. In order to prevent the cornea from swelling in solutions of dextran, a 4.75% solution must be used. This has an osmotic pressure of 865 mm.H_2O. Pieces of sclera are prevented from swelling when immersed in a 2.5% solution of dextran, which has an osmotic pressure of 325 mm. Hg. This gives some idea of the enormous capacity of the cornea to imbibe water. The swelling pressure can be neutralized by applying mechanical force to the surfaces of the excised pieces. In order to maintain normal corneal hydration, a mechanical pressure of 140 Gm./sq. cm. must be applied to pieces of corneal stroma immersed in distilled water and 40 Gm./sq. cm. when immersed in 1% sodium chloride, or a solution of HCl having pH 3.1. The actual swelling pressure of the stroma is of theoretical importance. If the swelling pressure of the living stroma were the same as the colloid osmotic pressure of the plasma in the limbal capillaries (assuming the epithelium and endothelium to be impermeable to electrolytes), there would be an equilibrium between these two forces, and the cornea would automatically be kept at a constant level of hydration. More recent measurements of this swelling pressure[50] showed a value of 865 mm. H_2O, which exceeds the colloidal osmotic pressure of the blood plasma by at least 500 mm. H_2O. This points to the need for some dehydrating mechanism in the cornea which prevents it from swelling in the normal state.

There can be no doubt that the imbibition of water is due to the stroma, but whether this is largely a property of the collagen fibrils or the ground substance surrounding the fibrils is at present debated. The evidence points largely to the mucopolysaccharides being chiefly responsible; the collagen fibrils themselves do not swell. The pH at which the swelling potential of the cornea is minimal is 4.5 to 4.7.[51] This is not the isoelectric point of collagen, pH 7.0; the diameter of the fibrils does not increase as the cornea swells, nor do the fibrils show any alteration or birefringence.[52] Further, the swelling is entirely an increase in thickness of the cornea and not in a direction parallel to its surfaces. This fact is of importance in corneal transplants. If the donor graft, which is nearly always swollen to some extent due to an increase in corneal hydration, were swollen in both thickness and in breadth, any shrinkage in breadth after insertion in the recipient eye would lead to opening of the anterior chamber, with serious consequences.

The living cornea is in the deturgesced state as long as its surface membranes are intact. However, swelling of the cornea occurs if either the epithelium or endothelium are damaged.[53] This is of great clinical importance. Abrasions of the cornea or any condition leading to loss of the corneal epithelium is likely to produce localized areas of corneal swelling and cloudiness. Fortunately, the corneal epithelium regenerates rapidly, and ordinarily the turgescence of the cornea is slight and transient. Damage to the endothelium is far more serious. Any loss of the endothelial cells results in marked and usually permanent swelling and loss of transparency, since the endothelium does not have the regenerative powers of the epithelium. This must always be kept in mind in any operative procedure in which the anterior chamber is opened. The endothelial surface must be scrupulously avoided when any instrument is introduced into the anterior chamber, and even flushing the anterior chamber with any solution carries with it some danger of damaging these fragile cells.

Although the normal water content of the living cornea is about 75%, it has been pointed out that this represents a relatively deturgesced state, since under conditions just outlined the corneal stroma will imbibe many times the amount of water and hold it. It has also been pointed out that there is little barrier to the entrance of water into the cornea from either its epithelial or endothelial surfaces or from its limbal blood supply. The epithelium is measurably permeable to water and the endothelium is highly permeable.[54] Water comes in readily along with salts from the limbal capillaries since there are no restraining membranes interposed. However, the cross-sectional area through which diffusion can take place is quite small compared to the total area of the cornea, and since no flow of water can be demonstrated in the cornea (p. 56), the limbal region is of minor importance when considering the water transport through the cornea as a whole.[47] Since living corneas are in the deturgesced state, it must be concluded that some mechanism is present which gets rid of the water. The water content of the living cornea must be maintained at a steady state between the water diffusing into the cornea and that being removed by some process.

Cogan and Kinsey first presented evidence that the mechanism which keeps the cornea deturgesced is an osmotic one. Their experiments indicated to them that the epithelial and endothelial surfaces were impermeable to salt and that neither sodium or chloride could enter the cornea if these membranes were intact. They believed that this impermeability to salt was sufficient to create a difference in osmotic pressure between the fluid in the corneal stroma and that bathing the cornea on either side. They pointed out that both the tear fluid bathing the epithelium and the aqueous humor bathing the endothelium were hypertonic, and they claimed that this was in part maintained by the impermeability of these cellular layers to salt. They therefore suggested that the intact cornea is maintained in a state of relative deturgescence by virtue of having a hypertonic salt solution in contact with its anterior and posterior surfaces. They pictured water entering the corneal stroma from the limbal capillaries, as illustrated in Fig. 13, and being pulled out by the osmotic force of the hypertonic salt solution covering the surface layers. The micelles of the corneal stroma hold some of the water against the osmotic forces

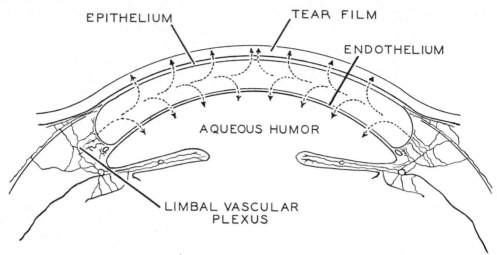

EPITHELIUM   TEAR FILM

ENDOTHELIUM

AQUEOUS HUMOR

LIMBAL VASCULAR
PLEXUS

Fig. 13. The movement of water into the cornea as suggested by Cogan and Kinsey.

withdrawing it from the surface layers, and the balance of these forces determines the degree of turgescence of the cornea. If either of the surface layers are destroyed, the imbibitory power of the corneal stroma no longer has any balancing force to oppose it since salt can then enter the cornea.

This hypothesis of an osmotic mechanism has been seriously questioned. It has been shown that the impermeability of the epithelium and endothelium to salt is only relative and not of an order to build up sufficient osmotic pressure required to pull water out of the cornea. Maurice[55, 56] has shown that the amount of sodium getting into the corneal stroma through either the epithelial or endothelial surfaces is too great to build up sufficient osmotic pressure to be effective. Further, a large amount of evidence has accumulated that the mechanism which gets rid of the water entering the cornea is a metabolic one, depending on aerobic glycolysis. Anaerobic glycolysis does not seem to play a role in this process.[57] Oxygen must be present. This ties in with the cloudiness of corneas that are covered

completely with a contact lens, mentioned previously (p. 48). It was shown that the cloudiness was due to turgescence of the cornea caused by oxygen lack. This itself pointed strongly to metabolic processes being involved in the mechanism of deturgescence. Other evidence of a metabolic role involving oxygen consumption has been produced by Harris and coworkers.[58] They found that reduction of temperature leads to corneal hydration, but that if the corneas were subsequently removed to room temperature and kept in air, the swollen corneas returned to their normal thickness. If oxygen was excluded, however, this temperature reversal effect did not take place, and the corneas remained swollen. Harris maintained that the accumulation of fluid during refrigeration was due to a reduction of metabolic activity. The effects of metabolic poisons, especially enzymatic, also could be interpreted as supporting the theory of a metabolic pump which required energy from aerobic glycolysis. In spite of a high level of anaerobic glycolysis in the cornea (p. 47), it seems that corneal deturgescence cannot be maintained in the absence of oxygen for any prolonged period.

It is not known with certainty where this metabolic pump is located or what actually is pumped out of the cornea, i.e., water or some ion primarily. The stroma itself cannot be responsible, nor can the limbus be concerned since the temperature reversal effect takes place with pieces of excised cornea taken from the central regions of the cornea. Either the epithelium, the endothelium, or both must be the seat of this metabolic activity. We have seen that the necessary anatomic structures and enzymes are present in these layers to make such metabolic activity plausible (p. 47). Harris's results indicated to him that the epithelium was probably the chief site of this pump mechanism. He produced evidence which suggested that the major cause of hydration of the cornea following endothelial damage was influx of water from the aqueous humor rather than decreased transport of water out of the cornea. According to his view, the endothelium provides a barrier to the influx of water from the anterior chamber, and Descemet's membrane is the barrier across which outflow occurs. The experiments of Knowles,[59] who inserted plastic membranes intralamellarly into the corneas of rabbits, cats, and monkeys, support this concept. Although no changes in the stroma occurred on either side of the membrane in monkeys, in the rabbit and cat corneas degeneration of the stroma anterior to the membrane took place. This was attributed to interference with the fluid exchange of this part of the cornea. Since no degeneration occurred in the stroma behind the membrane on the side of the endothelium, this was taken to be evidence that the endothelium is the chief site of the mechanism of deturgescence. These experiments were repeated by Bock and Maumenee,[60] who

reached the same general conclusions, although the changes in the stroma in their experiments were purely edematous and not degenerative changes. More recently Pollack[61] employed similar techniques and found that plastic membranes could be inserted in cat corneas which remained entirely clear after a period of swelling due to the operative trauma. Removal of the epithelium then led to swelling of the underlying cornea anterior to the plastic disk, while the posterior layers on the side of the endothelium remained clear. If two disks were inserted and the epithelium was removed, the middle and posterior segments of the stroma remained clear—only the segment on the side of the removed epithelium became swollen. Removal of the endothelium revealed a similar pattern. The posterior segment now became swollen, while the anterior segment or segments (in the case of two plastic disks) remained entirely clear. This suggests that active transport must occur across both the epithelium and endothelium. It also makes it possible that the stroma itself is the site of metabolic activity which maintains normal corneal hydration. There is some evidence that mucopolysaccharide synthesis does occur in the stroma.

It is well known clinically that abrasions of the epithelium seldom cause much swelling of the cornea and heal promptly, whereas endothelial damage is likely to produce marked and permanent swelling. In the rabbit removal of the epithelium experimentally produced on an average an increase of 200% in the cornea's thickness in 24 hours, whereas removal of the endothelium produced an increase of 500%.[56] The average rate of increase was initially 0.5% of the original thickness per minute when the epithelium was removed and 2% per minute when endothelium was removed. The fact that endothelial damage results in much more corneal swelling and more rapid swelling than epithelial damage supports the premise that the endothelium is of greater importance in deturgescence. It has been pointed out, however, that this might be the results of the additive effect of the intraocular pressure on the side of the endothelium. In effect, this would tend to prevent water coming into the cornea from the epithelial side and aid in driving water into the cornea on the endothelial side. Anseth and Dohlman[62] point out that the intraocular pressure counteracts the imbibition of fluid from the tears through the epithelium but not that of the aqueous humor through the endothelium. This hydrostatic pressure effect may account in part, at least, for the differences in swelling of the cornea between epithelial and endothelial removal.

As a working hypothesis, one can assume that either the epithelium, the endothelium, or both are concerned in the active transport of water or some solute out of the cornea. At present it is not known what this substance is. Any solute present to the extent of 5 mM/L. would be effective in overcoming the swelling force of the stroma.[55] If there is ion transport across one of these membranes involved in corneal dehydration, a potential difference across the cornea should be present, since there would likely be a difference in the mobility of the positive and negative ions involved. Such potential differences have been found.[63, 64] The epithelium is primarily responsible for this potential, and it is abolished if oxygen is removed. However, the fact that the potential is due to the epithelium and not to the endothelium, which as we have seen is most likely the seat of the dehydrating mechanism, casts some doubt on this potential having anything to do with the dehydrating mechanism. In fact, the

transparency of the corneas, which is often used as an index of corneal hydration, shows no correlation with the level of this potential.

If an electrolyte and not water is the substance excreted, sodium, according to Harris,[58] is the only one which can be considered on theoretical grounds. But we are completely confounded here by the fact that the polarity of the potential is in the wrong direction—the epithelial side of the cornea is negative to the endothelial side, which means that this mechanism would pump sodium *into* the cornea and not *out* of it. That sodium actually is pumped into the cornea across the epithelium has now been proved by Donn and co-workers.[64] To make matters still more perplexing, if the cornea is cooled, the inward transport of sodium is abolished, and *mirabile dictu* the cornea swells. These authors are unable to solve this paradox but point out that probably this inward transport of sodium into the cornea has nothing to do with the mechanism of corneal dehydration, and that many other possible substances may be pumped out of the cornea in addition to water or sodium, which has already been mentioned, such as uncharged salt molecules. This inward flux of sodium might be related to the normal state of the corneal colloids.

The failure so far to identify either the source of the metabolic activity of dehydration or the substance pumped out of the cornea by this mechanism has led some authors to question the entire theory of a metabolic pump. Langham[65a] has called attention to the well-known clinical fact that small areas of either epithelial or endothelial cell damage usually lead to strictly localized regions of corneal swelling in the immediate neighborhood of the damaged cells. Further, if the cornea be made to swell experimentally by denuding the epithelium over a large area, as the new epithelial cells cover the cornea there is a corresponding dehydration of this area of the cornea. The area still uncovered by new-formed cells remains swollen. In other words, the ability of the epithelium to induce recovery of turgesced cornea is strictly confined to those areas of stroma covered by epithelium. This and other considerations have induced him to present a new hypothesis, as follows.

"Normally in the living eye the swelling pressure is zero due to a balance between the imbibition pressure of the corneal mucopolysaccharides and the restraining or cohesive forces between the structural components of the stroma. Swelling would then result from a decrease in the forces of cohesion, and, in turn, the uptake of fluid by the mucopolysaccharide would cause a concurrent decrease in the imbibition pressure."*

In this scheme it would be necessary to propose that aerobic glycolysis was essential to the maintenance of the cohesive forces in the normal cornea and to their restoration in the swollen cornea undergoing recovery.

Another possibility which remains to be discussed is the role that purely passive osmotic forces in the corneal stroma play. What is the osmotic pressure of the interstitial fluid in the stroma? Does this factor bear on the problem of corneal turgescence? Determinations of the osmolality of interstitial fluid have been made by several different investigators. Davson[65] and Harris[66] consider the interstitial fluid hypertonic to plasma, whereas von Bahr and Giardini and Gandolfi[67] found this fluid to be hypotonic to aqueous humor. Recently Brubaker and Kupfer[67] found the interstitial fluid to be hypertonic to arterial serum

---

*From Langham, M.: Invest. Ophth. 1: 187, 1962.

by approximately 10 mM. These authors found the aqueous humor to have this same osmolality, i.e., 10 mM hypertonic to arterial serum.

The fact that the interstitial fluid is hypertonic to blood serum would imply that a large amount of fluid would tend to come into the cornea from the limbal blood vessels on an osmotic basis, which fluid would have to be gotten rid of by some mechanism. It would explain the strict localization of corneal swelling to the site of epithelial loss in abrasions of the cornea. On the whole it gives further support to the belief that some metabolic pump must be present in one or both of the cellular layers of the cornea.

CORNEAL TRANSPARENCY

The normal cornea is transparent, and any change in this property seriously interferes with the clarity of the retinal image. The anatomic peculiarities of the corneal structure, such as the uniformity and regularity in the arrangement of the epithelial cells, the closely packed corneal lamellae of uniform size running almost parallel to each other, and the absence of blood vessels, all contribute to the efficiency of the eye as an optical instrument. Because the individual corneal cells are living and are, therefore, constantly undergoing change and replacement, the cornea cannot maintain an unvarying constancy in its transparency and optical properties.

The transparency of the cornea depends on its physical makeup and, as we have seen from the discussion in the previous section, on the mechanisms which keep it from turgescing.

Physical factors

An explanation of corneal transparency based on the physical arrangement of the corneal micelles has been proposed by

Maurice.[52] He finds that the corneal collagen fibrils form a lattice structure so arranged that scattering of light is eliminated by mutual interference from individual fibrils.

The basic substance of the corneal stroma is collagen, saturated with a solution of mucoid. The index of refraction of the corneal collagen has been found to be 1.380 in cattle and 1.373 in pigs.[68]

The cornea remains clear when immersed in fluids of different refractive indexes up to 1.564. Therefore, the cornea can maintain its transparency even when the index of refraction of its collagen differs considerably from that of the surrounding medium. This property of remaining clear is believed to be due to the fibrils' being tightly and regularly packed together. It vanishes if the fibrils are broken up by artificial means. As long as the fibers are regularly arranged in a lattice and separated by less than a wavelength of light, the cornea will remain transparent. In Fig. 14 is shown the arrangement of the fibrils in a regular lattice, each fiber separated from the others by a regular spacing. The arrangement of the fibers when the cornea is swollen or distorted by pressure is shown in Fig. 15.

It has been shown that in order to maintain the transparency of the cornea it is necessary to keep it dehydrated. Since the structural and fluid components of the cornea have different refractive indexes, it is essential to keep the fluid constituents at a minimum.

The transparency of the cornea becomes temporarily impaired when abnormal pressures are applied to it. During the rise of intraocular pressure in acute glaucoma, the cornea becomes cloudy, and it is quite evident that this loss of transparency is not caused entirely by imbibition of fluid, which does occur, but also by physical changes in the stroma, since the

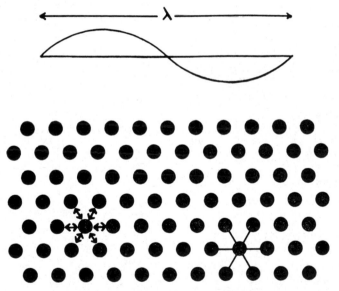

Fig. 14. Cross-sectional view of fibrils arranged in lattice. The size of a wavelength is shown above for comparison. Forces of repulsion and rigid links between fibrils are shown schematically. (From Maurice, D.: The physics of corneal transparency. In Duke-Elder, S.: Transparency of the cornea, Oxford, England, 1960, Blackwell Scientific Publications.)

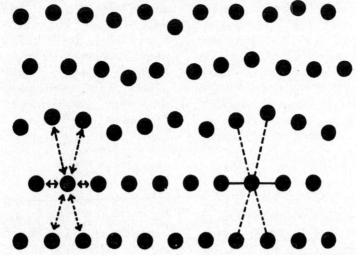

Fig. 15. Diagram illustrating swelling of cornea and disorder of the rows of fibrils consequent on weakening of forces of alignment from neighboring rows. (From Maurice, D.: The physics of corneal transparency. In Duke-Elder, S.: The physics of corneal transparency. In Duke-Elder, S.: Transparency of the cornea, Oxford, England, 1960, Blackwell Scientific Publications.)

cloudiness disappears immediately when the pressure is lowered. This can be demonstrated easily in an enucleated eye by applying pressure to the globe, whereupon the cornea immediately loses its transparency. As soon as the pressure is relieved, the transparency returns.

Effect of turgescence on corneal transparency

The cornea is a lyophilic colloid system inasmuch as its behavior is similar to that of gelatin and fibrin. Various physicochemical factors affect its transparency, acting through changes in the refractive index of either its intercellular fluid, the corneal micelles, or of both. The regulation of the water content of the cornea has already been discussed (p. 57). The absorbing power of the connective tissue must be due to its two chief components, collagen and mucoid. The collagen, split up into loose bundles of fine fibers, lies enmeshed in the mucoid.

The mucoid not only fills, as a gel, all spaces between the fiber bundles, but also penetrates the bundles and takes part in the formation of the micelles of the intermediate substance itself. These two components must be considered separately with regard to their contribution to the total absorptive power of the connective tissue. When dried corneas are exposed to water vapor of increasing concentration up to a water content of 30%, the water is taken up into the micelles of collagen, causing a demonstrable expansion of the crystalline lattice. Further absorption of water is ascribed mostly to the interfibrillar mucoid. Imbibition of collagen is intensified by the addition of acid and imbibition of mucoid by the addition of alkali. From the observations just mentioned, it should be expected that the mucoid of the cornea is also of importance to its transparency. This is confirmed by the fact that the increase in transparency of the corneas of chick embryos coincides with the appearance of the metachromatic mucoid staining. Van Walbeek and Neumann[69] investigated the transparency of the cornea after swelling in water. Maximal transparency occurred when the amount of water was 200 to 400% of the weight of the dry matter. This corresponds to the physiologic water content of fresh corneas. Their experiments lead them to believe that there is a complex relationship between collagen and mucoid and that these substances are not physicochemically independent.

In order to maintain its transparency, the cornea must be bathed with a fluid having an osmotic pressure as high as interstitial fluid. If the cornea is bathed with a hypotonic solution, it becomes cloudy due to the loss of the osmotic forces acting at the corneal epithelium. When the cornea is cloudy because it is turgescent, it can be temporarily cleared by bathing the eye with a hypertonic solution, such as 10% salt or glycerine solution. Solutions of drugs to be used in ocular therapeutics should be made equal to a 1 to 1.5% salt solution (p. 39).

In several pathologic conditions, such as glaucoma or endothelial dystrophy, fluid collects in the epithelial cells to such an extent that bullae are formed. Cogan[70] believes that this is due to an osmotic pressure greater in the epithelium than in tears, as a result of which water passes into the epithelium through the anterior surface from the tears. The experimental production of corneal vesicles supports this theory. Tears in the presence of corneal edema have not been sufficiently investigated, as Cogan points out, and the osmotic imbalance may result from either an increase in the salt content of the cornea or a decrease in the salt content of tears. If one grants that this is due to an increase in the salt content of the cor-

nea and not to a diminution in that of tears, it should be possible to produce fluctuations in the epithelial changes by variations in the composition of tears. Normally the tear film over the surface of the cornea is concentrated by evaporation. When evaporation at the surface does not occur, the edema becomes considerably worse. Cogan was able to prove this in bilateral endothelial dystrophy by having the patient wear airtight goggles, one side of which contained calcium chloride to absorb the moisture. The eye on that side showed improvement in corneal edema after the goggles had been worn for an hour. If evaporation was prevented, the edema became worse.

HEALING OF CORNEAL WOUNDS

The reactions which determine healing of corneal wounds start in the first few hours after injury, and most of these are initiated in the corneal epithelium. One of these changes, studied and elegantly documented by Weimar,[71] is that injury to the epithelial cell activates proteolytic enzymes which liberate chemotactic substances, presumably polypeptides inducing polymorphonuclear invasion. This process appears to be limited to the second hour following corneal injury and, if it is inhibited at this time, completely abolishes the invasion of the wounded cornea by polymorphonuclear leukocytes, at least up to the sixth postoperative hour. Several substances that specifically inhibit proteolytic enzymes, such as sodium salicylate and soybean trypsin inhibitor, were found to be effective.

Another change in the corneal stroma induced by wounding is its ability to take up and concentrate the vital dye neutral red. The normal stroma does not take up this dye but shortly after injury begins to show this property. The epithelium seems to be the source of the agent which stimulates the stromal cells to concentrate this dye, for crushing the epithelium in the region of the wound considerably accelerates the process. Further, the effect of the epithelium can be inhibited by soybean trypsin inhibitor and can be activated by trypsin only in the presence of the epithelium.

Weimar has also obtained evidence that the presence of the epithelium is necessary for transformation of the corneal stromal cells and monocytes into fibroblasts.

Superficial abrasions of the cornea which involve only the epithelium heal rapidly. It is not uncommon to find an abraded area measuring 2 or 3 mm. covered with epithelium in 24 hours. In a normal cornea phosphatase is found in faint traces in the cellular elements of the stroma.[72] In corneas having experimental abrasions there occurs a strong phosphatase reaction, with numerous lymphocytes which accumulate in the intralamellar spaces immediately underneath the injury. The lymphocytes showing this reaction increase greatly in number in the first 24 hours after the abrasion. After this, they decrease in number, and the cornea returns to a nearly normal appearance by the end of the fourth day. This observation suggests that the infiltration of the phosphatase-rich lymphocytes from the bloodstream into the avascular corneal stroma may be concerned in the process of phosphorylation which is apparently necessary for the repair of tissues.

Two processes are involved in the healing of wounds of the epithelial surface of the cornea: (1) cell migration to cover the injured area and (2) mitosis to reconstitute the normal number of epithelial cells. The migratory activity occurs first and almost immediately following an abrasion of the cornea. Cell division follows shortly afterward.

Small epithelial defects may be healed entirely without any cell multiplication,[73] simply by cell migration. The cells covering the defect are larger and flatter than normal and at first form a layer of only one-cell thickness. Thus, coverage of an epithelial defect can be accomplished with far fewer cells than were present initially. Recovery of the normal number of epithelial cells is accomplished by reduction in the rate of desquamation following closure of the wound, rather than by any marked increase in mitotic activity. Generally, the onset of the cellular movements takes place after a lag of about one hour following injury so that the stimulus for migration of cells becomes established during this period. In the repair of small wounds, mitosis has been found to decrease during the migratory phase.[74-76]

Drugs such as colchicine, ether, cocaine, and ephedrine have a definite deleterious effect on mitosis.[77] Colchicine arrests mitosis in metaphase but has little or no effect on the rate of entrance of the cells into mitotic activity. In the corneal epithelium of the living rat, ether, cocaine, and ephedrine all diminish the rate at which the cells begin mitosis, and under certain conditions ether appears to increase the duration of the mitotic cycle also. Corneal anesthetics definitely delay healing of corneal wounds when applied topically.[78, 79] Because of this inhibitory effect of some of the more commonly used anesthetics, a search was carried out by Smelser and Ozanics[80] to discover an anesthetic which would produce adequate surface anesthsia and yet not inhibit healing. In earlier experiments[81] these authors found considerable mitotic activity during the migratory phase of healing following extensive thermal burns of the cornea. They found 0.5% Nupercaine and 2% phenacaine hydrochloride caused a rather marked decrease in the number of mitotic figures in the normal cornea. Most of the anesthetics tested were harmful to mitosis, and after a burn had been incurred, they had an even more pronounced depressing action on mitosis than upon intact normal epithelium. Ointments containing the drugs were found to be less serious in their effect on mitosis than solutions of drugs in the same concentrations. Migration of cells was also found to be inhibited by some of the anesthetics. Aqueous solutions of Nupercaine had the greatest inhibitory action on movements of cells. Even boric acid with a pH of 4.1 inhibited migration of cells but to a slighter degree than the anesthetics. The ointments had a less deleterious effect on migration than did the aqueous solutions. This justifies the established opinion that many anesthetics interfere with corneal wound healing.

Although cocaine has been singled out as the anesthetic agent most damaging to the cornea, most synthetic anesthetic agents are as capable as cocaine of producing corneal erosions.[82] In addition to the toxic effect of repeated anesthetic agents on the cornea, Behrendt has found that further instillations of most anesthetic agents after the anesthesia has worn away show a progressive diminishing anesthetic effect until finally the effect is completely lost. It is not known just how this comes about. It does point up the fact that prescribing anesthetic drugs for patients to be used at home is dangerous and probably accounts for the fact that, although patients are directed not to use the anesthetic oftener than at one- or two-hour intervals, they frequently ignore these directions and begin to use the drops at more frequent intervals in order to obtain relief from pain.

An explanation of the basic mechanism involved must undoubtedly take into consideration the action of drugs on the intracellular processes, as shown by the studies of Michaelis and Quastel[83] and of Herrmann, Moses, and Friedenwald.[84] Since cocaine and ephedrine were found to inhibit the mitotic activity of the corneal epithelium, and both these substances sensitize various effector organs to the action of epinephrine, Friedenwald and Buschke[85] investigated the effect of epinephrine itself on the mitotic activity of epithelium in the rat. Ether inhibits mitotic activity and is known to stimulate the secretion of epinephrine by the adrenal glands during the stage of excitation. They found that excitement itself, particularly by painful stimuli, diminished the mitotic rate in the normal corneal epithelium, and that this decrease is an adrenergic response which could be stimulated by either local or systemic administration of epinephrine. If ergotamine or nicotine were given previously to the period of excitement, the inhibition of mitosis was eliminated or at least diminished. The effect of epinephrine is not due to a decrease in temperature of tissue or to local circulatory disturbances. Removal of the superior cervical ganglion led to a decreased mitotic rate in the epithelium after a lag of about 20 hours.

Ultraviolet light has an appreciable effect on the rate of corneal mitosis.[86] Low doses of an unfiltered quartz mercury arc stimulate mitotic activity in the corneal epithelium. With larger doses, this activity is inhibited. Severe exposures lead to nuclear fragmentation, mainly in the superficial layers of the corneal epithelium, and to loss of cohesion between the epithelium and the stroma. Since both of these phenomena are suppressed under anaerobic incubation, the pathologic processes involved are in part, at least, oxidative. The two phenomena appear to be independent of one another since they have different temperature coefficients, and at proper incubational temperatures the loss of cohesion between the epithelium and the stroma can be demonstrated in the absence of nuclear fragmentation. Nuclear fragmentation may be a form of pathologic mitosis. Experiments showed no inhibition in the healing of very small wounds after exposure to ultraviolet rays in the dosage used. This is in keeping with the general finding that posttraumatic cell movements are much more resistant to interference by various toxic agents than is mitotic activity.

Another factor which must be considered in the delay in healing of corneal wounds by anesthetics is the fact that some of the anesthetics used are good detergents, i.e., wetting agents. This property may be partly responsible for the inhibition of epithelization. Strong detergents act in this manner and if drugs are incorporated in ointments in which their detergent action is reduced, they fail to delay the migration of cells significantly. The least harmful anesthetics, as far as epithelial repair is concerned, seem to be Nupercaine and phenacaine ointments. These do not impair mitosis in normal epithelium or retard division and migration of cells in regenerating corneal epithelium, if used in moderation.

Although the studies of Smelser and Ozanics indicate that ointments rather than solutions of anesthetics are the most satisfactory in permitting epithelial repair, this does not seem to be the case in local administration of antibiotics. Here the reverse is true—ointments with or without antibiotics have generally been found to delay wound healing.

CORNEAL VASCULARIZATION

The normal cornea is entirely devoid of blood vessels for 1 to 2 mm. inside the limbus. If at any time blood vessels are present in this area, the cornea is, or has been, the seat of some pathologic process. The condition which produced the vascularization may have been either a local process or some more generalized pathologic condition, such as a nutritional disease. Certain diseases produce early and intense vascularization, and the situation and character of the new-formed blood vessels are sometimes guides to their diagnosis. For example, the straight branching vessels which enter the cornea at the limbus, coming in the deeper layers, are characteristic of interstitial keratitis, whereas the superficial tortuous vessels which can be traced onto the cornea from the conjunctival surface across the limbus are characteristic of various forms of keratoconjunctivitis. When they are confined to the upper limbus and associated with granulation tissue, they are pathognomonic of trachoma.

In many nutritional diseases vascularization of the cornea occurs early and is typical. Vascularization has been observed in rats on diets deficient in riboflavin,[87, 88] vitamin A, tryptophane, lycine, zinc, sodium,[89] or methionine[90] and in diets devoid of protein.[91, 92]

It has been suggested that acne rosacea keratitis (a disease of the cornea and conjunctiva associated with marked superficial corneal vascularization) is due to a deficiency of riboflavin.[93] This was a sequence of finding that corneal vascularization developed in rats placed on a riboflavin-deficient diet. This enzyme is an important factor in respiration of tissue and is thought to be especially significant in avascular tissue such as the cornea. The theory has been proposed that the corneal tissues become anoxic due to deficiency of riboflavin, and the corneal blood vessels grow in from the limbus in order to aid the supply of oxygen. As the result of the administration of riboflavin, cures in this disease have been reported, but Wise,[94] in a carefully controlled series, failed to effect a cure in any patient with acne rosacea.

Although vascularization may be considered a defensive mechanism by means of which the body protects itself against noxious influences, evidence also exists that the presence of vascularization considerably delays the healing of certain pathologic processes, particularly herpes corneae.

Many different theories have been proposed to account for the absence of blood vessels in the normal cornea and their ingrowth in diseased states. Among these are the following.

1. A substance is elaborated in the cornea as a result of the corneal pathologic process which stimulates the vessels to grow into the cornea to the site where this substance is manufactured. The substance is supposed to possess the power to initiate neovasculogenesis from already existing blood vessels and to have positive chemotaxis. While some experiments are suggestive that such a substance might exist, no substance has been isolated.[95] The accumulation of acid metabolites, histamine, a deficiency in ascorbic acid, and local anoxia have been suggested as factors which induce new vascularization. The relation of anoxia to the development of blood vessels is especially well documented by the work of Michaelson and co-workers, who showed that a capillary-free zone exists around the normal retinal arterioles, whereas no such capillary-free zone exists around the normal retinal venules. Campbell[96] found that litters of rats exposed to a low oxygen environment showed an encroachment of the capillaries on the retinal arterioles, indicating that oxygen tension is a factor which determines the growth of these normal vessels. In many disease conditions

anoxia has been held responsible for the characteristic development of new vessels, as in Eale's disease, diabetic retinopathy, and central vein occlusion. It goes without saying that anoxia may be effective in this respect by releasing some growth-promoting substance from the anoxic tissue, and carbon dioxide is not only a vasodilating agent, but also a strong stimulus to vasculogenesis.

2. The failure of blood vessels to grow into the normal cornea has been attributed to the properties of the cornea itself— either that it contains some substance which repels the growth of vessels or because of its compactness vessels are unable to penetrate it. In disease states associated with neovascularization it is suggested either that the inhibiting substance is lost to the cornea or that the swelling of the tissue by edema or turgescence allows the blood vessels to grow in. The mucopolysaccharide hyaluronic acid was thought to be such a vessel-inhibiting factor. Its presence in the corneal stroma and the ingrowth of blood vessels into corneas treated with hyaluronidase supported this concept. However, it has been shown that hyaluronic acid ester is not diminished to any degree in vascularizing corneas.[94]

No growth inhibiting substance has as yet been demonstrated in the cornea nor in other tissues normally devoid of blood vessels, such as cartilage, although such substances have been discovered in liver extracts and in tumors.

Cogan[97] was the first to suggest that the compactness of normal corneal tissue was the reason for its avascularity, and he pointed out that cartilage and the nails cannot be vascularized because they have no invadable intercellular substance. Reasoning along these lines, he suggested that the factor responsible for vasculogenesis in diseased states is a release of corneal tissue pressure. When the cornea becomes turgesced and therefore less compact, spaces are opened up through which vessels can grow. He reasoned that as a result of swelling of the cornea at the limbus the vessels normally present there become engorged and form saccular aneurysms which ultimately burst. This leads to the development of new vessels in these areas, with spread of the new-formed vessels into the now swollen corneal stroma.

Cogan[98] also suggested that swelling of the peripheral parts of the cornea sets up a cycle through neovasculogenesis which is self-corrective. The swelling of the cornea initiates the formation of new vessels, but this in turn corrects the swelling. He has observed that edematous corneas tend to deturgesce as new blood vessels grow into them. Those corneas, on the other hand, which do not become vascularized remain edematous and develop epithelial bullae. Luetic interstitial keratitis is an example of an edematous cornea accompanied by bullae formation which becomes deturgesced as new-formed vessels grow into it. On the other hand, the edematous corneas in endothelial dystrophy remain swollen and afflicted with bullae and never become vascularized. In endothelial dystrophy the cornea becomes swollen as a result of the impairment of endothelial function, with subsequent turgescence, but the swelling remains localized to the central regions of the cornea. In interstitial keratitis, both specific and nonspecific types, the alterations in corneal thickness correlate well with the progress of the disease. The ingrowth of vessels from the limbus is always preceded by corneal swelling at the limbus.[99]

Further experiments of Ashton and Cook[95] have shown that vascularization is usually produced if the corneal compactness is reduced by any means, provided that the zone of corneal swelling extends to the limbus, i.e., the site of the normal blood supply. The swelling of the stroma must persist for some time; the injection of saline solution, e.g., into the stroma, must be repeated a number of times in order to produce neovascularization, whereas viscous substances which remain in the cornea spreading the lamellae need only be injected once.

We may accept the conclusion that blood vessels are kept out of the cornea largely by the compactness of this tissue, and if this is modified so that the stroma becomes looser, vessels can gain access. This does not prove, however, that neovasulogenesis from the limbal vessels is initiated by changing the compactness of the stroma, and it seems very unlikely that this factor alone would stimulate the limbal vessels to send out new shoots. New vessels do not grow from previously existing ones in other parts of the eye where the tissue is loose, e.g., in the retina. It seems likely that some agent must be present in the cornea which reaches the limbal blood vessels when the stroma is loosened and acts on the vessels. Evidence pointing in this direction has been offered by Langham.[100] He was able to induce swelling of the cornea by injecting alloxan into the anterior chamber of rabbits. By proper selection of dosage this swelling could be reversed. In some cases he was able to show that after the vessels had grown into the stroma from the periphery a distance of 1 to 2 mm. they ceased to grow, although the cornea was extremely turgesced. Further, in some cases vascularization ceased at a time when the cornea was still twice its normal thickness.

The problem is still not solved, and it still seems likely that along with the change in the physical state of the stroma changes in the chemistry of the cornea occur which initiate neovasculogenesis when they reach the limbal vessels.

MECHANISM OF SENSATION
General considerations

In many sections of this book we will be dealing with sensory phenomena. The sensibilities of the cornea, the proprioceptive sense of the ocular muscles, and visual sensation itself are governed by the same general principles and organized on the same anatomic and physiologic plan. A review of this basic organization and function is given here.

The basic organization of all sense organs consists of a sensory receptor, a sensory nerve conducting afferent impulses into the central nervous system, a conducting path to the thalamus or similar subcortical station, and a conducting path to a localized sensory area of the cortex.

Three different types of sense organs are recognized: exteroceptive, proprioceptive, and visceroceptive. The first two are of chief interest in ocular physiology. The exteroceptors are divided into two groups, the distance receptors and the contact receptors. The senses of sight and hearing belong to the first group, and tactile, temperature, and pain receptors belong to the latter. The distance receptors give rise to sensations that are localized in space, i.e., psychically projected outside of the body. The sensations are referred to the origin of the stimulus, as far as their general direction goes; a ray of light entering the eye stimulating a photoreceptor gives rise to a sensation of light coming from the same direction as the entering ray. A prism introduced between the light source and the eye which deviates the entering ray gives rise to the impression that the light source has moved. Since the prism bends the light ray toward the base of the prism, the light will have appeared to have moved toward the apex of the prism. The contact receptors give rise to sensations that are localized on the stimulated receptor and are not psychically projected outside

of the body. The proprioceptors are generally placed inside the body, are connected to muscles and tendons, and may or may not give rise to any sensation or awareness of their effects.

Excitation of a receptor or of any part of its conducting pathway up to and including the cortical end station always gives rise to the same general quality of sensation, whatever the nature of the stimulus. Stimulation of the photoreceptors by light gives rise to a sensation of light, and mechanical or electrical stimulation of the photoreceptors gives rise to the same sensation. Further, stimulation of any part of the conducting pathways for vision up to and including the visual cortex gives rise to this same sensation. This is known as Müller's law of specificity of nervous energy. It tells us that the cortex is the seat of the transformation into consciousness of the message sent up from the sensory receptor. If one could successfully connect the auditory nerve to some part of the visual pathway we would "see" sounds.

The receptor or sensory unit. In the section on ocular muscles (p. 400) we will see that each motor nerve fiber supplies a number of muscle fibers. In the case of the ocular muscles only about ten muscle fibers are linked up with one motor nerve fiber, whereas in the muscles of the leg as many as one hundred and twenty muscle fibers may be supplied by one nerve fiber. The single motor nerve fiber, together with the muscle fibers it individually innervates, is known as the motor unit. In a similar way the individual sensory nerve fiber may be linked with many or with few sensory receptors, and the combination of sensory nerve fiber and receptors is known as the receptor or sensory unit. The distribution of the receptors supplied by one sensory fiber is known as the receptive field. Within this field or area, stimulation of any of the receptors will give rise to impulses in a single nerve fiber. It will be shown that the receptive fields vary considerably in different regions. In the cornea the receptive field may be 200 or more square millimeters, spreading out onto the conjunctiva and sclera. In the retina the receptive fields outside the fovea may be as small as one quarter of a millimeter, and in the fovea itself one optic nerve fiber may be linked with only one cone.

Quantitative relations between stimulus and response

Stimulus. Adrian[101] defines a stimulus as "any change in the environment of an excitable tissue which, if sufficiently intense, will excite the tissue, i.e., cause it to display its characteristic activity."* A stimulus is thus some external change which may be effective only if it is intense enough to excite. If, for example, the electric current used to stimulate a nerve fiber is very weak or if its duration is extremely short (less than $0.01\ \Sigma$), it is unable to excite. If the strength or the duration of the current is now increased just to the point at which the nerve responds with an action current, this is said to be the threshold of stimulation. At this threshold an impulse is set up in the nerve fiber which travels up the nerve at an extremely rapid rate. The impulses set up in the fibers of a nerve trunk do not all travel at the same speed. When, for example, a strong stimulus is applied to the saphenous nerve of a cat, the form of the action potential produced shows that a number of different kinds of nerve fibers are responding, having different voltages and different rates of conduction.

*From Adrian, E. D.: The basis of sensation, New York, 1928, W. W. Norton & Co., Inc.

In spite of these differences, which are inherent in the nerve fiber itself and are related to its structure, studies on different types of sense organs have proved that the impulses are approximately the same and that the differences in the sensations they produce are, as just stated, to be sought in their central nervous connections in the cortex and not in the fibers themselves. For each type of sense organ, there is one form of energy, called the adequate stimulus, to which the receptor is especially sensitive. Other forms of stimuli may excite the same sensation produced by the adequate stimulus, if strong enough.

Current of injury

If a cut muscle is connected with a galvanometer by means of two nonpolarizable electrodes so that one electrode rests on the cut end of the muscle and the other on the outside surface, the galvanometer will show a difference of electrical potential between the two electrodes. The cut end of the muscle will be electronegative and the intact surface will be electropositive, and a current will flow from one electrode to the other. This is called the current of injury or demarcation current. A similar electrical effect occurs in nerves and, for that matter, in almost all tissues, although the voltage observed elsewhere is low. Even plant tissues exhibit a kindred phenomenon, and a single bite taken out of an apple converts it into an electric battery of about 0.04 v. The current which this discharges is so minute that it is not capable of stimulating the mouth.

Action currents

Of even greater interest than this injury potential is the electrical wave which passes over a muscle or nerve when it is stimulated. If a muscle is contracted or a nerve is excited by applying a stimulus

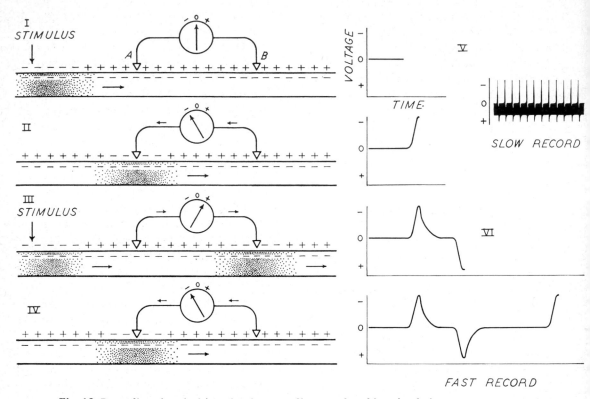

Fig. 16. Recording electrical impulses in nerve fibers produced by stimulation.

(mechanical, thermal, or electrical) at some point on its surface, the part where the activity starts becomes electrically negative to the remainder of the muscle or nerve (Fig. 16). As the wave of contraction passes along the muscle or the impulse along the nerve, this negativity decreases at the end from which the wave started. When the wave has reached the middle of the strip of muscle or nerve, neither end shows any difference in potential. As the excitation proceeds farther down the muscle, however, and finally reaches the far end, this in turn becomes negative.

These currents are called action currents, and they always precede the development of the mechanical effect when a muscle contracts. They are synonymous with the nerve impulses. In Fig. 16, *I,* is shown the action current in a nerve after the application of a stimulus. The two electrodes from which the action currents lead off to the galvanometer are placed on the nerve at *A* and *B*. The stimulus is applied to the left of *A*. As the impulse travels down the nerve, the active region comes to lie first under *A*, and this becomes electronegative. The galvanometer responds to this with a swing of the needle toward the left (Fig. 16, *II*). By the time the active region comes to lie midway between *A* and *B*, neither electrode shows a difference in potential, and the galvanometer needle comes to rest. The active region then passes under *B*, which in turn becomes electronegative, and the galvanometer needle swings toward the right (Fig. 16, *III*).

In this manner a record is produced which is made up of two distinct phases, an upward deflection, which represents the negative phase of *A,* and a downward deflection, which represents the negative phase of *B*. Such records are called diphasic.

Monophasic records may be obtained by using only one electrode on the nerve stimulated and by placing the indifferent electrode elsewhere on the body. If a muscle is tetanically stimulated, a fresh electrical disturbance accompanies each make and break of the tetanizing stimulus, although the mechanical response is a single prolonged contraction. Therefore, the tetanic contraction of a muscle is caused by the fusion of a series of discrete contractions or twitches.

The diphasic action current which results when a nerve is connected with two electrodes has just been described. The progress of two stimuli down the nerve past the electrodes is shown in Fig. 16, *III*. Each stimulus is a wave of electronegativity, represented in the illustration by a stippled area. The time course of these stimuli is plotted against the difference of potential between the two electrodes (Fig. 16, *V* and *VI*). If the photographic film on which the oscillographic records are made is moving fast, the action potentials appear as shown in the diagram, but if the film moves much slower, the potentials appear as spikes (upper right-hand corner of Fig. 16, *V*). In all the records which follow, the potential changes will appear in this form unless otherwise stated. The response of a sensory nerve to stimulation depends upon a number of different factors or parameters of the stimulus. We, thus, have thresholds for intensity, time, and area throughout which the stimulus is applied and difference thresholds.

Intensity threshold. The amount of energy required to stimulate a receptor depends upon (1) the nature of the stimulus, (2) the condition of the receptor, and (3) the locus of the stimulation.

1. The nature of the stimulus. The threshold is always lowest for the adequate or natural stimulus. When the adequate stimulus is not just one portion of the energy spectrum, as in the case of light, which is composed of wavelengths from 400 to 750 mμ, some parts of the adequate stimulus may be more effective than others. Species differences may also play a part. One species may have lower thresholds than others to certain portions of the stimulus. Bees respond to shorter wavelengths than man can see.

2. The condition of the receptor. Under certain conditions the threshold of the receptor may change enormously; the sensitivity of the retina increases many thousands of times after it has been kept in the dark for an hour. The simultaneous or previous application of a stimulus may raise the threshold for certain stimuli and lower it for others (see discussion of simultaneous and successive contrast phenomena, pp. 706 and 730).

3. The locus of the stimulation. The receptors in one area may have different thresholds from another, or the number of receptors per unit area may differ in different regions of the sense organ; e.g., the foveal cones are tightly packed together and are thinner than the cones in the rest of the retina. Further, rods are not present in the fovea.

Area threshold. If the stimulus is confined to a small area only, one or only a few sensory units may be stimulated, whereas if the area on which the stimulus falls is large, many units will be excited. If the stimulus is of near threshold for a single unit, no sensory response may ensue, but if a number of units are stimulated, the impulses they evoke may become summated in the conducting pathways, resulting in a sensory response.

Time threshold. A stimulus may be effective if it is delivered to the receptor for a certain period of time, but it may be ineffective if the presentation is shortened. This is just a question of the actual amount of energy which the receptor receives. In order to receive this minimal amount of energy, the time of presentation must be lengthened as the intensity of the stimulus is reduced. Within certain limits receptors follow the rule of $I \times T = K$. Further, since a stimulus as just defined (p. 73) is a change in the environment of the receptor, its effectiveness depends upon the rapidity with which the change takes place. The rate of change must be at a certain minimum. If slower than this, the receptor may adapt itself before the threshold can be reached (this will be explained more fully in the section on adaptation, p. 77).

Difference thresholds. All sense organs have the property of discriminating between different strengths and different durations of the stimulus. Some sense organs have other discriminatory powers, such as discrimination by the retina of different wavelengths of light, which give rise to the sensation of different colors. In differentiating between different strengths of stimulus, most sense organs obey Fechner's law which states that above the threshold and up to a certain maximal intensity sensation is a linear function of the logarithm of the stimulus. This is a more exact modification of Weber's original findings that in discriminating between tactile stimuli of different strengths the second stimulus must be increased by a definite percentage of the first stimulus. In general, Weber found that a change of 10% of the original stimulus was necessary for tactile discrimination. A tactile stimulus of 0.9 Gm.

could be distinguished from one of 1 gm. In order to distinguish a stimulus of 10 Gm. it was necessary to increase the second stimulus to 11 Gm., i.e., 10% of the first.

Receptors can also distinguish between successive stimuli, provided that the interval between their presentation is not too short. This minimal interval between successive presentations is known as the difference time threshold. In the case of the eye, for example, the interval between repeated flashes of light must be greater than 0.25 second in order for the flashes to be seen as separate. If the interval is shorter than this, the two lights will be fused, and the individual will have the impression of a continuous light.

Many other difference thresholds have been determined, such as difference thresholds of size, color, and color saturation (the amount of white light mixed with a particular color), which will be described later.

Way a nerve signals changes in intensity of a stimulus. It is well known that each sensory end organ or individual nerve fiber obeys the all-or-none law. As the stimulus is increased from a subthreshold level, a point is reached (the threshold) at which the end organ fires off. The response at this point is maximum, and further increases in strength of the stimulus fail to provoke larger action potentials. On the other hand, the impulses traveling up an individual fiber occur at a more rapid rate and persist longer after the stimulus stops (Fig. 17).

In any whole sensory nerve composed of many fibers it is found that only a few of the fibers become active as the strength of the stimulus reaches threshold value, but as the stimulus increases, more and more fibers respond. This must mean that the end organs do not all have the same threshold, but as the intensity of the

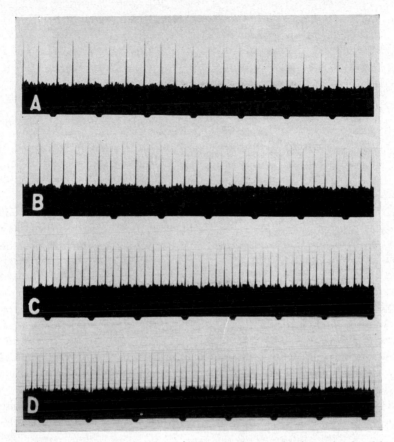

Fig. 17. Afferent impulses from a single end organ in the carotid sinus stimulated by constant pressures within the sinus. A, 40 mm. Hg; **B,** 80 mm. Hg; **C,** 140 mm. Hg; **D,** 200 mm. Hg. Time marker gives one fifth of a second. (From Bronk, D., and Stella, G.: Am. J. Physiol. **110:**708, 1935.)

stimulus increases, those with a higher threshold are gradually brought into play. This process is known as the recruitment of end organs.

The brain is made aware of changes in intensity of stimulation by means of two mechanisms—the increased rate and persistence of discharge in each fiber and an increase in the number of fibers actively signalling.

Adaptation in sensory receptors. When a strong but brief stimulus is applied to a sensory receptor, the response is a sudden burst of impulses in the nerve fiber. However, if the stimulus is maintained at a constant level, the rate of discharge of impulses in the fiber is not maintained but, after the initial burst, grows progressively slower until it reaches a minimum rate, which is held constant. This property, by means of which the end organ responds with an initial rapid burst of impulses which die down, is called adaptation. It is a property of all sensory receptors.

We think of excitation in a nerve as being due to the accumulation or segregation of ions in certain parts of the nerve fiber. This accumulation of ions upsets the balance of processes which maintain the fiber in its resting condition and leads to the further series of changes which constitute the nerve impulse. Unless the current is increasing rapidly, the rate of accumulation cannot keep ahead of the rate of leakage, and no excitation can occur. Or if the current rises to a maximum rapidly enough but stays at this level, excitation occurs, but soon fades out. It is a general rule, therefore, that the effectiveness of a stimulus depends not only on its intensity, but also on the rate at which it is applied.

The property of adaptation has an important influence on the nature of the message the brain receives from the sense organs. The degree of adaptation differs very markedly in different sense organs. Certain types of end organs adapt very little and maintain their initial rate of discharge for long periods of time, whereas other end organs adapt immediately. In general, the various receptors which are necessary for the maintenance of continuous function in the body adapt very little. Thus, the pressure receptors in the carotid sinus and the arteries in general, tension receptors in the lungs, and muscle spindles all belong to the class of recep-

tors which show very little adaptation, which is indeed fortunate. The receptors for pain in the cornea belong in this same group (p. 90). Touch receptors, on the other hand, adapt very quickly so that their burst of impulses is over within 0.2 sec., which is of decided advantage to the organism for the sense of touch. As a contact is perceived, adaptation wipes the slate clean and makes the end organ ready for a new impression.

The process of adaptation is pictured graphically in Fig. 18. The differences in rate of adaptation of different end organs are summarized in Fig. 19. It will be seen that adaptation is most marked in the nerve fiber itself and least in the muscle spindle.

Adaptation must not be confused with the property of fatigue, which is a decline in the activity of an organ caused by its previous activity. Fatigue usually implies the accumulation of the end products of metabolism, the result of the activity of the organ, which have to be removed before further activity is possible. Adaptation has nothing to do with the previous activity of an end organ, but is a fundamental property of the end organ itself.

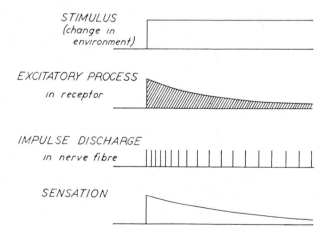

Fig. 18. Diagram illustrating the process of adaptation in sensory nerves. (After Adrian.)

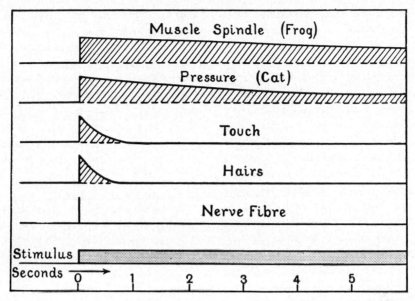

Fig. 19. Response to a continued stimulus in a nerve fiber and different types of end organ. Adaptation is most rapid in the nerve fiber and slowest in the sense organs in muscle. (From Adrian, E.: The Basis of Sensation, New York, 1928, W. W. Norton & Co.)

SENSIBILITIES
Sensibilities of the body in general

Throughout the body the sensory nerve endings are connected with specialized receptors built from connective tissue. These receptors take the form of filaments, nets, spirals or rings, and in some cases complex structures such as the organs of Ruffini, which initiate the sensation of warmth, and the pacinian corpuscles, which amplify the sensation of pressure. Their histologic structure is such as to indicate that they serve some special purpose, such as amplifying pressure, recording temperature changes, etc., by means of which various physical stimuli are able to send messages to the brain. By means of these receptors or end organs, the various sensibilities of pain, touch, heat, and cold are transmitted by appropriate nerve fibers into the central nervous system. In pain fibers, only, are there no specialized end organs. The sense of pain is elaborated from free nerve endings that form an exceedingly rich pattern of terminal nerve branches.

The sensory receptors in the skin are exteroceptors. They are excited by stimuli arriving from outside of the body. The receptors lying within the muscles and the tendons of the body, which are stimulated by their elongations or contractions, are called proprioceptors. The receptors lying in the linings of the gastrointestinal tract (the lungs, etc.) are called enteroceptors. Since the skin is so nearly akin to the cornea, the general principles of its sensibilities will be described as an introduction to those of the cornea, which is in reality a specialized skin for the eye.

Specialized nerve endings are not present in hairy skin, only free nerve endings.[102, 103] Similarly, only free nerve endings are present in the central regions of the cornea. Hence, if there are different sensibilities in the central cornea, such as touch, heat, cold, and pain, these must all be subserved by free nerve endings and not by specialized receptors.[104]

The concept that various modalities of sensation are subserved by specialized end organs has long been held and stems from the original work of von Frey, but this is now questioned.[105] It appears that as far as cutaneous and corneal sensibilities go there is no correlation between the specific modality of sensation and the presence of morphologically specific nerve endings. Four main modalities of sensation are considered to be separate entities: touch, cold, warmth, and pain. Although other sensations such as itching, tickling, roughness, smoothness, wetness, and stereognosis (tridimensional form sense) are recognized, they are generally believed to be the result of either a special type of response or simultaneous activation of two or more of the above-mentioned primary sensibilities. Thus, itching is considered a special type of response to weak stimulation of the pain receptors, and vibratory sensation is due to intermittent stimulation of touch and pressure receptors.

Sense of touch and pressure. The sense of touch is caused by stimulation of the nerve nets at the base of the hairs where these are present, as shown in Fig. 20. In the hairless regions of the body touch is produced by stimulation of the tactile corpuscles, called Meissner's corpuscles. Pressure sensations arise from large corpuscles lying deep in the true skin, called pacinian corpuscles. These measure about 1 mm. in length and have a structure something like that of an onion. They are also found in other parts of the body, particularly along the tendons and blood vessels, where they are stimulated by changes in blood pressure.

If the skin is dimpled with a stiff hair, the sensation one experiences is of movement, pressure, pull, or tension. The stimulus threshold of this sensation may be determined by finding the finest test hair which just produces a sensation. Care must be taken not to stimulate the hairs of the skin during the procedure.

In order to obtain quantitative data, one may calibrate the test hairs in grams per square millimeter. The hair to be calibrated is held vertically against one pan of any ordinary balance. Weights are placed in the other pan of the balance until the pan rising against the resistance of the hair succeeds in bending it. The weight which accomplishes this is recorded. The cross section of the hair is then measured under a microscope, and the number of grams per square millimeter which the hair could withstand without deformation is thus calculated. The normal stimulus threshold for a fingertip is 0.5 to 1.0 Gm./sq.mm.

If two stimuli are applied to the surface of the skin simultaneously, the subject will perceive two distinct sensations, provided that the distance between the two stimulated points is sufficiently great. When they are separated by a shorter distance, a single sensation is experienced. The minimal distance at which the recognition of two separate stimuli is possible varies considerably in different regions of the body. In the case of the fingertip, the distance is approximately 2.3 mm., whereas in the middle of the back, the upper arm, and the thigh, the distance is nearly 70 mm. These distances represent approximate distances between sensory receptors.

Rapid repetition of the mechanical stimulus of touching results in a sensation of vibration. The existence of a special vibratory sense is unproved. The sense of tickling is a modification of the pressure sense. It appears to be due to the summed effects of stimulating both touch spots and the free nerve endings subserving pain. Itching is likewise dependent upon impulses traveling by both tactile

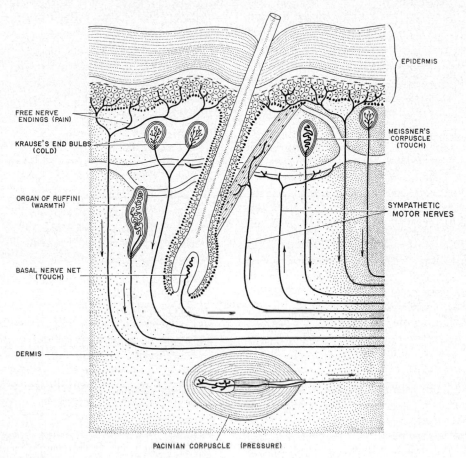

FREE NERVE
ENDINGS (PAIN)

KRAUSE'S END BULBS
(COLD)

ORGAN OF RUFFINI
(WARMTH)

BASAL NERVE NET
(TOUCH)

DERMIS

EPIDERMIS

MEISSNER'S
CORPUSCLE
(TOUCH)

SYMPATHETIC
MOTOR NERVES

PACINIAN CORPUSCLE (PRESSURE)

Fig. 20. Sensory endings in the skin. (Modified after Amberson and Smith.)

and pain fibers when the sensation arises, as it frequently does, in the healing of wounds when the adjacent skin is rubbed. Spontaneous itching that occurs under the same circumstances appears to be due to mild stimulation of the pain endings alone. In both cases the stimulation of the nerve endings is due to the liberation of a histamine-like substance by the cells of the skin.

The sensation of touch is transmitted in part to the ventral bundles of the spinal cord and in part to the posterior bundles. The final reception of the impulses is by the gyrus centralis posterior.

The sensation of pressure is not a true cutaneous sense. As stated, the pacinian corpuscles lie deep in the skin, as well as along the blood vessels and tendons and in the periosteum. Their nerve fibers run in the sensory nerves which supply the blood vessels, tendons, etc., and not in the cutaneous nerves.

Cold and heat. The adequate stimulus producing the sensation of cold is a reduction of temperature of at least 2.4 microcalories per minute when a cold spot is stimulated or a reduction of temperature of at least 0.15° C. per minute when larger surfaces are tested. This reduction of temperature must be below the indifferent point, which lies between 10° and 38° C., according to adaptation. Stimulation of a cold point with 45° C. or more results in a so-called paradoxical cold sensation.

The sensation normally produced by stimulating a cold spot is that which we commonly describe as cool or cold. When the temperature is very low, there is added to this a sensation of cutting or burning, which is really an added component of pain. The receptors are Krause's end organs, and the number of cold spots in the skin is usually about 10/sq.mm. The sensation is transmitted to the lateral bundles of the cord and is received in the gyrus centralis posterior.

The adequate stimulus producing the sensation of heat is an increase in temperature of the skin of at least 0.2° C. per minute above the indifferent point. The sensation produced by this is described as warmth. Above 48° C. the sensation is described as hot, which is the warm sense plus the paradoxical cold sense. At about 50° C. the sensation described is burning hot, which is a combination of warmth, paradoxical cold, and pain sensation. The receptors in the skin are the ruffinian bodies, which lie in the tela subcutanea. These are the deepest of all the skin receptors. The number of heat spots is 0.5 to 1/sq.mm. Transmission takes place through the lateral bundles of the cord, and the sensation is received in the gyrus centralis posterior.

Pain. Cutaneous pain is subserved by the fine medullated and nonmedullated nerve fibers bearing free endings. Since each nerve fiber ends in a number of fine bare nerve endings spread over a certain area of skin, the unit of sensation is not necessarily confined to one nerve ending. In 1943 Tower[106] introduced the useful concept of the sensory unit, as contrasted

with the single afferent nerve ending. A sensory unit consists of many nerve endings, all branches of a single fiber connected with a single cell in the dorsal root ganglion. Each single unit supplies an area of skin (or of the cornea) of about 1 cm. in diameter, but it is conceivable that larger units exist elsewhere in the body. Many pain fibers supply overlapping sensory units to a given area, but there is no connection between the endings of different fiber units. It would thus seem likely that the painful spot experienced as such, when an area of normal skin is exposed to noxious stimulation, is a centrally integrated experience projected onto the periphery for the specific purpose of localization (see discussion of local sign in the retina, pp. 837 and 842 to 847). The skin spot is, so to speak, a mind spot. Pain alone and no other sensation may be lost in limited regions of the body as a result of accidental injury to the spinal cord, and after surgical transection of the spinothalamic pathways, pain alone may be absent in circumscribed regions without associated loss of temperature or touch.

Certain structures are equipped for, and give rise to, the sensation of pain only. The pulp of the teeth, the middle meningeal artery, and the arteries of the brain are equipped with afferent fibers conducting only pain impulses.[107] Other areas in the body exist from which pain cannot be elicited, e.g., the parenchyma of the brain and an area on the inside of the cheek opposite the second lower molar tooth. Pain, therefore, is a sensation derived from noxious impulses traversing specific pathways. All the fibers conveying these impulses enter the spinal cord or brainstem through the dorsal root ganglia. The superficial pain impulses are usually conveyed by the somatic nerves and enter the cord more or less directly through the dorsal roots. Deep pain impulses reach the central nervous system in a number of ways. Some are conveyed part of the way by pain fibers that are attached to blood vessels, and they then join autonomic nerves. Others are closely associated from their beginning with autonomic nerves and remain so affiliated until nearly to the spinal cord.

After entering the spinal cord, all these impulses are conveyed across to the opposite side, where their pathways are localized in the anterolateral portion of the spinal cord. The fibers of the spinothalamic tract pass into the nucleus centralis posterior to the thalamus. The cortical projection is predominantly to the postcentral convolution.

Pain from the face seems to have both homolateral and contralateral cortical representations so that unilateral hemispherectomy does not result in analgesia of the face.

Discrimination of the intensity of pain has been investigated.[108] It has been found that there are approximately twenty-one just noticeable differences of intensity of pain which can be distinguished between the stimulus threshold and the stimulus beyond which no further discrimination is possible. Twenty-one discriminable steps are possible for a two-fold increase in the intensity of the stimulus. In contrast, there are only about nine steps of intensity of sensation distinguishable between the warmth threshold and the onset of pain. Also, the range of energy for vision from the threshold to the dazzle point is as 1 to 10 billion, and there are only 572 distinguishable steps in this enormous range, according to Hecht.[109]

It has been shown that in the case of light perception, there is spatial summation; i.e., the intensity of sensation from a fixed intensity of stimulus increases or decreases with increase or decrease in the size of the area stimulated. There is no quantitative evidence on this point for pain sensation. On the other hand, the sensory threshold for cutaneous temperature sensation is decreased or increased as the size of the area stimulated is decreased or increased. The usual explanation of this effect is that the subthreshold impulses from separate end organs are summated in the central nervous system.

The significance of spatial summation to the body economy is that it provides extreme sensitivity, thereby permitting sensation to be evoked by minute changes in the environment. For example, vision is stimulated by only a few quanta of energy when the entire eye is illuminated, and a sense of warmth is evoked by a rise in skin temperature of 0.0008° C. per second when the entire surface of the body is stimulated.[110]

There is some evidence that the skin is endowed with two types of apparatus for perceiving noxious stimuli; one gives rise to the quality of pricking which reaches the sensorium rapidly, and the other gives rise to the quality of burning which reaches the sensorium less rapidly. The latter is similar to the quality of pain experienced on some mucous membranes. This second quality would appear to be an intermediate between superficial pain and deep pain. It is a common observation that deep pain is followed by local contraction and sometimes by distant contraction of skeletal muscle. The head is a suitable place for the demonstration of such muscle rigidity and tenderness in association with visceral pain. Deep noxious impulses with pain from the head cause muscular contractions, especially of the frontal, masseter, and temporal muscles. These impulses may accentuate winking greatly and ultimately cause contractions of the occipital and cervical muscles. There may also be vasoconstriction or ischemia in the area of the muscle contraction. Lacrimation, edema of the eyelids, injection of the conjunctiva, nausea and vomiting, sweating, and photophobia are common accompaniments of severe pain coming from diverse portions of the body. Similar effects of contraction have followed the introduction of a foreign body into the conjunctival sac or the cornea and have occasionally followed diplopia experimentally induced through the use of lenses.[111]

Physiologic tests show that in most areas of the skin there are two sets of pain fibers which conduct their impulses at very different rates. One set, known as fast pain fibers because of their rapid conduction, is myelinated. The other set consists of thin unmyelinated fibers which conduct at a much slower rate.

The eye, like the skin, is supplied with nerves of common sensation, but, as will be shown, not all of the sensibilities present in the skin are equally represented in all of the ocular tissues, especially the cornea, and it has been seriously questioned whether the sensations of touch and heat occur in the cornea at all. Whatever sensibilities are present are conducted into the central nervous system from the eye by means of the first division of the fifth cranial nerve, some of whose physiologic properties will now be discussed.

Fifth cranial nerve

Although the peripheral distribution of the fifth cranial nerve is well known, the primary nuclei and the secondary paths in the central nervous system are still the subject of debate (Fig. 21). The trigeminal nerve may be regarded as a compressed group of afferent posterior roots and the gasserian ganglion as a fusion of all of their posterior root ganglia. The individual nerve terminals originating throughout the whole area of the face, including the eye and its adnexa, are gathered together into three main trunks or divisions which enter the gasserian ganglion and from there are distributed up and down the brainstem, from the midbrain on a level with the superior colliculi to the upper part of the cervical region of the cord. This collection of nerves, therefore, is a summation of all the posterior roots which correspond to all of the motor nerves originating from the brainstem.

Since the first or ophthalmic division of the fifth cranial nerve supplies the eyeball and surrounding structures, its physiologic constitution is important to us. Although it is largely a sensory nerve, it also carries sympathetic fibers into the eye. Thus, vasoconstrictor fibers and sympathetic fibers supplying Müller's unstriated muscle in the eyelids, coming from the cervical sympathetic nerve, reach the eyeball via the long ciliary nerves. The fibers supplying the dilator pupillae also travel by this route. There is also a possibility that these sympathetic fibers convey secretory impulses to the lacrimal gland, although section of this nerve does not stop the secretion of tears, and most authors feel that the fifth cranial nerve sends only sensory fibers to the gland. Antidromic vasodilator fibers are probably present in the nerve and account for the reflex ciliary flush caused by an imbedded corneal foreign body. The question of the existence of special trophic fibers has been raised because of the occurrence of neuroparalytic keratitis following section of the ophthalmic division of the fifth cranial nerve.

The cells of the fifth cranial nuclei are spread over a considerable portion of the brainstem, and the many connections with other important sensory and

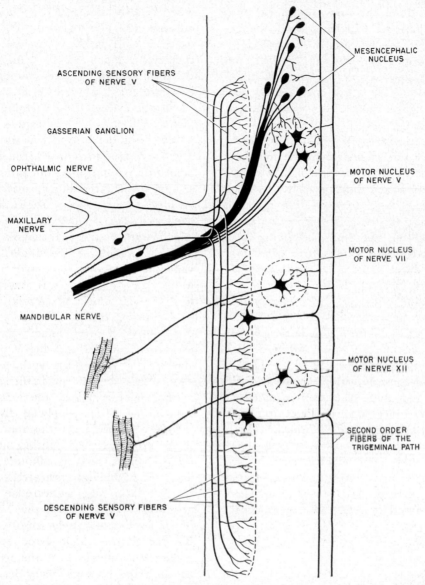

ASCENDING SENSORY FIBERS
OF NERVE V

GASSERIAN GANGLION

OPHTHALMIC NERVE

MAXILLARY
NERVE

MANDIBULAR NERVE

DESCENDING SENSORY FIBERS
OF NERVE V

MESENCEPHALIC
NUCLEUS

MOTOR NUCLEUS
OF NERVE V

MOTOR NUCLEUS
OF NERVE VII

MOTOR NUCLEUS
OF NERVE XII

SECOND ORDER
FIBERS OF THE
TRIGEMINAL PATH

Fig. 21. Diagram of the nuclei and central connections of the trigeminal nerve. (Modified after Ranson.)

motor nuclei in this region explain some of the associated symptoms of headache and ocular pain with disturbances in other parts of the body.

Thus, headache may result from innumerable different causes and is vague in its distribution. The reflex pain in ocular lesions usually follows the distribution of the fifth cranial nerve, but when it is very severe, it may spread to other nerves and produce reflex phenomena. In acute glaucoma, the pain is often accompanied by sweating and vomiting due to the connections of the fifth cranial nuclei with the nucleus of the vagus nerve. Refractive errors and muscle imbalances frequently cause occipital and suboccipital headaches, probably due to the close proximity of the nuclei of the first division of the fifth cranial nerve with the great occipital and upper cervical nerve roots.

Pressure on the eyeball slows the heart rate, the so-called oculocardiac reflex due to the association of the fifth cranial nerve and the vagus nerve. This may be of such severity as to be critical—cardiac arrest has occurred during ocular surgery. In order to evaluate better the factors producing a serious type of oculocardiac reflex, Kirsch and associates,[112] investigated the electrocardiographic changes induced during various types of operations performed on the eye. In 30% of the patients operated on, significant changes occurred in the electrocardiogram, and in two patients (4%) temporary cardiac arrest occurred. Digital pressure on the globe, manipulation of the ocular muscles, and direct pressure on the orbital contents following enucleation of the globe were implicated. The reflex could be eliminated entirely by retrobulbar anesthesia; therefore, these authors recommend that retrobulbar anesthesia be used in all operations performed for strabismus, retinal detachment, and enucleation, whether or not general anesthesia is employed.

Reflex weeping, sneezing, etc., are all explained by the association of the fifth cranial nuclei with the nuclei of other cranial nerves. Some effects on normal gastric motility have been shown in subjects who read for periods of time with incorrect glasses. Stimulation of the retina with excessive light results in tearing and causes photophobia and headache. Eckhardt, McLean, and Goodell[111] have shown that the fifth cranial nerve

is closely associated with the optic nerve and that the photophobia produced by excessive light is due to referred pain. They were able to rule out vasodilation which accompanies exposure to extreme illumination as the cause of photophobia. They found that the photophobia was relieved by surface anesthesia.

The term *photophobia* is sometimes erroneously used to denote dazzling, which is not true photophobia. The term should be used to denote only pain arising from exposure to excessive light. It has frequently been noted that in those corneal lesions accompanied by extreme photophobia the lesion is situated in the superficial layers of the cornea, and the more severe the photophobia is, the more superficial the pathologic process is likely to be. For example, extreme photophobia is always present with imbedded foreign bodies, phlyctenules, etc. This may be accounted for by the superficial arrangement of the corneal nerves, the plexuses being in the anterior stroma and subepithelium, with the fibrils from the latter almost reaching the surface. Photophobia may occur also in other than local ocular diseases, such as epidemic meningitis or trigeminal neuralgia. Lebensohn,[113] states that photophobia is due largely to the vasodilatation which occurs locally as an antidromic reflex. Most of this vasodilatation, he believes, takes place in the ciliary muscle and accounts for the fact that the photophobia generally disappears when the pupil is dilated and kept immobile.

A number of diseases of the eye are caused by lesions of the fifth cranial nerve. These may be divided into those in which the peripheral nerve terminals and peripheral fibers are affected and those in which the primary lesion is central—i.e., in the nucleus, in the brainstem, or in the gasserian ganglion. Recurrent erosion of the cornea, which sometimes follows abrasions of the cornea, belongs in the first group. The epithelium heals over an abrasion in the usual fashion and the eye seems cured, but a few days later, occasionally weeks or months later, the patient experiences severe pain in the eye, usually on awakening in the morning, and the epithelium is lifted up in a bleb which strips off easily. This process of healing and recurrent formation of blebs may occur many times before the condition finally yields to appropriate treatment. It is possible that the superficial plexus of nerve fibrils is damaged as the result of the original injury and forms small neuromas, instead of allowing the fibers to make their way into the new epithelial cells. As a result of this, the epithelium is without its normal nerve supply. Because of the absence of some trophic influence or other unknown factor, these cells never become firmly united to the underlying stroma (see discussion on healing of corneal wounds).

Superficial punctate keratitis is caused by a lesion (probably virus-induced) of the fifth cranial nerve endings in the corneal epithelium. The punctate character and position of the infiltrates suggest that they represent the distribution of nerve fibrils passing through Bowman's membrane from the deep plexus to the superficial plexus. Dendritic keratitis, which is also an inflammatory condition resulting from a virus infection, owes its characteristic features to the pattern of the nerve trunks as they course through the stroma from the limbus toward the center of the cornea.

Herpes zoster ophthalmicus and neuroparalytic keratitis are examples of conditions caused by disease or injury to the gasserian ganglion, sensory root, or first division. The former is undoubtedly due to a definite infection of the ganglion with a filtrable virus. The latter condition occurs after section of the ophthalmic division or of the sensory root of the fifth cranial nerve in the operation for tic douloureux. Various theories have been proposed to account for neuroparalytic keratitis. The most likely hypothesis is that of a trophic influence of the nerve on the nutrition of the cornea. As a result of section of the ophthalmic division and atrophy of the preganglionic fibers, the corneal nutrition suffers in much the same way as the skin becomes atrophic in the distribution of its nerve supply when the nerve is destroyed by disease or injury. Duke-Elder believes the trophic influences are based on a release of histamine into the tissues after the destruction of trophic fibers. This results in edema of the cornea, formation of blebs, and iridocyclitis. In addition to this trophic influence, it must be remembered that the cornea is no longer protected from the entrance of foreign bodies and from drying since sensation is lost entirely. If the eyelids are sewed together as soon as the keratitis manifests itself, the lesions usually clear up immediately, and as long as the eyelids are kept closed, no further damage occurs.

It has also been suggested that the primary cause of neuroparalytic keratitis is interference with the formation of tears due to damage of the great superficial petrosal nerve during operation. In support of this hypothesis, Dandy[114] observed that the incidence of neuroparalytic keratitis was greatest in those patients in whom operative trauma was considerable, especially when the seventh cranial nerve was damaged along with the fifth cranial nerve. In order to avoid this serious complication in the operation for tic douloureux, many surgeons now merely section the posterior two thirds of the sensory root, which seems to be successful in the majority of patients.

Sensibilities of the cornea

The nerve fibers are in large part myelinated as they enter the cornea from the limbus, but they lose their myelin sheaths as they pass from the periphery toward the center. The fine unmyelinated ramifications of these fibers form a plexus with terminal twigs, loops, or brushes whose branches penetrate the epithelium. They sometimes form a second plexus before entering individual epithelial cells. Within these plexiform arrangements there is no clue to the neuron unit. The terminal ramifications of a single sensory fiber are distributed over 50 to 200 or more square millimeters of cornea and adjacent sclera and conjunctiva. This forms a sensory unit, activity in any part of which affects the whole. There is no evidence that activity in this unit influences the activity of spatially coextensive units in any way.[115] The corneal sensory mechanism functions as an aggregate of units and not as a continuum. Nevertheless, there are possibilities of functional differentiation within the unit. The frequency and duration of impulses conducted to the central nervous system are determined not only by the intensity of the stimulation at any one point, but also by the site stimulated.

Sense of touch or pressure. The question of a true sense of touch in the cornea has been the subject of lively dispute. It was maintained by earlier workers that there is no true sensation of touch or pressure in the cornea. Mechanical stimulation of the cornea, according to these observers, results only in the sensation of pain. They showed that a vibratory stimulus applied to the cornea or conjunctiva results in a steady persistent sensation and not one of true vibration. Since the vibratory sense is a modification of the pressure sense, it was claimed that the failure to react to vibratory stimuli proves the absence of touch as a mode of corneal or conjunctival sensation. Further proof of the absence of a pressure sense was found in the lack of any stereognostic sensation in the conjunctiva. Stereognosis is best developed in the sense of pressure and is considerably weaker in the modality of pain. Tests show that the stereognostic sense is very poor in the cornea and conjunctiva. It has been claimed that in the majority of persons the sense of pressure is more highly developed on one side of the body than on the other, depending upon whether the person is right-handed or left-handed. It has been demonstrated that the response of the two eyes is equal when the threshold for the detection of hairs is determined. This has been suggested as further proof against the existence of a pressure sense. It has also been found that the rate of disappearance of sensation in the cornea after the administration of cocaine follows a simple arithmetical curve. It has been argued that if, in addition to the pain nerves, there were others carrying a pressure sense the curve of the fall in sensation would be complex, rather than the simple one obtained.

In the outer skin of the eyelid Strughold[116] found a threshold for pressure of 0.25 to 1 Gm./sq. mm. In order to obtain a painful sensation on these spots, the stimulus had to be increased tenfold. On the skin of the eyelid, therefore, two thresholds could be determined, yielding two different modes of sensation. The conjunctiva of the fornix and that covering the globe and the cornea, however, reacted entirely differently. In the middle of the cornea the threshold was very low, but the sensation remained purely painful. There was only one threshold; the reaction of the conjunctiva was apparently midway between that of the cornea and the skin of the eyelids. Strughold believed that the pressure sense is limited to the surfaces with two thresholds, namely, the outer skin and the edge of the eyelids, together with a small section of palpebral conjunctiva and the lacrimal caruncle. Corpuscles of Meissner are present in the skin of the eyelids and their edges, whereas they are entirely lacking in the cornea. The caruncle is covered with fine hairs; therefore, it is probable that here the receptors are the nerve nets spun around the hair shafts.

Not all observers are in accord with this point of view. Nafe and Wagoner[117] believe that the methods used by von Frey and Strughold were faulty and account for their erroneous conclusions. The stimulus used by the earlier investigators was a hair, capable of gradations in intensity. When used on the skin, it was capable of arousing touch or pressure. On the cornea it aroused only painful sensations; hence, von Frey concluded that the cornea was sensitive only to pain. Nafe and Wagoner point out that it is possible to stimulate the cornea either painfully or painlessly at will, and they conclude that the free nerve endings, which are the only afferent endings present, may transmit impulses associated with either touch or pain. The result depends upon one factor only, namely, the intensity of stimulation.

The reality of the sense of touch or pressure has been corroborated by the employment of Sjoqvist's operation of tractotomy. In this operation the descending root of the fifth cranial nerve is cut in the medulla for the relief of trigeminal neuralgia. Rowbotham[118] examined two patients after this operation and established the fact that, although the cornea was insensitive to pain, the contact of a wisp of cotton or of a camel's-hair brush was appreciated as touch. This has been confirmed by Grant, Groff, and Lewey.[119] Lele and Weddell[120] also found that if carefully graded stimuli are employed one can readily distinguish both touch and pain in the cornea.

It is now generally agreed that the cornea does possess a true sense of touch, and that contact with the cornea by a foreign body produces either a sensation of touch or a painful sensation, depending on the intensity of stimulation.

Cold and heat. Both the cornea and the conjunctiva contain many cold spots. In the cornea, the distribution of the spots is apparently greater at the limbus than at the center. Cold sensation resists anesthetics more than the sensation of pain. In this respect it is interesting to find that certain local anesthetics, such as Holocaine, when instilled in the eye cause a disagreeable sensation of cold which increases at first with each drop instilled. The cornea may be totally insensitive to pain after the first drop or two of a 1% solution of Holocaine; yet the instillation of another drop still produces a decidedly unpleasant cold sensation. Eventually this sensation of cold disappears, and further drops fail to produce it. It has been concluded from this that the cold receptors must lie at a deeper level in the cornea than the free nerve endings which yield the sensation of pain. The horizontal diameter is more sensitive to cold than the vertical diameter. This difference in sensitivity to cold in various meridians of the cornea is demonstrated even better in the conjunctiva where the region of the fissure is much more sensitive than the retrotarsal cul-de-sac. An area which is almost insensitive to cold is found occasionally above the limbus. The typography of the cold sense in the conjunctiva corresponds very well with the distribution of Krause's end organs, and the threshold for stimulation of the cold spots corresponds to the depth of these bodies in the tissues. Nafe and Wagoner[117] and Kenshalo[121] failed to confirm the existence of the sensation of cold in the cornea, however.

Most observers are agreed that the heat sense is almost entirely absent from the cornea and the conjunctiva. Only the conjunctiva bordering the eyelids, the eyelids themselves, and the lacrimal caruncle are sensitive to heat. Nafe and Wagoner found no sensation of heat when the cornea was stimulated with an applicator at 51.5° C. 2 mm. in from the limbus, but all of the stimulations produced a sense of pain. When the sclera was stimulated, however, they found that the sensation was described as burning hot.

From the fact that they found sensation to neither heat nor cold present in the cornea, Nafe and Wagoner believe that the only types of sensation present are those concerned with the free nerve endings, i.e., the senses of pressure and pain. The types of sensitivity which they find absent in the cornea are warmth, cold, heat, and pain aroused by heat. These types of sensitivity, they claim, are in general related to the existence of visceral afferent fibers terminating within the walls of blood vessels. Warmth seems to be correlated with the afferent discharge set up by vascular dilatation, cold by moderate constriction, heat by more severe constriction, and pain from heat when the constriction produced is extreme. Although the facts derived from their studies seem to support this hypothesis, it must be accepted with some reserve. It may be that the absence of heat in the cornea is due to the fact that the absence of blood vessels permits the temperature to heat up the whole cornea, whereas the sensation of heat is derived only from an area in which heat is applied at one point and is rapidly transported away from that point by the blood current—in other words, by establishment of a rapid gradient of temperature. Lele and Weddell have reported a sensation of heat produced by brief contact with a sheathed copper cylinder, with infrared heat, and with a fine jet stream of warmed air.

Pain. The conjunctiva and cornea are abundantly supplied with pain spots. More pain spots are located in the cornea and in the mucous membrane of the anus than in any other region of the body. In the cornea sensitivity to pain increases from the periphery to the center, at first quickly until a fairly high value is reached and then more slowly. This corresponds to the distribution of the corneal nerves, the center of the cornea being very richly supplied with free nerve endings. The horizontal meridian is more richly supplied than the vertical meridian, and the temporal half is more sensitive than the nasal half. The pain of a corneal foreign body and of all the diseases of the outer ocular coats which produce irritation of the conjunctiva and cornea is so characteristic as to be described as a foreign body sensation. It differs entirely from the deep-seated neuralgic pain of iritis and iridocyclitis. This latter pain is deep and throbbing and is always worse at night or early in the morning. It is frequently widespread in its reference, and patients may complain of earache, pain in the teeth, or pain over one of the sinuses.

The sensibilities of the other parts of the eye are important clinically, especially the sensibility for pain, and may be considered here briefly.

The ocular muscles produce very

marked painful sensations when they are put on a stretch. Both the retina and the optic nerve are said to be devoid of pain. In this respect they are like brain tissue. The sheaths of the optic nerve, like the meninges, must be supplied with pain fibers since patients with retrobulbar neuritis characteristically complain of pain behind the eyeball on moving the eye.

In experimental animals Tower[115] tested the sensitivity of the sclera, iris, and lens and the spontaneous discharge in the long ciliary nerves which took place when the intraocular pressure was artificially elevated. The sclera was found to be poorly supplied with nerve fibers, gauged by the response to equivalent stimulation applied to the cornea, but the form of the response to pressure, pinching, and pulling was similar to that in the cornea.

The iris, in contrast to the sclera, was found to be exceedingly sensitive. This is borne out well in clinical experience, since the pain of acute iritis is very severe. The lens was not found to be demonstrably sensitive to pricking or to touch, but pushing on its anterior curvature by means of a blunt glass rod provoked a small outburst of good-sized nerve impulses. The lens appeared to be without surface sensibility but seemed to possess what might be characterized as proprioceptive sensibility in modest proportions. The receptors in question are probably located in the ciliary body since no nerve fibers reach the lens itself. Raising the intraocular pressure produced an increase in the spontaneous activity of the nerve fibers, indicating the production of painful impulses.

REFERENCES

1. Marin-Amat, M.: The physiological variations of the corneal curvature during life; their significance in ocular refraction, Bull. Soc. Belg. Ophth. 113:251, 1956.
2. Von Bahr, G.: Corneal thickness; its measurement and changes, Am. J. Ophth. 42:251, 1956.
3. Mishima, S., and Maurice, D.: The effect of normal evaporation on the eye, Exper. Eye Res. 1:46, 1961.
4. Jakus, M.: The fine structure of the human cornea. In Smelser, G., editor: The structure of the eye, New York, 1961, Academic Press Inc., p. 344.
5. La Tessa, A., Teng, C., and Katzin, H.: The histochemistry of the basement membrane of the cornea, Am. J. Ophth. 58:171, 1954.
6. Mishima, S., and Maurice, D.: The oily layer of the tear film and evaporation from the corneal surface, Exper. Eye Res. 1:39, 1961.
7. Kaye, G., and Pappas, G.: Studies on the cornea, I, J. Cell. Biol. 12:457, 1962; Studies on cornea, II, J. Cell. Biol. 12:481, 1962.
8. Kaye, G.: Studies on the cornea, III, J. Cell. Biol. 15:241, 1962.
9. Wolter, J.: Innervation of the corneal endothelium of the eye of the rabbit, Arch. Ophth. 58:246, 1957.
10. Kawerau, E., and Ott, H.: The soluble proteins of the cornea, Exper. Eye Res. 1:137, 1961.
11. Maurice, D.: Eighteenth International Congress of Ophthalmology, Acta clin. belg. 1: 1958.
12. Finley, J., Berkowitz, D., and Croll, M.: The physiological significance of gerontoxon, Tr. Sect. Ophth. A.M.A., 1961, p. 114; Arch. Ophth. 66:211, 1961.
13. Meyer, K., and Chaffee, E.: The mucopolysaccharide acid of the cornea and its enzymatic hydrolysis, Am. J. Ophth. 23:1320, 1940.
14. Laurent, T., and Anseth, A.: Studies on corneal polysaccharides, Exper. Eye Res. 1:99, 1961.
15. Anseth, A.: Studies on corneal polysaccharides, Exper. Eye Res. 1:106, 116, 1961.
16. Philpot, F.: Factors affecting the hydration of the rabbit cornea, J. Physiol. 128:504, 1955.

17. Hermann, H., and Moses, S. G.: Content and state of glutathione in tissues of eye, J. Biol. Chem. **158**:33, 1945.

18. Philpot, F., and Pirie, A.: Riboflavin and riboflavin adenine dinucleotide in ox ocular tissues, Biochem. J. **37**:250, 1943.

19. deRoetth, A.: Glycolytic activity of the cornea, Arch. Ophth. **45**:1239, 1951.

20. Langham, M.: Glycolysis in cornea of rabbit, J. Physiol. **126**:396, 1954.

21. Kinoshita, J., and Masurat, T.: Aerobic pathways of glucose metabolism in bovine corneal epithelium, Am. J. Ophth. **48**: (pt. 2) 47, 1959.

22. Robbie, W., Leinfelder, P., and Duane, T.: Cyanide inhibition of corneal respiration, Am. J. Ophth. **30**:1381, 1947.

23. Langham, M.: Glycolysis in cornea of rabbit, J. Physiol. **126**:396, 1954.

24. Langham, M.: Utilization of oxygen by the component layers of the living cornea, J. Physiol. **117**:461, 1952.

25. Heald, K., and Langham, M.: Permeability of the cornea and the blood-aqueous barrier to oxygen, Brit. J. Ophth. **40**:705, 1956.

26. Smelser, G.: Relation of factors involved in maintenance of optical properties of cornea to contact lens wear, Arch. Ophth. **47**:328, 1952.

27. Cogan, D., and Hirsch, E.: The cornea; permeability to weak electrolytes, Arch. Ophth. **32**:276, 1944.

28. Swan, K., and White, N.: Corneal permeability. Factors affecting penetration of drugs into the cornea, Am. J. Ophth. **25**:1043, 1942.

29. Kinsey, V. E.: Personal communication.

30. O'Brien, C., and Swan, K.: Carbaminoylcholine chloride in the treatment of glaucoma simplex, Arch. Ophth. **27**:253, 1942.

31. Friedenwald, J., Hughes, W., and Hermann, H.: Acid bas tolerance of the cornea, Arch. Ophth. **31**:279, 1944.

32. Potts, A., and Johnson, L.: The nutritional supply of corneal regions in experimental animals, Am. J. Ophth. **53**: 504, 1950.

33. Janes, R., and Stiles, J.: The penetration of C^{14}-labelled atropine into the eye, Arch. Ophth. **62**:97, 69, 1959.

34. Potts, A.: The nutritional supply of corneal regions in experimental animals, Am. J. Ophth. **36**:127, 1953.

35. Maurice, D.: Influence on corneal permeability of bathing with solutions of differing reaction and tonicity, Brit. J. Ophth. **39**:463, 1955.

36. Cogan, D., and Kinsey, V.: Transfer of water and sodium chloride by osmosis and diffusion through the excised cornea, Arch. Ophth. **27**:466, 1942.

37. Cogan, D., and Kinsey, V.: Transfer of water and sodium chloride by hydrostatic pressure through the excised cornea, Arch. Ophth. **27**:696, 1942.

38. Cogan, D., and Kinsey, V.: Hydration properties of excised corneal pieces, Arch. Ophth. **28**:272, 1942.

39. Cogan, D., and Kinsey, V.: Hydration properties of excised corneal pieces, Arch. Ophth. **28**:449, 1942.

40. Cogan, D., and Kinsey, V.: Cornea: physiological aspects, Arch. Ophth. **28**: 661, 1942.

41. Cogan, D., Hirsch, E., and Kinsey, V.: Permeability characteristics of the excised cornea, Arch. Ophth. **31**:408, 1944.

42. Holt, M., and Cogan, D.: Permeability of the excised cornea to ions as determined by measurements of impedance, Arch. Ophth. **35**:292, 1946.

43. Davson, H., editor: The eye, vol. I, New York, 1962, Academic Press, Inc., p. 330.

44. Maurice, D.: The movement of fluorescein and water in the cornea, Am. J. Ophth. **49**:1011, 1960.

45. Beswick, A., Langley, R., and McCulloch, C.: Factors influencing the movement of fluorescein in the cornea, Am. J. Ophth. **46**:3, 1958.

46. Maurice, D.: The use of permeability studies in the investigation of submicroscopic structure. In Smelser, G., editor: The structure of the eye, New York, 1961, Academic Press, Inc., p. 385.

47. Donn, A.: The movement of ions and water across the cornea, Invest. Ophthal. **1**:172, 1962.

48. Maurice, D.: In Smelser, G., editor: The structure of the eye, New York, 1961, Academic Press, Inc., p. 390.

49. Kaye, G.: Studies on the cornea. III. The fine structure of the frog cornea and the uptake and transport of colloidal particles by the cornea in vivo, J. Cell. Biol. **15**:241, 1962.

50. Dohlman, C., and Anseth, A.: The swell-

ing pressure of the ox corneal stroma, Acta ophth. **35**:73, 1957.

51. Loeven, W.: The binding collagen-mucopolysaccharide in connective tissue, Acta anat. **24**:217, 1955.

52. Maurice, D.: The structure and transparency of the cornea, J. Physiol. **136**: 263, 1957.

53. vanWallbeek, K.: Turgescence and swelling pressure. In Duke-Elder, S., editor: Transparency of the cornea, Springfield, Ill., 1960, Charles C Thomas, Publisher, p. 51.

54. Potts, A., Cohen, B., and Goodman, D.: Corneal water transport as measured with tritiated water, Am. J. Ophth. **47**: 419, 1959.

55. Maurice, D.: Permeability to sodium ions of the living rabbit's cornea, J. Physiol. **112**:367, 1951.

56. Maurice, D., and Giardini, A.: Swelling of the cornea in vivo after the destruction of its limiting layers, Brit. J. Ophth. **35**:791, 1951.

57. Langham, M., and Taylor, I.: Factors affecting the hydration of the cornea in the excised eye in the living animal, Brit. J. Ophth. **40**:321, 1956.

58. Harris, J.: Transport of fluid from the cornea. In Duke-Elder, S., editor: Transparency of the cornea, Springfield, Ill., 1960, Charles C Thomas, Publisher, p. 73.

59. Knowles, W.: Effect of intralamellar plastic membranes on corneal physiology, Am. J. Ophth. **51**:274, 1961.

60. Bock, R., and Maumenee, A.: Corneal fluid metabolism, Arch. Ophth. **50**:282, 1933.

61. Pollack, I.: Corneal hydration studied in stromal segments separated by interlamellar discs, Invest. Ophthal. **1**:661, 1962.

62. Anseth, A., and Dohlman, C.: Influence of the intraocular pressure on hydration of the corneal stroma, Acta ophth. **35**: 85, 1957.

63. Potts, A., and Modrell, R.: The transcorneal potential, Am. J. Ophth. **44**:284, 1957.

64. Donn, A., Maurice, D., and Mills, N.: Studies on the living cornea in vitro, Arch. Ophth. **62**:741, 1959.

65. Davson, H.: Some considerations on the salt content of fresh and old ox cornea, Brit. J. Ophth. **33**:175, 1949.

65a. Langham, M.: The inter-relationship of metabolism and deturgescence of the living cornea, Invest. Ophth. **1**:187, 1962.

66. Harris, J.: The physiologic control of corneal hydration, Am. J. Ophth. **44**: 262, 1957.

67. von Bahr, Giardini, and Gandolfi. Cited by Brubaker, R., and Kupfer, C.: Microcryoscopic determination of the osmolality of interstitial fluid in the living cornea, Invest. Ophthal. **1**:653, 1962.

68. Aurell, G., and Holmgren, H.: Metachromatic substance in cornea, with special reference to question of transparency, Nord. Med. **30**:1277, 1946.

69. vanWalbeek, K., and Neumann, H.: Studies of corneal transparency under various experimental conditions, Arch. Ophth. **46**:482, 1951.

70. Cogan, D.: Bullous keratitis, Arch. Ophth. **25**:941, 1941.

71. Weimar, V.: Healing processes in the cornea. In Duke-Elder, S., editor: Transparency of the cornea, Springfield, Ill., 1960, Charles C Thomas, Publisher, p. 111.

72. Taylor, A., Goldsmith, E., and Bevelander, G.: Alkaline phosphase activity in the cornea following abrasion, Anat. Rec. **99**:634, 1947.

73. Friedenwald, J., and Buschke, W.: Mitotic and wound healing activities of corneal epithelium, Arch. Ophth. **32**: 410, 1944.

74. Arey, L.: Wound healing, Physiol. Rev. **16**:327, 1936.

75. Arey, L., and Covode, W.: Method of repair in epithelial wounds of cornea, Anat. Rec. **86**:75, 1936.

76. Mann, L.: Study of epithelial regeneration in living eye, Brit. J. Ophth. **28**: 26, 1944.

77. Buschke, W., Friedenwald, J., and Fleischmann, W.: Studies on mitotic activity of corneal epithelium; methods. Effects of colchicine, ether, cocaine and ephedrin, Bull. Johns Hopkins Hosp. **73**: 143, 1943.

78. Gunderson, T., and Liebman, S.: Effect of local anesthetics on regeneration of corneal epithelium, Arch. Ophth. **31**: 29, 1944.

79. Friedenwald, J., and Buschke, W.: Influence of some experimental variables on epithelial movements in healing of cor-

neal wounds, J. Cell. & Comp. Physiol. **23:**95, 1944.

80. Smelser, G., and Ozanics, V.: Effect of local anesthetics on cell division and migration following thermal burns of cornea, Arch. Ophth. **34:**271, 1945.

81. Smelser, G., and Ozanics, V.: Effect of chemotherapeutic agents on cell division and healing of corneal burns and abrasions in rat, Am. J. Ophth. **27:**1063, 1944.

82. Behrendt, T.: Corneal lesions after topical anesthesia, Am. J. Ophth. **41:**99, 1956.

83. Michaelis, M., and Quastel, J.: Site of action of narcotics in respiratory processes, Biochem. J. **35:**518, 1941.

84. Hermann, H., Moses, S., and Friedenwald, J.: Influence of pontocaine hydrochloride and chlorobutanol on respiration and glycolysis of cornea, Arch. Ophth. **28:**652, 1942.

85. Friedenwald, J., and Buschke, W.: Effects of excitement, of epinephrine, and of sympathectomy on the mitotic activity of corneal epithelium in the rat, Am. J. Physiol. **141:**689, 1944.

86. Buschke, W., Friedenwald, J., and Moses, S.: Effects of ultraviolet irradiation on corneal epithelium, J. Cell. & Comp. Physiol. **26:**147, 1945.

87. Bessey, O., and Wolbach, S.: Vascularization of the cornea of the rat in riboflavin deficiency, with note on corneal vascularization in vitamin A deficiency, J. Exper. Med. **69:**1, 1939.

88. Sydenstricker, V., Sebrell, W., Clockley, H., and Kruse, H.: Ocular manifestations of ariboflavinosis, J.A.M.A. **114:** 2437, 1940.

89. Dann, W., and Darby, W.: Appraisal of nutritional status (nutriture) of humans, with especial reference to vitamin deficiency diseases, Physiol. Rev. **25:**326, 1945.

90. Berg, J., et al.: Formation of capillaries and other tissue changes in the cornea of methionine-deficient rats, J. Nutrition **33:**509, 1946.

91. Hall, W., Sydenstricker, V., Hock, C., and Bowles, L.: Protein deprivation as cause of vascularization of cornea in rat, J. Nutrition **32:**509, 1946.

92. Ferraro, A., and Roizin, L.: Ocular changes in rats on amino-acid (valine)

deficient diet, Am. J. Ophth. **30:**330, 1947.

93. Johnson, L., and Eckhardt, R.: Rosacea keratitis and conditions with vascularization of cornea treated with riboflavin, Arch. Ophth. **23:**899, 1940.

94. Wise, G : Ocular rosacea, Am. J. Ophth. **26:**591, 1943.

95. Ashton, N., and Cook, C.: Mechanism of corneal vascularization, Brit. J. Ophth. **37:**193, 1953.

96. Campbell, F.: The influence of a low atmospheric pressure on the development of the retinal vessels in the rat, Tr. Ophth. Soc. U. Kingdom **71:**287, 1951.

97. Cogan, D.: Vascularization of the cornea, Tr. Am. Ophth. Soc. **46:**457, 1948.

98. Cogan, D.: Studies on the clinical physiology of the cornea, Am. J. Ophth. **32:** 625, 1949.

99. Cook, C., and Langham, M.: Corneal thickness in interstitial keratitis, Brit. J. Ophth. **37:**301, 1953.

100. Langham, M.: Observations on the growth of blood vessels into the cornea. Application of a new experimental technique, Brit. J. Ophth. **37:**210, 1953.

101. Adrian, E.: The basis of sensation, New York, 1928, W. W. Norton & Co., Inc.

102. Dastur, D.: Cutaneous nerves in leprosy, Brain **78:**615, 1955.

103. Weddell, G., Palmer, E., and Pallie, W.: Nerve endings in mammalian skin, Biol. Rev. **30:**159, 1955.

104. Weddell, G., and Zander, E.: A critical evaluation of methods used to demonstrate tissue neural elements, illustrated by reference to the cornea, J. Anat. **84:** 168, 1950.

105. Sinclair, D.: Cutaneous sensation and the doctrine of specific energy, Brain **78:** 584, 1955.

106. Tower, S.: Pain; definition and properties of unit for sensory reception, A. Research Nerv. & Ment. Dis. Proc. **23:** 16, 1943.

107. Ray, B., and Wolff, H.: Experimental studies on headache, Arch. Surg. **41:** 813, 1940.

108. Wolff, H., and Hardy, J.: On the nature of pain, Physiol. Rev. **27:**167, 1947.

109. Hecht, S.: The relation between visual acuity and illumination, J. Gen. Physiol. **11:**255, 1928.

110. Oppel, T., and Hardy, J.: Studies in

temperature sensation, J. Clin. Investigation **16:**525, 1937.

111. Eckhardt, L., McLean, J., and Goodell, H.: Experimental studies on headache; the genesis of pain from the eye, A. Research Nerv. & Ment. Dis. Proc. **23:** 209, 1943.

112. Kirsch, R., Samet, P., Kugel, V., and Axelrod, S.: Electrocardiographic changes during ocular surgery and their prevention by retrobulbar surgery, Arch. Ophth. **58:**348, 1957.

113. Lebensohn, J.: The nature of photophobia, Arch. Ophth. **12:**380, 1934.

114. Dandy, W.: Trigeminal neuralgia and trigeminal tic douloureux, Lewis' Pract. Surg. **12:**167, 1936.

115. Tower, S.: Unit for sensory reception in the cornea, J. Neurophysiol. **3:**486, 1940.

116. Strughold, H.: Mechanical threshold of cornea-reflex of the usual laboratory animals, Am. J. Physiol. **94:**235, 1930.

117. Nafe, J., and Wagoner, K.: Insensitivity of cornea to heat and pain derived from high temperatures, Am. J. Psychol. **49:** 631, 1937.

118. Rowbotham, G.: Observations on effects of trigeminal denervation, Brain **62:** 364, 1939.

119. Grant, F., Groff, R., and Lewey, F.: Section of descending spinal root of the fifth cranial nerve, Arch. Neurol. & Psychiat. **43:**489, 1940.

120. Lele, P., and Weddell, G.: The relationship between neurohistology and corneal sensibility, Brain **79:**119, 1956.

121. Kenshalo, D.: Comparison of thermal sensitivity of the forehead, lip, conjunctiva and cornea, J. Appl. Physiol. **15:**987, 1960.

CHAPTER 4

THE AQUEOUS HUMOR

CHEMICAL COMPOSITION AND PHYSICAL PROPERTIES OF NORMAL AQUEOUS HUMOR

The anterior and posterior chambers of the eye are filled with a clear fluid called the aqueous humor. This same fluid permeates the gellike vitreous humor. It represents the tissue fluid of the eye and has been called the ocular lymph. The use of the term *lymph* is inappropriate in view of the absence of any preformed lymphatics in the eye. The interior of the eye possesses no lymphatic channels. Even the so-called perivascular lymph spaces of the retinal arteries are denied by some authors. No true endothelial lined lymphatics are present within the orbit. The extension of the subarachnoid space around the optic nerve continues as a mesothelial-lined channel as far as the lamina cribrosa, but does not go any farther.[1] The conjunctiva alone has lymphatics. Furthermore, the use of the term *lymph* implies that the fluid possesses certain chemical characteristics and assumes certain functions similar to those of lymph found elsewhere in the body. The aqueous humor does not fulfill the functions of

ordinary lymph and possesses far different chemical and physical characteristics than those of the lymph contained in the receptaculum chyli.

The aqueous humor is a crystal-clear liquid having a refractive index relatively low compared to that of the lens which it bathes. The volume of the anterior chamber is approximately 285 ml. in the rabbit. The posterior chamber contains approximately 57 ml.—approximately 20% of the volume of the anterior chamber.[2] Of the usual laboratory animals having globes approximately the same size, rabbits have the smallest and cats the

Table 4. *Volume of anterior chamber compared to volume of globe**

Species	Anterior chamber/ Globe (%)
Owl	17.0
Chicken	3.0
Cat	22.0
Dog	12.5
Rabbit	14.0
Monkey	5.5
Man	2.5-4.0

*After Wessely.

largest anterior chambers. Table 4 shows the anterior chamber volume in relation to total globe volume.

The depth of the anterior chamber in the normal eye displays considerable variation.[3] In Fig. 22 is shown the depth of the anterior chamber in normal eyes, and the extreme differences in depth among normal persons is also illustrated. The refraction of the eye is of considerable importance in determining these wide variations. The anterior chamber is deepest in the young adult and shallows with advancing age. In the infant, the chamber is very shallow and gradually deepens until puberty is reached. The depth of the anterior chamber, as determined by the position of the ocular diaphragm, is not constant in any one individual, but shows definite changes throughout the day and from day to day, according to Bleeker.[4]

What circulation of fluid exists is suffi-

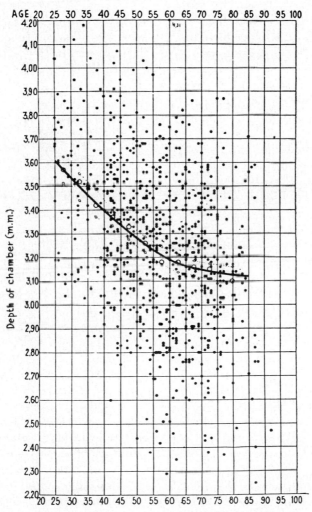

Fig. 22. Depth of the chamber in normal eyes. (From Rosengren, B.: Arch. Ophth. 44:529, 1950.)

cient to meet the metabolic demands of the structures which depend on it for their nutrition. The lens, and to some extent the cornea, is devoid of blood vessels; therefore, nourishment must be supplied largely by the bathing fluid, and waste products must be carried away in a similar fashion. The aqueous humor must, therefore, contain the building stones necessary for replacement of tissue, e.g., sugar and amino acids. Moreover, it must transport oxygen and carry away the waste products of metabolism, including carbon dioxide, from the interior of the eye to the blood. The normal aqueous humor fulfills these requirements, except that the oxygen supply of the aqueous humor is insufficient to maintain the metabolic needs of the cornea if it is denied contact with the air (p. 48).

Use of the term *aqueous humor* should be limited to the fluid in the healthy undisturbed eye. Any changes in the state of dilatation of the intraocular blood vessels, changes in the various membranes forming the blood aqueous barrier, changes in the intravascular pressure, or changes in the constitution of the blood lead to alterations in the chemical and physical properties of the aqueous humor. The resultant fluid can no longer be regarded as normal. Even slight irritation of the eye may lead to vasodilatation by axon reflexes and produce alterations in chemical constitution. Changes in permeability probably account for the wide variation in the analyses of this fluid reported in the literature. Under nonphysiologic conditions, the term *plasmoid aqueous* should be used. In the following discussion of the properties and mode of formation of aqueous humor, the normal aqueous humor as taken from the anterior chamber is referred to unless otherwise specified.

Chemical composition

Chemical analyses have been undertaken to shed light on the mechanisms concerned in the formation of the aqueous humor. When such analyses are made, the following precautions are necessary. The withdrawal of the aqueous humor and the blood samples must be made simultaneously because both can change their composition independently of each other in a brief period of time. The kind and the amount of anesthetic used are important because anesthetics influence the composition of the aqueous humor through changes in the blood-aqueous barrier and by varying the composition of the blood. Samples of aqueous humor and blood withdrawn after the death of an animal are totally unsuited for such analyses. Wherever possible, therefore, the analyses reported in this chapter are those which have been made with these factors controlled.

In the following discussion, unless otherwise stated, the figures given represent the chemical composition of the aqueous humor of the anterior chamber. The values in the aqueous humor withdrawn from the posterior chamber may differ considerably from those now presented. Further, the values of the aqueous humor in the posterior chamber are of much greater significance in the interpretation of the mechanisms concerned in the formation of aqueous humor than those in the anterior chamber. This will be emphasized later.

Protein. The most striking difference in the chemical composition of aqueous humor and blood serum is the total solid content. The former fluid contains about 1.08 Gm./100 ml. solids, whereas the latter fluid contains 9.5 Gm./100 ml. solids. Therefore, the aqueous humor is a much more dilute fluid than blood serum, and the chief difference in solids is due to the high percentage of protein present in serum. Blood contains over 7% protein, whereas aqueous humor contains 0.02%. Although the total amount of protein is considerably less in aqueous humor, most investigations show the relative proportions of globulin and albumin the same as in blood. Using a method of agar microelectrophoresis, François and associates[5] found a slight increase in the percentage of albumin and a more or less marked decrease in the percentage of gamma globulin. In keeping with the low gamma globulin content, one finds specific immune bodies present in a relatively low concentration in the aqueous humor. Even in an animal whose blood has been highly immunized against a particular organism, very few antibodies can be demonstrated in the aqueous humor. If the eye is inflamed or if the anterior chamber is tapped, the fluid which refills the anterior chamber, i.e., the plasmoid aqueous humor, contains a high per-

centage of protein and a high titer of antibodies. Table 5 shows the concentration of protein in the aqueous humor and serum of the cow and rabbit as determined by Duke-Elder.

In man, the protein content of the aqueous humor lies between 0.019 and 0.034 Gm./100 ml. Kronfeld[6] found less than 15% variation in repeated determinations of the protein content on the same eye and between the two normal eyes of human subjects. In senile cataract with cortical breakdown of the lens, the protein content is increased, probably because of the diffusion of lens protein into the anterior chamber.

Nonprotein nitrogenous substances. Table 6 gives the amount of urea present in aqueous humor and in blood serum in millimols per kilogram of water.

The average concentration of urea in the vitreous humor is intermediate between that in aqueous humor and that in blood. A comparison of the concentration

Table 5. *Concentration of protein in aqueous humor and blood serum in cow and rabbit*

	Cow		Rabbit	
Proteins	Intraocular fluid (%)	Blood serum (%)	Intraocular fluid (%)	Blood serum (%)
Total proteins	0.017	7.53	0.04	5.57
Globulin	0.009	3.73	0.009	1.16
Albumin	0.008	3.80	0.031	4.41
Quotient—globulin/albumin	1:1	1:1	1:4	1:4

Table 6. *Amount of urea in aqueous humor and blood serum (millimols per kilogram water)*

Animal	Aqueous humor	Blood serum	Ratio
Dog (Walker)	2.16	3.16	0.68
Cat (Adler)	7.58	9.55	0.79
Man (Adler)	5.00	5.95	0.84
Cat (Benham)	5.16	5.88	0.88
Dog (Benham)	7.43	8.29	0.90
Rabbit (Kinsey and Robinson)	4.50	5.37	0.84

Table 7. *Reducing substances in aqueous humor and blood plasma*

Investigator		Aqueous humor (%)	Blood plasma (%)	Ratio Aqueous/Plasma
Adler (1933)	Cat	0.113	0.135	0.84
Walker (1933)	Man	0.060	0.108	0.56
	Rabbit	0.136	0.146	0.93
	Dog	0.890	0.108	0.82
	Cat	0.078	0.119	0.66
Duke-Elder and Davson (1939)	Rabbit	0.125	0.146	0.86
	Cat	0.82	0.108	0.76

of urea in the aqueous humor in the two eyes of dogs showed that both eyes of the same animal had almost identical concentrations and that the concentration was less than in the blood.[7]

Amino acids. Experiments by Merriam,[8] with starch chromatography indicate that the distribution of amino acid in the aqueous humor is similar to that of the free amino acids in the blood plasma. He found the total concentration of free amino acids in pooled rabbit aqueous humor is about 70 mg./100 ml.

Reddy, Rosenberg, and Kinsey[9] compared the concentration of free amino acids in the aqueous humor of the anterior and posterior chambers, the vitreous body, and the plasma of rabbits by ion exchange chromatography. The concentration of all the amino acids that could be reliably determined was found to be greater in posterior chambers than in the plasma withdrawn at the same time, except for glycin, proline, and threonine. It is probable that most amino acids are transported actively across the ciliary epithelial cells.[10] The concentration of amino acids was found to be quite low in the vitreous, i.e., about one fifth that of the posterior chamber aqueous, which may indicate that there is active utilization by the surrounding intraocular tissues.

Reducing substances. Many of the analytical methods used in the estimation of sugars in body fluids are not specific.* This must be taken into account before drawing any inferences concerning the distribution of sugars in the aqueous humor and blood. Table 7 shows the concentration of reducing substances in the aqueous humor and blood plasma.

It is apparent from the information in Table 7 that, despite the inclusion in the analyses of ascorbic acid which, as will be shown, is in excess in the aqueous humor, the over-all concentration of reducing substances in this fluid is less than it is in the blood. Therefore, the concentration of sugar (predominantly glucose) must be still less.

Organic acids. The following organic acids have been found in the aqueous humor.

Ascorbic acid. The concentration of ascorbic acid (vitamin C) in aqueous humor is significantly higher than in circulating plasma in some animals, e.g., adult rabbits (Table 14). The concentration may be ten to fifteen times that of plasma. In young rabbits, the concentration is approximately the same as in

---

*A comparison of the results of estimations of aqueous humor-blood sugar ratios by different methods has been made by Janes and co-workers[10a] and should be consulted by persons wishing to make similar analyses.

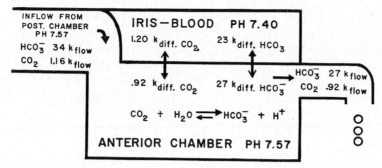

Fig. 24. Anterior chamber with flow in from posterior chamber, exit by flow, and diffusion across blood-aqueous barrier for bicarbonate and carbon dioxide. The relative concentrations are in millimols per kilogram water. (From Kinsey, V. E.: In Newell, F. W., editor: Glaucoma, New York, 1957, Josiah Macy, Jr. Foundation, p. 65.)

of the rabbit eye (Kinsey).[21] These figures are in substantial agreement with those of Becker.[22] Since the aqueous humor in the posterior chamber is about 0.20 of a unit of pH higher than the plasma, Kinsey calculates that 3.3% of the total bicarbonate exists as carbon dioxide or 1.16 mM/kg. water. The concentrations shown in Fig. 24 are analytical values. They suggest that due to the higher pH of the aqueous the carbon dioxide tension may be slightly higher in plasma than in aqueous humor from either the posterior or anterior chamber, despite a greater concentration of total carbon dioxide in the aqueous humors.

As is the case with other substances, there seems to be considerable difference in the distribution of bicarbonate between aqueous humor and plasma in different species (compare data given in Tables 14 and 15). It has been found that in general there is a rough correlation between the distribution of bicarbonate between aqueous humor and blood plasma and the size of the eye of the species. However, the rat[23] is an exception to this rule. In the human being the pH and the concentration of bicarbonate are lower in aqueous humor than in plasma.[24]

It has also been suggested[25] that the variation in bicarbonate concentration from species to species is determined by the buffering requirements of the ocular tissues, especially the lens, retina, and cornea, which produce organic acids. Since in small eyes the mass of metabolizing tissues in relation to the amount of aqueous is large, one might expect to find a higher concentration of bicarbonate than in large eyes where the reverse holds. This hypothesis would also offer an explanation for the fact that in the eyes of the monkey and the rat, which are both relatively small, the distributions are more characteristic of the large-eyed animals, for in the rat the rate of renewal of aqueous humor is two to three times greater than in the other mammalian species. According to Davson this rapid turnover of aqueous humor compensates for the low bicarbonate concentration.

Inorganic ions. Analyses of various inorganic ions in aqueous humor have shown great variability. This is understandable in view of the technical difficulties encountered in the accurate determination of these substances in small quantities of fluid.

Sodium. Table 8 gives the results of analyses of sodium in the aqueous humor and plasma in several species of animals.

Most investigators are agreed that the concentration of sodium in the anterior chamber is slightly less than in plasma, but if the concentration of sodium in the aqueous is compared with that of a dialysate of plasma, the concentration is greater than can be accounted for on the basis of a Donnan equilibrium.

It is interesting to note that cerebrospinal fluid, which like aqueous humor has a very low concentration of protein and is thought to be secreted, has a higher concentration of sodium than aqueous humor.

Chloride. The following table (Table 9) gives the concentration of chloride in aqueous humor and in blood.

The general agreement is that chloride values vary greatly in different species. For example, most workers agree that in the rabbit there is a deficit of chloride in the aqueous. Kinsey states that it is lowest in the posterior chamber, slightly higher in the anterior chamber, and highest in plasma. However, Becker has shown the reverse to be true in man, there being a surplus of chloride in the aqueous humor in both the anterior and posterior chambers.[24-26]

Calcium, potassium, magnesium, phosphate, and sulfate. Table 10 gives analyses of blood serum and aqueous humor from horses as determined by Stary and Winternitz.[27]

Table 11 shows Tron's complete analyses recalculated in millimols per kilogram of water.[28]

Salit[29] determined the calcium content

Table 8. *Sodium in aqueous humor and plasma (millimols per kilogram water)*

				Ratio
Investigator	*Species*	*Aqueous*	*Plasma*	*Aqueous/Plasma*
Davson (1939)	Cat	156	162	0.97
Duke-Elder (1939)	Cat	150	160	0.94
Kinsey (1951)	Rabbit	143	146	0.98

Table 9. *Chloride in aqueous humor and blood (millimols per kilogram water)*

				Ratio
				Aqueous humor/
Author	*Species*	*Aqueous humor*	*Blood*	*Blood*
Hodgson (1938)	Man	126	111	1.13
Davson and Weld (1941)	Dog			
Kinsey (1949)	Dog	124	125 (venous)	1.00
Kinsey (1949)	Man	121	117 (venous)	1.03
Kinsey (1953)*	Rabbit	105 (anterior chamber)	112	0.94
		100 (posterior chamber)	112	0.89
Becker (1958)†	Man	126 (anterior chamber)	117 (arterial)	
Becker (1958)‡	Man	121 (anterior chamber)	114	
		134 (posterior chamber)		

*Kinsey, V. E.: Arch. Ophth. **50:**401, 1953.
†Becker, B.: In Newell, F. W., editor: Glaucoma (Transactions Second Conference), New York, 1957, Josiah Macy, Jr., Foundation.
‡Becker, B.: Arch. Ophth. **58:**878, 1957.

of the aqueous and vitreous humors and blood serum in cattle of various ages, post-mortem.

Table 10. *Analyses of aqueous humor and blood serum in horses (millimols per kilogram water)*

Substance	Aqueous humor	Serum	Ratio
Ca	1.97	3.16	0.63
K	5.02	5.06	0.99
Mg.	0.70	0.78	0.90

Table 11. *Analysis of electrolytes in aqueous humor*

Substance	Aqueous humor	Serum	Ratio
Na	147.0	165.0	0.89
K	4.85	8.35	0.58
Ca	1.50	2.90	0.52
Mg	0.45	0.69	0.65
Cl	123.0	118.0	1.04
S	0.40	1.01	0.40
PO₄	0.30	0.57	0.53

Table 12. *Calcium content of aqueous humor, vitreous humor, and blood serum in cattle (millimols per kilogram water)**

	Calves	Young cattle	Old cattle
Aqueous humor	1.45	1.35	1.15
Vitreous humor	2.04	1.79	1.69
Blood serum	2.94	2.72	2.54

*Postmortem examination.

The calcium in the aqueous humor is lower than that in the vitreous humor and is still lower than that in blood serum. As is the case with most other inorganic ions, analyses show that the calcium content of the ocular humors is directly dependent on the calcium content of the serum. Merritt and Bauer[30] studied the variations in the concentration of calcium in the aqueous humor by inducing hypoglycemia with insulin shock.

Levene[31] found a slight deficit of potassium in the aqueous humor, whereas Harris and co-workers[32] report a small excess in the rabbit eye.

Inorganic phosphate in the aqueous humor is about 50% of that in the blood serum.[16] Winternitz and Stary[33] found both phosphates and sulfates to be lower in aqueous humor than in blood serum. Palm[34] gives the data shown in Table 13, collected from the reports in the literature, of the phosphate content of aqueous humor and plasma.

Oxygen. Langham[35] has shown that the rate at which oxygen accumulates in the anterior aqueous of a rabbit breathing pure oxygen follows an exponential curve to approach a new steady state at about 200 mm. Hg. The rate of diffusion of oxygen is similar to the value for ethyl alcohol, and it appears that this rate is in accord with the lipoid solubility and

Table 13. *Phosphate in aqueous humor and blood (millimols per kilogram water)*

Species	Aqueous humor	Corrected plasma	Ratio
Horse	0.31	0.33 (p*)	0.94
	0.28		
	0.23		
	0.16	0.36 (s†)	0.46
Rabbit	0.18 to 0.20	0.33 to 0.50 (s)	0.46 (mean)
Rabbit	0.35 to 0.48	0.55 to 0.90 (p)	0.57 (mean)

*Plasma.
†Serum.

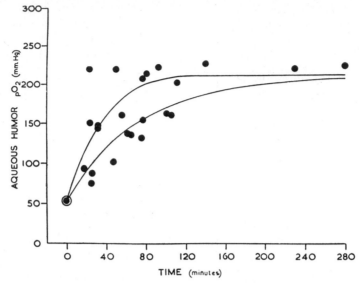

Fig. 25. Permeability of the blood-aqueous barrier to oxygen. The double circle represents the mean oxygen tension observed in normal eyes. The theoretical experimental curves $^k in =$ 0.027 min.$^{-1}$ and $^k in = 0.0135$ min.$^{-1}$ have been calculated on the basis that the maximal oxygen tension in the aqueous humor is 209.6 mm. Hg (see text). (From Langham, M.: In Duke-Elder, S., editor: Glaucoma, Springfield, Ill., 1955, Charles C Thomas, Publisher, p. 51.)

the known diffusion rates of molecules of similar size and physical characteristics (Fig. 25).

Miscellaneous chemical constituents. Various proteolytic enzymes are present in the aqueous humor[36] and are concerned with the breakdown of protein in the lens when the aqueous humor has access to the lens, e.g., after rupture of its capsule. Histamine has been found in the aqueous humor of the cat, dog, rabbit, and ox.[37] The histamine content of the aqueous humor does not rise significantly following an intravenous injection of histamine.

Other enzymes have been found in minimal concentration in normal aqueous humor of rabbits, such as lactic dehydrogenase and malic dehydrogenase.[38] Glucose 6-phosphate dehydrogenase was not detectable. The enzyme concentration rose in plasmoid aqueous six times its normal value, whereas the potein

concentration rose thirty to forty times its normal level.

Analyses of aqueous humor in posterior chamber

Kinsey was the first to point out that analyses of fluid in the posterior chamber differed considerably from those of fluid in the anterior chamber. This discovery has had a profound influence on the general theory of the formation of aqueous humor. The analyses reported in Table 14 are those taken from the anterior and posterior chambers of the rabbit; plasma was withdrawn almost simultaneously. It will be noted that the analyses from the posterior chamber show an even greater discrepancy between the concentration of various constituents in the aqueous humor and the blood than those from the anterior chamber.

Table 15 gives Becker's analyses for chloride, bicarbonate, and ascorbate, to-

Table 14. *Summary of composition of plasma and aqueous humor of anterior and posterior chambers of rabbit eye**

Substance	Anterior aqueous humor (mM/kg. H_2O)	Posterior aqueous humor (mM/kg. H_2O)	Plasma (mM/kg. H_2O)	Anterior aqueous humor/ Posterior aqueous humor	Anterior aqueous humor/ Plasma	Posterior aqueous humor/ Plasma	Anterior aqueous humor in excess of posterior aqueous humor (mM/kg. H_2O)
Anions							
Chloride	105.1 (73†)	100.0 (72)	111.8 (42)	1.051	0.94	0.89	+5.1
Bicarbonate	27.7 (23)	34.1 (23)	24.0 (23)	0.81	1.15	1.42	−6.4
Lactate	12.1 (24)	11.2 (24)	8.2 (12)	1.09	1.47	1.37	+0.9
Ascorbate	0.96 (16)	1.30 (16)	0.02 (5)	0.75	48.0	65.0	−0.3
Phosphate	0.89 (26)	0.52 (22)	1.49 (13)	1.80	0.60	0.35	+0.4
						Total	−0.3
Cations							
Sodium	146.5 (34)	144.5 (34)	— (2)	1.01	—	—	+2.0
Potassium	1154‡ (4)	1307.0 (4)	1545.0 (2)	0.89	0.75	0.85	−0.5 (estimate)
						Total	+1.5
Nonelectrolytes							
Carbon dioxide	1.0 (23)	1.2 (23)	1.2 (23)	0.83	0.83	1.0	−0.2
Nonprotein nitrogen	13.4 (25)	13.5 (25)	17.6 (16)	0.99	0.76	0.77	−0.1
Urea	6.3 (46)	5.8 (46)	7.3 (23)	1.08	0.86	0.80	—§
Glucose	6.7 (22)	7.1 (22)	8.3 (11)	0.96	0.81	0.85	−0.4
						Total	−0.7
						Grand total	+0.5

*From Kinsey, V. E.: Ophth. 50:401, 1953.

†Figures in parentheses refer to number of cases.

‡Expressed as counts per minute per kilogram.

§Figures for urea are omitted since they are included in values for nonprotein nitrogen.

Table 15. *Comparison of chemical composition of human aqueous humor (untreated) and arterial plasma (millimols per kilogram water)**

Patient	Chloride		Bicarbonate		pH		Ascorbate	
	AC†	Pl†	AC	Pl	AC	Pl	AC	Pl
1	122	114	25.5	28.6			0.58	0.04
2	126	110	22.3	26.3			0.39	0.06
3	122	113	22.1	25.3			0.87	0.07
4	124	117	20.6	23.7			0.47	0.05
5	124	119	22.1	27.3	7.20	7.38	0.81	0.07
6	130	120	19.5	25.8	7.23	7.42	0.89	0.06
7	130	124	19.6	25.4	7.24	7.42	1.33	0.07
8	132	121	21.3	26.9	7.21	7.40	0.51	0.05
9	124	117	20.8	23.5	7.18	7.40	1.43	0.09
10	121	115	21.9	26.8	7.20	7.40	1.03	0.04
11	135	124	17.3	23.6	7.19	7.38	1.64	0.10
12	127	117	18.4	24.9	7.27	7.41	0.15	0.03
13	127	116	20.0	25.8	7.24	7.41	1.21	0.08
14	125	116	21.5	26.1	7.19	7.40	0.37	0.03
19	122	113	22.6	28.0			1.10	0.04
20	123	115	21.8	24.6			1.72	0.08
21	127	117	23.1	26.7			0.75	0.03
22	129	116	22.4	26.2			1.20	0.09
23	125	121	22.3	25.0			1.17	0.07
24	128	117	23.1	28.1	7.19	7.38	1.53	0.10
25	121	113	21.8	24.5	7.20	7.37	0.36	0.04
26	118	113	23.1	27.4	7.23	7.41	0.84	0.06
Mean	126	117	21.5	25.9	7.21	7.40	0.92	0.06
Ac/Pl	1.08		0.83		—		15.3	

*From Becker, B.: Arch. Ophth. **57**:793, 1957.
†AC, anterior chamber concentration; Pl, arterial plasma concentration.

gether with the pH values, for the aqueous humor in the human being.[24]

Analyses of aqueous humor in vitreous

The fluid portion of the vitreous has been analyzed by many investigators (see section on vitreous), but Reddy and Kinsey have compared the chemical composition of this fluid with that of aqueous humor from the anterior and posterior chambers and plasma withdrawn simultaneously.[17] Table 14 shows the average values for all the analyses. The concentration of sodium in the vitreous is less than that in the plasma and in the aqueous humor of the anterior and posterior

chambers. This deficiency appears to be offset by an excess of potassium. It would appear that the vitreous seems to act as a source for those substances whose vitreous concentration exceeds that of the posterior chamber aqueous, e.g., chloride, and as a "sink" for those whose vitreous concentration is less than that in the posterior chamber aqueous, e.g., total carbon dioxide (see also Table 16).

Osmotic pressure

The osmotic pressure of the aqueous humor and its comparison with the parent blood plasma is of great theoretical importance in any consideration of aqueous humor formation and elimination

Table 16. *Concentration of various substances in intraocular fluids of rabbit eye (millimols per kilogram of water)**

Sample	Sodium	Potassium	Chloride	Total CO₂	Phosphate	Ascorbate	Lactate	Glucose	NPN
Vitreous	134	9.5	104.7	26.0	0.40	0.46	12.0	3.0	17
Posterior aqueous humor	136†	—	96.5	37.5	0.58	1.38	9.9	5.6	23
Anterior aqueous humor	138	5.0	101.0	30.2	0.89	1.11	9.3	5.4	25
Plasma	143	5.6	108.8	20.6	2.04	0 04	10.3	5.7	34

*From Reddy, D., and Kinsey, V. E.: Arch. Ophth. **63:**715, 1960.
†Estimated from ratios of concentrations in anterior aqueous and plasma found from a previous study.

from the eye. This will be elaborated in the section on aqueous humor formation (p. 123). Unfortunately, it cannot be said that the final figures are agreed upon by all investigators, and for the present we must be content with the reports, even though they are at variance. Although it is confusing and disappointing that many different values have been found that relate the osmotic pressure of the aqueous humor with that of blood withdrawn simultaneously, it must be remembered that the methods available for determining the osmotic pressure of minute amounts of fluid are subject to many variables and large experimental errors, such as those induced by general anesthesia.

It has been reasonably established that the aqueous humor from the anterior chamber is definitely hypertonic to that of the parent plasma. Kinsey[40] found it to be on the average 3 mM, sodium chloride equivalent, hypertonic to the plasma in rabbits. Similar findings have been reported by Roepke and Hetherington[41] and by Schaeffer.[42] Levene[43] found the normal osmolal values in rabbits obtained with the cryoscopic technique were 300.6 (0.9) mOsm. (milliosmols)/kg. water for aqueous humor and 298.5 (1.0) mOsm./kg. water for plasma. The excess of 2.1 mOsm./kg. of aqueous humor over that of plasma was statistically significant.

One is tempted to conclude from these figures that aqueous humor is hypertonic to the blood from which it is formed. Before this is possible, however, two facts must be recognized. First, the blood plasma on which all of these determinations of osmotic pressure were done was that circulating in the large arteries or the heart. It has been tacitly assumed that the osmotic concentration of the blood in the capillaries of the eye from which aqueous humor is formed is identical with that from these sources. This has not as yet been demonstrated, and Levene seriously considers that this may not be true. An even more important factor is that the figures we have quoted are those made on aqueous humor obtained by puncture from the anterior chamber. Since, as we shall see, the aqueous humor in the posterior chamber immediately after its formation from the ciliary processes has been shown to possess different chemical characteristics from aqueous humor found in the anterior chamber, it becomes a matter of the first importance to know whether the osmotic pressure of anterior chamber aqueous humor and that of posterior chamber aqueous humor are the same.

The studies of Kinsey made in 1951 demonstrated that the osmotic pressures of anterior and posterior chamber aqueous humors were identical. Recently, this concept has been challenged. Kass and Green[44] report that, while the osmotic pressure of the aqueous in the anterior chamber is considerably greater than that of the circulating blood plasma (blood withdrawn from the central ear artery), the osmotic pressure of the posterior chamber aqueous was equal to that of the plasma. Their figures show a hypertonicity of anterior chamber aqueous humor equal to 12—and 13.5 mM sodium chloride/1000 Gm. water. The posterior chamber aqueous humor was isotonic with plasma.

It is possible that some of the observed hypertonicity of the anterior chamber aqueous humor could occur through evaporation from the cornea. Mishima and Maurice[45] point out that a large part of the hypertonicity of the aqueous humor withdrawn from the anterior chamber could be due to evaporation, which if uncompensated by any osmotic attraction of water from the blood should concentrate the aqueous humor by about 2.6%.

PLASMOID AQUEOUS HUMOR

If the anterior chamber is opened and the aqueous humor is allowed to escape, the newly formed fluid which fills the chambers differs considerably in its physical and chemical properties from normal aqueous humor. This fluid has been called plasmoid aqueous. It more nearly resembles blood serum than normal aqueous humor.

The greatest change in plasmoid aqueous is an increase in protein content, which rises from a normal of 0.02 Gm. protein/100 ml. to that of serum, 7 Gm./100 ml. In most animals plasmoid aqueous clots, but in man normal aqueous contains very little fibrinogen and plasmoid aqueous shows very little disposition to form a clot. The low clotting power of human aqueous humor is of importance. It permits surgical procedures on the structures of the anterior chamber without danger of producing extensive postoperative adhesions. Plasmoid aqueous contains a marked increase in gamma globulin, so that immune bodies present in the bloodstream are now found in the same concentration in the aqueous humor.

It is not necessary to open the anterior chamber in order to produce plasmoid aqueous humor. Anything which dilates the intraocular blood vessels to an extent that the capillaries become more permeable will change the composition of the aqueous so that it resembles blood serum. Trauma to the eye and all inflammatory processes produce plasmoid aqueous. An aqueous flare is one of the first observable signs of inflammation of the anterior segment and is caused by an increased protein content of the aqueous, which becomes translucent in the beam of the slit-lamp. If the inflammatory process is severe, the dilatation of the intraocular blood vessels permits the passage of blood cells into the aqueous humor. All of the chemical constituents present in normal aqueous humor in different concentrations from that in the blood tend to equilibrate with the blood under these conditions. Sugar and urea increase, whereas ascorbic acid decreases. The unequal partitioning of electrolytes disappears. The specific gravity, the viscosity, and the refractive index increase in plasmoid aqueous.

All of the changes in the composition of aqueous humor which occur when the intraocular blood vessels are dilated lead to the conclusion that normally there is a barrier between the circulating blood and the fluid in the anterior and posterior chambers of the normal eye. This barrier shows selective properties. It has come to be known as the blood-aqueous barrier, without attempting to define it further in anatomic terms. The walls of the capillaries probably constitute the most important part of this barrier, although the ciliary epithelium cannot be excluded. The capillaries of the iris must be considered along with the capillaries in the ciliary processes.

Why should dilatation of the capillary bed produce such profound changes in permeability? It seems likely that the vasomotor activity of the metarterioles and the precapillaries determine the pressure and velocity of blood flow in all capillaries and thereby influence the exchange of fluid between the capillary and the surrounding tissues. When the muscles of the metarterioles and precapillaries are relaxed the precapillaries are open, and the pressure transmitted by the arteries is spread over the whole capillary network. The blood flow through the capillaries will be diminished, the intravascular pressure rises, and filtration out of the blood vessels is facilitated. Contraction of the muscles of the metarterioles and precapillaries, on the other hand, restricts the blood flow into a smaller capillary bed. Eventually the blood flows only through certain preferential channels directly into the venules so that the pressure conditions become more favorable for inward filtration, i.e., for the passage of fluid from the tissues into the blood. If this is the mechanism which changes the blood-aqueous barrier, we should find that the aqueous humor composition is affected by those drugs which relax or contract the blood vessel musculature. This is so. Drugs which dilate the peripheral vessels produce plasmoid aqueous as effectively as paracentesis, whereas vaso-

constricting drugs such as epinephrine will partially prevent the chemical changes induced by paracentesis from taking place. Electrical stimulation of the cervical sympathetics will do the same thing. Many drugs which are used in practice, such as eserine, di-isofluoro-phosphate, Humorsol, Phospholine iodide, and others, are known to increase the protein content of the human aqueous humor.[46]

All of the intraocular vascular bed probably contributes to the changes observed in the plasmoid aqueous humor. The iris vessels as well as those in the ciliary body become more permeable. This can be inferred from the fact that when the iris is totally removed from one eye of an experimental animal and after complete surgical recovery paracentesis is performed on both eyes the amount of protein found in the plasmoid aqueous humor of the side lacking the iris is always less than in the control side.[47]

Most of the transudate which forms plasmoid aqueous comes from the blood vessels, but it is possible that some of it comes into the anterior chamber from the vitreous. Radioactive phosphorus injected into the vitreous body of both eyes appears in greater concentration in the eye which has been subjected to a paracentesis than the fellow eye,[48] and fluorescein, similarly injected, diffuses more rapidly through the pupil in an eye after paracentesis.

The nature of the blood-aqueous barrier can be investigated by studying the rates at which substances injected into the bloodstream appear in the aqueous humor. If the blood level of the injected substance is kept constant, the rate of equilibrium of the aqueous humor with the blood can be measured. Substances can also be injected into the anterior chamber or into the vitreous, and the rates at which they disappear from the anterior chamber can be measured. In this way information can be obtained as to the factors which determine penetration of a substance across the barrier. The general principles of membrane permeability have been discussed in the chapter on the cornea (p. 49). They apply to the blood-aqueous barrier as they do to the permeability of the cornea. Water is able to pass freely into and out of the eye. Kinsey and co-workers[49] injected deuterium oxide (heavy water) into the bloodstream, and from the rate of acumulation of this substance in the anterior chamber the rate of movement of ordinary water into and out of this chamber was calculated. This was found to be equivalent to 20% per minute of the volume of the aqueous humor in the anterior chamber or 50 μl per minute in rabbits. More recent analyses using tritium as a tracer substance for water have yielded figures for the steady state rate of turnover of anterior chamber aqueous between 5.2 and 15.6% per minute for rabbits, essentialy in agreement with Kinsey's figures.[50]

As would be expected, very large molecules are held back in the blood by the blood-aqueous barrier. We have seen that protein is in very low concentration in aqueous humor. Large molecules such as inulin, dyes such as trypan blue, and the dextrans are found in very low concentration, either because of their large molecular size or because they are strongly adsorbed to the plasma proteins after injection into the bloodstream. Fluorescein enters both the anterior and posterior chambers after injection into the bloodstream and is of particular interest to us because of the use which has been made of this substance by Goldmann and others in measuring the minute volume of the aqueous humor in humans and by Becker to determine the changes in the

rate of aqueous humor production due to drugs.[51] Berggren[52] has shown that the time of appearance of fluorescent dyes is influenced by convection currents, so that the temperature outside the eye has to be controlled. Further, the time of appearance is not influenced by a reduction in the production of aqueous humor, e.g., by Diamox.

Apart from molecular size, the factor which chiefly determines penetration across the barrier is lipoid solubility, just as it is in the corneal epithelium. The penetration of various nonelectrolytes into the aqueous humor of the rabbit are shown in Fig. 26. The ordinates represent the concentration of the substance in the aqueous divided by the concentration present in the plasma at the same time. Ethyl alcohol and ethyl thiourea, both highly fat-soluble, penetrate very rapidly. Highly water-soluble substances such as creatine and sucrose penetrate much more slowly and to a much lesser extent.

Ross[53] has shown that the rapidity of penetration of a series of monosubstituted thiourea derivatives correlated positively with their lipoid solubility. The rate of penetration of these compounds did not depend upon molecular size or upon any chemical structure, other than that which affected lipoid solubility of the test substance. The selective permeability of the blood-aqueous barrier results from the selective affinity of the membranes of the barrier for lipoid-soluble substances so that these substances can more readily penetrate through the cells than through the water-filled pores of limited size between the cells. This same dependence of the rate of penetration on lipoid solubility applies to some antibiotics. Chloramphenicol, whose lipoid solubility is greater than that of the penicillins, penetrates the blood-aqueous barrier readily.[54] However, the penetration of sub-

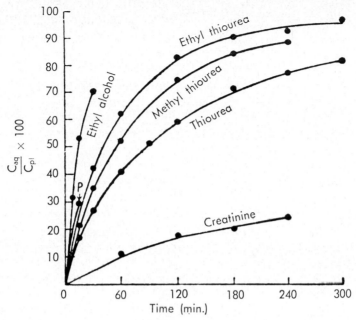

Fig. 26. Penetration of various nonelectrolytes into the aqueous humor of the rabbit. (From Davson, H., and Luck, J.: J. Physiol. **151:**202, 1957.)

stances such as urea, creatinine, amino-acetic acid, and various sulfonamide derivatives does not depend upon their lipoid solubility, according to Dobson.[55] Both cysteine and cystine can pass into the aqueous humor readily when injected into the bloodstream.[56]

At the present time there is no unanimity of opinion on the mechanisms involved in the transfer of many different substances from plasma to the aqueous humor. According to Kinsey,[57] the data for the entrance of labeled sodium into the posterior chamber from the blood fit a theoretical curve, suggesting that one third of the sodium enters the posterior chamber by diffusion and two thirds by secretion. Whereas similar data for chloride suggest that approximately three quarters enters by diffusion and only one quarter by secretion.

The case for ascorbic acid is so unique that the data for its transfer across the barrier are given in more detail (see also

p. 100). Kinsey[58] injected ascorbic acid intraperitoneally and observed that the concentration reached a maximum in the blood within 20 minutes (Fig. 27). The concentration in the aqueous humor also increased, but required a much longer time to reach maximum. In Fig. 28 is shown the concentration of ascorbic acid in the aqueous humor 1 hour after the injection of various quantities of this compound, plotted as a function of the concentration in the blood. Its increase was proportionate to the increase in the concentration of the serum up to 3 mg.%. At this serum level, the concentration in the aqueous humor was approximately 50 mg.%. With higher serum levels, no further increase in the quantity of ascorbic acid in the aqueous humor occurred within the time period studied (60 minutes), even though the concentration in the serum was elevated to 130 mg.%. Barany and Langham[59] also found that the secreting mechanism became sat-

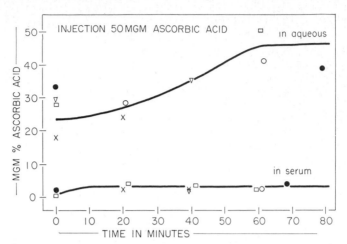

Fig. 27. Shows the change in concentration of ascorbic acid in the serum and aqueous humor at various intervals following intraperitoneal injection. (Courtesy Dr. V. E. Kinsey.)

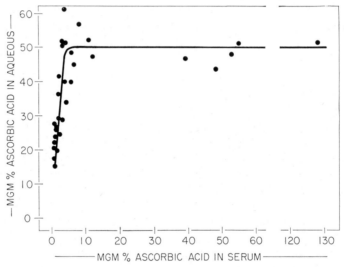

Fig. 28. Shows the concentration of ascorbic acid in the aqueous 60 minutes after the injection of various quantities of this compound plotted as a function of the concentration of the blood. (Courtesy Dr. V. E. Kinsey.)

urated with plasma levels of about 3 mg.%, but by waiting until steady state occurred, they obtained levels of aqueous humor of 65 mg.%.

In young animals, the concentration in the aqueous humor rose with increasing concentration in the blood and continued to rise throughout the entire range, contrasting sharply with the results in the adult animal. These results are consistent with the hypothesis that in adult animals ascorbic acid is transferred by a secretory process, since some factor other than availability of this compound in the blood limits the amount which can be transferred across the blood-aqueous barrier. In young animals the transfer probably takes place primarily by a process of diffusion, and since the hyaloid vessels are permeable to ascorbic acid, diffusion back into the blood must occur.

Linner[60] studied the effect of changes in blood flow through the uveal circulation on the concentration of ascorbic acid in the aqueous humor of the rabbit. Ligation of one common carotid artery led to a decrease in the concentration of ascorbic acid in the aqueous humor on the same side equivalent to the percentage of decrease in blood flow through the uveal tract. If the concentration of ascorbic acid was raised in the plasma, the concentration in the aqueous humor of the two eyes then became equal. From this he concluded that, when the amount of ascorbic acid transferred across the blood aqueous barrier is not maximal, the concentration of ascorbic acid in the aqueous humor is determined by the amount reaching the site of transfer. Following the work of Linner, Langham,[61] using rabbits, ligated the common carotid artery on one side and investigated to determine whether any of the ascorbic acid in the aqueous is formed within the eye or whether the relation between the concentration of ascorbic acid in plasma and in the aqueous humor of the operated animals supported the concept of Linner. His results supported Linner's contentions that the rate of transfer of ascorbic acid across the ciliary processes is determined by the amount reaching the site of transfer and is modified by changes in the rate of flow of blood through the eye.

Reducing substances

The kinetics of penetration into the aqueous humor of various reducing substances after injection into the blood-

Table 17. *Rate of penetration of various substances into the aqueous humor and vitreous humor*

Substances injected	Aqueous humor (K out min.⁻¹)	Vitreous humor (K out min.⁻¹)
Glucose	0.016	0.0080
Galactose	0.016	0.0069
3-methyl glucose	0.017	0.0080
Xylose	0.017	0.0119

stream has been studied by Davson and Duke-Elder.[62] They find that glucose, galactose, methyl glucose, and xylose all penetrate into the aqueous humor of the anterior chamber at about the same rate. Sucrose, on the other hand, penetrates much more slowly. The penetration of these substances into the vitreous humor was found to be different from that into the aqueous humor, as would be expected on the basis that their volumes are so different, if for no other reason. Table 17 shows the relative rates of penetration of these substances into the aqueous and vitreous humors.

The authors conclude that the barrier between blood and the vitreous humor is more selective than that between blood and the aqueous humor in its ability to discriminate between hexoses and pentoses.

The blood-aqueous barrier may be altered by a number of means and its change in permeability can be measured. Any inflammation of the eye, as stated, will alter the permeability of the blood-aqueous barrier in the same way that inflammation alters the permeability of all capillary beds. After irradiation, the blood-aqueous barrier has been found to be more permeable.[63] Anoxia accelerates the passage of fluorescein across the blood-aqueous barrier.[64] On the other hand, cortisone shows no effect on the

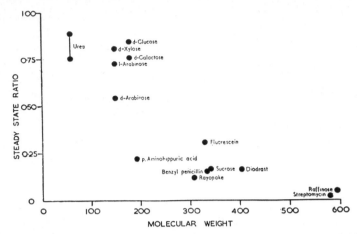

Fig. 29. Permeability of the blood-aqueous barrier to certain nonlipid-soluble compounds. Ordinate, steady state rates *caq/Cpl;* abscissa, molecular weight. (From Langham, M.: In Duke-Elder, S., editor: Glaucoma, Springfield, Ill., 1955, Charles C Thomas, Publisher, p. 51.)

permeability of the blood-aqueous barrier to fluorescein.[65] In Fig. 29 is shown graphically the characteristics of permeability of the blood-aqueous barrier to certain nonlipoid compounds. The concentration of lactate in the aqueous humor after occlusion of the carotid artery and after sympathectomy has been studied.[66] Four factors seem to determine the concentration of lactate in the aqueous humor: (1) influx of lactate in the primary secretion from the ciliary body, (2) liberation from the metabolizing tissues, particularly the lens, (3) outflow in bulk from the anterior chamber through the canal of Schlemm, and (4) diffusion across the blood-aqueous barriers. After occlusion of the carotid artery, there is a relative increase in the lactate and bicarbonate of the aqueous humor of the anterior chamber of the homolateral eye. After sympathectomy there is a relative increase in the lactate and bicarbonate of the aqueous humor of the anterior chamber of the contralateral eye. These operations are without effect on the concentration of chloride in the aqueous humor. The concentration of lactate in

the lens is unaltered, and the concentration of lactate in the aqueous humor of the posterior chamber is not affected. Occlusion of the carotid artery or sympathectomy has very little effect on the rate of flow of aqueous humor, but these experimental procedures change considerably the conditions governing the exchange of substances between the aqueous humor of the anterior chamber and plasma.

Up to now we have been concerned largely with the accumulation of substances in the chambers of the eye after their injection into the bloodstream. In a similar fashion substances have been injected into the anterior chamber and their rates of disappearance have been measured.

Substances may escape from the anterior chamber by two possible routes: diffusion into the blood vessels of the iris and by bulk flow out through Schlemm's canal. Most of these studies have been hampered by the trauma induced by the injection of the material to be studied into the anterior chamber. Davson and Spaziani[67] have overcome this difficulty recently by employing a continuous injection procedure, the rate of injection of the solution being so small as not measurably to alter the intraocular pressure. There is a striking similarity in the rates at which various substances leave the anterior chamber. This is in marked contrast to the rates at which these substances enter from the blood. For example, the rates of entry of sucrose, sodium, propyl thiourea, and ethyl alcohol differ widely, whereas the rates of escape from the anterior chamber of sucrose and sodium are the same, and those of propyl urea and ethyl alcohol are only slightly larger. This suggests that all these substances leave by bulk flow through an unselective channel, probably Schlemm's canal. Also the rate of escape is independent of the plasma concentration, which according to Davson proves that the escape is by a flow mechanism rather than by diffusion.

The rate of escape of para-aminohippurate was independent of the plasma concentration, which proves unequivocally that the escape of this substance is by a flow mechanism rather than by diffusion. Diamox had no decided effect on the rate of loss of injected material, which is further confirmation of the view put forward by Davson and Luck[08] that Diamox produces a fall in intraocular pressure, not by a large change in the rate of secretion of aqueous humor, but in part at least by some change in the physical factors affecting drainage. Langham[69] showed that there was a lack of linearity in the response of the intraocular pressure of the rabbit to injections of saline solution into the anterior chamber at different rates. This is probably due to a reduction in the episcleral venous pressure or the resistance to outflow from the anterior chamber rather than to reduced rate of secretion of aqueous hu-

mor, since it seems unreasonable that the injection of saline solution into the anterior chamber at different rates could have such an effect on secretion, especially when one recalls that when the drainage routes are blocked the secretion by the ciliary body may generate an intraocular pressure of 80 mm. Hg.

Substances can escape from the posterior chamber by flow into the anterior chamber, by diffusion backward into the vitreous, and possibly by selective absorption by the cells of the ciliary epithelium. This latter route is suggested by the work of Becker.[70] He found that many organic acids such as penicillin, para-aminohippurate, and iodopyracet which failed to gain access to the posterior chamber or vitreous across the blood-aqueous barrier were accumulated by the ciliary epithelium ten to fifteen times the concentration in the incubation media. After injection of iodopyracet into the vitreous of the rabbit eye, analysis of its rate of disappearance suggested an ocular transport mechanism which secretes iodopyracet out of the eye.

FORMATION OF AQUEOUS HUMOR
Basic concepts

The basic concepts which will be used in discussing dynamics of intraocular fluid are derived largely from the analogous behavior of gases and solutions. Like the molecules of gases, those of liquids are in continuous motion. This motion is of a random nature. The force which creates this motion is inherent in the molecules themselves, and its magnitude depends upon the temperature.

Diffusion. Diffusion is the process by which molecules of a gas or solution distribute themselves uniformly throughout the space in which they are contained. Diffusion in the body is of importance in the movement of substances across membranes. The simplest example is one in which a solution is divided into two portions by a membrane permeable to both the solvent and the solute, e.g., water and sodium chloride. In this instance, the molecules of both the salt and water on one side of the membrane will interchange continuously with those on the other side (Fig. 30, *A*). If the concentrations of the solutions on the two sides of the membrane are initially different, exchange in both directions will proceed as before, but (until equilibrium is reached) more salt will cross the membrane in a direction from a higher to a lower concentration of salt, and more water will move in the opposite direction (Fig. 30, *B*). It should be pointed out that, as in the case of the salt, the direction of the larger water movement is also from a higher to a lower concentration. The concentration of water is highest in pure water; i.e., 1 L. of pure water contains 1000 Gm. water; therefore, its molar concentration is 1000 Gm./18 or 55.5 M. Addition of salt reduces the amount of water present per unit volume; therefore, the water is less concentrated in a salt solution. It will be apparent later why emphasis is placed on this point of view. Movement of solvent or solute across a membrane in the manner just described has been expressed quantitatively (Fick's law) as follows:

Rate of transfer = k (C, side 1*; —C, side 2)
  C = concentration
  k = a constant, depending on permeability of membrane, temperature, nature of substance, etc.
  * = side containing higher concentration

A *semipermeable* membrane is one which is permeable to the solvent but impermeable to one or more solutes—e.g., one which will permit the passage of water but not salt or water and salt but not protein. The water will exchange across the membrane and more will move in the direction from a higher concentration of water to a lower concentration. The rate of net *transfer* will continuously decrease as the concentrations of water on the two sides approach each other.

The net transfer of water across the membrane can be explained on the basis that there are more molecules of water bombarding the membrane on one side than on the other side; thus, the chance of one molecule passing through the pores in one direction is correspondingly greater. This excess of molecules of water going through the membrane creates a potential force known as *osmotic* pressure

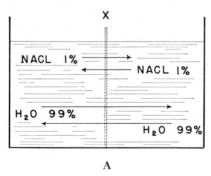 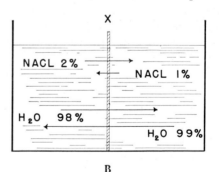

X — MEMBRANE
PERMEABLE TO NACL
AND H_2O

Fig. 30. Diffusion of solutes and solutions according to gas laws.

(Greek derivative meaning push), and the process is called *osmosis*.

Osmotic pressure. Osmotic pressure is measured by opposing this potential force with sufficient hydrostatic pressure from the side of the membrane containing the higher concentration of salt until there is no longer any net gain of water on that side.

It follows from this explanation of the source of osmotic pressure that sodium chloride or any other solute on one side of a semipermeable membrane does not attract the water from the other side, as is commonly stated.

The magnitude of osmotic pressure depends upon the number of dissolved particles to which the membrane is impermeable. In dilute solutions in which particles act essentially like gas molecules, e.g., in a tenth molar solution of a nonionizing solute such as glucose, a pressure of 2.24 atm. (atmospheres) (1700 mm. Hg) will be developed when the solution is separated from water by a membrane which will not permit passage of the solute. If in any solution the solute dissociates into two ions (for example, sodium chloride), twice the osmotic pressure is produced per mol fraction; i.e., a tenth molar solution in this case produces an osmotic pressure of 3400 mm. Hg.

An isotonic solution is one which has the same total osmotic pressure as the body fluids. A hypertonic solution is one with a higher osmotic pressure, and a hypotonic solution is one with a lower osmotic pressure than that of the reference fluid.

It is evident that relatively slight differences in concentration of salts can produce large differences in pressure; e.g., an osmotic pressure of 58 mm. Hg will be produced when solutions differing in concentration by only 0.01% (1.72 mM/L.)

sodium chloride are separated by a membrane impermeable to the salt. Since osmotic pressure depends upon the number rather than upon the mass of the dissolved particles, a difference in concentration of protein equal to 0.01% will produce a much smaller difference in osmotic pressure. If the molecular weight of the protein were 60,000 (albumin), the osmotic pressure of a 0.01% solution separated from water by a semipermeable membrane would be but 0.025 mm. Hg. The difference in osmotic pressure in plasma compared with interstitial fluids, which contain practically no protein, is approximately 30 mm. Hg. This is caused by a difference in protein of approximately 7%.

Dialysis and ultrafiltration. When a solution containing protein and salt is separated from pure water by a membrane permeable to salt and water, but not to protein, the salt will diffuse into the water, leaving the protein behind. In this case, as just stated, there will be a net transfer of water into the solution containing the protein. This process is called dialysis. If on the side of the membrane containing the protein a hydrostatic pressure is applied (e.g., the blood pressure), the transfer of salt across the membrane is accelerated. The term *ultrafiltration* is used to describe this process. Ultrafiltration may be defined, therefore, as dialysis in the presence of hydrostatic pressure.

Gibbs-Donnan equilibrium. If the solutions on both sides of a membrane impermeable to protein contain salt, but only one solution contains protein, an unequal distribution of the ions of the salt will occur. This effect is caused when positive ions (cations) such as sodium are bound by the protein which, at the hydrogen ion concentration of plasma, carries a negative charge. The magnitude of the unequal distribution of ions depends on the concentration of the protein. This unequal distribution was predicted by Gibbs and was confirmed later experimentally by Donnan and is known as the Gibbs-Donnan effect.

The following diagram may be used to illustrate the phenomenon. Two solutions, sodium proteinate and sodium chloride, are separated by a membrane which is permeable to the sodium and chloride, but not to the protein. The numbers are used to illustrate the relations that appear in the discussion that follows.

Side I		Side II	
Na	7	Na	21
Pr	7	Cl	21
		← Membrane	

Let us assume that these solutions have just been separated from one another by a membrane. If the membrane does not allow the protein anions to pass through it, but allows all the other ions to do so, then the following rearrangement of ions will take place.

Side I		Side II	
Na	16	Na	12
Pr	7	Cl	12
Cl	9		

The Gibbs-Donnan theory of equilibrium states: (1) that the product of the concentration of the sodium and chloride on one side of the membrane is equal to the product of the concentration of these ions on the other side and (2) that the amount of the sodium on any one side must equal the sum of the chloride and protein ions on the same side. Thus

$$(Na) \times (Cl) = (Na) \times (Cl)$$

where the concentrations of sodium and chloride are expressed in gram molecules per liter of solution. On Side I, which contains the nondiffusible substance, the

sodium comes from the sodium proteinate and the sodium chloride. On the other side of the membrane, the sodium comes only from the sodium chloride.

It, therefore, follows that on Side I the concentration of sodium must exceed that of the chloride because some of the sodium remains with the protein, in addition to that from the chloride.

On Side II the sodium and chloride must be equal. Since the products of the concentrations are the same on both sides, it follows that the sodium on Side I, which is greater than the chloride, must be greater than the sodium on Side II. The chloride on Side I must be less than the chloride on Side II.

The Gibbs-Donnan equilibrium determines, therefore, the distribution of ions across a membrane which is permeable to some ions and impermeable to others. Many experiments carried out in vitro between solutions of protein and of salt with semipermeable membranes have confirmed the equilibrium just described—namely, that on the side of the membrane where there is protein, the cations (e.g., sodium) are greater than on the other side, and the anions (e.g., chloride) are greater on the side of the membrane where there is no protein.

Flow. Flow is a unidirectional movement of a gas or a fluid involving no separation of its constituents due to an externally applied force. This force might be gravity, as in fluid running out of a tub, or the result of the action of a pump, as in the case of the circulation of the blood.

Potential differences on two sides of membranes. If suitable electrodes are placed on either side of a cellular membrane which separates fluids of different ionic concentration, an electrical potential difference will be found. This is also true of a single cell surrounded by a fluid of an ionic concentration different from that of the interior of the cell. By means of suitable dyes Friedenwald was the first to demonstrate the possibility of such an electrical potential difference between the ciliary epithelium and the stroma. The interpretation of such experiments with dyes is, however, open to question. Much more convincing proof of not only the existence of such a potential difference but its size has been obtained by direct measurements with electrodes.[71-72] A potential gradient of 28 mv. was found between the pigmented and nonpigmented epithelium of the rabbit.

The concentration difference and the resulting electrical potential difference are the result of a number of different forces, including such phenomena as the Donnan membrane equilibrium and membrane charge, as well as of the active transport of ions such as sodium. In general, the existence of such a potential is felt to be indicative of such secretory processes in cells called active transport (p. 127). Since acetazolamide depresses secretion, it would seem likely that after the administration of this drug a drop in the electrical potential of the ciliary epithelium would be found. Holland reports a decline in membrane potential to half the initial level after Diamox, but Miller and Constant were unable to demonstrate any change.[72]

Dynamics of aqueous humor

The dynamics of the aqueous humor is concerned with the movement of various components of plasma and substances which may be manufactured by the tissues of the eye into and out of the posterior and anterior chambers and with the forces which result from this movement.

Although a number of authors at one time or another have denied the existence of a through-and-through circulation of aqueous humor, experimental and clinical evidences are overwhelmingly to the contrary. Hamburger was the most staunch supporter of the theory that under normal conditions the aqueous humor was a stagnant fluid, and that its contents were renewed only by diffusion across a membrane impermeable to colloids. Magitot and later Duke-Elder denied any through-and-through circulation, but acknowledged that small mass movements of the aqueous humor would take place as the hydrostatic-osmotic pressure relationships were upset by movements of the eye, compression of the globe by the lids, and even by pressure of the pulse. All now agree that a constant though small amount of aqueous humor is being constantly formed and eliminated from the eye.

Main experimental evidence for through-and-through circulation. The main experimental evidence for through-and-through circulation is as follows.

1. Experimental blockage of the angle of the anterior chamber by mechanical means leads to an increase in intraocular pressure.

2. The normal rate of outflow in animals has been found experimentally.

3. Dyes or other substances injected into the anterior chamber disappear, and the rate of disappearance has been measured.

The clinical evidence* for through-and-through circulation of aqueous humor is as follows.

1. Inflammatory and neoplastic cells arising in the posterior part of the eye-

---

*Most of this evidence has been gathered from the study of eyes which are not normal and therefore can hardly be used as evidence for a through-and-through circulation in the normal eye. This factor should be understood, therefore, in evaluating such data.

ball behind the iris are usually deposited on the posterior corneal surface, which suggests that they are carried there by a mass movement of the aqueous humor.

2. High intraocular pressure develops in certain inflammatory diseases due to blockage of the angle by anterior synechiae or by inflammatory products. These can be seen on examination of the angle with a gonioscope. The rise of intraocular pressure in normal persons having a narrow angle may be demonstrated occasionally by keeping the subject in a dark room. This is due to dilatation of the pupil which results in the iris encroaching on the angle, thereby blocking the escape of fluid. In some instances, dilatation of the pupil with a mydriatic may so block the egress of fluid as to precipitate an attack of acute glaucoma.

3. A rise in intraocular pressure occurs in some cases of dislocation of the crystalline lens into the anterior chamber.

4. Iris bombé may develop. If the iris is bound down completely to the lens by posterior synechiae, thus obstructing the passage of fluid from posterior to anterior chamber, the iris bulges forward in a characteristic fashion and is called an iris bombé. The intraocular pressure rises, but the ensuing glaucoma can be relieved usually by making an opening in the iris so that the fluid can get from the posterior chamber into the anterior chamber.

The experimental and clinical evidence just cited indicates that normally fluid is constantly coming into the eye and leaving it by flow. This fluid arises in large part behind the iris, presumably from the ciliary body, fills the posterior chamber, flows between the iris and lens into the anterior chamber, and leaves the eye at the iris angle.

Thermal circulation. In addition to this bulk movement of fluid, there is a thermal circulation which is the result of differences in temperature between the various regions of the anterior chamber. The temperature difference arises as follows. When the eyelids are open, the cornea is exposed to the air and is cooled by the evaporation of the tear film on the corneal surface. The aqueous humor, on the other hand, is constantly heated by the blood in the vessels of the iris. As a result of this, a temperature gradient exists between the cornea and the iris. As the aqueous humor is heated by the blood in the iris, it tends to rise, and when it comes in contact with the cool cornea, it tends to sink. A constant circulation is established thereby which is of clinical importance because it determines the site of deposition of pigment and cellular debris on the posterior surface of the cornea. In inflammatory conditions of the eye in which the aqueous humor contains such cells, these are deposited on the posterior surface of the cornea in the form of a triangle with the base at the bottom of the chamber. Pigment is usually deposited in the pupil space in the form of a spindle or vertical line, the so-called Krukenberg spindle.

Since the evidence is strong that a through-and-through circulation of fluid takes place in the eye, two problems present themselves:

1. What is the mechanism by which the aqueous humor is formed?
2. What is the mechanism by means of which the aqueous humor escapes from the eye?

Theories of formation of aqueous humor

Four main theories have been proposed and will be dealt with in the order of their historical origin.

Ultrafiltration. The first theory is the process of ultrafiltration. As applied to the formation of all body fluids, this process may be described in the following manner. The capillary bed is the part of the vascular system in which transfer of water and metabolites takes place between the blood and the tissues. The capillary wall (endothelium) is a semipermeable membrane which hinders the passage across it of molecules above a certain size. The large protein molecules, especially, are held back. The smaller molecules and water are filtered off from the protein by the head of pressure in the capillaries. The force by means of which this movement of fluid across the capillary wall takes place is the hydrostatic pressure in the capillary bed.

If the osmotic pressure of the blood exceeds that of the filtrate, the hydrostatic pressure in the capillary bed must be greater than the osmotic pressure of the blood in order that filtration take place. Under these conditions there will then be a mass movement of water as a solvent out of the blood and of solutes such as sodium chloride, urea, and glucose—in fact, of all substances which are able to pass through the capillary endothelium (Fig. 31, *A* and *B*).

The blood contains about 7% protein and the interstitial fluid much less than that (p. 325). The osmotic pressure of the proteins in blood is about 30 mm. Hg. On the assumption that the osmotic pressure of the interstitial fluid is equal to that of the blood minus the 30 mm. Hg due to its protein content, a filtering pressure of more than 30 mm. Hg in the capillary bed would be required. In order to form a protein-free filtrate under such conditions, the blood pressure in the

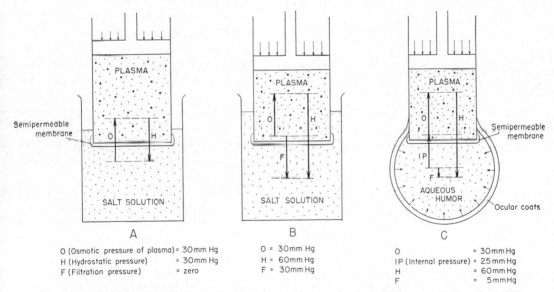

O (Osmotic pressure of plasma)	= 30 mm Hg	
H (Hydrostatic pressure)	= 30 mm Hg	
F (Filtration pressure)	= zero	

O = 30 mm Hg
H = 60 mm Hg
F = 30 mm Hg

O = 30 mm Hg
IP (Internal pressure) = 25 mm Hg
H = 60 mm Hg
F = 5 mm Hg

Fig. 31. A, No filtration of fluid will take place across the semipermeable membrane when the hydrostatic pressure just balances the osmotic pressure of the plasma proteins. **B,** When the hydrostatic pressure exceeds the osmotic pressure of the plasma proteins, filtration occurs. The amount of filtration will depend on the difference between the two forces when the filtrate is formed in a vessel open to the air—the effect of gravity being ignored. **C,** The same applies to the filtration of fluid when the filtrate is delivered into a closed vessel, such as the eye. Here the filtration pressure will be balanced by the pressure which develops in the eye as more and more fluid is formed and depends, therefore, partly upon the elasticity of the ocular coats.

capillaries must be greater than 30 mm. Hg. The effect of the filtration pressure (F) equals the hydrostatic pressure of the blood (H) minus the difference between the osmotic pressure of the blood and the interstitial fluid. When equilibrium has been attained in such a system, fluid will be constantly leaving the bloodstream at one end, where the filtration pressure is high, and will be entering the bloodstream downstream, where the hydrostatic pressure is low. The chemical properties of the interstitial fluid will have certain characteristics peculiar to filtrates. Depending upon the semipermeability of the capillary wall, there will be more or less protein in the interstitial fluid but always in amounts less than that in blood. Substances to which the capillary wall is freely permeable, such as crystalloids, will be present in a concentration equal to that in blood.

In the early part of this century Leber and his school applied these facts to the eye, and as such they constitute the ultrafiltration theory of the formation of aqueous humor. The capillary bed in the ciliary body was considered the main source of the fluid, although all of the vascular beds of the eye were thought to contribute also. The aqueous humor represents the interstitial fluid. Unlike the general tissue fluid in the body, in which the pressure in the tissue spaces is approximately zero, the aqueous humor is confined within the eye under a pressure of some 20 to 25 mm. Hg. In order to account for a mass movement of fluid into the eye from the capillary bed, it was assumed that the hydrostatic pressure is sufficient to overcome both the osmotic pressure of the colloids in the blood and the intraocular pressure. Leber believed that the osmotic pressure of the aqueous humor was lower than that of blood by 30 mm. Hg, this difference being due to

the absence of protein in the aqueous humor. Other than the difference in protein content, aqueous humor was thought to resemble plasma.

When these data are applied to the formula just given, the filtration pressure (F) equals the hydrostatic pressure of the blood (H) minus the difference between the osmotic pressure of the blood and that of the interstitial fluid. If one assumes the hydrostatic pressure of the intraocular capillaries to be 60 mm. Hg, then the following equations are true (Fig. 31, C).

$$F = 60 \text{ mm. Hg} - (30 \text{ mm. Hg} - 0)$$
$$F = 30 \text{ mm. Hg} - 25 \text{ mm. Hg (intraocular pressure)}$$
$$F = 5 \text{ mm. Hg}$$

Conditions in the eye are not strictly analogous to those in the rest of the body. For example, the aqueous humor is separated from the blood, at least in the ciliary body, by a complex epithelial membrane in addition to the capillary endothelium. Moreover, it is thought that the endothelium of the capillaries in the iris is unlike that existing in ordinary capillaries in the body. Thus, one would expect, a priori, that these different membranes might exert their influence on the nature of any fluid formed by ultrafiltration. That this is the case is suggested by the chemical analyses of the aqueous humor compared with those of other body fluids which are known to be formed by simple ultrafiltration. For example, freely diffusible substances such as urea and sugar should be found in equal concentrations in both aqueous humor and blood, but chemical analyses do not bear this out.

The concentration of glucose in the aqueous humor is less than that in blood. A similar deficiency is found for urea. In the case of glucose it can be argued that the aqueous humor as formed contains an amount equal to that in blood, but because of its utilization in the eye at any moment there is always less present in the aqueous humor than in the blood. This argument does not apply in the case of urea[7] since there is no evidence of utilization of urea by the eye.

The low concentration of urea in the aqueous humor in the anterior chamber has been explained by Kinsey on the basis of flow, as shown in Fig. 32. The top three figures illustrate conditions in a system in which conditions are static, i.e., no flow of fluid, and equilibrium is achieved on the two sides of a semipermeable membrane by diffusion. Starting with a high concentration of urea on the right side of the semipermeable membrane when equilibrium has been reached, there will be an equal number of molecules of urea on both sides of the membrane. In the lower three figures the factor of flow has been added to that of diffusion, and it can be seen that when a steady state has been reached, a number of molecules have gone down the outflow channels on the left side of the membrane, leaving a deficit on this side compared to the concentration on the right side of the membrane. The degree of this deficit is a measure of the number of molecules which have left the system

by flow. It is assumed that in the case of urea a steady state is reached by diffusion but that, because of a constant outflow at the chamber angle, some urea has left the eye by flow.

Not only are certain substances deficient in the aqueous humor, but it has been shown that a higher concentration of bicarbonate in rabbits, of chloride in man, and of ascorbic and hyaluronic acids in both species exists in aqueous humor than in blood. Furthermore, the osmotic pressure of aqueous humor is thought to be higher than that of plasma—notwithstanding the presence of proteins in the latter fluid (p. 108). It is obvious, therefore, on purely chemical grounds that some mechanism other than simple ultrafiltration alone must account for the formation of the aqueous humor. However, filtration is conceded to be part of the process.

Dialysis. The theory of dialysis for the formation of the aqueous humor assumes that the aqueous humor is in chemical equilibrium with blood and postulates that the hydrostatic pressure in the capillaries merely balances the intraocular pressure. From this point of view, the aqueous humor then becomes a static fluid. The interchange between blood and aqueous humor is, therefore, merely molecular, i.e., diffusional.

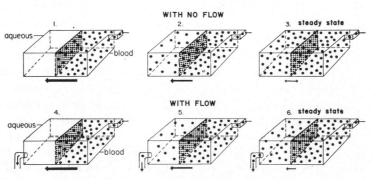

Fig. 32. Diffusion through membrane. (Courtesy Dr. V. E. Kinsey.)

In order to meet the theoretical requirements for dialysis, a fluid so formed must show certain chemical and physical characteristics. The nonelectrolytes must be in equal concentration in the parent fluid and in the dialysate. The dissociated electrolytes, which are subject to electrical constraints, must arrange themselves on the two sides of the membrane according to the Donnan equilibrium (p. 119). The osmotic pressure of the dialysate must be equal to that of blood less the osmotic pressure produced by the proteins in blood. Finally, the dialysate and the parent fluid must exhibit an electrostatic equilibrium due to the unequal distribution of diffusible ions on the two sides of the membrane. As a result of this, a difference in electrical potential must be set up on the two sides of the membrane.

It has been shown that a difference in potential actually does exist between the front and the back of the eye. Using the capillary electrometer, Lehmann and Meesman found a difference in potential between the aqueous humor and the blood of 6 to 10 mv., the aqueous humor being positive. Using entirely different methods, Friedenwald found a difference in potential between the two sides of the ciliary epithelium which he accounted for on the basis of oxidation-reduction systems present in the ciliary body (p. 131).

Can the theory of dialysis account for the formation of aqueous humor? From our present knowledge of its composition, the answer is No. It has already been pointed out that the majority of the requisites for dialysis are those of filtration, and that in the case of the eye the chemical composition of the aqueous humor, especially that of the posterior chamber, differs significantly from an ultrafiltrate.

We must still consider those properties which are requisite for a solution in static equilibrium with its parent fluid, the blood—namely, the unequal distribution of the ionized salts on the two sides of the membrane and the electrostatic forces which should be present on the two sides of the membrane. The distribution of the dissociated electrolytes varies so markedly in the different analyses reported in the literature that figures may be found which either support or deny the theory of dialysis. For the present, therefore, this cannot help us decide as to the validity of this theory. The chief evidences against the theory of dialysis are the following: (1) the excess and deficiencies of certain substances in the aqueous, (2) the higher osmotic pressure of the aqueous humor compared to the parent fluid, the blood, and (3) the evidence that the aqueous humor is not a static fluid, but that there is a constant through-and-through circulation of considerable size.

It should be recalled here that the finding of certain substances, such as urea and other nonelectrolytes, in a lower concentration in the aqueous humor than in blood is not in itself evidence against the theory of dialysis.

According to Hodgson, the osmotic pressure of the aqueous humor would have to be lower than that of the blood by 1.8 mM/kg. water for it to be a dialysate. It is thought to be higher than serum by an amount of 5 mM/L. sodium chloride equivalent. This converted into units of energy yields a figure of 4.34 calories, required for the production of 1 L. of aqueous humor. In other words, this is the amount of work which must be done in order to produce the aqueous humor in the concentration found in the anterior chamber. The evidence, therefore, points to the fact that work must be done for the elaboration of the aqueous humor.

Secretion. The term *secretion* has always been used to describe the work done by cellular activity in the elaboration of body fluids such as saliva, gastric juice, or bile. When the known chemical processes and physical forces present were insufficient to accomplish the work necessary for the elaboration of these fluids, the activity of the living cells which produced them was called secretion.

The idea of secretion of the aqueous humor in the sense of its being a fluid elaborated like saliva and gastric juice by gland cells was given impetus through the work of Seidel. There is evidence, however, for maintaining that the ciliary body is not a gland in the usual sense of the word and that the aqueous humor is not a secretory product such as saliva, gastric juice or bile.

A new concept of secretion is that in which the term is now used to describe the processes by means of which water and other substances are transferred across a membrane at the expense of cellular energy. This concept of secretion, now generally referred to as active transport, has been applied to the formation of the aqueous humor. Some of the evidence for secretion, as just defined, has already been given in presenting arguments against the formation of the aqueous humor by ultrafiltration or dialysis— namely, (1) the osmotic pressure of the aqueous humor is higher than that of plasma, and (2) there is an excess of certain substances, such as ascorbic and hyaluronic acids, in the aqueous humor.

Secretion-diffusion theory of formation of intraocular fluid. It has been shown that there is a mass movement of fluid from the posterior chamber into the anterior chamber and that this fluid leaves the eye by flow, resulting in a through-and-through circulation of the aqueous humor. The anterior segment of the eye consists of a complex series of membranes bathed by this fluid. It is not surprising, therefore, that in its passage through the eye the separate components of the aqueous humor may enter and leave the eye at different rates in different regions. In fact, as will be shown, emphasis has been laid on the fact that one cannot speak of the aqueous humor as a fluid of constant composition. Evidence has been provided that it is not even formed at any one point in the eye. The use of isotopes readily permits the investigator to follow separately some of these complex changes, and Kinsey has made excellent use of this method in tracing the different processes by which the separate components of the aqueous humor gain access to and emerge from the eye. As has been stated, Kinsey and co-workers,[49] using heavy water, have been able to determine the rate at which water enters and leaves the anterior chamber. Deuterium oxide (heavy water) was injected into the bloodstream, and from the rate of accumulation of heavy water in the anterior chamber the rate of movement of ordinary water into and out of this chamber was calculated to be equivalent to approximately 20% per minute of the volume of the aqueous humor in the anterior chamber, or 50 μl per minute. Measurements obtained with radioactive sodium indicated that the net movement of sodium into and out of the anterior chamber is equivalent to approximately 1.1% per minute. This rate corresponds to only 2.75 μl of aqueous humor per minute. Thus, not all the water and sodium enters or leaves the anterior chamber together. In other words, the aqueous humor as found in the anterior chamber is not formed as such and does not come from any one location in the eye. Some of it enters the anterior chamber from the posterior chamber by bulk movement (flow) and some of it comes by diffusion from the blood vessels of the iris. Nor can all of it leave the anterior chamber entirely by a flow process. Of the total movement of water out of the anterior chamber (50 μl per minute), 2.75 μl leave by flow and 47.25 μl by diffusion; 47.25 μl of water must, therefore, enter the anterior chamber by diffusion and 2.75 μl by flow, along with sodium, from the posterior chamber.

In regard to sodium, Kinsey and co-workers[13, 66] formerly believed that none leaves the anterior chamber by diffusion and therefore presumed that this also applied to other electrolytes. They arrived at this conclusion on the basis of the following reasoning. As indicated, they showed that 1.1% of the sodium leaves the anterior chamber each minute. In a series of separate experiments Barany and Kinsey[74] found that 1.1% of the aqueous humor leaves the anterior chamber by flow. Thus, all the sodium which is lost could be accounted for by flow. Because diffusion is a two-way process, the authors concluded that no sodium can enter the eye by this means.

A re-examination of these data by Kinsey and Palm brought out the fact that their previous estimate of the rate of turnover of sodium (1.1% per minute) was too low. This error in their early estimate was found to be due to failure to include in their calculations the loss of sodium ions by diffusion into the vitreous. The later estimate of the turnover rate of sodium is now calculated to be 26% .

This observation shows that some of the sodium in the anteror chamber exchanges with sodium in the blood across vessels in the iris, and not all, therefore, is lost by flow. Similar data have been obtained recently for chloride, showing

that this ion too is lost both by diffusion and flow.

As stated, one of the great advances in our conception of the formation of aqueous humor has been the demonstration by Kinsey that the fluid in the posterior chamber differs considerably in composition from that in the anterior chamber. Up to this point in our discussion we have considered the fluid in the anterior chamber. A comparison of the chemical composition of fluids in anterior and posterior chambers has already been referred to in previous tables. The differences in the rates of accumulation of the three major constituents of the aqueous humor in both chambers have been investigated, and the results are shown in Figs. 33 and 34. The original results were obtained by parenteral injections of isotopically labeled compounds. Analyses for each of these substances were made in the plasma and in the aqueous humor of both the anterior and posterior chambers. But under experimental conditions the concentration of each was not constant in the blood from the time of injection. To illustrate the actual rates of accumulation under normal physiologic conditions, the results for sodium and chloride have been recomputed on the assumption that the blood level remains constant.

The figures show that the concentration of each of these labeled ions rises more rapidly in the posterior chamber due chiefly to the fact that the volume of the posterior chamber is only one fifth that of the anterior chamber. However, after about 1 hour the situation is reversed in the case of sodium and chloride. These substances are now found to be in higher concentration in the anterior chamber than in the posterior chamber. How can this be explained? It has been found that the concentration of labeled sodium and chloride at this time is much

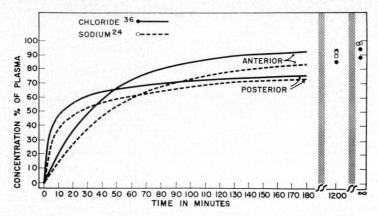

Fig. 33. The rate of accumulation of labeled sodium (Na^{24}) and chloride (Cl^{36}) in the anterior and posterior chambers of the rabbit eye following parenteral administration. (From Kinsey, V. E., and Reddy, D.: Acta ophth.)

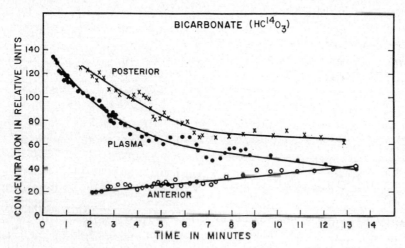

Fig. 34. The rate of accumulation of total carbon dioxide (HCO_3 ion and free CO_2) in the posterior and anterior chambers of the rabbit eye following parenteral administration of carbon[14]-labeled bicarbonate. (From Kinsey, V. E., and Reddy, D.: Acta ophth.)

less in vitreous than in blood and, in fact, is lower than that in the posterior chamber. It is a reasonable assumption that the labeled sodium and chloride diffuse backward into the vitreous from the posterior chamber. The same facts apply to the lens, so that there is a constant loss of labeled sodium and chloride into both the vitreous and the lens. This delays the piling up of sodium and chloride in the posterior chamber. When this fluid reaches the anterior chamber, labeled sodium and chloride are constantly added to it from the blood in the vessels of the iris, presumably by diffusion, and, in fact, in Fig. 33 the tangent to the line representing filling of the anterior chamber at the point of crossover is a direct measure of the rate of diffusion of either sodium or chloride through the vessels of the iris into the anterior chamber. The situation with regard to the relative con-

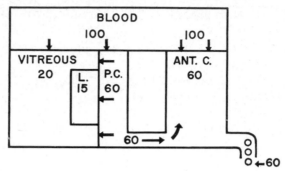

Fig. 35. Schematic representation of the relative concentration of Na²⁴ 65 minutes after parenteral administration in various parts of the eye. Arrows indicate direction of net transfer. (Courtesy Dr. V. E. Kinsey.)

centration in the various parts of the eye and the direction of net transfer at the point of crossover (approximately 65 minutes in the case of sodium) is shown by the highly schematic diagram in Fig. 35. The value for the lens and vitreous is simply a rough estimate used for the purpose of illustration.

The case for the bicarbonate ion is somewhat different. In the first place, from Fig. 34 it can be seen that the concentration of the total bicarbonate (bicarbonate ion, the bicarbonate radical, and carbon dioxide) rises with extreme rapidity in the posterior chamber. It is known that carbon dioxide can diffuse through biologic membranes much faster than the bicarbonate radical. In the posterior chamber labeled carbon dioxide is converted into labeled bicarbonate radical rapidly, a reaction presumably catalyzed by carbonic anhydrase. In effect, the bicarbonate radical becomes trapped; hence, the rise in concentration of total bicarbonate actually reflects the rate of movement of free carbon dioxide more than that of the ion itself. In the anterior chamber the concentration of total bicarbonate rises much more slowly due perhaps to the fact that there is less participation of carbonic anhydrase in the

blood vessels of the iris than in the ciliary epithelium.

On the basis of these data the actual proportion of sodium and chloride which enters the posterior chamber by secretion and by diffusion through the ciliary processes has been computed. In the case of sodium approximately two thirds enters by secretion and one third by diffusion, whereas in the case of chloride approximately one third enters by secretion and two thirds by diffusion. In the anterior chamber an equal amount of sodium comes in from the posterior chamber by flow and by diffusion across the blood vessels of the iris. For chloride, 40% comes in by flow and 60% by diffusion.

Analogous computations cannot be made for bicarbonate because of the rapidity of the exchange between blood and aqueous humor.

In order to determine the steady state of any substance between the blood and the aqueous humor it is necessary to know whether there is any loss or gain of the substance to or from the vitreous. One must know the concentration of the substance in both the vitreous and the aqueous of the posterior chamber. Studies involving the composition of vitreous and posterior chamber aqueous humor have

Table 18. *Concentration of various substances in intraocular fluids of rabbit eye (millimols per kilogram of water)*

Sample	Sodium	Potassium	Chloride	Total CO₂	Phosphate	Ascorbate	Lactate	Glucose	NPN
Vitreous	134	9.5	104.7	26.0	0.40	0.46	12.0	3.0	17
Posterior aqueous humor	136*†	—	96.5	37.5	0.58	1.38	9.9	5.6	23
Anterior aqueous humor	138	5.0	101.0	30.2	0.89	1.11	9.3	5.4	25
Plasma	143	5.6	108.8	20.6	2.04	0.04	10.3	5.7	34

*From Reddy, D., and Kinsey, V. E.: Arch. Ophth. **63:**715, 1960.
†Estimated from ratios of concentrations in anterior aqueous and plasma found from a previous study.[16]

Table 19. *Difference in concentration of various constituents in aqueous humor of posterior chamber and vitreous (millimols per kilogram of water)*

	Sodium	Chloride	Total CO₂	Phosphate	Ascorbate	Lactate	Glucose	NPN
(CH—Cv)	+2	−8	+12	+0.2	+0.9	−2	+2.6	+6

*From Reddy, D., and Kinsey, V. E.: Arch. Ophth. 63:715, 1960.

been carried out by Kinsey and Reddy,[75] as shown in Table 18. Table 19 shows the difference in composition of these constituents in posterior chamber aqueous and vitreous. This shows that sodium is slightly lower in vitreous than in aqueous humor and this is balanced approximately by an excess of potassium. Chloride, bicarbonate, and ascorbate are intermediate between that of plasma and posterior aqueous humor.

It has been shown that the aqueous humor cannot be accounted for by the known forces of filtration and dialysis. The flow process and, in particular, the chemical osmotic characteristics of the fluid in the anterior chamber demand that energy be expended. The energetic process necessary to achieve this has been defined as secretion. The possible mechanisms for this process have been extensively studied and will now be discussed.

Mechanism of secretion. Friedenwald and co-workers, in an extensive series of ingeniously conceived and beautifully executed experiments, tried to elucidate the secretory process in the ciliary body. Friedenwald reviewed this entire series of investigations in the Proctor Lecture for 1948.[76] These studies have been summarized further by Kinsey[77] and by Kessler.[78]

Friedenwald observed that the ciliary body exhibits irreciprocal permeability to positively and negatively charged dyes. He found that the former passes from the stroma into the epithelium and the latter passes from the epithelium into the stroma. The barrier at which the acid dyes (anions) are prevented from penetrating the epithelium and basic dyes (cations) from penetrating the stroma is at the junction of the epithelium with the stroma. No membrane to which these properties can be attributed is found histologically at this point, and Friedenwald suggests that this barrier may be a chemical monomolecular layer. The barrier is capable of being reversibly oxidized and reduced and possesses a negative charge. Its irreciprocal permeability depends upon the presence of oxygen, and it can be abolished by means of certain poisons.

The epithelium was found to have an oxidation-reduction potential of + 100 mv., whereas the potential of the stroma is –130 mv. (Fig. 36, *A*). The difference in potential is maintained only in the presence of oxygen and can be abolished by poisons such as cyanide (Fig. 36, *B*).

This observation suggests that the potential is maintained by enzyme systems. A search for these enzyme systems resulted in the discovery of both cytochrome-cytochrome oxidase and dehydrogenase systems in the epithelium. The stroma was found to contain only a dehydrogenase system. At least two and probably three substances (ascorbic acid, epinephrine, and glutathione) are believed to act as mediators between these enzyme systems.

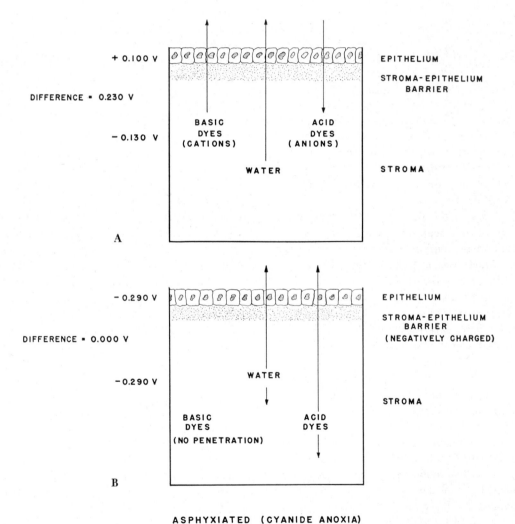

Fig. 36. A, Friedenwald's conception of the mechanism of secretion. **B,** Friedenwald's conception of the mechanism of secretion with the tissues asphyxiated.

Direct measurements by means of micro-electrodes have shown a potential gradient of 28 mv. between the pigmented and nonpigmented epithelium of the ciliary processes of rabbits.[72] This may or may not represent merely the resting potential of every living cell and cannot without caution be interpreted as representing evidence of secretion.

Barany[79] determined the rate of flow of aqueous humor in a normal guinea pig and in one which was scorbutic in order to ascertain whether the ascorbic acid-dependent dye transport mechanism which Friedenwald described was responsible for the production of the bulk of the aqueous humor. His data do not support the thesis that the bulk production of the aqueous humor is dependent upon the concentration of ascorbic acid in the plasma. The slight decrease in rate of flow of the aqueous humor in severely scorbutic animals can readily be accounted for on the basis of damage to tissue.

Friedenwald postulated that the irreciprocal permeability of the ciliary body is dependent upon an electric current which transfers water and cations from the stroma to the epithelium and anions from the epithelium to the stroma. He suggested that the source of energy for this current is supplied by differences between the aforementioned oxidation-reduction processes in the epithelium and stroma. The electric circuit is completed by transfer of electrons through the barrier, presumably through reversible oxidation-reduction of the barrier.

He assumed that the oxidative cycle begins with the oxidation of cytochrome oxidase by molecular oxygen with the transfer of electrons from the enzyme to oxygen.

(1) Reduced cytochrome oxidase + $\frac{1}{2}$ O_2 – oxidized cytochrome oxidase + $O^=$

(2) $O^= + H_2O \rightarrow \overline{2OH}$

He assumed that the hydroxyl ions produced react with carbon dioxide to produce bicarbonate ions.

(3) $\overline{2OH} + 2\ CO_2 \rightarrow 2\ \overline{HCO_3}$

The oxidized cytochrome produced in the system, he postulated, will be reduced by the barrier which in turn becomes oxidized only to be returned to its original reduced state by the stroma. The stroma provides electrons for this reduction at the expense of oxidation of a metabolite, according to the following formula:

$$RH_2 - 2e \rightleftarrows R + 2H^+$$

The excess of hydrogen ions is presumed to react with bicarbonate to form carbon dioxide

$$2H^+ + 2Na^+ + 2\overline{HCO_3} \rightleftarrows 2Na^\pm + 2H_2O + 2CO_2$$

Friedenwald pointed out that the net result of one cycle involving the reduction of one atom of oxygen in the epithelium and the oxidation of one hydrogen atom provided by a metabolite gives rise to two incompletely balanced anions in the epithelium and two incompletely balanced cations in the stroma. Under these circumstances in order for electrical neutrality to be maintained, anions would be transferred from the epithelium to the stroma, or cations from the stroma to the epithelium, or both.

The net product of such a secretory organ would be a slightly hypertonic fluid whose chief electrolyte constituent would be sodium bicarbonate. While sodium bicarbonate is not the chief electrolyte constituent of the aqueous humor, bicarbonate is significantly in excess in the aqueous humor in the rabbit. Additional evidence of the production of hydroxyl ions is the fact that the pH of the aqueous humor in the anterior chamber is in excess of that in plasma by approximately 0.17 pH unit. The higher pH of the aqueous humor results in a relatively lower

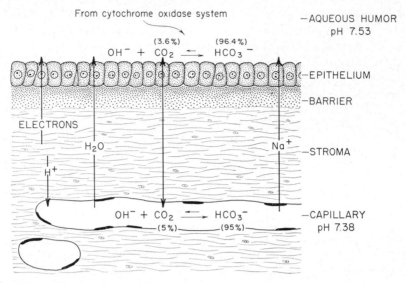

Fig. 37. The mechanism by means of which the aqueous humor is maintained hypertonic to plasma. (Courtesy Dr. V. E. Kinsey.)

tension of carbon dioxide in the aqueous humor compared with plasma, despite the higher concentration of total carbon dioxide in the aqueous humor (Fig. 37).

The production of unbalanced hydroxyl ions would seem to be sufficient to account for the hypertonicity of the aqueous humor. As just shown, the hydroxyl ions react with carbon dioxide to form bicarbonate which is then balanced electrostatically by sodium ions coming from plasma. Analytical data indicate that the concentration of bicarbonate in the aqueous humor is significantly in excess of that of plasma in the rabbit. Even if some of the bicarbonate can diffuse back out of the posterior chamber into plasma, the continuous production of this substance as an indirect result of the enzymatic reduction of oxygen to form hydroxyl ions would always maintain bicarbonate in excess in the aqueous humor. This could account for the aqueous humor's being hypertonic to plasma.

The Friedenwald-Kinsey hypothesis of the secretory mechanism of aqueous humor can be accepted as a working hypothesis in those animals who show an excess concentration of bicarbonate, a high pH, and a deficit of chloride in the aqueous humor as compared with plasma. But it runs into difficulty when applied to monkeys or to human beings. Both of these species have a lower pH and bicarbonate and a higher concentration of chloride in the aqueous humor than in plasma. Becker[80] has suggested that if the Friedenwald hypothesis is to hold true the transport of electrons may take place in the opposite direction in primate eyes than in rodents with the production of hydrogen ions which are secreted into the posterior chamber. This would resemble the redox pump mechanism as it has been applied to the gastric mucosa. In the posterior chamber an exchange of the cation sodium for hydrogen might take place, much as postulated for the renal tubule.

The active transport of sodium ions across a membrane in one direction will necessarily create a difference in electrical potential on the two sides of the barrier and will tend to influence the passage of other ions across the membrane. Thus, a transfer of sodium ions to the side of the aqueous humor would favor the migration of ions such as chloride to the aqueous side. This in turn would reduce the potential difference due to the transport of sodium. The active sodium pump potential is in the neighborhood of 30 mv. in both ox and rabbit eyes.[81]

Further objections to the Friedenwald hypothesis may be raised even when applied to the rabbit eye since it appears that this type of transport requires a greater utilization of oxygen than has been shown to occur in the ciliary processes.[81a]

NORMAL RATE OF FLOW OF AQUEOUS HUMOR

Although it has usually been conceded that the osmotic pressure of aqueous humor exceeds that of plasma by approximately 5 mv. sodium chloride equivalent, recent experimental evidence* indicates that the diffusion rate of water into the posterior chamber is too low to account for the normal rate of flow of the aqueous humor. Furthermore, both Barany* and Levene[81] have questioned the validity of applying values of osmotic pressure determined in vitro to conditions in the eye itself. That not all the water enters the posterior chamber as a result of an osmotic gradient, as previously held, is also supported by the significant proportion of sodium which appears to enter by secretion. The weight of evidence thus seems to favor the idea that most but perhaps not all of the net excess of water enters by flow (secretion), carrying with it solutes.

The question which now concerns us

is what is the total amount of fluid which comes into the anterior chamber and how much of this leaves the eye by flow through the exit channels. Kinsey's figures for the rate of movement of water into and out of the anterior chamber have been given previously on p. 128. This was calculated to be approximately 20% per minute of the volume of aqueous humor in the anterior chamber or 50 μl per minute. Of this 50 μl, only 2.75 μl enter and leave the anterior chamber by flow; the rest is accounted for by diffusion and filtration. It should be noted that of the total exchange of water in the anterior chamber only one seventeenth enters and leaves by flow.

Four main methods have been employed to determine the rate of flow in different species of animals and in man: fluorescein appearance time, perfusion experiments, tonography, and use of substances such as para-aminohippurate. Fluorescein and tonography have been the chief methods applied to human eyes. With all the various methods employed, the rates of flow have naturally varied somewhat, but are near enough that they may be accepted at the present as reasonably valid. They range from 1.1 to 1.9% of the volume of the anterior chamber per minute. In the rabbit eye from 2.5 to 3.5 c.mm. per minute flow through the eye. Goldmann's estimate of the absolute volume of flow per minute in normal human beings is 1.9%.[82]

The rate of flow may be expressed mathematically, provided that one knows the values for the head of pressure which maintains the flow and for the resistance which the fluid meets on its way through the outflow channels. This formula, published by Goldmann in 1947, is as follows:

$$F = \frac{\Delta P}{R}$$

*Barany, E.: Unpublished studies.

F is the number of cubic millimeters per minute flowing out of the eye.

F Δ P is the potential energy that maintains the movement of F against the resistance R. If there is no other source of energy, this movement comes to a standstill when the potential energy, FP, carried by the volume, F, has been used up. Between two pressure levels, P_1 and P_2, the fraction $(P_1 - P_2)$ is needed to overcome the resistance R between these two pressure levels. Thus the relationship $F = \dfrac{P}{R} = \dfrac{P_1 - P_2}{R}$ is valid. If we possess a method of measuring F directly, we are free to choose the region of resistance that interests us. If we determine the volume of flow per minute, the intraocular pressure, P, and the pressure in the aqueous veins, P_v, then the equation $R_1 = \dfrac{P_o - P_v}{F}$ expresses the resistance in the outflow system between the anterior chamber and the episcleral plexus, i.e., the actual resistance to the outflow of fluid from the eye, to which the outflow pressure, $P_o - P_v$, is related.

This formula $F = \dfrac{P_1 - P_2}{R}$ can be changed to determine the reciprocal of the resistance to outflow, which is the facility of outflow, and can be expressed as follows:

$$F = C (P_o - P_v)$$

In this formula C is Grant's coefficient of facility of outflow, which will be more fully discussed in the section on tonography. It can be derived from the above equation as follows:

$$C = \frac{F}{P_o - P_v}$$

ELIMINATION OF AQUEOUS HUMOR FROM THE EYE

Duke-Elder assumed that no outflow of aqueous humor occurs at normal pres-sures and that Schlemm's canal acts only as a safety valve mechanism when the pressure is elevated. It has been shown in a previous discussion (p. 121) that this concept is untenable in view of the demonstration by numerous authors—Kinsey and Grant[83] in rabbits; Ascher[84] and Goldmann[85] in man—of a considerable and continuous outflow of aqueous humor from the eye under conditions of normal pressure. The drainage mechanism functions constantly as an overflow mechanism, rather than as an occasional safety valve mechanism. An increase in the formation of the aqueous humor produced by a variety of means is compensated by an increased escape of the aqueous humor through the canal of Schlemm.[86]

The essential parts of the drainage mechanism have long been known, since Schlemm first described the canal which bears his name. Recent investigations have added considerably to our knowledge.[87]

The chief exit of the aqueous humor from the anterior chamber is found at the so-called filtration angle. The anatomic details of this region are shown in Fig. 38. Here the aqueous comes in contact with the trabecular fibers. Finding its way through this meshwork, it reaches Schlemm's canal. Entering this, it is conducted to the scleral and episcleral venous plexuses and thence into the aqueous veins and out of the eye.

It can readily be seen that access to the filtration angle is possible only if the iris is kept away from the back surface of the cornea. Under normal circumstances the angle is wide enough that full dilatation of the iris may occur without the folded iris blocking the angle. If the angle is very shallow, however, (which occurs in some eyes as an anatomic variant, e.g., the small hyperopic eye), dilatation of the pupil may block the angle and thus prevent the aqueous humor from reaching

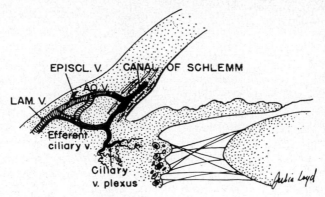

Fig. 38. Outflow channels of the aqueous bone.

the trabeculae and Schlemm's canal. The trabecular meshwork is rich in cells. Nerve fibers have been traced in the chamber angle of some species running into the trabecula, and the nature of the meshwork itself and the function of these nerves have raised considerable speculation.[88-90]

In 1934 Meyer and Palmer extracted an acid polysaccharide from the vitreous of cattle eyes and gave it the name of hyaluronic acid. This substance was then found in the aqueous. It is found in the synovial fluid in joints, in the umbilical cord, and in the capsule of some strains of pneumococci and streptococci. It binds water in the interstitial spaces in animal tissues and holds cells together in a jellylike matrix. A specific enzyme, hyaluronidase, breaks it up to acetyl glucosamine and glycuronic acid.

In 1956 this substance or a closely related one which was also hyaluronidase sensitive was discovered in the trabecular meshwork by Ashton[91] and since then has been confirmed by numerous other workers.[92] Since this substance could effectively cause resistance to the passage of water through the trabecular meshwork by forming a thin coating over the trabecular fibers, considerable interest was aroused by its discovery in the trabeculum. This interest was further heightened

by Barany's finding[93] that perfusion of animals' eyes with hyaluronidase produced a marked increase in the facility of aqueous outflow, about 50%. It is conceivable that the amount of mucopolysaccharide present in the trabecular fibers determines the rate at which aqueous humor can pass through the trabeculum into Schlemm's canal and that open angle glaucoma is due to either an excessive amount of this substance present in the trabeculum or an insufficiency of hyaluronidase to break down excessive amounts as formed.

The source of the trabecular acid mucopolysaccharide is at present not known. It is believed that it is either secreted by the endothelial cells covering the trabecular fibers or that it is derived directly from the aqueous humor, and that the large molecules of highly polymerized mucopolysaccharides are filtered out by the trabecular fibers. The aqueous humor, presumably, gets its hyaluronic acid from the vitreous. Although it is present in various ocular tissues such as the primary vitreous in the month-old embryo, in the fiber layers of the retina at four months, and in the rods and cones at six months, none has been found in the trabeculum prior to birth even though the chamber angle is completely differentiated by the seventh month.[94]

Since collagen probably forms a good part of the meshwork of the trabecula, it is intriguing to suggest that hyaluronic acid is present in the meshwork and that open-angle glaucoma might be due to this hyaluronidase-sensitive barrier. It has been shown[95] that the quantity of polymerized hyaluronate present in the aqueous humor itself cannot account for Barany's findings. Hence the polymerized hyaluronate is probably a part of the tissue of the filtration angle, and Zimmerman[96] has demonstrated that mucopolysaccharides can be removed by treatment with hyaluronidase—so that the part played by some polymer which is hyaluronidase-sensitive may well be of great importance in the decreased facility of outflow in open-angle glaucoma.[97]

Schlemm's canal is an annular vessel, approximately 0.25 mm. in cross section, running around the limbus deep in the limbal sclera, and is separated from the filtration angle by the trabecular meshwork. A number of collector channels varying from small capillaries to large trunks emerge from its lateral surfaces and immediately anastomose to form the deep scleral plexus of veins. Some collector vessels avoid these anastomoses and run directly out of the sclera to join the episcleral plexus of veins. The deep scleral plexus is connected with the episcleral plexus by a relatively small number of communicating vessels, and Ashton suggests that this may have some significance as a possible site of the increased resistance in chronic open-angle glaucoma.

The episcleral plexus communicates with the aqueous veins, and in this location the clear aqueous humor may under certain circumstances form a parallel column with the venous blood in the same vessel, remaining separate from it, which fact caused Ascher, their discoverer, to call them aqueous veins (p. 330).

The outflow channels for the aqueous humor include all the structures from the trabecular meshwork to and including the aqueous veins. The sum total of the resistance to flow offered by these structures determines the facility of outflow, whose formula was expressed mathematically on p. 171. In rabbit eyes, the size of the outflow channels is approximately 1.2 to 2.4μ. That is, particulate matter no larger than this can pass through the chamber angle and out of the eye in rabbits. In human beings the size of the pores has been estimated between 1.5 and 4.4μ and in monkeys between 1.5 and 2.25μ.[98]

The passage of substances out of the eye does not occur as unimpeded flow, however, but is influenced by the presence of spaces with different accessibilities, so that molecules of different sizes are separated. The small molecules, contrary to what might be expected, are retarded more than the large molecules in their passage out of the eye.[99, 100] Berggren[101] suggests that the situation is similar to gel filtration. Here, small molecules penetrate the gel grains to an extent that is determined by their molecular dimensions, the larger molecules being retarded to a lesser degree, since they do not penetrate the gel grains at all. The gel may be a coating of hyaluronic acid.

Thomassen[102] found that by injecting a 1% solution of methylene blue into the anterior chamber of human eyes in situ, the dye stained the epibulbar vessels, and the number of stained vessels increased according to the height of the pressure. When injection was performed after enucleation, a very strong staining of the epibulbar vessels was observed, even at a low pressure. These experiments show that the normal eye possesses a great capacity for compensating for any increase in intraocular pressure. Consequently, it is difficult to believe that glaucoma is caused by an increased production of the aqueous humor, only, and that in practically every kind of glaucoma a hampered escape of aqueous humor must be the principal factor.

The filtration angle and Schlemm's canal differ considerably in experimental animals from those in human beings, and this must be taken into account in the interpretation of experiments on aqueous humor outflow. In the dog the venous channels, known as the circle of Hovius, receive the aqueous humor directly from the anterior chamber. The veins anastomose with the branches of the anterior ciliary arteries.[103] In the rabbit a so-called trabecular plexus seems to perform the same function.[104, 105] Calkins[106] has made a comparative study of the filtration angle in Rodentia, Ungulata, Carnivora, and primates. This is a particularly valuable study since the extreme size variation in these different classes of eyes was eliminated by the use of selective magnification, and many of the recent gonioscopic findings on human eyes could be confirmed and explained phylogenetically and ontogenetically.

SUMMARY

This summary may be of value in achieving some comprehensive picture of the aqueous humor from the mass of data which often seems conflicting. It should be kept in mind, however, that as with reports on the weather, this can only attempt to record the present scene, and changes, perhaps far reaching, may have to be made at any moment.

A constant formation of fluid takes place from all the blood vessels inside the eye, the greatest part of which comes from the ciliary body, rich in blood vessels. Diffusion of nonelectrolytes takes place across the capillary beds whose walls act as semipermeable membranes, according to the gas laws, and diffusion of electrolytes occurs in accordance with the laws of the Donnan equilibrium. Filtration of fluid into and out of the capillary beds occurs, depending upon the hydrostatic pressure in the various parts of the circulation. In addition, there is an active transport, called secretion, of certain substances from the blood into the posterior chamber by the enzymatic activity of the cells of the ciliary processes covering the blood vessels in the ciliary body.

As a result of the enzymatic activity of the ciliary processes, a fluid called aqueous humor (whose composition differs considerably in the two chambers of the eye) is created. This fluid has an active circulation through the eye, the net rate of flow being in the order of 2.75 μl per minute or about 1% per minute of the volume of the aqueous humor in the anterior chamber.

Certain constituents of the fluid, notably sugar and urea, are lower in concentration in aqueous humor than in blood. The differences in concentration between aqueous humor and blood can be accounted for reasonably by either utilization or outflow. Other constituents are found to be higher. Ascorbic acid, e.g., is considerably higher in the aqueous humor and must be elaborated by the cells of the ciliary processes. Chloride is likewise considerably higher in man, and in some animals (the rabbit and guinea pig) bicarbonate is higher. The evidence that some or several substances are transported actively across the cell membranes lining the ciliary processes is convincing, but just what this substance is and which substances follow it according to physico-chemical laws are at present not decided. There are adherents to either belief that the principal ion secreted is bicarbonate, or that it is chloride, and some consider sodium the substance actively transported. The high chloride in the aqueous humor

of the human being, associated with a low pH, suggests that the hydrogen ion may itself be secreted, according to Becker.

REFERENCES

1. Patek, E., and Bernick, S.: Extravascular pathways of the eye and orbit, Am. J. Ophth. **49:**135, 1960.
2. Copeland, R., and Kinsey, V.: Determination of volume of the posterior chamber of the rabbit's eye, Arch. Ophth. **44:**515, 1950.
3. Rosengren, B.: Studies in depth of the anterior chamber of the eye in primary glaucoma, Arch. Ophth. **44:**523, 1950.
4. Bleeker, G.: Serial recordings of the depth of the anterior chamber, Arch. Ophth. **63:**821, 1960.
5. François, J., Rabaey, M., and Evens, L.: Agar microelectrophoresis of the aqueous humor, Arch. Ophth. **59:**692, 1958.
6. Kronfeld, P.: The protein content of the aqueous humor in man, Am. J. Ophth. **24:**1121, 1941.
7. Moore, E., Scheie, H., and Adler, F.: Chemical equilibrium between blood and aqueous humor, Arch. Ophth. **27:**317, 1942.
8. Merriam, F.: Personal communication.
9. Reddy, D., Rosenberg, C., and Kinsey, V.: Steady state distribution of free amino acids in the aqueous humor, vitreous body and plasma of the rabbit, Exper. Eye Res. **1:**175, 1961.
10. Kinsey, V., and Reddy, D.: Transport of amino acids into the posterior chamber of the rabbit eye, Invest. Ophthal. **1:** 355, 1962.
10a. Janes, R., Alert, H., and Johnson, N.: Dependence of aqueous-blood sugar ratios on method of determination, Arch. Ophth. **61:**720, 1959.
11. Nakamura, B., and Nakamura, O.: Uber das Vitamin C in der Linse und dem Kammerwasser der menschlichen Katarakte, Arch. Ophth. **134:**197, 1935.
12. Becker, B., Linner, E., and Barany, E.: Rate of turnover of ascorbic acid in aqueous humor of rabbits, Arch. Ophth. **45:**653, 1951.
13. Kinsey, V., and Barany, E.: The rate of flow of aqueous humor; derivation of

rate of flow and its physiologic significance, Am. J. Ophth. **32:**189, 1949.
14. Kinsey, V.: Dehydroascorbic acid—ascorbic acid in the aqueous humor of rabbits, Am. J. Ophth. **33:**257, 1950.
15. Purcell, E., Lerner, L., and Kinsey, V.: Ascorbic acid in aqueous humor and serum of patients with and without cataract; physiologic significance of relative concentrations, Arch. Ophth. **51:** 1, 1954.
16. Walker, A.: Comparison of the chemical composition of aqueous humor, cerebrospinal fluid, lymph and blood from frogs, higher animals and man, J. Biol. Chem. **101:**269, 1933.
17. Kinsey, V.: Comparative chemistry of aqueous humor in posterior and anterior chambers of rabbit eye, Arch. Ophth. **50:**401, 1953.
18. Fischer, F.: Ueber die tielchengrosse intravenous injizierter Farbstoffe im Serum und Kammerwasser, Arch. Augenh. **103:** 544, 1930.
19. Meyer, K., and Palmer, J.: On the nature of the ocular fluids, Am. J. Ophth. **19:**859, 1936.
20. Meyer, K., Smythe, E., and Gallardo, E.: On the nature of the ocular fluids; the hexosamine content, Am. J. Ophth. **21:** 1083, 1938.
21. Kinsey, V.: In Newell, F., editor: Glaucoma (Transactions Second Conference), New York, 1957, Josiah Macy, Jr. Foundation, p. 65.
22. Becker, B.: Symposium; recent trends in Diamox research, Am. J. Ophth. **40:** 129, 1955.
23. Davson, H.: Physiology of the ocular and cerebrospinal fluids, Boston, 1956, Little, Brown & Co., p. 227.
24. Becker, B.: Chemical composition of human aqueous humor, Arch. Ophth. **57:** 793, 1957.
25. Davson, H., and Luck, C.: Chemistry and rate of turnover of the ocular fluids of the bush baby (Galago Crassicaudatus Agisymbanus) J. Physiol. **145:**433, 1959.

26. Kinsey, V., and Reddy, D.: Documenta Opthalmologica. (To be published.)

27. Stary, Z., and Winternitz, R.: Zur Dhemie des Kammerwasser, Ztschr. physiol. Chem. **212**:215, 1932.

28. Tron, E.: Chemische Untersuchungen uber die Natur dar intraokularen Flussigkeiten. Anorganischer Schwefel und Phosphor in den intraokularen Flussigkeiten und dem Blutserum des Rindes. Die intraokularen Flusskeiten als Ultrafiltrat des Blutes, Arch. Ophth. **119**:659, 1928.

29. Salit, P.: Calcium content of aqueous and vitreous humors and serum, J. Biol. Chem. **104**: 275, 1934.

30. Merritt, H. H., and Bauer, W.: Equilibrium between cerebrospinal fluid and blood plasma; calcium content of serum, cerebrospinal fluid and aqueous humor at different levels of parathyroid activity, J. Biol. Chem. **90**:232, 1931.

31. Levene, R.: A study of aqueous humor formation (doctorate thesis), New York Postgraduate Medical School, New York, 1956; cited in Becker, B.: Glaucoma annual reviews 1956-1957, Arch. Ophth. **58**:878, 1957.

32. Harris, J., Carlson, A., Gruber, L., and Hoskinson, G.: The aqueous plasma steady-state ratios of potassium and sodium and the influence of Diamox and dibenamine thereon, Am. J. Ophth. **43**: 290, 1957.

33. Winternitz, R., and Stary, Z.: Zur Chemie des Glaskorpers, Arch. Augenh. **107**:191, 1933.

34. Palm, E.: On the phosphate exchange between the blood and the eye, Acta ophth. supp. **32**:1-120, 1948.

35. Langham, M.: In Duke-Elder, S., editor: Glaucoma: symposium, Springfield, Ill., 1955, Charles C Thomas, Publisher, p. 51.

36. Böck, J., and Popper, H.: Fermentbestimmungen und Kohlehydratuntersuchungen im Kammerwasser der Auges; Fermentehalt des Kammerwassers und Schrankendechte, Ztschr. ges. exper. Med. **90**:319, 1933.

37. Emmelin, N., and Palm, E.: On the presence of histamine in aqueous humor, Acta ophth. **22**:117, 1944.

38. Kuhlman, R., and Kaufman, H.: A microchemical study of the aqueous humor enzyme-protein interrelations, Arch. Ophth. **63**:41, 1960.

39. Reddy, D., and Kinsey, V.: Composition of the vitreous humor in relation to that of plasma and aqueous humors, Arch. Ophth. **63**:715, 1960.

40. Kinsey, V.: The chemical composition and the osmotic pressure in the aqueous humor and plasma of the rabbit, J. Gen. Physiol. **34**:389, 1951.

41. Roepke, R., and Hetherington, W.: Osmotic relation between aqueous humor and blood plasma, Am. J. Physiol. **130**: 340, 1940.

42. Schaeffer, A.: Osmotic pressure of the extraocular and intraocular fluids, Arch. Ophth. **43**:1026, 1950.

43. Levene, R.: Osmolality in the normal state and following acetazolamide, Arch. Ophth. **59**:597, 1959.

44. Kass, M., and Green, H.: Osmotic pressure measurements of intraocular fluids by an improved cryoscopic method, Am. J. Ophth. **48**:32, 1959.

45. Mishima, S., and Maurice, D.: The effect of normal evaporation on the eye, Exper. Eye Res. **1**:50, 1961.

46. Kadin, M.: Studies on total protein and radio-iodinated serum albumin (RISA) content of primary aqueous humor, Am. J. Ophth. **55**:93, 1963.

47. Scheie, H., Moore, E., and Adler, F.: Physiology of the aqueous in completely iridectomized eyes, Arch. Ophth. **30**: 70, 1943.

48. De Vincentis, D.: Further contributions to the study of the formation of the aqueous humor after paracentesis, J. Physiol. **146**:252, 1959.

49. Kinsey, V., Grant, W., and Cogan, D.: Water movement and the eye, Arch. Ophth. **27**:242, 1942.

50. Friedman, M., Newell, F., LeRoy, G., and Okita, G.: The steady-state turnover of tritiated water in the anterior chamber of rabbits, Am. J. Ophth. **44**: 375, 1957.

51. Becker, B.: The mechanism of the fall in intraocular pressure induced by the carbonic anhydrase inhibitor Diamox, Am. J. Ophth. **39**:177, 1955.

52. Berggren, L.: On the appearance of fluorescent dyes in the aqueous humor after intravenous injection, Am. J. Ophth. **42**:595, 1956.

53. Ross, E.: Transfer of non-electrolytes across the blood-aqueous barrier, J. Physiol. **112**:229, 1951.

54. Langham, M.: Factors affecting the penetration of antibiotics into the aqueous humor, Brit. J. Ophth. **35**:614, 1950.

55. Dobson, H.: The penetration of some sulfonamides into the intraocular fluids of the cat and rabbit, J. Physiol. **110**:416, 1950.

56. von Sallman, L., Dische, Z., Ehrlich, G., and Munaz, C.: Study on penetration of Cysteine and Cystine into the aqueous humor of rabbits and its relation to early x-irradiation effects on the eye, Am. J. Ophth. **34**:95, 1951.

57. Kinsey, V.: In Duke-Elder, S., editor: Glaucoma: symposium, Springfield, Ill., 1955, Charles C Thomas, Publisher, p. 84.

58. Kinsey, V.: Transfer of ascorbic acid and related compounds across the blood-aqueous barrier, Am. J. Ophth. **30**:1262, 1947.

59. Barany, E., and Langham, M.: On the origin of the ascorbic acid in the aqueous humor of guinea pigs and rabbits, Acta physiol. scandinav. **34**:2-3, 1955.

60. Linner, E.: Ascorbic acid as a test substance for measuring relative changes in the rate of plasma flow through the ciliary processes, Acta physiol. scandinav. (supp.) 26.

61. Langham, M.: The use of ascorbic acid to measure the rate of flow of plasma through the ciliary processes, J. Physiol. **130**:1, 1955.

62. Davson, H., and Duke-Elder, S.: Distribution of reducing substances between intraocular fluids and blood plasma, and kinetics of penetration of various sugars into these fluids, J. Physiol. **107**:141, 1948.

63. von Sallman, L., and Locke, B.: Experimental studies on early lens changes after roentgen irradiation, II. Exchange in penetration of radio-active indicators in normal and irradiated lenses of rabbits, Arch. Ophth. **45**:431, 1951.

64. Giardini, A., and Swanljung, H.: Effects of anoxia on the fluorescein permeability of the blood-aqueous barrier, Brit. J. Ophth. **35**:114, 1951.

65. Cook, C., and McDonald, R.: Effects of cortisone on the permeability of the blood-aqueous barrier to fluorescein, Brit. J. Ophth. **35**:730, 1951.

66. Kinsey, V., Grant, W., Cogan, D., Livingood, J., and Curtis, B.: Sodium, chloride and phosphorus movement and the eye, Arch. Ophth. **27**:1126, 1942.

67. Davson, H., and Spaziani, E.: The fate of substances injected into the anterior chamber of the eye, J. Physiol. **151**:202, 1960.

68. Davson, H., and Luck, J.: The effect of acetazoleamide on the composition of the aqueous humour and cerebrospinal fluid of some mammalian species and on the rate of turnover of 24 Na. in these fluids, J. Physiol. **137**:279, 1957.

69. Langham, M. E.: The influence of the intraocular pressure on the formation of the aqueous humor and the outflow resistance in the living eye, J. Physiol. **143**:11, 1958.

70. Becker, B.: The transport of organic ions by the rabbit eye, Am. J. Ophth. **50**:862, 1960.

71. Berggren, L.: Intracellular potential measurements from the ciliary processes of the rabbit eye in vivo and in vitro, Acta physiol. scandinav. **48**:461, 1960.

72. Miller, J., and Constant, M.: The measurement of rabbit ciliary epithelial potentials in vitro, Am. J. Ophth. **50**:855, 1960.

73. Holland, M.: Discussion of Miller, J., and Constant, M.: The measurement of rabbit ciliary epithelial potentials in vitro, Am. J. Ophth. **50**:861, 1960.

74. Barany, E., and Kinsey, V.: The rate of flow of aqueous humor; rate of disappearance of para-aminohippuric acid, radio-active Rayopake, and radio-active Diodrast from the aqueous humor of rabbits, Am. J. Ophth. **32**:177, 1949.

75. Reddy, D., and Kinsey, V.: Composition of the vitreous humor in relation to that of plasma and aqueous humor, Arch. Ophth. **63**:715, 1960.

76. Friedenwald, J.: The formation of the intraocular fluid. Proctor Award Lecture of Association for Research in Ophthalmology, Am. J. Ophth. **32**:9-27, 1949.

77. Kinsey, V.: The physiology of the aqueous humor and a new concept of the maintenance of intraocular pressure, Arch. Ophth.

78. Kessler, J.: Modification of the Frieden-

wald-Kinsey formula of intraocular pressure, Arch. Ophth. **57**:687, 1957.

79. Barany, E.: Rate of flow of aqueous humor in normal and scorbutic guinea pigs, Arch. Ophth. **46**:326, 1951.

80. Becker, B.: Glaucoma review, Arch. Ophth. **58**:878, 1957.

81. Cole, D.: Transport across the isolated ciliary body of ox and rabbit, Brit. J. Ophth. **46**:577, 1962.

81a. Newell, F. W.: editor: Glaucoma (Transactions Second Conference), New York, 1957, Josiah Macy, Jr. Foundation, p. 109.

82. Goldmann, H.: In Duke-Elder, S., editor: Glaucoma: symposium, Springfield, Ill., 1955, Charles C Thomas, Publisher, p. 108.

83. Kinsey, V., and Grant, W.: Further chemical studies on blood-aqueous humor dynamics, J. Gen. Physiol. **26**:119, 1942.

84. Ascher, K.: Aqueous veins, Am. J. Ophth. **25**:31, 1942.

85. Goldmann, H.: Abfluk des Kammerwassers beim Menschen, Ophthalmologica **111**:146, 1946.

86. Thomassen, T.: The safety valve of the eye, Acta ophth. **27**:413, 1949.

87. Ashton, N.: Anatomy and pathology of the drainage channels. In Duke-Elder, S., editor: Glaucoma: symposium, Springfield, Ill., 1955, Charles C Thomas, Publisher, pp. 13-42.

88. Holland, M., von Sallman, L., and Collins, E.: A study of the innervation of the chamber angle, Am. J. Ophth. **42**:148, 1956.

89. Vrabec, F.: L'Innervation de septeme trabeculaire de l'angle vein, Ophthalmologica **128**:359, 1954.

90. Vrabec, F.: The inner surface of the trabecular meshwork: Studied by a replica technique, Am. J. Ophth. **44**:7, 1957.

91. Ashton, N., Brini, M., and Smith, R.: Anatomical studies of the trabecular meshwork of the normal human eye, Brit. J. Ophth. **40**:275, 1956.

92. Zimmerman, L.: Demonstration of hya-

luronidase-sensitive acid mucopolysaccharide, Am. J. Ophth. **44**:1, 1957.

93. Barany, E.: Physiologic and pharmacologic factors influencing the resistance to aqueous outflow in glaucoma. In Newell, F., editor: Transactions First Conference on Glaucoma, New York, Josiah Macy, Jr. Foundation.

94. Thornfeldt, P., Reeh, M., and Kodama, J.: Investigation of acid mucopolysaccharides in fetal chamber angles, Am. J. Ophth. **50**:801, 1960.

95. Beswick, J., and McCullough, C.: Effect of hyaluronidase on the viscosity of the aqueous humor, Brit. J. Ophth. **40**:545, 1956.

96. Zimmerman, L., and Moss, L.: Phacolytic glaucoma: clinical pathology conference, Am. J. Ophth. **42**:97, 1956.

97. Vrabec, F.: The homophaces substance in the trabecular meshwork, Brit. J. Ophth. **41**:20, 1957.

98. François, J., Neetens, A., and Collegee, J.: Microradiography of Schlemm's canal, Am. J. Ophth. **40**:491, 1955.

99. Huggert, A.: Pore size in the filtration angle of the eye, Acta ophth. **33**:271 1955.

100. Huggert, A., Holmberg, A., and Esklund, A.: Further studies concerning pore size in the filtration angle of the eye, Acta ophth. **33**:428, 1955.

101. Berggren, L.: Passage out of the eye of substances of low and high molecular weights, Invest. Ophthal. **2**:305, 1963.

102. Thomassen, T.: On the exit of aqueous humor in normal eyes, Acta ophth. **28**: 479, 1950.

103. Duke-Elder, S.: System of ophthalmology, vol. I: the eye in evolution, St. Louis, 1958, The C. V. Mosby Co., p. 472.

104. Sheppard, L.: Intrascleral drainage channels of the normal rabbit eye, Tr. Am. Ophth. Soc. **57**:99, 1959.

105. Ruskell, G.: Aqueous drainage paths in the rabbit, Arch. Ophth. **66**:861, 1961.

106. Calkins, L.: The aqueous filtration angle; a phylogenetic and ontogenetic comparative histo-anatomic study of mammalian eyes, Tr. Am. Ophth. Soc. **58**:364, 1960.

CHAPTER 5

THE INTRAOCULAR PRESSURE

NORMAL INTRAOCULAR PRESSURE

The pressure in the inside of the eyeball is maintained at 15 mm. Hg above atmospheric pressure. This is the accepted value for the average of the normal human eye, based on readings taken with a tonometer. The range in physiologic intraocular pressure in man is now believed to extend from 10 to 22 mm. Hg.[1] This wide range makes it difficult to determine the physiologic limit for a given person. A pressure of 25 mm. Hg should be looked on with suspicion. In 1954 a new calibration scale was adopted by the Committee on Standardization of Tonometers. The normal readings in this scale range from 15 to 18 mm. Hg. Goldmann,[2] using an applanation tonometer, found that the physiologic limits lie between 10 and 22 mm. Hg. The methods by means of which intraocular pressure may be measured are as follows.

1. Manometry. A needle is inserted into the anterior chamber or into the vitreous chamber and is connected with a suitable mercury or water manometer. This method is naturally not applicable for clinical use.

2. Tonometry. The tonometer is an instrument which records the depth of indentation of the cornea produced by a given force acting over a constant area. The impressibility of an eye is determined in part by its internal pressure, but the impressibility is not identical with this pressure, nor does it vary absolutely with it. In a general way, however, the intraocular pressure may be inferred from the impressibility of the cornea. This method has the distinct advantage that it may be used clinically.

Usefulness of a high intraocular pressure

In experimental animals the pressures taken by manometry average 20 to 25 mm. Hg at normal levels of blood pressure. These values are higher, therefore, than those obtained in man by tonometry. This pressure is higher than that developed inside any other organ in the body and is much higher than the normal pressure of tissue, which is estimated at 2 to 3 mm. Hg. The normal pressure of cerebrospinal fluid is about 7 mm. Hg in the recumbent position.

The maintenance of this high pressure in the eye is necessary for the optical properties of the refracting surfaces. The corneal surface must be kept at an even and constant curvature, and the stroma must be under a constant and relatively high pressure in order to maintain a uniform refractive index.

When the eye becomes too soft, Descemet's membrane is likely to become wrinkled and show striae. This is a frequent occurrence after a cataract extraction; the fine straight folds in Descemet's membrane give a characteristic appearance called striate keratitis. Irregular folds in Descemet's membrane often occur in hypotension which follows trauma to the globe.

Variations in normal pressure

Variations in intraocular pressure frequently occur under normal conditions, but the range of pressures is relatively small. By means of tonometry, pressures in normal human eyes from a low of 10 mm. Hg to a high of 30 mm. Hg have been measured repeatedly, without any evidence of disease or any effect on the ocular functions, even when these pressures have been maintained for years. It has already been pointed out that tonometric readings do not measure intraocular pressure directly but are compounded from a number of factors (which will be discussed subsequently). The values thus obtained may not represent true intraocular pressure, therefore.

When the intraocular pressure is recorded manometrically in an animal, the level varies with respirations and the pulse beat, similar to the manner in which these factors cause variations in the blood pressure curve. Respirations produce a rise and fall of intraocular pressure of as much as 5 mm. Hg when the respirations are deep. The individual pulse beats

generally produce changes in pressure amounting to 1 to 2 mm. Hg. Changes in the general level of blood pressure give similar qualitative changes in intraocular pressure, but there is no quantitative relationship between the rise and fall of intraocular pressure and blood pressure, as will be shown later.

During the day, the intraocular pressure varies in a characteristic fashion. The pressure is lowest at about 5 to 7 o'clock in the evening but gradually rises during the night, reaching a peak in the early morning hours. When one first awakes, the pressure is at its highest level and gradually falls from this point throughout the day. In normal eyes the diurnal variations in pressure seldom exceed 3 to 4 mm. Hg. In chronic simple glaucoma the variation may be considerable. An abnormal elevation of intraocular pressure in the early morning hours may be of diagnostic significance in the detection of early chronic simple glaucoma.

It is not entirely clear what factors determine normal diurnal changes in intraocular pressure. The movements of the eye during the day may produce changes in intraocular pressure because of the changes in tone of the extraocular muscles. Vascular factors, such as a redistribution of blood due to postural changes during the day and night, have also been considered the causative agent. De Roetth[3] has suggested that osmotic changes in the blood might also play a part in these diurnal pressure variations, particularly in glaucoma, since he demonstrated that various artificially induced changes in osmotic pressure of the blood have an effect on the rate of flow of aqueous through the eye. Intake of food and water, exercise, and loss of fluids through perspiration certainly produce periods of relative dilution and concentration of the blood throughout the day, and these changes in osmotic pressure of the blood might be sufficient to cause the observed variations in ocular pressure.

These rhythmic changes seem to be characteristic for each person, and Duke-Elder[4] feels that they are unrelated to muscular activity, food intake, size of the pupil, and general blood pressure and can be altered only by changing a person's habits over a prolonged period of time. He likens this rhythm to other established rhythms, such as sleep, bodily temperature, diuresis, etc., all of which probably are under neurohumoral control. According to him the diurnal changes are caused by variations in facility of outflow due to pressure changes in the efferent veins brought about eventually by changes in sympathetic tonus. Other evidence, on the other hand, suggests that the diurnal variations are associated with changes in secretory activity of the ciliary body.[5, 6]

Variations in pressure probably occur in all persons with changes in the diameter of the pupil, but these cannot ordinarily be detected with the tonometer. In persons with very narrow filtration angles, on the other hand, the obstruction to the outflow of aqueous humor from the eye may be sufficient to change the intraocular pressure as the diameter of the pupil changes. Keeping such a patient in a dark room for one hour may build up the pressure by preventing the outflow from keeping pace with the formation of fluid, and tonometric readings may be 10 to 15 mm. Hg above the level observed when the pupil was contracted by light. The use of a dark room constitutes a convenient and poignant test for the obstructed angle type of chronic simple glaucoma.

Intraocular pressure in a normal person also probably undergoes changes with various other physiologic conditions, such as a concentration of blood, presence of commonly used drugs such as caffeine and alcohol, obstruction of the return flow of blood from the head area due to posture, etc., but in a normal person these changes in intraocular pressure rarely become evident. In open-angle glaucoma the mechanism of control of the intraocular pressure seems to be especially vulnerable to such factors, and the intraocular pressure rises to greater heights. If a person with this disease refrains from food and all liquids for 10 hours and then drinks a quart of water, the intraocular pressure will respond with a marked rise, far above that of a normal response. In the course of an hour the pressure subsides and may even fall below the normal. This marked lability of the intraocular pressure to changes in concentration of blood is characteristic of patients with the open-angle type of chronic simple glaucoma. Water-drinking is used as a provocative test for this disease. In this test, the rise in the intraocular pressure is due to an abnormal formation of aqueous humor as a result of the dilution of the blood and to the relative changes in osmotic pressure of blood and aqueous humor (p. 164). Scheie[7] has been unable to find any evidence of decreased facility of outflow during various phases of the water-drinking test.

Maintenance of normal intraocular pressure

The pressure inside an organ such as the eye or the skull is created by the volume of its solid and liquid contents and the elasticity of its coats. In the case of the skull the body casement is entirely inelastic, and the pressure depends entirely upon the volume of the contents. Since the volume of the brain cannot readily be changed, the only changes possible are due to displacements of blood or cerebrospinal fluid. There must be considerable resistance to a change in volume of any one constituent. When one changes, there must be an almost equal and opposite effect in one of the remaining contents. This is known as the Monroe-Kellie doctrine.[8, 9] The pressure inside the skull must respond immediately to any changes in displacement of fluid.

Under physiologic conditions the chief hemodynamic factor controlling the cerebrospinal fluid pressure is the venous return from the head area. Respiratory movements, compression of the diaphragm, etc., sufficiently affect the return flow of blood from the skull to raise the cerebrospinal fluid pressure immediately. On the other hand, an increase in bulk of the solid contents of the skull, unless very rapid, is compensated within wide limits by displacement of blood. It is only when the escape of cerebrospinal fluid from the ventricles is prevented that the cerebrospinal fluid undergoes rapid and marked changes in pressure.

The coats of the eye are more distensible than those of the brain, but the elasticity of the sclera is not considerable. The hemodynamics of the interior of the eye are similar to those of the brain, therefore. Internal pressure is created by the volume of the solid and fluid contents, and changes in the pressure are brought about largely by variations in the volume of the fluid contents or by pressure on the globe from the outside.

Rigidity of the sclera. Measurements of the distensibility of the eyeball have been made by a number of authors. Ridley[10] and Clark[11] both found that at low pressures the sclera is fairly distensible, but, as the internal pressure in the eye increases, the sclera becomes less and less distensible. This relationship was expressed by Clark in terms of a coefficient

of elasticity (Fig. 39). The coefficient of elasticity, *k*, changes continuously with the pressure, and Ridley showed that if the eye was exposed to a high internal pressure, its elasticity changed; so that when the pressure was lowered again, the coefficient of elasticity was different.

In animal eyes, *k* has been reported to increase with increasing pressure.[12] In human eyes, on the other hand *k* decreases as the intraocular pressure is raised.[13] The ocular rigidity in vivo varies somewhat from time to time, probably depending upon changes in the intraocular blood vessels and in the elastic properties of the ocular coats, depending upon their state of hydration. Reduction in the water content of the cornea and sclera results in an increase in ocular rigidity, but this effect is only observable with very gross changes in thickness of the tissues. Slight changes which might occur as a result of provocative tests for glaucoma such as the water-drinking test (p. 164) produce no changes in *k*.

Friedenwald[14] deduced a simple empirical formula for the relation between changes in pressure and volume in a given eye. He showed that this formula was applicable to tonometric measurements when the pressure was taken as the actual intraocular pressure with the tonometer resting on the cornea, and the volume was taken as the volume of the indentation in the cornea produced by the tonometer plunger. By using Schiøtz's original experimental data on which he based his tonometric chart, he computed the pressure which exists within the eye at each tonometer scale reading for each weight of the tonometer plunger and also the volume of the indentation corresponding to each tonometer scale reading. With the aid of these calculations and the empirical formula, he developed a nomogram (Fig. 46) from which the co-

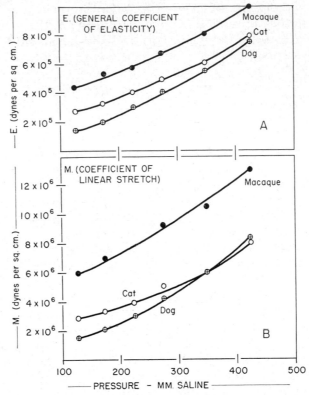

Fig. 39. A, General coefficient of elasticity of the eye as a whole. **B,** Coefficient of linear stretch of the coats of the eye. (After Clark.)

efficient of rigidity of an eye might be computed from two tonometric readings with two different weights. He found that the rigidity of the eye was increased in senile eyes and in extreme myopia. This was also true in some types of intraocular inflammatory disease, which not infrequently gave rise to the erroneous diagnosis of secondary glaucoma.

Many attempts have been made to compose a formula which best fits the data on ocular rigidity, i.e., the relationship of volume change per unit pressure change. The mathematical expression which relates pressure change to a corresponding volume change in the eye is known as the ocular rigidity function. The most recent (1960) and exact approximation to the facts as they relate to the excised cats eye is that given in an article by Holland, Madison, and Bean.[15]

The response of the living eye to artificial raising of the intraocular pressure differs considerably from that of the dead eye due to the fact that in the living eye increasing the intraocular pressure forces blood out of the eye. The amount of blood lost in this fashion reaches a maximum as the pressure approaches the arterial blood pressure.[16] It is apparent that one is not justified in assuming that the volume of fluid infused into an eye is a measure of the volume change in that eye. These same principles of the change in ocular rigidity with increasing pressure and the differences between the living and dead eye due to extrusion of blood from the globe have been found to be true not only for experimental animals but also for the human eye.[17]

Intraocular contents. The contents of the eye that contribute to the maintenance of normal intraocular pressure are the following.

Solid structures—lens and vitreous. All of the solid and semisolid intraocular structures, such as the lens, vitreous, uveal tract, and retina, aid in maintaining normal intraocular pressure and may by a change in volume cause an alteration in the intraocular pressure. The lens grows continuously throughout life and, in spite of the sclerosing process in the nucleus, increases in size. Its change in volume must be compensated by a displacement of fluid from the eye, or the intraocular pressure will increase. Under normal conditions the increase in volume takes place so slowly that it is fully compensated, but occasionally in the development of a cataract the lens may suddenly swell and cause an acute rise in pressure. In cataracts due to trauma the rapid development of opacification is often accompanied by such swelling of the lens that a rise in pressure results. This may demand surgical intervention. The same is true for the rapid swelling of the lens in congenital cataracts when a needling operation is performed. The fibers of the lens imbibe aqueous humor and swell, and as a result prompt emptying of the anterior chamber may be demanded to reduce the pressure.

The gradual and progressive growth of the lens may lead to changes in the position of the iris so that the anterior chamber is shallowed, and the root of the iris comes to lie in apposition to the posterior surface of the cornea, thus blocking the exit of fluid from the eye. It is well known that with age there is a gradual and progressive increase in the volume of the crystalline lens and that, similarly, there is a progressive shallowing of the anterior chamber as one grows older. Snydacker[18] found a direct relationship between the depth of the anterior chamber and the volume of the lens in patients with cataract, and as one would anticipate, the larger the lens, the shallower was the anterior chamber. There were exceptions to this relationship in which the lens was occasionally of much greater than normal volume, and yet the anterior chamber was not abnormally shallow. The converse was true likewise in isolated cases.

Changes in the volume of the vitreous body will lead to alterations in pressure unless compensated by loss of the fluid contents of the globe. The growth of neoplastic tissue in the eye will similarly increase the pressure unless fluid is displaced from the eye. One differential diagnostic feature of detachment of the retina caused by serous effusion from that caused by growth of a tumor is the behavior of the intraocular pressure. Where the detachment is due to growth of tumor tissue, in about 50% of the patients the intraocular pressure will be elevated. At first the pressure increase is slight since displacement of blood from the choroid and aqueous humor from the anterior chamber partially compensate for the increasing volume of the tumor. Eventually, a rapid rise of pressure occurs when this compensation is no longer adequate.

Fluid contents—blood and aqueous humor. Two fluids in the eye contribute to the volume of the intraocular contents, namely, the blood and the aqueous humor. Both of these are present in appreciable quantities, and variations in the amount of either will alter the intraocular pressure considerably.

ALTERATIONS IN INTRAOCULAR PRESSURE CAUSED BY VARIATIONS IN FLUID CONTENTS OF THE EYE
Variations in quantity and quality of the blood

When an eyeball is enucleated or if the circulation of the blood to the eye is interrupted, the intraocular pressure immediately falls. It does not drop to zero immediately but remains at about 5 mm. Hg for a considerable period of time. As postmortem changes set in, the pressure gradually drops to zero. The volume of blood in the intraocular blood vessels during life accounts for a large part of the volume of the intraocular contents. Of this, the largest amount is probably attributable to the blood in the choroid coat.

The choroid coat consists chiefly of several layers of blood vessels so that in cross section its histologic appearance resembles that of a spongy tissue similar to the corpus spongiosum of the penis. The state of contraction or dilatation of these blood vessels, particularly the choriocapillaris, will determine the volume of blood in the interior of the eye at any one time and, hence, will alter the internal pressure. Any factor which changes the filling of this choroidal reservoir must affect the intraocular pressure immediately. Whether such changes will result in an identical and persisting change in intraocular pressure will depend entirely upon whether an efficient mechanism is present for compensating for such changes.

Changes in general blood pressure. If the arterial pressure in an animal is suddenly raised by tightening a constricting band around the aorta, the intraocular pressure immediately rises. When the ligature is released, the intraocular pressure falls, following the drop in general blood pressure. Under these conditions, the changes in intraocular pressure are always in the same direction as the changes in blood pressure but as is to be expected, the quantitative relationship is not exact.

Many different factors account for this discrepancy. Intraocular pressure is dependent not only on blood pressure, but also on the quantity of the aqueous humor present in the eye at any one moment. Since changes in blood pressure will be reflected in changes in blood flow through the ciliary body, the secretory mechanism will undoubtedly be affected, and changes in the aqueous humor formation will result. The elasticity of the walls of the blood vessels determines the change in volume produced in the eye at any particular level of raised intravascular pressure. If the intraocular blood vessels were inelastic rigid tubes, their diameter would not change no matter what the pressure in their interior might be. A change in blood pressure would then cause no change in intraocular volume. If, on the other hand, the intraocular blood vessels were perfectly elastic, they would respond by dilating ad maximum to any increase in internal pressure, and the intraocular volume would be increased in like measure. Since the small blood vessels of a healthy person are fairly elastic, we find that changes in blood pressure dilate them and produce an increase in volume of the ocular contents and hence an increase in intraocular pressure. In persons with arteriosclerosis with high blood pressure, the peripheral vessels have lost their elasticity. They have become narrowed, and this factor probably caused the generalized hypertension. Because of their rigidity when organic changes have set in, they cannot dilate, even with a high internal pressure, and hence no corresponding change in volume occurs in the intraocular blood vessel bed. The pressure in the eye, therefore, does not rise.

A large rise in blood pressure results in a relatively small change in intraocular pressure, especially if the intraocular pressure is low to start with. As the intraocular pressure rises further, an increase in blood pressure will cause a greater change in the intraocular pressure as the distensibility of the sclera decreases. This is to be expected on the basis of the low elasticity of the sclera.

In an experimental animal if the blood pressure is elevated and maintained at a new high level, the intraocular pressure rises about one tenth that of the rise in blood pressure, but does not remain at the new high level, and soon returns to normal. This is due to the combination of a number of factors. (1) There is a loss of aqueous humor through the filtration angle. The moment the pressure increases in the anterior chamber, the aqueous humor flows out faster into Schlemm's canal. (2) The sclera becomes stretched. This must be of minor importance since the sclera is relatively inelastic. (3) Any change in hemodynamics upsets the steady state condition of the aqueous humor in many ways so that the rate of formation of its various constituents may be changed.

A sudden elevation of arterial pressure always tends to dilate the peripheral vascular beds, but in the intact animal the stretching of vessels incident to a rise in general blood pressure may produce reflex vasoconstriction. Most of the hollow viscera in the body react in this way to changes in the volume of their contents, either by a direct muscular response or by reflex action mediated through the central nervous system. Sudden elevations of general blood pressure produce cardiac inhibition and vasodilatation.

The blood vessels in the eye exhibit this same response to a minor degree. The sympathetic supply to the vessels maintains a certain amount of vasoconstrictor tone so that the intraocular pressure does not rise as high to a determined increment of general blood pressure as when the sympathetic supply to the eye has been destroyed. The effectiveness of this mechanism is small, and it cannot be looked upon as a homeostatic reflex protecting the eye against permanent changes in general blood pressure, as Barany pointed out.[19] He stated that the changes produced are quite short, lasting at most only some minutes, and therefore involve mainly a plethysmographic effect, and are no proof of the existence of a reflex which will affect the final level of equilibrium. Further, the total exclusion of the reflex increases the intraocular pressure by only 20%. This criticism is valid in that the effectiveness of the reflex in maintaining the final equilibrium level is slight. It does not invalidate the correctness of the statement that constrictor tone supplied to the intraocular blood vessels by way of the sympathetic nerves controls to some extent the caliber of these vessels.

Barany[19] studied the effects of lowering the blood pressure on the intraocular pressure. He was unable to show any reflex which significantly stabilized the intraocular pressure when the arterial blood pressure dropped. Barany feels that there is no proof of the existence of any homeostatic vasomotor reflex which protects the intraocular pressure from changes caused by alterations in blood pressure.

It has been shown that when the arterial pressure is either raised or lowered qualitatively similar changes occur in the intraocular pressure. These changes are due primarily to the dilatation or contraction of the distensible blood vessels in the eye, chiefly the choriocapillaris. When their internal pressure rises, these vessels dilate, and when their volume falls, they contract. The immediate changes in intraocular pressure under such conditions are not due to any interposed mechanisms such as changes in formation of fluid. This is made evident by the following factors. (1) The changes in intraocular pressure follow exactly the changes in blood pressure. They are qualitatively similar in all respects (Fig. 40). It would be difficult to conceive of any other mechanism which would be so rapidly adjustable. (2) Measurements of the latent period between the rise of blood pressure and that of intraocular pressure show that the latter responds in a period about equal to the time taken for the change in pressure to reach the eye. If a second mechanism were involved, such as an increase in the formation of the aqueous humor, the latent period would probably be longer. In a series of measurements, the latent period was found to be less than 0.1 second. When the recording of intraocular pressure is done with an ocular manometer so that friction is eliminated, pulse waves similar to the pulse in the arteries are present. At normal intraocular pressure, these pulsations are very slight, but as the pressure inside the eye is increased, they in-crease in amplitude until the intraocular pressure prevents the access of blood to the eye. Pulsations are frequently seen in the pointer of a tonometer when intraocular pressure in glaucomatous eyes is recorded. The blood pressure curve in a normal person shows variations which are caused by respiratory activity. These rhythmic changes, the Traube-Hering waves, are reflected in similar changes of smaller magnitude in the intraocular pressure.

Changes in venous pressure of the head area. If the venous return from the head is blocked, the intraocular pressure rises. When the blood is dammed up in the eye, all the blood vessels dilate ad maximum, and the intraocular pressure increases to levels present in pathologic conditions (Fig. 41).

The relation of the venous pressure in the eye to the intraocular pressure is not entirely clear, and the differences in opinion may be related to the differences in anatomic structure between man and the usual experimental animals used, such as the dog and cat. In man there are no substantial communications between the vortex bed of veins and the anterior ciliary system, whereas in dogs and cats

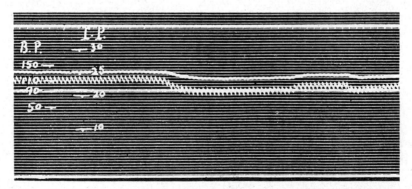

Fig. 40. Effect of lowering general arterial pressure. Dog (luminal anesthesia) ligature around inferior vena cava and abdominal aorta. *Upper tracing, B.P.,* blood pressure mm. Hg. *Lower tracing, I.P.,* intraocular pressure mm. Hg. (Time in seconds.)

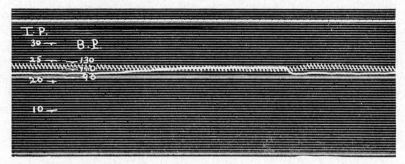

Fig. 41. The effect on intraocular pressure of changing venous pressure in a dog (luminal anesthesia). Both internal jugular veins were ligated and the external jugulars were compressed. *Upper tracing, B.P.,* blood pressure mm. Hg. *Lower tracing, I.P.,* intraocular pressure mm. Hg. (Time in seconds.)

these communications are numerous. In dogs changes in the pressure in the vortex veins will effectively change the pressure in the circle of Hovius and hence in the aqueous humor outflow pressure. In man the vortex system probably does not influence the episcleral venous system. In the cat there is a linear correlation between intraocular pressure and venous pressure.[20] In man the episcleral venous pressure has been found to be relatively constant in normal and glaucomatous eyes and apparently is not related to the intraocular pressure.[21]

Changes in blood flow. A growing body of evidence points to a complicated relationship between the intraocular pressure and the blood flow through the uveal tract. Changes in the arterial pressure, the venous pressure, or both will simultaneously change the blood flow through the uvea, and this in turn will influence the intraocular pressure by affecting the rate of aqueous humor secretion. It can readily be seen how difficult it is to control all the various factors concerned and to arrive at any conclusions as to the part played under normal conditions by each. The situation becomes even more complicated by the finding that an experimentally induced increase in the intraocular pressure itself causes a reduction in blood flow through the uvea and hence probably acts as a feedback mechanism to reduce the rate of secretion and thus maintain a balance of pressure.[22]

A further indication of a feedback mechanism whereby changes in intraocular pressure produce changes in other mechanisms which tend to bring about stabilization of pressure is the finding that the facility of outflow of aqueous humor is changed by a rise in intraocular pressure. In enucleated eyes of rabbits and cats the facility of outflow was found to depend on the intraocular pressure level. As the intraocular pressure rose, the facility of outflow increased, thus tending to keep the intraocular pressure at its previous level.[23]

Effect of the vasomotor nerves on the eye. The cervical sympathetic nerves contain fibers which supply the unstriped muscle in the orbit, the dilator pupillae, and the intraocular arterioles. It has just been shown that a vasoconstrictor reflex limits the dilatation of the intraocular vessels when the blood pressure is elevated. It might be supposed from this that stimulation of the sympathetic nerves to the head area would result in further vasoconstriction and lowering of pressure. Whatever vasoconstrictor activity is present on stimulation of sympathetic nerves, it is not sufficient to show any effect on the intraocular pressure, nor is there evidence that vasodilator fibers run to the intraocular blood vessels which when stimulated cause a rise in intraocular pressure. Removal of the superior cervical ganglion temporarily lowers the intraocular pressure by reducing the formation of aqueous humor.[24] In rabbits if the sympathetic nerve chain is cut in preganglionic fashion, the reduction in intraocular pressure does not occur.[25]

Schmerl and Steinberg,[26] using rabbits, implanted electrodes in the orbit in the region of the ciliary ganglion. Faradic stimulation caused pupillary contraction, flattening of the anterior chamber, and elevation of intraocular pressure.

If the sympathetic system has been effectively eliminated by a previous sympathectomy of the head area in cats, electrical stimulation of the parasympathetic pathway produces an immediate fall in intraocular pressure. This lowered pressure is generally maintained during the periods of continued stimulation.[27] These effects are still present after extraocular mechanical factors are eliminated such as severing attachments of the muscles to the globe. Armaly[28] believes that the immediate reduction in pressure is probably compounded from two effects, a rise in intraocular pressure due to muscular compression of the contents of the globe by the contraction of the ciliary muscle and at the same time a fall in pressure, which evidently is greater than the rise due to muscular contraction, caused by a reduction in the volume of the vascular bed of the ciliary muscle and iris. This is brought about through the effect of contraction of the ciliary muscle on the vessels coursing through it to form the major circle of the iris. The continued drop in pressure during stimulation is due to a number of factors working simultaneously, such as rate of inflow of aqueous, outflow resistance, and pressure in the collector channels, which cannot easily be isolated.

In a later paper Armaly[29] found that stimulation of the ciliary ganglion with either its central connections intact or previously severed caused an increase in the facility of outflow of aqueous. This could also be shown in the enucleated eye. Atropine abolished the effect. He believes this reduction of resistance to outflow takes place at the trabeculum, probably induced by contraction of the ciliary muscle.

According to Langham and Taylor[30, 31] the immediate effect of preganglionic and postganglionic sections of the cervical sympathetic is variable and transient. No sustained effect on the intraocular pressure of rabbits or cats is found after preganglionic section, but extirpation of the superior cervical ganglion in rabbits causes a slow fall in the steady state pressure of the eye which reaches a maximum after 24 hours. The pressure then returns to normal within three to four days. The authors found no change in the rate of flow of aqueous humor in these rabbits, but did obtain evidence that ganglionectomy changed the resistance to outflow between the anterior chamber and the episcleral veins, and that ganglionectomy increased the blood flow through the eye. They conclude, therefore, that the fall in intraocular pressure 24 hours after ganglionectomy is due principally to decreased resistance in the outflow system of the eye.

It is admittedly difficult to obtain satisfactory evidence of the existence of homeostatic mechanisms mediated through nerve impulses. Langham[32, 33] has presented evidence that in both the cat and the rabbit there is a marked difference between the dead and living eyes in the effect on the steady state pressure of raising or lowering the intraocular pressure. In the dead eye the steady state intraocular pressure increases linearly with the rates of infusion of fluid into the anterior chamber, whereas in the living eye the pressure-infusion relationship is not linear when plotted but exhibits a positive curvature. Preganglionic sectioning of the sympathetic nerve abolished this relationship in the living eye, from which Langham concludes that during life the steady state intraocular pressure is constantly under the influence of homeostatic impulses via the sympathetics to maintain the status quo pressure.

There is no doubt that the mechanism for the maintenance of intraocular pressure is under the control of the central nervous system and that either by nerve impulses, hormonal effects, or both the hemodynamics of the eye can be altered to meet the needs of the moment. How effective this mechanism is and by what channels it becomes operative are still matters of speculation. It is easy to postulate sympathetic and parasympathetic nerve effects in a manner which keeps the formation and elimination of the aqueous humor nicely balanced, but it is quite another thing to demonstrate these effects in the laboratory. Stimulation of selected areas in the diencephalon by electrodes produces widespread changes in the whole head area, and even under the most careful and painstaking setup it is difficult to state whether the effects observed on the intraocular pressure are due primarily to discharges from the stimulated area directed to this end or whether they are merely secondary to other changes in the head area. Von

Sallmann[34, 35] found that stimulation of a dorsal area of the hypothalamus and the ventral part of the thalamus produced changes in pressure in the eye which appeared as isolated events. In cats stimulation of numerous points in the diencephalon likewise produced changes in intraocular pressure associated with changes in systemic blood pressure, in the caliber of the vessels in the auricles of the ear, in the pupils, and in the nictitating membranes. These isolated changes in intraocular pressure are the most carefully controlled experimental proof of control by the central nervous system of the intraocular pressure yet presented.

In order to rule out the effect of contraction of the oculorotatory and smooth muscles on the intraocular pressure, von Sallmann and co-workers[36] eliminated the effects of the smooth muscle by cutting the trunks of the cervical sympathetic and vagus nerves and by an antecedent excision of the superior cervical ganglia. The effect of the oculorotatory muscles was eliminated by the use of a muscle relaxant (decamethonium). Stimulation of the region just cited, which produced isolated rises in intraocular pressure, then gave the following responses: (1) a sudden rise in intraocular pressure which was due to a coexistent rise in general blood pressure since it did not occur when the rise in general blood pressure was annuled and (2) a delayed rise of intraocular pressure, with augmentation of mydriasis, and moderate retraction of the denervated nictitating membrane, which apparently was mediated by the outpouring of epinephrine from the suprarenal gland.

Gloster and Greaves[37] observed changes in intraocular pressure due to stimulation of fixed points in the diencephalon by stereotaxic techniques, along with control of the general blood pressure, response of the nictitating membrane, and pupillary changes. In addition to changes which could be definitely attributed to changes in general blood pressure, they found responses of intraocular pressure independently, which provided an indication that the diencephalon might have a special role in maintenance of intraocular pressure. However, they could not be sure that the pathways involved in these responses originated in the diencephalon since they might have been due to effects obtained from stimulation of nerve tracts running through the diencephalon and emanating from other nervous centers. They are compatible with the view that the diencephalon influences the intraocular pressure, but they do not allow the conclusion that any such influence is in the nature of a controlling mechanism.

The parasympathetic fibers in the seventh cranial nerve do not appear to control either blood flow through the eye or intraocular pressure since stimulation of the seventh cranial nerve intracranially in the monkey is without effect on the intraocular pressure, nor does similar stimulation of the third cranial nerve have any effect on intraocular pressure.[38-40] Nerve fibers terminating in the trabecular system have been reported[41] and the existence of terminal corpuscles which might record changes in pressure between the canal of Schlemm and the episcleral venous plexus.[42] Electron micrography has confirmed the existence of both medullated and unmyelinated nerve fibers in the fine structure of the angle in both man and rhesus monkey.[43, 44] It is not known what function these nerves subserve although it is tempting to associate their presence with some kind of a regulating mechanism controlling the intraocular pressure. That this speculation is somewhat justified is suggested by the findings of Perkins.[45] Recording from the long ciliary nerves of cats and monkeys, he found an increase in frequency of potentials with elevation of the intraocular pressure and a decrease in frequency when the pressure was lowered. There was no exact parallel between the change in pressure and the frequency of the spikes, however.

Effect of drugs which dilate or contract the intraocular vessels. Intraocular pressure may be effectively varied by the action of a number of drugs on the peripheral vessels in the eye similar to their action on peripheral vessels elsewhere in the body. In order to study the action of such drugs on the eye, it is necessary to eliminate the effect of the drugs on the general blood pressure by employing an artificial perfusion apparatus in the head area, as has been done by Duke-Elder. With an apparatus of this sort, an oxygenated flow of blood to the eye is maintained at a constant rate and at a constant pressure. After the injection of the drug in the perfusion fluid, the changes in the blood vessels are determined by recording the intraocular pressure and the changes in intraocular temperature. Alterations in the size of the vessels can also be determined by direct observation of the vessels of the iris.

Drugs which constrict peripheral vessels. In an intact animal an intravenous injection of epinephrine nearly always causes a marked and sudden rise in intraocular pressure coincident with the rise in blood pressure (Fig. 42). Since epinephrine constricts the smaller peripheral blood vessels all over the body, one would expect the vessels in the eye to be constricted and the intraocular pressure to fall. This will occur if the blood pressure is kept from rising by means of a perfusion apparatus (Fig. 43). When tested in this way, epinephrine in large

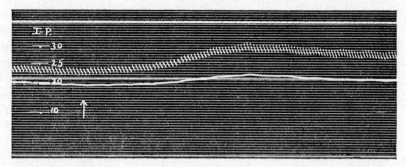

Fig. 42. The effect of epinephrine when injected in a dog (luminal anesthesia). Injection of 0.1 ml. 1:1000 epinephrine in external jugular vein shown at arrow. *Lower tracing, B.P.,* blood pressure mm. Hg. *Upper tracing, I.P.,* intraocular pressure mm. Hg. (Time in seconds.)

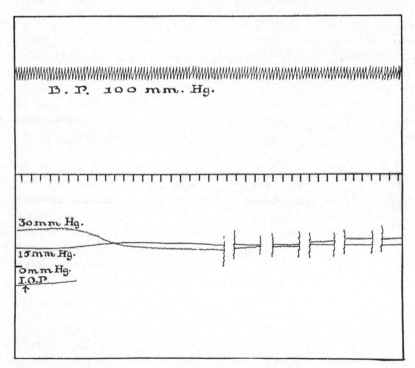

Fig. 43. Effect of epinephrine on the intraocular pressure of the perfused eye. (After Duke-Elder.)

doses constricts the arterioles and capillaries and lowers intraocular pressure. In small doses, the capillaries in the eye are dilated passively by the rise in the general blood pressure, and intraocular pressure may rise accordingly.

Barium chloride injected intravenously also causes marked vasoconstriction in all the peripheral vessels and a rise in the general blood pressure. When large doses are injected, the intraocular pressure increases as the peripheral vessels are forced open by the rise in general blood pressure. If small doses are injected, the general blood pressure is not elevated very much, whereas the intraocular pressure falls due to the peripheral vasoconstriction. Pituitrin acts very much like epinephrine but is relatively slow in onset, and the vasoconstriction produced is usually not so great as when epinephrine is used (Fig. 44, *A*).

Drugs which dilate peripheral vessels. Inhalation of amyl nitrite by an intact animal dilates the peripheral vessels, as is evidenced by the dilated capillaries in the mucous membranes. The general blood pressure falls. It is possible to obtain a slight rise of intraocular pressure by the dilatation of the intraocular capillaries before the fall in general blood pressure becomes very marked (Fig. 44, *B*). When the blood pressure falls considerably, the intraocular pressure also falls as the blood leaves the head area.

Histamine administered in perfusion

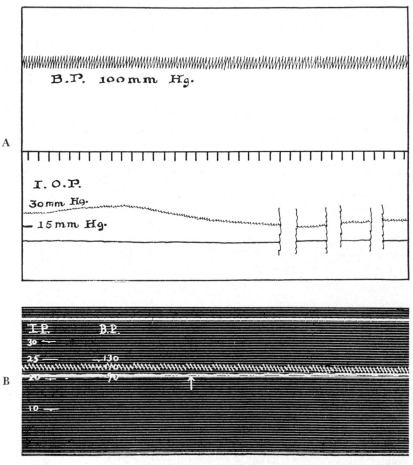

Fig. 44. A, Effect of pituitrin on the intraocular pressure of the perfused eye. B, Effect of amyl nitrite. Inhalation of amyl nitrite begins at arrow. *Upper tracing, B.P.,* blood pressure mm. Hg. *Lower tracing, I.P.,* intraocular pressure mm. Hg. (Time in seconds; A, after Duke-Elder.)

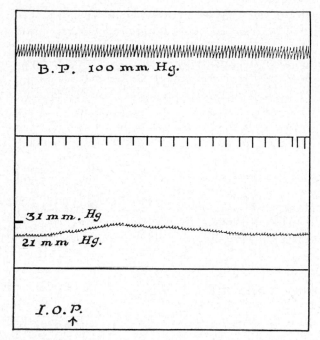

B.P. 100 mm Hg.

31 mm. Hg

21 mm Hg.

I.O.P.

Fig. 45. Effect of histamine on the intraocular pressure of perfused eyes. (After Duke-Elder.)

fluid gives a variable reaction. When epinephrine is not present in the fluid, a fall in intraocular pressure occurs due to vasoconstriction. When a constant amount of epinephrine is present, however, a rise in intraocular pressure occurs due to vasodilatation. In order for any effect to be produced from histamine, the peripheral vessels must possess a certain amount of tone. The presence of epinephrine in circulating blood imparts this tone to the capillaries, and the histamine can then relax the tone (Fig. 45). This same effect has been shown for the capillaries in a perfused hind limb.

Choline and acetylcholine also dilate the peripheral vessels but complicate the reaction, even in the perfused eye, by contracting the rectus muscles (p. 413). This causes enophthalmos and a rise of intraocular pressure because of the external pressure on the globe.

Other drugs. Atropine produces a slight fall in pressure in the normal eye. Duke-Elder found that the administration of trypan blue caused dilatation of the minute intraocular blood vessels and an increase in their permeability. He attributes the fall in pressure to relaxation of the tone of the unstriped muscle in the orbit. A rise in pressure of smaller degree which comes on later is regarded as the result of dilatation of the capillaries. In a normal animal the changes in intraocular pressure caused by the administration of atropine are quite insignificant when compared to its effect in a patient with obstructed angle glaucoma. In the normal eye, there is plenty of room in the angle to accommodate the iris as it dilates under the influence of atropine, and any change which occurs is probably due to its effect on the permeability of the capillaries.

Physostigmine dilates the capillaries and increases their permeability to protein. The dilatation of the capillaries causes a slight rise in intraocular pressure in the normal eye. In chronic simple glaucoma, both obstructed angle and open-angle types, the pressure is usually reduced by the administration of eserine.

The action of all miotic drugs is apparent in glaucoma of the obstructed angle type. The miosis pulls the iris away from the filtration angle and allows the aqueous humor to escape into the canal of Schlemm. On the other hand, it is not known how these drugs reduce the elevated pressure in chronic simple glaucoma of the open-angle type. The action of the drug cannot be to open the angle since it is open already. Further, in these patients drugs which dilate the pupil, such as atropine, do not produce elevation of the pressure to any degree. It has been suggested that this is due to diminution in the formation of aqueous humor,[46] but it has been shown that under the influence of these drugs patients with open-angle glaucoma show marked reduction in resistance to outflow.[47] The mechanism through which the outflow is facilitated is still obscure.

Barany[48] concludes that the effect of pilocarpine in open-angle glaucoma is complex. The facility of outflow of aqueous is increased by two components. The first is the effect of contraction of the ciliary muscle. It has been shown[49] that the intraocular pressure is reduced by contraction of the ciliary muscle in normal human beings, and this same action is achieved by the increase in tonus of the ciliary muscle under the influence of pilocarpine. This effect of pilocarpine is nullified within 3 to 5 minutes by an intravenous injection of atropine. The second component is thought to be a direct action of pilocarpine on the endothelial cells lining Schlemm's canal. Pilocarpine probably has a histamine-like effect on the endothelium, causing the cells to swell and to separate from one another in the wall of the canal.

The action of mydriatics and miotics in changing the intraocular pressure is still somewhat obscure. The action of mydriatics in precipitating an attack of acute glaucoma in a patient with a narrow angle can be readily explained by stating that the iris, by dilating, closes up the channel through which the aqueous humor must flow in order to reach the trabecular meshwork and the canal of Schlemm. Chandler[50] has suggested that the dilatation does not mechanically push the iris up against the trabecular wall, but that the dilatation of the pupil produces relaxation of the iris and allows the normal pressure in the posterior chamber to push the more yielding parts of the iris forward to close the angle. Previously, Scheie and Frayer[51] had suggested this same mechanism as the cause for the rise in intraocular pressure when air is injected into the anterior chamber of the eye.

In addition to the effect of atropine on the dilatation of the pupil and in blocking the filtration angle, Nash and Woodbury[52] give evidence that in dogs the administration of atropine, because of its vascular effects, modifies the circulation of the aqueous humor.

On the same grounds miotics pull the iris out of the angle and reinforce anchorage of the stroma of the iris to the sphincter when it is contracted.

Pilocarpine, eserine, and DFP are all parasympathomimetic drugs and provoke a strong contraction of the ciliary muscle. The anatomic diposition of the meshwork may be altered in some way by this contraction. It has also been suggested that these drugs have a vasomotor effect on either the canal of Schlemm or the scleral plexuses leading from the canal of Schlemm.[53]

Most drugs which affect the normal intraocular pressure lower it, and no drugs have been found which permanently elevate it.[54] In some patients continued use of steroids locally has been shown to produce glaucoma. It is probable that these eyes are predisposed to the disease. As yet nothing is known of the mode of action of the steroids in producing an elevation of pressure.

Changes in osmotic pressure of the blood. Intraocular pressure may be altered by changing the osmotic pressure of the blood, as previously shown. If the concentration of the crystalloids in the blood is increased, as by injection of a hypertonic salt solution, intraocular pressure is lowered independently of any change in general blood pressure. Since the injection of saline solution into the bloodstream finally results in the passage of the salt out of the blood into the tissues, the lowering of intraocular pressure is but momentary. If substances such as sorbitol or urea to which the blood-aqueous barrier is less permeable are injected, a considerable reduction of intraocular pressure may be obtained and last for some time. If the blood is made hypotonic, water will leave the blood vessels at normal pressures and enter the aqueous humor. This results in a rise in intraocular pressure.

Alterations in the concentration of colloids in the bloodstream lead to changes in osmotic pressure of the blood and cause marked and lasting changes in intraocular pressure. If the concentration of colloids in the blood is increased by an intravenous injection of 15% gum acacia, the intraocular pressure will fall, whereas if the colloids of the blood are diminished by removing the corpuscles and replacing them with an equal volume of isotonic saline, the intraocluar pressure will rise.

Changes in hydrogen ion concentration of the blood. Normal intraocular pressure depends somewhat indirectly upon the reaction of the blood. It can be shown experimentally that increasing the alkalinity of the blood increases the pressure, but it is difficult to alter the hydrogen ion concentration of the blood without at the same time changing its osmotic properties.

The changes in pressure in the eye caused by altering the pH of the blood are claimed by most authors to be due to swelling or shrinking of the vitreous body. Since the blood is kept very constant in its pH by buffer systems, it is unlikely that alterations in pH occur in the animal body which could cause any change in intraocular pressure. Alterations in the metabolic activity of the vitreous body might conceivably cause changes in its reaction which lead to volume changes, but they have not been demonstrated. In patients with glaucoma who have been examined, the hydrogen ion concentration and osmotic pressure of the blood have been found to be within normal limits by most observers.

One of the characteristic signs of diabetic coma is a very low intraocular pressure. The hypotonia is probably not due to an increase in crystalloids in the blood, for this is kept fairly constant, an increase in glucose and ketonic acid being compensated for by a corresponding loss of chlorides.

Alterations in intraocular pressure due to formation and elimination of the aqueous humor

As a result of the constant accumulation of aqueous humor in the anterior chamber and the constant exit of this fluid, the volume of the contents of the eye must depend upon the balance which is struck between these opposing processes. The volume of fluid in the anterior chamber must be maintained, in part by a balance between the rate at which fluid enters the eye and the rate at which it leaves. When the factors are in equilibrium, there will be a definite quantity of fluid coming into the eye from the blood, and the same quantity will be leaving the eye in unit time. The volume of the fluid present will be kept constant, therefore, and the intraocular pressure will be maintained at a constant level. The intraocular pressure will be increased if either the rate of formation of fluid is increased or the rate of outflow is diminished. Similarly, the intraocular pressure will fall if the rate of formation is diminished or the rate of outflow is increased.

Kinsey[55] has pointed out that if the osmotic pressure of the aqueous humor is higher than that of the plasma by about 5 mM/L. equivalent of sodium chloride this small difference in concentration would be capable of creating a relatively enormous difference in pressure, as it would between two solutions when separated by a semipermeable membrane, i.e., one which will permit the passage of water but not the dissolved material.

A simple calculation will show that theoretically a difference of 5 mM/L. in concentration can cause an intraocular pressure of approximately 170 mm. Hg. The calculation is as follows: A difference in concentration of 1 mol of an ion on two sides of such a membrane will create a pressure of 22.4 atm. or 17,000 mm. Hg (22.4 atm. × 760 mm. Hg/atm.). Since sodium chloride dissociates into two ions, 1 molar difference in concentration of sodium chloride would cause a pressure of 34,000 mm. Hg. Thus a difference of 5 mM/L. in concentration would equal 0.005 × 34,000 = 170 mm. Hg.

In addition to this force, a hydrostatic force of 50 mm. Hg is available afforded by the capillary pressure in the eye. Thus, a total pressure of 220 mm. Hg. is available, tending to move water into the anterior chamber which, if allowed to build up, would create an intraocular pressure of 220 mm. Hg.

This pressure is never able to develop in the eye, however, because there is a constant outflow of fluid. The outflow in the human being is about 2 μl per minute.[56]

As a result of the outflow of fluid, the intraocular pressure under normal conditions is only about one tenth of the totally available pressure. According to this conception the following factors are of significance in maintaining intraocular pressure.

1. The rate of outflow: Any factor which changes the rate of outflow will be extremely effective in producing changes in intraocular pressure.

2. The difference in osmotic pressure between the aqueous humor and blood.

3. The hydrostatic pressure of the blood: This as has been shown, is a relatively minor factor and accounts for the fact that large changes in blood pressure effect a relatively small change in intraocular pressure.

These relationships may be more readily visualized from the following schema:

$$\text{IOP} = k \ [\text{OP}_{Aq} - \text{OP}_{Pl}) + \text{CP}]$$
$$\text{IOP} = k \times (170 \text{ mm. Hg} + 50 \text{ mm. Hg})$$
$$\text{IOP} = k \times 220 \text{ mm. Hg}$$

IOP = intraocular pressure; OP_{Aq} = osmotic pressure of aqueous humor; OP_{Pl} = osmotic pressure of plasma; CP = capillary pressure; k = a factor

The resistance to outflow is expressed by k. Thus, the less the resistance (greater outflow), the lower the pressure will be. Experience shows that k is generally equivalent to 0.1. Hence the intraocular pressure is maintained normally at about 22 mm. Hg.

This concept beautifully fits all of the observed phenomena connected with normal intraocular pressure and logically explains most of the abnormal changes seen clinically. It is not known exactly where the aqueous humor meets its greatest resistance on its way out of the eye. Three possible sites have been considered, and experimental evidence has been offered for each.

1. Schlemm's canal[57-59]
2. Caliber variations of the collector channels and of the intrascleral vessels (Kleinert)
3. Trabecular meshwork[60-62]

Rohen[57] comes to the conclusion that the site of resistance to aqueous outflow lies in the inner wall of Schlemm's canal. He believes that an "endothelium-basement-membrane-system" exists as an active mechanism which regulates and varies the rate of aqueous outflow.

The following are some examples of changes in intraocular pressure induced by variations in the factors which normally maintain the pressure at physiologic levels.

1. Normal intraocular pressure in most of the laboratory animals is approximately 20 to 25 mm. Hg. This is consistent with the theory on the basis of experimentally observed rate of outflow, of the difference in osmotic pressure between the aqueous humor and blood, and of the generally accepted value of the capillary hydrostatic pressure. The relatively small influence of changes in blood pressure on the intraocular pressure follows from the fact that the hydrostatic pressure contributes only one fourth of the total available pressure (50 mm. Hg out of a total of 220 mm. Hg).

If, for example, the hydrostatic pressure is raised 100% (from 50 to 100 mm. Hg), the increase in the total available pressure rises only 23% (from 220 to 270 mm. Hg).

2. Changing the difference in osmotic pressure between the aqueous humor and blood by only a slight amount produces a large change in intraocular pressure. It has been shown that a difference of only 5 mM/L. sodium chloride equivalent accounts for an available pressure of 170 mm. Hg. A difference of 1 mM/L. sodium chloride equivalent, therefore, will produce a change in available pressure of 34 mm. Hg. Provided that no compensating mechanism such as an increase in the rate of flow of fluid out of the eye comes into the situation, an increase in the difference in osmotic pressure between aqueous humor and blood of 1 mM/L. sodium chloride equivalent will change the intraocular pressure from 22 mm. Hg to 25.4 mm. Hg, and a decrease of 1 mM/L. will lower it to 18.6 mm. Hg.

It has been shown that the total osmotic pressure available from the proteins of the blood is only 30 mm. Hg. A change in concentration of the protein fraction of the serum, therefore, will cause very slight changes in intraocular pressure. None of the disease conditions in which there is hypoproteinemia, or the reverse should produce much change in the intraocular pressure, and this is generally the case. Nephritic patients, with considerable loss of blood proteins, show no change in intraocular pressure.

Any change in the salt concentration of the blood, on the other hand, will produce large changes in intraocular pressure, until they are compensated. This affords us a reasonable explanation of the changes which occur in intraocular pressure when the serum is diluted by drinking large amounts of water during a short period of time. These changes, which are observable in normal persons, occur to a marked degree in patients who have open-angle glaucoma. When such a patient drinks a quart of water, the intraocular pressure generally increases considerably.

The water-drinking test has a reliability of approximately 70%.[63] Next to this, the Priscoline test has a reliability of 60%. In both these tests the facility of outflow changes but little. Both tests are effective in increasing the total flow of the aqueous humor, and in the water-drinking test this increased total flow can be diminished by the administration of acetazolamide. The principle underlying the rise in pressure may be illustrated as follows.

By diluting the blood, the concentration of salt falls, reducing the osmotic pressure of the plasma. It will be assumed that before the ingestion of the water, the total molecular concentration of the plasma was 160 mM/L. and that of the aqueous humor 165 mM/L. sodium chloride equivalent.

Table 20 shows the changes which theoretically could take place in the relationships in osmotic pressure between plasma and the aqueous humor and how these changes would affect the intraocular pressure. Such marked changes probably would never occur in normal circumstances because they are compensated, and these values are used merely for illustration.

The intraocular pressure is normal (1) before the ingestion of water. By (2) the osmotic pressure of the plasma has begun to fall, and the intraocular pressure is slightly elevated. This continues at (3), although by this time the water is beginning to leave the tissues and gets into the eye, diluting the aqueous humor slightly. The fall in osmotic pressure of the blood continues, and at (4) the osmotic pressure of plasma and the aqueous humor has attained a difference of 15 mM/L. sodium chloride equivalent, raising the intraocular pressure to 56.0 mm. Hg. At (5) the osmotic pressure of the blood is beginning to rise, whereas that of the aqueous humor is still falling. This situation continues through (6, 7, and 8), at which time the difference between the osmotic pressure of the aqueous humor and that of the plasma has

Table 20

Reading number	Time	Plasma osmotic pressure (mM/L.)	Aqueous humor osmotic pressure	Difference $OP_{Aq} - OP_{Pl}$	Intraocular pressure (mm. Hg)
1	10:00	160	165	+ 5	22.0
		1 qt. water ingested			
2	10:15	158	165	+ 7	28.8
3	10:30	154	164	+10	39.0
4	10:45	148	163	+15	56.0
5	11:00	152	160	+ 8	32.2
6	11:15	154	159	+ 5	22.0
7	11:30	156	158	+ 2	11.8
8	11:45	160	161	+ 1	8.4
9	12:00	160	164	+ 4	18.6
10	12:15	160	165	+ 5	22.0

fallen to 1 mM/L., and accordingly the intraocular pressure drops to 8.4 mm. Hg. Following this, the osmotic pressures of both fluids gradually return to their previous levels, and the intraocular pressure returns to normal.

3. Any interference with the outflow of the aqueous humor by way of Schlemm's canal results in an immediate and marked change in intraocular pressure. If the outflow of the aqueous humor is entirely prevented, the intraocular pressure could rise to the level of the available pressure inherent in the mechanisms just described, i.e., to 220 mm. Hg. It has always been difficult to explain the high pressures observed clinically in patients with absolute glaucoma on the basis of a theory of filtration or dialysis since, according to these theories, the intraocular pressure could never rise above the available hydrostatic pressure in the capillary bed. Although there are no available records of the height which the intraocular pressure can reach in man when the outflow mechanism is completely closed, tonometric readings of 80 to 90 mm. Hg are occasionally found. The tonometer is not suitable for measuring pressure in this range, and it is likely that higher pressures would be recorded by manometry.

4. It seems paradoxical that in many patients with acute inflammatory disease of the anterior segment, even when the aqueous humor shows a marked flare and is full of cells and fibrin, the pressure, instead of being elevated, is frequently subnormal. This hypotonia is caused by the equalization of the osmotic pressures of the aqueous humor and the plasma by an amount of protein in the anterior chamber equal to the amount in the serum and, what is more important, by the loss of the barrier to diffusion of electrolytes out of the anterior chamber. The blood vessels of the iris, being dilated, allow diffusion of the substances, which accounts for the higher osmotic pressure of the aqueous humor back into the bloodstream, and accordingly the 5 mM/L. of excess osmotic pressure in the aqueous humor disappears or at least diminishes. It has been shown that this will result in a lowering of the intraocular pressure well below normal levels.

Many patients with inflammatory disease of the anterior segment go through phases of high and low intraocular pressure, and it can be assumed that at one moment blocking of the outflow of aqueous by cells and fibrin raises the pressure, whereas at another moment, the equalization of osmotic pressure reduces the intraocular pressure. The combination of these two forces in varying proportions will determine what the intraocular pressure will be.

In many eyes with secondary glaucoma studied histologically, there is evidence of blockage of the avenues of escape of fluid from the eye. The increased viscosity of the aqueous humor from cells and fibrin may retard the outflow of the aqueous humor and lead to deposition of material in the trabeculae so that the fluid cannot get into Schlemm's canal. Adhesions of the iris to the cornea in the iris angle may shut off the approach of the aqueous humor to Schlemm's canal. As a result, the fluid is dammed back in the anterior chamber, and the intraocular pressure is elevated. In most of these patients the anterior chamber is deeper than normal, and tonographic measurements[64] show that the increased pressure is caused by increased resistance to outflow of the aqueous humor.

5. A fall in intraocular pressure can be induced by the administration of a carbonic anhydrase inhibitor, such as acetazolamide. It has been pointed out (p. 103) that in some species the bi-

carbonate ion is present in aqueous humor in higher concentration than it is in blood. It was postulated by Friedenwald and Kinsey that the bicarbonate ion which is catalyzed by an enzyme, carbonic anhydrase, is secreted into the aqueous humor from the parent blood. The enzyme carbonic anhydrase would then by an important part of this mechanism. Subsequently it was shown by Becker that certain drugs, which inhibit carbonic anhydrase, notably acetazolamide (Diamox) cause partial suppression of the secretion of aqueous humor, with resulting lowering of the intraocular pressure. In rabbits and guinea pigs, which have a high concentration of bicarbonate in their aqueous humor, the mechanism by means of which acetazolamide suppresses the secretion of aqueous humor was interpreted to be due to its action as a carbonic anhydrase inhibitor, since there is a rapid fall in the amount of bicarbonate in the aqueous humor well correlated with a decrease in secretion of aqueous humor and with the lowering of the intraocular pressure.

This conception of the action of acetazolamide runs into difficulties in those species in which bicarbonate is not present in excess in the aqueous humor over that in blood plasma, which is true for man. Becker[65, 66] showed that in human beings the administration of Diamox resulted in other alterations in the chemistry of the aqueous humor. The drug partially abolished the excess of chloride in the aqueous humor, and at the same time there was an increase in the concentration of bicarbonate. The pH of the aqueous humor, which in human beings lies below that of the plasma, was elevated. It has been shown repeatedly that the drug is ineffective in lowering the intraocular pressure when injected subconjunctivally, intraocularly, and intraarteri-

ally, although the activity of carbonic anhydrase is probably inhibited. Further, Langham and Lee[67] have shown that ammonium chloride, which is not a specific carbonic anhydrase inhibitor, lowers the intraocular pressure, and the fall in bicarbonate content of the aqueous humor corresponds to a similar fall in that of the blood.

Duke-Elder believes that there is no evidence that acetazolamide has any effect on a secretory mechanism, but that its hypotensive action can best be explained by a decrease in the base-binding capacity of the blood. This disturbs the relationship between the osmotic pressure of blood and aqueous tumor, presumably reducing the hypertonicity of the aqueous humor. Becker considers the simplest assumption is as follows.

"The enzyme provides bicarbonate buffering capacity directly to the secretory cell or cells. Thus, the cell secreting an acid may itself sustain a rise in pH. This requires buffering much as does the acidosis of the cell secreting an alkaline product. The less adequate buffering capacity introduced by carbonic anhydrase inhibitors results in a partial suppression of the secretory process."*

A still different concept of the mechanism of acetazolamide in lowering the intraocular pressure has been suggested by Macri.[69] Macri had found that the intraocular pressure at steady state is dependent upon the venous pressure, and that a 1:1 relationship exists between venous pressure and iris artery pressure.[70] Since acetazolamide produced a sustained increase in resistance to perfusate flow through the iris arteries in the cat in his experiments, he concluded that the action of acetazolamide in lowering intraocular pressure is due to constriction of the arterial vessels of the iris. This decreases

---

*From Becker, B.: Arch. Ophth. **58:**86, 1957.

the volume and pressure within the vessels of the ciliary body and/or choroid, which diminishes the intraocular pressure by decreasing the bulk volume within the eye.

Kass and Green,[71] as noted on p. 110, found the osmotic pressure of the anterior chamber aqueous to be considerably hypertonic to blood plasma, whereas the osmotic pressure of the aqueous humor of the posterior chamber was nearly equal to that of blood plasma. They found that Diamox considerably decreased the osmotic pressure of the anterior chamber aqueous humor, but did not affect the osmotic pressure of the posterior chamber aqueous humor; hence they deny any action of Diamox in changing the osmotic pressure relationships of aqueous humor as it is formed from the blood in the ciliary processes.

In summary, it can be said that the exact mechanism by means of which Diamox reduces the inflow of fluid into the eye is not at all clear, although there is no question that carbonic anhydrase seems to have something to do with the formation of aqueous humor. Green[72] has put very clearly the requirements which are basic for any proof that an enzyme is a primary determinant of any physiologic process. According to him these are the following.

"(1) The reaction mediated by the enzyme is fundamentally related to the physiologic processes; (2) inhibition of the enzyme activity results in a disruption or suppression of the physiologic processes, dependent upon the enzyme activity, with either an accumulation of the substrate of the reaction or a disappearance or decrease in the concentration of the product of the reaction; (3) the existence of a good correlation between the rate of the physiologic processes and the rate of the enzymatic reaction."*

------

*From Green, H.: Am. J. Ophth. **49:**385, 1960.

The evidence in support of carbonic anhydrase having a primary part in aqueous humor formation consists of the following: a potent carbonic anhydrase such as Diamox injected intravenously inhibits the enzyme in the anterior uvuea of the rabbit eye, produces a lowering of the bicarbonate ion concentration in the aqueous humors, and reduces the rate of flow of aqueous humor and hence the intraocular pressure. Other evidence, however, has been brought forward to prove that carbonic anhydrase cannot be directly concerned in the formation of aqueous humor as just outlined. This evidence has been summarized by Green as follows.

"Subconjunctival injections of Diamox completely inhibit the carbonic anhydrase activity of the anterior uvea of the rabbit, but have no apparent effect on either the bicarbonate ion concentration of the aqueous or on the rate of inflow of aqueous, and the intraocular pressure. There is a lack of correlation between the biochemical parameters of the aqueous humor and the pharmacological responses which cannot be reconciled on the basis of any theory of the action of Diamox on carbonic anhydrase."*

Cardiac glycosides such as digoxin and ouabain have been found to lower the intraocular pressure of human beings and to decrease the rate of aqueous humor formation in experimental animals.[73] This effect is supposed to be the inhibition of the enzyme sodium potassium-activated adenosine triphosphatase in the ciliary epithelium. Becker has found that intravitreous injection of ouabain is more effective than intravenous injection, and suggests that the sodium potassium-adenosine triphosphatase transport system is more sensitive to inhibition by ouabain approaching it from the vitreous than from the bloodstream.[74]

------

*From Green, H.: Am. J. Ophth. **49:**385, 1960.

Hypothermia. Lowering the temperature of the body of experimental animals results in a profound decrease in the rate of formation of aqueous humor and a fall in the intraocular pressure. At a body temperature of 19° to 20° C. the rate of aqueous humor formation is reduced to approximately 10 to 20% of normal.[75-77] It is probable that many different factors involved in aqueous humor production are adversely affected by low temperatures, and at the present time one cannot deduce from this phenomenon much information regarding the mechanisms of aqueous humor formation. The facility of aqueous humor outflow is diminished by hypothermia, probably due to the increased viscosity of aqueous humor at low temperatures, but in spite of this the fall in aqueous humor formation is so much greater that the net result is a marked lowering of intraocular pressure.

TONOMETRY

Tonometry is the usual method of obtaining a quantitative measurement of the intraocular pressure in human beings. Unlike manometry, it is an indirect method and thereby suffers from discrepancies—in fact, so many that Schiøtz, whose instrument is now the recognized standard, advised against interpreting the recorded readings in millimeters of mercury. In spite of his exhortation, however, it is customary to translate the tonometric reading into millimeters of mercury and to consider this the intraocular pressure.

In principle the tonometer is an instrument which applies a determined weight on a known area of the cornea and measures the impressibility of the cornea by this weight. In addition to determining the intraocular pressure, a tonometric reading, therefore, also measures the rigidity of the ocular coats. Other factors also determine the tonometric reading. These factors include the following: (1) the volume of the corneal indentation produced by the tonometer plunger, (2) the distortion of the cornea by the footplate, irrespective of the indentation by the plunger, (3) the expulsion of intraocular fluid by the weight used, (4) the manner in which the tonometer is applied, and (5) the mechanical accuracy of the tonometer itself, according to whether it was made accurately and whether it is functioning properly, i.e., devoid of friction.

A form of tonometry called applanation tonometry[78] is based on the principle that the pressure in a sphere filled with liquid and surrounded by an infinitely thin membrane can be measured by the counterpressure necessary to flatten this membrane to a plane.

Whenever a tonometer such as the Schiøtz tonometer is applied to the eye the internal pressure of the eye is increased by the identation of the plunger. The pressure which is recorded by the tonometer is, therefore, somewhat higher than the actual internal pressure of the globe before the tonometer was applied. Since relatively heavy weights are employed in the Schiøtz tonometer, this increase in internal pressure due to the change in internal volume is considerable. If P_o is the actual pressure before the tonometer is applied, the recorded pressure P_t may be significantly higher. The magnitude of this increase is a function of the elasticity of the ocular coats so that any single calibration is valid only for a given figure of normal elasticity. The Schiøtz scale has been calibrated to read directly in the P_o values of an eye with average scleral rigidity and, therefore, average volume change. If the eye being examined does not have average scleral rigidity, the value of P_t may be markedly different from the true intraocular pressure P_o. For this reason the Schiøtz tonometer cannot be entirely relied on to give accurate readings of the intraocular pressure. If the scleral rigidity is low, the tonometric reading will be too low, and if the scleral rigidity is high, the reading will be higher than the actual internal pressure.

The scleral rigidity can be calculated, however, when it is deemed expedient to check the tonometric readings. This is done by taking the pressure with the tonometer using several different weights. By using Friedenwald's 1955 pressure rigidity nomogram for the Schiøtz tonometer, shown in Fig. 46, the scleral rigidity factor can be determined, and the corrected intraocular pressure can be obtained. As Olmstead[78a] points out, this is only a rough approximation, as there is a very small spread of the V_c (volume change) values obtained with the available weight variations, and the factor of corneal curvature also changes the results.

For this reason, applanation tonometry has recently gained considerable favor as a means of determining the intraocular pressure with the factor of scleral rigidity eliminated.

The applanation tonometer differs from the indentation type, such as the Schiøtz tonometer, in that the displacement is constant and minimal. The cornea is indented to the same degree in each eye examined, and the force necessary to produce this constant indentation is measured. In the Schiøtz tonometer, the force applied is constant, i.e., the weight of the plunger (i.e., the plunger itself and added weights, 5.5 Gm., 7.5 Gm., etc.)

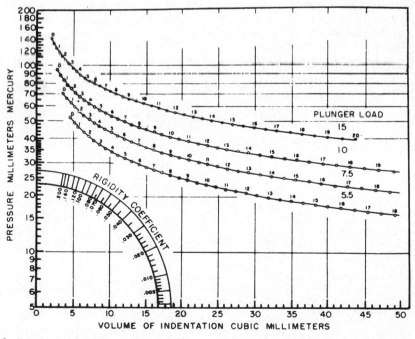

Fig. 46. Friedenwald 1955 pressure rigidity nomogram for Schiøtz tonometer. (From Olmstead, E.: Arch. Ophth. 62:140, 1959.)

and the amount of indentation vary and are measured (the scale reading).

The actual indentation by the applanation tonometer of Goldmann is an area of 3.06 mm., and the force used to obtain this area of indentation is read directly. By this means scleral rigidity is eliminated from the reading.

Phillips and Quick[79] performed experiments on hollow water-filled rubber spheres and found that a given change in volume produced by indentation results in a change in pressure which is an inverse function of the initial volume of the sphere. Hence, eyes which are larger than the standard eye for which the Schiøtz tonometer was calibrated will give too low a reading, whereas those eyes which are smaller will give an abnormally high reading.

Sampson and Girard[80] confirm Phillips and Quick's findings that the factor of structural pliancy of the scleral walls is an important cause of the discrepancies between the findings of indentation and applanation tonometry. They find that the effect of the variation of the initial intraocular volume is of greater importance and must be considered along with variations in scleral rigidity.

TONOGRAPHY

Moses and Bruno[81] and Grant[82] have computed the rate of outflow of aqueous humor in normal eyes by making continuous recordings of intraocular pressure with an electric tonometer, with variable pressures applied to the eye. Normal eyes show an average facility of outflow of 0.22 c.mm./min./mm. pressure, the individual values ranging from 0.11 to 0.44 c.mm. The normal net rate of flow (or rate of formation of aqueous humor) averages 2.4 c.mm./min, with a range of from 1.1 to 5.3 c.mm. Age does not seem to be a factor in determining either facility of outflow or rate of formation. In every instance measurements made in glaucomatous eyes show the elevation of tension above normal to be due exclusively to an abnormal resistance to outflow of the aqueous humor (Fig. 47). No case of glaucoma due to hyperformation of aqueous humor was observed by Grant. In obstructed angle glaucoma, the resistance to outflow and the degree of closure of the angle as estimated by gonioscopic examination were well correlated. In open-angle glaucoma a decreased facility of outflow of the aqueous humor was found consistently, although the angle was open gonioscopically. In secondary glaucoma, an obstruction to the outflow of aqueous humor also seemed to be responsible for the elevation of pressure. However, this form of glaucoma was peculiar in that spontaneous return to normal or low pressure levels in some cases was the result of return of facility of outflow to normal, whereas in others it was apparently the result of a decrease in rate of formation of the aqueous humor, with abnormal resistance to outflow persisting. Surgical treatment in general was beneficial only when it improved the facility of outflow of the aqueous humor. Treatment with miotics also seemed to be effective principally in improving the facility of outflow of the aqueous humor, but in a small proportion of cases there was some indication of a depressant effect on the formation of aqueous humor.

Tonography can yield useful information on both the rate of formation of aqueous humor and the resistance to its outflow from the eye. It was shown on p. 136 that the resistance, R, is equal to $\dfrac{P_o - P_v}{F}$ where P_o is the intraocular pressure, P_v is the episcleral venous pressure,

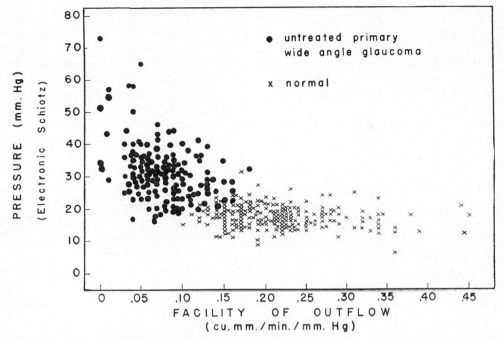

Fig. 47. Comparison of the intraocular pressure and facility of outflow of the aqueous in 118 normal eyes and 75 untreated glaucomatous eyes. (From Grant, W.: Arch. Ophth. 46:116, 1951.)

and F is the rate of formation of aqueous humor.

The reciprocal of the resistance is the facility of outflow, C. This may be determined by the following equation:

$$C = \frac{\Delta V}{t \,(\text{average } P_t - P_o)}$$

Where ΔV is the change in ocular volume for the initial and final tonometric readings, P_t is the intraocular pressure during tonography, and P_o is the intraocular pressure immediately before tonography.

C, the facility of outflow, is expressed as cubic millimeters per minute per millimeter pressure. In a study designed to determine the accuracy of methods employed in clinical tonography, Scheie and associates[83] found no significant change in C values in different age groups in normal eyes. The C value was 0.16

c.mm./min./mm. pressure in 94% of normal eyes. A probable error of approximately 0.04 c.mm./min./mm. pressure must be assumed for any one tracing on a given eye. Any value of C below 0.16 should be regarded as suspicious.

The net rate of outflow (equivalent to the rate of formation) is calculated by the following formula:

$$k = C(P_o - P_v)$$

Where k is the net rate of flow expressed as cubic millimeters per minute, C is the coefficient of facility of outflow of aqueous humor, P_o is the intraocular pressure immediately before tonography, and P_v is the episcleral venous pressure. The value now accepted for the episcleral venous pressure is 8 mm. Hg. Grant[84] gives the following values (Table 21) for the normal.

Table 21. *Normal values of episcleral venous pressure according to Grant*

C = 0.233	
P_o = 13.5 mm.	
P_v = 8 mm.	
F (k) = 1.69 cu. mm./min.	

Somewhat similar values (Table 22) are reported for the normal by Goldmann[85]

Table 22. *Normal values of episcleral venous pressure according to Goldmann*

Normal intraocular pressure = 14.5 mm. Hg
C = 0.135
Outflow pressure = 5 mm. Hg (approximately)
Flow = 1.9 cu. mm. /min.

The facility of outflow varies in different species. Becker[86] found the following values for the facility of outflow of aqueous humor in various species (Table 23).

Table 23. *Coefficient of facility of outflow of aqueous humor in various species*

Cat	1.54
Rabbit	0.35
Guinea pig	0.08

Although the coefficient of facility of outflow varies considerably if one calculates the formation of aqueous expressed as the per cent of the volume of the anterior chamber, the figures are remarkably alike in the different species, from 1.3 to 1.6% in all four species, including man.

Sufficient data have now been collected to allow at least an approximate calculation of the factors influencing the resistance to outflow of the aqueous humor in both a normal eye and one with open-angle glaucoma. McEwen[87] has pre-

sented some interesting conclusions by using Poiseuille's law in connection with the normal facility of outflow and the pressures developed when the facility is diminished. He cautions, of course, that these calculations are only as good as the data, offered by other authors, which must be used in the equations. Also Poiseuille's law is strictly applicable only when two important conditions are met. The flow must be laminar and the tube should be cylindrical. The first criterion is met in the case of the outflow of the aqueous humor, but the criterion of a cylindrical hole is based on the premise that the length is considerably greater than the diameter. McEwen states that even our best assumptions do not seem to meet this condition. Since, however, Poiseuille's law does apply to filter beds which are composed of a network of interstices and do not have tubular holes, it seems reasonable to accept its application here. He finds that, if the total outflow of aqueous humor were confined to only one opening, that hole need only be 12 μ in diameter. The trabecular network, having interstices greater than 12 μ, cannot contribute to the resistance to outflow. Hence McEwen feels the uveal and corneoscleral openings described by Flocks[88] are not a factor in the normal resistance to outflow. Using a figure at the lowest extreme of uniform holes of 0.6 μ in diameter, McEwen calculates that some 110,000 holes would be needed. Since the filtration area of the eye is calculated to be about 11 mm.^{2}, it follows that there would have to be about 10,000 holes per each square millimeter. If one assumes an average somewhere between the two extremes if each hole measured 2 μ, 1200 holes would be needed, which is about 1 hole in a square 0.1 mm. on a side. This can be visualized by drawing a square 100 mm. on each side and placing a circle 2 mm. in diameter in its center.

The major resistance to the outflow of aqueous humor is due to a low-porosity tissue barrier with holes about 2 μ in diameter every 0.01^2. Open-angle glaucoma, according to McEwen, is due to a decrease in the diameter of these holes by a change too small to be detected histologically, since changes in the diameter of the individual holes would produce very large changes in the facility of outflow. If the diameter of each hole is reduced by one half, the facility of outflow would be decreased by one sixteenth and the pressure drop ($P_o - P_v$) would increase sixteen times, raising the intraocular pressure from 15 mm. Hg to 90 mm. Hg. If the diameter were reduced by one quarter, the intraocular pressure would rise to 27 mm. Hg. On the other hand, diminution in the number of holes without any change in the diameter of the holes would not be nearly as effective in decreasing the facility of outflow. It would require that three quarters of the holes be closed in order to produce a pressure rise to 30 mm. Hg. It is reasonable to suppose that since no detectable changes have been found in the channels of outflow in open-angle glaucoma the increase in resistance is due to a diminution in the diameter of the pores, which as McEwen points out could still be so small as to be undetectable by measurements and yet raise the pressure to the levels occurring in this disease.

Consensual changes in intraocular pressure. It has been known for a long time that manipulation of one eye may produce changes in intraocular pressure not only of that eye but also of the opposite undisturbed eye. Trauma and even massage of an eye produce an immediate fall in intraocular pressure in this eye and simultaneously in the opposite eye. The fall in pressure was termed the *ophthalmotonic consensual reaction*[89] and is now now generally called the consensual intraocular pressure reaction.

The fall in pressure in the undisturbed eye is generally small, from 1 to 4 mm. Hg, but is statistically significant. The degree of trauma to one eye necessary to elicit a fall in intraocular pressure in the other eye may be extremely slight. Even resting a tonometer on an eye for several minutes may cause a fall in pressure in the fellow eye.[90] The occurence of the consensual reaction is common after tonography.

The mechanism of the consensual reaction has been disputed: The most obvious explanation would be that changes in blood pressure are induced by manipulation of one eye, such as a fall in pressure due to slowing of the pulse by the oculocardiac reflex, and that this fall in blood pressure was accompanied by a fall in intraocular pressure in the opposite eye. This cannot be the explanation, however, as it has been shown that the consensual fall in intraocular pressure occurs with no changes in either blood pressure or pulse rate.[91]

Evidence has been presented that the consensual fall in pressure is associated with a reduced flow of aqueous humor, while the coefficient of facility of outflow, the episcleral venous pressure, and the ocular rigidity remain normal. In rabbits systemically atropinized, the consensual reaction does not occur, which suggests that the parasympathetic nervous system is concerned in the reflex.

Changes in the circulation of the fellow eye on the basis of neural or hormonal transmission have been postulated, and the effect has been used as evidence for the existence of hypothalamic centers controlling intraocular pressure. An increase in the tonus of some of the extraocular muscles of the fellow eye has likewise been suggested, produced by proprioceptive impulses from the muscles of the eye being examined. The various theories have been reviewed by Perkins.[92] Recently Grant and English[93] have given convincing evidence that the effect is due to loss of fluid by evaporation from the eye which is kept open during the tonography in order to maintain fixation. The consensual drop in pressure is eliminated if this eye is covered with a plastic film which prevents evaporation from the cornea but still permits the eye to be used for fixation.

PATHOLOGIC PHYSIOLOGY OF GLAUCOMA

Much of the material in this section has already been developed in the preceding pages and will be reassembled here to present a picture of the changes which lead to the maintenance of an intraocular pressure higher than the normal. It has already been stressed that there is a wide range of physiologic values for intraocular pressure but that a persistent pressure of 25 mm. Hg or over should indicate the condition called glaucoma. By definition *glaucoma* is a term applied to a number of conditions having in common one sign, i.e., a persistent elevation of intraocular pressure. For those conditions in which the elevated pressure is obviously the result of some antecedent disease such as uveitis, the term *secondary glaucoma* is applied. For those conditions in which no obvious cause is present, the term *simple glaucoma* is used. *Acute* and *chronic* are terms generally applied to the patient whose disease either develops suddenly and with devastating severity (acute) or slowly and insidiously (chronic). The term *acute glaucoma*, however, is now usually restricted for those patients in whom the

disease develops suddenly and with devastating severity due to one condition, i.e., obstruction to the filtration angle.

Glaucoma is not a disease entity but a sign that something has gone wrong with the pressure-regulating mechanism in the eye, in much the same manner that fever is not regarded as a disease but as a manifestation that something has disturbed the temperature-controlling mechanism of the body. All glaucoma is secondary to something. The terms *primary* and *simple* should be eliminated as the factor or factors which produce the rise in intraocular pressure in each different type of glaucoma are discovered. Two types of glaucoma are now reasonably understood. Angle-closure glaucoma has been solved, and open-angle glaucoma is well on the way to solution. We are not sure what causes the rise in pressure in iridocyclitis, thrombosis of the central retinal vein, dislocation of the lens into the vitreous, intraocular tumors, epidemic dropsy, infantile glaucoma and many other types, but we may make reasonable guesses how these glaucomas are produced. For this purpose the physiology will be reviewed, and a division of the various types of glaucoma seen clinically will be attempted on this basis.

The factors responsible for the maintenance of the normal intraocular pressure are as follows:

1. Elasticity of cornea and sclera
2. Volume of intraocular contents
   (a) Volume of blood in uveal tract
   (b) Volume of aqueous
   (c) Volume of vitreous
   (d) Volume of lens
3. Difference in osmotic pressure of plasma and aqueous humor

Elasticity of the ocular coats

The internal pressure of the eye is influenced by the scleral rigidity in that a small increase in the internal volume of the eye will cause a greater pressure rise in a globe whose coats are more rigid than normal and a lesser pressure rise if the coats are less rigid. The measurement of the intraocular pressure by any method of indentation tonometry will be influenced by the scleral rigidity. A rigid sclera will give rise to a higher internal pressure (lower Schiøtz scale reading) and a less rigid sclera will give a lower internal pressure (higher scale reading). This factor is eliminated by applanation tonometry.

Volume of the contents of the globe
Solid contents

The volume of the iris, lens, vitreous solids, retina, and choroid account in part for the internal pressure of the eye. Under normal conditions these do not change to any appreciable degree after full growth has been attained and what changes do take place with age are compensated, so that the internal pressure is not affected materially. Sudden alterations in volume, as are induced by swelling of the lens, can cause abrupt rises in intraocular pressure. Changes in volume of the vitreous with changes in pH, salt concentration, etc., can be produced in vitro but do not take place in the body as far as is known.

Fluid contents

The amount of fluid present in the eye at any one time is the chief determinant of the intraocular pressure. The volume of the three different fluids present—vitreous fluid, blood, and aqueous humor—must be considered separately.

Vitreous fluid. The vitreous body is very largely fluid. If the normal vitreous body of an animal's eye is placed on a filter paper in a glass funnel, the fluid separates from the solid portion, and almost the entire volume of the original vitreous body will be found in the glass beaker below the funnel. The portion remaining on the filter paper is very small. As stated previously, the volume of a gel can be changed considerably under altered conditions of its milieu, but in the human body the milieu is kept so constant that volume changes of the vitreous never occur.

Blood. The amount of blood circulating within the eye is subject to considerable change which could produce sufficient alteration in the volume of the intraocular contents to affect the intraocular pressure. The amount of blood in the choriocapillaris does affect the intraocular pressure, and any alteration in this reservoir of blood will change the intraocular pressure accordingly. An obstruction to the outflow of venous blood from the eye will cause marked temporary elevation of pressure. Changes in arterial pressure in the head area, on the other hand, produce little change in intraocular pressure—generally about one tenth that of the arterial pressure change. The intraocular pressure is not elevated in generalized high blood pressure because the factor which brings about the hyperpiesia is constriction of the arterioles. The arterioles of the ophthalmic artery constrict, as do those of the splanchnic vessels, and therefore no increase in blood volume occurs in the eye.

Even changes in the blood flow through the eye, which must regulate to a certain extent the formation of aqueous humor, do not appear to be very effective in changing intraocular pressure. Experimental reduction of blood flow through the eye has no effect on the rate of formation of aqeous humor until the flow is reduced to a critical level, when the formation of aqueous stops entirely. There is no evidence that increasing the blood flow increases aqueous formation.

The arteries of the interior of the eye, similar to those of the brain, are not actively controlled by the autonomic nervous system.

In general, the volume of blood in the eye cannot be looked on as a factor responsible for any sustained rise in intraocular pressure found in glaucoma.

Aqueous humor. The volume of the aqueous present in the eye at any one moment is the chief determinant of the normal intraocular pressure. Physiologists are agreed that the main factor responsible for the maintenance of the intraocular pressure is the balance between the rate of formation and the rate of elimination of this fluid. In an enucleated eye, where there is no pressure in the veins into which the aqueous flows after passing through Schlemm's canal, the intraocular pressure can be expressed by the formula $P = \dfrac{F}{C}$, where P is the intraocular pressure, F the rate of inflow, and C the facility of outflow. In the intact eye the pressure in the veins has to be taken into account. This is a fairly constant 10 mm. Hg. The formula, then, will be $P = \dfrac{F}{C} + P_v$. P_v equals the pressure in the veins.

Rate of aqueous humor formation. In the normal human eye there is a constant formation of fluid from the ciliary epithelium into the posterior chamber of about 2.3 cm. per minute. This fluid enters the anterior chamber through the iris-lens diaphragm from the posterior chamber by flow. In addition to this, a constant and much larger volume of fluid is entering the anterior chamber by diffusion from the arterial capillaries of the iris and at the same time is leaving the anterior chamber by diffusion into the venous capillaries of the iris. The volume of aqueous present in the eye at any one time is made up, therefore, of two portions—one enters and leaves the eye by flow and the other enters and leaves the eye by diffusion. Considering for the moment the latter, an increased rate of diffusion of fluid into the eye will cause a temporary rise in intraocular pressure, and a decreased rate of diffusion into the eye will cause a temporary fall in intraocular pressure. Changes in the rate of diffusion of fluid into the eye are brought about by alterations in the difference in osmolality between the aqueous humor and the blood. If the osmotic pressure of the blood is lowered or that of the aqueous is raised, an increased diffusion of water from the blood takes place into the anterior chamber, and the increased volume produces a rise in intraocular pressure. Conversely, if the osmotic pressure of the blood is raised or that of the aqueous is lowered, water diffuses more rapidly out of the anterior chamber into the blood, the volume of aqueous is diminished, and the intraocular pressure is lowered.

The production of aqueous humor from the ciliary processes into the posterior chamber by flow takes place through some sort of a secretory process which at present is not well understood. The most recent evidence indicates that the mechanism involves a sodium pump with a diffusional transport of water as a result of osmotic forces. The concentration of certain substances in the aqueous is quite different from that in the circulating blood. These differences in chemical composition cannot be accounted for on the basis of the hemodynamic forces present. No other data would be needed to prove that the aqueous humor must be formed by a process of secretion in addition to the processes of dialysis and filtration.

Rate of aqueous humor elimination. In the normal human eye there is a constant outflow of aqueous humor by way of Schlemm's canal of about 2.3 c.mm. per minute, in addition to the diffusion of fluid out of the eye as previously described. The amount of this outflow is determined by the resistance offered by the outflow channels themselves plus the venous pressure in the veins which drain Schlemm's canal. The principal restrictive control over the outflow of aqueous from the normal eye is the trabecular meshwork. The size and circuitousness of the passages through this meshwork determines the resistance, and the character of the trabecular passages seems to be determined by the properties of the structural proteins, their endothelial sheaths, and possibly their mucopolysaccharide.

• • •

The various types of glaucoma can now be discussed in terms of pathogenesis, using the factors listed on p. 174 and pigeonholing each type according to its known or suspected causes.

1. **Elasticity of the ocular coats.** None known at present. In the glaucoma of epidemic dropsy, swelling of the sclera might possibly be the underlying cause, but there is no evidence for this.

It is generally accepted that the glaucoma in epidemic dropsy is due to contamination of cooking oils with argemone oil. However, the alkaloid sanguinarine, which is a constituent of argemone oil, does not produce a persistent rise in intraocular pressure in laboratory animals.[94]

2. **Volume of the solid contents.** Neoplasms arising from any of the solid structures of the interior of the eye may cause an increased volume sufficient to produce a rise of internal pressure, but this takes place so slowly that it is usually compensated. Swelling of the lens following traumatic cataract formation does give rise to an acute glaucoma, probably more on the basis of angle closure than on an increase in volume of the intraocular contents.

3. **Volume of the vitreous.** The theory of swelling of the vitreous gel as a cause of glaucoma has no evidence to support it and has been discarded. There may be some tie-up between the manufacture of hyaluronic acid or similar mucopolysaccharides by the vitreous which influences the deposition of this material on the trabecular meshwork. Again, no evidence for this exists.

4. **Volume of the blood.** I have pointed out that there is no evidence that the factor of blood volume per se is ever a cause of any of the recognized types of glaucoma. Even ligation of all the vortex veins in an animal results in a very temporary rise in intraocular pressure. I have also pointed out that the evidence of neurogenic control of the intraocular pressure is not convincing. The question of neurovascular crises will be discussed later.

5. **Rate of aqueous humor secretion.** An increase in the rate of inflow of aqueous humor as a cause of glaucoma is a hypothetical possibility, but if it occurs, it is extremely rare. A type of hypersecretion glaucoma has been described by Becker but has not been confirmed by others.

6. **Increased rate of diffusion of water into the eye.** No form of glaucoma has as yet been proved to be due to this factor. The sudden lowering of the pressure following trauma and in inflammatory conditions could be accounted for on this basis in theory, however. Increased permeability of the blood-aqueous barrier to ions which are in excess in the aqueous and which give it 5 mM sodium chloride

equivalent hypertonicity to the blood would cause a fall in the osmotic pressure of the aqueous, and water would diffuse more rapidly out of the eye, thus lowering the pressure.

7. **Resistance to the passage of aqueous humor through the iris-lens diaphragm.** This is certainly the cause of the glaucoma in inflammatory conditions in which there is seclusion of the pupil and the production of an obvious iris bombé. Aphakic glaucoma is probably due to a pupillary block mechanism arising from adhesions between the iris and the vitreous. The pressure in the posterior chamber rises, since aqueous cannot get into the anterior chamber. This results in a bulging forward of the peripheral portions of the iris, which come in contact with the cornea in the chamber angle. Anterior peripheral synechiae form and, if allowed to persist, permanently close off the filtration angle.

Angle-closure glaucoma arises from a somewhat similar process. The obstruction to the outflow of aqueous is due to the apposition of the periphery of the iris against the trabeculum, thus effectively blocking the escape of aqueous into Schlemm's canal. Two concepts are current as to how this takes place. The older concept was that, given a shallow anterior chamber and narrow angle, dilatation of the pupil permitted the whole iris to completely fill the angle. The aqueous humor could not reach the trabeculum and filter out of the eye. A more recent concept considers that the primary block occurs at the iris-lens diaphragm. Given a shallow anterior chamber and narrow angle, partial dilatation of the pupil results in creating a tighter junction between iris and lens. The result is a bulging forward of the peripheral portions of the iris, which then comes in contact with the trabeculum and effec-

tively blocks the egress of aqueous from the eye. This theory, first proposed by Curran in 1920,[95] is now generally accepted. It explains the fact that occasionally full dilatation of the pupil relieves the pressure in an eye suffering an acute attack of angle-closure glaucoma, and also the fact that most patients who get an acute attack of glaucoma following mydriasis have their acute rise in pressure not when the pupil is widely dilated but later as the pupil is coming back to its normal size when the area of iris-lens contact is increasing. "The critical degree of dilatation which seems to bring on an attack of acute glaucoma in a predisposed eye is 3.5 to 6 mm."* This degree of dilatation allows enough relaxation of the peripheral portions of the iris so that it can bulge forward while not entirely abolishing the resistance to flow through the iris-lens diaphragm. Constriction of the pupil with miotics not only prevents the iris from folding into the angle, but also keeps the periphery of the iris on the stretch so that the increased pressure in the posterior chamber due to aqueous humor formation cannot push the peripheral portions of the iris forward into the angle.

Both of these theories of angle-closure glaucoma are based on an anatomic peculiarity of the eye, a shallow anterior chamber and narrow angle. This is due in all probability to disproportion between the size of the anterior chamber and the size of the lens, known to be present in the hyperopic eye and in the microphthalmic eye in which acute attacks of angle-closure glaucoma are most prone to occur. Angle-closure glaucoma in myopes is extremely rare.

As indicated, the cause of obstructed

---

*From Chandler, P.: Arch. Ophth. **47:**702, 1952.

angle glaucoma is blockage of the filtration angle by the iris. It seldom occurs unless the anterior chamber, particularly the filtration angle, is narrow to begin with. Hence, there is usually an anatomic predisposition necessary for its development. The narrow filtration angle is usually found in a small eye, which is generally hyperopic because it is small. These individuals cannot be said to have glaucoma until blockage of the filtration angle raises the intraocular pressure, and since this usually occurs suddenly, the rise of pressure is swift and severe. It is like the blockage which occurs in a drainpipe. If the pipe is merely narrowed, nothing startling occurs until suddenly some debris is sucked into it, stopping the outflow, and water starts accumulating in the sink. If the water keeps accumulating in the sink and it is a closed semielastic container, the internal pressure would immediately rise.

The normal flow of aqueous humor is shown in Fig. 48. In Fig. 49 is shown the situation which occurs in a filtration angle when the pupil dilates in open-angle glaucoma. In Fig. 50 is shown what happens to the outflow when the angle is obstructed. If the iris is dilated, it closes the angle.

Many circumstances bring about pupillary dilatation—a prolonged stay in the dark as in a movie theatre (during sleep the pupil is contracted, p. 200), use of cycloplegics for refraction which also cause mydriasis, emotional states (p. 203), etc. Added to the dilatation of the pupil, which as Chandler points out (p. 178) need not be maximal, may be vasomotor factors which cause engorgement of the blood vessels of the ciliary body, forcing the iris diaphragm forward.

Although this purely mechanistic concept of angle-closure glaucoma is fully supported by experimental and clinical evidence, Duke-Elder and a few others believe a neurovascular factor must be present in addition to the narrow angle in order to produce an acute attack. Their chief argument is that it is difficult to explain why so many acute attacks of

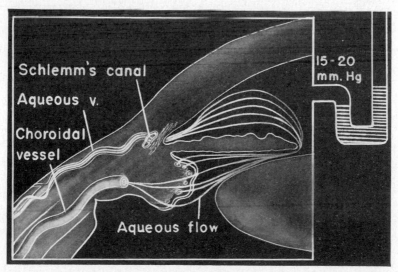

Fig. 48. Normal dilating narrow angle of the anterior chamber. (Modified from Shaffer, R.: In Newell, F. W., editor: Glaucoma, New York, 1956, Josiah Macy, Jr. Foundation.)

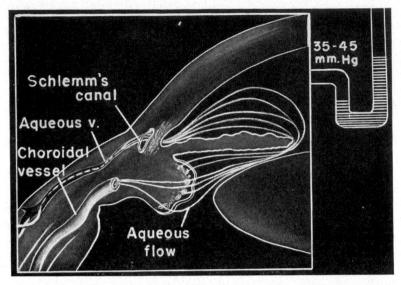

Fig. 49. Angle in the open-angle type of glaucoma. (Modified from Shaffer, R.: In Newell, F. W., editor: Glaucoma, New York, 1956, Josiah Macy, Jr. Foundation.)

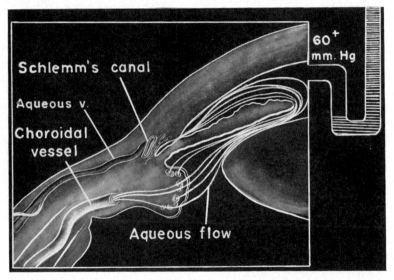

Fig. 50. Angle in the obstructed angle type of glaucoma. (Modified from Shaffer, R.: In Newell, F. W., editor: Glaucoma, New York, 1956, Josiah Macy, Jr. Foundation.)

angle-closure glaucoma occur after emotional stress. The answer to this could be the semidilatation of the pupil which occurs during emotional stress. In predisposed eyes an increase in pressure can readily be obtained by merely keeping the patient in a dark room, dilating the pupil slightly. It has never been shown that a predisposed patient could be thrown into an acute attack by emotional stress when the pupil was kept contracted with a miotic. The neurovascular hypothesis cannot be accepted until more compelling evidence is presented. This does not imply that neurovascular factors are unimportant in influencing the clinical picture of the disease after the pressure has become elevated, but it denies neurovascular factors as the primary cause of the acute attacks.

The clinical picture can be profoundly influenced by the effect of the raised intraocular pressure on the blood flow through the eye. The situation is comparable to the change in the clinical picture of a hernia when it becomes strangulated. As soon as the pressure in the hernial sac is sufficient to cause embarrassment to the blood flow, strangulation occurs, i.e., venous stasis and all the signs of inflammation. In the same way increased intraocular pressure sufficiently severe and sudden to cause impairment of blood flow through the eye leads to increased diffusion of fluid into the eye, a further acute rise in pressure, and all the signs of venous stasis and inflammation. The condition is then usually spoken of as inflammatory glaucoma, acute or chronic as the case may be.

8. **Narrowness of the filtration angle.** This factor is the underlying cause of all cases of angle-closure glaucoma.

It has been shown that if the anterior chamber is less than 2.5 mm. dilatation of the pupil with mydriatics will produce an abnormal elevation of intraocular pressure. The depth of the anterior chamber influences the facility of outflow even in eyes with normal chamber depth, the resistance to outflow increasing with decreasing depth of chamber. The relationship is approximately linear.[86, 97] The resistance to outflow attains pathologic values when the depth of the anterior chamber is less than 2.2 mm.[98] This figure is comparable to that of the average depth of the chamber in patients with angle-closure glaucoma, i.e., 2.30 mm.[99]

9. **Resistance to the passage of aqueous through the trabecular spaces.** This is probably the chief cause of most glaucomas other than angle-closure glaucomas. The normal resistance to outflow is considerable, as is evidenced by the fact that the normal pressure in the eye is around 15 to 20 mm. Hg. We have seen that the trabecular spaces are quite small, and although the filtering area is enormous, the small size of each individual passageway creates a larger resistance. Hence, it is reasonable to suppose that the increase in resistance to outflow found in most open-angle types of glaucoma is due to diminution in size of the individual pores rather than to a reduction in their number.

In this type of glaucoma the angle is open and the disease process is slow and insidious. The elevation of pressure, being moderate and developing over a period of time, causes no symptoms until late and is usually detected only by routine tonometry. The disease may be well established, with cupping of the disc and marked loss of the visual field, without the patient's being aware of anything wrong with his eyes. The central visual acuity remains normal until devastating loss of the peripheral fields has occurred. The elevation of pressure is due in the vast majority of patients to obstruction to outflow. In some patients, open-angle glaucoma has been attributed to the excessive formation of aqueous humor,[100] but these patients must be rare. The site of the obstruction to outflow is not agreed on. Since the filtration angle is open, it must be in one or more of the following structures: the trabecular meshwork, Schlemm's canal, the collector channels, the deep scleral plexus, the connecting vessels between the deep scleral plexus and the episcleral veins, and the aqueous veins. The literature is full of suggestive evidence, but not convincing proof, that each of these structures or various combinations are to blame.

Goldmann states that there are two possible alternatives—the increased resistance lies between the anterior chamber and Schlemm's canal or it lies beyond Schlemm's canal in the outflow vessels. Since the pressure in the aqueous veins is slightly lower than normal in glaucomatous eyes with raised pressure, but rises in normal eyes when the anterior chamber pressure is artificially elevated, and since obstruction to the circulation of blood in the episcleral plexus leads to the appearance of blood in Schlemm's canal in the normal eye but not in glaucomatous eyes, the site of the increased resistance must be in the trabecular meshwork. Goldmann admits that the last word in this argument will be the determination of whether or not the pressure in Schlemm's canal is found to be elevated in glaucoma, a measurement which as yet no one has attempted, for obvious reasons. Also favoring the trabecular meshwork as the site of the obstruction to outflow are the experiments of Linner.[101, 102]

The trabecular meshwork may be removed from a quarter to a third of the circumference of the filtration angle, however, without necessarily altering the facility of outflow.[103] As Grant points out, conclusions drawn from these experiments that the site of resistance must necessarily be located in the intrascleral portions of the outflow channels are only tentative. In the enucleated eyes in which these experiments were performed, the resistance to outflow might differ in some fundamental aspect from that of normal eyes in vivo, even though quantitatively the resistances encountered were similar.

Evidence for the collector channels or aqueous veins as the site of the resistance has been offered by Perkins who found that in monkey's eyes cannulating Schlemm's canal or cutting it transsclerally reduced the resistance to outflow. This was confirmed in one human eye. But Becker[104] was able to cannulate Schlemm's canal with polyethylene tubing in vivo in eyes with absolute open-angle glaucoma and no synechiae, and he noted no alteration in the tonographic estimates of outflow facility. Beskey repeated Perkins' experiment of incising Schlemm's canal transsclerally in cannulated enucleated human eyes and found only a small (less than 20%) reduction in resistance to outflow, in spite of the fact that he could demonstrate histologically that the canal had been successfully opened from the outside. Ascher has offered numerous experiments and deductions in support of his belief that the aqueous veins are responsible, but these have not convinced most authors. Grant has reported stripping the globes of all episcleral tissue without producing any change in resistance to outflow.

Recognizing that chronic simple glaucoma is a disease of older age and that the sclera is composed of a considerable amount of collagen, Theobold and Kirk[105] consider that hypertrophy and sclerosis of the collagenous scleral fibers could produce narrowing or occlusion of the intrascleral veins and lead to glaucoma. A microscopic study of the aqueous veins in a series of glaucomatous eyes supports this hypothesis and suggests that in some cases of chronic simple glaucoma the rise of pressure is secondary to hypertrophy and sclerosis of the sclera, with resultant closure of the veins and obstruction to aqueous outflow.

In some glaucomatous eyes a progressive dystrophy of the trabecular meshwork has been found, consisting of a diffuse nodular proliferation of extra-cellular long-spacing collagen. This might be the cause of the obstruction to the trabecular meshwork.[106]

On anatomic grounds Ashton incriminates the collector channels running between the deep scleral plexus and the episcleral veins (p. 136), and Duke-Elder considers organic changes in the venous channels leading from Schlemm's canal to be the primary cause of the increased resistance in the anterior segment of the globe and similar vascular changes in the posterior segment of the globe to cause the cupping of the disc and the loss of visual field.

For many years the thought has been expressed that chronic simple open-angle glaucoma is not a local disease of the eye alone, but "a sick eye in a sick body." This point of view has been championed recently by Duke-Elder who marshalled the evidence in a most convincing manner in the Bowman Lecture for 1957.[107] He emphasizes the evidence for the existence of a center in the hypothalamic region for the control of intraocular pressure and the many associated symptoms in patients with glaucoma which suggest a disturbance of autonomic imbalance. The present effort on the part of investigators to localize the resistance to outflow in one portion of the outflow mechanism suggests to him the following.

"[that they] . . . have come to believe that the be-all and end-all of glaucoma lies in a small corner of the eye, that the entire pathology is centered in the drainage channels, that the secret of the disease can be expressed in terms of a mathematical formula defining mechanical events in terms of flow, resistance, and a pressure-gradient. But glaucoma cannot be expressed in terms of increased pressure alone; for increased pressure is merely a symptom and by no means an invariable symptom of the disease."*

*From Duke-Elder, S.: Tr. Ophth. Soc. U. Kingdom **77**:205, 1957.

It is indeed sound advice, and there is no dearth of literature on changes found throughout the body in patients with glaucoma, but so far they have not advanced our knowledge of the disease as much as have those studies confined to that "small corner of the eye."

Duke-Elder gives the following definition of open-angle glaucoma:

". . . a vascular dyscrasia manifesting itself initially as a periodic sympatheticotonia involving periodic constriction of the small vessels of the eye. Therefore, as functional changes progress to become structural and a periodic constriction evolves to become a permanent obliteration, a gradual condition of tissue-sclerosis due to a lack of adequate blood supply spreads throughout the globe."*

The cupping of the disc and the loss of visual fields according to this point of view are not due primarily to the raised pressure, but to involvement of the posterior segment of the globe by this vascular dyscrasia which likewise, involving the vessels of the outflow mechanism, produced the embarrassment of outflow and the raised intraocular pressure.

Some of the forms of open-angle glaucoma in which the underlying cause is probably diminution in size of the pores are the following.

(a) *Pigmentary glaucoma.* The dissemination of pigment from the back surface of the iris is seen in the stroma of the iris and on the back surface of the cornea, generally in the form of a Kruckenberg spindle. Transillumination of the eye shows the loss of pigment from the back surface of the iris. Gonioscopy shows the angle deeply pigmented due to deposition of pigment on the trabeculae.

(b) *Glaucoma capsulare.* Although it was formerly believed that the exfoliation

*From Duke-Elder, S.: Tr. Ophth. Soc. U. Kingdom **77**:205, 1957.

of the lens capsule came from the zonular lamellae, most authors now consider this material which is found in the angle and deposited on the trabeculae to come from some other source. Wherever this material comes from, it undoubtedly causes glaucoma by obstructing the pores in the trabeculum.

(c) *Glaucoma following hyphemia.* The cause of the rise in pressure is probably blockage of the trabeculum by red cells and fibrin.

Secondary glaucoma occurs in the course of many affections of the eye or orbit which are the cause of the elevated intraocular pressure. The rise of pressure may be insidious and of small degree, but generally it is sudden and severe. Sudden changes in pressure are characteristic— subnormal pressure following high pressure and alternations occurring without obvious reason.

PHYSIOLOGIC PRINCIPLES UNDERLYING OPERATIONS FOR GLAUCOMA

The operations designed to reduce the pressure in the glaucomatous eye aim at affording a means of escape of the aqueous humor from the eye.

Paracentesis. In paracentesis when the anterior chamber is opened, the escape of aqueous humor reduces the intraocular pressure to zero. The chamber gradually re-forms with fresh fluid or plasmoid aqueous humor, and the pressure rises. This affords but temporary relief from the hypertension, but may be of value in the treatment of secondary glaucoma due to plastic iritis in which the aqueous humor contains so much fibrin and so many cells that it temporarily blocks the normal avenues of escape. Since the use of atropine is indicated in the treatment of such inflammatory conditions, paracentesis may be performed to relieve the

acute rise of pressure which may follow its use.

It is generally agreed by clinicians that the rise of pressure in uveitis, unless severe and causing pain, had best be accepted and the treatment confined to the ocular inflammation. The use of steroid therapy frequently results in lowering of the pressure, and the elevation of the pressure itself seldom leads to loss of visual field. Surgical treatment for secondary glaucoma is, therefore, being resorted to less frequently.

Iridectomy. The various forms of iridectomy designed to reduce pressure in the eye aim to open the angle, which has been blocked by the iris. The operation has been termed a basal iridectomy since the portion of iris which is cut away is that directly attached to the ciliary body. This is the operation of choice in closed-angle glaucoma, if it can be done before any anterior synechiae form. In place of a wide basal iridectomy, a small basal iridectomy may be performed early in an acute attack before synechiae form. Weekers[108] has shown that a reduction in the resistance to outflow follows iridectomy in patients with closed-angle glaucoma. If peripheral anterior synechiae have formed, the resistance to outflow is normalized only by iridencleisis, as a rule, or by a procedure such as Scheie has devised.[109]

The proper treatment of the condition is, obviously, its prevention. This depends entirely on the ability of the clinician to recognize a narrow filtration angle. Generally, the ophthalmologist has little opportunity to detect obstructed angle glaucoma until an acute attack occurs in one eye, although prodromal symptoms do occur. Ideally, every person with narrow angles should be safeguarded against closed-angle glaucoma by receiving proper advice, by using miotics, or by undergoing surgery—according to the individual condition. Gonioscopy can evaluate the narrowness of the angle, and provocative tests can determine the degree of impending obstruction.

It is a well-known clinical fact that cuts in the iris do not heal, and a small iridotomy or iridectomy remains open throughout life. It has been assumed that the adult stroma of the iris has no proliferative capacity. The second possibility is that local influences in the anterior chamber prevent proliferation of connective tissue. In order to test this hypothesis, Snell[110] implanted granulation tissue produced in guinea pigs subcutaneously by inserting foreign bodies under the skin. The foreign bodies in their envelopes of granulation tissue were then transferred to the anterior chambers of the animals' eyes. On the third, fourth, or fifth day after transplantation, diathermy burns of the iris were created. After a suitable period the eyes were enucleated and sectioned. The healthy transplanted granulation tissue of subcutaneous origin failed to provide effective fibrosis for healing of the iris burns. This suggests that something in the environment of the anterior segment of the eye either inhibited proliferation or prevented cohesion.

Iris inclusion operations. Iridencleisis and iridotasis fulfill the same purpose as an iridectomy but are based on the idea that iris tissue left in the wound forms a filtering cicatrix which conducts fluid out of the eye by a new route. These operations are, therefore, useful in the treatment of chronic simple glaucoma of the closed-angle type in which acute attacks have led to the formation of peripheral anterior synechiae.

It has been shown[111] that iridencleisis acts as a tension-normalizing operation in chronic open-angle glaucoma by creating new drainage channels for the intraocular fluid. It has been advocated that the operation acts by modifying the circulation of the anterior uvea, possibly by the inhibition of axon reflexes,[112] but the recent studies of Weekers,[52, 108] support the general belief that following this operation the aqueous humor flows into the subconjunctival space along the iris enclosed in the scleral opening.

Trephine and sclerectomy. These operations also create a new channel for the escape of fluid from the eye by making a permanent connection between the anterior chamber and the subconjunctival tissue. A bleb is formed under the conjunctiva produced by the intraocular fluid seeping out from the interior of the eye, where it is absorbed by the veins of the subconjunctival spaces. The trephine operation, or one of its modifications, is of greatest usefulness in chronic simple glaucoma of the open-angle variety. Here, the fluid can gain access to Schlemm's canal or at least to the angle readily, and the trephine opening merely substitutes another avenue of escape for the mechanism of Schlemm's canal. The effectiveness of the operation seems to depend upon the formation of a filtering cicatrix, which depends in turn upon the outgrowth of endothelium from the anterior chamber into the subconjunctival space.

Filtering operations may create three routes of aqueous drainage, according to Teng and associates[113]: (1) by the transconjunctional route, (2) through areas of perivascular degeneration, and (3) by direct recanalization. These authors believe the aqueous has a direct effect on collagen, and that when aqueous leaks through the transconjunctival route, the collagen degenerates and becomes more permeable. The epithelium and basement membrane of the conjunctiva are also affected, so that aqueous oozes through the bleb. A similar principle produces the perivascular route when the aqueous affects the collagen around the blood vessels. New recanalization occurs where the scleral wound is close to the trabecular region, rich in capillaries. These authors do not explain why the aqueous humor does not normally affect the collagen of the connective tissue and blood vessels surrounding the unoperated anterior chamber.

DeVoe[114] feels that in the treatment of most types of glaucoma success in fistulizing operations is not due to mechanical fistulization, but more probably to trauma of the uveal tract and readjustment of the neurovascular system. This opinion was based on gonioscopic examination of patients after surgery, and it is quite conceivable that filtration was going on but could not be detected by this method. The only evidence that is entirely satisfactory to determine whether filtration is taking place would be a microscopic examination of the area and probably serial sections.

Cyclodialysis. This operation was devised by Heine, who noted that when the choroid was detached the intraocular pressure fell and fluid could seep out of the eye from the anterior chamber into the subchoroidal space. The operation consists of separating the ciliary body and the iris from the sclera over the ciliary body. The greatest usefulness of this operation is in the treatment of glaucoma which occurs following cataract extraction. Some authors employ it in place of a trephine in treatment of open-angle glaucoma. Goldmann[115] has shown that in open-angle glaucoma cyclodialysis is effective by reducing the formation of the aqueous humor and by establishing new surfaces of resorption.

The experiments of Epstein[116] suggest that cylodialysis, when successful in advanced glaucoma, is probably due to reopening of an occluded angle.

Cyclodiathermy. No studies are available to suggest the mechanism of action of this operation, but it would seem likely that it reduces the formation of the aqueous humor by destroying the secreting cells of the ciliary processes, either directly or by shutting off their blood supply.

Other fistulizing operations. A number of fistulizing operations, such as the Preziossi procedure, have been devised recently. More recently, Scheie[109] has devised a fistulizing procedure in which retraction of the edges of a scleral wound is induced by cautery. All these procedures create new channels of exit.

REFERENCES

1. Weekers, R., Watillon, M., and deRudder, M.: The limits of pressure, Ann. ocul. **188:**920, 1955.
2. Goldmann, H.: Applanation tonometry. In Newell, F. W., editor: Glaucoma (Transactions Second Conference), New York, 1957, Josiah Macy, Jr. Foundation, p. 167.
3. De Roetth, A., Jr.: The effect of changes in the osmotic pressure of the blood on aqueous humor dynamics, Arch. Ophth. (To be published.)
4. Duke-Elder, S., editor: Glaucoma: symposium, Springfield, Ill., 1955, Charles C Thomas, Publisher, p. 147.
5. Grant, W. M.: Aqueous production and flow. Proceedings symposium on glaucoma, New Orleans Academy of Ophthalmology. Quoted by Becker, B.: Glaucoma annual reviews, 1956-1957, Arch. Ophth. **58:**860, 1957.
6. MacDonald, R.: Symposium on clinical assessment of glaucoma, Tr. Canad. Ophth. Soc. **7:**178, 1956.
7. Scheie, H.: In Duke-Elder, S., editor: Glaucoma: symposium, Springfield, Ill., 1955, Charles C Thomas, Publisher, p. 164.
8. Weed, L.: Some limitations of the Monroe-Kellie hypothesis, Arch. Surg. **18:** 1049, 1929.

9. Weed, L., and Flexner, L.: Further observations upon the Monroe-Kellie doctrine, Bull. Johns Hopkins Hosp. **50:** 196, 1932.

10. Ridley, E.: Intraocular pressure and drainage, Brit. J. Exper. Path. **11:**217, 1930.

11. Clark, J.: Method for measuring elasticity in vivo and results obtained on eyeball at different intraocular pressures, Am. J. Physiol. **101:**472, 1932.

12. Perkins, E., and Gloster, J.: Further studies on the distensibility of the eye. Brit. J. Ophth. **41:**475, 1957.

13. Saiduzzafar, H.: Studies in ocular rigidity, Brit. J. Ophth. **46:**717, 1962.

14. Friedenwald, J.: Contribution to the theory and practice of tonometry, Am. J. Ophth. **20:**985, 1937.

15. Holland, M., Madison, J., and Bean, W.: The ocular rigidity function, Am. J. Ophth. **50:**958, 1960.

16. Eisenlohr, J., and Langham, M.: The relationship between pressure and volume changes in living and dead rabbit eyes, Invest. Ophthal. **1:**63, 1962.

17. Eisenlohr, J., Langham, M., and Maumenee, A. E.: Manometric studies of the pressure-volume relationship in living and enucleated eyes of individual human subjects, Brit. J. Ophth. **46:**536, 1962.

18. Snydacker, D.: The relation of the volume of the crystalline lens to the depth of the anterior chamber, Tr. Am. Ophth. Soc. **54:**657, 1956.

19. Barany, E.: The influence of derangement of the vasomotor system of the eye on the relation between local arterial blood pressure and intraocular pressure, Upsala läkaref. förh. **52:**1, 1946.

20. Macri, F.: Acetazolamide and the venous pressure of the eye, Arch. Ophth. **63:**953, 1960.

21. Linner, E.: The outflow pressure in normal and glaucomatous eyes, Acta ophth. **33:**101, 1955.

22. Bill, A.: Intraocular pressure and blood flow through the uvea, Arch. Ophth. **67:** 336, 1962.

23. Armaly, M.: The effect of intraocular pressure on outflow facility, Arch. Ophth. **64:**125, 1960.

24. Ridge, J.: The effect of unilateral common carotid occlusion and of acute preganglionic cervical sympathectomy on

25. Linner, E., and Prijot, E.: Preganglionic cervical sympathectomy and aqueous flow, Arch. Ophth. **58:**77, 1957.

26. Schmerl, E., and Steinberg, B.: The role of ciliary and superior cervical ganglia in ocular tension, Am. J. Ophth. **32:** 947, 1949.

27. Armaly, M.: Studies on intraocular effects of the orbital parasympathetic pathway. I. Technique and effects on morphology, Arch. Ophth. **61:**14, 1958.

28. Armaly, M.: Studies on intraocular effects of the orbital parasympathetics. II. Effect on intraocular pressure, Arch. Ophth. **62:**145, 1959.

29. Armaly, M.: Studies on intraocular effects of the orbital parasympathetic pathways. II. Effect on steady-state dynamics, Arch. Ophth. **62:**817, 1959.

30. Langham, M., and Taylor, C.: The influence of pre- and post-ganglionic section of the cervical sympathetic on the intraocular pressure of rabbits and cats, J. Physiol. **152:**437, 1960.

31. Langham, M., and Taylor, C.: The influence of superior cervical ganglionectomy on the intraocular pressure, J. Physiol. **152:**447, 1960.

32. Langham, M.: Influence of the intraocular pressure on the formation of the aqueous humor and the outflow resistance in the living eye, Brit. J. Ophth. **43:**705, 1959.

33. Langham, M.: Steady-state pressure flow relationships in the living and dead eye of the cat, Am. J. Ophth. **50:**950, 1960.

34. von Sallmann, L., and Lowenstein, O.: Responses of intraocular pressure and cutaneous vessels to electric stimulation in the diencephalon, Am. J. Ophth. **39:** 11, 1955.

35. von Sallmann, L.: Central control of intraocular pressure. In Newell, F. W., editor: Glaucoma (Transactions Second Conference), New York, 1957, Josiah Macy, Jr. Foundation, pp. 81-123.

36. von Sallmann, L., Macri, F., Wanko, T., and Grimes, P.: Some mechanisms of centrally induced eye pressure responses, Am. J. Ophth. **46:**130, 1956.

37. Gloster, J., and Greaves, D.: Effect of diencephalic stimulation upon intra-

ocular pressure, Brit. J. Ophth. **41**:513, 1957.

38. Greaves, D., and Perkins, E.: The seventh cranial nerve and intraocular pressure, J. Physiol. **134**:393, 1956.

39. Greaves, D., and Perkins, E.: Influence of the sympathetic nervous system on the intraocular pressure and vascular circulation of the eye, Brit. J. Ophth. **36**:258, 1952.

40. Greaves, D., and Perkins, E.: Influence of the third cranial nerve on intraocular pressure, Brit. J. Ophth. **37**:54, 1953.

41. Vrabec, F.: L'innervation du système trabéculaire de l'angle irien, Ophthalmologica **128**:359, 1954.

42. Vrabec, F.: The topography of encapsulated terminal sensory corpuscles of the anterior chamber angle of the goose eye. In Smelser, G., editor: The structure of the eye, New York, 1962, Academic Press, Inc., p. 325.

43. Chapman, G., and Spelsberg, W.: The occurrence of myelinated and unmyelinated nerves in the iris angle of man and rhesus monkey, Exper. Eye Res. **2**:130, 1963.

44. Feeney, L.: Ultrastructure of the nerves in the human trabecular region, Invest. Ophthal. **1**:462, 1962.

45. Perkins, E.: Sensory mechanisms and intraocular pressure, Exper. Eye Res. **1**: 160, 1961.

46. Barany, E.: Action of atropine, homatropine, eserine, and prostigmine on osmotic pressure of aqueous humor, Acta physiol. scandinav. **13**:95, 1947.

47. Weekers, R.: The mode of action of medical and surgical methods of reducing the intraocular pressure-tension. In Duke-Elder, S., editor: Glaucoma: Symposium, Springfield, Ill., 1955, Charles C Thomas, Publisher.

48. Barany, E.: The mode of action of pilocarpine on outflow resistance in the eye of a primate, Invest. Ophthal. **1**:712, 1962.

49. Armaly, M., and Jepson, N.: Accomodation and the dynamics of the steady-state intraocular pressure, Invest. Ophthal. **1**:480, 1962.

50. Chandler, P.: In Newell, F. W., editor: Glaucoma (Transactions First Conference), New York, 1956, Josiah Macy, Jr. Foundation, pp. 26-28.

51. Scheie, H., and Frayer, W.: Ocular hypertension induced by air in the anterior chamber, Arch. Ophth. **44**:691, 1950.

52. Nash, C., and Woodbury, R.: Influence of atropine on the intraocular pressure of dogs, Am. J. Physiol. **176**:65, 1954.

53. DeLong, S., and Scheie, H.: Dibenamine. An experimental and clinical study, Arch. Ophth. **50**:289, 1953.

54. Schenk, F.: Uber die Wirkung von Atropine, etc. auf den Augendruck des Kaninschens, Ophthalmologica **118**:42, 1949.

55. Kinsey, V. E.: The physiology of the aqueous humor and a new concept of the maintenance of the intraocular pressure, Arch. Ophth. **44**:215, 1950.

56. Goldmann, H.: Uber fluorescine in der menschlichen vorder-kammer, Ophthalmologica **119**:65, 1950.

57. Rohen, J.: On the aqueous outflow resistance, Ophthalmologica **139**:1, 1960.

58. Ashton, N., Brini, A., and Smith, R.: Anatomical studies of the trabecular meshwork of the normal human eye, Brit. J. Ophth. **40**:257, 1956.

59. Speakman, J.: Aqueous outflow channel in the trabecular meshwork in man, Brit. J. Ophth. **43**:129, 1959.

60. Grant, H.: Facility of flow through the trabecular meshwork, Arch. Ophth. **54**: 245, 1955; **60**:523, 1958.

61. Tang, C., Katson, H., and Chi, H.: Primary degeneration in the vicinity of the chamber angle, Am. J. Ophth. **43**: 193, 1957.

62. Berggren, L., and Vrabec, F.: Demonstration of a coating substance in the trabecular meshwork, Am. J. Ophth. **44**: 200, 1957.

63. Swanljung, H., and Blodi, F.: Tonography and some provocative tests for glaucoma, Am. J. Ophth. **41**:187, 1956.

64. Weekers, R., Delmarcelle, Y., and Prijot, E.: A propos du diagnostic différentiel entre le glaucome chronique simple et le glaucome congestif non inflammatoire, Ann. ocul. **186**:873, 1953.

65. Becker, B.: The mechanisms in the fall of intraocular pressure induced by the carbonic anhydrase inhibitor, Diamox, Am. J. Ophth. **29**:177, 1955.

66. Becker, B.: The effects of the carbonic anhydrase inhibitor, acetazoleamide, on the composition of aqueous humor, Am. J. Ophth. **40**:129, 1955.

67. Langham, M., and Lee, P.: Action of

Diamox and ammonium chloride on formation of aqueous humor, Brit. J. Ophth. **41:**65, 1957.

68. Becker, B.: Glaucoma review, Arch. Ophth. **58:**86, 1957.

69. Macri, F., and Brown, J.: The constrictive action of acetazolamide on the iris arteries of the cat, Arch. Ophth. **66:**148, 1961.

70. Macri, F.: Interdependence of venous and eye pressure, Arch. Ophth. **65:**442, 1961.

71. Kass, M., and Green, H.: Osmotic pressure measurements of intraocular fluids by an improved cryoscopic method, Am. J. Ophth. **48:**32, 1959.

72. Green, H.: Dr. Green's reply, Am. J. Ophth. **49:**385, 1960.

73. Simon, K., and Bonting, S.: Possible usefulness of cardiac glycosides in treatment of glaucoma, Arch. Ophth. **68:**227, 1962.

74. Becker, B.: Ouabain and aqueous humor dynamics in the rabbit eye, Invest. Ophthal. **2:**325, 1963.

75. Becker, B.: Hypothermia and aqueous humor dynamics of the rabbit eye, Tr. Am. Ophth. Soc. **58:**337, 1960.

76. Pollack, I., Becker, B., and Constant, M.: The effect of hypothermia on aqueous humor dynamics. I. Intraocular pressure and outflow facility of the rabbit eye, Am. J. Ophth. **49:**1126, 1960.

77. Holmberg, A., and Becker, B.: The effect of hypothermia on aqueous humor dynamics. II. Ultrastructural changes in the rabbit ciliary epithelium, Am. J. Ophth. **49:**1134, 1960.

78. Goldmann, H.: Applanation tonometry. In Newell, F. W., editor: Glaucoma (Transactions Second Conference), New York, 1957, Josiah Macy, Jr. Foundation, pp. 167-220.

78a. Olmstead, E.: An evaluation of tonometric techniques, Arch. Ophth. **62:**460, 1959.

79. Phillips, C., and Quick, M.: Impression tonometry and the effect of eye volume variation, Brit. J. Ophth. **44:**149, 1960.

80. Sampson, W., and Girard, L.: The coefficient of scleral rigidity. Effect of variation of the intraocular volume, Am. J. Ophth. **52:**357, 798, 1961.

81. Moses, R., and Bruno, M.: The rate of outflow of fluid from the eye under increased pressure, Am. J. Ophth. **33:**389, 1950.

82. Grant, W. M.: Clinical measurements of aqueous outflow, Arch. Ophth. **46:**113, 1951.

83. Scheie, H., et al.: Tonography, Arch. Ophth. **54:**515, 1955.

84. Grant, W. M.: In Duke-Elder, S., editor: Glaucoma: symposium, Springfield, Ill., 1955, Charles C Thomas, Publisher, p. 137.

85. Goldmann, H.: In Duke-Elder, S., editor: Glaucoma: symposium, Springfield, Ill., 1955, Charles C Thomas, Publisher, p. 124.

86. Becker, B., and Constant, A.: Species variation and facility of aqueous outflow, Am. J. Ophth. **42:**189, 1956.

87. McEwen, W.: Application of Poiseuille's law to aqueous outflow, Arch. Ophth. **60:**290, 1958.

88. Flocks, M.: The anatomy of the trabecular meshwork as seen in tangential sections, Arch. Ophth. **56:**708, 1956.

89. Prijot, E., and Stone, H.: On the ophthalmotonic consensual reaction and its relationship to aqueous humor dynamics, Am. J. Ophth. **42:**50, 1956.

90. Stocker, F.: On changes in intraocular pressure after application of the tonometer, Am. J. Ophth. **45:**192, 1958.

91. Drance, S.: Relationship of consensual changes in intraocular pressure to arterial blood pressure, Arch. Ophth. **66:**619, 1961.

92. Perkins, E.: Consensual changes in intraocular pressure under experimental conditions. In Newell, F., editor: Symposium on glaucoma, (Transactions of Third Conference), New York, 1958, Josiah Macy, Jr. Foundation, pp. 143-201.

93. Grant, M., and English, F.: An explanation for so-called consensual pressure drop during tonography, Arch. Ophth. **69:**314, 1963.

94. Dobbie, G., and Langham, M.: Reaction of animals' eyes to Sanguinarine and Argemone oil, Brit. J. Ophth. **45:**81, 1961.

95. Curran, E.: New operation for glaucoma involving a new principle in aetiology and treatment of chronic primary glaucoma, Arch. Ophth. **49:**131, 1920.

96. Chandler, P.: Narrow-angle glaucoma, Arch. Ophth. **47:**702, 1952.

97. Barany, E., and Woodin, A.: Hyaluronic

acid and hyaluronidase in the aqueous humor and the angle of the anterior chamber, Acta physiol. scandinav. **33:** 257, 1955.

98. Nihard, P.: Influence of the depth of the anterior chamber on the resistance to flow of aqueous humor, Exper. Eye Res. **1:**229, 1962.

99. Weekers, R., and Grieten, J.: Study of the dimensions of the anterior chamber of the human eye. III. In closed-angle glaucoma and in open-angle glaucoma, Ophthalmologica **143:**56, 1962.

100. Becker, B., et al.: Hypersecretion glaucoma, Arch. Ophth. **56:**180, 1956.

101. Linner, E.: The flow pressure in normal and glaucomatous eyes, Acta ophth. **33:** 101, 1955.

102. Linner, E.: Further studies of the episcleral venous pressure in glaucoma, Am. J. Ophth. **41:**646, 1956.

103. Grant, W. M.: Facility of the flow through the trabecular meshwork, Arch. Ophth. **54:**245, 1955.

104. Becker, B.: Glaucoma review, Arch. Ophth. **56:**902, 1956.

105. Theobold, G. Dvorak, and Kirk, H.: Aqueous pathways in some cases of glaucoma, Am. J. Ophth. **41:**11, 1956.

106. Speakman, J., and Leeson, T.: Site of obstruction to aqueous outflow in chronic simple glaucoma, Brit. J. Ophth. **46:** 321, 1962.

107. Duke-Elder, S.: The etiology of simple glaucoma, Tr. Ophth. Soc. U. Kingdom **77:**205, 1957.

108. Weekers, R.: The mode of action of medical and surgical methods of reducing ocular tension. In Duke-Elder, S., editor: Glaucoma: symposium, Springfield, Ill., 1955, Charles C Thomas, Publisher, pp. 257-272.

109. Scheie, H.: Retraction of scleral wound edges: as a fistulizing procedure for glaucoma, Am. J. Ophth. **45:**220, 1958.

110. Snell, A., Jr.: Wound healing of the iris, Am. J. Ophth. **41:**499, 1956.

111. Kronfeld, P., and McGarry, H.: The mode of action of iris inclusion operations, Tr. Am. Ophth. Soc. **48:**107, 1950.

112. Duke-Elder, S.: The dependence of surgery on physiology, Am. J. Ophth. **33:** 11, 1950.

113. Teng, C., Chi, H., and Katzin, H.: Histology and mechanism of filtering operations, Am. J. Ophth. **47:**16, 1959.

114. DeVoe, A.: A gonioscopic study of fistulizing operations, Tr. Am. Ophth. Soc. **48:**118, 1950.

115. Goldmann, H.: Cited in Weekers, R.: The mode of action of medical and surgical methods of reducing ocular tension. In Duke-Elder, S., editor: Glaucoma: symposium, Springfield, Ill., 1955, Charles C Thomas, Publisher, pp. 257-272.

116. Epstein, E.: Fibrosing response to aqueous, Brit. J. Ophth. **43:**641, 1959.

CHAPTER 6

THE IRIS AND
THE PUPIL

THE IRIS
THE PIGMENT OF THE IRIS

Color of the iris at birth. The color of the normal iris varies from a light blue to a deep brown. All shades of blues and browns are seen, and the pigmentation may be diffuse or patchy. At birth all irises in members of the Caucasian race are light blue. The color of the Negro infant's iris is slate or steel blue. It is never brown. This is due to the absence of individual pigment cells, called chromatophores, from the iris.

The posterior surface of the iris is lined by two rows of deeply pigmented epithelial cells containing between them the potential cavity of the primary optic vesicle. In front of these pigmented cells is the iris stroma formed from mesoderm. In the central so-called ciliary zone of the iris are two layers of mesoderm. In the central or pupillary zone the stroma is thinned down to one layer of mesoderm. In the fetus both layers are continuous up to the margin of the pupil, but shortly before birth one of these layers, the anterior one, disappears. No pigment cells,

or chromatophores, are present in the stroma at birth. Light, entering the eye, passes through the stroma and strikes the deeply pigmented epithelial cells on the back surface of the iris. It is then reflected back through the stroma again. In its passage, certain of the rays are absorbed, i.e., those of longer wavelength. Hence, the color of the iris appears blue or grayish. Light is absorbed by the iris stroma in much the same way as light is absorbed by a body of water. The reflected rays give the water a blue color.

Color of the adult iris. Shortly after birth, isolated pigment cells, chromatophores, develop in the iris stroma. These cells increase in number in some persons and when numerous give the iris a brown color. The color of the adult iris depends upon the number of these pigment cells and their distribution.

Heterochromia; iris freckles. In some persons the color of the two irises is quite different. Slight differences occur in nearly every person. In fact, the markings of the iris are so distinctive that it has been proposed to use photographs of the iris as a means of identification instead of fingerprints. When the difference in color between the two irises is very marked, e.g., a brown iris on one side and a blue on the other, the condition is called heterochromia. This may be found in perfectly normal eyes, but frequently the eye with the lighter iris suffers from attacks of inflammation and secondary glaucoma. Domestic animals, especially cats, are frequently heterochromic, and as far as can be told, the eyes are entirely healthy.

It has been suggested that the sympathetic nervous system plays a part in determining the color of the adult iris by its influence on the chromatophores, but the experiments to support this have not been convincing.

In many persons collections of chromatophores are grouped together on the surface of the iris to form spots called iris freckles. These have no significance in themselves and are sometimes called benign melanomas. On the other hand, they are frequently associated with malignant melanomas of the choroid, according to Wilder.[1] She found that 50% of eyes removed for trauma had benign melanomas (freckles) of the iris, and of 200 eyes removed for malignant melanomas of the choroid, 66.5% had freckles of the iris. In 55 eyes removed for malignant melanomas of the iris, freckles were found in all. These findings support the belief that iris freckles are either potentially malignant or at least frequently associated with other intraocular malignant melanomas.

Dissemination of pigment. Changes in the retinal pigment of the iris (that in the epithelial cells on the back surface) occur in many pathologic conditions and as a result of senility. A definite though slight depigmentation occurs in all irises with advancing age. In some the pigment in the epithelial cells gets loose and is scattered on the surface of the iris, on the lens capsule, and on the posterior surface of the cornea, deposited there by the thermal current of the aqueous humor. In this latter situation it collects in the form of a vertical line or spindle, called Krukenberg's spindle. Pigmented cells may be found in small numbers floating in the aqueous humor but, unless associated with other changes, have no pathologic significance.

In large numbers these cells may be an important factor in the etiology of some forms of chronic simple glaucoma. The dissemination of the cells through the iris stroma has no significance itself since it is a common change in senility, as just indicated, but with the experience gained from the use of the gonioscope it is now recognized that pigmentation of the iris angle is frequently seen in association with open-angle glaucoma. It is too early to evaluate this association properly, but it is logical to explain the elevation in pressure by the deposition of particles of pigment in the trabecular meshwork, preventing the escape of the aqueous humor.

MUSCLES OF THE IRIS

The iris contains two muscles, the sphincter pupillae and the dilator pupillae.

Embryologic development. The pigment epithelium of the retina in the region of the iris undergoes a peculiar transformation. It becomes the dilator pupillae.

Anatomic studies show that Bruch's membrane is not a true elastic membrane but is formed of fibers similar to smooth muscle cells without nuclei. This membrane is of epithelial origin. The epithelial part of the iris, which corresponds to the rim of the optic vesicle, gives rise to both the pigmented epithelial cells on the back surface of the iris and to the dilator and sphincter muscles of the iris. All of the musculature of the iris, therefore, arises from epithelial structures or ectoderm, instead of mesoderm, as is customary in most unstriated muscle in the body.

In man, the sphincter muscle develops at about the beginning of the fourth month and arises from the epithelial cells of both layers of the optic vesicle. The dilator muscle develops at about the seventh month from the anterior layer of epithelial cells of the optic vesicle. The transition from epithelial cell to muscle cell goes on to completion in the case of the sphincter muscle, whereas transition of the dilator muscle proceeds in only part of each muscle cell. The remainder retains its epithelial character and, in part, its pigmentation, even after birth.

Mention will be made in a later chapter of the movements of the pigment in the pars optica retinae under the influence of light. An ingenious suggestion has been made as to how these muscle fibers come to be developed from cells of the neural epiblast. In some of the vertebrates, such as amphibians and fish, the iris responds directly to light after all nerve connections with the eyeball have been severed. The pigmented cells, which compose the outer layer of the secondary optic vesicle, when stimulated by light manifest amoeboid movements. They send out processes which protrude between the rods and cones. These phototactic movements are most easily produced by light of short wavelength, suggesting that they are the result of some chemical change. The pigmented epithelial cells are continued directly on to the back of the iris and still retain phototactic power. The cells lining the retina receive the stimulus on their outer surface which has processes protruding from it and produce movement of the pigment under the influence of light. The cells on the back surface of the iris do not project forward in the iris stroma, but run radially, so that when

they retract in the dark, the pupil dilates. In the course of evolution, the contractile power of the muscle tissue of the iris is changed from a direct action to the stimulus of light into an indirect reflex act. No contraction to light of the iris tissue takes place in mammals when the iris has been severed from its connections with the central nervous system. It loses its direct reflex phototactic action, but retains its contractile power under nervous control. It is interesting to see how a transition in function from an amoeboid type of motion to that of true muscular contraction proceeds hand in hand with the elaboration of structure. In the frog, contraction of the pupil occurs when the internal edge of the iris is illuminated,[2] and the rate of contraction is unaffected by excision of the eye. Light from the violet end of the spectrum is sixty times more effective than that from the red part of the spectrum in bringing about autonomous contraction of the iris. The effect on the pupil and the migration of granules in the retina of the frog seem to be definitely connected.

Sphincter pupillae.

Anatomy. The sphincter pupillae is a typical sphincter muscle composed of unstriated fibers. It lies in the posterior iris stroma just in front of the pigment epithelium, next to the margin of the pupil. The fibers resemble ordinary smooth muscle fibers in other parts of the body, but they shorten on contraction much more than any other unstriated muscle. The excursion of the pupil can be extraordinarily large. When maximally contracted, the pupil may be 1.5 mm., and with maximal dilatation it may be 8 mm. The muscle shortens about 87% of its length, a change seldom found in other smooth or striated muscles in the body. It is generally believed that those muscles which move their insertions through large distances have long fibers. Haines[3] finds that the length of a muscle fibril bears a constant relation to its range of movement. The amount of contraction possible in a muscle fiber is about 57% of its length when fully stretched. In most muscles, this amount of contraction corresponds to the range of movement allowed by the bones to which the muscle is attached. The unusual shortening ability of the sphincter pupillae has been explained by assuming that the fibers telescope into one another on contraction. This would increase the thickness of the muscle as a whole.

The fibers are intimately connected with the underlying stroma and with the dilator muscle to such an extent that contraction of the muscle, causing constriction of the pupil, is possible even after a section of the sphincter has been cut, i.e., following iridectomy. In many diseased states, contraction of the pupil to appropriate stimuli occurs only in segments of the sphincter.[4]

Nerve supply. The sphincter is supplied by a branch of the oculomotor nerve. This nerve divides into two branches after reaching the orbit. The superior ramus supplies the superior rectus and levator palpebrae, whereas the inferior ramus

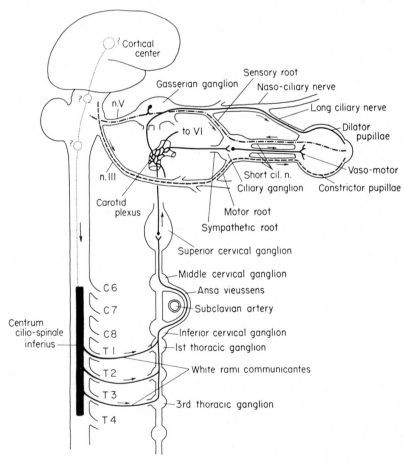

Fig. 51. Diagram of the ciliary ganglion with its connections and of the origin and course of the pupillodilator sympathetic nerve fibers. (Modified after Whitnall.)

breaks up into three twigs, supplying the inferior rectus, the medial rectus, and the inferior oblique. From this latter twig, a small filament runs to the ciliary ganglion (Fig. 51), called the short or motor root of the ganglion, and from the ganglion new fibers run to the eyeball in the short ciliary nerves. Usually about twenty of these nerves surround the optic nerve and penetrate the sclera to reach the suprachoroidal space. A layer of ganglion cells, from which fibers come off to supply the sphincter muscle, has been described in the suprachoroidea.

In the orbit and the anterior part of the cavernous sinus the pupillary fibers may be distributed among the somatic fibers of the inferior division of the third cranial nerve, or they may occupy a superficial, independent, and sharply localized position as far as the superior orbital fissure. In the front part of the cavernous sinus some of these fibers may be associated with fibers of the superior division. Back of this, between the middle of the sinus and the brainstem, the pupillary fibers are concentrated at and around the superior surface of the nerve.[5]

The so-called sympathetic and the sensory roots of the ciliary ganglion are not found in the cat, according to Christensen.[6] The short ciliary nerves as they leave the ciliary ganglion contain only postganglionic parasympathetic fibers. Sympathetic fibers, however, become incorporated in the short ciliary nerves before they enter the eyeball. In the orbit of the cat, therefore, there is partial separation of the postganglionic sympathetic and parasympathetic fibers which innervate the eye. Careful operative procedures should make it possible to deprive the eye of its postganglionic parasympathetic nerve supply by removal of the ciliary ganglion without disturbing the sympathetic nerve supply.

In man, the ciliary ganglion has a long or sensory root. This comes from the nasociliary nerve, which is a branch of the ophthalmic division of the fifth cranial nerve. It conducts sensory impulses from the whole eyeball back into the brain. It may also contain some efferent sympathetic fibers.

While the pupillomotor fibers of the sphincter undoubtedly synapse in the ciliary ganglion, there seems to be a question whether the sympathetic fibers synapse or pass through the ganglion. Weinstein[7] finds that after a retrobulbar injection of tetraethylammonium bromide, which paralyzes all the synapses in the ciliary ganglion, the pupil dilates, the accommodation is paralyzed, and the intraocular pressure is decreased. He interprets this as proof that the vasomotor fibers, innervated by the sympathetic, have a synapse in the ciliary ganglion.

Dilator pupillae.

Anatomy. The dilator pupillae extends from the ciliary border of the sphincter muscle to the root of the iris. Its presence was first proved physiologically by the classic experiments of Langley and Anderson before the muscle was found histologically. Prior to their work, there were three theories concerning the cause of the dilatation of the pupil produced by stimulating the cervical sympathetic: (1) inhibition of the sphincter muscle, (2) action of the sympathetic vasoconstrictor fibers on the blood vessels of the iris, and (3) contraction of a radially arranged muscle. Since histologic sections failed to show such a muscle, it was assumed that the sphincter had no active antagonist. It is now known that the dilator muscle is unusual in its histologic characteristics in that it contains pigment. Until the sections are depigmented, the muscle cannot be visualized.

Langley and Anderson showed that

changes in the size of the blood vessels could be eliminated as the cause of dilatation of the pupil by stimulating the sympathetic nerve in an animal which had been bled to death, first. The pupil dilated as in normal animals. They then made two radial cuts close together in the iris, obtaining a wedge-shaped piece isolated from the rest except at the ciliary border (Fig. 52). Contraction or relaxation of the sphincter muscle in such a strip might cause a slight narrowing or widening of its pupillary edge, but could not cause any radial movement inward or outward of the whole piece. They found that in this strip radial shortening was produced by direct stimulation and, more important, by stimulating the cervical sympathetic nerve in the neck. This movement could only be explained by the presence of an active radially arranged dilator muscle in the strip. Following this physiologic demonstration, the muscle was located histologically. In spite of this demonstration, from time to time the existence of a dilator muscle continues to

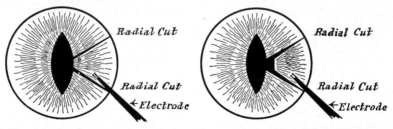

Fig. 52. Physiologic demonstration of the dilator muscle. The left-hand figure shows the electrodes placed on a pie-shaped piece of iris ready for stimulation. The right-hand figure shows the retraction of the pupil margin of this pie-shaped piece on stimulation.

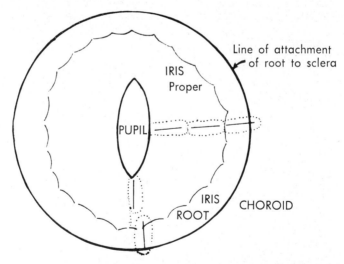

Fig. 53. Cat iris with cornea and corneoscleral junction removed. Whole iris and its root, overlying the ciliary body, is exposed. Slits *(solid radial lines)* were cut through the iris in three locations in the lateral iris and in two locations at the apex of the pupil. The iris segment surrounding the slits was removed by cutting with a de Wecker scissors on the dotted line. Segments from the sphincter, middle, and root portions of the iris are thus isolated. (From Apter, J.: Am. J. Ophth. **48:**316, 1959.)

be questioned. Recently Apter[8] has performed experiments the results of which are sufficiently convincing to reopen this debated question. Apter made radial slits in the iris in three situations as shown in Fig. 53, and removed the three sections of the iris surrounding each slit. These segments were then connected with a suitable apparatus for measuring changes in tension and were tested individually for their responses to electrical stimulation, Mecholyl, and epinephrine. The sphincter region contracted to Mecholyl and to the electric current, but relaxed to epinephrine. The root portion of the iris contracted equally to both Mecholyl and epinephrine and with even greater force to the electric current. The middle portion, however, containing the so-called dilator pupillae, did not respond to either drugs or electrical stimulation. From this Apter concludes that radial contractility in the iris arises in the sphincter and ciliary muscles but not in a so-called dilator pupillae.

The same technique was applied to enucleated human eyes, with the same results. The portion which is supposed to contain the dilator muscle failed to show contractility. In fact, the behavior of this section of the iris to temperature changes indicated that it contained no muscle, and the responses were characteristic of an elastic polymer. Further, isolated strips from the three sections of the iris showed that the sphincter contracted both radially and circumferentially to Mecholyl and electric current, but relaxed to epinephrine. The ciliary muscle contracted equally in both directions to epinephrine, to Mecholyl, and to the electric current. The dilator section, on the other hand, did not respond at all (Fig. 54).

It is apparent that an answer will have to be given to these seemingly strong arguments in favor of the nonexistence of a dilator muscle, but until either this work is confirmed or the interpretations are shown to be incorrect, we must adhere to our previous belief that a dilator muscle is present and, although in no way a match for the sphincter, acts in a recipro-

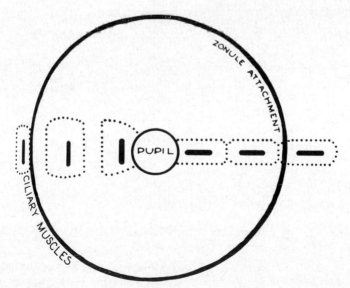

Fig. 54. Diagram of the human iris. *Solid lines,* slits; *dotted line,* outline of the excised segments. (From Apter, J.: Am. J. Ophth. **49:**1179, 1960.)

cal fashion to the sphincter and aids dilatation of the pupil under certain conditions by active contraction.[9] Other evidence will be presented throughout this chapter which proves that in man at least the dilator muscle, even if anatomically present, has far less to do with changes in pupil size than the state of contraction or relaxation of the sphincter muscle.

Nerve supply. The dilator muscle is supplied by sympathetic fibers. Stimulation of certain cortical areas in the brain will produce dilatation of the pupil, but this is due not to stimulation of a sympathetic center in the cortex but to in-

hibition of the third cranial nerve supply to the sphincter. In the cat, an area of the frontal cortex with a caudal extension backward through the basal telencephalon to the hypothalamus in which stimulation produces pupillary dilatation has been mapped out by Hodes and Magoun.[10] The dilator responses are effected entirely by inhibition of the third cranial nerve, however, since they cannot be elicited in the parasympathectomized iris.

Centers for the origin of sympathetic impulses are probably located in the hypothalamus. Stimulation over a wide

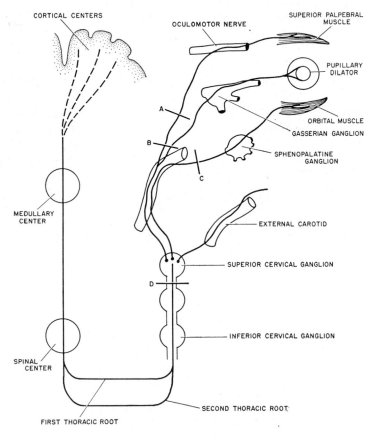

Fig. 55. Distribution of the cervical sympathetic nervous system. **A,** Lesion here would produce ptosis. **B,** Lesion here would produce ptosis and narrowing of the pupil. **C,** Lesion here would produce enophthalmos, theoretically. **D,** Lesion here would produce all the symptoms of Horner's syndrome. (After Walsh.)

area of this region produces dilatation of the pupil, but it is difficult to tell whether the effects are due to stimulation of the dilator pupillae or to inhibition of the sphincter. From such hypothetical centers, fibers travel down the cord as far as the eighth cervical and first dorsal ventral nerve roots. They leave the cord with these roots and proceed as white rami communicantes to the superior thoracic ganglia. They ascend the sympathetic chain as far up as the superior cervical ganglion (Fig. 55). Here they terminate, forming a synapse with the cells of the ganglion. New fibers now proceed to the dilator muscle by two routes. (1) Fibers run from the superior cervical ganglion to the gasserian ganglion and join the nasal branch of the ophthalmic division. They follow the nasal branch to the point where the two long ciliary nerves are given off. Here they follow the long ciliary nerves and penetrate the sclera, entering the suprachoroidal space, where they form a plexus from which fibers pro-

ceed to the dilator muscle. (2) From the superior cervical ganglion, fibers are given off which run to the various plexuses on the branches of the internal carotid artery. One of these is the cavernous plexus, which sends a fine branch to the ciliary ganglion.

Sympathetic fibers, therefore, run to the ciliary ganglion and enter the eyeball with the short ciliary nerves, along with the fibers destined for the sphincter muscle. In man, the short ciliary nerves contain both pupilloconstrictor and pupillodilator fibers. In the cat, the sympathetic fibers join the short ciliary nerves only between the eyeball and the ganglion where the short ciliary nerves are joined by branches from the long ciliary nerves.

Some general uncertainty exists about the preganglionic outflow of sympathetic fibers to the pupil, however. In man, Foerster[11] obtained homolateral dilatation of the pupil by stimulation of the anterior roots of the eighth cervical nerve and roots of the first and second thoracic

CASE NO.	C. 8	TH. 1	2	3	4	5
1	+	+	+	+	0	
2	0	+	0	0		
3	0	+	0	0		
4	0	+	+	0		
5	0	+	+	0		
6	0	+	+	0		
7	0	+	+	0		
8	0	+	+	+	0	
9	0	+	+	+	+	0
10	0	+	+	+	+	0

Fig. 56. Spinal levels for pupillary control. Stimulation at these levels produces pupillary control. (From Ray, B., Hinsey, J., and Geohegan, W.: Ann. Surg. 118:647, 1943.)

nerves. Hyndman and Wolkin[12] found that in five patients in whom the anterior roots of the first to the fifth thoracic nerves were sectioned bilaterally three showed bilateral miosis and ptosis, whereas two showed only unilateral changes. Ray, Hinsey, and Geohegan[13] exposed the anterior roots by laminectomy in a series of ten patients and in one patient found that, on stimulation, the preganglionic outflow to the pupil was through the anterior roots of the eighth cervical nerve to the root of the third thoracic nerve. In two patients stimulation of the first thoracic nerve alone caused pupillary dilatation. In four patients the anterior roots of the first and second thoracic nerves contained pupillary fibers. In one patient the roots of the first, second, and third thoracic nerves and in two patients the roots of the first through the fourth thoracic nerves contained pupillary fibers (Fig. 56). These observations show that the sympathetic innervation travels through one or more roots and between the levels of roots of the eighth cervical and fourth thoracic nerves. They amply demonstrate the great variability in the segmented sympathetic innervation of the pupil in man, a variation which is found not only in different persons, but also between the two sides of the same person.

Reciprocal innervation of the sphincter and dilator muscles. The sphincter and dilator muscles are antagonistic and have generally been thought to exhibit the phenomenon of reciprocal innervation (p. 414). Stimulation of a part of the sensorimotor area of the brain is followed by dilatation of the pupil, even though the sympathetic nerve has been cut, as stated. Inhibitory fibers must run from this portion of the cortex to the nucleus of the third cranial nerve, therefore, and dilatation of the pupil in this case has been regarded as due to a diminution in tone of the sphincter muscle.

Not all authors accept this reciprocal relationship, however. Apter,[14] e.g., studied this question by recording the electrical responses in the sympathetic and third nerves when the pupil was made to change size from a number of different stimuli. She found marked potentials for action in the ciliary ganglion during the response of the pupil to both light and darkness, whereas the superior cervical ganglion showed no change in electrical activity. On the other hand, the superior cervical ganglion did show activity in the pupillary dilatation which occurs when one awakens from sleep. During sleep the pupil is constricted, and the superior cervical ganglion is silent during sleep. From this, one might conclude that the constriction of the pupil during sleep is due to the absence of sympathetic tonus. Apter concluded that the sympathetic and parasympathetic innervations of the iris are independent variables—the sympathetic varying slowly through narrow limits and the parasympathetic varying swiftly through wide limits. Superimposed on this activity are the variations in the size of the pupil induced by changes in the vasoconstriction of the iridal blood vessels.

Lowenstein,[15] however, believes that the results obtained by Apter are due to the fact that the animals were under anesthesia, and according to him, anesthesia always inhibits the sympathetic mechanism. This, he says, can be shown easily because under anesthesia both pupils dilate equally at the same speed and to the same extent when the cat is unilaterally sympathectomized, and pupillary dilatation is abolished on the parasympathectomized side when the third nerve is cut, the ciliary ganglion is removed, or atropine is instilled into one conjunctival sac.

The majority of authors now believe that in cats pupillary dilatation following painful stimuli is due entirely to a diminution of tone of the third cranial nerve center.[16] From their experiments, Seybold and Moore[17] believe that inhibition of the activity of the third cranial nerve constitutes the principal factor in the reflex pupillodilatation elicited by the withdrawal of light, by painful stimulation, or by emotional excitement. If the sympathetic path only is interrupted in an animal, the sympathectomized pupil dilates readily on withdrawal of light and also in response to faradic stimulation of the sciatic nerve or to emotional excitement.

Although it is generally accepted that in the cat, and perhaps in the rabbit, inhibition of the parasympathetic mechanism is predominant in producing pupillary dilatation by all reflex stimulation, Weinstein and Bender[18] claim that in the monkey excitation of the sympathetic mechanism is of greater importance. These authors point out that the cat and monkey differ markedly in the response of the denervated iris to epinephrine and acetylcholine. They showed[19] that the sensitized denervated iris of the cat has a predominantly adrenergic dilator response, whereas the monkey reacts with a cholinergic constrictor effect to the introduction of either acetylcholine or epinephrine.

It is of interest, and not too surprising, that there should be a difference between these species in the neural as well as in the humoral aspects of pupillary dilatation. In recent years, evidence has been accumulating that the two muscles of the iris are not simple antagonists, as had been stated. Although it had been assumed that the sphincter muscle is inner-

vated by the parasympathetic third nerve, alone, and the dilator by the sympathetic fibers, alone, it is now believed that the sphincter is supplied by both cholinergic and adrenergic fibers. The dilator, on the other hand, is still thought to be supplied with only adrenergic fibers. It has been shown that certain drugs which are known to stimulate sympathetic nerves; e.g., epinephrine, have a distinct relaxing effect on the tone of the isolated sphincter muscle. If the iris is excised and the sphincter muscle is cut and suspended in an oxygenated Ringer solution, it shows rhythmic movements. These spontaneous movements last for an hour or so and are the expression of slight changes in tone of the muscle, which is not entirely relaxed. If a minute amount of epinephrine is added to the Ringer solution, the sphincter immediately relaxes and the rhythmic movements cease. On the basis of such experiments, together with more indirect reasoning, it has been concluded that the sphincter muscle is not innervated by the third cranial nerve alone but contains fibers from the sympathetic nerve which, when stimulated, inhibit the tone of the muscle.

It is evident that the sphincter muscle is much more powerful than the dilator, and the two can hardly be thought of as equal antagonists. It is believed by some that dilatation of the pupil occurs chiefly by inhibition of the sphincter. In some animals, and probably in man, this is aided by contraction of the dilator as well.

Constriction of the pupil takes place by contraction of the sphincter alone. Other unstriated muscles in the body have a double innervation. The bronchial muscle is inhibited by epinephrine and by stimulation of sympathetic fibers.

Variability in the size of the pupil, even if due to variation in oculomotor tonus alone, is in itself a summation of various nuclear events and is, therefore, complex. All the factors which are summated in pupillary reactions may be represented in a diagram (Fig. 57).

It must be assumed that the multitudinous factors which determine the size of the pupil operate around an inherent tonus of the pupilloconstrictor cells, i.e., the Edinger-Westphal nucleus. Keller[20] found that these cells continue to discharge impulses when they are completely deafferented by two transections of the brainstem, one placed above and the other below the oculomotor nuclei. Under these conditions, the pupils remain permanently and markedly constricted, except when they are dilated by sympathetic efferent impulses during spurts of somatic activity, such as struggling movements. Unilateral section of the cervical sympathetic nerve in the neck prevents dilatation of the pupil on that side under these conditions. Atropine applied to one eye results in dilatation of that pupil, whereas the other one remains constricted. It seems reasonably certain that the discharge of pupilloconstrictor impulses is due to an inherent mechanism within the cell bodies. The possibility that the dis-

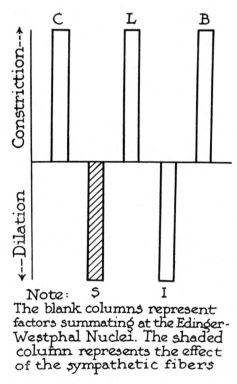

Note: The blank columns represent factors summating at the Edinger-Westphal Nuclei. The shaded column represents the effect of the sympathetic fibers

Fig. 57. Schematic representation of factor influencing pupillary diameter. S, Sympathetic dilator tonus which does not vary. Its effect is peripheral; whereas the four remaining elements enter into events occurring at the Edinger-Westphal nucleus. I, Central inhibition. C, Cortical component of pupillary constriction. It is obtainable in cats upon stimulation of the visual cortex. B, Constrictor tonus, independent of the light reflex. This is the basal tonus of the Edinger-Westphal nucleus. The paralytic dilatation during deep anesthesia signifies cessation of this spontaneous neural discharge and usually the death of the animal. (From Ury, B., and Oldberg, E.: J. Neurophysiol. 3:201, 1940.)

charge is due to an irritative stimulation of these cells by factors incident to the transection seems unlikely because the condition persists in a preparation that has been maintained for eleven weeks after operation. The only other possibility of extraneous stimulation would be a chemical one by way of the bloodstream. The increased tonus of the sphincter when the nuclei of origin of its motor nerves are isolated from incoming stimuli will be mentioned later in connection with the Argyll Robertson pupil (p. 219).

THE PUPIL

THE NORMAL PUPIL

Size and appearance. The size of the normal pupil varies at different ages. In the newborn infant, the pupils are small and usually remain so until about the first year of life. During childhood and adolescence the pupils are at their maximum size and gradually become smaller again with the passage of time. The pupils in advanced age are often miotic.

The pupils are in a state of constant change, depending upon the changing balance of power between the tonus of the sphincter and the dilator muscles. So many factors influence this balance of power that it is extremely difficult to isolate one from the others and to determine its effectiveness. Psychic influences are potent. Surprise, fear, and pain dilate the pupil markedly. The emotional reactions of the pupil depend not so much upon an increase in tonus of the dilator as upon an inhibition of the tonus of the sphincter. The reaction is initiated in the cerebral cortex, but some part of it is probably subcortical. Sustained dilatation of the pupil may occur in the presence of any emotion. Psychic dilatation can be brought about by almost any strong emotion,[21] pleasant or unpleasant, but it is most characteristic of anxiety or fear. During these disturbances, not only is the pupil dilated, but also the contraction to light is markedly diminished.

So many factors which influence the size of the pupil are operating constantly that normally it is in a constant state of movement. The excursions of this so-called *play* of the pupil are not great enough in a normal person to be noticed on casual observation, but in certain pathologic conditions they may become very marked. The condition is then called hippus.

The various factors which influence the state of the pupils may be divided into those determined by external circumstances and those which have no obvious cause in a person's surroundings. The former will be considered more fully in the discussion of pupillary reflexes.

Carefully controlled studies have shown that the reactions of the pupil do not depend on the activity of an isolated reflex arc, but are conditioned by the state of the whole central nervous system. For example, in subjects who are calm and well rested, adaptation to dim background illumination causes the pupil to become slightly smaller than in darkness, but if the subject is tired, the same background illumination has a profoundly depressing effect. The pupil become quite small and the reaction to standard light flashes follows abnormal patterns.[22]

The diameter of the normal adult pupil is somewhere between 3 and 4 mm. The pupil is generally larger in women than in men, in general is larger in myopic persons than in hyperopic persons, and is larger in blue-eyed persons than in brown-eyed persons. If the two pupils are unequal, the condition is termed anisocoria. About 17% of normal persons show slight but perceptible anisocoria, and in 4% of normal persons[23] the difference in pupillary size is pronounced. Probably anisocoria should never be dismissed as normal, however, since Lowenstein[24] considers anisocoria to be due always to a unilateral or bilateral lesion. Although it may be harmless, it is never physiologic. In fact, it is impossible to produce "physiologic" anisocoria in man or monkeys by unequal illumination of the two eyes.[25] In cats, however, unequal illumination causes a greater reaction in the stimulated eye than in the opposite eye. This difference among the species is due to the fact that in cats the crossed fibers greatly outnumber the uncrossed fibers whereas in man the crossed and uncrossed pupillary fibers are about equal in number.

The color of the iris plays a part in the reactions of the pupil to drugs. It is well recognized that mydriatics are more effective in light-colored than in dark-colored eyes. Mydriasis is difficult to obtain in Negroes.

The pupil during sleep. The pupil during sleep is contracted rather than dilated. One would expect to find the pupil dilated when the lids are closed and no light enters the eyes. The miotic pupil during sleep, however, is such a constant finding that it serves as an aid in differentiating true from simulated sleep. Two possible explanations may be offered to account for the miosis of the pupil during sleep. It may be due to shutting out the stimuli from the cortex, which keep the sympathetic center constantly alive. On this basis the miosis would be due to changes in tonus of the sympathetically innervated muscles. The miosis may also be due to shutting off inhibitory impulses to the constrictor center. In the waking state it is assumed that the cortex constantly inhibits the activity of subcortical centers. This loss of cortical inhibition during sleep allows the sub-

cortical center full play, with the result that the pupil becomes miotic.

Morphine causes miosis so marked that in man pinpoint pupils are almost never due to any other cause, and the morphine habitué may thus be detected. The cause of this miosis is not known.

The pupil during anesthesia. During anesthesia, the behavior of the pupil is an aid in determining the depth of narcosis. In Stages I and II of anesthesia the pupil is generally dilated because of emotional stress. In Stage III, i.e., the stage of surgical anesthesia, the pupil constricts and becomes smaller than normal. Stage IV, which heralds medullary paralysis and death, is generally ushered in with dilatation of the pupils. On occasion it is confusing from the behavior of the pupils to determine whether the patient is re-entering Stage II of anesthesia and approaching consciousness or entering Stage IV. This can be determined only by other associated signs, such as the presence of movements of the eyeball, corneal reflex, and lacrimation, all of which indicate that the patient is re-entering Stage II and should be given more anesthetic. The dilatation of the pupil in Stage II is reflex in character in contrast to the paralytic dilatation of Stage IV. The pupillary reflex to light is always present in Stage II.

Stage III of surgical anesthesia is often divided into four planes, according to the depth of the anesthesia. The pupils are contracting in Planes 1 and 2 and attain a size about that commensurate with deep sleep in this, the desired plane of surgical anesthesia. As the patient passes into Planes 3 and 4, however, the pupils begin to dilate again, and as Stage IV is approached, they dilate widely and often suddenly. Provided that no morphine or other drugs have been given beforehand, the behavior of the pupils is an excellent guide for the experienced anesthetist.

Functions of the pupil. The functions of the pupil are principally optical and will not be considered here in detail. Contraction of the pupil reduces the amount of light entering the eye. It acts as an emergency mechanism, therefore, giving the retina time during which it can adapt to a change in illumination (p. 706). Narrowing the pupil cuts off the peripheral parts of the refracting system. Hence, it diminishes spherical and chromatic aberrations and the astigmatism caused by oblique pencils of light. It also increases the depth of focus. The focal length of the eye is about 20 mm., and the pupil can expand from approximately 1.5 mm. to 8 mm. Thus, the effective aperture varies between f. 13 and f. 2.5, which is a range of nearly 30 to 1 in the amount of light admitted.

Shape of the pupil and its position in the eye. It makes no difference in the shape or the clarity of the image whether the pupil is centrally situated or on one side of the center, provided that the eye be properly focused. Even double pupils have no effect on the image if the eye is in focus. If the location of the pupil is not close to the optic axis, the rays which enter the optical system of the eye will not be paraxial and will suffer therefore from certain aberrations, even though they will be focused on the retina. This fact should be borne in mind when considering the proper place in the iris to perform an optical iridectomy. It makes no difference what portion of the iris is cut away, provided that it be close to the optic axis of the eye. The shape of the opening makes no difference, as long as it is large enough to admit sufficient light. It also makes no difference whether one or several openings be made in the iris so long as the eye is emmetropic or is made so with correcting glasses.

PUPILLARY REFLEXES
Reflexes constricting the pupil

Light reflex, direct and consensual. Whenever the intensity of illumination increases above a threshold value within a certain minimum period of time, the pupil constricts. The constriction of the pupil when light is thrown directly into the eye is called the *direct light reflex*. Not only does the pupil in which the light is thrown contract, but the pupil on the opposite side contracts also. The constriction of the opposite pupil is called the *consensual light reflex*. This pupil is said to react consensually. The reaction of the pupil, either directly or consensually, is a true reflex, independent of the will. Like other reflexes, it has a threshold value in both time and intensity. If the illumination is changed very gradually, no constriction of the pupil will occur unless the illumination becomes very intense. On the other hand, a slight but rapid increase in illumination produces prompt constriction of the pupil.

Direct light reflex. In general it can be said that there is no definite quantitative relation between the size of the stimulus on the one hand and the reaction of the pupil on the other. The same change in intensity of illumination may at one time cause contraction of the pupil and at another dilatation. This is due to the multiplicity of factors which affect the tonus of the constrictor and dilator mechanisms. The chief factor which determines what effect a given change in illumination will have on the pupil is the state of adaptation of the retina (p. 706). The second most important factor in determining the effect of a given stimulus on the contraction of the pupil is the portion of the retina which is stimulated. Not all parts of the retina are of equal value in producing the light reflex, any more than they are of value in the visual function.

It has been claimed that only the fovea and a small portion around the fovea are capable of causing a contraction of the pupil. The fovea undoubtedly has the greatest ability to elicit a pupillomotor reaction, just as it has the greatest visual acuity. As soon as the illumination is directed off the fovea, the pupil responds considerably less than when the same stimulus is directed on the fovea. The retina surrounding the optic nerve hardly responds at all. If the size of the stimulus, on the other hand, is increased considerably, the response of the periphery of the retina may nearly equal that of the fovea.

The light reflex, like other reflexes, has a definite latent period. An average latent period of 0.18 second has been determined by means of motion pictures. This is a relatively long latent period as compared to most reflexes. The patellar reflex, for example, has a latent period of about 0.06 second. The long latency in the light reflex points to many synapses being involved, for the rapidity with which a nerve conducts an impulse is known to be very great. Certainly the transformation of the light energy in the retina into a nerve impulse, whether visual or pupillomotor, is an extremely rapid one if we are to judge by the visual process and by the action currents in the retina.

The reflex time, i.e., the time elapsing between the beginning of the stimulus and the maximum contraction, is about 0.94 second. Following maximum contraction, the pupil often dilates slightly and then constricts again. One finds great variability in the state of the pupil thereafter in different subjects. Some pupils may stay contracted for a considerable length of time after the stimulus is applied; others dilate again almost immediately.

The contraction of the pupil to light may be fatigued by repeated stimuli. If the same spot of the retina is stimulated repeatedly, this so-called fatigue can be noticed easily. The size of the contraction diminishes gradually. It is not true fatigue of the sphincter muscle, but is caused by adaptation of the retinal receptors.

The rate of the constriction shows considerable individual variations. The average pupil reaches its maximum contraction in less than 5 seconds, and the greatest part of the contraction occurs within the first 2 seconds. When the stimulus is removed, the pupil dilates quite slowly, the time for dilatation being several times that required for contraction of the pupil.

Adaptation to light naturally influences the pupillary light reflex, since light adaptation reduces the sensitivity of the retina (p. 707). Exposure to a bright light will reduce the effect of a weak stimulating light flash so that the pupil response may even be abolished. If the adapting light is weak and the stimulating light flash is intense, the pupil will respond with a strong reaction. Evidence has also been presented that adaptation to dim light alters the functional state of the Edinger-Westphal nucleus.[22]

The details of the changes in pupil size and the speed of the various parts of the pupil contraction under the influence of light have been carefully documented by Lowenstein.[26]

Consensual light reflex. The stimulation of one retina by light produces a contraction of the pupil in the opposite eye in all animals in which there is partial decussation of the optic nerve fibers in the chiasm. In the lower vertebrates, in which the chiasmal decussation is complete, a consensual reaction is absent. Although the latent period of the consensual reaction in man is the same as that of the direct reflex, the pupil reacting consensually takes longer to attain its final constrictive size, and when this is reached, the diameter of this pupil is generally greater than that of the pupil reacting directly.

If the light is thrown simultaneously into both eyes, the response is greater than that which results from the stimulation of one eye, for both types of response (direct and consensual)—summate. The question of whether simultaneous stimulation of both retinas produces a greater response than stimulation of one retina only has interested investigators for some time.

Thomson[27] devised several experiments to find out if summation of afferent impulses occurred when a purely objective effect, such as contraction of the pupil, is measured. Since the nervous pathways of the pupillary light reflex do not ascend higher than the midbrain, the results might help to localize the site of summation of visual phenomena within the nervous system. He found that the degree of constriction of the pupil which results from the stimulation by light of the retina of the single eye was significantly less than that obtained when both eyes were stimulated. This binocular summation was equivalent to that obtained by increasing the area of the stimulating flash between two and four times and observing a single eye throughout. It did not seem to be influenced by cerebral cortical activity. He points out that the afferent neurons of the light reflex do not utilize coordinating neurons above the level of the midbrain; therefore the binocular and areal summations in these experiments probably occur at the synapses within either the pretectal regions or the oculomotor nucleus. It is possible, therefore, that the binocular summation found in measurements of the dark-adaptation threshold occurs at a level below that of the cerebral cortex, perhaps in this case in the lateral geniculate body.

Afferent pathway of the light reflex.

There can be little question that the receptors for the pupillary light reflex are identical with those concerned in the act of vision, i.e., the outer limbs of the rods and cones. The question arises whether two separate sets of fibers convey the afferent pupillary and the visual impulses, or whether these impulses reach the brain by one and the same fiber. Each optic nerve is composed of fibers of two different sizes, large and small. It has been assumed that the thick fibers conduct the afferent pupillary impulses and the smaller fibers the visual impulses. No physiologic evidence is available to decide this point.

The pupillary fibers are probably collaterals given off by the visual fibers, and the same optic nerve fiber probably conducts both visual and afferent pupillary impulses. These separate from each other before reaching their appropriate cell terminations.

As far as we can tell, the pupillary fibers follow the course of the visual fibers in every respect and undergo semidecussation in the chiasm. They travel with the visual fibers in the optic tract up to the lateral geniculate body. Up to this point, it is not possible to separate the afferent pupillary fibers from the visual fibers by lesions produced either experimentally or as the result of disease processes. At the level of the lateral geniculate body, however, the afferent pupillary fibers separate from the visual fibers, and it is possible to produce lesions which affect one or the other functions separately.

Pupilloconstrictor responses are obtained from stimulation of the optic chiasm, of the optic tract on the lateral surface of the brain stem and ventral to the lateral geniculate body, of the brachium of the superior colliculus, of the pretectal region, and of the posterior commissure and the fibers emerging from it and arch-

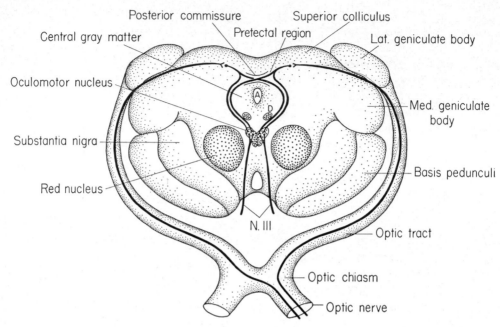

Fig. 58. Diagram of the path for the pupillary light reflex. Abbreviations: **A,** aqueduct; **D,** nucleus of Darkshevitch; **N. III,** oculomotor nerve. (After Ranson.)

ing ventrally around the central gray matter at the level of transition between the third ventricle and the cerebral aqueduct (Fig. 58). Pupillary constriction is never obtained from stimulation of the superior colliculus itself. It was previously thought that the afferent pupilloconstrictor fibers ended in the superior colliculus, but the work of Ranson, Magoun, and others,[28-30] using the Horsley-Clarke apparatus, has demonstrated conclusively that the fibers do not run into the superior colliculus.

Barris, Ingram, and Ranson[31] traced crossed and uncrossed fibers of retinal origin through the stratum zonale of the thalamus to the pretectal area where they appeared to terminate. This was done by the usual methods of staining for degeneration of nerve fibers following enucleation of one eye. Using the same method, Barris[32] traced fibers from the cortex to the pretectal area where they appeared to end.

Stimulation of this area after degeneration of the optic tract produces constriction of the pupil, which indicates that the pretectal area is the site of a synapse in the pathway concerned with constriction of the pupil. Several groups of cells lie in this region, and when it is destroyed bilaterally, the response of the pupil to light can be permanently abolished.

In the rabbit, the pretectal cell masses consist of three separate nuclear groups.[33] In the monkey, the pretectal region includes the nucleus of the optic tract, the pretectal nucleus, and the nucleus of the posterior commissure.[34] Magoun and Ranson[35] have summarized the evidence bearing upon the participation of the pretectal region in the pupillary light reflex in the cat.

From the pretectal region, the pathway swings ventrally around the rostral gray matter of the aqueduct to the oculomotor nucleus, undergoing partial decussation in the posterior commissure and another decussation ventral to the central gray matter. The pathway includes the pretectal region of the brain but, as stated, not the superior colliculus. After the fibers reach the brachium of the superior colliculus, they do not enter the superior colliculus itself but turn rostrally and medially into the pretectal region. Here, the synapse is made as just described, and from the pretectal region the pathway descends around the rostral end of the central gray matter to the oculomotor nuclei. In the cat and in the monkey, central crossings in the path have been found, both in the posterior commissure and ventral to the aqueduct in the immediate vicinity of the oculomotor nuclei. Bilateral responses are obtained from electrical stimulation of the posterior commissure and the region dorsilateral to it, whereas marked ipsilateral and weak contralateral constriction are obtained from stimulation of the fibers arching ventrally around the central gray matter.

Szentagothai[36] has confirmed the findings of Ranson and Magoun by histologic examination of the region following degeneration of the fibers as a result of experimentally induced lesions. The afferent pupillary fibers of retinal origin were found to end in the central lamellae of the lateral geniculate ganglion. From here, a second afferent intercalated neuron begins and runs in a quite superficial position over the superior colliculus and the pretectal region toward the posterior commissure where the majority of the fibers seem to cross. The reflex fibers lie in the most dorsal part of the posterior commissure immediately under the ependyma of the recessus pinealis. Crossed and uncrossed reflex fibers join together outside of the interstitial nucleus, running around to the posterior longitudinal bundle in a ventrocaudal direction. From here, they

immediately go to the small ganglion cells (Edinger-Westphal nuclei) lying in front of the large-celled oculomotor nuclei, where they terminate.

The results of pathologic lesions, in man, suggest *complete* decussation of the pathway of the light reflex in the posterior commissure, but this has not been found in experimental animals. Ranson and Magoun have shown a *partial* crossing of the pathway of the light reflex in the posterior commissure of the cat. This was confirmed by Magoun, Ranson, and Mayer.[37] Following destruction of the posterior commissure in the midline, the light reactions were reduced but not abolished. Lesions in the pretectal region do not in any sense produce an Argyll Robertson pupil in experimental animals.

No observable pupillary reaction to accommodation can be shown obviously in the cat. Miosis does occur following lesions of the pretectal region, but this lasts for only a few days and then disappears as the irritation caused by the lesion subsides. In the chronic stage, the pupils of these experimental animals are widely dilated. One cannot say, therefore, whether the miosis in Argyll Robertson pupils (p. 219) is due to a chronic irritation of some part of the pupilloconstrictor path or to an associated lesion in the pupillodilator pathway. However, Magoun and Ranson[38] do not see how it is possible for both the pupilloconstrictor and the pupillodilator pathways to be interrupted by a single lesion of any moderate extent in this region.

Efferent pathway of the sphincter mechanism. The Edinger-Westphal nucleus is generally considered to be the part of the nucleus of the third cranial nerve which controls the sphincter pupillae. The oculomotor nucleus in man lies under the aqueduct of Sylvius and extends from about 5 mm. from the rostral to near the caudal border of the superior colliculus. The length of 5 mm. for the entire nucleus of the third cranial nerves does not include allowance for shrinkage in the preparation of the specimen, nor does it include the nucleus of Darkshevich. It consists of three readily distinguishable portions (Fig. 186, p. 448). The first portion, called the large-celled nucleus, is made up of cells which are polygonal or multipolar in shape. These large cells possess a large-celled nucleus which is less sharply bounded than the nucleus of the small cells because of the relatively greater quantity of cytoplasm. The cells are typical somatic motor cells. The mass of cells may be subdivided into dorsal, ventral, and scattered groups. The second portion of the oculomotor nucleus is a compact mass of cells in the midline, which is called Perlia's nucleus. These are typical efferent cells but are smaller than those of the first portion. They form an almond-shaped mass which lies between the right and left large-celled masses. The sharper and more tapered end of the mass is directed forward, the caudal end being more blunt, like those of the lateral chief masses. The third portion, called the Edinger-Westphal nucleus, consists of small cells of the visceral motor type. They are usually slightly more elongated than those of the other two portions. These small cells have a bilateral representation, and each half is divided into medial and lateral portions.

The oculomotor nucleus of the cat is similar to that of man in position and in relation to the aqueduct of Sylvius, the raphe, and the medial longitudinal fasciculus. The subdivisions of this nucleus in the cat are the same as in man, except that the median or central nucleus of Perlia is wanting in this animal (p. 448).

Benjamin,[39] using Horsley-Clarke stereotaxic instruments, has investigated the various regions of the nucleus of the oculomotor nerve in a series of cats. He believes that the caudoventrally arching fibers of the posterior commissure constitute a part of the pathway for the constrictor reflex of the pupil. He considers it possible that the anterior median small-celled group of the oculomotor nucleus may form a part of the constrictor center in the cat, but that the Edinger-Westphal cells form a more important and extensive portion of such a center and have for at least one of their functions the contraction of the sphincter pupillae. The large cells in the caudal third of the oculomotor nucleus of the cat have nothing to do with the constriction of the pupil. Crouch[40] has shown that each iris is innervated by both the homolateral and contralateral portions of the Edinger-Westphal nucleus. Each iris is, therefore, under the control of both the crossed and the uncrossed fibers. Each side of the nucleus, therefore, influences both pupils. This clarifies the mechanism by means of which both pupils react as a unit to constrictor impulses in the consensual light reflex and to central inhibition.

Boeke has carefully described the minute innervation of the iris and ciliary body in man and in the monkey.[41] He describes an anastomosing plexus of nerve fibers in the ciliary body with nerve endings in two regions. Two types of endings are present. Small rings and bulbous endings are found among the connective tissue cells, and also present are fine anastomosing nets of neurofibrillar bundles which run between the muscle fibers and send fine branches into them where they end as intraprotoplasmic rings near the nucleus. The same two types of endings are found in the sphincter muscle. Boeke considered the first type of ending to be sensory and the second type to be motor.

Although it is still debated whether the Edinger-Westphal nucleus is concerned with the innervation of the sphincter pupillae, the evidence is distinctly in favor of the conclusion that the efferent pathway begins in these cells. As Cogan[42] points out, however, no fibers have been traced from the Edinger-Westphal nucleus into the oculomotor group, and section of the oculomotor nerve does not result in retrograde degeneration into the Edinger-Westphal nucleus.

Accommodation-convergence reaction (near reflex). When a person is requested to direct his eyes to an object held close to the face, the pupils contract. This contraction is independent of any change in illumination and depends upon an association of the sphincter pupillae with the ciliary muscle and the medial recti. It is not a true reflex but an associated movement or synkinesis for which there is an anatomic basis. The medial recti muscles and the ciliary muscles, as well as the sphincter pupillae, are all innervated by branches of the third cranial nerve. It is natural that the impulse to look at an object close at hand should always associate these three mechanisms, for they serve a common purpose. The medial recti contract so that the image of an object close to the eyes will be thrown on both foveas. Contraction of the ciliary muscles takes place so that the image will be in focus on each fovea, and contraction of the pupil takes place, probably as a further optical aid to increase the depth of focus. Since this reaction of the pupil is a synkinesis, dependent on the nearness of the object of regard, it is generally considered best termed the near point reaction, or near reaction of the pupil.

Afferent pathway. The contraction of the pupil does not depend on either the accommodation or the convergence any more than does the convergence or accommodation depend upon others of the triad. All three must be looked upon as being associated in a common function. Normally they work together, but one may be dissociated from the others. Thus, it is possible to have contraction of the pupil with convergence of the visual axis without accommodation by placing plus lenses in front of each eye to take the place of the accommodation needed for the near point. Likewise, convergence can be prevented by placing base-in prisms in front of each eye. When a person is asked to read fine print under both these circumstances, the pupil will contract.

Renard[43] claims that the contraction of the pupil is not associated in any way with accommodation. He calls attention to the fact that pupillary contraction takes place if the effort of convergence is imposed by the interposition of a prism, even if the subject looks in the distance. Pupillary contraction exists in myopic persons and in very old people who have lost all accommodation. The contraction of the pupil begins only at the moment that the fixated object comes within 0.5 M. and not at the moment that accommodation begins. It is abolished in paralysis of convergence when accommodation is intact. He points out that the contrary arguments, based on the persistence of pupillary contraction in one-eyed persons and during isolated paralysis of a medial rectus muscle, have no value because synkinesis exists with the effort of convergence, which is effected even in these cases. The accommodation thus plays no part in its production. The reaction, according to Renard, should be termed "pupillary synergy during convergence." The constriction of the pupil takes place equally in both eyes, even though one be covered. This is true even though the vision in one eye is considerably impaired.

Although the center for the near reaction of the pupil is probably the cells in the Edinger-Westphal nucleus, the stimulus which initiates the contraction of the pupil comes to this nucleus by an entirely different route than that which contracts the pupil due to the stimulus of light. It is, therefore, possible to have a lesion which destroys the reaction of the pupil to light and yet the near reaction of the pupil is kept intact. This type of abnormal pupillary response is known as the Argyll Robertson pupil, which will be discussed later. The reverse of an Argyll Robertson pupil—namely, contraction of the pupil to light but absence of the near reaction—is theoretically possible.

Efferent pathway. It has been claimed that the impulses of the sphincter in response to the near reaction may be relayed partially outside the ciliary ganglion since miosis is said to occur with accommodation, even after removel of the ciliary ganglion.[44] Nathan and Turner[45] have suggested two efferent pathways for pupillary contraction, one passing through the ciliary ganglion and subserving the light reflex and the other subserving the near reaction which runs outside the ciliary ganglion. On the basis of the presence of a unilateral Argyll Robertson pupil in a patient following an attack of herpes zoster ophthalmicus, Naquin[46] believes that there are two separate efferent pathways to the sphincter—one for the light reflex and one for the near reflex. The latter passes without synapse from the convergence-accommodation center in the midbrain to the iris sphincter. The constrictor fibers, for the light reflex, on the other hand, synapse in the ciliary ganglion on their way to the iris sphincter (for a discussion of the significance of this in the site of the Argyll Robertson pupil see p. 219).

Further evidence will have to be presented before it can be accepted that any of the pupilloconstrictor fibers run outside of the ciliary ganglion, or that there is a separate pathway for the fibers which contract the pupil to light and those which contract the pupil to the stimulus of the near point reaction.

Lid-closure reaction (orbicularis reflex). If a person is told to try to close one eye while the two lids are held apart so that they cannot close, a constriction of the pupil may be observed. This phenomenon occurs only when the orbicularis muscle is actively innervated. It is of value in proving the integrity of the efferent pupillary pathway in patients in whom the pupil fails to respond either to light or at the near point. The presence of a constriction when this test is applied proves that the sphincter is functioning. The reaction is said to occur if the eyelids are closed reflexly as well as voluntarily. It is a typical associated movement of synkinesis that occurs only in the eye under examination and never consensually in the other eye. It is not always present, however.

This reaction is usually regarded as proof of the direct connection between the facial nucleus and the cells of the third cranial nerve supplying the superior rectus and the inferior oblique. It will be recalled that this accounts for an upward deviation of the eyeball when the eyelids are closed and is referred to as Bell's phenomenon (p. 27). When the eyelids are voluntarily closed, contraction of the pupil takes place, associated with upward rolling of the globe. It also occurs during spontaneous blinking and during closure of the eyelids caused by corneal stimulation.

Afferent pathway. The cortical, nuclear, and internuncial pathways for this associated act are not known. In man, the act of closing the eyelids is widely represented in the motor cortex.[47]

Efferent pathway. The efferent pathway of the orbicularis reflex is the same as that for the near reaction, as far as is known.

Trigeminal reflex (oculopupillary reflex). It is a matter of common experience that the pupil is constricted if an eye is irritated in any way, such as by a cinder imbedded in the cornea. Any marked irritation of the cornea or conjunctiva or even of the lids results in constriction of the pupil. It is true that painful stimuli result in dilatation of the pupil, but only if the painful irritation lasts but a short time. When the irritation is long continued, the pupil constricts and finally stays constricted. Both pupils may be constricted, but the pupil of the affected side is usually narrowed to a greater extent. The pathway for this reflex is the ophthalmic branch of the fifth cranial nerve to the gasserian ganglion and the nucleus of the fifth cranial nerve. Connecting fibers finally run to the sphincter nucleus by way of the medial longitudinal bundle.

The constriction of the pupil is due also to a local reflex dilatation of the iris capillaries, called an axon reflex (Fig. 59). Stimulation of the endings of the fifth cranial nerves causes reflex dilatation of the capillaries in the iris, similar to the dilatation of the skin capillaries when a sensory nerve in the skin is stimulated. Whenever the peripheral end of a posterior root is stimulated, dilatation of the capillaries of the skin occurs in the area supplied by the posterior root. The fibers conducting these vasodilator reflexes have their cell stations in the ganglia of the posterior root. These vasodilator impulses have been designated antidromic since

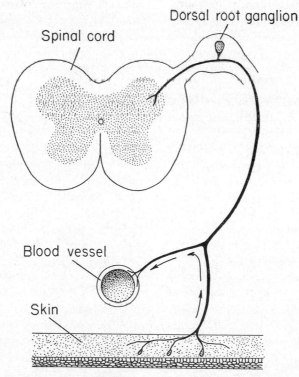

Fig. 59. Diagram illustrating the axon reflex.

they are opposite in direction to those which the nerve usually carries. Antidromic impulses may be carried in the fifth cranial nerve, and the gasserian ganglion may be regarded as the ganglion of its posterior root. Thus the vasodilator impulses may reach the iris, and the dilatation of the blood vessels gives rise to a constricted pupil. The role of changes in the blood vessels of the iris in the production of variations in size of the pupil has recently been emphasized by Longworthy and Ortaga[48] and by Apter.[14] Such changes may undoubtedly cause change in the width of the pupil. It is common experience to find a very narrow pupil in a person with beginning cyclitis. In spite of the prolonged use of atropine, an increase in the severity of cyclitis always produces lessened pupillary dilatation. This is a good guide, therefore, to the progress of the cyclitis. Dilatation of the pupil cannot be accounted for satisfactorily by contraction of the blood vessels of the iris.

Reflexes dilating the pupil

Withdrawal of light. The withdrawal of light from the eyes causes dilatation of the pupil. In a conscious normal subject the pupils will remain dilated in the dark, but if the light is simply subdued, the pupils generally constrict again to physiologic size. This is further proof that the size of the pupil depends not only on the illumination, but also on the adaptation of the retina. Gullberg, Olmstead, and Wagman[49, 50] showed by means of infrared photographs that the dilatation of the pupil in the dark is the result of two mechanisms: (1) passive elasticity of the iris tissue and (2) actual contraction of the dilator pupillae. The maximum pupil diameter during normal dark adaptation is reached when the added effect of these two mechanisms just balances the residual tone of the constrictor pupillae. After the sympathetic nerve is cut, the maximum diameter of the pupil is less than normal and is now determined by the balance between the passive elasticity of the iris on the one hand and the residual tone of the constrictor pupillae on the other.

Stimulation of the sensory nerve. Stimulation of most sensory nerves causes dilatation of the pupil, especially if the stimulation results in pain. It was shown that in most experimental animals the dilatation of the pupil to painful stimuli was generally thought to be due to parasympathetic inhibition. This may not be true for man, however. Arieff[51] studied patients with complete lesions of the spinal cord in the cervical region. Painful stimulation of regions of the body above the site of the lesion of the cord failed to produce pupillary dilatation, whereas similar stimuli applied below the site of the lesion did cause pupillary dilatation. In man, therefore, dilatation of the pupil from painful stimuli may be due to sympathetic activity and not to parasympathetic inhibition.

Vestibular stimulation. Stimulation of the vestibular apparatus, either rotatory or caloric, generally causes dilatation of the pupil during and for a short time after cessation of the stimulus. Some fibers of the sympathetic nerve connected with the iris muscle probably run through the middle ear because it has been noted that after a radical mastoid operation, paresis of the pupillary fibers of the sympathetic nerve is occasionally found on the operated side. The pupil on this side is contracted, and cocaine fails to dilate it as widely as its fellow.

Psychic stimulation. Dilatation of the pupils is observed as a result of psychic stimuli, especially in emotional states such as fear and anxiety. The dilatation is caused by stimulation of the sympathetic nerve.

REACTIONS OF THE PUPIL TO LESIONS OF VARIOUS PARTS OF THE REFLEX ARC
Studies to be made in determining location of lesions

The location of a lesion in the pupillomotor pathways is suggested by the characteristic behavior of the pupillary re-

sponses. If some schematic representation of the pupillary pathways, such as shown in Fig. 60, is adopted it is possible to determine the location of a lesion in different parts of the pathway with some accuracy. One may trace the course of an impulse through the various afferent tracts to the oculomotor or sympathetic nuclei and thence along the efferent or motor pathway to the sphincter or dilator muscle of the iris. An interruption of the im-

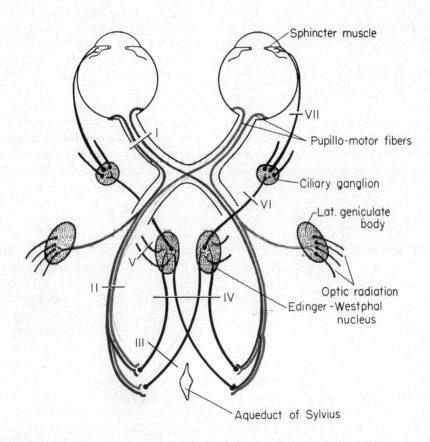

Fig. 60. Diagrammatic representation of the pupillomotor pathways. **I** to **VII**, Lesions at various levels in the pathways. These are some examples used for illustration and do not refer to the numbers given on p. 216 indicating all the possible lesions. **I**, Lesion between the photoreceptors and the lateral geniculate body. **II**, Lesion of the tracts beyond the lateral geniculate body, as far as the tegmentum. **III**, Lesion of the intercalated fibers on one side. **IV**, Same on both sides. **V**, Lesion of the fibers impinging on the Edinger-Westphal nucleus, which produce the near point reaction and the orbicularis reaction. **VI**, Lesion of the preganglionic third nerve fiber. **VII**, Lesion of the postganglionic third nerve fiber.

pulses at any point will necessarily result in an altered response of one or both pupils, and this will be more or less characteristic for the particular part of the pathway affected. In order to determine what part of the pathway in a particular patient is affected, it may be necessary to observe the reactions of the pupil not only to the ordinary reflexes, but also to certain drugs. The effect of drugs on the pupil will be considered more fully on pp. 222 to 233.

The following may have to be studied in any individual patient: (1) the physiologic state of each pupil—size, shape, and equality with its fellow, (2) the presence of atrophy of the iris, anterior or posterior synechiae, or other evidence of pathologic disorder in the iris, (3) the play of the pupil, whether it is normal, increased, or decreased, (4) the light reflex, direct and consensual, of each pupil, (5) the near reaction of each pupil, (6) the sensory and psychic reflexes, (7) the orbicularis reaction, and (8) the reaction to certain drugs such as eserine, pilocarpine, atropine, the cholines, cocaine, and epinephrine.

Various pathways and parts of pathways of the pupil involved in lesions

The following pathways and parts of pathways of the pupil may be involved by lesions: (1) the ascending or afferent pathway of the light reflex, which includes the structures from the rods and cones up to the pretectal region, (2) the intercalated fibers from the synapse in this region into the posterior commissure from which the fibers bifurcate and run to the Edinger-Westphal nuclei of both sides, (3) supranuclear afferent pathways coming from undetermined regions of the brain having to do with associated movements of the pupil, such as the near or orbicularis reaction, (4) the oculomotor nucleus itself, that is, the Edinger-Westphal nucleus, (5) the oculomotor nerves from the Edinger-Westphal nucleus to the ciliary ganglion, (6) the ciliary ganglion and short ciliary nerves and their endings in the sphincter muscle, both cholinergic and adrenergic, (7) the myoneural junction of the third cranial nerve in the sphincter muscle, (8) the cells of the sphincter muscle, themselves, (9) any part of the afferent sympathetic pathway from the hypothalamus through the brainstem to the superior cervical ganglion and thence into the eye by the long ciliary nerves and possibly by way of the short ciliary nerves also, and (10) the dilator muscle.

Lesions of the afferent pathway of the light reflex. There are various types of lesions of the afferent pathway of the light reflex.

Lesions between receptors and the chiasm. A lesion situated between the rods and cones in the retina and the chiasm will give rise to visual disturbances, as well as pupillomotor disturbances, on that side. The visual disturbance will depend upon the involvement of the visual fibers and will vary in extent and intensity, depending upon the situation and severity of the lesion. The nearer it is to the cones in the macula or their ascending fibers in the papillomacular bundle, the greater will be the effect on the central visual acuity and the pupillomotor response. A lesion situated away from the macula or the papillomacular bundle will produce no effect on the central acuity, but will result in some type of defect of the visual field, e.g., a scotoma, a nerve fiber bundle defect, etc., depending upon its situation. There will be little if any demonstrable change in the pupillary reactions unless the visual defect is gross. Gross lesions will show the following reactions. (1) The reaction to direct light on the affected side is weak or abolished, but, if the pupil responds at all, its contraction will be prompt and concentric. (2) The extent of the movement will be diminished, and the pupil will not remain contracted as long as normal. (3) The consensual reflex in the opposite eye will be affected to the same degree.

If the opposite eye is normal and its afferent pathway is intact, the reaction to direct light of this eye will be normal, and the consensual reaction of the affected side will also be normal. This assumes, of course, that the *efferent* pathway on the affected side is normal. The near reaction and the orbicularis reaction will be normal in both eyes. The response of both pupils to drugs will be normal.

In order for a lesion of this part of the pathway to have a demonstrable effect on the reactions of the pupil, the lesion must be gross. The effects of a small lesion on the visual acuity may be evident, while at the same time no change may be noted in the pupillomotor response. Opacities in the ocular media, e.g., will materially influence the visual acuity, whereas they do not alter the light reaction of the pupil. The light reaction of the pupil should be normal, therefore, in patients who have cataracts, even though they be sufficiently dense to prevent any view of the fundus with an ophthalmoscope. The state of the retina and whether the eye will secure good vision if the cataract is removed successfully can thereby be predicted. Failure of the pupil to react under these circumstances is indicative of severe macular damage. The pupil should react normally to light, and the opposite pupil should react consensually.

When there is a lesion in the pathway from the retina to the chiasm, the pupil of the affected side, according to some authors,[52] is usually several millimeters wider than the normal side. Since the pupillomotor fibers from each eye are connected with each sphincter nucleus, it would appear that the effect of a lesion on one side would be equally distributed to both nuclei. It has been suggested, however, that each optic tract is more intimately related functionally with the contralateral nucleus and that the tonus of the pupillomotor fibers coming from the nasal half of each retina is more effective than that from the temporal half of each retina. This is in harmony with the fact that the visual elements of the nasal half of each retina are more sensitive than those from the temporal half.

Since the fibers from the nasal half of the retina on the side of the lesion travel up the contralateral tract, after crossing in the chiasm, and are then chiefly related to the sphincter nucleus of the same side as the affected eye, it follows that the pupil on this side will not receive as much tonic innervation as the sound side and will therefore be semidilated. This assumes, of course, that the illumination of the two eyes is equal. This explanation has been confirmed in recent years by the discovery of the connections of the retina to each Edinger-Westphal nucleus. When there is a unilateral lesion in this part of the pathway and the pupil of the affected side is larger than that of the opposite side, the difference between the two pupils can be intensified or diminished according to the way in which one illuminates the retina of the normal side. If the light is thrown onto the temporal half of the retina of the normal eye, the anisocoria diminishes and the two pupils become equal. Occasionally, the pupil of the affected side may become smaller than that of the normal side. If light is thrown only on the nasal half of the retina of the normal eye, the anisocoria is increased, and the pupil on the side of the lesion becomes much more dilated.

Dilatation of the pupil of the affected side is denied by Lowenstein, who claims that in lesions of the first neuron, no matter what their location (from the photoreceptors to the lateral geniculate ganglion), the two pupils are always equal. Both are larger than normal during ordinary diffuse illumination, but are normal in size in darkness, and there is no anisocoria. Since the light reaction of the pupil, either direct or consensual, may be impaired while the near reaction is normal, this may simulate an Argyll Robertson pupil, and Lowenstein[53] lays some stress on the lack of anisocoria in differentiating the two conditions because anisocoria is found in the vast majority of cases of Argyll Robertson pupils.

In bilateral lesions both pupils are often semidilated. This is particularly characteristic in optic atrophy. The explanation for this mydriasis is difficult. It has been shown that the sphincter is under the influence of both cholinergic and adrenergic innervations. One must assume that when the afferent fibers fail to reach the third nerve nucleus, which initiates the cholinergic mechanism, the inhibitory adrenergic fibers gain the upper hand. They, along with the normal tonus of the dilator muscle, succeed in dilating the pupil.

Lesions between the chiasm and the lateral geniculate body. A lesion in the pathways from the chiasm up to the lateral geniculate body will result in some form of hemianopic defect of the visual field, depending upon the situation of the lesion in the chiasm (p. 673) and should also result in a hemianopic disturbance of the pupil. Bitemporal pupillary paralysis should occur if the crossing fibers from each nasal retina are caught in the chiasm. Similarly, if the lesion involves the optic tract from the chiasm up to the lateral

geniculate body, a lesion should produce homononymous hemianopsia and homonymous hemianopic pupillary disturbances. This reaction is called Wernicke's hemianopic reaction of the pupil.

Lesions above the lateral geniculate body. The visual fibers, in man, all run to the lateral geniculate body and end by synapsing with cells in this primary optic center. The pupillomotor fibers, on the other hand, do not stop in the lateral geniculate body, but continue backward to the tegmentum. At the level of the lateral geniculate body the visual and pupillomotor fibers separate from each other, and each function may be interfered with independently of the other. As stated, a lesion in the optic tract, where both sets of fibers run together, should produce both homonoymous hemianopsia and homonymous hemikinesia. That is, when light is thrown onto the eye and falls on the blind half of each retina, it would fail to produce a response in the pupil, whereas when light is thrown onto the seeing half of each retina, it would cause prompt contracion of the pupil (hemianopic reaction of the pupil). Although this is theoretically possible, it is quite difficult to demonstrate because of the diffusion of light within the eye.

A lesion above the level of the lateral geniculate body in the optic radiations produces homonymous hemianopsia but no disturbances in the function of the pupil, no matter whether the light falls on the blind or the seeing halves of either retina.

A lesion above the level of the lateral geniculate body which involves the tegmentum, but does not involve the optic radiations, on the other hand, will produce a disturbance of the pupil but no interference with visual fields. This type of lesion is described in the next section.

Lesions of the intercalated fiber. Evidence has been presented that the afferent fibers for the light reflex, after reaching the brachium of the superior colliculus, do not enter the superior colliculus itself, but turn rostrally and medially into the pretectal region. From here the pathway descends around the rostral end of the central gray matter into the posterior commissure. Some of the fibers proceed to the Edinger-Westpahl nucleus on the same side, while others cross over to that of the opposite side. In this fashion each afferent pathway reaches both Edinger-Westphal nuclei. The evidence indicates that there is a synapse of these fibers in the pretectal region so that the fibers in the pretectal region which run into the Edinger-Westphal nuclei are intercalated neurons.

Argyll Robertson pupil. Lesions of these intercalated neurons are of considerable clinical importance, for it is thought that these are the ones which cause the so-called Argyll Robertson pupil. In 1869, Argyll Robertson published a paper entitled *Four Cases of Spinal Miosis With Remarks on the Action of Light on the Pupil.*[54] These cases were peculiar in that the direct and consensual reactions of the pupils to light were absent, and yet the pupils all contracted promptly at the near point. Since the publication of this paper, all such pupils have been denoted Argyll Robertson pupils or pupils showing reflex paralysis. The presence of a prompt reaction in accommodation and convergence proves that the efferent pathway of the pupillary light reflex is intact and suggests that the lesion is in some portion of the afferent pathway at a point which involves the pupillomotor fibers of both sides and yet which spares the visual fibers.

Since Argyll Robertson's first description, many papers have appeared differentiating these pupils more exactly from others with which they might be confused. Lesions of the afferent pathway just described (p. 216), when bilateral and complete (e.g., blindness from bilateral optic atrophy), may simulate Argyll Robertson pupils. These pupils with bilateral amaurotic paralysis exhibit the same phenomena as typical Argyll Robertson pupils, but the blindness clearly indicates that the lesion is situated in that portion of the pathway where both visual and motor fibers are in contact, i.e., in the optic nerves or optic tracts as far as the lateral geniculate bodies. The definition of Argyll Robertson pupils must be confined, therefore, to those pupils in which the visual acuity, or rather light perception, is sufficient to yield a prompt response of pupil. It used to be common to see patients with tabetic optic atrophy who had typical Argyll Robertson pupils, but their vision was so poor (e.g., questionable light perception) that a diagnosis of an Argyll Robertson pupil could not positively be made.

Since there are other types of pupils which somewhat resemble the Argyll Robertson pupil, it may be well to examine more carefully the characteristics by means of which Argyll Robertson himself first differentiated these pupils as a clinical entity. In all of his cases the patients had neurosyphilis. It has been well established since that pupils which have all of the characteristics which he originally described are almost pathognomonic of syphilis of the central nervous system. If the presence of this pupillary phenomenon is to have any clinical significance in the diagnosis of neurosyphilis, it seems reasonable to insist that the term be applied to only those pupils which show all of the characteristics described by Argyll Robertson. The moment one admits into the group pupils that are somewhat similar but lack one or more of the peculiarities which he described, the diagnosis of neurosyphilis become less certain, and the phenomenon loses its clinical importance.

Robertson described the following characteristics which pupils should have in order to be typical of this syndrome. (1) The patient's sensitivity to light must be good enough to evoke a pupillomotor response, as just stated. (2) The pupil must not contract directly or consensually on exposure to light. Although Argyll Robertson's original pupils showed complete absence of pupillary response to light directly and consensually, if one were to limit the diagnosis of an Argyll Robertson pupil to one which was completely immobile to light, the early stage of this syndrome would naturally be missed. Every pathologic process interfering with function must pass through a state in which the function is impaired before it is finally abolished. It seems reasonable, therefore, to include pupils in which the direct and consensual reaction to light is impaired, instead of confining the diagnosis to those pupils in which it has been entirely lost. If, however, one prefers to wait until the end stage of the process before making a positive diagnosis, the patient may be tentatively labeled an Argyll Robertson pupil suspect. (3) The pupil contracts normally at the near point. (4) The pupils are miotic. Frequently the pupils are unequal in size, but both pupils are definitely smaller than normal. (5) The pupil dilates poorly to the administration of atropine and cocaine and to painful stimuli. (6) Even when the patient is kept in the dark, the pupils show no dilatation for long periods of time.

The Argyll Robertson pupil is of importance since it is one of the earliest diagnostic signs of tabes and taboparesis and occurs in a fairly large proportion of these patients. At the present time it cannot be said with certainty where the lesion is located, but the evidence supports the theory of its being in the intercalated fibers just before they reach the sphincter nucleus.

The lesion must be close to the oculomotor nucleus so that both the crossed and uncrossed pretectal fibers are caught. This would interrupt the light reflex, both direct and consensual, but would spare the near reaction of the pupil since these fibers descend to the oculomotor nucleus away from the vicinity of the intercalated fibers. The miosis can be explained as follows. Interruption of the pretectal fibers isolates the oculomotor nucleus by depriving it of its afferent innervation. The isolated oculomotor nucleus then becomes hypersensitive to cholinergic substances always present in the blood. Such hypersensitivity is well known on the sympathetic side where the superior cervical ganglion, e.g., if isolated by section of its preganglionic roots, becomes hypersensitive to epinephrine, with dilatation of the pupil from the normal adrenergic substances circulating in the blood.

The occurrence of a unilateral Argyll Robertson pupil and other findings which are not entirely compatible with the theory of pathogenesis in the central nervous system have directed attention to the possibility that the changes producing the phenomenon must be located in either the efferent pathway, which must therefore consist of two separate neurons,[46] or perhaps in the iris itself.[55] The evidence has been summarized recently by Lowenstein,[53] who upholds the generally accepted notion that the lesion is in the intercalated pathway close to the nucleus of the third cranial nerve. This excellent paper should be read before one accepts any other localization of the lesion.

Lesions of the efferent pathway from the nucleus to the sphincter muscle. We have no means at hand, except for the use of drugs, for differentiating lesions in the various portions of the efferent pathway. We cannot differentiate a lesion of the Edinger-Westphal nucleus from one involving the preganglionic fibers of the third cranial nerve. Complete mydriasis with paralysis of both the sphincter pupillae and of the ciliary muscle as well (accommodation) points to a lesion of the ciliary ganglion or the postganglionic fibers, but one cannot be certain of this. It is possible to differentiate between a preganglionic and a postganglionic lesion because of the acquisition of sensitivity to cholines, which is acquired when the postganglionic fibers have degenerated.

Lesions of the nucleus. An isolated lesion of one Edinger-Westphal nucleus is possible theoretically and would result in paralysis of the pupil on the affected side. This would be complete to all stimulation. The reaction to light, direct and consensual, the near reaction, and the orbicularis reaction would all be lost. The pupil would be widely dilated but would dilate still further if sympathomimetic drugs such as cocaine were instilled. The accommodative power of this eye would be lost. This lesion could only be differentiated from one involving the pupillary fibers alone in the nucleus or in the third cranial nerve by the retention of accommodation in this eye.

Lesions of the fibers of the third cranial nerve. A lesion involving the pupilloconstrictor fibers in the third cranial nerve, running from the nucleus to the sphincter muscle, would resemble a lesion of the nucleus in all respects. It would be more likely to have associated with it paralysis of other muscles supplied by the third cranial nerve, i.e., both the ciliary muscle on that side and the extraocular muscles supplied by the third cranial nerve.

Lesions of the ciliary ganglion and postganglionic fibers. A lesion involving the ciliary ganglion and the postganglionic fibers should produce the same reactions as a lesion of the nucleus and of the fibers of the third cranial nerve. In addition the pupil should respond to the administration of cholines. It is thought that a form of abnormality of the pupil occasionally seen, called Adie's pupil, is due to a lesion in this part of the pathway. For that reason it is described here.

Adie's or tonic pupil: This form of abnormality of the pupil is characterized by a very slow reaction of the pupil to light and to the near point. In 80% of the patients it is unilateral, and the opposite pupil is normal. The affected pupil is usually larger than its fellow. It may be mistaken easily for an Argyll Robertson pupil if the light is flashed into an eye and it is noted that no immediate contraction of the pupil takes place. Generally, a little more patience is expended in eliciting the near point reaction, and if it is found that the pupil does contract, albeit after some time, under these circumstances an erroneous diagnosis of Argyll Robertson pupil may be made. In a tonic pupil, however, the pupil will contract on prolonged exposure to light, but the rate of contraction is so slow as to be hardly noticeable. The pupil will also dilate if the patient is kept in a dark room. Adie termed the pupil a pseudo-Argyll Robertson pupil and pointed out that it was frequently associated with absent tendon reflexes.

Scheie[56] noted that tonic pupils contract when a 2.50% solution of Mecholyl is instilled into the conjunctival cul-de-sac of the eye, exhibiting the tonic pupil. The pupil on the normal side, like all normal pupils, fails to react to Mecholyl in this concentration. Because of this, Scheie postulated that the site of the lesion is in the postganglionic fibers after they have left the ciliary ganglion.

This is now generally accepted by most authors. deHaas,[57] on the other hand, disagrees with this on the basis of his findings that the pupil in Adie's syndrome does react better to highly dilute solutions of eserine and neostigmine than the non-tonic pupil. On the basis of this and other associated findings, he considers this disturbance to be due to some lesion situated in the hypothalamic vegetative centers.

During an acute attack of glaucoma the pupil is dilated, fixed, and resistant to miotics. It has been shown by Tyner and Scheie[58] that the mydriasis which is seen with increased intraocular pressure is independent of the preganglionic and postganglionic motor nerve supplies to the sphincter, of the local neuroheumoral mechanism, and probably of the sympathetic innervation of the dilator muscle. If the intraocular pressure is raised beyond a certain critical level, the pupil will no longer respond to miotics and will not constrict until the pressure is lowered again.

Lesions of the sympathetic system. The most striking feature of a lesion of the sympathetic nerve supply to the eye is a contracted pupil, or miosis, on the affected side. Frequently there is narrowing of the palpebral fissure due to the paralysis of Müller's muscle and apparent enophthalmos due to narrowing of the palpebral fissure. When these changes are associated with anhydrosis on the same side, the condition is called Horner's syndrome. Cocaine instilled into the eye fails to dilate the pupil, whereas epinephrine, which has little or no effect on the normal pupil, will dilate it if the sympathetic fibers have degenerated.

PHARMACODYNAMICS OF THE SPHINCTER AND DILATOR MUSCLES
The neurohumoral theory

Transmission of the nerve impulse across synapses and motor end plates. The origin of a nerve impulse and its transmission down a nerve fiber to its termination has been described in another section of this book (p. 616). At its terminus, the axon connects either with dendrites of another nerve cell or with a motor end plate connected with a muscle cell or a cell concerned with some function such as secretion. The stimulus carried down the axon is designed to set these effector cells in motion, so to speak. How does the nerve impulse bridge the synapse between axon and dendrite or between axon and muscle cell?

Although the distance between the cell membranes of the functional synaptic contacts is only 10 to 20 mμ, the impulse cannot travel across the gap. Some other process must take place which continues the message through the synapse to other nerve cells or through the motor end plate in order to excite the muscle fiber. This process is a chemical one, generally known as the neurohumoral mechanism of transmission.

Along each nerve terminal the electron microscope reveals synaptic vesicles filled, it is believed, with acetylcholine. Even in the absence of any stimulation of the nerve these vesicles are discharging acetylcholine at random intervals. In the resting condition, packets of acetylcholine, perhaps containing thousands of molecules, are released at each nerve-vesicle junction every second. This amount, while not sufficient to cause the muscle fiber to contract, can be recorded as a small drop in potential of the muscle membrane. When the membrane potential is further lowered by an incoming nerve impulse, however, the rate of release of these packets of acetylcholine increases enormously, in fact, about one hundred times for each 30 mv. lowering of the membrane potential.

The theory[59] postulates, then, that impulses are transmitted from one nerve fiber to another and finally to the effector organ through the mediation of a chemical substance called an effector substance.

This is liberated at the nerve endings upon the arrival of a nerve impulse. The theory offers a rational explanation for the transmission of nerve impulses and logically explains the mechanism of action of various drugs used to stimulate or depress muscular activity.

Upon the arrival of a nerve impulse at a synapse, the effector substance is liberated at the nerve ending (Fig. 61). This substance, in turn, initiates a similar impulse in the next nerve cell in the pathway, and the process is repeated at each synapse. An antagonistic substance that destroys the effector substance rapidly is present constantly in the nerves, thereby permitting only momentary stimulation of the next nerve fiber in the chain. Once the impulse has arrived at the organ or muscle which the nerve is supplying, a similar process occurs, with the liberation of an effector substance causing the cells to assume their physiologic activity. An antagonistic substance is likewise present here so that the activity is short lived unless more effector substance is kept constantly liberated by stimulation of the nerve.

Acetylcholine is the chemical substance responsible for transmission across all synapses throughout the nervous system. This substance likewise activates all the structures supplied by the parasympathetic nervous system and the voluntary motor system. Acetaylcholine, therefore, performs three functions: (1) the transmission of nerve impulses across all synapses in the body, (2) the transmission of nerve impulses to skeletal muscle, causing this type of muscle to contract, and (3) the activation of structures supplied by postganglionic fibers of the parasympathetic nervous system (blood vessels, sweat glands, certain smooth muscles, and the muscles of the ciliary and sphincter pupillae). The first two of these effects can be produced

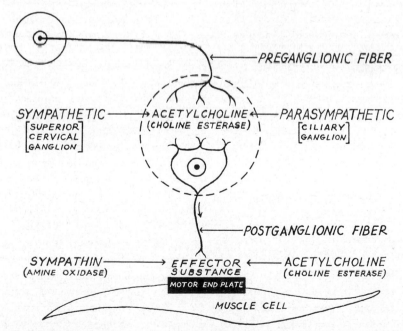

Fig. 61. Neuroeffector mechanism. The diagram shows the terminal ganglion and myoneural junction. (From Scheie, H.: Tr. Am. Acad. Ophth. **53**:186, 1949.)

by small amounts of nicotine. Hence, the transmission of nerve impulses across synapses and the activation of skeletal muscles by acetylcholine are spoken of as the nicotinic action of acetylcholine. The third function, that of stimulating the effector organs innervated by postganglionic parasympathetic fibers, can be produced by muscarine, and for that reason it is referred to as the muscarinic action

of acetylcholine. As stated, acetylcholine is manufactured at the interneuronic synapses of both the sympathetic and the parasympathetic nervous systems and also at the junction of the second parasympathetic neuron and the reacting cell (Fig. 62, *A* and *B*).

The antagonistic substance which is produced by all the tissues of the body and which has the property of entering into

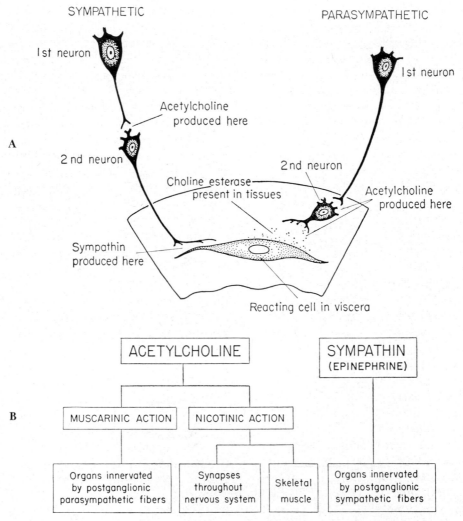

Fig. 62. **A,** Diagram of balance between sympathetic and parasympathetic nerves and esterase. **B,** Diagram showing structures stimulated by acetylcholine and sympathin. (**A,** After Myerson and Thau. **B,** From Scheie, H.: Tr. Am. Acad. Ophth. 53:186, 1949.)

chemical union with acetylcholine and thus destroying its effectivity is called cholinesterase. Cholinesterase brings about an inhibition of activity of acetylcholine, probably by accelerating the hydrolysis of the ester radical.

Organs supplied by the sympathetic nervous system are activated through the liberation of an epinephrine-like substance at the nerve endings called sympathin.* Two types of sympathin are liberated: (1) sympathin E, which produces excitation of structures innervated by the sympathetic nervous system, and (2) sympathin I, which causes inhibition of these structures. Several substances probably serve as antagonistic agents to sympathin, the chief among which is amine oxidase.

As stated, acetylcholine is rapidly destroyed in the body by cholinesterase which is present in all tissues. Although it is destroyed very rapidly in the myoneural junctions of the voluntary nerves and in the synapses of the central nervous system, its destruction is much slower at the autonomic endings of the parasympathetic system, so that a certain amount may diffuse into the surrounding tissue fluids and exert an effect on neighboring cells. It is normally present, therefore, in the iris and ciliary body and has been detected in the aqueous taken from rabbits' eyes treated with physostigmine after they have been exposed to light.[60] It is absent after degeneration of the parasympathetic system. Since acetylcholine is the effector substance for the muscles supplied by the parasympathetic system, it has been called the cholinergic system and the nerves, cholinergic nerves. For the same reason, the sympathetic system has been spoken of as the adrenergic system since it is stimulated by sympathin which is an epineph-

rine-like substance, and the nerves are called adrenergic nerves.

Drugs which mimic either the nicotinic or the muscarinic action of acetylcholine are referred to as cholinergic drugs, and those which produce muscarinic effect by stimulating structures supplied by the parasympathetic nervous system are described as parasympathomimetic. Drugs which depress these structures are called parasympatholytic. Likewise, drugs which stimulate structures innervated by postganglionic sympathetic fibers are called adrenergic or sympathomimetic, and drugs which depress these structures are called sympatholytic drugs.

Sensitization to effector substances

The phenomenon of sensitization of an organ to its effector substance was described by Anderson in 1903. He demonstrated that an organ deprived of its postganglionic nerve supply responded to much greater dilutions of its effector substance. If the parasympathetic nerve supply to the ciliary and sphincter muscles is interrupted at the ciliary ganglion or peripheral to it, the short ciliary nerve endings supplying the ciliary muscle and the sphincter pupillae shortly degenerate. Within 24 to 48 hours, these muscles become sensitized to their effector substance (acetylcholine). They then contract to much greater dilutions of these substances than they did previously. This can be demonstrated in both man and animals. Specifically, Mecholyl, which is a choline substance, ordinarily contracts the normal pupil in solution of 15 to 20%. Scheie[56] showed that pupils sensitized by postganglionic denervation constrict to solutions as weak as 2.5%. If the sympathetic nerve fibers are interrupted by a lesion at the superior cervical ganglion or peripheral to it and denervation is allowed to occur, sensitization of the dilator

---

*Sympathin is a mixture in variable proportions of epinephrine and norepinephrine.

muscle to sympathin and epinephrine results. Such a denervated pupil dilates to 1:1000 epinephrine, whereas the normal pupil requires much stronger concentrations.

The mechanism of sensitization of the denervated muscles to acetylcholine and epinephrine is not fully understood. It has been suggested that the permeability of the muscle cells is increased by the denervation, and this point of view is supported by the fact that the increased sensitivity is not absolutely specific for acetylcholine and epinephrine, but is also manifest with other stimulating agents. For example, the denervated nictitating membrane is found to be sensitive not only to epinephrine, but also to acetylcholine, pilocarpine, histamine, and potassium ions. Further, the electrical potential of denervated muscle accompanying its contraction is also decreased following denervation, probably due to diminished polarization of the cell membranes resulting from the increase in permeability of the muscle cells.

Sensitization of the iris of the cat to pilocarpine after removal of the ciliary ganglion was studied in detail by Neidle.[61] Sensitization developed when the drug was administered either intravenously or into the conjunctival sac. It set in immediately after operation and was maximal on the fifth to eighth day, with intravenous doses of pilocarpine, and in the case of topical application the sensitization was maximal immediately after the operation. Repeated administration of pilocarpine did not alter the course of sensitization. Sensitization decreased gradually and reached its minimum one hundred days after the operation.

Pharmacodynamics of cholinergic substances

The cholinergic or parasympathomimetic substances either act directly upon the motor end plate of the sphincter muscle, exactly as does acetylcholine, or they may act indirectly on the sphincter muscle by inactivating cholinesterase. By binding cholinesterase and preventing it from destroying acetylcholine, the acetylcholine may accumulate in high concentrations. It is enabled, therefore, to act effectively on the muscle cell (Fig. 63).

The cholinergic drugs which stimulate the sphincter muscle may be divided into the following two groups: (1) agents which directly stimulate the motor end plate, such as acetylcholine and (2) agents which protect acetylcholine by binding cholinesterase, such as eserine. Although acetylcholine itself is the substance which physiologically stimulates muscle cells by acting directly upon the motor end plate, it is so rapidly destroyed by the cholinesterase of the tissues that it produces no miosis when instilled into the conjunctival cul-de-sac. Certain other substances, however, some of which are derivatives of acetylcholine, have an identical effect upon the motor end plate and are sufficiently resistant to destruction by cholinesterase to reach the iris in concentrations sufficient to produce miosis.

Mecholyl (acetyl - β - methylcholine). This substance is a choline derivative which, although destroyed by cholinesterase, is much more resistant than acetylcholine and is of clinical value when instilled locally in the eye. It is used in aqueous solutions, which are unstable and cannot be kept for long periods of time. Aside from stimulating the sphincter pupillae, when instilled into the eye, it causes marked dilatation of the conjunctival blood vessels and probably has a similar effect upon the vessels of the uveal tract. Swan and Hart[62] showed that Mecholyl very markedly increased the permeability of the blood-aqueous barrier. Since it is destroyed by cholinesterase, it should be

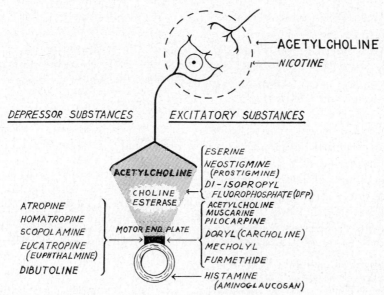

Fig. 63. Diagram illustrating mechanism of action of drugs upon the myoneural junction of the sphincter iridis. (From Scheie, H.: Tr. Am. Acad. Ophth. **53**:186, 1949.)

used in combination with eserine or Prostigmin.

Carbamylcholine (Doryl). This is a choline derivative and a powerful miotic agent which is more stable when instilled into the eye than Mecholyl. According to VanDyke[63] it has a double action, for it not only stimulates the motor end plate, as do all of the choline substances, but also to some degree inhibits the action of cholinesterase. Its action, therefore, is not augmented by the simultaneous use of Prostigmin or of eserine, like Mecholyl; therefore, it can be used by itself. In addition to being more powerful than Mecholyl, it has a more prolonged action. Swan and Hart found that Doryl increases the permeability of the blood-aqueous barrier but to a less degree than does Mecholyl or eserine. It is poorly absorbed through the cornea and conjunctiva and should, therefore, be used in combination with one of the wetting agents, such as Phemerol or Zephiran. It is commonly

sold under the trade name of Carcholin in powder form containing a wetting agent and ready for dilution to strengths of 0.75 or 1.5%. Clark[64] states that Doryl is more effective when instilled locally than 2% pilocarpine and believes that it compares favorably to a mixture of 2% pilocarpine and 0.50% eserine.

Pilocarpine. Pilocarpine is an alkaloid obtained from the South American shrubs *Pilocarpus jaborandi* and *Pilocarpus microphyllus*. It is one of the two oldest miotic agents in ophthalmic use, physostigmine being the other. Its mode of action is comparable to that of acetylcholine. The effect of pilocarpine administered systemically is similar to muscarine, for it stimulates the organs innervated by postganglionic cholinergic nerves. The sweat glands are particularly responsive, and it has been used in this way for therapeutic purposes. Its ocular actions were first described in 1876 by Weber. When applied locally to the eye, pilocarpine causes contraction of the ciliary and sphincter pupillae muscles. The miosis usually persists for several hours. Spasm of accommodation may last for 2 hours. Following postganglionic denervation, sensitization to pilocarpine occurs, just as it does to acetylcholine. It may be used in strengths from 0.50 to 10%. It is effective in overcoming mydriasis produced by Paredrine and similar substances, but very poor in counteracting the action of homatropine and the atropine group of drugs. Scheie[65] has pointed out the advisability of using pilocarpine to contract the pupil following the extraction of cataract in which retrobulbar injections of procaine are employed for anesthesia. Retrobulbar injection of procaine temporarily produces an effect identical to the removal of the ciliary ganglion. The pupil is dilated and fixed. It fails to constrict to eserine, but does so promptly to pilocarpine.

Anticholinesterase drugs. These drugs inactivate cholinesterase (Fig. 64), thereby allowing acetylcholine to accumulate in the tissues in concentrations sufficient to give miosis by stimulation of the sphincter pupillae. The effect of these substances depends upon the supply of acetylcholine, and they are ineffective, therefore, if the postganglionic nerve fibers have been sectioned and allowed to undergo degeneration. Acetylcholine can be liberated only by intact functioning postganglionic parasympathetic nerve fibers. Anderson demonstrated this fact in 1903 when he found that after removal of the ciliary ganglion in cats the pupil on the operated side became widely dilated as the result of the loss of the nerve supply to the sphincter. Following this, all the anticholinesterase drugs such as physostigmine then failed to constrict the pupil on the op-

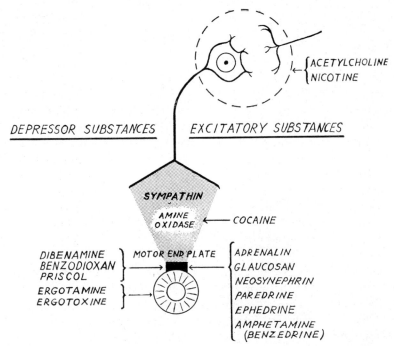

Fig. 64. Diagram illustrating mechanism of action of drugs upon the myoneural junction of the dilator iridis. (From Scheie, H.: Tr. Am. Acad. Ophth. **53**:186, 1949.)

erated side, whereas the same solutions were effective in the unoperated eye.

Physostigmine (eserine). Physostigmine is an alkaloid obtained from the calabar bean. It is one of the oldest and most commonly used miotics in ophthalmology. The bean from which it comes was once used as an ordeal poison used by native tribes. The suspect was forced to eat a quantity of these beans. If he promptly became ill and vomited, he would survive and was assumed to be innocent. In 1863 Fraser[66] first observed the pupillary contraction associated with the use of physostigmine when the drug was applied locally.

This drug, applied locally, causes pupillary constriction and spasm of accommodation. Miosis begins in a few minutes and is maximal in one-half hour, after which it may persist in some degree for as long as several days. The spasm of accommodation lasts a shorter time. Eserine dilates the intraocular capillaries and increases their permeability. In ophthalmology, eserine is commonly used in strengths varying from 0.25 to 1%. Sensitivity to the drug is rather common after prolonged local use, with the development of follicular conjunctivitis, occasionally associated with allergic dermatitis of the eyelids.

Prostigmin. Prostigmin is a synthetic alkaloid chemically related to physostigmine. It is prescribed as a methylsulfate or bromide salt and is to be used in 3 to 5% solution. It acts in the same way as does physostigmine but is somewhat less effective as a miotic agent.

Di-isopropyl fluorophosphate (DFP). This drug has been studied extensively by Leopold and Comroe.[59] This substance, commonly called DFP, is one of several fluorophosphate compounds which exert muscarinic effects through the inhibition of cholinesterase. It is a more effective agent than either eserine or Prostigmin, having a much more powerful, as well as a more prolonged, effect. There is reason to believe, according to Leopold and Comroe and to Quilliam,[67] that DFP either destroys or irreversibly combines with cholinesterase, which must then be resynthesized by the tissues. Consequently, in man, miosis which may last as long as twenty-seven days is produced. Ciliary spasm occurs which gradually disappears during the 48 hours following instillation. Dilatation of the capillaries of the iris and ciliary body occurs, which according to von Sallmann and Dillon[68] may produce elevation of the ocular tension.

Leopold and Comroe have also suggested that DFP produces an associated increase in permeability of the blood-aqueous barrier. The capillary dilatation and increased permeability associated with edema of the ciliary body may account for the occasional precipitation of an acute attack of glaucoma in patients predisposed because of an anatomically narrow angle. Because it is such a marked miotic agent, this drug is of use when other drugs fail to produce miosis. It is commonly used in strengths of 0.035 to 0.05%. It must be dissolved in peanut oil since it is unstable in aqueous solutions. It is particularly valuable in the treatment of aphakic glaucoma and certain types of strabismus.

Substances which act on the muscle cells directly

Histamine. Histamine is thought to be the most powerful miotic agent known. Scheie and Ojers[69] found that this was not true in the dog. The conflicting reports in the literature, they believe, may be due to differences among species. Histamine is supposed to counteract mydriasis produced by atropine, but these authors were not able to confirm this in the dog. The drug is a marked vasodilator, particularly affecting the capillaries and increasing their permeability, with the resultant escape of fluid and protein through the capillary wall.

Friedenwald[70] showed that congestion of the anterior uveal tract due to the release of histamine may play a part in the precipitaton of acute attacks of glaucoma. The vasodilatation produced by histamine persists even in the presence of epinephrine, the walls being in an unresponsive or refractory state. It should be recalled that the release of histamine following injury to the anterior segment of the eye brings about the so-called triple response of Lewis (p. 321). The drug is of no clinical value because of the marked pain and local reaction which it causes, associated with extreme chemosis and injection.

Some other substances such as barium and potassium ions, also stimulate the muscle cells of the sphincter directly, but these have no practical clinical value as miotics.

Parasympatholytic depressor drugs

With the exception of dibutoline sulfate, substances which are used clinically to depress structures innervated by postganglionic parasympathetic nerve fibers are alkaloids obtained from belladonna or are chemically related to it (Fig. 63).

Atropine. Atropine was first obtained in pure form by Mein in 1831. The effect of belladonna upon the pupillary size had been known for centuries, however. Atropine paralyzes the sphincter muscle of the iris and the ciliary muscle, evidently by preventing the action of acetylcholine upon the motor end plate of the muscle cell. Atropine either has a greater affinity for the motor end plate of the cell than has acetylcholine, thereby blocking

its action or depresses the motor end plate to an extent sufficient to prevent stimulation of the muscle cells.

Pupillary dilatation from the local instillation of atropine into the conjunctival sac begins in a few minutes and may last from ten to twelve days. Paralysis of the ciliary muscle requires a few minutes longer and passes off in three to five days. Atropine may have a direct action on blood vessels of the eye, causing a decrease in their permeability to protein. It has been found that the increase in the protein content of the aqueous humor is less in an atropinized eye than in a normal control eye, following the irritation of both Dionin or oil of mustard in equal amounts. This may account for some of the beneficial action of atropine in inflamed eyes. It is generally stated that the good effects of atropine in inflammatory conditions is the result of putting the ciliary and sphincter muscles at rest.

Scopolamine (hyoscine). Scopolamine is also obtained from the belladonna plant. It produces mydriasis and paralysis of the ciliary muscle, but its effect lasts approximately only two days. It is ordinarily used in 0.5% solution. Care must be taken in its prolonged use to watch for toxic reactions such as hallucinations and other psychic disturbances.

Homatropine. Homatropine is a synthetic compound possessing a mandelic acid base rather than troponic acid, as do the naturally occurring members of this group. It has an effect comparable to scopolamine but is effective for a somewhat shorter period—the mydriasis lasting 24 to 36 hours. It is best used in 1 to 2% solution, 1 drop in the eye every 15 minutes for 5 to 6 drops in order to obtain the greatest cycloplegic effect.

Euphthalmine. Euphthalmine is also a synthetic member of the group with a considerably weaker action than the aforementioned drugs. It has little effect on the ciliary muscle. It is usually used in 5 to 10% solution to dilate the pupil for examination of the fundus because its effects can be counteracted quickly. Mydriasis persists for 5 to 10 hours if not counteracted by miotic drugs.

Sympathomimetic drugs

Antioxidase drugs which protect sympathin. There are antioxidase drugs which act as protectors of sympathin (Fig. 57).

Cocaine. Cocaine instilled into the conjunctival sac in strengths of 2 to 10% produces slight to maximal mydriasis, beginning within a few minutes and reaching a maximum in 45 minutes. The mydriasis persists for approximately 4 hours. Its effect is probably comparable in the sympathetic nervous system to the action of eserine and the eserine group of drugs on the parasympathetic side; i.e., it probably prevents the destruction of sympathin by the oxidases which are present in the tissues. An alternative explanation suggests that cocaine might increase the permeability of the muscle cell to sympathin, permitting these cells to be stimulated by much smaller amounts of sympathin and thus explaining the mydriasis.

Agents which stimulate the motor end plate. There are agents which act as excitatory substances on the motor end plates (Fig. 64).

Epinephrine (Adrenalin). Epinephrine, like sympathin, causes mydriasis by acting on the motor end plate of the muscle cell. Epinephrine was first studied in its natural state as isolated from the adrenal medulla. However, early in the century it was synthesized in pure form, and since then many derivatives have been obtained and studied. Epinephrine produces mydriasis following intravenous injection or subconjunctival injection. Dilutions of 1:1000 instilled into the conjunctival sac

do not affect the normal pupil, but a solution of 1:100 is a powerful mydriatic agent and is frequently used to break up posterior synechiae, especially when applied with cotton pledgets saturated with the solution.

If the sympathetic nerves are sectioned peripheral to the superior cervical sympathetic ganglion and the postganglionic fibers have degenerated, sensitization is produced, and dilution of 1:1000 of the drug then produces mydriasis. Very small doses dilate the capillaries of the uveal tract, but larger doses cause marked constriction of the arterioles and capillaries of the eye. Following the vasoconstriction, a period of vasodilatation or reactive hyperemia occurs which can be of considerable importance in the clinical use of the drug. In perfusion experiments in which the general blood pressure is maintained stable, Duke-Elder[52] showed that very small doses of epinephrine cause a rise in intraocular pressure due to capillary dilatation, but larger doses result in a fall in intraocular pressure due to vasoconstriction. When the drug is injected subconjunctivally or into the eye, an initial rise of pressure occurs, followed by a fall due to vasoconstriction.

Swan and Hart have shown that epinephrine causes little change in the permeability of the blood-aqueous barrier during the first hour after administration, but it does cause an increase in permeability subsequent to this, probably due to secondary hyperemia. Epinephrine can be obtained in dilutions of 1:1000 and 1:100. Several other derivatives or substances, chemically related, produce mydriasis in a similar way, among which are synephrine, Neo-Synephrine, Benzedrine, ephedrine, and Paredrine. Neo-Synephrine and Paredrine are the only ones of clinical value.

Neo-Synephrine. Neo-Synephrine is a

synthetic substance chemically related to epinephrine and having a similar effect. It is much more stable, however, than epinephrine and produces a more lasting response. It is available in a 1% solution, a 10% solution, and a 10% emulsion. When instilled into the conjunctival cul-de-sac, it is an extremely powerful mydriatic and is effective in breaking up posterior synechiae. It is also a powerful vasoconstrictor drug.

Paredrine. Paredrine is frequently used as a mydriatic agent in ophthalmoscopic examination. It is more stable than epinephrine. It also acts as a vasoconstrictor. A 1% solution gives a pupillary dilatation lasting from 1 to 2 hours. In some patients more than one instillation must be made. It is very easily counteracted by pilocarpine or eserine in contradistinction to homatropine, which is very poorly neutralized by pilocarpine. Tassman[71] has suggested its use in combination with homatropine, feeling that the two might have a synergistic action. It can be obtained as an ophthalmic solution containing 1% Paredrine hydrobromide and 2% boric acid in distilled water.

Sympatholytic drugs

The usefulness of this group of drugs has as yet been practically unexplored by ophthalmologists. Ergotoxin and ergotamine depress structures innervated by sympathetic fibers, probably by acting directly on the effector cell itself. The question of sensitization of the sphincter and dilator muscles as a pharmacological phenomenon has been extensively studied by Sachs and Heath.

Combinations of miotics might be supposed to yield more intense miosis[72-75] and hypotensive effect than can be achieved by the use of a single drug. Swan and Gehrsitz[76] present data, however, which indicate that, instead of a synergic or additive action, a weaker miotic may reduce the effectiveness of a stronger drug. In the albino rabbit, for example, pilocarpine decreased the activity of the iris sphincter to physostigmine and DFP, as well as to physiologically produced acetylcholine. The exact mechanism of this modifying action of pilocarpine has not been established as yet, but the authors suggest that pilocarpine competes with acetylcholine for the receptor mechanism of the iris sphincter. These results are in agreement with observations on patients with glaucoma in whom it is possible to reduce the clinical effectiveness of physostigmine and DFP by the prior or simultaneous administration of pilocarpine.

Intra-arterial injections of histamine, pilocarpine, or 5-hydroxytryptamine[77] (5-HT) close to the superior cervical ganglion caused both stimulation of the ganglion and potentiation of the response to submaximal preganglionic stimulation. A variety of chemically unrelated substances potentiate ganglionic transmission. These may be divided into three general groups: (1) nicotine-like substances such as choline (p. 226), choline esters, and nicotine, (2) sympathomimetic amines such as epinephrine and norepinephrine, and (3) histamine, 5-HT, and pilocarpine. These can all potentiate the sympathetic synaptic transmission. Substances in the first two groups alone are able to yield depression. The superior cervical ganglion in the cat possesses not only acetylcholine receptors, but also separate receptors for histamine, pilocarpine, and 5-HT and for sympathomimetic amines.

Extracts of freshly excised rabbit's iris contain a hitherto unknown smooth muscle-stimulating substance to which the name irin has been given.[78] It can be distinguished from various active substances, such as choline esters, histamine, 5-HT, and substance T, that are present in mammalian tissues. The substance is capable of contracting iridial and intestinal smooth muscles. It is not antagonized by atropine. The discovery of this substance arose out of a study of the prolonged atropine-resistant spasm of the sphincter irides which occurs in rabbits on mechanical stimulation of the trigeminal nerve.[79] It is believed that this substance is released as the result of an axon reflex from the trigeminal nerve when it is stimulated antidromically or when the iris itself is stroked. Irin produces prolonged spasm of the sphincter pupillae; since it differs from other smooth muscle substances found in tissue extracts, it has been given the name *irin.*

REFERENCES

1. Wilder, H.: Relationship of pigment cell clusters of the iris to malignant melanoma in the uveal tract, New York Acad. Sc. **6:** 137, 1948.
2. Weale, R.: Observations on the direct effect of light on the irides of rana temporaria and xenopus laevis, J. Physiol. **132:**257, 1956.
3. Haines, R.: On muscles of full and of short action, J. Anat. **69:**20, 1934.
4. McGreggor, I.: Segmental movement of pupil, Brit. M. J. **1:**629, 1945.
5. Sunderland, S., and Hughes, E.: The pupillo-constrictor pathway and the nerves to the ocular muscles in man, Brain **69:** 301, 1946.
6. Christensen, K.: Sympathetic and parasympathetic nerves in the orbit of the cat, J. Anat. **70:**225, 1936.
7. Weinstein, P.: Pharmacodynamics of the ciliary ganglion, Am. J. Ophth. **40:**202, 1955.
8. Apter, J.: Distribution of radial contractile forces in the iris of cats, Am. J. Ophth. **48:**316, 1959.
9. Apter, J.: Responses and distribution of of the human intraocular muscles, Am. J. Ophth. **49:**92, 1960.
10. Hodes, R., and Magoun, H.: Pupillary and other responses from stimulation of the frontal cortex and basal telencephalon of the cat, J. Comp. Neurol. **76:**461, 1942.
11. Foerster, O.: Operative-experimentelle Erfahrungen beim Menschen über den Einfluss des Nervensytems auf, den Kreislauf, Ztschr. ges. Neurol. u. Psychiat. **167:** 439, 1939.
12. Hyndman, O., and Wolkin, J.: Sympathectomy of the upper extremity, Arch. Surg. **45:**145, 1942.
13. Ray, B., Hinsey, J., and Geohagen, W.: Observations on the distribution of the sympathetic nerves to the pupil by stimulation of the anterior roots in man, Ann. Surg. **118:**647, 1943.
14. Apter, J.: Studies on the autonomic innervation of the iris, Am. J. Ophth. **42:** 122, 1956.
15. Lowenstein, O.: Discussion of Dr. Apter, J.: Studies on the autonomic innervation of the iris, Am. J. Ophth. **42:**1956.
16. Ury, B., and Gelhorn, E.: Role of the sympathetic system in reflex dilatation of the pupil, J. Neurophysiol. **2:**268, 1939.
17. Seybold, W., and Moore, R.: Oculomotor nerve and reflex dilatation of the pupil, J. Neurophysiol. **3:**436, 1940.
18. Weinstein, E., and Bender, M.: Pupillo-dilator reactions to sciatic and diencephalic stimulation; comparative study in cat and monkey, J. Neurophysiol. **4:** 44, 1941.
19. Bender, M., and Weinstein, E.: Actions of adrenalin and acetylcholine on the denervated iris of the cat and monkey, Am. J. Physiol. **130:**268, 1940.
20. Keller, A.: The striking inherent tonus of the deaffernated central pupillo-constrictor Neurons, Fed. Proc. **5:**55, 1946.
21. Gang, K.: Psychosomatic factors in the control of pupillary movements, J. Clin. Psychopath. **6:**461, 1945.
22. Lowenstein, O., and Lowenfeld, I.: Influence of retinal adaptation upon the pupillary reflex to light in normal man, Am. J. Ophth. **51:**644, 1961.
23. Meyer, B.: Incidence of anisocoria and difference in size of palpebral fissures in 500 normal subjects, Arch. Neurol. & Psychiat. **57:**464, 1947.
24. Lowenstein, O.: Clinical pupillary symptoms in lesions of the optic nerve, chiasm and optic tract, Arch. Ophth. **52:**390, 1954.
25. Jones, I.: Anisocoria, attempted induction

by unilateral illumination, Arch. Ophth. **42**:249, 1949.

26. Lowenstein, O.: Clinical pupillary symptoms in lesions of the optic nerve, optic chiasm and optic tract, Arch. Ophth. **52**: 385, 1954.

27. Thomson, L.: Binocular summation within the nervous pathways of the pupillary light reflex, J. Physiol. **106**:59, 1947.

28. Ranson, S., and Magoun, H.: The central path of the pupillo-constrictor reflex in response to light, Arch. Neurol. & Psychiat. **30**:1193, 1933.

29. Magoun, H., Atlas, D., Hare, W., and Ranson, S.: The afferent path of the pupillary light reflex in the monkey, Brain **59**:234, 1936.

30. Magoun, H., Ranson, S., and Mayer, L.: Pupillary light reflex after lesions of the posterior commissure in the cat, Am. J. Ophth. **18**:624, 1935.

31. Barris, R., Ingram, W., and Ranson, S.: Optic connections of the diencephalon and midbrain of the cat, J. Comp. Neurol. **62**:117, 1935.

32. Barris, R.: A pupillo-constrictor area of the cerebral cortex of the cat and its relationship to the pretectal area, J. Comp. Neurol. **63**:353, 1936.

33. Kuhlenbeck, H., and Miller, R.: Pretectal region of the rabbit's brain, J. Comp. Neurol. **76**:323, 1942.

34. Atlas, D., and Ingram, W.: A note on the typography of the pretectal area of the monkey, J. Comp. Neurol. **66**:291, 1937.

35. Magoun, H., and Ranson, S.: The afferent path of the light reflex: a review of the literature, Arch. Ophth. **13**:862, 1935.

36. Szentagothai, J.: Arch. Psychiat. **115**:136, 1942.

37. Magoun, H., Ranson, S., and Mayer, L.: The pupillary light reflex after lesions of the posterior commissure in the cat, Am. J. Ophth. **18**:624, 1935.

38. Magoun, H., and Ranson, S.: The central path of the light reflex, Arch. Ophth. **13**:791, 1935.

39. Benjamin, J.: The nucleus of the oculomotor nerve with special reference to innervation of the pupil and fibers from the pretectal region, J. Nerv. & Ment. Dis. **89**:294, 1939.

40. Crouch, R.: Efferent fibers of Edinger-Westphal nucleus, J. Comp. Neurol. **64**: 365, 1936.

41. Boeke, J.: Innervationsstudien; zur Nervenversorgung der augenhaute; die Beziehungen der Nervenfasern der Iris zu den Bindegewebszellen beim Affen. Die "interstitiellen" Elemente des Irisstromas und der sympathische Grundplexus, Ztschr. mikr.-anat. Forsch. **39**:477, 1936.

42. Cogan, D.: Neurology of the ocular muscles, ed. 2, Springfield, Ill., 1956, Charles C Thomas, Publisher, p. 34.

43. Renard, G.: La synergie pupillaire a la convergence, Rev. oto-neuro-opht. **19**:240, 1947.

44. Foerster, O., Gazell, O., and Mahoney, W.: Ueber die Anatomie Physiologic und Pathologie der Pupillarinneration, Verhandl. deutsch. Gesellsch. inn. Med. **48**: 386, 1936.

45. Nathan, P., and Turner, J.: Efferent pathway for pupillary contraction, Brain **65**: 343, 1942.

46. Naquin, H.: Argyll Robertson pupil, Am. J. Ophth. **38**:23, 1954.

47. Bender, M.: Eyelid closure reaction, Arch. Ophth. **29**:435, 1943.

48. Longworthy, O., and Ortaga, L.: Innervation of the iris of the albino rabbit as related to its function; theoretical discussion of abnormalities of the pupils observed in man, Medicine **22**:287, 1943.

49. Gullberg, J., Olmstead, J., and Wagman, J.: Reciprocal innervation of the sphincter and dilator pupillae, Am. J. Physiol. **122**:160, 1938.

50. Gullberg, J., Olmstead, J., and Wagman, J.: Reciprocal action of the constrictor and dilator pupillae during light adaptation, Proc. Soc. Exper. Biol. & Med. **38**: 616, 1938.

51. Arieff, A.: Pathways for darkness and reflex pupillary dilatation, Am. J. Ophth. **40**:119, 1955.

52. Duke-Elder, S.: Textbook of ophthalmology, vol. 2, St. Louis, 1937, The C. V. Mosby Co., p. 512.

53. Lowenstein, O.: The Argyll Robertson pupillary syndrome, Am. J. Ophth. **42**: 105, 1956.

54. Robertson, D.: Four cases of spinal miosis with remarks on the action of light on the pupil, Edinburgh M. J. **15**:487, 1869.

55. Apter, J.: The significance of the unilateral Argyll Robertson pupil, Am. J. Ophth. **38**:34, 1954.

56. Scheie, H. G.: Site of disturbance of

Adie's syndrome, Arch. Ophth. **24:**225, 1940.

57. deHaas, E.: Adie's syndrome, Arch. Ophth. **61:**866, 1959.

58. Tyner, G., and Scheie, H.: Mechanism of the miotic resistant pupil with increased intraocular pressure, Arch. Ophth. **50:**572, 1953.

59. Leopold, I., and Comroe, J.: Effect of diisopropyl fluorophosphate (DFP) on the normal eye, Arch. Ophth. **36:**17, 1946.

60. Engelhart, E.: Der Humorale Wirkungsmechanismus der Oculomotoriusreizung, Arch. ges. Physiol. **227:**220, 1931.

61. Neidle, E.: Pilocarpine sensitization in the parasympathetically denervated pupil of the cat, Am. J. Physiol. **160:**467, 1950.

62. Swan, K., and Hart, W.: A comparative study of the effects of mecholyl, doryl, eserine, pilocarpine, atropine and epinephrine on the blood-aqueous barrier, Am. J. Ophth. **23:**1311, 1940.

63. VanDyke, H.: Autonomic nervous system and action of drugs important in ophthalmology, Arch. Ophth. **38:**145, 1947.

64. Clark, S.: Mecholyl and prostigmine in the treatment of glaucoma, Am. J. Ophth. **22:**249, 1939.

65. Scheie, H., and Ojers, G.: The choice of a miotic agent following retrobulbar anesthesia, Am. J. Ophth. **32:**1369, 1949.

66. Fraser, T.: On the characters, actions and therapeutic uses of the bean of calabar, Edinburgh M. J. **9:**35, 1863.

67. Quilliam, J.: Di-iso propylfluorophosphate (DFP), its pharmacology and its therapeutic uses in glaucoma and myasthenia gravis, Postgrad. M. J. **23:**280, 1947.

68. von Sallman, L., and Dillon, B.: The effect of Di-isopropyl fluorophosphate on the capillaries of the anterior segment of the eye in rabbits, Am. J. Ophth. **30:**1244, 1947.

69. Scheie, H., and Ojers, G.: Personal communication.

70. Friedenwald, J., and Pierce, H.: The pathogenesis of acute glaucoma, Arch. Ophth. **3:**574, 1930.

71. Tassman, I.: The use of paredrine in cycloplegia, Am. J. Ophth. **21:**1019, 1938.

72. Sachs, E., and Heath, P.: The pharmacological behavior of the intraocular muscles, I: Problem of sensitization and methods for its study, Am. J. Ophth. **23:**1199, 1940.

73. Sachs, E., and Heath, P.: The pharmacological behavior of the intraocular muscles, II: Sensitization phenomena in the dilator and sphincter iridis, Am. J. Ophth. **23:**1376, 1940.

74. Sachs, E., and Heath, P.: The pharmacological behavior of the intraocular muscles, III: "Cholinergic" behavior of the dilator iridis, Am. J. Ophth. **24:**34, 1941.

75. Sachs, E., and Heath, P.: Antagonism between adrenergic drugs and atropine in the isolated iris dilator, Am. J. Ophth. **24:**142, 1940.

76. Swan, K., and Gehrsitz, L.: Competitive action of miotics on the iris sphincter, Arch. Ophth. **46:**477, 1951.

77. Trendelenburg, U.: Modification of transmission through the superior cervical ganglion of the cat, Am. J. Physiol. **132:**529, 1956.

78. Ambache, N.: Properties of irin, a physiological constituent of the rabbit's iris, Am. J. Physiol. **135:**114, 1957.

79. Maurice, D.: Constriction of the pupil in the rabbit by antidromic stimulation of the trigeminal nerve, Am. J. Physiol. **123:**45, 1953.

CHAPTER 7

THE LENS AND THE VITREOUS BODY

THE LENS

The lens forms one of the refractive media of the eyes. It must, therefore, be perfectly transparent. Its surfaces must possess the proper curvature, and its index of refraction must conform with that of the other refractive media to make the eye emmetropic. The geometric center of the lens must coincide with the optical center of the refracting system. The lens must be free from contact with the surrounding structures which might hamper changes in the curvature of its surfaces, for, as will be shown subsequently, as the organ of accommodation it must increase its dioptric power within relatively wide limits by changes in the curvature of its surfaces. The lens is a living structure with definite metabolic needs. Throughout the life of a person, new fibers are constantly forming. It must be supplied with nourishment, therefore, and the end products of its metabolism must escape from it. These functions must all be car-

ried on without interfering in any way with its transparency.

THE LENS CAPSULE

The lens is entirely surrounded and enclosed by a capsule. This is a noncellular laminated membrane secreted by the epithelium. It is elastic, and when it is cut, it rolls back on itself as if the outer layers were under tension. The capsule is tough and may be stripped off easily. There is a layer of epithelial cells on the front surface under the capsule. The posterior capsule is considerably thinner than the anterior capsule. There is no epithelial layer under it, however.

By phase-contrast and electron microscopy the capsule seems to possess a fine fibrillar structure, and small channels have been visualized by phase-contrast by Monahan.[1] These channels are found on the anterior capsule only, coursing from a small area near the anterior pole in contact with the aqueous humor toward the equator of the lens to end in the bow area of germinative cells. It is questionable whether these structures are in reality channels through the capsule or, as Dart believes from his studies, filaments in the substance of the capsule.[2]

STRUCTURE OF THE LENS

The arrangement of the lens fibers in parallel bundles, with the nuclei at the equator, is designed to give optical homogeneity to the mass, and the growth of new fibers from the epithelium in the region of the equator assures the greatest transparency in the middle of the lens, through which the light rays have to pass. Any interference with this uniform development produces an optical defect and destroys the transparency of the lens. As the formation of new fibers takes place, the older fibers are compressed and pushed in toward the center. This results in increasing density of the lens from the surface to the center.

There is no sharp boundary line between the various portions of the lens, but in general two main parts are recognized, i.e., a dense center or nucleus and the surrounding cortex. This arrangement has a peculiar optical advantage in making the total refractive power of the lens greater than if the index of refraction were uniform throughout. The lens may be considered to be made up of three optical portions—a central biconvex portion of greater density and two concavoconvex menisci of lesser refractive index which surround the biconvex portion. The effect of these concave menisci is to diverge the rays of light entering the lens. Were they of equal density with the central nucleus, their effect would be very pronounced and might offset the converging effect of the nucleus. Their refractive index is considerably less than that of the nucleus, however, so that the bicon-

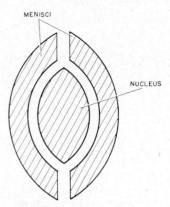

Fig. 65. Artificial division of the lens into two portions having different refractive indices. (After Cowan.)

vex nucleus, which forms a strong plus lens, is not appreciably neutralized by them (Fig. 65).

The increasing density of the center or nucleus with increasing age is the result of loss of water and compression of the lens fibers. The lens is entirely an epithelial structure and is no exception to the general rule that such structures keep on growing throughout life. In the case of the hair, nails, and epidermis, the old cells become keratinized and are shed or lost by being rubbed off as they come in contact with the outside world. In the lens, the growth of fibers keeps up throughout life, but the cells cannot be shed. If there were no sclerosing process, the lens would soon grow to a size incommensurate with the eyeball. Even with this compensating sclerosis and the formation of a dense hard nucleus, the lens does increase somewhat in volume as time goes on. Patients under 30 years of age may be operated on safely for traumatic cataract by needling the lens or by doing what is called a linear extraction. After a person reaches the age of 30 years, the eyeball must be opened sufficiently to remove the large nucleus which has formed by that time. This dense nucleus cannot be broken up and absorbed by the aqueous humor.

CHEMISTRY OF THE LENS CAPSULE

The capsule is largely composed of a single major constituent, an insoluble protein containing about 10% carbohydrate.[3] This has many of the characteristics of collagen but is not identical with collagen. It differs from the protein of the vitreous in that the vitreous protein can be entirely separated from the carbohydrate. The vitreous protein has been identified as collagen from a study of its physical and chemical properties.[4] The capsule contains 14% nitrogen, 9 to 10% carbohydrate, 9 %reducing sugars after hydrolysis, and about 1% hexosamine. No phosphorus is present.

In tissue sections the lens capsule stains deeply by the Hotchkiss method for the detection of polysaccharide. Descemet's and Bruch's membranes also take these stains, and a basement membrane lining the whole vascular tree[5] has been demonstrated by this method. Insoluble proteins rich in carbohydrate are present in many membranes of the body. Other evidence has been offered[6] that the lens capsule is similar to basement membranes in other parts of the body. Roberts has shown that both the lens capsule and most basement membranes contain fluorescent antibodies not found in collagen itself.

The lens capsule is not an inert membrane. Even after removal of its epithelium the capsule shows glycolytic activity. Aerobic metabolism is not present.[7] The metabolic activity of the capsule seems to depend on its contact with the lens itself, for adenosine triphosphate (ATP) which is found in the capsule in contact with the lens rapidly disappears due to adenosine triphosphatase activity after the capsules are removed. High energy phosphate componds are found in much greater concentration in the capsule (including the posterior capsule) than in the cortex.[8]

At present the part of the capsule responsible for its activities (p. 236) is not known. Sperekalis and Potts[42] have speculated on the possibility of a basement membrane being revealed by electron microscopy similar to that which has been found for the corneal epithelium.[9] The epithelial cells of the ciliary processes have been shown to have extensive elaborations of their cell membranes, consisting of highly interdigitated membranes forming their margins and infoldings of the surface facing the posterior chamber. The marginal interdigitations are thought to be involved in the secretion of aqueous humor while the surface infoldings facing the posterior chamber have been considered sites of absorption of some of the constituents of aqueous humor.[10]

Sperekalis and Potts call attention to the fact that the lens may be considered analogous to an inside-out epidermis due to the ectodermal origin of the lens and the invagination of the primary lens vesicle. The analogy may be carried further by comparing it with frog's skin which has known mechanisms for active transport of ions. The inside of the lens is comparable to the outside of the frog's skin, and both are charged negatively. The lens capsule may be responsible, therefore, for the transport of ions across it by metabolic processes so that it, as well as the lens fibers, may be concerned with keeping sodium out of the lens and retaining potassium inside the lens.

CHEMISTRY OF THE NORMAL LENS

Water content. Compared to most body tissues, the lens is a relatively dehydrated structure since the water content of the adult lens is only 65% of its total weight. The absolute amount of water in the lens

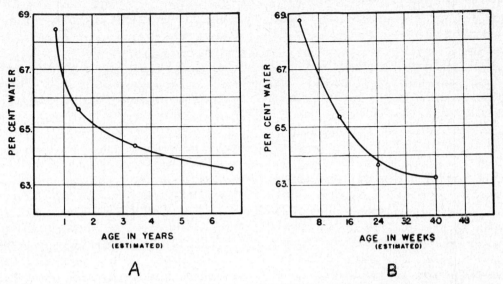

Fig. 66. A, Relationship of age to water content of bovine lens. **B,** Relationship of age to water content of rabbit lens. (From Ely, L.: Am. J. Ophth. **32:**215, 1949.)

increases as the lens grows, but decreases relatively with age[11, 12] (Fig. 66). There is a greater proportion of water (i.e., 65 to 75%) in the cortex due to the fact that the cortex contains the youngest fibers.[13] The amount of water in all tissues depends somewhat upon the procedure used for its analysis, for water exists in both a free and a bound form. There is very little bound water in the majority of tissues. The unbound water can be removed by the usual methods of dehydration, but it is more difficult to remove bound water. An estimated 20% of the water in the lens remains, even when the temperature is raised to over 200° C. A considerable amount of energy is required, therefore, to release water from the lens, and no sharp line of demarcation exists between its bound and free contents. Their relative proportions depend upon the amounts of energy expended in the procedure.[14]

The relative dehydration of the lens with advancing age may be a factor in the development of presbyopia (p. 300). Changes in the water content of the lens probably account for the changes in refraction frequently present in diabetic persons. When the blood sugar is suddenly lowered, as by the withdrawal of sugar and starches from the diet, marked but transitory hyperopia may occur, and similarly, when the blood sugar rises suddenly, myopia may develop. These refractive changes are the result of a deranged water exchange between the lens and its surroundings, brought about by sudden alterations in the osmotic pressure of the fluid bathing the lens. If the osmotic pressure of this fluid rises, the lens becomes dehydrated with so-called dry salt retention, its index of refraction rises, which increases its dioptric power and results in myopia. On the other hand, if the osmotic pressure of the fluid bathing the lens is lowered, water retention follows so that its refractive index drops and hyperopia develops. Other factors which may also account for changes in refraction in a diabetic person will be considered in the section on the vitreous humor (p. 267).

Protein content. The lens contains a higher percentage of protein than any other organ in the body.[15] The total amount of protein is 35% of the lens mass. By comparison, muscle has 18% and kidney 17%. The protein can be divided into soluble and insoluble portions. Until recently the soluble portion was considered to consist of three substances, each of which had characteristic properties. These were called alpha and beta crystallin and albumin. Nearly twice as much beta crystallin is present in the normal lens as alpha crystallin. In the bovine lens at 1 year of age, Krause[15] found the following percentages of protein fractions in the lens (Table 24). Krause[15] deter-

mined the distribution of the various protein fractions in the lens after dividing the lens into six layers, estimating the percentage of each of the proteins in each layer. Table 25 shows the protein-nitrogen distribution in these various layers.

As is to be expected, the nucleus contains a higher percentage of the total protein than the cortex. The soluble proteins are concentrated in the cortex and decreases steadily until the center is reached. The insoluble protein, albuminoid, on the other hand, is most concentrated in the nucleus. The cortex of the young lens contains practically no albuminoid, whereas the nucleus of old lenses is composed almost entirely of this protein fraction. Since the concentrations of albuminoid and alpha crystallin are nearly inversely proportional, a close chemical relationship probably exists between the two. As the lens ages, the soluble alpha crystallin is gradually converted into the insoluble albuminoid. The close relationship of alpha crystallin and albuminoid is shown further by the fact that albuminoid and alpha crystallin are immunologically similar. Some believe that they are identical.[16, 17]

Table 24. *Percentages of protein fractions in bovine lens*

Insoluble albuminoid	12.50%
Alpha crystallin	31.74%
Beta crystallin	53.39%
Albumin	1.46%
Nucleoprotein	0.07%

Table 25. *Protein-nitrogen distribution in six layers of one hundred bovine lenses (age 1 year)*

Nitrogen of lamellar fractions from without inward	Outer		Fraction			Inner
	I	II	III	IV	V	VI
Per cent of total nitrogen of lens present in each layer	14.7	12.3	18.5	19.6	21.5	13.4
Nitrogen distribution of each protein in per cent of total nitrogen of each lamellar fraction						
Albuminoid nitrogen	0.4	4.8	7.0	9.9	13.2	38.4
Alpha crystallin nitrogen	37.4	35.1	34.9	33.3	30.7	12.4
Beta crystallin nitrogen	55.3	54 4	53.5	53.9	53.9	47.2
Albumin nitrogen	2.3	2.4	1.5	1.2	1.1	0.9
Mucoprotein nitrogen	1.3	1.1	1.1	0.4	0.3	0.4
Peptone nitrogen	0.4	0.4	0.1	0.1	0.1	0.1
Nonprotein nitrogen	2.9	2.8	1.9	1.2	0.7	0.6

In addition to the proteins just mentioned, traces of other proteins—gamma crystallin, mucoprotein, nucleoprotein, and phosphoprotein—have been reported.

Bellows has commented on the possible significance of the various proteins and their distribution in the individual lens fiber. He suggests that the mucoprotein is extracellular and serves as a cement substance holding the individual fibers loosely together. In this way, coherence without rigidity is obtained. The coherence is obviously necessary for the maintenance of the optical properties of the lens, and the flexibility is needed for the changes in curvature of the fibers, which take place during accommodation. The outer layer of each fiber is probably albuminoid in nature, combined with lipids, forming a phospholipid protein, which enables the cell to maintain its form and its characteristic permeability. The nucleoprotein is in the nucleus, and the other soluble proteins—alpha and beta crystallins and albumin—are incorporated in the body of the fiber. As has been stated, until recently only three different protein fractions have been isolated and identified by standard chemical analysis. With the advent of more refined techniques of electrophoresis, many more protein fractions have been separated. The number of different fractions found depends on the method of electrophoresis used, but there seems little doubt that of the original three proteins only alpha crystallin can now be considered a single entity. Beta crystallin is probably made of a large number of other protein fractions that are less electronegative than alpha crystallin. Albuminoid, the insoluble protein, is likewise now considered to be complex. As van Heyningen[18] points out, the fact that the lens is known to contain many enzymes which are all proteins themselves would of itself lead us to suspect that the protein makeup of the lens was much more complicated than the findings of the earlier workers in this field indicated.

The basic or acidic character of the amino acids present in any protein imparts an electrical charge to the protein molecule (Fig. 67). At a certain degree of acidity, the net charge on the molecule may be positive, and under the influence of an imposed current it will migrate to the negative pole. At a different concentration of hydrogen ions, the net charge on the protein molecule may be negative, and then the migration of the molecule will be toward the positive pole. At some pH or, more properly, within some pH range, the net charge on the protein molecule will be zero—in other words, the protein will be electrically neutral and will not migrate. The pH at which this occurs is called the isoelectric point.

The isoelectric point is of importance because the solubility of a protein is at a minimum at this pH. Therefore, the protein will tend to be precipitated. In the case of the lens, the protein may become opaque at this point. The isoelectric point of any protein depends upon the nature of the individual amino acids which compose it. If basic amino acids predominate, the isoelectric point will be at a high pH, whereas if acid amino acids are the chief constituents of the protein, the isoelectric point will be at a low pH. The whole bovine lens has been reported to have an isoelectric point of 5.16.[19] The isoelectric point of the cortex is 5.10, whereas that of the nucleus is 5.44.

Nordman found three separate isoelectric points, presumably representing the different proteins present. The albuminoid fraction ranged from 5.2 to 6.8. Alpha and beta crystallins gave isoelectric points of 3.5 to 4, and beta crystallin had an isoelectric point of 8 to 9.5. Hesselvik[20]

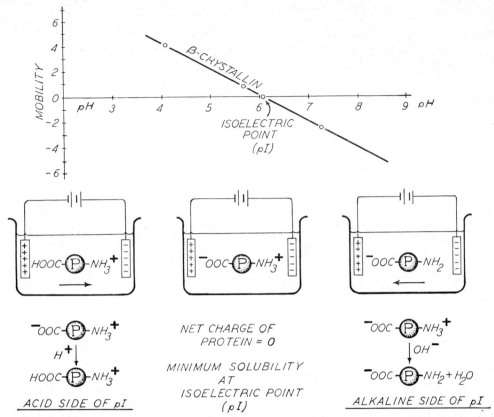

Fig. 67. Electrophoresis of lens protein and the mechanism of change in mobility with pH. (Graph at top of illustration from Hesselvik, L.: Skandinav. Arch. f. Physiol. **82**:151, 1939.)

found alpha crystallin had an isoelectric point of pH 5.1, whereas beta crystallin showed an isoelectric point of pH 6.1. The various protein fractions of the lens may be separated by making use of the differential rate of migration of the different proteins in an electrical field, according to the charges they carry. This method, as just stated, is called electrophoretic separation. Various methods have been devised,[21] and with the different methods a different number of proteins become separable. By paper electrophoresis, François and associates[22] isolated three distinct fractions. More recently, using an agar microelectrophoresis method, François and Rabaey[23] found thirteen dif-

ferent fractions in the lenses of infants.

Some of the changes that occur in the lens with increasing age have already been pointed out. The lens is a very favorable organ to use in following changes in advancing age since it has a rather simple morphology unobscured by blood vessels, has a fairly simple and uniform chemical composition, and is readily accessible to view where its physical characteristics, such as index of refraction or transparency, can be easily determined. Two changes have already been pointed out—the continuous loss of water and the increase in insoluble albuminoid. This increase in albuminoid continues throughout the life span of an animal (rat) at a slowly declining rate. There is evidence that the aging of the lens is associated with a continuous net oxidation of the cysteine of lens proteins to cystine, along with the continuous precipitation of albuminoid. Dische and co-workers[24] intrepret this to be a continuing process of differentiation of cells of ectodermal origin analogous to the keratinization of epidermis. These authors also believe that ascorbic acid and glutathione may play a role in the regulation of the protein synthesis of the lens.

Types of protein. Chemical analyses of each of the lens proteins into their constituent amino acids are of considerable physiologic interest. The amino acid composition of the whole lens proteins has been determined by microbiological assay and by starch chromatography. In Table 26 are given representative values which were calculated by Merriam* from the data obtained by Schaeffer and Murray who used the bovine lens and the microbiological procedure. Their data are similar to those obtained by Merriam, using starch chromatography and the rabbit lens. The latter worker also found that ammonia is obtained from the hydrolyzed proteins in an amount approximately equivalent to the glutamic acid present.

Each of the lenticular proteins contains a carbohydrate residue which is believed to be mannose or one of its derivatives.[25] Mucoprotein contains hyaluronic acid or a similar mucopolysaccharide. Of the various amino acids which composed the soluble proteins of the lens, it is of interest to find a relatively high concentration of cysteine and cystine. According to Krause, cystine forms 1.25% of albuminoid, 1.11% alpha crystallin, 3.18% of beta crystallin, 3.58% albumin, and

*Personal communication.

Table 26. *Composition of bovine lens proteins*

Amino acid	Mol (%)
Leucine	7.40
Isoleucine	5.74
Phenylalanine	6.52
Tryptophane	1.46
Valine	5.74
Methionine	1.98
Tyrosine	4.68
Proline	2.58
Glutamic acid	11.00
Alanine	4.69
Threonine	3.46
Aspartic acid	7.90
Serine*	9.23
Glycine*	9.35
Arginine	8.21
Lysine	4.80
Histidine	3.48
Cystine ($\frac{1}{2}$)	1.79
Total	100.01

*Average values for different animals.

3.25% of the lens capsule. The importance of cysteine and cystine will be discussed in the section on metabolism of the lens. It is also noteworthy that the lens proteins contain very small amounts of glycine. Urea, which is the end product of normal metabolism of protein, comprises approximately 20% of the nonprotein nitrogen fraction of bovine lenses.[26]

Immunologic properties of the lens. The protein of most of the tissues of the body is species-specific; i.e., an animal immunized against the proteins in the blood serum of one species will react only to a subsequent injection of blood serum from that species and not to the blood serum of any other species. In the lens, however, the proteins are not species-specific, but organ-specific. An animal immunized against lens protein will react to a subsequent injection of lens protein regardless of the species from which it is obtained. This suggests that the proteins in lenses of different species must be very nearly alike.

Why does not the body become sensitive to its own lens proteins? It is possible to produce experimentally a hypersensitive reaction in an animal to its own lens protein by repeated injections of its own ground-up lens. It seems, therefore, that the answer is probably the fact that from embryonic life on the animal's lens is confined within a capsule which does not permit the lens proteins to come in contact with the antibody-forming cells of the rest of the body. This concept is given further support by the occurrence of sensitivity reactions to their own lens protein in cataract patients. In some patients who have had a previous extracapsular cataract extraction performed on one eye, with the retention in that eye of considerable lens material, extracapsular extraction of a cataract in the opposite eye at a later date is immediately followed by a severe allergic inflammatory reaction. This was called endophthalmitis phacoanaphylactica by Verhoeff and Lemoine. It is believed that this anaphylactic reaction is due to the patient's having become sensitized to his own lens protein in the anterior chamber of the first eye operated on, with the production of antibodies which then react to the lens protein in the second eye when lens material is allowed to remain in the anterior chamber. This suggests that intracapsular extraction of the lens in the fellow eye should always be done whenever possible in patients who have had an extracapsular extraction in the first eye with the retention of lens material. Strangely, no detectable antibodies have been found in the blood of these patients, but the skin sensitivity to lens protein is said to be increased.

Three immunologically distinct proteins have been found by the older methods of precipitin titrations—alpha and beta crystallins and gamma crystallin or albuminoid. When agar precipitin methods were used, at least six organ-specific components have recently been revealed.[27] Alpha crystallin possesses the greatest immunological activity, whereas beta crystallin and albuminoid tend to neutralize the activity of the alpha crystallin fraction.

Autolysis. Autolysis takes place in the isolated lens kept under aseptic conditions. Some protective mechanism must be present in life which prevents proteolytic breakdown. Sauermann[28] suggests that the proteolytic enzymes are kept inactive in the normal lens because of its pH. At the pH of the normal lens, 7.4, no autolysis occurs. If the lens becomes more acid, the proteolytic enzymes become active. Krause[29] found considerable difference in the resistance of the individual lens proteins to proteolysis. Albuminoid and alpha crystallin are resistant to proteolysis whereas beta crystallin is broken down much more readily. Krause termed the proteolytic enzymes alpha and beta protease. Alpha protease is active over a wide range of hydrogen ion concentration (pH 8 to pH 3). Alpha protease can hydrolyze only protein which has been partly broken down. The preliminary hydrolysis is accomplished by beta protease. Beta protease is active only on the acid side from pH 7.0 to pH 4.0, with a maximum activity at pH 5.0 (normal pH 7.4).

Evidence has been presented[30] that indicates that the proteins of the lens are continuously being degraded and resynthesized. In rabbit lenses cultured in vivo, glycine labeled with C-14 in the carboxyl or in the methylene position has been shown to turn over at a rate between 2.5 and 5% per day. This amino acid was also shown to be rapidly converted by the lens to serine, which in turn is incorporated into protein at a comparable rate.

The enzymes mentioned previously which break down tissue proteins under acid conditions are known as cathepsins. Recently attention is being directed to neutral proteinases. In view of the evidence that in the normal lens the processes of breakdown and re-formation are constantly going on, considerable importance can be attached to the discovery of such proteases, not only for the better understanding of normal lens metabolism, but also for their possible role in the development of cataract. Cataract formation is characterized among other changes by an increasing loss of protein, so that one of the processes must be an increased rate of proteolysis over synthesis. A proteinase has been found in ox lenses which can break down alpha crystallin. Beta crystallin contains inhibitors and is not catalyzed.[31, 32]

Salt content. The ash of a completely desiccated and incinerated lens is about 0.5 to 1% of the original lens weight. This increases with age, corresponding to the relative loss of water.[33] In the normal lens, the cortex has a greater mineral content than the nucleus.[13] Table 27 shows the relative proportions of different ions in the lens, according to Fischer.[34]

The figures for sodium and potassium given by Lebensohn[13] are indicated in Table 28.

The sodium and chloride are found chiefly in the fluid bathing the lens fibers and not inside the fibers. The potassium, on the other hand, is found inside the fiber. As the lens ages, the potassium content decreases, whereas the sodium and chloride increase. This is probably due to the death of lens fibers. It is a well-known fact that for proper function of most body cells the electrolyte composition of the intercellular fluid must be quite different from that of the intracellular fluid. This, it will be recalled, is the case with all highly cellular tissues such as muscle. Sodium and chloride are found chiefly outside the cell, whereas potassium is found in greatest concentration inside the cell.

Many cells also contain practically no chloride but are rich in phosphate. The intercellular fluid, on the other hand, contains a high proportion of chloride. These differences in electrolyte composition are maintained, in spite of the fact that the cell membrane is not entirely impermeable to any kind of ion. The permeability, both to water and to all substances in solution, is affected by the electrolyte composition of the external fluid.

The calcium content of the external fluid has a great deal to do with maintaining the permeability of the cell membrane. In the absence of calcium, the per-

Table 27. *Relative proportion of different ions in fresh cattle lenses*

Ion	Mg. (%)
Sodium	46
Potassium	404
Calcium	6
Magnesium	8
Chloride	60
Phosphate	43
Sulfate	468

Table 28. *Milliequivalents per liter of available water*

	Sodium (Na)	Potassium (K)	Total	Potassium/Sodium equivalent values
Ox cortex	54.5	90.1	144.6	1.65
Nucleus	90.0	120.6	210.6	1.34

meability is increased. In some cases, the presence of polyvalent ions can counteract the reduction of permeability produced by calcium. If all the electrolytes are removed, the permeability of the cell membrane is increased still further. The cell can function only if its membranes are normally permeable.

The potassium content of the lens is very high, in fact, many times higher than that of any other tissue of the eye. It is not known exactly how potassium accumulates inside the lens fiber, but in general it may be stated that body cells are more permeable to potassium than to other cations. Once inside the cell, the potassium combines with proteins, phospholipids, or other nonelectrolytes to which the cell membrane is not permeable. This is one factor, at least, which prevents the potassium from diffusing out of the cell. The potassium content is so vital to the integrity of the cell that the proportion of potassium to sodium found in a tissue has been used as a measure of its vitality. A high potassium content is found in rapidly growing tissues such as tumors, but this is probably the result rather than the cause of the rapid growth.[35]

Traces of calcium are present in the normal lens, probably to maintain the normal permeability of the cell membranes. As shown in Table 27, Fischer found 6 mg. of calcium per 100 Gm. of fresh cattle lens. In the calf and the pig, the amount was 0.5 and 0.4 per 100 Gm., respectively, Salit[36] could detect no calcium in the normal lens of the rabbit or ox. As the lens ages, the deposition of calcium increases, and in old sclerotic lenses, particularly cataractous lenses, calcium is present in considerable amounts. Table 29 shows the consistent rise of calcium in the eye of the pigeon from the embryo to the adult, with a corresponding fall in the potassium-calcium ratio.[37]

The lens fibers can live in media with a variable calcium content. Using tissue culture techniques, Kirby[38] showed that the lens fibers could withstand a high concentration of calcium salts without showing any changes in their growth.

The magnesium content of the lens is approximately the same as that of calcium. It is a recognized component of certain glycolytic systems, but whether it fulfills this function in the lens is not known. The retina has the highest glycolytic activity in the body and has a magnesium content greater than that of any other ocular tissue.[39] Traces of other cations are also present in the lens.

Of the anions, the sulfates form almost half of the total ash (45.8%) of the normal lens.[40] Table 30 gives the percentage of dry weight and percentage of ash of chlorides, sulfates, and phosphates in hu-

Table 29. *Relation of potassium and calcium content to age in pigeon according to Kaufman and Laskowski*

Age of pigeon	K (Mg./Gm.)	Ca (Mg./Gm.)	K/Ca
In embryo			
13 days	1.40	0.27	5.70
17 days	1.23	0.38	3.30
Postnatal			
7 days	0.97	0.86	1.20
13 days	0.94	1.11	0.87
6 weeks	1.05	3.26	0.32
Adult	0.92	4.30	0.21

Table 30. *Percentage of anions in human lenses*

Anions	Dry weight (%)	Ash (%)
Sulfates	1.20	45.8
Chlorides	0.097	3.4
Phosphates	0.537	18.6

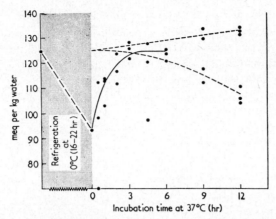

Fig. 68. Accumulation of potassium during incubation of the previously refrigerated rabbit lens. *Dotted lines,* extrapolations designed to show that some lenses lose activity and some continue to concentrate potassium. The steady state is reached in 6 hours. (Tyrode solution modified with 0.01 M 1-glutamic acid; from Harris, J., Gehristz, L. B., and Nordquist, L.: Am. J. Ophth. **36:**39, 1953.)

man lenses, according to Mackay and associates.

No figures are available for the carbonate and bicarbonate concentrations in the lens. The concentration of lactic acid in the lens is higher than in aqueous humor, ranging from 56 to 69 mg.%.[41]

Mechanism of maintenance of salt and water concentration in the lens. The difference in concentration of sodium and potassium inside body cells and in the surrounding fluid is governed by active secretory processes in the cell membrane. The normal body cell excretes sodium and concentrates potassium. Interference with this secretory mechanism brings about an increase of sodium within the cell and loss of potassium. Water tends to move with the sodium, so that interference with the secretory mechanism carries with it increased hydration of the cell as sodium piles up. In the lens the effective mechanism of cation transport seems to reside largely in the lens capsule, and it has been shown that any injury to the capsule such as massage or incision leads immediately to increase in sodium and loss of potassium within the lens. The individual lens fibers, each acting as a cell, also contribute to the maintenance of salt and water balance in the lens, and as Sperelakis and Potts state:

"In this respect, the organization of the lens is not as one giant cell with the capsule as the cell membrane, but rather of many individual cells within one giant cell."*

The mechanism of ion transport is probably a metabolic one. It is immediately affected by a drop in temperature and is recoverable when the temperature is raised again to normal levels, provided that the exposure to cold has not been too severe. In Fig. 68 is shown the accumulation of potassium in the lens during incubation at 37° C. following refrigeration.

As would be expected in the presence of any mechanism of active ion transport, potential gradients have been found across both the anterior and posterior

*From Sperelakis, N., and Potts, A.: Am. J. Ophth. **47:**408, 1959.

lens capsule[43, 44] and deep in the lens substance.

Potential differences amounting to about 70 mv. have been found between the inside of the lens and the vitreous.[43] Similar membranes have been postulated surrounding each lens fiber since the lens is known to lose potassium and gain sodium if the metabolic activity is depressed by cooling, metabolic poisons, or lack of glucose.[45] Sperelakis and Potts[44] have provided evidence that electric potential differences exist across the individual lens fiber membranes and across the lens capsule which depend on metabolic activity. Both the fiber membranes and the lens capsule have active metabolic ion pumping mechanisms whose function is to maintain electrochemical gradients across them. The transmembrane potentials of the lens fibers have a mean value of $-23.3 + 1.2$ mv. negative inside. The transcapsular potential had a mean value of $-30.2 + 1.4$ mv. negative inside. Another potential between the extracellular space and the bathing medium was found to have a mean value of -10.3 mv. Since the three potentials were in series, the potential between the inside of a fiber and the outside of the capsule is the sum of the three or minus 63.8 mv.

Hydrogen ion concentration. Table 31

Table 31. *pH of the lens*

Animal	Portion of lens	pH range	pH average	Method of determination	Author
Dog	Whole		7.35	Antimony electrode	Nordmann (1935)
Rabbit	Whole	7.1 to 7.50	7.30	Antimony electrode	Nordmann (1935)
Rabbit	Cortex	7.35 to 7.45	7.40	Antimony electrode	Nordmann (1935)
Rabbit	Nucleus	7.20 to 7.65	7.42	Antimony electrode	Nordmann (1935)
Ox	Nucleus	7.20 to 7.85	7.44	Antimony electrode	Nordmann (1935)
Ox	Cortex	7.25 to 7.95	7.43	Antimony electrode	Nordmann (1935)
Ox	Whole	7.40 to 7.60	7.44	Colorimetric	Sauermann (1933)
Calf	Whole		7.56	H₂ electrode	Salit (1939)
Man	Whole	7.00 to 7.35	7.37	Antimony electrode	Nordmann (1935)

Table 32. *Lipids of bovine lens (1 year old)*

Lipid	Moist (Grams/1000 Gm.)	Dry (Grams/1000 Gm.)
Total lipids	3.237	9.646
Fats (glycerides of fatty acids)	0.041	0.122
Total phospholipids	1.939	5.751
Lecithins	1.242	3.701
Cephalins	0.310	0.924
Sphingomyelins	0.378	1.126
Cerebrosides	0.042	0.125
Cholesterol	0.660	1.967
Carotenoids		
Carotene	0.0023	0.007
Xanthophyll	0.0000	0.000
Undetermined nonsaponifiable substances	0.538	1.603
Free fatty acids	0.010	0.029
Lipids recovered after alkaline hydrolysis	0.014	0.042

gives the hydrogen ion concentration of the lens as determined by various authors.

The buffering capacity of the lens is large, but no comparison has been made between the buffering capacities of the cortex and nucleus.

Osmotic pressure. The osmotic pressure of the human lens is equivalent to a solution of 0.91% sodium chloride.

Lipid content. Table 32 gives the lipid content of the lens, according to Krause.[46]

Of the total lipids of the lens, 80% are made up of phospholipids and cholesterol. The significance of the phospholipids is not known. It has been shown that the phospholipids form an integral part of every cell membrane and probably ac-

count for the characteristic permeability of the membrane. It is uncertain whether the phospholipids of the lens increase with age, but it is generally agreed that the cholesterol content increases both absolutely and relatively up to the age of maturity. The increase of cholesterol content of the bovine lens with increasing age[47] is shown in Fig. 69.

D'Asaro and co-workers[48] have made a comparison of the lipid content of the various structures of the eye. The results of their study are shown in Table 33. The factor of interest in this lies in the belief that the wide quantitative differences in lipid content of the different tissues implies a marked range in metabolic activity, and the lens and vitreous seem to

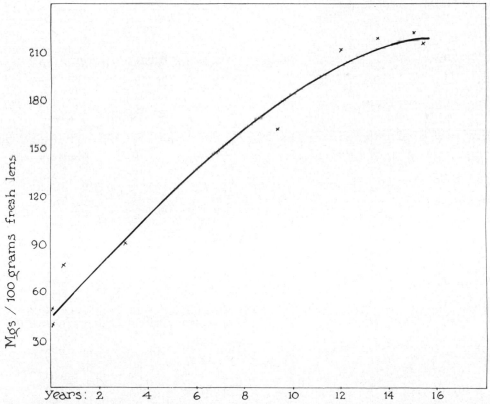

Fig. 69. Cholesterol content of bovine lens. (From Bellows, J.: Cataract and anomalies of the lens, St. Louis, 1944, The C. V. Mosby Co.)

Table 33. *Lipid content of various parts of eye**†

Eye tissue	Total fatty acids and cholesterol	Cholesterol	Fatty acids‡	Phospholipids					
				Total	Choline-containing		Fatty acids§		
					Amount	Per cent of total	Amount	Per cent of total	
Lens	0.80 (0.69-0.89)	0.26 (0.22-0.30)	0.54	0.65 (0.53-0.86)	0.29 (0.25-0.32)	45	0.44	82	
Cornea	1.45 (1.39-1.52)	0.43 (0.36-0.52)	1.02	1.07 (0.95-1.24)	0.76 (0.62-0.98)	71	0.72	70	
Retina	2.86 (2.58-3.02)	0.65 (0.61-0.67)	2.21	2.72 (2.66-2.85)	1.40 (1.15-1.58)	51	1.82	82	
Iris	3.23 (2.99-3.64)	0.67 (0.56-0.78)	2.56	3.94 (3.49-4.30)	2.23 (2.08-2.38)	57	2.64	100	
Ciliary body	4.25 (3.38-4.90)	0.76 (0.61-0.85)	3.49	5.23 (4.80-5.85)	3.19 (2.84-3.72)	61	3.50	100	

*From D'Asaro, B., Young, R., and Williams, H.: Arch. Ophth. **51**:596, 1954.
†Expressed in per cent of dry weight except where noted. Figures in parentheses are the range of values obtained on three or more samples obtained at different times. They are given for the directly determined values only. All other values have been calculated from these.
‡Total fatty acids equal the difference between columns 1 and 2.
§Phospholipid fatty acids equal total phospholipids times the factor 0.67, on the basis that two thirds of the phospholipids are fatty acids.

be relatively inert structures in this respect.

Ascorbic acid. The amount of ascorbic acid in the lens varies greatly in different animals. Horses, sheep, and cattle have the highest amount, whereas very little is found in the lens of the dog. Table 34 gives the values reported in different species by numerous authors, collected by Heath.[49]

The distribution of ascorbic acid in the various tissues of the eye of the same species also varies considerably, being greatest in the corneal epithelium, 47 to 94 mg./100 Gm. wet weight. The lens is next with 34 mg., the ciliary body with 30 mg., the retina with 22 mg., the aqueous humor with 19 mg., and the vitreous with 15 mg.[50] In almost all animals more ascorbic acid is present in the lens than in the aqueous humor, except in the rabbit and guinea pig in which the lens contains less than the aqueous humor. It was pointed out on p. 100 that the concentration of ascorbic acid in the aqueous is very much higher than that in the circulating blood. Because of this it was suggested that the lens synthesizes ascorbic acid and by diffusion through the lens capsule raises the aqueous humor concentration. Another suggestion has been made that the ciliary

body secretes ascorbic acid in its oxidized form and that this is reduced by the lens. Both these theories have been discarded by most workers in this field. The concentration of ascorbic acid in the aqueous humor has been found to vary with the concentration in the serum of human beings, regardless of whether the lens was clear or cataractous and after removal of the lens. It seems reasonably certain that the mechanism involved in the production and maintenance of ascorbic acid in the aqueous humor is not dependent in any way upon the presence of or the condition of the lens.[51]

The amount of ascorbic acid in the lens varies with the age of the animal, being greatest in young animals. More is present in the cortex than in the nucleus.[52] The greatest amount has been found in the cortex just under the capsule, and the concentration falls as one gets closer to the nucleus.[53] The guinea pig is the only animal in which the excess of ascorbic acid is greater in the aqueous humor than in the lens, and in guinea pigs with experimental scurvy the outer layers of the lens lose their ascorbic acid first, but regain it more quickly after the return to a normal diet containing vitamin C.

What part ascorbic acid plays in the metabolism of the lens is unknown. Since it exists in both oxidized and reduced forms, it may act as a carrier in the transport of hydrogen in tissue respiration. Almost all of the ascorbic acid present in the lens is in the reduced form. Ascorbic acid is necessary for the formation of mucopolysaccharide, and a deficiency leads to abnormal mucopolysaccharide biosynthesis.

Glutathione. Glutathione consists of the amino acids, glycine, cysteine, and glutamic acid. The cysteine fraction, containing a sulfhydryl group (-SH) is the most reactive constituent and enables gluta-

Table 34. *Ascorbic acid content of the lens in different species (mg./10 Gm. wet weight)*

Species	Ascorbic acid
Rat	3
Dog	8
Guinea pig	13
Rabbit	15
Sheep	21
Frog	25
Pig	26
Man	30
Cow	34
Horse	57

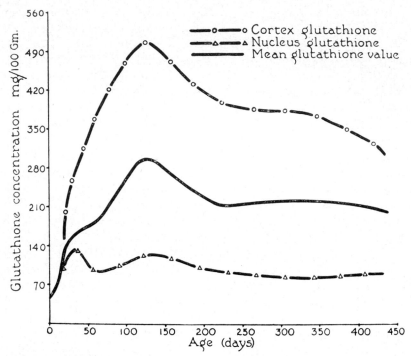

Fig. 70. Relation between age and the concentration of glutathione in the lens. (From Rosner, L., Farmer, C., and Bellows, J.: Arch. Ophth. **20**:417, 1938.)

thione to exist in two forms, oxidized (S-S) and reduced (SH). Reduced glutathione contains cysteine, whereas oxidized glutathione contains cystine. In most tissues a rough correlation exists between the concentration of glutathione and the activity of the tissue.

Glutathione is found in the lenses of all animals but only in traces in the aqueous and vitreous humors. Its concentration changes with age, and in cattle it rises rapidly in the first few months of life and then levels off (Fig. 70).[54] In rats, it rises during the first few months of life and then decreases. Table 35 gives the concentration of reduced glutathione in the lens.

Glutathione is synthesized in the lens.[55]

Although it has been postulated that glutathione may act as a hydrogen carrier and thus be concerned in oxidation in lens metabolism, no mechanism has been found in the lens whereby this oxidation of glutathione can be accomplished. The enzyme glutathione-reductase, together with the coenzyme reduced triphosphotyridine nucleotide (TPNH), reduces glutathione; this is a one-way reaction, and once glutathione is reduced, there seems to be no way by which oxidation can be brought about.

It will be pointed out later that in nearly all forms of cataract glutathione disappears from the lens. This has led to

Table 35. *Concentration of reduced glutathione in lens*

	Mg./100 Gm. tissue (fresh weight)
Lens cortex	388-570
Lens nucleus	64-100

the belief that glutathione plays an important part in the metabolism of the normal lens.

METABOLISM OF THE LENS

There is no obvious reason for the lens to have a high rate of metabolism, for it does very little work. Its energy requirements are limited to the maintenance of its transparency, nourishment for the development and growth of new lens fibers, and whatever metabolic interchange is necessary to maintain the elasticity of its capsule. After birth, the lens has no blood supply. The transport of foodstuffs and waste products to and away from the lens takes place by an exchange between the lens substance and the aqueous humor. Any changes in the composition of the aqueous humor or of its rate of formation might be expected to influence the metabolism of the lens (p. 110). Further, since the lens is enclosed in a capsule, changes in the permeability of this membrane are of importance in the maintenance of normal metabolism.

Oxygen consumption. The amount of oxygen which the aqueous humor supplies to the lens is relatively small and is comparable to the amount of oxygen physically dissolved in most body fluids. Those tissues which are bathed by the bloodstream have the advantage of a fluid containing from 13 to 19 vol.% oxygen. Plasma, devoid of red cells, contains only 1 or 2% of this amount. The aqueous humor contains from 0.08 to 0.12 vol.% oxygen[56] and has an oxygen tension under normal conditions of 40 to 50 mm. Hg.

The mean oxygen consumption of young rabbit lenses has been found to be approximately 30 to 45 c.mm./Gm. wet weight per hour at 30° C. and 37° C., respectively.[57] Calculation of the oxygen consumption of the rabbit lens from these in vitro measurements indicates that the lens uses about a quarter of a milligram per day. Almost the entire amount of this utilization of oxygen is by the epithelium and cortex. The epithelium probably plays the chief role. The utilization of oxygen by the nucleus of the lens decreases with age because of the decreased metabolic activity of all older tissues. Ely[58] studied the oxygen uptake of the lens capsule, the epithelium, the cortical fibers, and the nucleus of the lens. The lens capsule and the nucleus of both bovine and rabbit lenses consumed negligible amounts of oxygen, as can be seen from Table 36.

The oxygen uptake of the lens increases if the lens capsule is ruptured. This has been interpreted as indicating that the capsule is relatively impermeable to oxygen. Pirie points out that this conclusion is unjustified, however, since it is well

Table 36. QO_2* *of various segments of crystalline lens of cattle and rabbits*

	QO₂		QO₂ teased cortex	
Kind of lens	Nucleus	Capsule	Mean	Standard deviation†
Rabbit	0	0	0.145	0.028
Cattle	0	0	0.168	0.042

*QO_2 is defined as the microliters of O_2 consumed per mg. dry tissue per hour.

†Standard deviation $\sigma = \sqrt{\dfrac{\Sigma\ X^2}{N}}$

X = deviation of individual items from the mean.
N = total number of cases.

known that injury to tissues often by itself causes increased oxygen consumption.

The oxygen uptake is one measure of the rate of metabolism of a tissue. The low rate of oxygen uptake by the lens indicates a rather sluggish respiration compared with other tissues. The oxygen uptake alone, however, does not necessarily measure the total metabolism of a tissue since in some tissues, notably the lens, about two thirds of the energy requirements are provided by glycolytic processes which do not involve oxygen. Since different metabolites require different amounts of oxygen for their combustion, in proportion to the amount of carbon dioxide produced, one may determine the type of metabolite being burned by ascertaining the respiratory quotient (R_q).

It is to be expected that the metabolic processes in the lenses of young animals would exceed those of older animals, and this has been found to be true. When all conditions were equalized, lenses from 1-month-old rabbits could produce greater amounts of lactic acid anaerobically than lenses from 3-year-old rabbits.[59] There is some evidence that young lenses use different metabolic processes than older lenses since their responses to cation shifts has been found to be different.[60]

Carbohydrate metabolism. Carbohydrate seems to be the sole substrate for the energy requirements of the lens. Fischer[61] compared the oxygen and carbon dioxide contents of the blood obtained from the vortex veins with that from the carotid artery and found a respiratory quotient of 1.0, indicating that carbohydrate was the main food being utilized by the whole eye. He inferred from this that it was true of the lens alone.

Kinsey* did direct measurements on guinea pig lenses, using the Warburg

---

*Personal communication.

technique and found a respiratory quotient of 1.0. The addition of glucose to solutions bathing the lens does not change its oxygen consumption immediately, indicating considerable reserves of glucose. Moreover, the addition of ten times as much glucose to the bathing solution as is normally present in the aqueous humor does not alter the oxygen uptake.

It has been found that the concentration of sugar in the aqueous humor increases in an aphakic animal,[62] which also indicates that the lens utilizes sugar and that this utilization accounts in part for the low concentration of sugar in the aqueous humor (p. 100). It will be recalled that glucose can be utilized as a source of energy for tissues in either the presence or absence of oxygen. When oxygen is present, glucose may be completely broken down to carbon dioxide and water. In the absence of oxygen, glucose can be converted only into lactic acid by a series of complex steps.

Anaerobic breakdown of glucose. Most of the carbohydrate metabolism of the lens is by way of anaerobic utilization of glucose, i.e., glycolysis. The various steps by means of which glucose is broken down to lactic acid are the same as in all other tissues and follow the Embden-Meyerhof scheme. In addition, it has been shown that the hexosephosphate shunt, in which there is direct oxidation of the 6-carbon glucose structure, is also of importance in the lens.[63] The citric acid cycle in which the lactic acid formed by glycolysis is broken down aerobically to carbon dioxide is not utilized. Instead, the hexosephosphate shunt takes its place in the lens.

If the lens employs cellular respiration, i.e., the oxidation of substrates by molecular oxygen, it does so to a very limited extent. The oxidation of cytochrome C is the usual reaction which most tissues employ for the utilization of molecular oxygen, and cytochrome C, cytochrome oxidase, and flavoprotein are almost confined to the lens epithelium and there in low concentration.

Carbonic anhydrase. This enzyme, which is of such interest in the formation of aqueous humor, is present in greater concentration in the lens than in any other ocular tissue. It is not present in aqueous humor.

PERMEABILITY OF THE LENS CAPSULE

The lens capsule forms an inert nonselective semipermeable membrane. It is permeable to water and electrolytes and to some dyes. Alcohol passes freely into the lens.[64] The capsule is freely permeable to sodium salicylate and fluorescein.[65] On the other hand, the capsule provides a barrier to some substances of large molecular weight, such as albumin and globulin. Lenses in young animals are more permeable to most substances than the lenses of older animals.[66] The lens capsule shows selective permeability only with respect to the molecular size of the substances tested. No visible pores are found in the capsule with the ultramicroscope.

The capsule carries a negative charge when immersed in physiologic sodium chloride solution. If two electrodes immersed in a solution containing electrolytes are separated by a semipermeable membrane on which there is an electric charge, water will be transported from one side of the membrane to the other. If the membrane carries a positive charge, the transport of water will be from the negative pole toward the positive pole. If the membrane carries a negative charge, the transport will be in the reverse direction. Experiments with the lens capsule[66] under such conditions reveal a flow of water in the direction from the positive side to the negative side, confirming the negativity of the membrane.

As would be expected from the negative charge which the capsule carries, it is slightly more permeable to electropositive colloids than to electronegative colloids, but no evidence of anomalous permeability has been discovered. Compared to other biologic membranes, the permeability of the capsule is high, exceeding that of the capillaries, which are normally impermeable to hemoglobin.

Once inside the capsule, substances in solution have to pass through the epithelium on the anterior surface of the lens in order to gain access to the lens fibers. There is no layer of epithelial cells underneath the posterior capsule, which itself is quite thin. The penetration of substances into the lens, as stated, now appears to be much more complex than can be accounted for by simple laws of diffusion, and it is generally acceded that selective transport of substances must take place and that the capsule and/or the epithelium is the site of the active forces brought into play. Even the maintenance of a constant water content is an energy-consuming process dependent upon metabolic activity of the epithelial cells. It has been shown that this is true for both hydration and dehydration of the lens.[67]

PATHOLOGIC PHYSIOLOGY OF THE LENS—CATARACT
Cataract and nuclear sclerosis

The transparency of the lens depends on the physicochemical state of the proteins of the lens. These, like the protein in other organs, are sensitive to changes in the properties of their surrounding fluid. Changes in the concentration of dissolved salts, in the osmotic pressure, in the pH, or in the enzyme activity of this fluid profoundly alter their properties. It is to be expected, therefore, that variations in any of these factors might cause harmful effects on the lens. If the osmotic pressure of the aqueous humor is altered, as sometimes occurs in diabetic persons who permit sudden changes in the dietary regime, the lens imbibes or loses fluid, which results in swelling or shrinking of the lens. This is a reversible change involving variations in the size of the complex protein micellae. The result is an optical disturbance that causes changes in diffraction and refraction. The only pathologic changes which the lens can undergo are alterations in water content and opacification of its fibers since the lens has no blood supply after birth. It cannot react to deleterious physical and chemical agents by an inflammatory or allergic process, as do other tissues.

The changes in water content which occur with advancing age have already been mentioned, and the growth of the nucleus, which increases the refractive index and partially accounts for the loss of accommodation, has been described. Nuclear sclerosis reduces visual acuity, especially when it is associated with the deposition of pigment (so-called cataracta nigra). This sclerosing process of the nucleus is different from the changes which are described as true cataract formation, but since both lead to loss of vision, they have been generally regarded as one and the same pathologic entity. True cataract formation concerns loss of transparency of the lens cortex. Some authors, Salit,[33] e.g., speak of two types of sclerosis of the nucleus—normal, which is strictly an aging process, and pathologic. The aging process, as we have seen, is due to the continued formation of new lens fibers throughout life, which pushes the older fibers into the center of the lens. Here, they lose their nuclei and become compressed into a firm unyielding mass. The nucleus loses water and its soluble proteins and increases its refractive index so that the eye becomes myopic. When this process has gone on to a point at which the transmission of light is so impaired that visual acuity suffers, it can be considered pathologic. There is probably no other difference between the two types of sclerosis of the nucleus, save that of degree. It should be pointed out, however, that the amount of sclerosis of the nucleus varies greatly among individuals. Many people attain extreme old age, i.e., 85 to 90 years, with little change in their refractive status toward the myopic side and with little interference with visual acuity. Again, nuclear sclerosis of a severe degree, while not common, is seen in relatively young persons and may be an unsuspected cause for diminution in vision and may not be detected until a careful slit lamp examination of the lens through a dilated pupil and utilizing a narrow beam demonstrates a dense nucleus. Further, the amount of pigment deposited in the nucleus of sclerotic lenses is extremely variable. The nature of this pigment is not known, but it does not appear to be melanin[68] and is probably related to urochrome.

True cataracts, on the other hand, are always pathologic. They cannot be considered an aging process, and many people live a long life with entirely transparent lenses. Cataracts are opacities in the cortex of the lens due to an irreversible chemical change that produces permanent derangement of the micellar structure of the proteins.

The type of cataract which occurs in elderly people and known as senile cataract has no known etiology, and none of the forms of cataract produced experimentally closely resemble this type. A vast amount of work has been done on the experimental production of cataracts in animals, and an excellent review of this has been given by Pirie and van Heyningen,[69] which should be consulted. The chief methods employed to produce experimental cataracts are radiation, changes in concentration of sugar in the blood, lowering the ratio of calcium to phosphorus in the blood, dietary deficiencies, anoxia, and administration of poisons such as dinitrophenol.

In all of these methods the striking difference between the cataracts produced when compared with senile cataracts is the fact that the younger the animal the easier it is to create opacities of the lens and the shorter the latent period between the experimental procedure and the onset of opacification. In experimental cataracts the changes are unquestionably due to a primary action on the epithelial cells just in front of the equator of the lens which manufacture new lens fibers. In cataracts due to radiation, e.g., it has been proved[67] that, unless the epithelium of the lens is radiated, cataracts do not develop, and irradiation of the ciliary body alone does not produce cataracts.[70]

Experimental cataract

Cataracts may be caused by many different agents, some of which produce types of opacification of the lens which are more or less characteristic. Many cataracts produced experimentally are reversible if the noxious agent is withdrawn in time, in contradistinction to senile cataracts which, for the most part, are progressive or seem to come to a standstill, but almost never regress. Only a few of the many different types will be described here.

Dietary cataracts. Cataracts may be produced by feeding certain sugars such as galactose or xylose and by withholding certain substances from the diet such as

protein-deficient diets or by omitting certain amino acids such as tryptophan. Diabetic cataract, which is a specific clinical type that occurs as a complication of diabetes in young people, is quite rare, although diabetics seem to be more prone to the ordinary senile cataract than the general nondiabetic population.

Galactose and xylose cataracts. The presence of high levels of *d*-galactose or *d*-xylose in the aqueous inevitably leads to the formation of cataract. Galactose cataract can be produced experimentally by feeding a diet containing more than 25% galactose. Galactose also occurs in a rare inborn error of metabolism in human infants known as galactosemia in which the infant is unable to metabolize one of the components of lactose, i.e., galactose. This is due to the deficiency of an enzyme, galactose 1-phosphate uridyl transferase, necessary for the conversion of galactose to glucose.

As a result of this metabolic block, galactose and galactose 1-phosphate accumulate in the blood and in the aqueous humor. Infants with this deficiency are normal at birth but soon feeding becomes a problem and they fail to thrive. Cataracts begin to appear very early in over half the patients. If the disease is detected early, and if all milk and other foods containing lactose or galactose are eliminated from the diet, recovery may be rapid, with the disappearance of the lens opacities.

The changes found in the lens consist of a complete or interrupted circle of vacuoles under the capsule in the pre-equatorial zone. These changes are found as early as five days after feeding has been started. In contrast to the experimental cataracts induced by radiation, which will be described later, the bow fibers are uninvolved, and proliferation of nucleated elements at or behind the equator are entirely lacking. The severe changes noted involve primarily the cytoplasm of newly formed fibers.[71]

Cataracts can be produced in rats by feeding a diet containing 25 to 50% xylose, but only weanling rats are affected. Further, the cataracts are only temporary and disappear even though the diet is continued. Human beings apparently are not affected.[72]

Diabetic cataracts. Diabetes may be produced in experimental animals in a number of ways, and cataracts can be produced by injections of alloxan, dehydroascorbic acid, and diphenylthiocarbazone. The appearance of the cataracts seems to depend upon the level of the blood sugar, and if the blood sugar level is lowered with phlorizin, insulin, or a high protein or high fat diet, the cataract may be prevented from developing. Osmotic changes in the aqueous humor, although they occur with changes in blood sugar, are not of themselves responsible for the opacification of the lens.[73]

Diets deficient in protein, especially those containing tryptophan will produce cataracts in young guinea pigs.[74] Unlike most forms of experimental cataract studied, the changes in the lens in this type of cataract are not found at the lens equator, all components of which retain their normal appearance, but at the ends of the lens fibers, particularly at the suture lines. A diet deficient in many other amino acids has likewise been found to be cataractogenic. This is particularly true of diets deficient in phenylalanine, valine, and histidine.[75] Cataract formation has never been noted in human infants due to such dietary deficiencies.

Cataracts produced experimentally by toxic substances. Cataracts have been produced experimentally by the introduction of many different toxic substances, either fed or injected, such as naphthalene, mimosene, and quinoid substances. Dinitrophenol was one of the first to attract attention because of the high incidence of cataracts in human beings taking this drug for obesity. The drug Myleran, used in the treatment of myeloid leukemia, has likewise been found to be cataractogenic in rats, and recently Mer/29, used for the control of hypercholesteremia, has definitely produced cataracts in human beings and has now been withdrawn from the market. We must be constantly on the alert for such untoward side effects when new drugs are prescribed.

Radiation cataract

The cornea is normally impermeable to wavelengths shorter than 315 mμ, so that very little of the ultraviolet radiation in sunlight reaches the lens. At the other end of the visible spectrum, the infrared waves readily penetrate the cornea up to 1250 mμ, so that the lens is exposed constantly to these wavelengths. Cataracts have been known to occur in individuals exposed to intense radiation from this part of the spectrum. The lens changes are largely confined to the anterior capsule and consist of breaks in the anterior layer of the capsule called the zonular lamella, with curling up of the edges. This is often referred to as true capsular exfoliation to distinguish it from the pseudoexfoliation sometimes seen on the lens capsule in chronic uveitis.

Microwaves of a frequency around 24,000 megacycles have produced cataracts in rabbits.[76] The effect on the lens seems to be related to the rise in temperature of the whole body and/or to environmental factors that affect the capacity of the body for dissipating heat. While cataract formation on this basis has not been reported in man, it points out the need for precautions in the administration of diathermy to the eye or for those individuals who operate microwave generators.

The chief interest in the effects of radiation on the lens centers around the production of cataracts by ionizing radiation as a result of the applications of x-rays and radium around the head area and the effects of atomic explosion. The cells of the lens, like all living cells, are sensitive to all types of ionic radiation, and the younger the cell, the more sensitive it is. The younger the animal, the more likely will the lens develop cataractous changes.[77] The effect on the lens is due primarily to damage to the nuclei of the newly formed fibers; hence irradiation of the lens periphery or of the whole lens will produce cataract with a dosage which is totally ineffective if applied only to the center of the lens. This germinative zone shows the greatest number of mitotic figures. The number of mitoses per epithelium decreases markedly with the age of the animal, and this suggests that the primary effect of radiation is on the mechanism of cell division. This is borne out by the observation of von Sallmann that within 30 minutes after irradiation to 1500 r of x-rays there is an almost complete disappearance of dividing cells in the germinative zone.[78] The absence of mitotic figures lasts two to six days, depending upon the dose, and is followed by a period of excessive mitosis, with breakdown of the cells. Opacification of the lens follows the development of these affected fibers.

It is believed that the effect is the inactivation of an enzyme or enzymes by the production of some chemical substance which reacts with cysteine. This is borne out by the finding that the injection of certain substances such as cysteine, thiourea, and glutathione prior to exposure to an effective cataractogenic dose of x-rays will protect the lens from opacification.

Changes known to occur in cataracts

Increase in water. There is a relative increase in water which disappears gradually as the cataract becomes mature. The total amount of water eventually decreases, and at the same time the weight of the lens diminishes.

Increase in the percentage of ash. The nucleus is said to contain a greater percentage of ash than the cortex[13, 33] after cataract formation.

Increase in sodium. It has already been stated that the potassium-sodium ratio may be taken as an index of tissue vitality.[13, 79] In the normal cortex this ratio equals 1.65 and in the nucleus, 1.34. In cataract this falls to 0.41 in the cortex and 0.32 in the nucleus due to the rise in sodium and the fall in potassium.

Decrease in potassium. Potassium decreases sharply, dropping from 21.8% in the ash of normal lenses to 8.45% in immature senile cataract and 2.4% in mature cataract.[40] There is a loss of potassium in almost all forms of experimental cataract. In galactose cataract, the potassium falls from 0.222% in normal lenses to 0.165% in the cataractous lens.[80] The loss of potassium is probably due to the breakdown of complexes of organic potassium, after which the potassium diffuses away from the lens. This probably indicates death of the cell. At the same time, this loss of potassium permits sodium to penetrate into the lens fibers and accounts for the increased sodium content of cataractous lenses. The potassium content decreases in traumatic cataract and in cataract following experimental parathyroidectomy as well.

Increase in calcium content. The calcium content increases. This is not a primary change in the cataractous process,

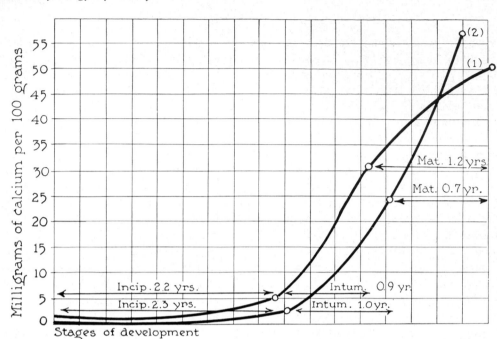

Fig. 71. Stage of cataract and calcium content. **Curve 1,** Classification by slit lamp; **Curve 2,** relative calcium content (Salit). (From Bellows, J.: Cataract and anomalies of the lens, St. Louis, 1944, The C. V. Mosby Co.)

however, since Bellows has shown that in galactose cataract the calcium deposition follows the primary cataractous changes (Fig. 71). The increased calcium content has always been of interest because cataract develops in man and in experimental animals when the normal calcium relationshps of the body are disturbed in conditions such as rickets and following parathyroidectomy. In normal lenses, the ash contains 1% calcium, in immature cataract it contains 2.3%, and in mature cataract it contains 5.5%. This relationship between calcium content and stage of maturity is so intimate that Salit classifies cataracts on this basis. Those whose calcium content is below 10 mg.% (net weight) are classified as incipient, those with a calcium content from 10 to 35 mg.% as immature, and those with a

calcium content above 35 mg.% as mature.

Decrease in oxygen consumption. The oxygen consumption of the lens decreases.[81]

Disappearance of glutathione. Glutathione disappears from the lens.[24] In experimentally produced cataract, the freely diffusible cysteine is first changed to its oxidized form and then diffuses out of the lens, whereas the bound cysteine (beta crystallin) is decreased in quantity.[82] It is not known whether the disappearance of glutathione is the cause of cataract formation or whether it is secondary to the cataractous process. As just stated, some evidence exists that the ability of the lens to consume oxygen depends on the presence of glutathione. With the loss of this substance, therefore, the vital power of oxidation of the lens fibers fails. When rats receive galactose, the loss of glutathione precedes the appearance of cataract, and when they are placed back on a normal diet, the glutathione content of the lenses rises so that eventually the rats recover from the incipient cataract.[54] No evidence is available to substantiate this in the case of senile cataract, however, but there is evidence that the experimental cataract due to the administration of naphthalene may be caused by the withdrawal of cystine from the body and consequently from the lens. Naphthalene is detoxicated in the body of the rabbit by conjugation with cysteine and is excreted as alpha-naphthylmercapturic acid.[83] If cystine is given to such experimental animals, the toxicity of naphthalene is reduced and the formation of cataracts is delayed or prevented.[84] No evidence exists that the loss of cysteine or glutathione from the body as a whole or any disturbance in the sulfur metabolism of human beings accounts for senile cataracts.[85] Blood-glutathione determinations done on patients with senile cataracts[86] show no changes from those of normal persons.

Diminution in weight. A gradual diminution in the weight of the lens occurs as it become cataractous. This is true both of experimental cataract and of ordinary senile cataract.[87]

Concentration of ascorbic acid. The concentration of ascorbic acid has been reported to be reduced in the lens.[88] What ascorbic acid is present in the aqueous humor of cataractous eyes is in the oxidized form (dehydro-ascorbic acid) and not in the reduced form as normally occurs.[89] However, the loss of ascorbic acid is probably an effect of the cataract rather than the cause of the changes in the lens. It has been suggested that the reduction in the concentration of ascorbic acid in

the aqueous humor in cataract is due to a reduction in the rate of flow of plasma through the ciliary processes, and recent experiments indicate that the rate of flow of plasma is smaller in senile cataract than in eyes with clear lenses.[90]

Some authors believe that the ascorbic acid in the lens remains the same in cataractous lenses as in normal lenses. Purcell and associates[91] found the concentration of ascorbic acid in the aqueous humor to be the same in cataractous eyes as in those with clear lenses.

Loss of protein. A gradual loss of protein, as judged by the nitrogen values in terms of wet weight, occurs both in the processes of pathologic sclerosis of the lens and in the formation of cataracts. The average nitrogen content of "practically normal" human lenses is 5.36%, decreasing to 4.83% during pronounced sclerosis and to 4.43% in advanced sclerosis.[92] In mature cataracts there is a loss of about 25% of the nitrogen.[93] The loss is proportional to the degree of damage to the lens and, according to Salit, consists chiefly of the soluble proteins, i.e., alpha and beta crystallins. The insoluble albuminoids are left behind and impart increased rigidity and hardness to the nucleus, where they predominate. Analyses of the amino acids yielded by cataractous and sclerosed human lenses do not support the hypothesis that the loss in protein consists chiefly of the soluble proteins unless it is also assumed that the pattern of amino acids of the crystallins and albuminoids is approximately the same.

A good deal of interest has centered around changes in blood flow through the ciliary processes and the rate of formation of the aqueous humor in cataractous eyes as compared with normal eyes. While Kronfeld[94] found no change in formation of the aqueous humor in cataractous patients, Linner,[95] using a suction cup method, reports a definite reduction in flow in the presence of cataracts. There was no correlation between the decrease in the rate of flow and the stage of development of the cataract.

THE VITREOUS

EMBRYOLOGY OF THE VITREOUS

The development of the vitreous is of some importance in understanding its structure, differences in composition of various regions, and developmental abnormalities and disease processes which affect different parts.

The primary vitreous is derived from the lens plate and optic vesicle and is therefore purely ectodermal in origin. At about the 13 mm. stage or sixth week of gestation mesodermal elements begin to invade this fibrillar structure. The hyaloid vessels running from the optic nerve head aborize around the lens, developing within the primitive vitreous body. The second stage is signaled by the further development of a fibrillar mass that fills the space between the now fully formed lens vesicle and the developing retina. This secondary vitreous is derived from the glial cells of the retina, Müller's fibers. These fibers also form the internal limiting membrane of the retina, so that in a certain sense the fibrils in the main mass of the fully developed vitreous are part and parcel of this membrane. As the optic cup enlarges, filled with this developing secondary vitreous, the hyaloid system of vessels surrounding the lens begins to atrophy, and eventually only the remnants of the hyaloid artery, now empty of blood, remain, persisting in different individuals to various degrees. Usually only a small tag of fibrous tissue is left on the nasal side of the optic disc, but occasionally the residual tissue remains as a fibrous stalk, more or less projecting into the vitreous

toward the posterior surface of the lens. In some cases the whole stalk remains attached to the lens. These remnants are known as retained hyaloid and should be recognized as embryonic in nature and not the result of disease. The spot on the back of the lens where the hyaloid was originally attached often persists as a small opaque dot, known as a Mittendorf dot. The potential space through which the hyaloid courses on its way to the lens is known as the canal of Cloquet.

The third stage in development consists in the growth of fibers from the region of the developing ciliary body and iris. The ciliary epithelium is covered with an internal limiting membrane, similar to the retina, and from this membrane fibers grow into the vitreous toward the lens, forming the suspensory ligament of the lens or so-called zonular fibers.

Abnormalities in development of the vitreous at any of these three stages may give rise to conditions which are of serious import. Retention of the primary vitreous usually results in a completely opaque mass behind the lens, which obviously results in an almost blind eye and which may be mistaken for tumor. The extreme degrees of retention of the hyaloid system may affect vision likewise. Failure of development of the tertiary vitreous may result in absence or weakness of the zonular fibers, with resulting subluxation of the lens.

STRUCTURE OF THE VITREOUS

The vitreous body is a transparent jellylike substance that fills the posterior cavity of the eye. On its back surface is the internal limiting membrane of the retina which, as we have seen, gives rise to the fibrillar structure of the main vitreous mass. The anterior surface is concave, forming the patellar fossa in which the lens rests. It is debated whether or not this anterior surface is covered with a separate membrane. It is difficult to explain in any other way the presence of the retrolental space seen with the slit lamp as an optically empty space between the more peripheral portions of the back of the lens and the face of the vitreous, as identified by its fibrillar structures. The stability of the face of the vitreous after the intracapsular extraction of cataract likewise suggests the presence of a retaining membrane. Occasionally a distinct membrane can be detected, as demonstrated by Cowan[96] and Kirby.[97] At the region of contact between the vitreous face and the lens in some species there is a distinct membrane which firmly attaches the vitreous to the lens and is known as the ligamentum capsulohyaloidea. In most laboratory animals if the eye is cut in such a way that the whole anterior segment can be lifted up, the entire vitreous body will remain intact and firmly adherent to the back of the lens. In man, this attachment is not so easily demonstrable, and the lens generally separates easily from the face of the vitreous as it is removed at operation. Occasionally, following cataract extraction a hernia of the vitreous into the anterior chamber occurs, but usually the anterior face of the vitreous presents a smooth curved front to the aqueous humor and remains as such. It frequently bulges through the pupil space as a smooth spherical surface, protruding more or less with changes in the pupillary aperture. If the membrane or whatever supports the vitreous face is ruptured, the vitreous fibrils stream into the anterior chamber. When marked, this may become a serious complication of an otherwise successful cataract operation, resulting in localized corneal edema in the regions where the vitreous becomes adherent to the corneal endothelium and in secondary glaucoma if vitreous blocks

the anterior chamber angle, preventing the entrance of aqueous humor to Schlemm's canal (p. 137).

The vitreous is firmly adherent to the ciliary body in a ring-shaped area running forward from the ora serrata over the ciliary body for about 2 mm. This forms the vitreous base. It is not generally adherent to the retina but Grignolo describes firm adhesion of the vitreous to the retina in the macular region[98] and to the optic disc itself. The internal limiting membrane which forms the posterior limits of the vitreous does not continue over the optic disc, but runs forward joining in the walls of the canal of Cloquet.

The fact that the vitreous framework arises from the internal limiting membrane makes it easy to see why contraction of the vitreous as a whole or the formation of inflammatory bands in the vitreous creates a pull on the delicate retina behind it and may give rise to tears in the retina. Since the strongest point of attachment of the vitreous is anterior at the vitreous base, the forces developed from such bands will be effective in separating the vitreous from the retina, causing detachment of the vitreous (a condition so often found in elderly people as to be almost physiologic) or to detachment of the retina if the retina tears and permits fluid vitreous to seep in behind it.

If the vitreous body is lifted out of an eye and is placed on filter paper, within a very short time its fluid contents drain out on to the paper, eventually leaving an extremely small residue. It is obvious that the vitreous body is mainly fluid— hence its name, the vitreous humor. Strictly speaking this term should be used only for the fluid part of the vitreous. The residue which remains on the filter paper represents the mass of vitreous fibrils just described as forming the structural elements of the vitreous. By far the greater part of the vitreous is fluid. The volume of vitreous of an ox eye is about 18 ml. Of this the residual fibrous structure after all the fluid has drained away is about 2 to 3 mg.

These fibrils are composed of protein having nearly all the characteristics of collagen; their amino acid composition is like that of collagen, with the characteristic high concentration of aminoacetic acid, 18%, hydroxyproline, 15%, and proline, 8%.[99] The electron microscopic picture of these fibrils is likewise that of collagen, and they are hydrolyzed by collagenase. In only one particular do they seem to differ from collagen, in that they seem bound to a comparatively high amount of carbohydrate which does not appear to be hyaluronic acid since it is not broken down by hyaluronidase. This protein has been given the name vitrein or residual protein. In an attempt to determine the nature of the carbohydrate in the vitreous collagen, Dische and Zelmanes[100] found that the central portions of the vitreous contained three separate proteins, each associated with a different carbohydrate. In some respects the vitrein is comparable to the collagen found in the lens capsule, and it should be remembered that both the primary vitreous and the lens capsule are embryonically purely ectodermal structures.

The fibrillar structure of the vitreous is not uniform but varies in different regions. At least three different-sized fibers have been identified. The largest fibers have been found in the periphery of the vitreous and especially in the region of the vitreous base, which is not surprising when one recalls that the zonular fibers run through the vitreous here on their way to the lens.

The vitreous fibers are broken down by collagenase and are, especially the large fibers, easily attacked by trypsin. This has been put to good clinical use in the development of methods of tryptic digestion of the zonular fibers as an aid to removal of the cataractous lens by the intracapsular method. The use of chymotrypsin to weaken the zonular fibers has been found to be highly successful in selected cases. At the same time it must not be forgotten that such digesting substances, if allowed to spread backward into the vitreous, can produce liquefaction of the entire vitreous and undoubtedly can affect the retina as well.

From what has been said, it seems certain that the vitreous has a formed structure of collagenous fibers which act as a skeleton to give it support. It cannot, as formerly, be considered a pure gel. The early workers in this field doubted that the gossamer wavy fibers as seen in the vitreous with the slit lamp represented true anatomic structures, but were merely optical artifacts. The histologic appearance of fiberlike structures in the vitreous was explained by the action of the fixatives, and it was shown that the size, shape, and pattern of these histologic structures varied, depending upon the type of fixation fluid employed. It was therefore claimed that the vitreous body was a gel similar to ordinary gelatin, without anatomic structure. When gelatin is dissolved in water, the protein molecules attract water and eventually become completely surrounded by layers of water bound to them. In this form they are called micelles and are able to move about in the water with the same freedom of all dissolved molecules. In this state the protein is known as a sol. If the amount of water is reduced, the micelles cannot move about in the solution but become more or less firmly fixed. In this form they are said to be a gel.

With the advent of phase microscopy, the idea that the vitreous consists entirely of a simple gel has had to be abandoned. Although representing a minute portion of the total vitreous volume, the fibrous structure of the vitreous is an anatomic entity. Through this gossamer-like structure substances in solution can readily diffuse. There is no evidence of flow, however, as in the case of the aqueous humor in the anterior and posterior chambers (p. 121). The framework of the vitreous offers no apparent resistance to the diffusion of relatively large molecules within it, such as albumin.[101] This is not surprising in view of the small size of the fibrils, i.e., around 20 mμ in diameter, and the average interfibrillar distance, which is of the order of 2.0 μ.[102]

The main resistance to diffusion of substances throughout the vitreous concerns the viscosity of the fluid component. This part of the vitreous is a true gel. The various parameters which influence its viscosity will be discussed in the following sections.

CHEMICAL COMPOSITION OF THE WHOLE VITREOUS

Most of the analyses made on vitreous have been on the whole vitreous. Since the fibrillar components are so small com-pared to the volume of fluid present, the resulting analyses can be considered to represent almost entirely the chemistry of the true vitreous humor.

The vitreous has a chemical composition similar to that of the aqueous humor, with the exception of two proteins peculiar to the vitreous humor—mucoid and vitrein (also called residual protein). Table 37 gives the chemical composition of the vitreous body compared with that of the aqueous humor and blood plasma, as determined by Reddy and Kinsey.[103]

It will be seen that the composition of the vitreous differs from that of the aqueous humor in the posterior chamber and plasma, chiefly in the concentration of total carbon dioxide and possibly chloride and ascorbic acid.

The amount of water in the vitreous is about the same as that in the aqueous humor. The vitreous contains no oxygen and about the same amount of carbon dioxide as the aqueous humor. The concentration of reducing substances, estimated as glucose, is considerably lower in the vitreous than in the aqueous. The layers of the vitreous in contact with the

Table 37. *Composition of vitreous humor in comparison with that of aqueous humor and plasma in rabbit**

	Vitreous (mM/Hg H₂O)	Plasma (mM/Hg H₂O)	Anterior aqueous (mM/Hg H₂O)	Posterior aqueous (mM/Hg H₂O)	Number of rabbits
	S.D.	S.D.	S.D.	S.D.	
Chloride	103.0 ± 4.2	107.0 ± 4.6	100.0 ± 1.5	96.0 ± 3.4	21
Total carbon dioxide	26.0 ± 1.8	21.0 ± 1.7	30.0 ± 0.63	37.5 ± 1.1	9
Lactate	12.0 ± 3.6	10.3 ± 3.6	9.3 ± 1.4	9.9 ± 0.2	14
Phosphate	0.4 ± 0.17	2.0 ± 0.22	0.9 ± 0.23	0.6 ± 0.005	16
Ascorbate	0.5 ± 0.11	0.04 ± 0.006	1.1 ± 0.13	1.4 ± 0.24	12
Sodium (pooled)	134.0	143.0	138.0	—	6
Potassium (pooled)	9.5	5.6	5.0	—	6
Glucose	3.0 ± 0.59	5.7 ± 1.3	5.4 ± 1.4	5.6 ± 1.2	13
Nonprotein nitrogen	16.8 ± 3.9	34.4 ± 3.0	25.4 ± 1.4	22.9 ± 3.9	16

*From Reddy, D., and Kinsey, V.: Personal communication.

retina contain less glucose than the more anterior layers, as shown in Table 38. This is probably due to the fact that the retina utilizes glucose rapidly so that the low concentration of glucose in the vitreous is due to its rapid utilization by the surrounding tissues. The vitreous is practically surrounded on all sides by the retina, and all the fluid entering the vitreous from the bloodstream must first pass through the retina, whether it comes from the capillaries of the central artery of the retina or from the choriocapillaris. Thus, there would be ample opportunity for the retina to use up some of the glucose before it reaches the vitreous. If this is correct, one should find a gradient in the concentration of glucose to be highest in the anterior layers and lowest in the posterior layers of the vitreous because in this latter situation the vitreous is directly exposed to the glycolytic activity of the retina. In order for this point to be determined, a series of eyes were frozen solid with dry ice, and the vitreous was shelled out and cut into two portions.[104] The aqueous and blood sugar were determined at the same time. Table 38 shows that in nearly every case the posterior

layers of the vitreous contain less glucose than the anterior layers.

These experiments indicate that the low concentration of glucose in the vitreous is due in part to its rapid utilization by the retina. The findings of the following experiment supports this view.[104] In a series of cats the optic nerve on one side was cut and after time was allowed for degeneration of the nerve and retina to take place, the animals were killed, and the aqueous humor and vitreous of the two eyes were analyzed for glucose. In some of the cats the posterior segments of the normal and operated sides were compared as to their relative rates of glycolysis. It is known that cutting the optic nerve leads to atrophy of the retina. The vitreous on the side of the atrophied retina should have a higher glucose content than the normal side and should approach that of the aqueous humor because the atrophied retinas should not use as much glucose as the normal retinas. Table 39 gives the percentage of glucose in the aqueous humor and in the vitreous of three of these cats, in all of which the pupillary reactions indicated a complete lesion of the afferent

Table 38. *Glucose content of blood and aqueous and vitreous humors**

Eye no.	Blood	Aqueous humor	Anterior vitreous	Posterior vitreous	Difference
1†	284	86	63	53	−10
2†	284	86	81	64	−17
3	108	99	71	44	−27
4	104	73	63	70	7
5	104	83	63	52	−11
6	118	96	65	67	2
7	118	127	64	47	−17
8†	281	158	129	106	−23
9	127	65	42	35	− 7
10	150	–	68	57	−11
11	150	114	88	51	−37

*From Adler, F.: Tr. Am. Ophth. Soc. **28**:307, 1930.
†These animals were anesthetized with ether and chloroform, hence the high glucose values in blood.

Table 39. *Percentage of glucose in aqueous humor and vitreous*

Cat no.	Aqueous humor control (mg.%)	Experimental (mg.%)	Vitreous control (mg.%)	Experimental (mg.%)
1	89	102	59	96
2	83	89	69	153
3	95	125	68	113

Table 40. *Rate of glycolysis per gram tissue per hour*

Cat no.	Normal posterior segment (mg.%)	Optic nerve cut segment (mg.%)
1	18.5	14.6
2	5.7	1.7
3	17.7	6.2
4	12.8	1.8

pupillomotor pathway on the operated side and in which the retinas were all grossly atrophic. In all three cats the glucose in the vitreous was much higher on the operated side than on the normal side, and the glucose in the aqueous humor was likewise higher on that side.

Table 40 gives the rate of utilization of glucose of the posterior segments of four of these eyes. The atrophied retinas use considerably less glucose than the normal retinas.

Mention has been made of the fact that the concentration of sugar increases in an aphakic animal,[62] indicating that the lens utilizes sugar. A similar increase in the concentration of sugar in the vitreous has been found after removal of the lens.

The most striking difference between the vitreous humor and the aqueous humor is the content of phosphate, which is in a much smaller concentration in the vitreous body than in the aqueous humor. Analysis of rabbit eyes, ox eyes, and horse eyes showed that the phosphate content was appreciably lower in the vitreous than in the aqueous humor. In the rabbit, e.g., the phosphate content of the aqueous humor is about 30 μg/ml., whereas in the vitreous body it is about 10 μg. The concentration of phosphate is rather uniform in different parts of the vitreous, although a significantly higher concentration can be detected in the parts in the immediate vicinity of the ciliary body. Here, the concentration of phosphate approaches that in the aqueous humor. The aqueous humor and the vitreous body are not separated by a membrane that could be conceived of as impairing an exchange of ions. This seems to demonstrate that the liquid permeating through the gel structure of the vitreous body is not identical with that of the aqueous humor. It is possible to account for both the low phosphate and the low glucose in the vitreous on the basis that the glucose and the phosphate leave the vitreous body by a common process, i.e., phosphorylation.[105]

Recent experiments confirm the fundamental difference between the anterior and posterior environments of the lens so far as phosphate is concerned. The exchange of phosphate between blood and the interior of the lens must take place, therefore, largely by way of the aqueous humor, especially in the equatorial and anterior surfaces of the lens.[106] In cats the oxygen tension of normal vitreous was found to be 53 mm. Hg. Under conditions of hypoxia the oxygen tension of the vitreous fell to an average of 28 mm. Hg when the animal was submitted to moderate hypoxia such as 15% oxygen in the inspired air. When the oxygen in the inspired air was raised, a corresponding increase in the oxygen tension of the vitreous resulted. When the inspired air had a tension of 609 mm. Hg, the vitreous had a tension of 175 mm. Hg. At this level more is being taken into the vitreous than can be accounted for on the basis of the increased oxygen which goes into solution in the blood plasma.[107]

The various crystalloid constituents of the vitreous must come from the bloodstream in much the same way as they do in the aqueous humor. It has been shown that changes in the crystalloid content of the blood, both electrolytes, such as sodium chloride, and nondissociable crystalloids, such as glucose, are reflected promptly in a corresponding change in the aqueous humor. There is very little lag before a chemical equilibrium between the aqueous humor and blood is reached. The vitreous, being a more solid substance, might take longer to equilibrate with changes in the bloodstream, and this is found to be the case. When an animal's blood sugar is raised by an intravenous injection of glucose, a prompt rise in the glucose in the aqueous humor results, but it takes a longer time for a corresponding increase in the glucose in the vitreous.

Proteins. The fluid portion of the vitreous contains soluble proteins such as are present in the aqueous humor.

Hyaluronic acid. The viscosity of the vitreous fluid is due to its content of the mucopolysaccharide hyaluronic acid (400 mg./L. in vitreous humor of cattle, according to Pirie), consisting of equal parts of glucuronic acid and acetylglucosamine. This substance, first isolated from the vitreous by Meyer and Palmer in 1934[108] was subsequently found in the umbilical cord, in synovial fluid, and in most connective tissues. It probably exists in different molecular size in different tissues, and since the vitreous hyaluronic acid is less viscous than that from these other sources, it is presumed that vitreous hyaluronic acid has a smaller molecular size.[109]

Hyaluronic acid is not present in the bloodstream. It is found in the aqueous and in the structures bordering the anterior chamber, i.e., the iris and trabeculum (p. 95). It is not known where it is manufactured, but it has been suggested that stellate cells found on the surface of the vitreous body secrete this substance. The enzyme hyaluronidase has the capacity of hydrolyzing hyaluronic acid. It is not present normally in the vitreous, but if injected, it depolymerizes the hyaluronic acid and reduces the viscosity of the vitreous fluid.

Substances injected into the vitreous humor diffuse into the aqueous humor and also into the bloodstream. Radiosodium, e.g., injected into the vitreous of rabbits diffuses rather rapidly into the aqueous humor, and after a few hours the ratio of the concentration of radiosodium in the aqueous humor to that in the vitreous humor reaches a steady value of 0.20. In 24 hours nine tenths of the radiosodium injected into the vitreous is lost, and of this 60% leaves by way of the anterior chamber. The exchange of radiosodium between aqueous humor and vitreous can be explained entirely by diffusion, but substances leaving the vitreous and gaining entrance to the bloodstream are apparently impeded by a membrane of low permeability on the surface of the vitreous, probably the external limiting membrane of the retina.[110]

Liquefaction of the vitreous occurs in certain pathologic conditions and frequently in what seem to be otherwise healthy eyes. The unexpected presence of fluid vitreous at the time of extraction of a cataract poses a serious problem, and although the present methods of careful suturing of the wound by methods which allow almost immediate closure have reduced vitreous loss to a minimum during cataract operations, nevertheless, it still remains one of the chief factors for poor visual results. The numerous complications which vitreous loss at operation causes are beyond the scope of this book, but they are well documented in any book on cataract surgery. High myopes are always prone to fluid vitreous, and in my experience patients with cupuloform cataracts and nuclear sclerosis are prone to have fluid vitreous. When the patient has had previous inflammation of the posterior uveal tract, fluid vitreous can usually be anticipated. The investigation of whether the vitreous is fluid is too often not attempted prior to the operation. While frequently this is not possible because of the density of the cataract, in many cases the anterior portion of the vitreous can be visualized with the slit lamp through the cataractous lens, and with movement of the patient's eye some evaluation of the solidity of the vitreous can often be made.

We are entirely ignorant of the factors which cause fluid vitreous in human eyes, although experimentally liquefaction may be easily produced. When whole blood is injected into the vitreous, liquefaction of the vitreous occurs. This effect has been traced to the hemoglobin of the blood. If hemoglobin is injected into rabbit vitreous, considerable liquefaction takes place.[111]

Vitreous opacities. Opacities in the vitreous occur so frequently in normal individuals and are so often disturbing when they are first noticed that the ophthalmologist is constantly faced with the problem of differentiating nonpathologic opacities from those which are known to be associated with disease. Further, when they are nonpathologic, he is constantly asked what they are due to. It is not always easy to tell which opacities are pathologic from the character of the opacities themselves, but in general so-called stringy opacities and small isolated spots are generally not associated with disease. They are especially prevalent in myopes. While not necessarily harbingers of disease, even these opacities are in a certain sense not normal since the vitreous must have undergone some abnormal change, however slight, for their appearance. Large irregularly shaped opacities in the anterior vitreous are probably always pathologic, are occasionally the precursors of retinal separation, but are commonly seen without any further change. Dust-like opacities are always pathologic and are suggestive of inflammation in the uveal tract.

What is the nature and the origin of those opacities which may be considered nonharmful? No chemical studies have been made on them, and one can only surmise that either they are collections of cells, probably blood cells which have leaked from blood vessels, or represent small hemorrhages from broken vessels, or are coagulated protein resulting from increased permeability of the blood-vitreous barrier. They may also be condensations of the soluble protein of the vitreous following posterior detachment of the vitreous. What induces this change in the physical state of these proteins is not known at present, but from the complexity of the chemistry of normal vitreous fluid one wonders how it is maintained in its crystal-clear state without undergoing minimal opacification as a result of its metabolic processes.[112] Some opacities have been proved to be blood cells, such as those which follow visible hemorrhages from the retinal blood vessels, but the claim that the majority of the floaters

seen in the normal eye are on this basis cannot be true.[113]

REFERENCES

1. Monahan, R.: Channels in human lens capsule and their relationship to senile cataract, Am. J. Ophth. **36:**24, 1953.
2. Dart, A.: Formed elements in the human lens capsule, Brit. J. Ophth. **45:**298, 1961.
3. Pirie, A.: Composition of ox lens capsule, Biochem. J. **48:**368, 1951.
4. Pirie, A., Schmidt, G., and Waters, S. J.: Ox vitreous humor: I. The residual protein, Brit. J. Ophth. **32:**321, 1948.
5. Bray, R.: Polysaccharides in ocular tissue, Am. J. Ophth. **33:**224, 1950.
6. Roberts, D.: Studies on the antigenic structure of the eye using the fluorescent antibody technique, Brit. J. Ophth. **41:** 338, 1957.
7. Dische, Z., and Erhlich, G.: The breakdown of glucose and its phosphoric esters in the bovine lens capsule, Am. J. Ophth. **39:**99, 1955.
8. Frohman, C., and Kinsey, V.: Studies on the crystalline lens. V. Distribution of various phosphate-containing compounds and its significance with respect to energetics, Arch. Ophth. **48:**12, 1952.
9. Tenz, C., and Katzin, H.: The basement membrane of corneal epithelium, Am. J. Ophth. **36:**895, 1953.
10. Pappas, G., and Smelser, G.: The fine structure of the ciliary epithelium in relation to aqueous humor secretion. In Smelser, George, editor: The structure of the eye, New York, 1961, Academic Press, Inc., p. 453.
11. Salit, P. W.: Biochemical investigation of the nitrogen, weight and water content of crystalline lenses, Arch. Ophth. **5:** 623, 1931.
12. Ely, L.: Metabolism of the crystalline lens: water content and growth rate, Am. J. Ophth. **32:**215, 1949.
13. Lebensohn, A. E.: Biochemistry of the lens: mineral metabolism in normal and cataractous lenses, Arch. Ophth. **15:** 217, 1936.
14. Fischer, F. P.: Der Wasserhaushalt des Auges und seiner Teile, Docum. Ophth. **1:**79, 1938.
15. Krause, A. C.: Chemistry of the lens: relation of the anatomic distribution of the lenticular proteins to their chemical composition, Arch. Ophth. **10:**788, 1933.
16. Burky, E. L., and Woods, A. C.: Lens extract; its preparation and clinical use, Arch. Ophth. **6:**548, 1931.
17. Woods, A. C.: Chemical and immunologic researches on lens protein, Arch. Ophth. **4:**96, 1930.
18. van Heyningen, R.: The lens. In Davson, H., editor: The eye, vol. 1, New York, 1962, Academic Press, Inc., p. 244.
19. O'Brien, C. S., and Salit, P. W.: Isoelectric point of lens protein, Arch. Ophth. **6:**870, 1931.
20. Hesselvik, L.: Electrophoretical investigation on proteins of eye lens and vitreous body, Skandinav. Arch. Physiol. **82:** 151, 1939.
21. Pirie, A., and van Heyningen, R.: Biochemistry of the eye, Springfield, Ill., 1956, Charles C Thomas, Publisher, pp. 3-6.
22. François, J., Rabaey, M., and Wieme, R.: Nouvelle technique de fractiounement des protéines cristalliniennes, Bull. et mém. Soc. franç. opht. **67:**26, 1954.
23. François, J., and Rabaey, M.: Agar microelectrophoresis at high tension of soluble lens proteins, Arch. Ophth. **61:** 351, 1959.
24. Dische, Z., Borenfreund, E., and Zelmenis, G.: Changes in lens proteins of rats during aging, Arch. Ophth. **55:**471, 1956.
25. Krause, A. C.: Chemistry of the lens: composition of beta crystallin, albumin and capsule, Arch. Ophth. **9:**617, 1933.
26. O'Brien, C. S., and Salit, P. W.: Chemical constituents of aqueous, vitreous and lens; a comparative study on animal eyes, Am. J. Ophth. **14:**582, 1931.
27. Halbert, S., and FitzGerald, P.: Studies on the immunologic organ specificity of ocular lens, Am. J. Ophth. **46:**187, 1958.
28. Sauermann, A.: Contribution to problem of enzyme-action in mechanism of cataract, Am. J. Ophth. **16:**985, 1933.
29. Krause, A. C.: Chemistry of the lens: autolysis of lenticular proteins, Arch. Ophth. **10:**631, 1933.

30. Merriam, F. C., and Kinsey, V. E.: Studies on the crystalline lens; incorporation of clycine and serine in the proteins of lenses cultured in vitro, Arch. Ophth. **44:**651, 1950.

31. van Heyningen, R., and Waley, S.: Search for a neutral proteinase in bovine lens, Exper. Eye Res. **1:**336, 1962.

32. Waley, S., and van Heyningen, R.: Purification and properties of a neutral proteinase in the lens, Exper. Eye Res. **1:**343, 1962.

33. Salit, P. W.: The water content and solids of the cataractous and sclerosed human lenses, Am. J. Ophth. **21:**755, 1938.

34. Fischer, F. P.: Der Mineralbestand des Auges, Arch. Augenh. **107:**295, 1933.

35. Fenn, W. O.: Role of potassium in physiological processes, Physiol. Rev. **20:**377, 1940.

36. Salit, P. W.: Calcium determinations on cataractous human lenses, Am. J. Ophth. **13:**1072, 1930.

37. Kaufman, L., and Laskowski, M.: Wachstumsgeschwindigkeit und K/Ca-Quotient, Biochem. Ztschr. **242:**424, 1931.

38. Kirby, P. B.: Calcium in relation to cataract in vivo, Arch. Ophth. **5:**868, 1931.

39. Wolff, R., and Bourquard, A.: Sur las repartition du magnesium dans quelques tissues de l'oeil, Compt. rend. Soc. biol. **124:**319, 1937.

40. Mackay, G., Stewart, C. P., and Robertson, J. B.: A note on the inorganic constituents of normal and cataractous human crystalline lenses, Brit. J. Ophth. **16:**193, 1932.

41. Weekers, R.: L'acide lactique du cristallin, Arch. opht. **1:**707, 1937.

42. Sperekalis, N., and Potts, A.: Additional observations on the biolectric potentials of the lens, Am. J. Ophth. **47:**408, 1959.

43. Brindley, G.: Resting potential of the lens, Brit. J. Ophth. **40:**385, 1956.

44. Sperekalis, N., and Potts, A.: Additional observations on the biolectric potentials of the lens, Am. J. Ophth. **47:**395, 1959.

45. Harris, J., and Gehrsitz, L.: Significance of changes in potassium and sodium content of the lens, Am. J. Ophth. **34:**131, 1951.

46. Krause, A. C.: Chemistry of the lens: lipids, Arch. Ophth. **13:**187, 1935.

47. Bunge, E.: Der Cholesteringehalt Normaler und Getrubter Menschlicher Linsen, Arch. Ophth. **139:**50, 1938.

48. D'Asaro, B., Young, R., and Williams, H.: Lipids of the lens, cornea, iris, ciliary body, and retina, Arch. Ophth. **51:**596, 1954.

49. Heath, H.: The distribution and possible functions of ascorbic acid in the eye, Exper. Eye Res. **1:**363, 1962.

50. Heath, H., Beck, T., Rutter, A., and Greaves, D.: Vision Res. **1:**274, 1961.

51. Ourcell, E., Lerner, L., and Kinsey, V.: Ascorbic acid in aqueous humor and serum of patients with and without cataract, Arch. Ophth. **51:**1, 1954.

52. Glick, D., and Biskind, G. R.: Studies in histochemistry: distribution of vitamin C in the lens of the eye, Arch. Ophth. **16:**990, 1936.

53. Henkes, H. E.: Ueber die Verteilung des Vitamin C in die Linse des Auges, Ophthalmologica **108:**11, 1944.

54. Rosner, L., Farmer, C. J., and Bellows, J.: Biochemistry of the lens: studies on glutathione in the crystalline lens, Arch. Ophth. **20:**417, 1938.

55. McMillan, P., Ryerson, S., and Mortensen, R.: The metabolism of lens glutathione studies with clycine-C[14], Arch. Biochem. **81:**119, 1959.

56. Friedenwald, J. S., and Pierce, H. F.: Respiratory function of the aqueous, Tr. Am. Ophth. Soc. **31:**143, 1933.

57. Field, J., Jr., Tainer, E. G., Martin, A. W., and Belding, H. S.: Studies on the oxygen consumption of the rabbit lens and the effect of 2-4 dinitrophenol thereon, Am. J. Ophth. **20:**779, 1937.

58. Ely, L.: Metabolism of the crystalline lens: respiration of the intact lens and its separated parts, Am. J. Ophth. **32:**220, 1949.

59. Green, H., and Solomon, B.: The effect of age upon lens metabolism, Arch. Ophth. **58:**23, 1957.

60. Heinrichs, D., and Harris, J.: Lens metabolism as studied with the reversible cation shift, Arch. Ophth. **57:**207, 1957.

61. Fischer, F. P.: Ber. ü. Versamml. deutsch. ophth. Gesellsch. **48:**95, 1930.

62. Duke-Elder, S., and Davson, H.: Studies on the intra-ocular fluids: the reducing substances in the aqueous humor and

vitreous body, Brit. J. Ophth. **33:**21, 1949.

63. Kinoshita, J.: Carbohydrate metabolism of the lens, Arch. Ophth. **54:**360, 1955.
64. Nicloux, M., and Redslob, E.: Passage de l'alcool ingere dans le corps vitre et le cristallin, Ann. ocul. **168:**593, 1931.
65. Gifford, S., Lebensohn, J., and Puntenny, I.: Biochemistry of lens: permeability of the capsule of the lens, Arch. Ophth. **8:** 414, 1932.
66. Friedenwald, J. S.: Permeability of the lens capsule with special reference to the etiology of senile cataract, Arch. Ophth. **3:**182, 1930; Permeability of the lens capsule to water, dextrose and other sugars, Arch. Ophth. **4:**350, 1930.
67. Schwartz, B., Danes, B.: and Leinfelder, P.: The role of metabolism in the hydration of the isolated lens and cornea, Am. J. Ophth. **38:**182, 1954.
68. McEwen, W.: The yellow pigment of human lenses, Am. J. Ophth. **47:**(pt. 2) 144, 1959.
69. Pirie, A., and Van Heyningen, R.: Biochemistry of the eye, Springfield, Ill., 1956, Charles C Thomas, Publisher.
70. Apter, A., and Leinfelder, P.: Roentgen-ray cataract, Arch. Ophth. **49:**257, 1953.
71. von Sallmann, L.: The lens epithelium in the pathogenesis of cataract, Am. J. Ophth. **44:**159, 1957.
72. Van Heyningen, R.: Metabolism of xylose by the lens; calf lens in vitro, Biochem. J. **69:**481, 1958.
73. Patterson, J.: Cataracts caused by hydrocarbohydrates, Am. J. Ophth. **36:**143, 1953.
74. von Sallmann, L., Reid, M., Grimes, P., and Collins, E.: Tryptophan-deficiency cataract in guinea pigs, Arch. Ophth. **62:**662, 1959.
75. Hall, W., Bowles, I., Sydenstricker, V., and Schmidt, H.: Cataracts due to deficiencies of phenylalanine and histidine in the rat. A comparison with other types of cataract, J. Nutrition **36:**277, 1948.
76. Williams, D., Monohan, J., Nicholson, W., and Aldrich, J.: Biologic effects studies on microwave radiation, Arch. Ophth. **54:**863, 1955.
77. Cogan, D., and Donaldson, D.: Experimental radiation cataract, Arch. Ophth. **45:**508, 1951.
78. von Sallmann, L.: Experimental studies on early lens changes after roentgen irradiation, Arch. Ophth. **47:**305, 1952.
79. Salit, P. W., Swan, K. C., and Paul, W. D.: Changes in mineral composition of rat lenses with galactose cataract, Am. J. Ophth. **25:**1482, 1942.
80. Meesmann, A.: Experimentelle Ultrarotkatarakt durch Langdauernde Schwachdosierte Bestrahlungen Erhielt, Ber. ü. Versamml. deutsch. ophth. Gesellsch. **48:** 348, 1930.
81. Tsuji, T.: Experimentelle Untersuchungen uber des Linseneiweiss bei Katarakt, J. Biochem. **15:**33, 1932.
82. Bourne, M. C., and Young, L.: Metabolism of naphthaline in rabbits, Biochem. J. **28:**803, 1934.
83. Nakashima, T.: Chemische Untersuchungen uber die Entstehung des Naphthalin-Katarakts, J. Biochem. **19:**281, 1934.
84. Bourne, M. C., and Campbell, D. A.: Sulphur metabolism in senile cataract, Brit. J. Ophth. **20:**684, 1936.
85. Campbell, D. A.: Glutathione in the blood in senile cataract and other ocular conditions, Brit. J. Ophth. **20:**33, 1936
86. Kubik, J.: Sur Pathologic Menschlicher Stare, Arch. Augenh. **102:**657, 1930.
87. Bellows, J. G.: Biochemistry of the lens: cevitamic acid content of the blood and urine of subjects with senile cataract, Arch. Ophth. **15:**78, 1936; Some studies on vitamin C and the lens, Arch. Ophth. **16:**58, 1936.
88. Goldmann, H., and Buschke, W.: Blutkammerwasserschranke und Vitamin C; die Permeabilitat der Blutkammerwasserschranke und der Askorbinsaurespiegel der Vorderkammer, Arch. Augenh. **109:** 205, 1935.
89. Day, P. L., Langston, W. C., and O'Brien, C. S.: Cataract and other ocular changes in vitamin G deficiency, Am. J. Ophth. **14:**1005, 1931.
90. Linner, E.: The rate of plasma flow through the ciliary processes in senile cataract measured by means of ascorbic acid, Acta ophth. **32:**213, 1954.
91. Purcell, E., Lerner, L., and Kinsey, V.: Ascorbic acid in aqueous humor and serum of patients with and without cataract, Arch. Ophth. **51:**1, 1954.
92. Salit, P. W.: Nitrogen content of cataractous and sclerosed human lenses, Acta ophth. **17:**81, 1939.

93. Block, R. J., and Salit, P. W.: A note on the amino acids of cataractous and sclerosed human lenses, Arch. Biochem. **10**:277, 1946.

94. Kronfeld, P.: Tonography, Arch. Ophth. **48**:393, 1952.

95. Linner, E.: The rate of aqueous flow in human eyes with and without cataract, Arch. Ophth. (To be published.)

96. Cowan, A.: Concerning a membrane between the vitreous and the anterior chamber seen after removal of the crystalline lens and its capsule, Tr. Am. Ophth. Soc. **29**:179, 1931.

97. Kirby, D. B.: The anterior vitreous in health and disease, Tr. Am. Ophth. Soc. **29**:193, 1931.

98. Grignolo, A.: Fibrous components of the vitreous body, Arch. Ophth. **47**:768, 1952.

99. Young, R., and Williams, H.: Biochemistry of the eye. II. Gelatinous proteins of vitreous body, Arch. Ophth. **51**:593, 1954.

100. Dische, Z., and Zelmanes, G.: Polysaccharides of the vitreous fibers, Arch. Ophth. **54**:528, 1955.

101. Maurice, D.: Protein dynamics in the eye studies with labelled proteins, Am. J. Ophth. **47**:361, 1959.

102. Grignolo, A.: Fibrous components of the vitreous body, Arch. Ophth. **47**:760, 1952.

103. Reddy, D., and Kinsey, V.: Composition of vitreous humor, Arch. Ophth. **63**:717, 1960.

104. Adler, F. H.: Metabolism of the retina, further notes, Arch. Ophth. **6**:901, 1931.

105. Palm, E.: The phosphate content of the vitreous body, Acta ophth. **27**:553, 1949.

106. Christianson, J., and Palm, E.: The exchange of substances in the anterior part of the vitreous body bordering upon the lens, Acta ophth. **32**:197, 1954.

107. Krause, A., and Goren, S.: The effects of hypoxia and hyperoxia, Am. J. Ophth. **42**:764, 1956.

108. Meyer, K., and Palmer, J.: The polysaccharide of the vitreous humor, J. Biol. Chem. **107**:629, 1934.

109. Balazs, E.: Physical chemistry of hyaluronic acid, Fed. Proc. **17**:1086, 1958.

110. Maurice, D.: The exchange of sodium between the vitreous body and the blood and aqueous humor, J. Physiol. **137**:110, 1957.

111. Karg, J., and McEwen, W.: The effect of beef hemoglobin on rabbit vitreous, Am. J. Ophth. **43**:293, 1957.

112. Discussion on papers on vitreous, Am. J. Ophth. **38**:37, 1954.

113. White, H., and Lavatin, P.: "Floaters" in the eye, Scient. Am. **206**:119, 1962.

CHAPTER 8

ACCOMMODATION

NECESSITY FOR CHANGING THE DIOPTRIC POWER OF THE EYE

The normal eye is so constructed that when it is at rest rays of light coming from infinity are focused on the retina. The refractive indices of the various ocular media, the curvatures of the refracting surfaces, and the position of the retina are such that rays of light entering the eye parallel to its optic axis are focused on the sensitive outer layers of the retina, i.e., the rods and cones. By definition, an emmetropic eye is one in which the retina coincides with the posterior principal focus of the optical system when the eye is at rest. Actually, the normal eye is never really at rest. Even in the dark, the state of the human lens corresponds to about 0.8 D. of accommodation.[1] Rays of light coming from a distance of 6 M. or more are considered parallel and come, therefore, to a focus on the retina of the emmetropic eye.

The emmetropic eye at rest will focus exactly only those objects situated at infinity. Objects situated within this distance may remain in sufficiently good focus to be seen distinctly without any change taking place in the refractive power of the eye. An object may be moved, e.g., from 10 M. to 9 M. distance from the eye and still be in such good focus that the subject (assumed to have no accommodation) fails to notice any difference in the clarity of the image. The region through which an object may be moved in space without causing noticeable blurring of the image is called the depth of field. This increases considerably as the pupillary aperture is narrowed. An emmetropic eye with a pupil of 2 mm. has a depth of field from infinity to approximately 15 M., but if the pupil enlarges to 4 mm., the depth of field narrows from infinity to 30 M. The distance in the retina within which an image may move and still not produce a perceptible blur is called the depth of focus. Over a range of pupil size from 2.5 to 8 mm., the total depth of focus decreases about 0.12 D./mm. increase in size of pupil. The total depth of focus increases with increase in target size.[2]

The resolving power of the eye as an optical instrument is measured by the smallest visual angle at which two objects can be distinguished separately. This is called the minimum separable and is approximately 40 to 60 seconds of arc. In the emmetropic eye an object that subtends an angle of 60 seconds of arc has a retinal image of approximately 0.005 mm. (4.55 μ). When an object is not clearly focused on the retina, it forms a diffusion image or blurred circle which takes the form of the pupil. An object may still be seen even when it is out of focus as long as its diffusion image does not subtend an angle greater than the minimum separable (60 seconds of arc), i.e., as long as the image does not spread more than 0.005 mm. over the retina. An object may be moved a certain distance in space, nearer or farther away from the eye, without the diffusion image increasing more than 0.005 mm. on the retina, as is shown diagrammatically in Fig. 72. If the object is moved closer to the eye than the depth of focus permits, the

blurred circles of diffusion, falling on the percipient elements, subtend an angle greater than 60 seconds of arc. In order to obtain a clear focus under these circumstances, either the dioptric power of the eye must increase or the eyeball must become longer.

It is obvious that the human eye cannot change its axial length under physiologic conditions; therefore this change of focusing power must take place by changing the dioptric power of its refracting surfaces. Experience teaches us that we can focus objects closer to the eye than 6 M. and that, when this is done, all objects situated farther away are out of focus. If one observes an ink spot on a windowpane a foot or so away with one eye, the spot appears clearly focused,

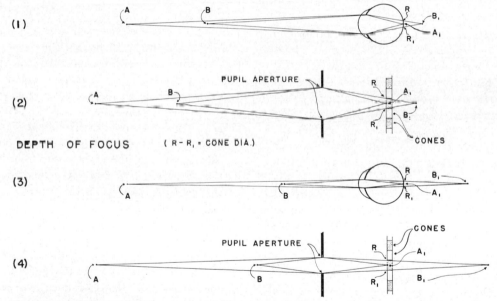

Fig. 72. 1, Object *A* is focused on the retina at *A'* in an emmetropic eye at rest. Object *B*, nearer the eye than *A*, will therefore be focused at *B'*, back of the retina. 2, The same optical principles expressed in 1, with the retina magnified so that the diameter of each cone, *r-r'*, will still receive all the rays emanating from *B* when the pupil is opened wide, e.g., 4 to 5 mm. 3 and 4, An increase in the distance between *A* and *B* is made possible by narrowing the pupil, e.g., to 2 mm. In spite of the fact that there is wider separation between the conjugate foci *A'* and *B'*, rays emanating from *B* still fall within the diameter of one cone and can still be seen, therefore.

whereas objects outside the window are blurred. When an object in the background is then focused clearly, the spot on the windowpane blurs and may even disappear. Two objects cannot be in focus at one and the same time, therefore, when the difference between the distance of each from the observer exceeds the depth of focus of the eye. When a person gazes from one to another, the dioptric power of the eye must change.

This change is brought about by altering the form of the crystalline lens, and this is accomplished by contraction of the ciliary muscle. The process by means of which the dioptric power of the eye is changed is called accommodation.

ANATOMY OF THE PARTS OF THE EYE CONCERNED WITH ACCOMMODATION

Accommodation is the result of a change in the form of the lens, brought about by contraction of the ciliary muscle. No general agreement exists concerning the anatomic details of some of these structures so that anatomy alone cannot be relied upon to formulate a theory of the mechanism of accommodation.

Lens capsule. The lens capsule is a thin transparent membrane that encloses the lens. Although it is seemingly structureless, it is composed of two layers which can be demonstrated by appropriate staining methods. The outer of these two layers is derived from the zonule and hence is called the zonular lamella (Fig. 73). In persons exposed to heat and glare this may become exfoliated, forming a type of opacity known as glassblower's cataract because it occurs frequently in persons in this occupation.

The chief characteristic of the lens capsule is its elastic property. If a wound is made in the capsule, the edges roll outward, and the lens substance bulges through the wound. If the lens is removed from the eye with the capsule intact and the capsule is grasped on either side by two forceps, the surfaces of the lens are flattened when the forceps are pulled gently apart. When the traction is released, the lens returns to its original shape. Years ago, Bowman called attention to the elasticity of the lens capsule in the following words.

"Its elasticity, which is one of its most remarkable properties, is evidenced by a curious experiment which presented itself to me accidentally when I was occupied with a series of researches into the anatomy of these parts. When removed from the eye and placed in water, the lens imbibes fluid through its capsule, which thereby becomes distended and separated from the contained lens, being raised in the form of a vesicle. If it be taken from the water and punctured with a needle, the fluid is ejected with violence by the resilience of the distended capsule which instantly contracts to its former bulk and grasps the lens closely."

The capsule does not have the same thickness throughout its entire extent, and this fact is of importance in any theory of the mechanism of accommodation, as pointed out by Fincham (p. 294). The anterior capsule is much thicker than the posterior capsule and varies in thickness from the equator to the anterior pole, as illustrated in Fig. 74, *A*.

Lens substance. The anterior surface of the lens is faced with a layer of epithelial cells lying directly beneath the capsule. There is no epithelium on the posterior surface of the lens. The lens itself is composed of layers of fibers which take the form of concave meniscus plates, thinner near the center. They run from the equator on one side to the equator on the other side. All new fibers arise at the equator and, as they are formed, push the older fibers in toward the center as they grow (Fig. 74, *B*).

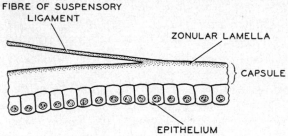

Fig. 73. Lens capsule and zonular lamella. (Modified after Wolff.)

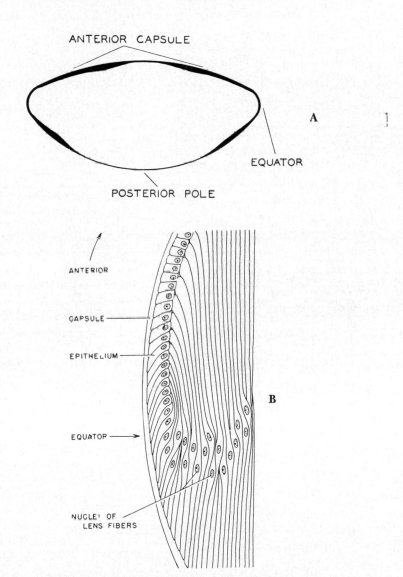

Fig. 74. A, Diagram of the relative thickness of the capsule in various portions, as measured by Fincham. **B,** Meridional section of the equatorial region of the lens showing growth of new fibers at equator. (**B,** After Otto Becker; from Wolff.)

Growth. The lens continues to grow throughout life.[3] In Fig. 75 are shown the growth of the lens in weight from birth to 90 years of age and the growth in volume from 20 to 90 years of age.

Donaldson and King[4] have measured the rate of growth in man and in animals. The rate of increase in the weight of lenses is approximately similar in all the species they measured (Fig. 76). In Fig. 77 is shown the increasing thickness of the lens in emmetrophic persons as measured by Raeder (quoted by Bellows[5]). The postnatal growth in mass and in volume of the human lens shows two distinct phases. During infancy and early childhood the lens grows like other structures associated with the nervous system, and after this early stage of rapid relative increment, it enters a period of slow, steady growth which continues throughout life. A loss of plasticity is associated with continued growth.

Since the older fibers cannot be cast off as is usual with epithelial cells in other parts of the body, they are crowded together into the center of the lens. Here they lose water and form a dense nucleus.

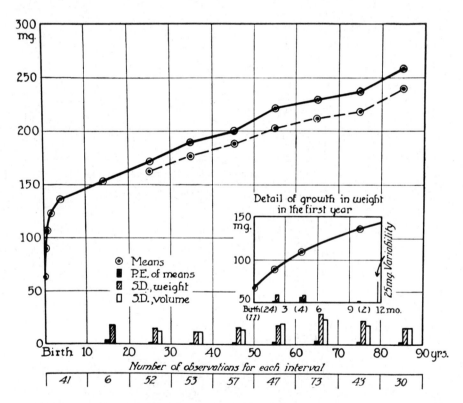

Fig. 75. *Solid line,* growth of the lens in weight from birth to 90 years of age. *Broken line,* growth of lens in volume from 20 to 90 years of age. The curve for the weight of the lens in the first decade was drawn from inspection. The curves for the weight and volume of the lens from 25 years of age onward were drawn by connecting mean points. *Inset,* Growth of the lens in weight during the first year of life. This curve was drawn from inspection. **P.E.,** Probable error; **S.D.,** standard deviation. (From Scammon, R., and Hesdorffer, M.: Arch. Ophth. **17**:104, 1937.)

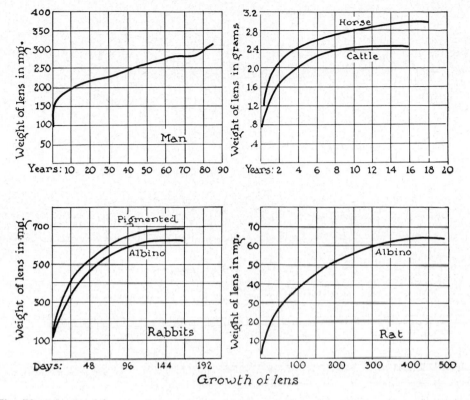

Fig. 76. Growth of lens in various mammals. (From Bellows, J.: Cataract and anomalies of the lens, St. Louis, 1944, The C. V. Mosby Co.)

This nucleus is of little physiologic or pathologic significance until the age of 30 years, by which time it has become so large and dense that it interferes with the deformation of the lens during accommodation.

The growth of the lens with age is due to an increase in the thickness of the cortex. The rate of increase in thickness of the anterior cortex at different ages is constant, corresponding to an increase in growth of the anterior cortex of 0.007 mm. per annum.[6]

The anterior and posterior cortices are approximately of equal thickness. The nucleus varies from 2.26 to 3.60 mm., with an average of 2.80 mm., which is about the size of the whole lens at birth.

The nucleus does not show any consistent variation with age.

Since the lens at birth is more spherical than the adult lens, i.e., the sagittal diameter is greater than the equatorial, the equatorial diameter must grow at a greater rate postnatum than does the sagittal. The growth of the human lens as calculated by Weale[7] from the data of Scammon and Hesdorffer, Johansen, and Salmony is shown in Fig. 78. This continued growth of the equatorial diameter must cause the lens equator to approach the ciliary processes as the individual gets older, which according to Weale has several consequences of significance in the development of presbyopia and perhaps in glaucoma (p. 178). In Fig. 79 is shown

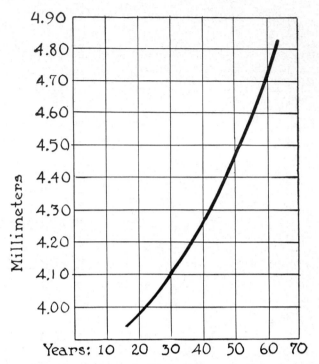

Fig. 77. Thickness of lens in emmetropes. (From Bellows, J.: Cataract and anomalies of the lens, St. Louis, 1944, The C. V. Mosby Co.)

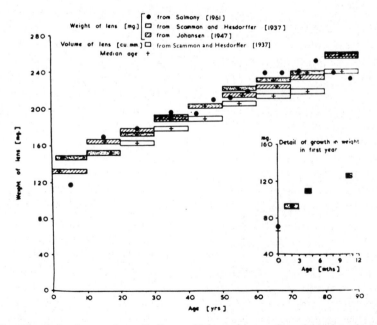

Fig. 78. Growth of the human lens. Ordinate: Volume in cm. (based on data from Scammon and Hesdorffer, 1937, and Johansen, 1947.) (From Weale, R.: Brit. J. Ophth. **46:**660, 1962.)

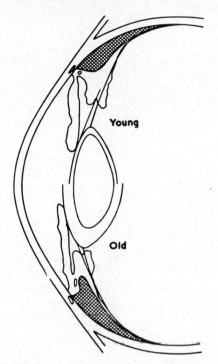

Fig. 79. Schematic comparison of the anterior parts of the eye in the second and seventh decades, respectively. *Shaded parts,* ciliary muscle. (After Stieve, 1949; from Weale, R.: Brit. J. Ophth. **46:**660, 1962.)

a schematic cross section of the eye with the relationships of the lens to the ciliary body shown in both young and old persons.

The lens substance itself is probably not very elastic. The term which has been used to describe its physical state is *plastic,* which by definition implies that its shape can be modified by an external force, and that this shape will then be maintained when the molding force is withdrawn. Weale[7] has criticized this conception since he found evidence that the lens does not exactly maintain its shape after deformation by an external force which is then released.

Evidence that the lens is not entirely unelastic has been offered by Kikawa and Sato,[8] who measured the recovery in form of rabbit's lenses after deformation. These authors found the lens capsule highly elastic, and in addition they found that the lens does tend to return in some measure to its original shape after an external deforming force has been removed. It cannot therefore be stated categorically that the lens substance is entirely inelastic, but exactly what proportion of the two elastic forces, the lens capsule and the lens substance itself, is useful in restoring the spherical shape of the lens when the zonule is relaxed must await further experimentation. At the present time the evidence is distinctly in favor of the capsule.

The cortex consists of soft viscous material which can be easily deformed, whereas the nucleus, as stated, becomes increasingly hard as one approaches the center of the lens. The posterior cortex has greater malleability than the anterior, and the difference between the two becomes more marked with increasing age.[9]

The change from soft cortex to hard nucleus leads to an increase in the refractive index of the various layers of the lens. The rate of change of the refractive index is not uniform throughout the lens, but various isoindicial surfaces exist (isoindicial surfaces are those having the same index of refraction). These isoindicial surfaces are irregular in contour, accounting for the characteristic starshaped figures which small distant lights assume, even in the emmetropic eye. With increasing age, these layers become more and more sharply differentiated from one another and can be seen to form zones of discontinuity when looked at with the slit lamp. The more central fibers, having a greater refractive index and also a more spherical contour than the superficial fibers, largely account for the total refractive power of the lens. These isoindicial surfaces change their shape along with the outside surface of the lens during the act of accommodation.

Radii of curvature. The radii of curvature of the anterior and posterior surfaces of the lens and those of the central layers of the lens, which are considered to form a unit or core lens, are given in Table 41.

Table 41. *Radii of curvature of lens*

Surface	Radius of curvature (mm.)
Anterior surface	11.0 (8.4-13.8)
Posterior surface	5.7
Anterior surface of core lens	4.6 to 7.5
Posterior surface of core lens	7.9

The zonule

The lens is supported by the ciliary body in much the same way a hammock is hung between two posts. The zonule serves as the ropes and appears to be made of separate, individual fibers when looked at with a slit lamp. According to Duke-Elder,[10] the zonule is part of the vitreous body, which is a gel consisting of a network of fine fibrils, and therefore has no real structure. He believes that the zonular fibers which can be visualized are merely condensations of the gel material, and the fibrils which compose the zonule are of the same nature as the micellar aggregates of the vitreous body, although they are more compactly oriented together. Between them lies a clear, transparent, nonstaining gellike substance showing the physicochemical properties of the vitreous gel.

Both the anterior and posterior surfaces of the zonule appear as glistening, shiny, unbroken surfaces. These show marked striation from the lens to the ciliary body. This is rendered very evident by traction upon the lens. The space between these two surfaces shows an irregular crisscrossing of similar strands, surrounded by homogeneous gellike ma-

terial through which the aqueous humor can diffuse with ease from the vitreous into the posterior chamber. Material may be injected into the potential space between the posterior surface of the zonule and the anterior face of the vitreous, as was done by Petit, or into the softer gel between the anterior and posterior surfaces of the zonule, as was done by Hanover, thus leaving intact the continuous membranous appearances described by most anatomists.

The zonule, like the lens capsule, was thought to be an elastic membrane and not a system of inextensible fibers, such as appear in the preparations that have been treated with a fixing agent and described as such by the older anatomists. This view has been challenged by Wolff,[11] however, who believes on good evidence that the fibers of the suspensory ligaments forming the zonule are very real. In appropriate sections, a zonular fiber can be seen to be continuous with the zonular lamella of the anterior capsule so that, if the zonular fiber is regarded as an artifact, the capsule of the lens must also be an artifact (Fig. 73).

The method by means of which the zonular fibers become fixed to the ciliary body is still disputed. Some believe that the zonular fibers are processes of the clear cells of the pars ciliaris retina, others that the fibers can be followed through the cells to the membrane beneath them, and still others that the attachment is intercellular.

The ciliary muscle

Salzmann recognizes three groups of muscle fibers which make up the whole of the ciliary muscle—a meridional bundle, a radial portion, and a circular portion.

The meridional bundle. The meridional bundle is located on the scleral aspect of the muscle, which is much thicker anteriorly than posteriorly. At the forepart it thins again, however, and has its insertion in the scleral roll. The origin of this part of the muscle, therefore, is at the corneoscleral junction just in back of Schlemm's canal (Fig. 80). It thins off posteriorly and becomes intimately connected with the fine trabeculae which cross the suprachoroidal space. The insertion of this bundle is in the choroid coat near the posterior pole of the eye. No distinct line of insertion of the fibers can be seen, but since the anterior portion of the suprachoroidal space is empty and the posterior portion back of the equator contains these fibers joined to pigmented trabeculae, it may be inferred that the insertion lies back of the equatorial zone.

The radial portion. These fibers are so interspersed with the framework of the connective tissue that it is difficult to determine the exact topography of the bundle as a whole. No definite origin or insertion can be distinguished. The anterior end seems to unite with that portion of the scleral framework which does not enter the scleral roll.

The circular portion (so-called Müller's muscle). These fibers form a circular bundle at the inner anterior aspect of the ciliary body. They act as a sphincter muscle and on contraction narrow the ring formed by the ciliary processes. The form of the ciliary muscle as a whole is determined largely by the grade of development of this circular portion. It is always poorly developed in myopic eyes

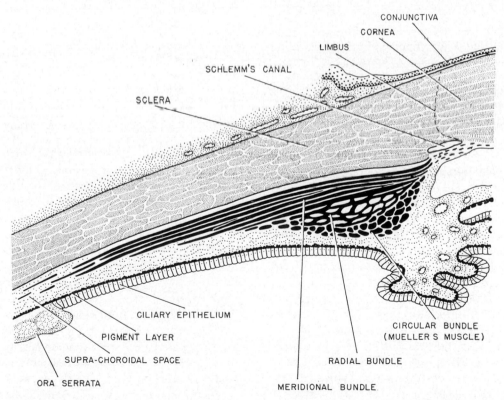

Fig. 80. Anteroposterior section through the anterior portion of the eye. (Modified after Wolff.)

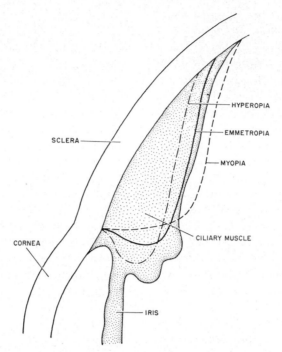

Fig. 81. Relative size of ciliary muscle in hyperopia, emmetropia, and myopia. Note that the major increase in the hyperope is in the region of Müller's muscle.

and well developed in hyperopic eyes, which suggests that this bundle is important in accommodation (Fig. 81).

Contraction of the circular portion of the ciliary muscle alone must result in relaxation of the zonule. Contraction of the meridional and radial portions of the ciliary muscle might result in either relaxation or increased tension of the zonule, and from the present state of our knowledge of the anatomy of the muscle, one cannot decide between these two possibilities.

It must be emphasized that the separation of the ciliary muscle into three components as anatomic entities is for descriptive purposes only, and there is no proof that these portions can act independently of each other. In fact, all the evidence points to the fact stated by Weale that "the ciliary muscle is a functional entity and that its meridional, radial, and circular portions represent different perspectives of the same structure."*

Innervation of the ciliary muscle

The ciliary muscle is innervated by the third cranial nerve. The cells serving this muscle probably lie in the Edinger-Westphal nuclei. From here the axons run into the mass of fibers coming from the main nuclei of the third cranial nerve and thence to the ciliary muscle. Extirpation of the ciliary ganglion leads to ipsilateral degeneration of the fibers in the Edinger-Westphal nucleus.[13] Fibers to the ciliary muscle take the same route as that taken by the fibers to the sphincter muscle, and both sets of fibers make a synapse in the ciliary ganglion. The short ciliary nerves

---

*From Weale, R.: Brit. J. Ophth. **46:**664, 1962.

convey postganglionic fibers into the eye, and they reach the muscle after traversing the suprachoroidal space.

Evidence has been presented that the sympathetic nervous system is also involved in innervation of the ciliary muscle, and certain clinical and experimental phenomena can best be explained by assuming an active participation of the sympathetic nervous system. A dual innervation of the ciliary muscle would seem likely on the basis of analogy with other organs of the body whose functions are regulated by involuntary muscles. These organs generally have a dual system whose two components—the sympathetic and the parasympathetic nervous systems—are mutually antagonistic. For example, parasympathetic fibers to the heart constitute cardiac depressors, whereas sympathetic fibers innervating the heart are cardiac accelerators. In some organs the parasympathetic system is excitatory. In the gastrointestinal tract the parasympathetic system excites motility, whereas the sympathetic system has the opposite effect. As Cannon has shown, in an animal the sympathetic innervation is invoked in response to certain environmental emergencies and in protective reactions such as fear, anger, and pain. The parasympathetic system is effective under conditions of repose and when the environment is stationary. It is known that the iris is innervated by both the sympathetic and the parasympathetic systems, the latter supplying the sphincter pupillae and the former the dilator pupillae. There is no reason why the ciliary muscle should be an exception to this general rule of the dual innervation of unstriated muscle in the body.

If observations on lower animals are applicable to human beings, a wide field for speculation is opened. For example, the action of the sympathetic system might be the cause of the change in axis which occurs occasionally in astigmatism during active accommodation, as reported by Hughes.[14] A difference in the amount of astigmatism during rest and accommodation, has occasionally been noted, an increase in the cylindrical correction being required at the near point. The axis in astigmatism likewise may change. Two explanations for this have been given: (1) asymmetrical changes in the crystalline lens during the act of accommodation and (2) cyclotorsion of the eye during convergence. O'Brien and Bannon[15] examined twenty-five subjects and found an increase in astigmatism for near of approximately 10%. It was possible to determine a shift in the axis in high degrees of astigmatism only. The change averaged 2 degrees. They do not believe that this change is correlated with changes in cyclotorsion during convergence, but that asymmetrical changes in the crystalline lens take place during accommodation.

Although, in man, dual innervation of the ciliary muscle has been assumed,[16] Cogan[17] was the first to present clinical evidence for such dual innervation. He measured the accommodation in a series of patients in whom portions of the sympathetic nervous system had been removed from one side for various conditions. Since these patients all had unilateral Horner's syndrome, it is evident that all had a unilateral lesion of the sympathetic system. The Horner's syndrome was incomplete, i.e., paresis and not complete paralysis. A greater accommodative amplitude was found on the side from which the sympathetic system had been partially removed. One patient presented the opposite condition, i.e., an irritative excitation of the sympathetic chain. In this patient the accommodative amplitude was diminished. These facts suggest that stimulation of the sympathetic system adapts the eye for distance and opposes accommodation for near. The reduction in accommodative amplitude on stimulation of the sympathetic system amounted to 1 to 2 D.

Observations of an increase in accommodative amplitude have been reported in patients with Horner's syndrome,[18] but it may be questioned whether the effect is not due to narrowing of the pupil on the side with the paralyzed sympathetic nerve. Cogan believed that he had ruled out this factor in his observations, using a 2 mm. diaphragm before each eye as an artificial pupil.

Drugs which have a sympathomimetic action produce partial loss of accommodation. Subconjunctival injections of epinephrine hydrochloride, which produce sympathetic stimulation, cause partial loss of accommodation on the side of the injection.[19] More recent studies show that subconjunctival injection of epinephrine causes marked loss of accommodative amplitude, with virtually all the change occurring at the near point.[20] The effect is prompt and transient. The recession of the far point is not as marked as that caused by parasympathetic blocking alone. It is postulated that negative accommodation is mediated via the sympathetic nervous system and positive accommodation via the parasympathetic nervous system. The effect of the sympathetic nervous system may be explained either as a result of vascular change[21] or as due to a direct stimulation of certain portions of the ciliary muscle, as Cogan has done.

In cats, no degeneration of the fibers supplying the sphincter muscle of the iris or of any portion of the ciliary muscle has been found after removal of the superior cervical sympathetic ganglion. Operative removal of the ciliary ganglion results, however, in complete degeneration of the fibers supplying both the sphincter muscle of the iris and the ciliary muscle.

This suggests that in the cat no sympathetic fibers run to the ciliary muscle.

It has been claimed that stimulation of the sympathetic system causes flattening of the lens in the eyes of cats, rabbits, dogs, and monkeys.[22, 23] It has been shown also that, in cats, sympathomimetic agents could counteract the contraction of the ciliary muscle which was induced by stimulation of the parasympathetic nerves.[24] In cats, when the movements of the various portions of the ciliary muscle were observed after the sympathetic nerves had been stimulated, it was noted that the stimulation resulted in a movement directed backward caused by contraction of the radial muscle fibers of the ciliary body. When the parasympathetic fibers were stimulated, the principal movement was in a radially forward direction. This was construed by the investigators to represent an inhibition of autonomic tone of the radial fibers.

Further evidence of dual innervation of the ciliary muscle is found in the fact that even in the dark the state of the human lens corresponds to about 0.8 D. of accommodation. This means that in order for one to focus for infinity, there must be active flattening of the lens from this state of partial accommodation; even though the change is small, it would indicate that there is some mechanism designed to accomplish the change.

CHANGES IN THE EYE DURING ACCOMMODATION

All observers agree that the following changes take place in the eye during accommodation, but the interpretation of some of these phenomena is still a matter of dispute.

1. The pupil contracts during accommodation and convergence. This is a synkinesis and not a true reflex in that it does not depend upon either accommodation or convergence alone for its appearance. If convergence is prevented by the interposition of suitable base-in prisms before each eye, contraction of the pupil will take place during accommodation alone. If accommodation is prevented by placing suitable plus spheres in front of each eye and the person converges to the near point, the pupil will likewise contract.

2. The anterior pole of the lens moves forward, carrying the iris with it. Hence, the anterior chamber becomes slightly shallower in the center as the anterior pole of the lens approaches the back surface of the cornea. The posterior pole does not change its position to any extent.

3. The anterior surface of the lens becomes more convex so that its radius becomes smaller. The posterior surface increases its curvature slightly. This has been ascertained by a study of the images reflected from the various refracting surfaces of the eye. If the image of a candle or some small source of light is thrown into an eye from one side and if the images reflected from the surfaces of the eye are examined, three distinct, separate images will be seen. In Fig. 82, *IA* is a bright erect image, *B* is also erect, much larger but not so bright, whereas *C* is a small, faint, inverted image.

Image A is from the anterior surface of the cornea, *B* is from the anterior surface of the lens, and *C* is from the posterior surface of the lens. If these images are now measured and their distances from each other are determined while the eye is at rest, then during active accommodation the following changes will be observed, as shown in Fig. 82, *II*. No change will occur in *image A*, demonstrating that the corneal surface has undergone no alteration in either position or curvature; *image B* will become smaller and approach *image A*; *image C* will remain in the same position but become smaller.

From the laws governing reflection of light, one can calculate the exact position and curvature of a reflecting surface from the character of its reflected images. A

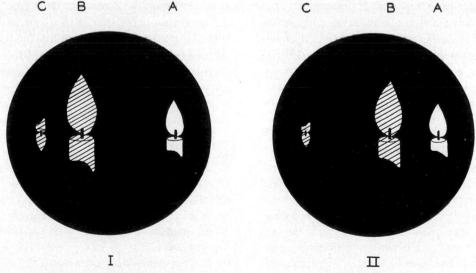

Fig. 82. Catoptric images from the refracting surfaces of the eye. **I,** When the eye is at rest. **II,** During active accommodation.

convex mirror forms an erect and virtual image. If a luminous object such as a candle flame is moved in front of it, the image will be seen to move in the same direction. A concave mirror forms a real inverted image, and its motion is in the opposite direction to that of the object. In a convex mirror, the size of the image of a given object is proportional to the radius of the mirror. Hence, if the curvature of the mirror increases, the image becomes smaller.

The *image A* is formed by the anterior surface of the cornea and is erect and virtual because it is formed by a convex mirror. Since it is nearest the candle flame, its image is the closest to the candle. It is the brightest because the difference between the refractive index of air and of the cornea is greater than between any of the other reflecting surfaces. Since the curvature of the cornea is greater than that of the anterior surface, but less than that of the posterior surface of the lens, the size of this image lies midway between the other two.

Image B is largest since the surface which produces it is least convex, i.e., the anterior surface of the lens. It becomes smaller during accommodation and moves closer to *image A,* proving that the anterior surface of the lens becomes more convex as it approaches the cornea.

Image C is inverted, being formed by a concave mirror, i.e., the posterior surface of the lens or anterior surface of the vitreous. It becomes slightly smaller but remains in position, proving that this surface increases its curvature slightly but does not alter its position.

Young was the first to show that during accommodation the anterior surface of the lens does not become uniformly more curved, but that the central portions increase their dioptric power more than the peripheral portions. Tscherning repeated Young's experiments and concluded that in accommodation the central portions became more curved than the peripheral portions, forming thereby a lenticonus. Tscherning based his theory of the mechanism of accommodation by an increased tension of the zonule on this fact. He believed that the periphery of the anterior surface was flattened by traction of the zonule when the ciliary muscle contracted. This pulled the soft cortex back on to the hard and more convex nucleus. This theory will be considered in more detail later (p. 293).

4. Since the posterior pole remains fixed and the anterior pole moves forward, the thickness of the lens at the center increases.

5. As the lens increases in axial thickness, it diminishes in diameter.

6. Changes occur in the tension of the lens capsule. In a unique case of aphakia following trauma in a 30-year-old man, Graves observed the anterior and posterior capsules of the lens with a slit lamp and studied the changes which accommodation and various drugs produced in them.[25] From his drawings (Fig. 83), it seems indisputable that both during normal accommodation and following the administration of a drug such as eserine that stimulates contraction of the ciliary muscle the anterior capsule becomes slack and separates from the posterior capsule.

7. The accommodated lens sinks due to the effect of gravity. During accommodation the lens sinks in the direction of gravity. Hess first called attention to this fact by observing the apparent upward displacement of the entoptic image of an opacity in his own lens when he accommodated. Fincham confirmed this by finding the distance from the anterior surface of the lens to the cornea in the accommodated state to be 0.2 mm. less

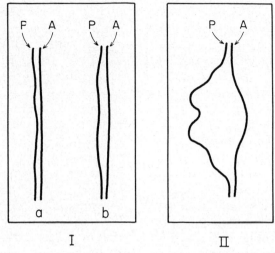

Fig. 83. I, The normal state of the capsule at rest. The posterior capsule, *P,* is more mobile than the anterior capsule, *A,* and sometimes floats forward almost to touch the anterior capsule, *a,* and at other times floats backward, *b.* **II,** The capsule under the influence of eserine. It has now become very lax. (After Graves.)

when the head was held forward parallel to the floor than when the head was held erect, showing the effect of gravity on the position of the lens during accommodation. No change in this distance was observable with a change in position of the head when the eye was not fully accommodated. Little doubt exists, therefore, that the lens is displaced in the direction of gravity during accommodation.

As previously stated, changes within the lens substance create a change in refractive power of the lens in addition to the changes in curvature of the surface when the ciliary muscle contracts. These internal changes are brought about by changes in curvature of the various portions of the lens having different indices of refraction. The total dioptric power of the lens has been found to be greater during maximal accommodation than could be accounted for on the basis of changes in the curvature of the surface. Gullstrand suggested that the changes in the isoindical surfaces made up this deficit.

THEORIES OF THE MECHANISM OF ACCOMMODATION

Although numerous theories have been proposed to account for the changes taking place in the accommodated eye, as just described, only two have sufficient evidence in their favor to warrant serious consideration. These theories may be best described as the relaxation theory and the theory of increased tension. The first was proposed by Thomas Young and was elaborated by Helmholtz, by whose name it is known generally. This theory has recently been supported by a number of original observations contributed by Fincham, whose monograph should be consulted for a more detailed account of the experimental data.[26] The theory of increased tension was developed chiefly by Tscherning, was modified by Pflugk, and in recent years has been upheld by Luedde.[27]

The relaxation theory. The relaxation theory assumes that when the eye is at rest or unaccommodated, the lens is compressed in its capsule by the zonule. In the compressed form its surfaces are curved the least, and the dioptric power, accordingly, is at a minimum. The zonule is kept constantly stretched by its attachments to the ciliary body. In the original theory of Helmholtz, it was supposed that the elasticity of the choroid sustained this. The pull of the choroid balanced the tension of the zonule. When the ciliary muscle contracts, two things happen. The choroid is pulled forward, releasing the tension of the zonule, and the ring formed by the ciliary processes is narrowed by the sphincter or circular fibers of the ciliary muscle, thus making the zonule still more lax. When this occurs, the lens is freed of any compressing force, and by virtue of the elasticity of its capsule, it assumes the shape taken by all elastic bodies freed of constraint, i.e., the shape of a sphere. This increases the dioptric power of the eye.

Although at first Helmholtz regarded the lens as a highly elastic body, which of itself would assume the spherical shape, he soon realized the fallacy of this. The lens is a semisolid mass which may be de-formed but which is not so elastic that, when the deforming force is removed, it returns completely to its original shape. Helmholtz found it necessary, therefore, to attribute elastic properties to the lens capsule to account for the change in the shape of the lens when it was freed from compression by the zonule.

In Fig. 84 is shown a mechanical model of accommodation devised by Gullstrand, based on the Helmholtz hypothesis. The cord between the two springs represents the zonule, the upper spring represents the lens, and its contraction represents the change of the form of the lens during accommodation. The lower spring represents the elasticity of the choroid. In the eye at rest this spring is sufficiently strong to overcome the pull of the upper spring, which must always be slightly on the stretch and therefore must be the weaker of the two. A cord passed over the pulley, supporting the weight, represents the pull of the ciliary muscle. In the unaccommodated eye, the weight is at rest and exerts no pull. When accommodation takes

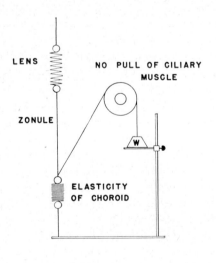
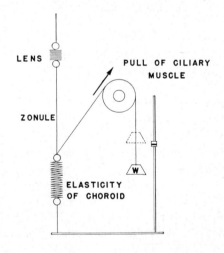

UNACCOMMODATED   ACCOMMODATED

Fig. 84. Mechanical model showing the forces which produce accommodation according to the Young-Helmholtz theory.

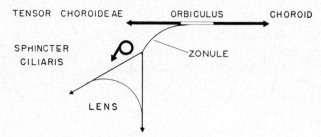

Fig. 85. Traction on the zonule according to Henderson.

place, the weight moves down, pulling against the elastic choroid, and slackens the zonule, thus allowing the upper spring to contract. This represents accommodation by relaxation of the zonule.

As stated, Helmholtz assumed that the choroid sustains the elastic traction of the lens capsule while the eye is at rest. Hensen and Volckers showed that during accommodation the choroid coat moves forward. This suggests that, when the eye is at rest, the choroid does pull against the zonule. It does not seem logical, however, to expect the choroid to constitute a counterweight to such a continually acting force. The choroid, being a richly vascular network, is hardly a structure to be constantly stretched without showing pathologic changes. In fact, where the choroid is known to be under traction, as is the case in high myopia, the parts subjected to pull undergo atrophy and show the effects of stretching. No such changes are noted in the normal choroid where the pull from the ciliary muscle would be exerted.

To overcome this objection to the relaxation theory, Henderson suggested that the traction of the zonule was borne chiefly by the radial and longitudinal portions of the ciliary muscle. He pointed out that the zonule in its course from the ora serrata to the lens presents a curve and not a straight line (Fig. 85). The mechanical significance of this, he thought,

had been overlooked, and he stated the following:

" . . . a curvature in a nonrigid structure, such as the zonule, which is bearing or transmitting a strain cannot exist unless the curvature is supported and the support so given takes a part in sustaining the strain."

In other words, some structure must be supporting the zonule or pulling on it in such a manner that it forms an arch. Henderson offered anatomic evidence to prove that the ciliary muscle supports this arch. He divided the ciliary muscle into the usual three sets of fibers—longitudinal, radial, and circular—but ascribed different functions to each part. The longitudinal fibers act as a support to the distal extremity of the zonule; the radial fibers support the zonular arch (Fig. 86) and increase its tension. The circular fibers act as a sphincter in the generally accepted manner. He was convinced that the zonule is constantly stretched by means of the longitudinal and radial fibers and that the pull on the zonule, due to the elasticity of the lens capsule, is not counterbalanced by the elasticity of the choroid coat, but by the tone of the longitudinal and radial fibers of the ciliary muscle. It is more plausible to consider this a function of muscle than to ascribe it to a vascular structure such as the choroid.

Henderson considered that the ciliary muscle had two different nerve supplies.

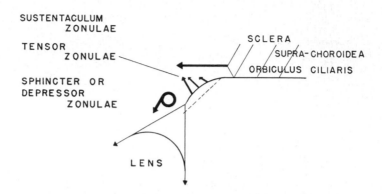

Fig. 86. Henderson's theory of the support of the zonular arch.

The radial and longitudinal fibers maintain a constant postural activity which counterbalances the pull of the zonule, whereas the sphincter or circular muscle overcomes the tension on the zonule and permits it to become slack.

Henderson's theory fits into the evidence, just given, that both parasympathetic and sympathetic innervation are concerned in accommodation. He considered that accommodation is accomplished by inhibition of the postural activity of the longitudinal fibers of the ciliary muscle and by active contraction of the circular fibers. The former, he believed, is due to activity of the third cranial nerve. He regarded the sympathetic nerve as excitatory and the third cranial nerve as inhibitory. According to him, atropine paralyzes accommodation by releasing inhibition, perhaps similar to its action in paralyzing the vagus nerve.

According to the relaxation theory, when the ciliary muscle contracts, the zonule is relaxed. It has been shown already that during accommodation the lens is displaced in the direction of gravity and that both the anterior and posterior capsules of the lens become slack, particularly the former. This is strong evidence in favor of the relaxation theory, which demands that during accommodation both surfaces of the lens become more convex.

One of the fundamental objections to the Helmholtz theory is the fact that the choroid does not move forward when the longitudinal fibers of the ciliary muscle contract. Assuming that the fibers connecting the longitudinal fibers of the ciliary muscle to the choroid are elastic, Stuhlman offers the following solution to the problem, on mechanical grounds.

"In [the] figure [87] the ciliary muscle, suspensory ligaments, and lens are shown diagrammatically. The longitudinal muscle is shown sloping at an angle of 45 degrees; the circular fibers (*c.f.*) lie directly below them. Let F represent the force of contraction developed by the longitudinal muscles in a coordinate system whose Y axis represents the direction of a radius of the lens passing through the circular fibers above it and perpendicular to the optical axis of the lens. This force may be resolved into two components at right angles to each other, F_a, acting along the optical axis of the lens, and F_r, acting along a radius of the lens in a direction pointing from the periphery at right angles to the optical axis.

"If the radial ciliary muscles contract, lying as they do in the base of the ciliary processes, this contraction causes the apices of the processes to come together and form a smaller circle. In such a circular constriction the forces

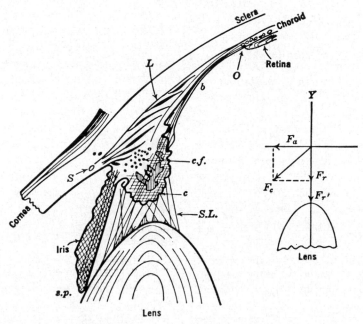

Fig. 87. Diagrammatic representation of the mechanical interactions of ciliary muscle, **L**, suspensory ligaments, **S.L.**, and lens. If **L** contracts, the choroid is stretched, **b** and **c** move down, removing tension from **S.L.** The vector diagram is supposed to show how the external forces act on the lens. S, Canal of Schlemm; s.p., sphincter pupillae, circular muscle of the iris; c.f., circular fibers of the ciliary muscle; L., longitudinal fibers of the ciliary muscle; c, ciliary processes; O, ora serrata end of retina. (From Stuhlman, O.: An introduction to biophysics, New York, 1948, John Wiley & Sons, Inc.)

must again act radially to decrease the circumference of the circle; this latter force is F_r' in the diagram. It will be noted that both F_r and F_r' act in the same direction, tending to slacken the tension on the suspensory ligaments. The horizontal component of the force F_a which is directed forward tends to slacken the tension in those suspensory ligaments which originate at b and which are attached to the anterior face of the lens. This force does not change the tension on those suspensory ligaments running from the anterior surface of the ciliary processes to the posterior side of the lens. These keep the posterior face of the lens under constant tension and do not allow the hydrostatic pressure in the lens to change the radius of curvature of that face. The decreased tension over the anterior surface of the lens allows the lens to bulge in the anterior direction, but not with a uniform change in curvature. The distribution of the suspensory ligaments and the changed thickness of the capsule tend to prevent a uniform change in curvature."[*]

The Tscherning theory (theory of increased tension). The Tscherning theory attributes the increased curvature of the lens to compression of the capsule by increased tension of the zonule. Contraction of the ciliary muscle pulls on the zonule directly and increases the tension on the capsule. This results in compression of the capsule at the equator of the lens so that the poles bulge. Accommodation is brought about, therefore, by increasing the tension of the zonule instead

---

[*]From Stuhlman, O.: An introduction to biophysics, New York, 1948, John Wiley & Sons, Inc.

of relaxing it, as the relaxation theory postulates.

Tscherning considered that it was impossible to account for the lenticonus assumed by the anterior surface, mentioned previously (p. 288) on any basis other than increased tension of the zonule. Contraction of the ciliary muscle, according to him, pulled the periphery of the lens backward against the unyielding vitreous, and this made the central portions of the lens bulge. Fincham[26] confirmed Tscherning's measurements and agreed that the lens did assume a conoid shape. He pointed out, however, that the capsule of the lens, particularly the anterior portion, does not have the same thickness throughout its entire extent, and he made use of this to account for the conoidal form assumed during accommodation. If the lens capsule is elastic and exerts a compressing effect on the lens, the compression will be least in those parts where the capsule is thinnest. As a result, the lens will bulge there. In lenses in which the anterior capsule is uniform throughout, the anterior surface will assume a spherical shape, but if the anterior capsule is very thin at the anterior pole and thick at the edges, as occurs in some lenses, the hyperbolic or conoidal shape will be taken. Thus the properties of the capsule itself not only determine the increase in curvature of the lens, as the relaxation theory demands, but also account for the conoidal form which the lens assumes.

Nordensen[29] has criticized this suggestion and does not believe that the difference in curvature between the center and the periphery is great enough to justify the notation conoidal. In his own experiments Nordensen showed that during accommodation the peripheral parts of the lens assumed an aspect quite different from that described by Fincham. Nordensen's figures showed marked increase of the curvature of the whole anterior surface of the lens. He also showed that the radius of the peripheral parts, although still greater than that of the central part, is always smaller in accommodation than at rest.

Odqvist[30] placed lenses extracted in their capsule in a hypotonic solution so that they absorbed water and swelled, causing the capsule to become considerably stretched. The lenses assumed a spherical form and did not form a lenticonus.

Fincham[26] has shown that the anterior surface of the lens of a child becomes more convex when the zonule is severed than when the zonule is intact. He showed further that this change was not equal throughout the entire anterior surface (Fig. 88, *A* and *B*). Fincham agreed that the anterior surface of the lens underwent a considerable change in radius of curvature, e.g., from 12 mm. to 5.50 mm. He pointed out that if a lens with a spherical surface, having a diameter of 8 to 9 mm., changed its curvature by this amount and remained spherical a considerable movement of lens substance would be necessitated. This would entail a large reduction in the equatorial diameter and a marked forward movement of the pole. It has been shown, however, that the movements of these parts are small and are consistent with only a small change in the general form of the lens. The conoidal form of the lens surface, therefore, produces a great increase in power for that part of the lens which is exposed through the pupil, while necessitating the minimum amount of movement of the lens substance. He points out that this probably results in an economy in contraction of the ciliary muscle. It is now generally accepted that the anterior surface of the lens becomes more convex, as described by Tscherning, and that during

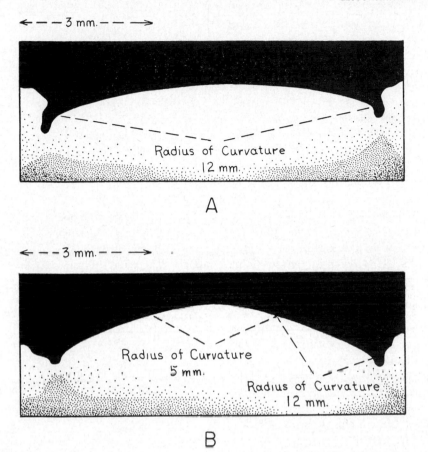

Fig. 88. A, Shadow graph of the anterior surface of the lens of a child before the zonule is severed. B, Lens after the zonule has been severed. Note that change is not equal through whole anterior surface. (After Fincham.)

accommodation it becomes conoidal in form.

When all the evidence for the two theories is viewed impartially, the weight of evidence is in favor of the relaxation theory. At the present time it cannot be said that either theory has been proved, however.

The changes seen in the angle by gonioscopy appear to bear out the Helmholtz theory.[31] The general impression gained is that there is relaxation of the zonule during accommodation, with recurving of the relaxed lens capsule to create greater curvature of the central surface of the lens. In addition, these observations support the belief that during accommodation the vitreous body does press on the periphery of the lens.[32]

THE STIMULUS TO ACCOMMODATION

An emmetropic individual employs no accommodation when fixating a distant target (theoretically at infinity) under normal daylight viewing conditions. However, if the illumination is reduced considerably, in most individuals but not in all the far point of the eye changes to within infinity. In other words, most individuals become slightly myopic under conditions of dark adaptation, the average change being from 0.5 to 2 D. This disappears when the eye is light-adapted again. This so-called night myopia has been the subject of many experiments, but at present it is still not entirely clear what causes it. Since it does not occur in the aphakic eye, it is evidently connected with some change in the lens. Various theories have been proposed to account for it, including spherical and chromatic aberration due to a wide pupil, forward displacement of the lens as the pupil dilates, and eccentric fixation in the scotopic eye compared to foveal fixation in the photopic eye. The myopia persists, however, even when the target is viewed through an artificial 2 mm. pupil, so that spherical aberration is ruled out. To complicate matters it has been shown that this same increase in the refractive power of the eye occurs under bright photopic conditions if the subject's visual field is empty.[33]

Accommodation cannot be voluntarily induced (except the accommodation which is induced by convergence, carried out voluntarily) or voluntarily changed. It is therefore almost entirely reflex in nature. Unlike unconditioned reflexes such as contraction of the pupil to light, the accuracy of the mechanism is augmented by use. If some of the normal stimuli which control the accuracy of accommodation are experimentally eliminated, the remaining stimuli may be enhanced by practice.[34] What are the normal stimuli which call accommodation into play?

The chief stimulus to accommodation is a change in vergence of the rays of light on the retina. When an object which is in focus on the retina is brought closer to the eye, the focus is moved to a point back of the retina and the image is blurred. This change in vergence of the light normally produces accommodation of the lens to bring the focus back on the retina.

Conscious awareness of the distance of an object assists in producing a correct degree of accommodation, but accommodation can be elicited without any awareness of the distance of the object from the eye by placing negative lenses in front of the eye. The adjustment to this change in the vergence of the light occurs rapidly (p. 298) without any conscious effort on the part of the subject. As stated, the act is reflexly carried out.

Accommodation is activated only when the light energy reaching the retina from the test object exceeds a critical value. This has been found to be about twice the light energy necessary to produce foveal vision.[35] This is suggestive that the receptors involved in the accommodation reflex are the foveal cones. Changes in the vergence of light on the cones produces blurring, and it is the appreciation of this blurring, consciously or unconsciously, which elicits the reflex. While this might seem an entirely satisfactory explanation, it can easily be shown that one must inquire farther into the process, for a blurred retinal image per se does not produce accommodation. Unless the blurring is produced by a change in the vergence of the light rays on the retina, no accommodation takes place. If one presents a clear series of letters on a screen at 20 feet to an individual, and then puts these letters out of focus, no accommodation takes place. How then does the individual discriminate between blurred images on his retina due to changes in vergence of light and those not so produced? The answer is not entirely clear at present.

Fincham[36] found that if the target was viewed in monochromatic light about 60% of his subjects lost the power to accommodate correctly when the vergence of light on the retina was changed. From this he concluded that the stimulus for accommodation rests in part on the chromatic aberration of the eye and in part on small scanning movements of the eyes over details whose images are blurred. He points out that there is no mechanism by means of which the retina can send information to the brain of blurring of the image falling on it; the retina can only report two types of information, namely, differences in the amount of illumination and differences in color. Hence when a target is viewed in monochromatic light, chromatic aberration is eliminated, and faulty accommodation develops.

The mechanism by which chromatic aberration becomes effective is as follows. In the emmetropic eye (or one made so with correcting glasses) white light from a target at infinity is somewhat broken up into the component colors (wavelengths) of the spectrum by the chromatic aberration of the eye, and the yellow or wavelengths of 580 mμ are exactly focused on the retina. The shorter wavelengths, e.g., blue, being more strongly refracted, fall in front of the retina, whereas the longer waves, e.g., red, being less refracted, fall in back of the retina. If the target is now brought closer to the eye, the focus shifts backward, so that the blue rays now fall exactly on the retina and the yellow and red rays now fall behind the retina. From this it can be seen that the movement of a target within infinity, let us say at the reading distance, to which the eye has accommodated exactly so that the yellow waves fall on the retina will produce a shift of colors on the retina as the target is moved either closer to or farther away from the eye. This shift will provide information from which fine changes in accommodation may be made (chromatic aberration and its use in the duochrome test are discussed further on p. 756).

In the remaining 40% of his subjects, prevention of scanning movements of the eye over the target by keeping the eye fixed succeeded in eliminating accurate accommodation. The effect of scanning was interpreted by Fincham to indicate that the Stiles-Crawford effect (p. 774) is the other possible means by which the visual mechanism interprets differences of vergence in terms of difference of light stimulus. As the eye makes small movements over the target, the limiting rays of the blur circles acquire different degrees of obliquity at the retina. When the vergence of light rays is such that the image is focused behind the retina, the rays nearer the center of the fovea become more perpendicular to the retina, whereas when the focus is in front of the retina, the rays farther from the center of the fovea become more perpendicular. Hence, during scanning movements a difference of brightness stimulus between the two sides of the area is produced by the Stiles-Crawford effect, and the brain can detect thereby whether the light at the retina is convergent or divergent.

Other stimuli normally employed in accommodation are apparent size and apparent distance and possibly stereopsis.

Spherical aberration and astigmatism may also be used to decide whether a monocularly viewed out-of-focus target requires an increase or decrease of accommodation for it to be refocused.[37]

It has been assumed that accommodation can be kept in abeyance when doing a manifest refraction in patients under the presbyopic age by the method of fogging, i.e., inserting plus lenses in the trial frame sufficiently strong to blur distance vision. This in effect brings the conjugate focus of the test letters well in front of the retina, and hence any accommodative effort would blur the patient still further. Evidence has been produced, however, that fogging may stimulate accommodation instead of relaxing it maximally or allowing it to remain passive.[38]

Once the eye has accommodated accurately on a target, small fluctuations in accommodation take place. This is not surprising since most motor systems show the same thing. Thus, the pupil shows constant fluctuations in size at any constant illumination (p. 203), and the eyeball shows constant micronystagmus during steady fixation (p. 500). Similarly, it has been found that under steady viewing conditions the accommodation undergoes small fluctuations which disappear when the subject views a target at infinity or when a cycloplegic is instilled in the eye, paralyzing accommodation.[39]

Reaction time. The accommodative response follows the presentation of an accommodative stimulus after a reaction time which averages about 0.36 second.[40] When the response is carried out in a single sweep, the time required to make the movement is independent of the amplitude of the movement and averages 0.64 second for far-to-near accommodation and 0.56 second for near-to-far accommodation. The reaction time for an accommodative response is considerably longer than that for the contraction of the pupil to light, 0.26 to 0.30 second,[41] or for eye movements, with a minimum of 0.12 second. However, the reaction time of the pupil response to near (p. 211) is longer than the reaction time of the pupil to light, 0.32 second. This is probably due to the fact that in the near response of the pupil there is a longer central component, since the near response of the pupil shares with the accomodation and convergence reaction a central pathway capable of making distinctions between and interpretations of retinal images which we usually associate with cortical areas. The latency of a convergence response is about 0.20 second.[42]

Other evidence suggests that in the case of accommodation the accommodation itself can be halted during its progression and that some continuous monitoring system must be present which guides the accommodation mechanism once it has begun to act, up to a point at which the satisfactory amount of accommodation has been produced (see discussion of effect of chromatic aberration, p. 756). This can be contrasted with the behavior of the extraocular muscles system in which pulse stimuli, if they yield a response, produce saccadic movements which cannot be modified during their progress.

AMPLITUDE OF ACCOMMODATION

The amplitude of accommodation is somewhat dependent on extraneous factors such as the background luminance of the object of regard. As the level of luminance is diminished, the amplitude of accommodation is lessened.[43] In other words, as the visibility of the test target against its background is reduced, the accommodative power is lessened. This is in no way related to any change in the accommodation-convergence/accommodation (A-C/A) ratio, however, which does not change significantly with decreasing retinal illuminance.[44]

RELATION BETWEEN ACCOMMODATION AND CONVERGENCE

In normal binocular vision accommodation and convergence operate in unison. The chief stimulus to accommodation is a change in the vergence of light striking the retina. Assuming an object at 6 M. to be in focus on the fovea, as it approaches the eyes, the pencil of rays entering the pupils becomes divergent. This produces accommodation. If the object approaches the individual on a line midway between the two eyes, the image moves away from each fovea in a temporal direction. This temporal displacement of the retinal images relative to each other provides the stimulus for convergence of the visual axes. The basic stimuli to the *binocular* adjustment for near vision are, therefore, (1) change in the vergence of the light reaching each fovea and (2) temporal disparity of the two images relative to the two foveas.

The relationship of these two functions is not strictly fixed, although under normal conditions a unit change in one is accompanied by a unit change in the second. Thus, one diopter of accommodation is ordinarily accompanied by one meter angle of convergence. But it has been shown by most investigators that some latitude of action is possible between accommodation and convergence. There is an amplitude of accommodation corresponding to each convergence value, and convergence can vary somewhat relative to a fixed condition of accommodation. In order to show the amplitudes of either accommodation or convergence, each function in turn must be held in a fixed state of action while the other is varied. Provision must be made in the experimental setup to change either the vergence of the light or the temporal disparity of the image, but not both at the same time. Such measurements will tell us then how far either function, being unstimulated, responds in sympathy to stimulated changes in the other.

The change in convergence produced by a change in accommodation is known as the accommodative convergence. This will be considered in the section on convergence on p. 484. The change in accommodation produced by a change in convergence will be considered here. Until recently it has been debated whether or not convergence alone, without any accompanying change in the vergence of light on the retina, was able to change accommodation. In 1956 Christoferson and Ogle[45] stated that the difficulties of measurement were such that they prevented any investigation as to what extent convergence-accommodation exists. Fincham and Walton, however, have succeeded in measuring the controlling effect of convergence upon accommodation in the absence of the effects of light vergence. They find that in young subjects, up to the age of 24 years, the convergence-induced accommodation is equal to the convergence, but above that age it gradually diminishes. Accommodation is induced by convergence as an unconditioned reflex. It is probable that the diminution of the convergence-induced accommodation with age is due to the progressive sclerosis of the crystalline lens causing a reduced response to a given innervation and contraction of the ciliary muscle rather than to a change in the relative innervations to the two functions.[46]

Accommodation can be produced, therefore, by convergence alone, and up to 24 years of age the physiologic maximum can be produced by this stimulus. In older persons the rate of increase of accommodation with increasing convergence is reduced. Fincham[47] has produced evidence which shows that this is caused by the need for greater ciliary force to produce a given amount of accommodation. Further, he found that artificial paresis of the ciliary muscle with homatropine sufficient to produce the slightest reduction in accommodation relative to convergence also causes the maximum of accommodation to be reduced at all ages. Therefore, maximal accommodation requires the maximal force of the ciliary muscle. Miotics enhance the contraction of the ciliary muscle accompanying convergence. This results in an increase of accommodation relative to convergence, and the maximal accommodation is increased above the physiologic maximum. These facts support the idea that it is not the elasticity of the lens which makes it more spherical when released from the tension of the zonule during contraction of the ciliary muscle, but the elasticity of the lens capsule, which deforms the plastic lens. As the lens substance becomes harder with age, greater force from the elastic capsule will be required to produce a given change in curvature. This force can only be applied by greater contraction of the ciliary muscle. This explains why we are unable to maintain our full accommodation for more than a short time and why the presbyope requires optical aid although his near point may not lie outside his working distance. The fact that he has to contract his ciliary muscle to a greater extent in order to produce even minimal accommodation naturally gives rise to fatigue, headaches, and all the symptoms of asthenopia.

PRESBYOPIA

The amplitude of accommodation gradually diminishes with age. At the age of 8 years the dioptric power of the eye can be raised by accommodation approximately 12 D., at the age of 20 years this has fallen to 11 D., at the age of 30 years it falls to 9 D., and at the age of 50 years it is less than 2 D. The nearest point for which the eye can accommodate so that a clear image is formed on the retina is called the near point or the punctum proximum. If the eye is emmetropic or is made so with the proper corrective lenses, the near point will vary with the age of a person as just stated. It is closest to the eye at the age of 8 years and recedes gradually until about the age of 45 years when a much more rapid recession occurs. Further loss of the accommoda-

tive power, with recession of the near point, continues unabated until about the age of 60 years, by which time all the accommodation has been lost.

By the time the near point has become so far removed that the subject cannot read fine print, the eye is said to have become presbyopic. Presbyopia is the normal recession of the near point due to age and usually begins around the age of 46 years. Convex glasses must then be prescribed as a substitute for the decrease in the accommodative power of the lens.

It is generally believed that presbyopia is the result of sclerosis or hardening of the nucleus of the lens so that the forces which normally deform the soft lens during youth (capsular elasticity or compression of the lens by the zonule) are now no longer effective. It has also been suggested that the decrease in malleability of the cortex is due to a loss of water content of the lens with age. In the young lens during accommodation the water leaves the fibers in which it is bound and becomes intermicellar in nature rather than intramicellar, but as the lens grows older and contains relatively less water, it becomes more difficult to make this intermicellar exchange. Fincham found the surfaces of lenses which had been removed from the eye to be less strongly curved in older people than in children, which implies that the elasticity of the capsule is no longer able to deform the senile lens.

Some of the phenomena of presbyopia are easier to understand if one admits that accommodation is effected by direct stress applied to the lens (Tscherning theory). As long as any displaceable lens substance surrounds the nucleus, the lens should be able to change its shape as formerly. No change should occur in the malleability of the human lens due to increase in size of the nucleus until late in life, at least not until after the age of 30 years, but, as just stated, accommodation begins to diminish at 8 to 10 years of age. This suggests a direct stress applied to the lens from without. Any increase in its resistance creates opposition to the external stress and thus would interfere immediately with its malleability.

Duane pointed out a third possibility—that loss in accommodation is due in part, at least, to progressive diminution in the power of the ciliary muscle. The expansion of the lens depends on two factors: the physical constitution of the lens itself and the strength of the ciliary muscle. Several facts suggest that the power of the ciliary muscle diminishes with age, almost in proportion to the manifest diminution in accommodation.

A person 45 years of age loses his remaining power of accommodation when homatropine is instilled in the eyes much more quickly than a 20-year-old person. The loss of accommodation produced by homatropine at different ages is illustrated in Fig. 89. This is best explained by assuming that the total energy of the ciliary muscle varies in different subjects at the same age and undergoes a steady reduction year after year, as does accommodation. If one accepts Tscherning's theory or some hypothesis which ascribes accommodation to external stress applied to the lens, the facts may bear a different interpretation. As the lens becomes sclerosed, a greater and greater degree of power of the ciliary muscle is required to deform the lens. The amount of power in the ciliary muscle, instead of decreasing from youth on, as is necessary according to the Helmholtz theory, either would remain the same or would actually increase during adolescence. The third possibility is that both processes cooperate to produce a steady reduction in the accommodative power.

Although the evidence of presbyopia is

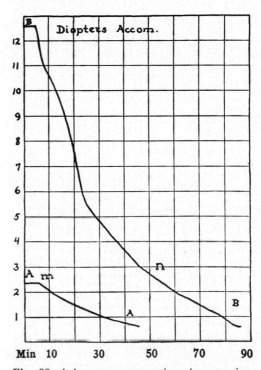

Fig. 89. **A,A** curve representing the recession of the accommodation under homatropine in a man 45 years of age. **B,B,** similar curve in a girl 12 years of age. If the original accommodation in each case is supposed to be 18 D., the fall in 6 minutes in the first case would be 15.6 D., or 78%, whereas the fall in the second case would be 6 D., or 33%. But if the original accommodation in the first case is supposed to be 3 D. and in the second case 15 D. each curve really would be alike, representing a fall in the geometric ratio of 20% each 6 minutes—i.e., at the end of each 6-minute period the residual accommodation would be 80% of what it was at the beginning of the period. This more plausible assumption seems borne out by the following fact. Curve **A** from **m** onward is almost precisely like curve **B** from **n** onward. One may reasonably infer that the small portion of curve **A** before **m** (representing in this case the diminution in the latent accommodation) and an equally small portion of curve **B** before **n** are also alike. In this case the starting point of curve **A** would be somewhere about 3 D. (From Duane, A.: Arch. Ophth. 5:1, 1931.)

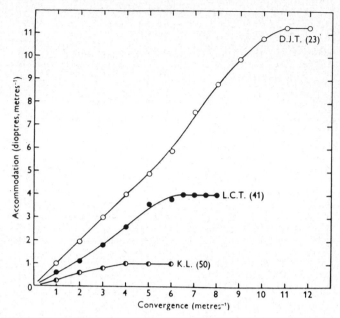

Fig. 90. Accommodation induced by convergence. Results on three subjects of different ages. Both the maximum and the rate of increase of accommodation relative to convergence become less with age. Convergence is shown in the units metres^{-1} as comparable with diopters of accommodation. (From Fincham, E.: J. Physiol. **128:**105, 1955.)

in favor of the Tscherning hypothesis, Goldmann and Aschmann[48] present evidence that the Helmholtz theory is indeed correct, but that with age the power of the ciliary muscle weakens, probably from disuse. Such an explanation reconciles the otherwise conflicting data.

The capsular theory, according to Fincham, leads to the conclusion that, as the lens substance becomes harder with age, greater force from the elastic capsule will be required to produce a given change of curvature. He states:

". . . [this force,] in view of the elasticity of the suspensions, can only be applied by greater contraction of the ciliary muscle. Consequently a force approaching the full capacity of the muscle may be required to produce maximal accommodation, whether it be some 15 or 16 diopters in youth or only 1 or 2 diopters in presbyopia. This view explains why we are unable to maintain our full accommodation for more than a short time, and why the

presbyope requires optical aid, although his near point may not lie outside his near working distance."*

Fincham[49] compared the accommodative response to varying degrees of convergence under normal conditions and under conditions of paresis and artificial stimulation of the ciliary muscle produced by the action of drugs. In sixteen normal subjects with good fusion, every increase in convergence was found to be accompanied by an increase in accommodation. The relation of these two functions varied with age of the subject (Fig. 90). Both the rate of increase of accommodation relative to convergence and the maximum accommodation become less with age. When drugs were used to cause slight paresis of the ciliary muscle, it was found that in no

*From Fincham, E.: J. Physiol. **128:**105, 1955.

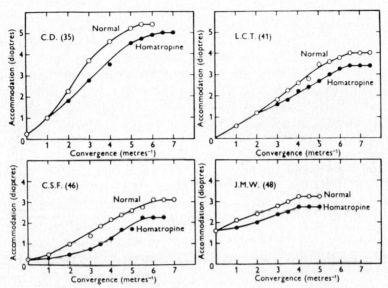

Fig. 91. Effect of slight paresis of the ciliary muscle upon accommodation induced by convergence. (From Fincham, E.: J. Physiol. **128**:107, 1955.)

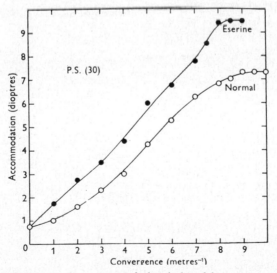

Fig. 92. Effect of eserine upon the accommodation induced by convergence. (From Fincham, E.: J. Physiol. **128**:108, 1955.)

subject was the reduction of accommodation relative to convergence detected without a corresponding reduction in the maximum of accommodation (Figs. 91 and 92). These experiments indicate that the hypothesis of a unit of power of the ciliary muscle (called the *myodiopter* by van der Hoeve and Flieringa), which is obtained by measuring the effect upon the lens of the muscular contraction and is constant throughout life, is invalid. Fincham found that the physiologic maximum of accommodation can be induced by convergence. Artificial paresis of the ciliary muscle sufficient to produce the slightest reduction of accommodation relative to convergence also causes the maximum of accommodation to be reduced at all ages; therefore, maximum accommodation requires the maximal

force of the ciliary muscle. Eserine enhances the contraction of the ciliary muscle which accompanies convergence. This results in an increase of accommodation relative to convergence. When eserine is instilled in the eye, the maximal accommodation is increased above the physiologic maximum.

Alpern[50] has postulated the two theories of presbyopia and collected the evidence favoring each. The theory of Helmholtz and Gullstrand is based on the belief that to produce a diopter change of accommodation at any age requires the same amount of change in length of the ciliary muscle, whereas the theory of Donders, Duane, and Fincham assert that the amount of shortening of the ciliary muscle required to produce a diopter change of accommodation increases with age.

REFERENCES

1. Campbell, F., and Primrose, J.: State of accommodation of the human eye in darkness, Tr. Ophth. Soc. U. Kingdom **73:** 359, 1953.
2. Ogle, K., and Schwartz, J.: Depth of focus of the human eye, J. Optic. Soc. America **49:**273, 1959.
3. Scammon, R. E., and Hesdorffer, M. B.: Growth in mass and volume in postnatal life, Arch. Ophth. **17:**104, 1937.
4. Donaldson, H. H., and King, H. D.: On growth of eye in three strains of Norway rat, Am. J. Anat. **60:**203, 1937.
5. Bellows, J. G.: Cataract and anomalies of the lens, St. Louis, 1944, The C. V. Mosby Co.
6. Huggert, A.: Thickness of cortex of crystalline lens in different ages, Acta ophth. **24:**43, 1946.
7. Weale, R.: Presbyopia, Brit. J. Ophth. **46:**660, 1962.
8. Kikawa, Y., and Sato, T.: Elastic properties of the lens, Exper. Eye Res. **2:** 210, 1963.
9. Jaeger, A., and Vogelsang, K.: Uber Dehnungs- und Hartemessungen an tierischen Linsen, Arch. Augenh. **109:**103, 1936.
10. Duke-Elder, W. S.: The nature of the vitreous body, Brit. J. Ophth. (supp. 4), 1930.
11. Wolff, E.: Some aspects of the normal histology of the suspensory ligament of the lens, Proc. Roy. Soc. Med. **39:**252, 1946.
12. Weale, R.: Presbyopia, Brit. J. Ophth. **46:** 664, 1962.
13. Kure, K., Susuki, T., Kaneko, Y., and Okinaka, S.: Histologische Studien über die extrapyramidalen Bahnen; die Kerne der extrapyramidalen Fasern für die Augenmuskeln, Ztschr. Zellforsch. u. mikr. Anat. **17:**453, 1933.
14. Hughes, W. L.: Change of axis of astigmatism on accommodation, Arch. Ophth. **26:**742, 1941.
15. O'Brien, J. M., and Bannon, R. E.: Accommodative astigmatism, Am. J. Ophth. **30:**289, 1947.
16. Nicolai, C.: Der Mechanismus der Akkommodation, Eine neue Theorie, Klin. Monatsbl. Augenh. **94:**617, 1935.
17. Cogan, D. G.: Accommodation and the autonomic nervous system, Arch. Ophth. **18:**739, 1937.
18. Cobb, S., and Scarlett, H. W.: Report of eleven cases of cervical sympathetic nerve

injury, causing the oculopupillary syndrome, Arch. Neurol. & Psychiat. **3**:636, 1920.

19. Heath, P.: Neosynephrin hydrochloride, some uses and effects in ophthalmology, Arch. Ophth. **16**:839, 1936.

20. Biggs, R., Alpern, M., and Bennett, D.: The effect of sympathomimetic drugs upon the amplitude of accommodation, Am. J. Ophth. **48**:169, 1959.

21. Fleming, D.: The role of the sympathetics in visual accommodation, Am. J. Ophth. **43**:789, 1957.

22. Mohney, J., Morgan, M., Olmstead, J., and Wagman, I.: Pathways of sympathetic nerves to ciliary muscles in the eye, Am. J. Physiol. **135**:759, 1942.

23. Olmsted, J.: Role of autonomic nervous system in accommodation for far and near vision, J. Nerv. & Ment. Dis. **99**:794, 1944.

24. Meesman, A.: Experimentelle Untersuchungen über die antagonistische Innervation der Ciliarmuskulatur, von Graefes Arch. Ophth. **152**:335, 1952.

25. Graves, B.: The response of the lens capsules in the act of accommodation, Tr. Am. Ophth. Soc. **23**:184, 1925.

26. Fincham, E. F.: Mechanism of accommodation, Brit. J. Ophth. (supp. 8) pp. 5-80, 1937.

27. Luedde, W. H.: What subluxated lenses reveal about mechanism of accommodation, Am. J. Ophth. **24**:40, 1941.

28. Stuhlman, O.: An introduction to biophysics, New York, 1948, John Wiley & Sons, Inc., p. 207.

29. Nordensen, J. W.: Some remarks on Fincham's capsular theory of accommodation, Brit. J. Ophth. **27**:127, 1943.

30. Odqvist, B.: Studien über den Akkommodations Mechanismus, Acta Soc. Med. Suec., 1937.

31. Burian, H., and Allen, L.: Mechanical changes during accommodation observed by gonioscopy, Arch. Ophth. **54**:66, 1955.

32. Busacca, A.: La physiologie du muscle ciliare etudiee par la gonioscope, Ann. ocul. **188**:1, 1955.

33. Whiteside, T.: Accommodation of the human eye in a bright and empty visual field, J. Physiol. **118**:65, 1952.

34. Marks, H.: On the accuracy of accommodation, Brit. J. Ophth. **46**:742, 1962.

35. Campbell, F.: The minimum quantity of light required to elicit the accommodation reflex in man, J. Physiol. **123**:357, 1954.

36. Fincham, E.: The accommodation reflex and its stimulus, Brit. J. Ophth. **35**:381, 1951.

37. Campbell, F., and Westheimer, G.: Factors influencing accommodation responses in the human eye, J. Optic. Soc. America **49**:568, 1959.

38. Flom, M.: Variations in convergence and accommodation induced by successive spherical lens additions with distance fixation, Am. J. Optom. Monograph 176, 1955.

39. Campbell, F., Robson, J., and Westheimer, G.: Fluctuations in accommodation under steady viewing conditions, J. Physiol. **145**:579, 1959.

40. Campbell, F., and Westheimer, G.: Dynamics of accommodation response of the human eye, J. Physiol. **151**:285, 1960.

41. Loewenstein, O., and Loewenfeld, I.: Electronic pupillography, Arch. Ophth. **59**:352, 1958.

42. Westheimer, G., and Mitchell, A.: Eye movement responses to convergent stimuli, Arch. Ophth. **55**:848, 1956.

43. Alpern, M., and David, H.: The effects of illuminance quantity on the accommodation of the eyes, Indust. Med. **27**:551, 1958.

44. Alpern, M., and Larson, B.: Vergence and accommodation. IV. Effect of luminance quantity on the AC/A, Am. J. Ophth. **49**:1140-54, 1960.

45. Christoferson, K. W., and Ogle, K. N.: Effect of homatropine on accommodation-convergence association, Arch. Ophth. **55**:779, 1956.

46. Fincham, E., and Walton, J.: The reciprocal actions of accommodation and convergence, J. Physiol. **137**:488, 1957.

47. Fincham, E.: The proportion of ciliary muscular force required for accommodation, J. Physiol. **128**:99, 1955.

48. Goldmann, H., and Aschmann, A.: Studien über Akkommodation, Ophthalmologica **111**:182, 1946.

49. Fincham, E.: The proportion of ciliary muscular force required for accommodation, J. Physiol. **128**:99, 1955.

50. Alpern, M.: Muscular mechanisms. In Davson, H., editor: The eye, vol. 3, New York, 1962, Academic Press, Inc., pp. 209-217.

CHAPTER 9

THE OCULAR CIRCULATION

GENERAL CHARACTERISTICS OF OCULAR CIRCULATION

In man all of the blood reaches the eye by way of the internal carotid artery. In the lower mammals, particularly those used for experimental purposes such as the cat, dog, and rabbit, the blood supply is from both the internal and the external carotid arteries. In the dog blood reaches the circle of Willis through an anastomosis between the spinal branches of the vertebrals and the deep cervical artery and, as Bouckaert and Heymans have shown,[1] also through the ophthalmic branch of the internal maxillary artery. The internal maxillary artery, which is a branch of the external carotid artery, communicates with the internal carotid artery within the skull.

The ophthalmic artery is the direct branch of the internal carotid artery, and the two separate and independent systems, i.e., the retinal and the uveal arteries which supply the eye in man, both come directly from the ophthalmic artery (Fig. 93). The detailed anatomy of the ophthalmic artery has recently been reinvesti-

gated by new techniques by Hayreh and Dass.[2-4] The uveal circulation is formed by the anterior and posterior ciliary arteries, and the retinal circulation is formed by the central retinal artery. The retinal system supplies the inner layers of the retina as far as the inner nuclear layer. It ends in two capillary plexuses—an inner plexus in the nerve fiber layer and a second or outer plexus whose terminal branches end in the inner nuclear layer (Fig. 94). The uveal circulation supplies the outer layers of the retina, from the inner nuclear layer outward, and the remainder of the outer coats of the eye. The entire posterior portion of the uveal circulation terminates in a large capillary bed, the choriocapillaris. This is of importance in the nutrition of the eye and also in the maintenance of the intraocular volume.

There is a very free anastomosis between the branches of the uveal circulation, but the branches of the central retinal artery are independent of each other as far as their capillary beds. They are considered to be end arteries. The

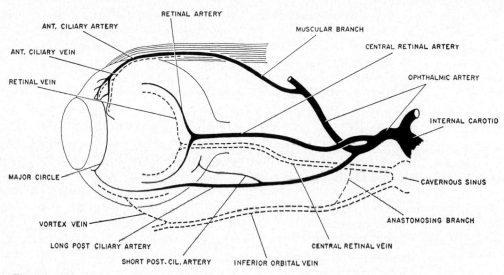

ANT. CILIARY ARTERY
ANT. CILIARY VEIN
RETINAL VEIN
MAJOR CIRCLE
VORTEX VEIN
LONG POST CILIARY ARTERY
SHORT POST. CIL. ARTERY
RETINAL ARTERY
MUSCULAR BRANCH
CENTRAL RETINAL ARTERY
OPHTHALMIC ARTERY
INTERNAL CAROTID
CAVERNOUS SINUS
ANASTOMOSING BRANCH
CENTRAL RETINAL VEIN
INFERIOR ORBITAL VEIN

Fig. 93. The retinal and uveal circulations of the eye. (Modified after Duke-Elder.)

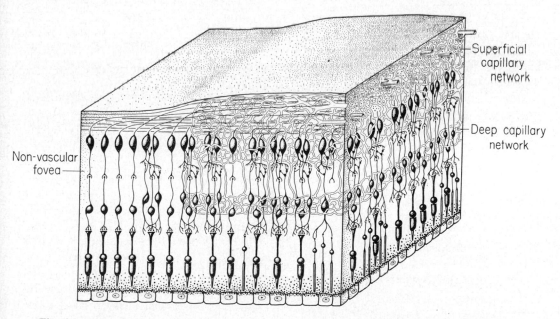

Non-vascular fovea

Superficial capillary network

Deep capillary network

Fig. 94. Stereogram of retina in the macular region showing the synapses between the various cellular components of the retina. The superficial and deep capillary plexuses are shown in the right-hand half of the picture, only, since the vessels do not enter the foveal area.

retinal circulation has always been compared with the cerebral circulation. For many years the latter was thought to consist of a system of end arteries, in the sense that there were no anastomoses between the individual branches. However, Lorente de No[5] showed that this conception of the cerebral circulation was erroneous. In 1927, he described the connections of the cerebral blood vessels and came to the conclusion that the arteries were not end arteries, stating:

"One can go from each vessel over into another without leaving the capillary net. I believe I am not exaggerating if I say that one could pass through the capillary net from the olfactory bulb all the way to the occipital lobe."*

This is not true of the retinal circulation because the branches of the central retinal artery makes no gross anastomoses. The arteries only interconnect through capillaries.[6] The smaller veins around the ora serrata do anastomose, however. The central vein of the retina does have numerous anastomoses with the choroidal and scleral vessels.[7] Wolff[8] injected normal cadaver material and made serial sections of the region around the lamina cribrosa. These sections showed that there is a capillary anastomosis between the branches of the central artery and those of the circle of Zinn, the latter giving by far the largest supply to this region. This has been confirmed by finding an anastomosis between the central retinal artery and the arterial plexus of the pia mater surrounding the anterior portion of the optic nerve. There is also an anastomosis between the central retinal artery and the intrascleral circle of Zinn.[9] In spite of the existence of these

---

*From Lorente de No, R.: Quoted in Penfield, W.: Cytology and cellular pathology of the nervous system, New York, 1932, Paul B. Hoeber, Inc.

collateral channels, vision is generally lost following occlusion of the central retinal artery. The fact that uveal retinal arterial anastomoses exist warrants the use of any measure which promotes vasodilatation in the treatment of central retinal artery occlusion in the hope that it will facilitate the opening up of collateral circulations. The procedures which have been suggested to serve this purpose are paracentesis of the anterior chamber to lower the intraocular pressure suddenly, retrobulbar injection of acetylcholine, and administration of oxygen.[10]

Various methods have been employed to demonstrate the intraocular circulation. The intrascleral vessels related to the filtration angle have been visualized by injection methods from which neoprene casts could be made.[11] The choroidal vessels have been directly visualized by creating windows in the sclera.[12] The uveal veins have been studied by radiographic injection techniques, and reconstructions have been made on the basis of regional x-ray pictures. In Fig. 95 is shown a composite picture of the intraocular venous system in the cat as made by Cohan.[13]

There can be no doubt that the integrity of the retina is dependent upon the retinal circulation since closure of the central artery, if complete, leads to permanent blindness. In fact, the metabolic requirements of the retina are of such a high order that any slight vascular disturbance leads to marked interference with its function.

The effects of temporary arrest of the circulation on the central nervous system have been studied.[14] In a series of experiments on cats the circulation to the entire body was temporarily interrupted, abruptly and completely, by clamping the pulmonary artery. The moment at which the circulation returned to the cerebrum

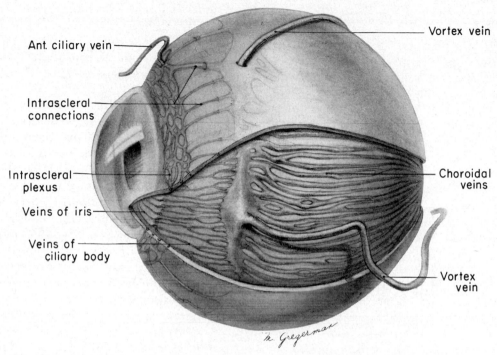

Ant. ciliary vein

Intrascleral connections

Intrascleral plexus

Veins of iris

Veins of ciliary body

Vortex vein

Choroidal veins

Vortex vein

n. Gregerman

Fig. 95. Schematic composite of the radiographic anatomy of the intraocular venous circulation of the cat. The sclera is drawn as if it were semitransparent in order to demonstrate the veins within it and the location of the vortex sinus in the underlying uveal system. A strip of sclera has been removed to reveal the pattern of the uveal venous circulation. (Modified from Cohan, B.: Arch. Ophth. **63**:145, 1960.)

could be determined accurately by observations of the retinal vessels. Arrest of the circulation for 3 minutes, 10 seconds or less was tolerated without any obvious neurologic disturbances. Permanent alterations in behavior and psychic function occurred in animals subjected to 3 minutes, 25 seconds or more of circulatory arrest. After 6 minutes of circulatory arrest, vision and sensation suffered permanent injury. After 7 minutes, 36 seconds, there were permanent defects—dementia, blindness, serious sensory, motor, and postural defects, and reflex abnormalities. Life could not be restored for more than a few hours if the circulation was interrupted for 8 minutes, 45 seconds or longer. Definite histologic changes

were seen in the brain after circulatory arrest of 3 minutes, 10 seconds. At these relatively short periods, the spinal cord and medulla were uninjured, but the third and fourth laminae of the cerebral cortex appeared to be particularly susceptible to injury. The lateral geniculate body was found to be the most vulnerable of the basal nuclei in the cat.

It may be assumed that the ocular circulation, like that of the brain, is of extreme importance to the nervous tissues of the globe and visual pathways. Interference will not be tolerated, save for the briefest periods of time.

Pilots of aircraft traveling at high speeds are likely to experience serious disturbances in the retinal circulation.

A sudden change in the direction of flight at high speed, such as occurs when the pilot is pulling out of dives or making sharp turns, sets up centrifugal forces of such magnitude that the blood cannot reach the retina, and a form of temporary blindness known as blackout occurs. A pilot flying at a speed of 300 mph, e.g., will experience a force of 4 g while making a turn with a radius of 1,500 feet.[15] Under normal circumstances a pressure of 25 mm. Hg is required to overcome the force of gravity in order to raise blood from the heart to the head level, i.e., a distance of 0.3 M. With a specific gravity of 4 the pressure required would be about 100 mm. Hg. Assuming the subject's systolic arterial pressure at the heart level is 120 mm. Hg, the pressure of blood at the head level during exposure to a force of 4 g would be 120 minus 100 mm. Hg. Assuming that the normal intraocular pressure is approximately 20 mm. Hg, it is evident that the blood flow will cease under these conditions. Blackout generally occurs with a force of 4 g after an exposure of 3 seconds.[15a]

The arterial pulse

The following types of pulsation have been described in the retinal arteries.

1. Pulsations in which the course of the artery shifts slightly from side to side at each heartbeat, becoming manifest either as a lateral displacement of some portion of the arterial tree or, more often, as a slight bending or unbending of some twist or knuckle in the artery. This type of pulsation is called locomotion pulse or serpentine pulsation.

2. Pulsations in which the arterial channel itself enlarges and collapses during systole and diastole. It is appropriate to speak of this type of pulsation as expansile pulsation.

Unless otherwise specified, this is the type meant by the term *arterial pulsation,* which is usually used.

The locomotion pulse (serpentine pulsation). The retinal vascular dynamics which produce the locomotion pulse have been thoroughly explored by Friedenwald.[16] If one considers the constant flow of fluid through a system of frictionless elastic tubes, the total energy of the body of fluid confined in any one of the tubes may be divided into potential energy, which is manifested as lateral pressure, and kinetic energy, which is manifested as flow pressure (Fig. 96, *A*). The lateral pressure is measured by the height to which fluid will rise against gravity in a side channel which enters perpendicularly into the tube. The flow pressure is measured by the difference between the lateral pressure and the height to which fluid will rise in a side channel entering the tube parallel to the direction of flow, the mouth of this measuring tube being arranged to open upstream. The lateral pressure plus the flow pressure is the total pressure head of the system. Lateral pressure will rise or fall as the stopcock letting water out of the system is opened or closed. It can, therefore, be stated that the greater the velocity of outflow from the system (greater flow pressure), the lower will be the lateral pressure and vice versa (Fig. 96, *B* and *C*).

If the tube is bent, a part of the flow pressure is added to the lateral pressure on that side of the wall of the tube which is convexed outward, and the lateral pressure will be correspondingly diminished on the opposite side of the tube (Fig. 97). The difference between the pressure on the two sides of the tube constitutes a force tending to displace the tube toward the convex side, a phenomenon which is easily observed in the wriggling of a garden hose through which a steady stream of water is passing. No such undulating movement as that typified by a garden hose is observed in the retinal vessels since the excess pressure on the one side of the vessel is compensated by the elastic tension of the tissues in which the vessel is imbedded, but when the linear velocity of flow through the vessel increases and with it the flow pressure, the force which tends to produce the undulating movement increases and creates a tendency toward tortuosity in the vessel.

In a garden hose with a moderate flow through the hose, the tube accommodates

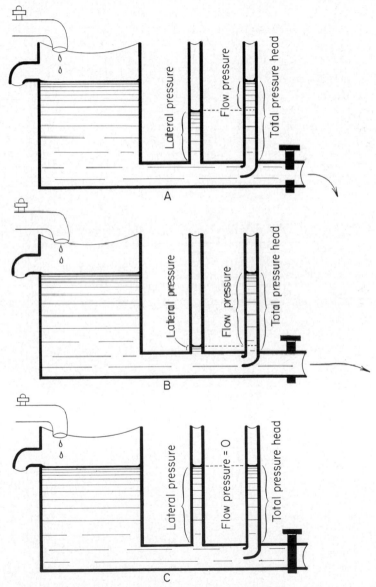

Fig. 96. Physical principles underlying the dynamics of circulation.

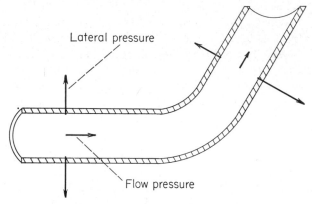

Lateral pressure

Flow pressure

Fig. 97. Addition of flow pressure to lateral pressure in a bent tube.

itself by assuming a slight degree of tortuosity in which the bends have a wide radius of curvature. With increased flow, not only does the velocity of displacement increase, but also the curvature becomes more acute, and each bend represents a greater fraction of the circumference of a circle than before. This is one explanation for the increased tortuosity of the retinal arteries. Tortuosity should be expected whenever the linear velocity of the flow of blood in the vessel is abnormally great. If the blood pressure is normal, we may expect increased tortuosity to result from diminished peripheral resistance. If the peripheral resistance remains unchanged, we may expect increased tortuosity to result from increased arterial blood pressure, which leads to increased flow.

So far, we have considered the effect of a steady flow of blood through the retinal vessels. The heartbeat introduces variations in the force which tend to produce a lateral displacement of the vessel in regions where the vessel bends, causing a serpentine pulsation. The following factors favor the presence of serpentine pulsation: (1) tortuous arteries, (2) dilated arteries (this is equivalent to a diminished resistance to flow), (3) pliable walls, (4)

large pulse pressure, (5) high systolic pressure, (6) slight peripheral resistance, and (7) minimal viscosity of the blood.

Serpentine pulsation never occurs in straight vessels. It is never seen when the entire arterial retinal tree is narrow, even in the presence of aortic regurgitation. It may be present with dilated retinal arteries, even in the absence of abnormal circulatory states. It is commonly seen in healthy young children with dilated, tortuous, and presumably pliable retinal vessels and is very rarely seen in the aged, even though the retinal vessels are dilated and tortuous. It is commonly present in persons with a large pulse pressure, i.e., aortic regurgitation, and is often present in anemia, provided that the retinal vessels are full and tortuous, but not in polycythemia, in spite of the extreme tortuosity of the arteries in this condition.

Expansile pulsation. The mechanics of this type of pulsation are far simpler than those of the serpentine variety. We have to deal here with the elasticity and tone of the vessel's wall and the balance between the intravascular and the extravascular pressures, i.e., the intraocular pressure. The state of the rigidity and the muscle tone of the vessel walls must be taken into account. The visibility of the expansile pulse in the retinal arterial tree depends upon the magnification used in the examination of the eyeground. No expansile pulsation is visible in a normal person when the ordinary ophthalmoscope is used, which has a magnification of about 16 diameters. If, however, one uses the Gullstrand binocular ophthalmoscope, pulsation can be seen in practically all normal persons.

An expansile pulse becomes visible with the usual methods of examination as soon as the difference between the diastolic and systolic arterial pressures rises, or as soon as the intraocular pressure rises above the diastolic arterial pressure. The maximum pulse is reached when the intraocular pressure just equals the diastolic blood pressure. Under these conditions, the artery empties blood during diastole and expands to its full extent at the height of systole. Conditions are most favorable for the oscillation of the wall of the vessel when the pressures on both sides of the wall are the same during the diastolic phase. The arterial pulse is transmitted to the interior of the eye, and since the sclera is very poorly distensible, the volume pulse is almost entirely transposed into a pressure pulse.

Although the retinal arteries are the ones which can be seen to pulsate when observed with the ophthalmoscope, the pulse is present in both the retinal and the uveal circulations. In fact, the pressure pulse is essentially the pulse of the uveal vessels since it remains unaltered after complete occlusion of the central retinal artery. The uveal vessels carry many times the amount of blood present in the retinal system. The ratio of the blood volume of the choroid to retina has been found to be 37:1.[17] The pressure pulse is best seen in the oscillations of the pointer of the tonometer during the measurement of intraocular pressure. Under conditions

in which the volume pulse is increased, the pressure pulse readily becomes apparent and may amount to as much as 5 mm. Hg. An increase in amplitude of the arterial expansile pulse occurs under the following conditions.

1. Rise in the intraocular pressure. This may occur from artificial pressure on the globe, as by pressure from the finger. In a normal person if the retinal arteries are observed with an ophthalmoscope and pressure is made on the globe gradually, a point will be reached at which the vessels can be seen to pulsate. In patients with glaucoma in whom the intraocular pressure is already raised, pulsation may be present, or it may be brought on by applying a degree of pressure to the globe that would not produce pulsation in a normal person.

2. Fall in blood pressure. When the diastolic pressure is low, as in general anemia, or when there is an exceptionally large pulse pressure, as in aortic regurgitation and thyrotoxicosis, an expansile pulse may be visible in the retinal arteries, even when the intraocular pressure is normal.

The venous pulse

In the majority of normal persons, pulsation is seen in the veins as they emerge from the disc. This is due to the pulse being transmitted directly from the arteries to the veins through the vitreous and is not the result of a pressure pulse transmitted from the right auricle into the veins. When the intraocular pressure rises above the venous pressure, as it does during systole, some blood must be expelled from the veins. This results in partial or complete collapse of the segment of the vein which is nearest the outlet of blood from the eye. The length of the region of collapse can be affected by the gradient of pressure in the veins, by the velocity of blood flow, by the viscosity of the blood, and by the degree and duration of time involved in the rise of intraocular pressure, i.e., the duration and height of systole. A large pulse pressure and a slow pulse are, therefore, more likely to be accompanied by marked venous pulsation than are a small pulse pressure and a rapid pulse. If no spontaneous pulsation is present in the veins, the slightest pressure on the globe generally suffices to bring it out since it increases the arterial pulse. Any back pressure on the veins in the eye, e.g., compression of the jugular veins, generally suffices to stop a spontaneous pulse in the veins. On theoretic grounds, absence of normal pulsation in the veins in the disc should be one of the early signs of papilledema. This has been generally taught, and even in recent publications it is stated that increased intracranial pressure can be excluded if spontaneous venous pulsation is present or occurs after slight pressure is exerted on the eye. This is denied by Huber,[18] who claims that such a sign is of no significance for the diagnosis of increased intracranial pressure, especially not for the early diagnosis of choked disc.

Normal pressure in the retinal and uveal arteries and veins

The pressure in the retinal and uveal arteries is probably higher than in most peripheral vessels since the internal carotid artery constricts immediately after giving off the ophthalmic artery (Fig. 98). This arrangement ensures a high pressure in the ophthalmic artery. The ophthalmic artery is also comparatively short so that the blood is delivered to the eye only a short distance from the internal carotid artery. Therefore, the high pressure is transmitted directly to the interior of the eye. This suggests that the circulation takes place at a considerably higher pressure level than the circulation in most organs supplied by an artery the size of the ophthalmic artery. The anatomic conditions are akin to those in the kidney where a short renal artery delivers blood to the organ at a pressure slightly under that in the aorta. In the cat the pressures in the ophthalmic artery have been estimated to be as follows:

Systolic:	average	115 mm. Hg
Diastolic:	average	78 mm. Hg

The systolic pressure in the central retinal artery was found to be 88 mm. Hg and the diastolic pressure 64 mm. Hg.

In human beings, the retinal blood pressure has been estimated by means of ophthalmodynamometry. In the method of dynamometry, the intraocular pressure is raised artificially by applying pressure to the outside of the globe until maximum pulsation occurs in the arteries observed with the ophthalmoscope. The intraocular pressure reading at this time is a measure of the diastolic arterial pressure. Raising the intraocular pressure further to the point at which all pulsations cease is the measure of the systolic arterial pressure.

The determination of the pressures in the intraocular circulation by such a method involves a number of fallacies. Any pressure applied to the globe which tends to obstruct the flow of blood from the eye must necessarily increase the pressure in the veins. This increase in pressure then spreads back through the capillaries to the arterial side of the circulation, and if the pressure on the outside of the eye is continued at a level higher than that in the arteries in the eye, the pressure will build up in these arteries to the level in the main feeding vessel, namely, the ophthalmic artery. On theoretic grounds, therefore, the method is not measuring the

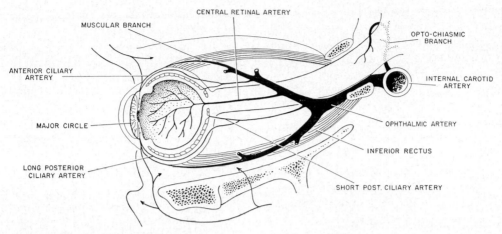

Fig. 98. Ocular arteries. (After Jayle.)

pressure in the central artery of the retina, but the level of pressure somewhere between this artery and the ophthalmic artery, depending upon how rapidly the measurements are taken. The method may have value in affording comparative figures, but it cannot yield exact values on which calculations can be based for physiologic purposes, such as the determination of the pressures available for the formation of the aqueous humor.

Although the determination of the retinal arterial blood pressure has its limitations, as just pointed out, the figures obtained by ophthalmodynamometry are valid for comparing the pressures in the two eyes of the same animal or person. Hence this method is of value in showing differences between the two eyes when aneurysm of the internal carotid artery or spontaneous occlusion of the carotid artery is suspected.[19]

The intraocular venous pressure is believed to be slightly higher than the intraocular pressure; otherwise, the veins without rigid walls would collapse. Duke-Elder estimates the intraocular venous pressure to be approximately 2 mm. higher than the normal intraocular pressure. The ve-

nous pressure varies with the intraocular pressure. When the intraocular pressure is raised, the venous pressure rises, until eventually it is equal to the arterial pressure in the opthhalmic artery. This may not be true of the intrascleral veins around the canal of Schlemm since these are supported by a dense scleral framework and would not necessarily collapse with a rise in intraocular pressure. The pressure in the intrascleral veins may remain below the intraocular pressure since the veins are not directly compressed, and thus it would still allow an outflow of the aqueous humor into Schlemm's canal, even when the intraocular pressure was elevated abnormally.

Although the pressure in the central retinal vein is slightly above the normal intraocular pressure, a sudden drop in venous pressure occurs in the region of the lamina cribosa. At this point as the venous blood leaves the eye, the pressure in the central vein drops to zero in the upright position and to about 10 mm. Hg in the recumbent position. It would seem as though the high intraocular venous pressure was maintained by a high "flow resistance" which fixes the maximum rate of blood flow through the vein. It has been suggested that this accounts for the facility with which retinal venous obstruction occurs in many different pathologic conditions.[20] Under conditions in which a high resistance to outflow is present it is easy to see why obstruction to the central vein occurs in all patients whose blood viscosity is elevated, such as in polycythemia vera, sickle cell disease, the various forms of macroglobulinemia and cryoglobulinemia, etc. Further, if the lamina cribrosa is the site of the resistance, a displacement of the lamina backward might increase this normal resistance, accounting for the frequency of central vein obstruction in open-angle glaucoma.

Capillary pressure

It is of theoretic importance to know the capillary pressure in the eye. Various theories of the formation of the aqueous humor depend on the determination of the capillary pressure. No satisfactory direct determinations have been made, nor is it likely that, in man, they ever will be, and since the blood pressure in experimental animals differs considerably from that in the human being, such measurements cannot be used to decide theories of the formation of the aqueous humor in man.

It is generally agreed that the greatest fall in arterial pressure takes place in the arteriolar bed and not in the capillary bed (Fig. 99). This means that on the arteriolar side of the capillaries the pressure is probably not much below that of the diastolic pressure of the entering arteriole (50 mm. Hg).

Blood volume and circulation time

The abrupt fall in blood pressure in the arteriolar bed is due to frictional re-

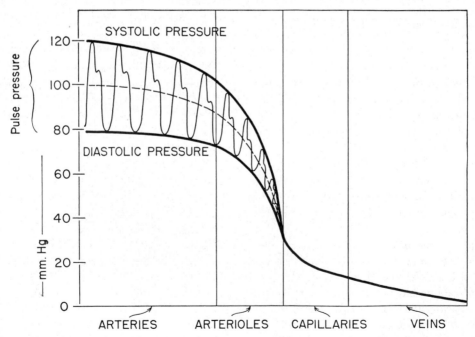

Fig. 99. Fall in blood pressure in various regions of the circulatory tree. (After Best and Taylor.)

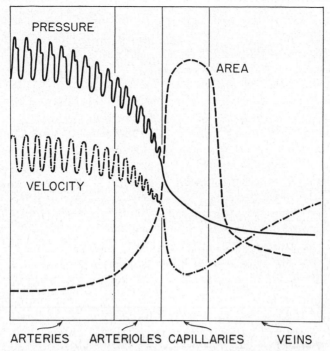

Fig. 100. Diagram showing the pressure and velocity of the blood in different parts of the vascular system (modified from Fredericq.) Note the relation between blood velocity and vascular area and the absence of rhythmical variations in pressure and velocity in the capillaries and veins. (After Best and Taylor.)

sistance, which is greatly increased as the result of the breaking up of the arterioles into small capillaries. The sum of all of the capillary surfaces is enormously greater than that of the large blood vessels such as the aorta. The fall in the velocity of the blood through the various portions of the circulatory system from arteries to capillaries is shown in Fig. 100. Also, the fall in velocity and the fall in pressure are compared.

The volume of blood present in the eye at any one time has been estimated to be 211 c.mm. The blood flow through the eye of rabbits has been estimated to be in the neighborhood of 0.32 ml./min./Gm., which is 46% of the value obtained for cerebral blood flow.[21] The cerebral circulation time is calculated as about 3 sec-

onds, i.e., the time elapsed for a corpuscle to travel from the internal carotid artery as it enters the skull to the jugular vein as it leaves it. In many respects conditions in the eye resemble those in the skull. The Monroe-Kellie doctrine of the invariability of the volume of the intracranial contents is based on the firm rigidity of the bones of the skull which enclose the brain. It can be shown that the sclera has some elasticity, and by the amount of this elasticity, therefore, the pressure relationships depart from the Monroe-Kellie doctrine. The total contents of the cranium can alter relatively little, and it is not possible for a greater volume of blood to flow through the skull without the velocity of flow through the individual vessels being increased. The only way the brain can be assured of obtaining an extra supply of oxygen, when the physiologic demand is increased, is by increasing the speed of the circulation through the blood vessel bed, rather than by enlarging the total capacity of this bed. The conditions in the eye probably fall somewhere between those existing in the brain and those found in other organs, such as the kidney, liver, or muscle, in which the whole organ can expand and the blood vessels can dilate widely. In the eye it may be assumed that any increased call for oxygen, necessitated by functional demands, can be met by both a slight increase in the volume of blood in the eye at any one moment and an acceleration of the blood flow through the eye.

Control of circulation

Although each part of the body is dependent upon the output of the heart to maintain its circulation, individual organs can alter the state of their own vascular bed to a considerable degree. The walls of the arterioles are composed chiefly of involuntary muscle fibers which can change the size of the vessel as the result of stimulation of constrictor or dilator nerves supplying the arteriolar musculature. The capillary bed can also change its volume, not only passively, as the result of changes in the general blood pressure or by reflecting local changes that occur in the arteriolar bed, but also quite independently.

The capillary bed is the most important part of the circulatory apparatus in any organ since it is here that the interchange of substances between the bloodstream and the tissues takes place, determining the activities of the tissue. It is important to find, therefore, that the capillaries do not play merely a passive role but are capable of independent activity. In muscle and in some organs such as the kidney the number of capillaries which are open and permit blood to pass through them is directly related to the activity of the tissue. In the resting state, only a few capillaries are open, whereas during muscular activity or diuresis, a great increase in the number of visible capillaries takes place. In most organs of the body the capillary bed is not a simple web of vessels between the arterial and venous systems but is composed of two components, one of which forms a thoroughfare into which the blood flows from the arteriole. The other is a secondary network formed by the true capillaries connected with the thoroughfare channel. Scattered along the thoroughfare channel are isolated smooth muscle fibers, wrapped around the endothelial wall of the channel, which by contracting can close and shunt the blood from one capillary bed to another. These sphincter muscles occur where the capillary beds are joined to the main thoroughfare channel; hence various portions of the tissue can be irrigated, so to speak, independently of other portions, depending upon their needs. In other organs such as the brain all of the capillaries are probably open and stay open the entire time. The literature contains no data on the condition of the capillaries in the eye.

Nervous control of the arterioles and probably of the capillaries themselves comes from the sympathetic nervous system. If the sympathetic supply to an organ is cut, the blood flow through the organ is increased. One may infer from this that a steady stream of constrictor impulses travels by way of the sympathetic nerves to the peripheral blood vessels, keeping them in a semiconstricted state. Since the vessels fail to constrict after the sympathetic supply has been cut, one may conclude that changes in the caliber of the peripheral blood vessels are determined chiefly by an increase or decrease of vasoconstrictor impulses. This is further borne out by the fact that, when the sympathetic supply is stimulated under suitable conditions, the blood vessels throughout most of the body are diminished in caliber. The degree of constriction varies in different organs. The vessels of the skin and alimentary tract are intensely constricted, whereas the vessels of the brain and the lungs show only slight constriction.

The peripheral vessels affected by such vasoconstrictor impulses are the peripheral arterioles, the veins, and probably to a less extent the capillaries. The nerve fibrils to the capillaries are extensions from a nervous plexus that surrounds the arteriolar bed. They innervate the capillaries with constrictor fibers. The evidence for dilator fibers is not nearly so certain nor their distribution so widespread as that for the constrictor fibers, and dilatation of the capillaries, at least in muscles, is probably dependent mainly upon the production of acid metabolites.

The vasoconstrictor fibers to the peripheral arterioles arise from nerve cells situated in the lateral horns of the spinal cord. In man these extend from the cells

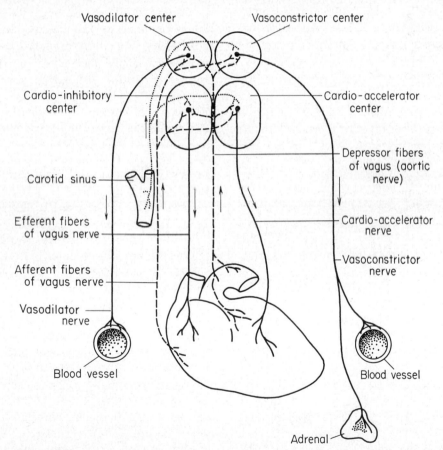

Fig. 101. Diagrammatic presentation of the cardiovascular reflex mechanisms. *Broken line,* afferent vagal fibers; *dotted line,* sinus nerve; *solid line,* efferent fibers to the heart and to the blood vessels. The afferent fibers are represented as causing reciprocal effects upon the medullary centers. (After Best and Taylor.)

of the first thoracic segment to the second or third lumbar segment, inclusive. All of the arterioles in the body are supplied with vasoconstrictor fibers from this rather condensed group of cells. The origin of the vasodilator fibers to those vessels which have been found to have such a supply is more diffuse than that of the vasoconstrictors.

Both the constrictor and dilator vascular effects are controlled by the vasoconstrictor and the vasodilator centers, and the maintenance of vasomotor tone is intimately dependent on the integrity of these groups of nerve cells lying in the floor of the fourth ventricle close to the vagus nuclei (Fig. 101). The constrictor center is also connected to a subsidiary center in the cord, constituted of those cells in the thoracolumbar region already mentioned, extending in man from the first thoracic segment to the second or third lumbar segment. The vasoconstrictor center occupies the apex of the ala cinerea or the fovea inferior in the floor of the fourth ventricle. The vasodilator center lies just lateral to the obex. Both centers are bilaterally represented. Still higher centers probably exist in the central nervous system, and recent work indicates that these are situated in the hypothalamus and even in the cerebral cortex.

Vasomotor tone and its regulation. The tone of the vasomotor centers depends (1) upon afferent impulses received from various organs and regions of the body, as well as those from other nervous centers such as the cerebral cortex, respiratory center, etc., and (2) upon the chemical composition of the blood.

Neurogenic control. The vasoconstrictor center exhibits tone, as just stated. Although dilator tone does exist to a slight degree, it is much less effective than the tone of the vasoconstrictor center under ordinary circumstances. If the cord is sec-

tioned in the lower cervical region, the stream of impulses passing from the medullary centers to the spinal centers is interrupted, and the peripheral vessels dilate, with a subsequent fall in blood pressure. After a time the blood pressure rises again, and the spinal centers exhibit their inherent power of autonomous action and assume the duties previously exercised by the medullary centers. Section of the splanchnic nerves in the splanchnic region doubles the blood flow in the vessels of the denervated area, which indicates the high degree of vasoconstrictor tone which is normally maintained. Removal of the lumbar sympathetic nerves causes a corresponding increase in the flow through the femoral artery, and this greater flow persists for several months. If the cord is sectioned, and if sufficient time is allowed for the tone of the peripheral vessels to return, it falls again when the splanchnic nerves are sectioned. Some of this tone may be regained after a certain time. This final tonus resides in the vascular muscle itself and is called peripheral tone.

Chemical control. The vasomotor centers are influenced to a great extent by the chemical composition of the blood, particularly by the blood gases. A high carbon dioxide or a low oxygen tension causes an increase in vasoconstrictor tone, with a subsequent rise in blood pressure. Similarly a rise in the hydrogen ion concentration of the blood, such as occurs if lactic or other organic acids are injected into the bloodstream, also produces a rise in blood pressure. In addition to the effect on the vasomotor centers, the chemical composition of the blood is very important in determining the state of the peripheral capillaries. The local effect of an excess of carbon dioxide or lactic acid upon the peripheral vessels is dilatation. In the vasomotor center the effects of the hydrogen ion content of the blood are in the opposite direction when compared with the peripheral control of the circulation.

Another factor capable of changing the state of the peripheral vessels is the liberation of histamine in the tissues. A diffusible substance called the H substance, which resembles histamine in its action, acts as a humoral mechanism, bringing about dilatation of the capillaries by direct action upon their walls. If the skin of the body is stroked with sufficient vigor with a blunt instrument, a so-called triple response may be seen. This comprises (1) a red reaction, (2) a flare, and (3) a wheal.

The red reaction consists of a red band which appears on the skin approximately 3 to 15 seconds after the skin is stroked. It is due to dilatation of the capillaries and is independent of any nervous mechanism since it occurs after degeneration of the cutaneous nerves. If the stimulus is quite strong, a flare occurs that consists of a reddening of the skin outside the area of the red reaction, probably due to dilatation of the arterioles, and depends upon local nervous mechanisms. The wheal, which occurs if the stimulus is still more intense, is due to local edema and comes on from 1 to 3 minutes after quite severe stroking. It is due to increased permeability of the capillary wall which permits edematous fluid to come through it.

Lewis has extended this conception of the triple response due to both nervous and humoral mechanisms to include the vasodilator effects of certain antidromic impulses that are discharged under ordinary circumstances through the posterior roots into the nerves supplying the skin. It is thought that these antidromic impulses cause release of the H substance from the cells of the epidermis, which

then affects the vessels. Certain characteristic cutaneous lesions—herpes zoster, e.g.—are ascribed to the liberation of H substance by abnormal antidromic impulses. In the case of zoster ophthalmicus, the abnormal antidromic impulses are produced by lesions of the gasserian ganglion. It is quite possible that other types of cutaneous lesions are due to similar abnormal liberation of H substance. The capillaries are undoubtedly under the control of the corticosteroids, epinephrine, and norepinephrine which are released by both the adrenal gland and by the endings of nerves in the muscles. As described previously, these substances cause contraction of the muscle cells in the capillary thoroughfare channels, and if they are absent, the blood vessels lose their tone and the circulation collapses. Acetylcholine is also liberated at the nerve endings, and the effect of this substance on the capillary wall is the same as for histamine, causing the muscle cells to relax. There is good reason to believe that the capillaries inside the eye are affected by chemical substances in the same way as other capillaries throughout the body. Axon reflexes, acting through the sensory nerves, produce vasodilatation through the liberation of H substance. A foreign body on the cornea produces an immediate flush of the conjunctiva, and if the irritation is long continued, dilatation of the deeper vessels in the eye will occur, producing a circumcorneal injection or the so-called ciliary flush. This does not occur so readily if the eye is thoroughly anesthetized, which prevents the antidromic reflex from taking place.

Axon reflexes in the iris have been demonstrated.[22] If the iris of an albino rabbit is stroked with a blunt instrument, marked dilatation of the capillaries occurs over the region stroked, and there is dilatation of the arterioles over the entire iris. At the same time, an increase in the permeability of the vessels is demonstrated by the appearance in the anterior chamber of a dye, such as trypan blue, previously injected into the circulation. An increase in the temperature of the eye of from 1° to 2° C. and a rise in intraocular pressure occur also. If the eye has previously been anesthetized, the local dilatation and increased capillary permeability are still evident, but the spreading vascular reaction in the arterioles, which depends upon nerve impulses for its propagation, is absent.

During the stage of arteriolar and capillary dilatation due to H substance, any attempt to constrict the blood vessels with vasoconstrictor drugs is quite ineffective. This has been termed the unresponsive state. It is met with clinically in all inflammatory conditions of the eye when the capillaries are maximally dilated. It is of considerable importance in the vascular reactions which may occur in any form of glaucoma and which are known as the congestive or incompensated stage of glaucoma. The unresponsive state may also be responsible for the continued ciliary flush after any injury or operation on the eye. After an operation for cataract, e.g., marked dilatation of the ciliary and conjunctival vessels may not appear until the fourth or fifth postoperative day, but then persists in most patients for one to two weeks, even when the condition is completely uncomplicated. During the marked stages of this reaction, the instillation of epinephrine may blanch the eye temporarily, but the flush returns in a very short time and remains until the vessels gradually regain their normal appearance. It may be due to the liberation of H substance from the partly devitalized tissues. During this postoperative period the administration of steroids locally considerably lessens the injection of the vessels.

Vasomotor control of cerebral vessels. The intraocular blood vessels are direct branches of the cerebral vessels. It is probable, therefore, that the control of the retinal and choroidal circulations is similar to that of the cerebral vessels. It is established that vasoconstrictor impulses are conveyed to the vessels of the brain by the sympathetic nerves, and nerve fibers going to the blood vessels within the brain substance have been described.[23] Vasodilatation follows stimulation of the central end of the vagus nerve. The cerebral vessels are held in a state of tonic dilatation, rather than of tonic constriction, as prevails in the vascular system of the rest of the body.[24] Reduction of vasodilator tone is probably of greater importance than sympathetic impulses bringing about constriction of the cerebral vessels. The facial nerve is apparently the only nerve carrying dilator fibers to the cerebral vessels.

Regional differences in cerebral blood flow may occur as a result of localized functional demands. Thus, Fulton observed an increase in blood flow through the blood vessels in an hemangioma of the occipital lobe when the subject read fine print. In animals a rise in temperature of the optic pathway has been recorded with a thermocouple when the eyes were illuminated. This demonstrates that the cerebral vessels can vary their caliber independently of changes in the caliber of the systemic vessels. On the other hand, there is good evidence that this independence is quite limited and that, in general, the blood flow through the vessels of the brain normally follows the general blood pressure in a passive fashion. In a study of patients on whom a stellate ganglion block had been performed, Risteen and Volpitto[25] observed the diameter of the pial vessels through bur holes in the skull. The cerebral blood flow was determined using the method of Kety and Schmidt.[26] No significant changes due to the block were found. Others likewise have failed to obtain significant changes in cerebral blood flow and vascular resistance following stellate ganglion block.

Under normal conditions the sympathetic nervous system plays little part in the intrinsic control of the cerebral circulation. The cerebral blood flow is probably determined largely by the systemic blood pressure. Next to the general systemic pressure, the carbon dioxide and oxygen tensions of the blood constitute the most important factors in its control.

Carbon dioxide is a potent cerebral vasodilator, as is anoxia, whereas high oxygen tensions and low carbon dioxide pressures produce mild and severe vasoconstrictions, respectively.[27] In man the dominant control of cerebral vessels is probably a chemical one, activated by levels of carbon dioxide, oxygen, and hydrogen ions. Procaine block of both stellate ganglia produces no change in cerebral circulation or resistance, which suggests that the known channels of the sympathetic nervous system to the brain do not exert an appreciable tonic effect on cerebral vessels.[28]

Vasomotor control of ocular vessels. In the intraocular vessels, the evidence points to a similar lack of effective control by the sympathetic nervous system. The experiments which have been performed in the past to demonstrate the effectiveness of the sympathetic vasoconstrictor fibers on the intraocular blood vessels have frequently failed to take into account the marked effect stimulation of these fibers has on the smooth muscle in the orbit of animals. This sympathetically innervated muscle when stimulated causes marked exophthalmos, raises the intraocular pressure by compression of the globe, and frequently produces venous stasis in the eye by compression of the veins at their outlets.

The rate of formation of fluid in the eye has been measured while the intraocular pressure was maintained at a constant level.[29] It was found that the rate of formation of this fluid was diminished by stimulation of the cervical sympathetic nerves, even after Müller's muscle had been effectively eliminated. This can be explained adequately only by constriction of the intraocular blood vessels, thus affording evidence of vasoconstrictor fibers to the eyeball. No evidence of vasodilator fibers was obtained by this method.

No tonic influence of the sympathetic nerves on the intraocular blood vessels has been found[30] which would indicate that these vessels are kept normally in a semiconstricted state. No effect on the intraocular pressure is shown on cutting the sympathetic nerves. On the other hand, sudden elevation of the blood pressure obtained by tightening a ligature placed under the aorta above the superior mesenteric artery produces a rise in intraocular pressure, and this rise is greater if the cervical sympathetic nerves have been cut previously. As Barany[31] points out, these experiments do not demonstrate the existence of any reflex that under normal conditions effectively regulates the intraocular pressure via vasoconstrictors coming from the sympathetic. The changes are of very short duration, lasting at most some minutes, and there is no proof that they are effective at all in establishing or altering the final equilibrium level, which, as is well known, is not dependent on the blood pressure level except within wide limits.

The blood pressure in the artery at

the origin of the ciliary arteries has been found to be elevated by 5 to 10 mm. Hg by electrical stimulation of the cervical sympathetic chain, with no simultaneous change in the general blood pressure as measured in the femoral artery. This rise lasted only 1 to 2 minutes, however.[32] Further, Bill[33] has shown that after carotid ligation stimulation of the cervical sympathetic ipsilaterally results in a rise of pressure at the origin of the ciliary arteries, as well as in the distal part of the ligated carotid artery, and that the rise in the ciliary blood pressure results in an increase in the blood flow through the uveal tract. The resistance to blood flow through the uveal tract of cats and rabbits is somewhat increased by electrical stimulation of the cervical sympathetics, according to Bill.[34]

It may be concluded that the intraocular vessels, like those of the brain, are little affected by neurogenic tone. They, like the cerebral vessels, react with local changes in blood flow in certain regions, depending upon functional activity, e.g., the macular supply during photopic vision, the periphery during scotopic vision, the vessels of the ciliary body during active formation of the aqueous humor, etc. It is also possible that the intraocular blood flow, like that of the brain, is an extremely rapid one in order to take care of the greater need for oxygen.

A rise or fall in the general blood pressure will affect the state of the intraocular capillaries, but they may change independently. The effect on the intraocular contents will vary, depending upon whether the arterioles and the capillaries change their caliber in the same direction or in opposite directions.

1. If the arteriolar bed dilates and the capillaries themselves passively dilate, the pressure in the capillary bed will rise and lead to active hyperemia, with an increase in temperature and increased capillary permeability. This in turn should lead to increased intraocular pressure. If, however, the capillaries themselves contract in spite of an active arteriolar dilatation, the effects may be partly or completely neutralized.

2. If the arteriolar bed itself contracts, the blood flow through the capillary bed is decreased so that the temperature and the pressure fall. If the capillaries themselves also contract, they may be entirely emptied of blood. Accordingly, the intraocular pressure may fall considerably due simply to loss of volume of the intraocular contents. If the capillaries dilate, the pressure remains low and fluid may come from the tissues across the capillary wall into the blood.

3. If the capillaries dilate independently and no other changes occur in the circulation, the blood flow will be increased at a higher pressure, and the formation of fluid across the capillary wall will increase.

Independent constriction of the capillaries will, of course, lead to the opposite result.

4. Constriction of the veins leaving the eye will immediately raise the pressure in the capillary bed until it reaches that of the arteriolar pressure. If this is associated with capillary dilatation, marked transudation of fluid from the capillary bed will occur, with resultant marked increase in intraocular pressure.

The effects just mentioned take into account only the changes which will occur in the filtration of fluid across a semipermeable membrane. In addition, the effects on active secretion must be considered. An increase in blood flow should per se increase the secretory activities of the ciliary processes, and likewise a decrease in blood flow will work in the opposite direction.

Capillary permeability

The capillary wall permits water and many dissolved substances to pass more easily than does the surface membrane of most tissue cells. The capillary wall appears to be about 3000 times more permeable than most cellular membranes when studied quantitatively under comparable conditions. Capillary permeability cannot always be judged by an increase or a decrease of the passage of a substance into the tissues. In vivo, the capillary wall may be permeable to proteins and unable to retain any fluid, and yet external conditions prevent this change from becoming grossly obvious. Conversely, more fluid may pass through the capillary wall, not because its permeability is greater, but merely because the pressure within the capillaries has been increased.

Water passes most easily through the capillary membrane. Urea, potassium, sodium, chloride, and nitrate pass almost as easily as water. Hevsey and Jacobsen[35] observed in the rabbit that it required only half a minute for heavy water to pass through the capillary wall. Merrell, Gellhorn, and Flexner[36] found that 73% of heavy water and 60% of radioactive sodium in the blood pass to and fro through the capillary wall between blood and tissue fluid in each minute. Calculated on the basis of plasma only, water is exchanged twice as rapidly as sodium. Substances such as calcium, magnesium, and glucose still pass relatively easily so that equilibrium of concentration is reached with only moderate delay, and their osmotic effects on movement of fluid, though definite, are comparatively slight and transitory.

Large molecules such as gelatin are held back by the capillary wall, but eventually these too get into the tissue fluid and pass into the urine at rates as high as 50% in half an hour.[37] These substances have an equatorial diameter of about 1.6 to 1.8 μ. The plasma proteins have an equatorial diameter of from 3.2 to 3.8 μ.

As a working concept, Landis[38] pictures the capillary endothelium to consist of a meshwork with pores of many sizes, of which a few have diameters of 3.8 μ or possibly more. Protein is retained or passes with difficulty. Diffusible substances, such as urea, salt, glucose, and amino acids, are able to move back and forth quite freely through the smaller and larger pores by simple diffusion. This diffusion need not be accompanied by a transport of water in either direction. Landis assumes that the small pores predominate and that only a very few have diameters of 1.6 to 3.8 μ. He cautions us that this purely mechanical concept may be far too simple and that other forces as yet unknown may explain more easily and logically those facts which are extremely difficult to reconcile with present information. The normal capillary filtrate probably contains from 0.2 to 0.5% protein. It is difficult to understand how a normal capillary wall can retain most of the molecules of plasma protein and yet permit some albumin, with a molecular weight of 69,000, some globulin, with a molecular weight of 160,000, and even minute amounts of fibrinogen, with a molecular weight of 500,000, to pass through it into the tissue spaces.

If the capillary leaks any of the larger protein molecules, why does it not leak all of the smaller protein molecules? How does it retain any protein? Knisely[39] states that two possible hypotheses may explain this.

1. The molecules of the three important proteins of the blood just mentioned all have about the same equatorial diameter. They differ greatly, however, in

length. All are narrow, but some are much longer than others. We may imagine the capillary endothelium to consist of a meshwork of pores of different sizes, as Landis does. A few pores must have a diameter of at least 3.8 μ or possibly more. As the blood column moves lengthwise through a capillary, most of the long, narrow, tumbling protein molecules would strike the inner surface of the endothelium flatwise or at oblique angles. A few would be forced, by chance, endwise into the larger pores of the capillary wall and hence would be forced out into the adjacent tissue spaces (Fig. 102). Thus, most protein molecules of each category would be retained while a few might escape.

2. Although blood is generally flowing through the capillaries fast enough to maintain an adequate supply of oxygen at each point along its course, in some parts of the body during various phases of normal activity the capillaries are shut off for various periods, during which their walls must become anoxic. Knisely has shown this to be true in the case of contracting muscles. During the phase of anoxia, the capillaries would leak protein, and various amounts of these substances having larger molecules with high

molecular weight might be able to pass through.

Capillary blood pressure affects the permeability of the capillaries directly, but a high capillary pressure may also increase manyfold the visible effects of the given increase in permeability, and conversely a very low capillary pressure may also obliterate the visible effects of a marked increase in capillary permeability. In the normal capillary, filtration occurs at an increasing rate when the hydrostatic pressure is above the colloid osmotic pressure. When the hydrostatic pressure is below the colloid osmotic pressure of the blood, absorption occurs, also at an increasing rate. The capillary wall thus acts as an inert filter, i.e., nonsecreting. Certain capillary poisons, such as alcohol or mercuric chloride, injure the capillary wall so that no absorption and no equilibrium are seen at any pressure, and the slope of the line relating pressure and filtration indicates that permeability to fluid is increased seven to nine times above normal. The absence of absorption at any pressure indicates that the effect of the colloid osmotic pressure of the plasma proteins is reduced to almost zero and that most, if not all, of the plasma proteins are able to escape freely with the fluid. A capillary

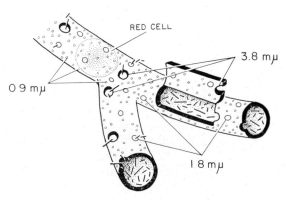

Fig. 102. Knisely's conception of the leakage of protein molecules of different size through the capillary wall.

filtrate with a high concentration of protein will occur, therefore, particularly if the hydrostatic pressure is high. Even under these circumstances, however, a very low hydrostatic pressure may almost completely mask the effect of increased permeability.

Injury to the tissue by any means, chemical, thermal, or mechanical, is always accompanied by prompt leakage of a large volume of capillary filtrate, rich in protein, into the tissues. The accumulation of carbon dioxide has no measurable effect on capillary permeability, nor do changes in the hydrogen ion concentration, when tested within physiologic limits, affect capillary permeability. If a pH of 4.0 is reached, the permeability is increased. This is clearly due to gross damage far outside the physiologic range. Mild lack of oxygen has little effect on increased permeability. In order to obtain an irreversible change in capillary permeability due to lack of oxygen, it is necessary that the grade of anoxia be very severe. There can be no doubt of the gross capillary damage which is observed in the extreme prolonged anoxia of total arterial occlusion, but under reasonably physiologic conditions, we do not know what oxygen tension and what duration at each tension are necessary to produce a uniform increase in capillary permeability.

Whenever the capillaries are dilated, their permeability is increased. This increase ranges from a slight increased permeability to plasma, which Ricker termed prestasis, to a degree of permeability at which the white blood cells come through the wall of the vessel, called peristasis, and finally to a degree of permeability which leads to the escape of red blood cells from the capillary. Ricker has called this true stasis or rubrostasis. A good example in which to follow the various

phases of increased permeability of the capillary bed in the eye to oxygen want is found in spasm or closure of the central artery of the retina or one of its branches. If spasm occurs in an arteriole, the diminished blood flow into the capillary bed supplied by this branch immediately produces anoxia. As a result, the capillaries dilate in this region and become more permeable. The outpouring of serum is manifested by edema of the retina. If the obstruction is complete, hemorrhages and tissue necrosis occur. Recovery may take place if the offending spastic vessel can be dilated in time. If the obstruction to the circulation occurs in the venous end of the system, as in obstruction of the central vein or one of its branches, the capillary dilatation is more acute due to the back pressure of the venous blood. Rubrostasis, therefore, occurs at once, with a marked tendency for severe hemorrhage throughout the layers of the retina.

The normal capillary is composed of endothelial cells resting on a basement membrane, around which is a network of reticulin fibers. Surrounding this is a discontinuous second layer of cells, called *pericytes*, which are supposed to have contractile properties. Whereas arteries and veins have smooth muscle in their walls controlling the diameter of the vessel lumen, the capillaries must depend on the contractility of the pericytes for similar changes in lumen size (p. 331).

Lymph

It has been shown that the filtrate from the capillaries of the blood in practically all parts of the body contains all of the proteins of the blood in fairly high concentration. Drinker and Field[40] state the following about the capillaries throughout the body.

". . . [they] practically universally leak protein. This protein does not re-enter the blood vessels unless delivered by the lymphatic system. The filtrate from the blood capillaries to the tissue spaces contains water, salts, and sugar in the concentrations found in the blood, together with serum globulin, serum albumin, and fibrinogen in low concentrations, lower probably than that of tissue fluid or lymph. Water and salts are reabsorbed by the blood vessels, and the protein enters the lymphatics together with water and salts in the concentration existing in the tissue fluid at the moment of lymphatic entrance. The lymph from any given drainage area contains a varying amount of protein, depending upon the amount of water absorption which has taken place in the region from which the collection is made, and represents a cross section of the tissue fluid of the area in question. This leakage of protein out of the capillaries constitutes a pool of protein from which any body cell needing protein or capable of storing some surplus protein receives it."*

From this protein pool, new plasma protein, hemoglobin, or cell protein may be derived. As stated by Whipple and Madden, "The circulating plasma protein is the medium of exchange and the body is solvent just so long as there is adequate protein supply for any emergency."†

The exceptions to this seem to be the capillaries of the glomeruli in the kidney, the capillaries of the choroid plexus in the cerebrospinal axis, and the uveal and retinal capillaries. The aqueous humor, which probably represents the tissue fluid of the ocular tissues, contains practically no protein in its normal state (0.02 mg./ 100 ml.) (chemical analysis of the normal aqueous humor is given in Chapter 4). There are no lymphatics in the interior of the eye to pick up the protein and return it to the bloodstream. Why does the eye have no lymphatics? This is probably due to the fact that the intraocular blood vessels are highly impermeable to protein, and there is no need for a system whose function is to return protein to the blood stream.

Functions of the capillary bed

The capillary bed is the part of the vascular system in which transfer of food materials and metabolites takes place between the blood and the tissues. As far as is known, three physical processes account entirely for the interchange of substances between blood and the tissue spaces. These processes are filtration, absorption, and diffusion. Filtration is the mass passage through the capillary wall, from within outward, of the following: (1) water as a solvent, (2) solutes such as sodium chloride, urea, and glucose, and (3) such substances as are able to pass through the pores of the capillary wall whenever capillary pressure exceeds the colloid osmotic pressure of the blood. Absorption refers to the mass passage through the capillary wall, from without inward, of water as a solvent and of the substances mentioned which may be situated outside the capillary and may be able to pass through the pores of the capillary wall whenever the colloid osmotic pressure exceeds the capillary blood pressure.

Filtration and absorption cannot occur except when different pressures are exerted on the fluids separated by the membrane. Hence, osmotic pressure, capillary blood pressure, and the permeability of the capillary wall are all essential factors in these two processes. Diffusion refers only to the movement of a substance, solvent or solute, from a region of high concentration to a region of low concentration as a result of the random and interfering movement of single molecules.

*From Drinker, C. K., and Field, M. E.: Am. J. Physiol. **97**:32, 1931.

†From Whipple, G. H., and Madden, S. C.: Medicine **23**:215, 1944.

In the absence of a membrane or other barrier, diffusion is free. In the capillary network diffusion is impeded in that the rate of diffusion is slow, depending upon the relative permeability of the capillary wall. Capillary blood pressure and colloid osmotic pressure should not affect diffusion, except secondarily where rapid filtration might add to, or rapid absorption subtract from, the effects of poor diffusion.

Circulation in localized regions of the eye

The capillary beds in various portions of the eye naturally serve different functions. Because of the importance of the capillary circulation in all physiologic and pathologic processes, numerous observations of the circulation in various portions of the eye have been made.

Conjunctival circulation. The conjunctiva is supplied by branches of the ophthalmic (medial palpebrals) and lacrimal arteries which are the main blood supply of the lids. In addition to this, the anterior ciliary arteries send branches to the conjunctiva as they travel along the tendons of the recti muscles. These anterior conjunctival vessels anastomose with the posterior conjunctival vessels to form a pericorneal plexus just before they enter the globe. The conjunctival portion of this plexus forms a superficial layer of vessels which branches irregularly and is freely movable, whereas the deeper portion is situated in the episcleral tissue and runs in a relatively straight line, radiating out from the margin of the limbus. In inflammations of the conjunctiva, only the superficial vessels are dilated, whereas in inflammations of the iris and cornea the deeper layer or ciliary vessels are dilated. The former is called conjunctival injection, whereas the latter is called a ciliary flush.

In a number of pathologic conditions the blood cells are agglutinated into masses which change the blood from its normal relatively fluid state to that of a so-called circulating sludge.[42] The aggregation of corpuscles thus produced reduces the surface between the corpuscles and plasma. This must affect the gas exchange of the corpuscles in an unfavorable manner. Further, agglutinated blood-cell masses may act as emboli, and the reduced suspension stability of the blood may play an important part in the genesis of thrombi. The resistance of sludged blood to its own passage through the bottlenecks of the circulatory system, namely, the capillaries, reduces the rate of blood flow in all the open vessels of the body. It is believed, therefore, that sludged blood provides a common, easily understandable set of factors whereby many diseases in animals and man can and do damage the body.

In man, the appearances of the capillaries and arterioles in the conjunctiva vary so from vessel to vessel that caution must be observed in connecting any changes with a particular disease or even, for that matter, of interpreting them as indicating a diseased state.

Conjunctival lymphatics. Although no lymphatics are present in either the interior of the globe or of the orbit, lymphatics are present in both the bulbar and palpebral conjunctivas, beginning in the former at the limbus in a series of arcades. It must be remembered that the lymphatic system not only performs a nutritive service to the body by returning protein from the interstitial fluid back to the blood, but also represents one of the first lines of defense against infection. The skin and presumably the conjunctiva, containing lymphatics, cannot be injured without introducing foreign material directly into the lymph channels. Severed lymphatics, unlike blood vessels, may remain open for a long time, and infectious material may therefore readily enter them. The transportation of foreign substances by way of the lymph is much more rapid than the volume of lymph flow would lead one to suspect.[43]

Aqueous veins. In 1942, Ascher[44] first described what he called aqueous veins in the conjunctiva. These veins are usually seen a short distance from the corneoscleral limbus, between either the 2 and 4 o'clock positions or the 8 and 10 o'clock positions. They are found in 20 to 75% of the persons examined, according to various authors who have verified their presence. They are identified by the fact that their lumens are either entirely clear or show a stratification or layering of clear and bloody fluid in the same vessel, forming two and sometimes three parallel strata.

These vessels are pathways that carry the aqueous humor from Schlemm's canal and the deep scleral venous meshwork to the superficial scleral and conjunctival veins. The aqueous humor, after leaving the canal of Schlemm, either mixes rapidly with the blood in the scleral venous meshwork or passes through the scleral meshwork without being mixed with blood and enters the conjunctival or subconjunctival veins as perfectly clear fluid. Leber, Maggiori, and Theobald have described collaterals connecting both these venous systems which finally empty into the vortex veins or into the anterior ciliary veins. Most of the veins of the human ciliary body are drained into the vortex veins, but some of the veins that leave the ciliary muscle pierce the sclera and empty into the anterior ciliary veins. These join with the conjunctival veins. The connection between these two independent venous regions is highly important in the understanding of the mechanism of con-

gestive glaucoma, according to Ascher. As the intraocular pressure rises, increasing quantities of blood that should leave the choroid by way of the vortex veins are forced into a collateral detour via the scleral plexus and thence into the anterior ciliary veins.

The experiments of Goldmann[45] have given added support to the belief that the clear fluid in the aqueous veins is aqueous humor.

Aqueous veins have been observed in animals in which no Schlemm's canal exists. In the exterior part of the sclera the aqueous veins have the ordinary wall of a vein, whereas in the portion close to Schlemm's canal they have the structure of a canaliculus. While running through the sclera they have one or more connections with the intrascleral blood veins. There is, therefore, no real difference between an aqueous vein and other epibulbar veins that are in direct connection with the canaliculi. In either case, it is the canaliculus that empties intrasclerally into a blood vein. The canaliculi and the aqueous veins have a tendency to accompany each other in the sclera and run in a common canal, separated from each other only by the wall of the vein and the one-layered endothelium. It is obvious, therefore, that the ratio between the pressure in the two vessels in the scleral canal must be of importance in determining the quantity of liquid that each of them empties into the recipient vein. If the pressure in the vein is high, it will compress the canaliculus in such a manner as to reduce the escape of the aqueous humor or even arrest it. On the other hand, if the pressure in the vein is low, the vein will be compressed, causing a larger flow of the aqueous humor.

Retinal arterioles. The retina is richly supplied with blood from the branches of the central retinal artery and also from the choriocapillaris on which it rests being separated from it only by the cuticular layer of Bruch's membrane. The inner portion of Bruch's membrane is secreted by the pigmented epithelium and fuses with the portion derived from the choroid, corresponding in this respect to Descemet's membrane in the cornea, which is secreted by the endothelium.

The major portion of the arterial tree visualized with the ophthalmoscope consists of arterioles. The central artery of the retina as it travels down the optic nerve resembles a true artery in that it has a well-developed muscular coat and an internal elastic lamina. The intima consists of a single layer of endothelium, lying directly on the internal elastic lamina. The muscular coat is well developed, and the adventitia or outside coat is intimately fused with the surrounding dural sheath of the optic nerve and with the cribriform lamina where the vessel penetrates these two tissues.

As the artery passes through the cribriform plate, however, it undergoes marked histologic changes. The internal elastic lamina is reduced to a single thin layer and disappears completely after the first or second bifurcation. The muscular coat is reduced to a single layer of muscle fibers which no longer form a continuous layer but are separated from each other by gaps. In other words, the artery at this point ceases to be an artery and becomes an arteriole because, by definition, vessels which do not possess an internal elastic lamina or a continuous muscular coat are classified as arterioles. All the branches of the central retinal artery, therefore, except those close to the main vessel on the disc, are arterioles. Since the main disease process with which we are concerned in the retinal circulation is sclerosis, it is important to recognize that true arteriosclerosis, i.e., atherosclerosis, is largely confined to the main branch of the central retinal artery, whereas the arterioles are affected chiefly by the process of arteriolar sclerosis.[46]

Retinal capillaries. The retinal capillaries consist of three layers, endothelial cells, a discontinuous single layer of pericytes, and a thick basement membrane. In nearly all respects they resemble the capillaries found elsewhere in the central nervous system.[47, 48] The pericytes are cells surrounding the outside of the endothelium.[49] Their function is not entirely agreed upon. The number of pinocytic vesicles found along the cell membrane suggests that the pericytes are active in the transfer of substances, but some investigators consider them to be contractile, controlling the patency of the lumen of the vessel (see discussion of mural cells that follows). Like most of the capillary beds of the central nervous system, the retinal capillaries are devoid of endothelial fenestrations or pores. In their place the endothelial cells contain an abundance of spherical vesicles which may serve as a means of active and selective transport through the capillary walls.

The retinal capillaries are further invested in glial elements. It has been claimed that these glial elements surrounding the central nervous system capillaries constitute a blood-brain barrier, and Kissen and Bloodworth[48] suggest that this forms a blood-retina barrier in a similar fashion.

The retinal capillaries contain two types of cells in their walls, (1) ordinary endothelial cells that line the lumen and (2) mural cells, so called by Kuwabara and Cogan[50] because they are encased within the vessel wall, covered on both inner and outer surfaces by basement membrane. Mural cells are not found in the capillaries of the conjunctiva, of the choroid, or of connective tissue, but are pres-

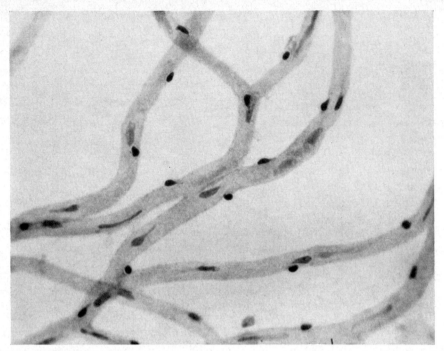

Fig. 103. Capillaries of human retina prepared as flat mount after trypsin digestion. Mural cells are characterized by small, dark-staining nuclei on outer portion of wall, whereas endothelial cells have lighter, larger, more elongated nuclei internal to the capillary wall. (Hematoxylin-PAS stain; from Kwabara, T., and Cogan, D.: Arch. Ophth. **69:**492, 1963.)

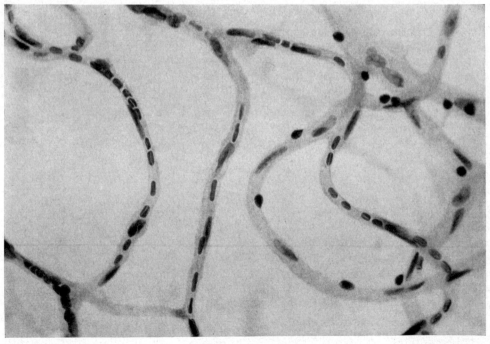

Fig. 104. Capillaries illustrating red blood cells (small ellipsoid bodies) preferentially in those capillaries which have lost their mural cells. The capillary second from the bottom is the only one with mural cells and the only one containing no red blood cells. (Hematoxylin-eosin stain; from Kwabara, T., and Cogan, D.: Arch. Ophth. **69:**492, 1963.)

ent in all the mammals studied (man, monkey, cat, dog, beef, hamster, mouse, and rat). These cells have been described by others as pericytes, but since there is no clear definition of what a pericyte is, Kuwabara and Cogan prefer the term *mural cell,* and point out that actually these cells are within the vessel wall and not around it. Also mural cells have not been found elsewhere in the body, whereas so-called pericytes have been described rather widespread (Fig. 103).

These mural cells may be an effective mechanism for controlling the patency of any particular arteriolar-capillary-venule unit, although at present there is no clear-cut proof of this. The normal retinal capillary is characteristically empty of red blood cells, and loss of mural cells seems to increase significantly the frequency with which red blood cells are found in these capillaries (Fig. 104). Further, mural cells seem to inhibit neovasculogenesis. New vessels develop only from vessels which do not have mural cells, and it has been shown experimentally that hyper-

oxia causes vaso-obliteration and new vessel formation in fetal retinas prior to the development of mural cells only.[51] It may be of significance that loss of mural cells is characteristically and most extensively seen in diabetes, in which neovasculogenesis is such a prominent feature.

The arrangement of the capillaries in the retina is of significance in the understanding of certain pathologic states. According to Michaelson and Campbell, two capillary networks are present, as shown in Fig. 105 (see also Fig. 94, p. 307). A superficial capillary net is found in the nerve fiber layer at the level of the retinal artery and vein. A deep capillary network lies in the boundary plane between the inner nuclear layer and the outer plexiform layer. These two capillary networks are connected by intercommunicating branches. The two capillary networks are not independent. Anastomotic capillaries run from one to the other, but the markedly lamellar structure of the retina causes the nets to be largely two dimensional, in contrast to the three dimensional networks present in most other organs, e.g., the brain. Afferent and efferent vessels, the so-called arteriae afferentes and vena efferentes, are distributed along the main arteries (Fig. 106). From these interdigitating vessels, precapillaries arise which feed and drain the superficial and deep capillary nets. Each of the networks consists of true capillaries and is not predominantly arterial or venous. The deep capillary net is more complex than the superficial net.

Surrounding each artery is a zone which is quite free from capillaries.[52] The capillary-free zone extends on either side of the artery for an average of 15 μ. The capillaries do not avoid the neighborhood of the veins in this way, but are found right up to the vein itself. As one approaches the venous precapillaries and their drain-

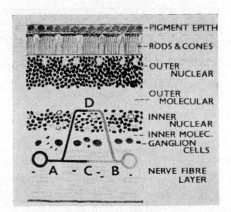

Fig. 105. Diagrammatic representation of the situation of the superficial and deep capillary networks. **A,** Arterial precapillary. **B,** Venous precapillary. **C,** Superficial capillary plexus. **D,** Deep capillary plexus. (From Michaelson, I., and Campbell, A. C. P.: Tr. Ophth. Soc. U. Kingdom **60:**71, 1940.)

Fig. 106. Field from equatorial zone of retina. *Left,* a vein; *right,* an artery. Note the interdigitation of the venae efferents, **v,** with the arteriae afferentes, **A.** Note also the capillary-free zone around the artery. (From Michaelson, I., and Campbell, A. C. P.: Tr. Ophth. Soc. U. Kingdom **60:**71, 1940.)

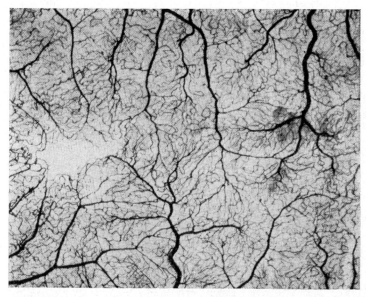

Fig. 107. Lateral part of the macula. Note its greater vascularity as compared with the field shown in Fig. 106 due to a narrower capillary mesh and to the appearance of a third capillary layer. (From Michaelson, I., and Campbell, A. C. P.: Tr. Ophth. Soc. U. Kingdom **60:**71, 1940.)

ing vena efferentes, the more dense the capillary network becomes so that the retina shows a regular alternation of dense capillary areas centered around the veins and open areas around the arteries. This is to be expected since the poor oxygenation of the blood in the venous ends of the capillaries must be compensated by a denser distribution of the capillaries in this region if the tissue is to be uniformly supplied with oxygen.

In the macular region, the two layers are replaced by a three-layered pattern (Fig. 107). This area appears much more vascularized than the region outside the macula due to a closer capillary mesh and to the appearance of the third capillary layer. In and around the optic disc another more superficial capillary net is found, which is the densest of all those present in the retina. The fovea shows a completely avascularized area (Fig. 108), varying from 0.4 to 0.5 mm. in diameter. The blood supply of the fovea comes entirely from the choriocapillaris of the cho-

roid. In man the choriocapillaris can supply nutrition to the retina for a distance of about 130 μ.[53] Hence, in regions where the retina is no thicker than this, there is no need for an additional intraretinal circulation. Since the retina is only from 0.075 to 0.12 mm. in thickness in the foveal area, the metabolic needs of this region can be well supplied from the underlying choroidal vascular bed. Toward the periphery of the retina the mesh of the capillary net becomes wider and the capillary-free periarterial space becomes increasingly prominent. Still farther toward the periphery the deep net disappears entirely, leaving only a single net of wide-mesh, large-caliber capillaries. All over the posterior part of the retina the width of the mesh of the deep net is approximately constant, having a range of about 15 to 130 μ, with an average of about 50 μ.

The disposition of the retinal capillaries, as just described, seems to be an important factor in the pathogenesis and evolu-

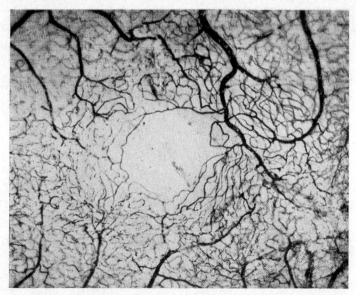

Fig. 108. Fovea with its capillary-free area. (From Michaelson, I., and Campbell, A. C. P.: Tr. Ophth. Soc. U. Kingdom **60**:71, 1940.)

tion of certain pathologic patterns associated with most retinopathy. In hypertension and nephritis, the hemorrhages in the retina are flame-shaped or linear-shaped, indicating that they lie in the nerve fiber layer. In diabetes, on the other hand, the hemorrhages are characteristically dotted or rounded and lie in the deeper layers. In hypertension and nephritis, the initial mechanism is increased pressure within the constricted arterioles and capillaries. The arterial capillary, which lies in the nerve fiber layer, is usually longer than the venous capillary. This follows from the fact that the capillary-free space around the arteries is larger than that around the veins. If the hemorrhage is precapillary in origin, it is easy to understand why it is flame-shaped and superficial. It is very unusual to see one actually overlying an artery, which is in keeping with the capillary-free space around the artery. Why should the bleeding which occurs in hypertensive disease take place from the superficial capillary plexus, rather than from the deep one? The most likely explanation is that the superficial plexus is higher up the vascular circuit and the impact of the increased pressure within the arterial system is felt here more strongly than in the deep capillary plexus. The deep plexus is a more closely knit meshwork than the superficial one so that the circulation there tends to be relatively more sluggish.

In diabetes, the most outstanding visible change in the large retinal vessels is a fullness of the retinal veins. If the veins are congested, the congestion is bound to be felt in the venous capillary system. The deep plexus is that part of the system where the meshwork is closest and the circulation, therefore, slowest. Therefore, the back pressure from venous stasis is felt chiefly at this point. In this way, the

incidence of microaneurysms and punctate hemorrhages that occurs in diabetes becomes explicable. Leakages from the deep plexus find their way into the outer molecular layer where, because of the looseness of that tissue, they assume a circular outline.

So far it has not been found possible to reproduce typical diabetic retinopathy in experimental animals. The lesions found in the retina of human diabetics does not seem to be duplicated in any other part of the body. This has led to the suggestion that the occurrence of diabetic retinopathy is due to some peculiar property of the human retinal capillaries, and studies are under way to identify if possible what these peculiar properties are. However, Patz and Maumenee report typical findings of human diabetic retinopathy in a dog which developed diabetes spontaneously. This dog showed microaneurysms and exudates and diffuse glomerulosclerosis similar to that described in diabetic human beings with diffuse glomerulosclerosis. No Kimmelstiel-Wilson nodules were noted so that the nephropathy was considered compatible with but not pathognomonic for diabetes.[54]

On the basis of electron microscopic studies of rat retinal capillaries Kissen and Bloodsworth[48] suggest that differences in basement membranes, the presence or absence of fenestrations or pores, and the presence of pericytes may all have a determining influence on the permeability characteristics of any particular capillary bed. Similar thinking along these lines has been applied to the brain capillaries, where it has been shown that the blood-brain barrier is maintained by the investment of the brain capillaries in glial elements. Kissen and Bloodsworth find all of the retinal capillaries of the rat completely invested in glial elements.

The capillaries in diabetes characteristically lack mural cells, as stated. This may result in pathologic arteriovenous shunts, according to Kuwabara and Cogan.[50] Each shunt will deprive competing capillaries of their circulation, the result being that capillaries adjacent to the shunt dry up. The microaneurysms and tubular proliferation of the endothelium are mostly found in these vessels.

In recent studies of the retinal circulation, using a method which digests the nonvascular components of the retina prior to staining with PAS, Cogan and co-workers find some disagreement with the concepts of the vessel architecture just set forth and based largely on Michaelson's studies. They find that[55] human retinal arteries show both sidearm and dichotomous branching. The arteries in the posterior retina have mainly the sidearm type that comes off at right angles, whereas those arteries in the periphery have Y-shaped branches with arms of equal diameter. This would indicate that the capillaries in the central portions of the retina are served with a higher head of vascular pressure than those in the periphery. On the other hand, there are more capillaries in the central portions so that this may equalize the effects of the different types in the two positions.

The capillary-free zone characteristic of the arterial bed is seen chiefly in the periphery and is absent or least evident in the macula.

The capillary walls have both endothelial and glial cells incorporated within them and are occasionally connected by intercapillary bridges, which are strands of tissue that do not seem to be obliterated vessels and have no lumina.

It will be recalled that Michaelson emphasized a laminar distribution of the retinal capillaries—a superficial capillary plexus in the nerve fiber layer and a deep capillary plexus at the junction of the internal nuclear and outer plexiform layer. In the macular layer the superficial plexus was split to form an additional plexus between the internal nuclear layer and the inner plexiform layer. By using three-dimensional preparations Cogan and associates[56] do not find the lamination of the capillary plexus thought to be characteristic of the retina, except in the region just around the optic disc and in the extreme periphery. Elsewhere capillaries anastomose throughout all layers without any tendency to lamination.

In some patients with diabetes the circulation in the veins is obstructed sufficiently to produce a block in the main vessels or one of their branches. Central venous thrombosis occurs frequently in diabetic persons. If there is endophlebitis or a clot within the vein, sudden stoppage of the return flow of blood from the eye may occur, and the sudden alterations in intravascular pressure are severe. The back pressure in the veins is felt in the entire capillary system, and the results are not only hemorrhages in the deep layers of the retina, but also flame-shaped hemorrhages in the superficial layers. Even the larger vessels leak blood, and the variety of hemorrhages occurring in venous thrombosis and in Kimmelstiel-Wilson disease is equaled only by that occurring in leukemic retinopathy in which the hemorrhages may be of all sizes and situated anywhere in the retinal tree. The hemorrhages in these conditions are due, therefore, to extreme stasis in the venous circuit.

Superficial and deep hemorrhages occur close to and radiate out from the optic disc in papilledema (edema of the head of the optic nerve caused by pressure somewhere behind the eyeball—usually increased intracranial pressure) but are not as marked. These hemorrhages probably come from the peripapillary plexus of the capillaries just described.

Newly formed vessels in the retina occur after venous thrombosis and in any condition in which there has been repeated hemorrhage, such as tuberculous periphlebitis. It is generally believed that these vessels are newly formed and not dilatations of pre-existing capillary channels. They probably arise as a result of the same forces which are active in the cornea in vasculogenesis (Chapter 3). Some authors, on the other hand, believe that the diffuse capillary networks just described form a sufficient basis for these vessels and that it is unnecessary to invoke pathologic changes such as the budding of endothelial tubes from the larger veins. They point out that the capillaries all over the body are capable of hypertrophy to an enormous extent.

The retinal capillaries and the choriocapillaries may differ somewhat in their permeability. Certain dyes when injected intravenously come through the choroidal capillaries and can be seen in the choroid and in the outer layers of the retina. They do not come through the retinal capillaries, however, and are not seen in the inner layers of the retina.[57]

Choroidal circulation. A transverse section of the choroid shows that it is made up almost entirely of a series of blood vessels ranging from large arteries and veins on the scleral aspect to a network of capillaries on which the pigmented epithelium of the retina rests (Fig. 109). The capillaries constituting the choriocapillaris consist of a meshwork of very wide endothelial tubes. The width of each of these tubes is important since a very large lateral pressure will be generated by the blood passing through them. The degree of filling of the choriocapillaris and the other blood vessels of the choroid determines sudden, though slight, changes of intraocular pressure to some extent. In this respect, the choroid acts like an erectile tissue such as the corpus spongiosum.

Although at one time it was believed that the short posterior ciliary arteries were end arteries functionally and that the vessels in the choroid had a strict segmental distribution, there is no anatomic evidence for the concept that these arteries are true end arteries.[58] In fact, there is no evidence to support the belief that the choroidal circulation is divided into separate zones, which could explain certain disease pictures in the same way that the distribution of the retinal arterioles and capillaries explains the type of hemorrhage that occurs in hypertension and diabetes (p. 336). At one time it was thought that the ring scotoma which occurred characteristically in the early stages of pigmentary degeneration was due to the fact that the retinal degeneration resulted from a defect in the underlying choroidal circulation and that there was a zone at the equator which represented the meeting place of the terminal twigs of the short posterior ciliary arteries, running forward, and of the recurrent choroidal arteries from the anterior part of the uveal tract, running backward. Such a strictly localized zone based on the arrangement of the choroidal blood vessels does not exist, however. The same can be said for the choroidal circulation in the macular region. No specialized characteristics of the choriocapillaris can be found to explain the localization of hemorrhages in the macular region which occurs so commonly in juvenile and senile macular degeneration or in extreme myopia, and some factor other than the vascular must account for the predilection of certain disease processes for certain regions of the choroid. Variations in the choroidal circulation influence the formation of the aqueous humor by changing

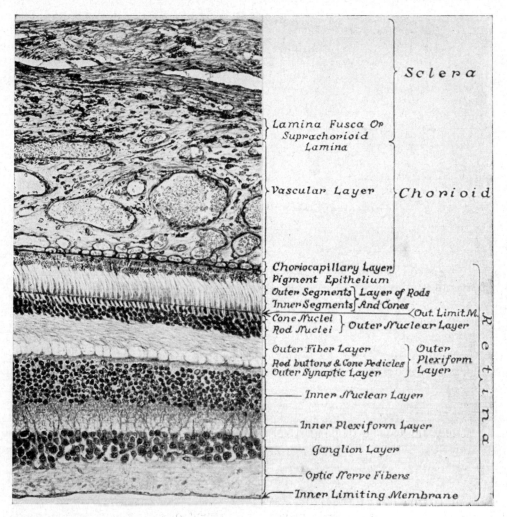

Fig. 109. Cross section through the coats of the human eyeball in the region of the central area (medium magnification). Uppermost is a portion of the tough outer tunic or sclera, chiefly made up of connective tissue and pigmented melanophores. The middle or vascular tunic, the chorioidea, is composed of blood vessels, the innermost forming the choriocapillary layer. The inner tunic, the retina, made up of several cellular and fibrous layers, is preponderantly nervous tissue, the only nonnervous tissue layer being the pigment epithelium immediately adjoining the photoreceptive layer of rods and cones. (From Polyak, S.: The retina, Chicago, 1941, University of Chicago Press.)

the rate of blood flow through the ciliary processes. The arteries and arterioles of the choroid are identical with those vessels in other parts of the body, except that the choroidal vessels are generally smaller in caliber (Fig. 110).

Undoubtedly the choroidal circulation is equally or more important to vision than the retinal vascular tree since the fovea is nourished entirely by the choriocapillaris. It is of value to know the conditions of blood flow through the choroidal ves-

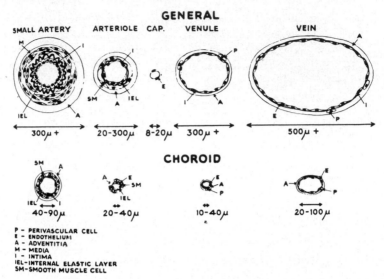

Fig. 110. Schematic drawing showing the comparative structure and size of choroidal vessels and those of other parts of the body. (From Hogan, M., and Feeney, L.: Am. J. Ophth. **51:** 1084, 1961.)

sels, therefore, and to find out what factors influence the blood flow and blood volume. Many methods have been tried with varying success. Direct observation or photography of the vessels in their normal state is rarely possible since the choroidal circulation is ordinarily not visible because of the pigmented epithelium of the retina. Leopold[59] has succeeded experimentally in visualizing the larger choroidal vessels through a scleral window with the insertion of a plastic disk in the suprachoroidal space. By this means vasoconstrictor drugs could be seen to cause narrowing of the choroidal vessels, but dilatation of these vessels did not occur with any drugs. Either the choroidal vessels are in a state of maximal dilation under normal conditions, or the trauma of the method used dilates them ad maximum. Bettman and Fellows[57] have determined changes in the total blood volume which involve minimal trauma to the globe, using a method of injecting radioactive phosphorus. Although the method

gives information as to the change in total blood volume within the eye (or rather within the scanning range of the Geiger counter), it does not give any indications of changes in rate of flow. Drugs acting on the peripheral vessels had marked effects when injected retrobulbarly but not when given by systemic administration. What primary active dilatation of the intraocular blood vessels they were able to show was weak and probably dominated by the results of contraction or dilatation of the peripheral blood vessels. Carbon dioxide administered systemically was found to produce some vasodilation. The simultaneous administration of oxygen did not prevent this effect; therefore, it would seem wise to administer mixtures of carbon dioxide and oxygen when it is desirable to obtain vasodilatation of the intraocular blood vessels and maintain oxygenation of the retinal tissues.[60, 61]

It has been pointed out that the uveal vessels can be influenced by stimulation of the cervical sympathetics. Bill[32] found that the resistance to blood flow through the uveal tract could be raised about 100% at the highest levels of physiologic stimulation frequencies. He also found that an increase in intraocular pressure reduced the uveal blood flow in both rabbits and cats. This was due to an increase in the pressure in the proximal part of the uveal veins and an increase in uveal vascular resistance.[62]

ROLE OF THE SYMPATHETIC NERVOUS SYSTEM IN ESSENTIAL HYPERTENSION AND ITS EFFECTIVENESS ON OCULAR CIRCULATION

The hemorrhages, exudates, and degenerative changes that occur in the retina in chronic renal disease are always accompanied by vascular hypertension. Clinicians have come to believe, therefore, that the retinopathy is due primarily to the hypertension. In the disease entity of essential hypertension, the retinal changes are considered to be dependent likewise upon the elevation of blood pressure. It is logical, therefore, to inquire into the cause of the vascular hypertension in these two conditions in order to find an explanation for the retinopathy common to both.

It is generally agreed that the elevation of blood pressure that occurs in essential hypertension is due to a widespread increase in peripheral vascular tone, with heightened peripheral resistance. The blood volume, viscosity, and cardiac output remain within normal limits.

The peripheral resistance is considerably increased above the mean normal value in every hypertensive subject. The total peripheral resistance indicates that the total cross section of the peripheral vascular bed must be constricted, but it is quite possible that this could be caused by either generalized constriction in all parts of the bed or marked constriction in certain parts with dilatation in others, the constricted areas being greater than the dilated ones. In patients with essential hypertension, the peripheral resistance has been found to be elevated in all of the organs examined; therefore, it is generally conceded that the elevated resistance is widespread and not confined to just a few localities.

It is agreed also that the elevation of blood pressure comes about as the result of narrowing of the peripheral arteriolar bed since capillary and venous pressures throughout the body, as well as blood flow, remain normal.[63]

What causes narrowing of the peripheral arterioles?

Is it a functional narrowing produced by an increase in vasoconstrictor tone or is it an anatomic narrowing produced by organic change in the walls of these vessels? Is the evidence in favor of functional vasoconstriction initiating the hypertension, at least in the early stages of essential hypertension, and are the organic changes which are detectable in the vessels after the hypertension has existed for some time secondary processes, independent of the hypertension, or, as some believe, determined by the hypertension itself?

The evidence against primary organic change in the vessels is strongest in the case of the arterioles distributed throughout the general bodily musculature. As far as can be determined, these are histologically normal during the early stages of essential hypertension. When organic vascular disease has been found, it has not been possible to demonstrate that it was the cause per se of the increased resistance to blood flow.[64] The vascular lesions are generally thought to be a manifestation of aging, as suggested by Evelyn, rather than the cause or the effect of the increased blood pressure. Arteriolar sclerosis may occur without hypertension and hypertension of long standing may be associated with little or no change in the walls of the vessels. It is probable that the two conditions are independent, but it is also possible that each tends to accelerate the other; i.e., hypertension tends to accelerate aging, and senescence may predispose to the development of hypertension.

Medial arteriosclerosis affecting the large vessels is excluded from consideration in essential hypertension since the diastolic pressure is seldom elevated in this form of arteriosclerosis. We are dealing here with the disease process of arteriolar sclerosis which affects those vessels which have no continuous muscular coat and no internal elastic lamina, namely, arterioles.

Patients with long-standing hypertension show a marked increase in the incidence and severity of arteriolar sclerosis, not only in the kidney, but also in almost all the organs and tissues which have been studied by quantitative methods. Observers agree that in a small percentage of patients with essential hypertension, arteriolar sclerosis is completely absent from the kidneys, even when the disease has been of long standing. Evelyn thinks that arteriolar sclerosis and essential hypertension are both primary, independent processes which may undergo parallel development, but which are capable of intensifying one another in the later stages of their evolution.

In the case of the arterioles of the kidney, the evidence is conflicting. According to some authors, arteriolar lesions occur frequently in the kidneys.[65] In order to link essential hypertension in its benign phase with experimental hypertension of renal origin, some authors, notably Goldblatt, have stressed the organic changes which are found in the smaller vessels of the kidney in essential hypertension. Goldblatt observed that intrarenal stenosing arterial sclerosis and arteriolar sclerosis occur with great frequency in both the benign and malignant phases of essential hypertension. He assumed that, if stenosing vascular disease limited to the kidneys were the primary factor in producing essential hypertension, he should be able to reproduce essential hypertension in animals by simulating intrarenal stenosing vascular disease. As is well known, he was able to produce a disturbance of renal hemodynamics similar to that caused by intrarenal stenosing vascular disease by constricting the main renal artery, and in experimental animals this resulted in persistent elevation of blood pressure. This form of experimental hypertension resembles essential hypertension in man more nearly than any other form, either experimentally produced or resulting from a number of widely different disease processes. In experimental renal hypertension, both the benign and the malignant phases of human essential hypertension can be reproduced.

Not all authors agree, however, that the renal blood vessels show pathologic change in patients with essential hypertension. Castleman and Smithwick[66] reported a series of renal biopsies from one hundred hypertensive patients in which the most striking finding was the high percentage of patients in whom there was no renal vascular disease or at least minimal renal vascular disease. Twenty-eight had histologically normal kidneys; in twenty-five the organic vascular disease was too slight to be solely responsible for the hypertension, and this was borne out by studies of renal blood flow in twenty of these patients.[67] These authors concluded, therefore, that in over half their patients hypertension must have been due to some functional vascular disturbance and not to organic disease of the renal vessels. This conclusion is disputed by Goldblatt,[68] however, who does not consider such biopsy material sufficient to draw conclusions on the state of the vasculature of the entire kidney. He points out that the study of a few arterioles in the periphery of the cortex of a kidney can hardly afford an estimate of the vasculature of the entire kidney and that the stenosis of even one large intrarenal artery could easily account for profound hemodynamic disturbances in a large mass of kidney substance supplied by thousands of arterioles that are not themselves diseased.

It cannot be definitely decided at present whether organic disease of the renal arterioles is the primary cause of essential hypertension in human beings. It is possible that the discrepancy in the various pathologic reports is due to the failure to separate cases of essential hypertension from those in which the hypertension is a result of primary kidney disease, i.e., acute and chronic nephritis. Even if it is granted that intrarenal vascular sclerosis is present and causes essential hypertension, it is still necessary to find the cause of the vascular disease itself.

The arterioles of the retina generally show ophthalmoscopic signs of sclerosis by the time the patient is known to have essential hypertension, and in fact the ophthalmologist may be the first to call attention to the hypertension. This does not mean, however, that sclerosis is the initial stage. We are accustomed to describe the changes in the retinal vessels in terms of both sclerosis and hypertension, and frequently the term *spasm* is used to denote a functional change capable of complete restitution. This term is justifiable, strictly speaking, only when one has had the opportunity of seeing the constriction of the vessel disappear. This is seldom the case in essential hypertension. The narrowing, either localized or generalized, of the retinal artery persists throughout the period of observation of the patient. The time one is most justified in using the term *spasm* is for patients with late toxemia of pregnancy. In this condition it is common to find that one or more constricted arteries regain their normal caliber after delivery.

It would seem that the evidence favors the point of view that the primary change in the peripheral arterioles throughout the body is functional rather than organic in the early stages of essential hypertension, with the exception that the evidence is equivocal in the case of the renal arteries.

What produces functional arteriolar constriction?

If the first change which takes place in the arterioles is functional vasoconstriction, the following question must be answered: What produces it? There are several possible answers. (1) It may be initiated by direct stimulation of the vasoconstrictor nerve supply, i.e., by an increase in neurogenic tone. (2) It may be due to some humoral vasoconstrictor agent which acts directly on the vessel wall. (3) It may be due to a humoral agent which acts on the vasoconstrictor centers and thereby increases the peripheral vasoconstrictor tone. Evidence for the existence of each of these possible mechanisms has been sought in both experimental animals and in hypertensive patients.

Experimental renal hypertension. Most of the experimental evidence comes from so-called experimental renal hypertension. Here, the evidence is strongly in favor of a humoral origin, and perhaps it is because of this that there have been few who have adhered to a neurogenic etiology of human essential hypertension.

Carotid sinus denervation and aortic depressor nerve section. A form of experimental hypertension can be produced in animals by bilateral denervation of the carotid sinus and section of the aortic depressor nerves. This hypertension is due to interruption of the afferent nerve impulses which normally buffer or depress the activity of the vasomotor centers in the medulla. The amount of hypertension produced and its duration vary considerably, and the results seem to be contradictory in different animals and with different procedures used. There is also a considerable difference of opinion as to the effect of sympathectomy on this type of hypertension. Although the evidence is somewhat contradictory, elevation of the pressure apparently does not result in histologic alterations in the arterioles throughout the body. It is questionable whether this type of experimental hypertension is related in any manner to essential hypertension in man. In both essential hypertension and in experimental hypertension due to removal of the moderator nerves, increased vasoconstriction is present. However, this does not prove that essential hypertension is due to an abnormality of the carotid sinus and aortic depressor nerve mechanism. The similarity, as Nowak and Walker[69] state, lies in the end result rather than in the cause. It is of interest to note that experimental hypertension due to section of the moderator nerves and essential hypertension in man are usually affected very little by division of the splanchnic nerves only. This form of experimental hypertension differs from experimental hypertension of the renal type in that blood pressure is usually much more labile and tachycardia is more marked.

Increased intracranial pressure. In animals, increasing the intracranial pressure produces hypertension in both acute and prolonged experiments. This type of hypertension, however, cannot be maintained in a predictable fashion for extended periods of time. In experimental animals when the intracranial pressure is increased acutely to a level approaching the diastolic blood pressure, brief asphyxial elevations of systemic arterial pressure can be produced. Similarly, attempts to produce persistent hypertension, as by the injection of colloidal kaolin into the cerebral subarachnoid spaces, have resulted in only transient and unpredictable elevations of blood pressure.[70]

Cerebral anemia. Occlusion of various cerebral arteries may cause chronic hypertension in animals, but these procedures do not always result in hypertension, probably because of the development of a collateral circulation.

All of the forms of experimental neurogenic hypertension are due apparently to disturbances in the neurogenic vasomotor control. The hypertension produced is quite different in its characteristics, however, from human essential hypertension. Removal of the carotid sinus produces hypertension and a fast pulse, which is uncommon in essential hypertension. The rise in pressure in this form of experimental hypertension is due, therefore, to cardiac acceleration and not to increased peripheral arteriolar tone.

Human essential hypertension

Vasomotor instability. The evidence that the sympathetic nervous system initiates peripheral arteriolar constriction in human essential hypertension is far from convincing, but again there is little evidence against it. Although the blood pressure of hypertensive patients, as a whole, reacts abnormally to a few stimuli, such as immersing the hand in cold water, inhalation of carbon dioxide, and prolonged holding of the breath (Valsalva's maneuver), local vascular responses studied have proved to be normal thus far. The cutaneous vessels react normally to local heat and cold. The arterioles of the muscles react normally to exercise and to the general constrictor effects of epinephrine, Pituitrin, and Tyramine. It has been suggested that the sympathetic nervous system of patients with essential hypertension reacts too strongly to normal vasoconstrictor influences, as a result of which the blood pressure of these patients shows marked deviations from the mean level throughout the day. In fact, it has been frequently emphasized that the variations in the level of blood pressure that occur in essential hypertension are characteristic of this disease.[71] There seems to be little question, therefore, that unusual rises in blood pressure in response to different stimuli such as pain, cold, emotional disturbance, holding the breath (carbon dioxide), and postural changes do occur in the hypertensive patient. This form of increased tone has been called hyperreactivity by Hines and Brown.[72, 73]

Whereas there can be no doubt that the responses to vasopressor influences are more pronounced in the hypertensive subject than in the normotensive subject, Landis[73a] has pointed out that this may be more apparent than real. Since the blood pressure of the hypertensive patient and of the normotensive subject does not start from the same base line of arteriolar diameter and tension (the mean blood pressure of the hypertensive patient being considerably higher than that of the normotensive), the same vasopressor activity may well produce a greater rise in blood pressure in the hypertensive patient. This does not mean that his sympathetic nervous system is necessarily more sensitive or more responsive than the normal person's, however, and one is not justified in concluding that hyperactivity of the sympathetic nervous system has anything to do with initiating essential hypertension. It is readily admitted that sympathectomy successfully abolishes the vasopressor reactions in the hypertensive patient, but it would in all probability do the same in the normotensive subject.

Effect of sympathectomy on blood pressure in essential hypertension. Whereas partial or even total sympathectomy has very little effect on the various forms of experimental hypertension in animals, it is effective in lowering the blood pressure in a large proportion of the patients with essential hypertension. Whether this difference between experimental animals and man is due to the fact that animals do not assume an erect posture, with its consequent hemodynamic effects on the vasomotor apparatus, cannot be stated with certainty.

The most striking immediate effect on the blood pressure of patients with essential hypertension following sympathectomy is the reduction in pressure upon standing. The difference in reaction may be due also to the fact that control of the peripheral vessels by the nervous system is less in animals than in man. This fact is borne out by the more labile responses of the blood pressure to emotional stress in man.

One of the most striking things about sympathectomy in hypertensive patients is the unpredictability of its effect on the mean blood pressure level. In some patients, the mean pressure is lowered and stays down persistently. In others, there is only temporary lowering of the pressure. In a still larger group, the mean pressure is not affected although the patient may experience subjective benefit from the operation, and in some patients there may even be objective improvement, such as disappearance of retinopathy.

The extent of the sympathectomy appears to determine in large measure the result on the blood pressure. The more nearly total the sympathectomy, the more likely is the patient to have permanent lowering of the mean pressure.

The fact that only a relatively small proportion of the patients operated upon obtain permanent lowering of the blood pressure suggests that some factor other than a neurogenic one accounts for the persistent elevation of the pressure and points to the presence of a humoral agent. There is some evidence, however, that the persistence of hypertension after operation may be due merely to the failure to eliminate sufficient neurogenic control.

In the majority of the patients sympathectomy abolishes certain vasopressor responses. These vasopressor responses, which have been described previously, are normally mediated in part by the splanchnic sympathetic nervous system. The abolition of these responses by sympathectomy may be therapeutically beneficial to hypertensive patients by avoiding peaks of arterial pressure during which gross or microscopic vascular rupture or other types of damage might occur. These normal constrictor impulses, representing vasopressor reflexes from the sympathetic nervous system, can easily increase peripheral resistance, which is already elevated by excitement, pain, exercise, or even simple standing.[74]

It is difficult to explain the lowering of arterial pressure by sympathectomy save on the basis of widespread decrease in peripheral resistance. No consistent changes in cardiac output after sympathectomy have been found. No great change in blood flow has been found in any organ, even in the liver, when arterial pressure has been lowered and has become stabilized after sympathectomy. Investigators who have studied renal hemodynamics in hypertensive patients, using the clearance method, are agreed that there are no significant changes in renal blood flow following splanchnicectomy. Therefore, they have found it difficult to attribute any fall in arterial pressure that may occur after such operations to a change in the effective renal circulation.

There is a definite decrease in the splanchnic vasoconstrictor response to the upright position and a decrease or abolition of vasopressor overshoots of arterial pressure. All these postoperative effects occur whether or not the mean arterial pressure has been lowered. The results indicate that the observed direct hemodynamic effects of splanchnicectomy do not account adequately for the persistent lowering of arterial pressure that may occur. However, it is possible that in some patients indirect physical or chemical mechanisms resulting from these hemodynamic effects may in time act to cause widespread decrease in peripheral resistance or lowering of arterial pressure.

Effect of sympathectomy on retinopathy. It has been shown previously that the intraocular vessels such as those of the brain are affected but little by neurogenic tone.

In the usual thoracolumbar sympathectomy, the sympathetic nerve supply to the head area is not touched. What neurogenic control of the intraocular vessels exists is not disturbed, therefore. It seems likely that whatever effect sympathectomy has on hypertensive retinopathy must be related to diminished vascular resistance in distant parts of the body rather than to a direct effect on the ocular blood vessels.

In those patients for whom sympathectomy is beneficial, it would appear to be due largely to the removal of vasopressor activity, which may suddenly raise an already dangerously elevated pressure to the breaking point. Whatever benefits are derived as far as retinopathy is concerned are due to the elimination of this factor.

CHANGES IN THE OCULAR CIRCULATION DUE TO EXTERNAL FACTORS

The effects of acceleration and deceleration on the body have become increasingly important because of the high velocities that are now attained in military aviation. Sudden changes in direction or speed produce profound physiologic effects on the crew of an airplane. The accelerative forces are called g forces and are expressed as multiples of the gravitational attractive force. Military maneuvers such as dive bombing and steep inside turns produce characteristic symptoms, resulting in the physiologic effects of positive g forces, which end in blackout and unconsciousness. Two theories have been held as to the origin of blackout: (1) it results from ischemia of the retina and (2) it is caused by ischemia of some other portion of the visual tract. Duane[75] found by direct observation of the fundus oculi during blackout, with carefully controlled observations on the peripheral circulation, that retinal ischemia is the important, if not the sole, cause of blackout. When the positive acceleration reaches a magnitude and duration sufficient to produce loss of vision, the arteriolar tree collapses. In the first stage, collapsile pulsation is observed in the arteries, and this is followed immediately by complete exsanguination and complete collapse of the retinal arteries. During the first stage some subjective phenomena, such as peripheral light loss and graying of the visual field, occur. Within 2 or 3 seconds after the arteries empty of blood, blackout occurs. It seems evident that retinal anoxia occurs within seconds after retinal ischemia appears and that the retina will not function more than 2 to 5 seconds after its blood supply is impaired. It is probable that the ganglion cell and nerve fiber layers are most susceptible to retinal ischemia and that choroidal circulatory changes, which would primarily affect the rod and cone layers, are relatively unimportant. It will be pointed out that the changes in dark adaptation due to anoxia are not concerned with the photochemical processes but with conduction in the neural elements of the retina.

REFERENCES

1. Bouckaert, J., and Heymans, C.: On reflex regulation of cerebral flow and cerebral vaso-motor tone, J. Physiol. **84**:367, 1935.
2. Hayreh, S., and Dass, R.: The ophthalmic artery. I. Its origin and intracranial and intracanalicular course, Brit. J. Ophth. **46**:65, 1962.
3. Hayreh, S., and Dass, R.: The ophthalmic artery. II. Intraorbital course, Brit. J. Ophth. **46**:165, 1962.
4. Hayreh, S.: The ophthalmic artery. III. Branches, Brit. J. Ophth. **46**:212, 1962.
5. Lorente de No, R.: Quoted in Penfield, W.: Cytology and cellular pathology of the nervous system, New York, 1932, Paul B. Hoeber, Inc.
6. Arey, L. B.: Quoted in Penfield, W. G.: Cytology and cellular pathology of the nervous system, New York, 1932, Paul B. Hoeber, Inc.
7. Beauvieux, and Gouelmino, R.: Anatomy of central vessels of retina and optic nerve, Compt. rend. Soc. biol. **90**:1241, 1924.
8. Wolff, E.: Blood supply to the lamina cribrosa, Tr. Ophth. Soc. U. Kingdom **60**:69, 1940.
9. Wybar, K.: Anastomosis between the retinal and ciliary circulations, Brit. J. Ophth. **40**:65, 1956.

10. Patz, A.: Oxygen in retinal artery occlusion, Am. J. Ophth. **40:**789, 1955.

11. Ashton, N.: In Duke-Elder, S., editor: Glaucoma: symposium, Springfield, Ill., 1955, Charles C Thomas, Publisher.

12. Wudka, E., and Leopold, I.: Experimental studies of the choroidal vessels, Arch. Ophth. **55:**605, 1956.

13. Cohan, B.: Experimental intraocular venography, Arch. Ophth. **63:**489, 1960.

14. Weinberger, L. M., Gibbon, M. H., and Gibbon, J. H., Jr.: Temporary arrest of circulation to central nervous system, pathologic effects, Arch. Neurol. & Psychiat. **43:**961, 1940.

15. Behrman, S.: Amaurosis fugax et amaurosis fulminans, Arch. Ophth. **45:**458, 1951.

15a. Duane, T.: Communication, Arch. Ophth. **59:**317, 1957.

16. Friedenwald, J. S.: Retinal vascular dynamics, Am. J. Ophth. **17:**387, 1934.

17. Chao, P., and Bettman, J.: The relative volume of blood in the choroid and retina, Am. J. Ophth. **43:**294, 1957 (abst.).

18. Huber, A.: Eye symptoms in brain tumors, St. Louis, 1961, The C. V. Mosby Co., p. 108.

19. Van Allen, M., Blodi, F., and Brintnall, E.: Retinal artery blood pressure measurements in diagnosis and surgery of spontaneous carotid occlusion, J. Neurosurg. **15:**19, 1958.

20. Behrman, S.: Retinal vein obstruction, Brit. J. Ophth. **46:**336, 1962.

21. Levene, R.: Studies on ocular blood flow in the rabbit, Arch. Ophth. **58:**19, 1957.

22. Colle, J., Duke-Elder, P. M., and Duke-Elder, W. S.: Studies on intraocular pressure; action of drugs on vascular and muscular factors controlling intraocular pressure, J. Physiol. **71:**1, 1931.

23. Penfield, W.: Intracerebral vascular nerves, Arch. Neurol. & Psychiat. **27:**30, 1932.

24. Schmidt, C.: The present status of knowledge concerning intrinsic control of cerebral circulation and effects of functional derangements in it, Fed. Proc. **3:**131, 1944.

25. Risteen, W. A., and Volpitto, P. P.: Role of stellate ganglion block in certain neurologic disorders, South. M. J. **39:**431, 1946.

26. Kety, S. S., and Schmidt, C. F.: The nitrous oxide method for the quantitative determination of cerebral blood flow in man, J. Clin. Investigation **27:**476, 1948.

27. Kety, S. S.: Blood flow and metabolism of the human brain in health and disease, Tr. & Stud. Coll. Physicians Philadelphia **18:**103, 1950.

28. Harmel, M. H., Hafkenscheil, J. H., Auston, G. M., Krumpkin, C. W., and Kety, S. S.: The effect of bilateral stellate ganglion block on the cerebral circulation in normotensive and hypertensive patients, J. Clin. Investigation **28:**415, 1949.

29. Adler, F. H.: Local control of ocular circulation, Arch. Ophth. **53:**1, 1924.

30. Adler, F. H., Landis, E. M., and Jackson, C. L.: The tonic effect of the sympathetic on ocular blood vessels, Arch. Ophth. **53:**239, 1924.

31. Barany, E.: Influence of derangement of vasomotor system of the eye on the relation between local arterial blood pressure and intraocular pressure, Upsala läkaref. förh. **28:**1, 1946.

32. Bill, A.: Blood pressure in the ciliary arteries of rabbits, Exper. Eye Res. **2:**20, 1963.

33. Bill, A.: Effects of cervical sympathetic tone on blood pressure and uveal blood flow after carotid occlusion, Exper. Eye Res. **2:**203, 1963.

34. Bill, A.: Autonomic nervous control of uveal blood flow, Acta physiol. scandinav. **56:**70, 1962.

35. Hevsey, G., and Jacobsen, C. F.: Rate of passage of water through capillary and cell walls, Acta physiol. scandinav. **1:**11, 1940.

36. Merrell, M., Gellhorn, A., and Flexner, L. B.: Studies on rates of exchange of substances between blood and extravascular fluid, exchange of sodium in guinea pig, J. Biol. Chem. **153:**83, 1944.

37. Little, J. M., and Dameron, J. T.: Plasma retention, urinary excretion and effect upon circulating total red cell volume of intravenous gelatin in normal dogs, Am. J. Physiol. **139:**438, 1943.

38. Landis, E. M.: Capillary permeability and factors affecting the composition of capillary filtrate, Ann. New York Acad. Sc. **46:**713, 1946.

39. Knisely, M. H.: Discussion of papers of Landis and Drinker, Ann. New York Acad. Sc. **46:**818, 1946.

40. Drinker, C. K., and Field, M. E.: Protein content of mammalian lymph and relation

of lymph to tissue fluid, Am. J. Physiol. **97**:32, 1931.

41. Whipple, G. H., and Madden, S. C.: Hemoglobin, plasma protein and cell protein—their interchange and construction in emergencies, Medicine **23**:215, 1944.

42. Knisely, M. H., Block, E. H., Elliott, T. S., and Warner, L.: Sludged blood, Science **106**:431, 1947.

43. McMaster, P. D.: Conditions of the skin influencing interstitial fluid movement, lymph formation and lymph flow, Ann. New York Acad. Sc. **46**:743, 1946.

44. Ascher, K. W.: Aqueous veins, Am. J. Ophth. **25**:31, 1942.

45. Goldmann, H.: Abfluss des Kammerwasser beim Menschen, Ophthalmologica **111**:146, 1946.

46. Friedenwald, J. S.: Retinal and choroidal arteriosclerosis. In Ridley and Sorsby: Modern trends in ophthalmology, New York, 1940, Paul B. Hoeber, Inc.

47. Ishikawa, T.: Fine structure of retinal vessels in man and the macaque monkey, Invest. Ophthal. **2**:1, 1963.

48. Kissen, A., and Bloodworth, J.: Ultrastructure of the retinal capillaries of the rat, Exper. Eye Res. **1**:1, 1961.

49. Wolter, J.: The pericytes of the human retina, Am. J. Ophth. **53**:981, 1962.

50. Kuwabara, T., and Cogan, D.: Retinal vascular patterns. VI. Mural cells of the retinal capillaries, Arch. Ophth. **69**:492, 1963.

51. Ashton, N., and Pedler, C.: Studies on developing retinal vessels, Brit. J. Ophth. **46**:257, 1962.

52. Michaelson, I. C., and Campbell, A. C. P.: Anatomy of finer retinal vessels and some observations on their significance in certain retinal diseases, Tr. Ophth. Soc. U. Kingdom **60**:71, 1940.

53. Michaelson, I. C.: The role of the choroid in the nutrition of the retina and some observations on its significance in certain retinal diseases, Tr. Ophth. Soc. U. Kingdom **70**:8, 1950.

54. Patz, A., and Maumenee, A.: Studies on diabetic retinopathy, Am. J. Ophth. **54**:532, 1962.

55. Kuwabara, T., and Cogan, D.: Studies of retinal vascular patterns, 1. Normal architecture, Arch. Ophth. **64**:904, 1960.

56. Toussaint, D., Kuwabara, T., and Cogan, D.: II. Human retinal vessels studied in three dimensions, Arch. Ophth. **65**:575, 1961.

57. Bettman, J., and Fellows, V.: A technic for the determination of blood volume changes in the choroid and retina by the use of radioactive phosphorus, Am. J. Ophth. **42**:161, 1956.

58. Wybar, K. C.: Vascular anatomy of the choroid in relation to selective localization of ocular disease, Brit. J. Ophth. **38**:513, 1954.

59. Leopold, I. H.: Autonomic drugs and their influence on choroidal vessel capacity, Tr. Am. Ophth. Soc. **49**:625, 1951.

60. Stein, H., Wakim, K., and Rucker, C.: In vivo studies on the choroidal circulation of rabbits, Arch. Ophth. **56**:726, 1956.

61. Wybar, K.: A study of the choroidal circulation of the eye in man, J. Anat. **88**:94, 1954.

62. Bill, A.: Studies on uveal circulation and aqueous humor drainage, Acta Universitatis Upsaliensis, Abstract of Thesis No. 7, Uppsala, Sweden, 1962.

63. Eichna, L., and Bordley, J.: Capillary blood pressure in man, direct measurements in the digits of normal and hypertensive subjects during vasoconstriction and vasodilatation experimentally induced, J. Clin. Investigation **21**:711, 1942.

64. Bradley, S.: Physiology of essential hypertension, Am. J. Med. **4**:37, 1948.

65. Moritz, A., and Oldt, M.: Arteriolar sclerosis in hypertensive and non-hypertensive individuals, Am. J. Path. **13**:679, 1937.

66. Castleman, B., and Smithwick, R.: The relation of vascular disease to the hypertensive state, J.A.M.A. **121**:1256, 1943.

67. Talbot, J., Castleman, B., Smithwick, R., Melville, R., and Pecora, L.: Renal biopsy studies correlated with renal clearance observations in hypertensive patients treated by radical sympathectomy, J. Clin. Investigation **22**:387, 1943.

68. Goldblatt, H.: Symposium on hypertension. Recent studies in hypertension, Am. J. Med. **4**:1, 1948.

69. Nowak, S., and Walker, I.: Experimental studies concerning the nature of hypertension, New England J. Med. **220**:269, 1939.

70. Griffith, J., Jeffers, W., and Lindauer, M.: A study of the mechanism of hypertension

following intracisternal Kaolin injection in rats, Am. J. Physiol. **113:**285, 1935.

71. Ayman, D.: An evaluation of therapeutic results in essential hypertension, J.A.M.A. **96:**2091, 1931.

72. Hines, E., and Brown, G.: A standard test for measuring the variability of blood pressure. Its significance as an index of the prehypertensive state, Ann. Int. Med. **7:** 209, 1933.

73. Hines, E.: The significance of vascular hyper-reaction as measured by the cold pressor test, Am. Heart. J. **19:**408, 1940.

73a. Landis, E. M.: Personal communication.

74. Wilkins, R., and Culbertson, J.: The effects of surgical sympathectomy upon certain vasopressor responses in hypertensive patients, Tr. A. Am. Physicians **60:**195, 1947.

75. Duane, T.: The effect of anoxia. Observations on the fundus oculi during blackout, Arch. Ophth. **51:**343, 1954.

CHAPTER 10

OCULAR MOTILITY

ARTICULATION OF THE EYEBALL IN THE SOCKET

Fascia. Each eyeball is held in position in the orbital cavity by various ligaments and fascial expansions which surround it. These form a scaffolding which keeps the eyeball in the same position in the orbit while it is being rotated by the external ocular muscles; otherwise, contraction of these muscles would displace the globe laterally, vertically, or in an anteroposterior direction. The fascia of the orbit extends from the apex to the orbital rim, varies considerably in structure and serves different functions in various parts. It has been given different names to identify its various portions, but in reality it is one indivisible tissue Thus, the fascia surrounding the front of the globe is fixed at the orbital rim and is condensed in places to form thick ligaments, the so-called check ligaments. These are so arranged that they check the action of each muscle that would otherwise carry the globe too far in any one direction (Fig. 111). That portion of the fascia which is condensed in back of the globe and lines the inside and the outside of the muscle cone is called Tenon's capsule.

The fascia of the orbit is a continuation of the dural sheath as it comes through the optic foramen that surrounds the optic nerve (Fig. 112). At the rim of the optic foramen this dural sheath splits into two portions, as shown in the diagram. The outer part adheres firmly to the bones of the orbit, where it forms the orbital periosteum, and in this location is called the periorbita. This continues forward to the orbital rim, although it is penetrated by all of the structures which enter the orbital cavity through the orbital fissures. At the orbital rim it joins the periosteum covering the bones of the face but is adherent to the bones of the orbital rim so that it cannot be lifted up easily here. At this location it splits and sends a firm sheet of fascia vertically to cover the entire orbital aperature except for the opening between the margins of the lid which forms the fissure of the lid (Fig. 1, p. 19). The portion of the fascia blocking off the orbital cavity is called the orbital septum. Because this dense fascia continues over the walls of the orbit and closes in the front of the orbital opening, blood and inflammatory products tend to remain confined to each orbit, although spread across the nose to the lids of the opposite side is possible due to the weak

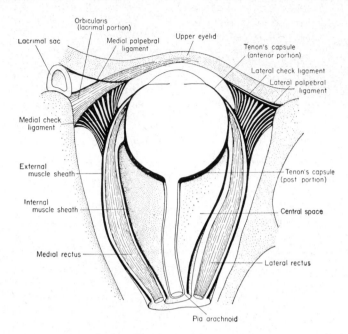

Fig. 111. Horizontal section through the orbit showing fascial sheaths and check ligaments. (Modified after Duke-Elder.)

spots in this fascia where it covers the lacrimal sac. Hemorrhage in an orbit may be confined at first to the lids of the same side, but eventually it spreads over the nose to the opposite lids.

At the orbital end of the optic canal the dural sheath not only lines the inside of the orbit, but also splits into two further divisions which cover the outside and inside of the ocular muscles as they arise from the annulus of Zinn. As has been said, the coverings of the muscle cone form part of Tenon's capsule, the rest being formed by the fascia covering the posterior part of the eyeball and firmly adherent to it (Figs. 113 and 114). The space formed inside the muscle cone and occupied by the optic nerve, blood vessels, nerves, and fat is called the central space. This space allows freedom of the optic nerve during movements of the eye and prevents compression of the blood vessels during such movements.

The fascia covers the globe from the entrance of the optic nerve forward to the limbus. It is not tightly bound down to the globe, although trabeculae run between it and the sclera, so that a potential space is found here, known as Tenon's space. At one time it was thought that this space was lined with endothelium and that the globe rotated freely inside it, but this concept is erroneous.

The fascia covering the outside of the muscle cone is quite tenuous at the back of the orbit but becomes thicker as the tendons of the individual recti are approached. Just before reaching the tendons, the fascia on both the outside and the inside of the muscles becomes so thick that it looks as though the muscles had actually to pierce through the fascia in order to attach to the globe at their insertions. In this forward location the combined two layers of the fascia covering the globe between each rectus muscle is

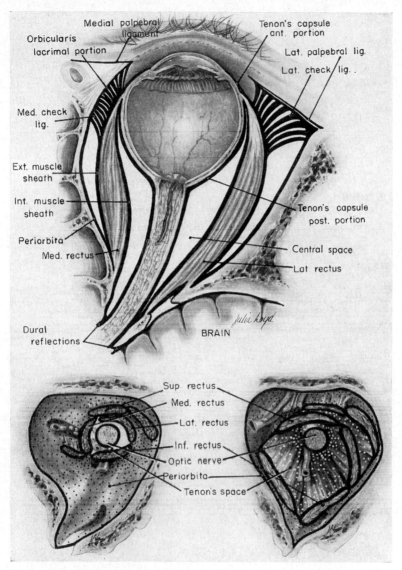

Fig. 112. Orbital contents seen in various cross sections.

called the intermuscular fascia and is of considerable importance in surgery of the muscles. If a muscle is recessed (i.e., placed farther back on the globe then its original insertion), unless the intermuscular fascia is cut on each side of the muscle, it will not retract into the orbit as far as may be intended. Hence, in order to get the maximal effect of a recession, it is advisable to free the muscle carefully from the intermuscular fascia by cutting this on each side of the muscle.

Check ligaments. Over each of the rectus muscles, particularly the lateral and medial rectus muscles, the outer layer of fascia becomes enormously thickened where the tendon inserts into the globe. This thickened fascia flares out to the

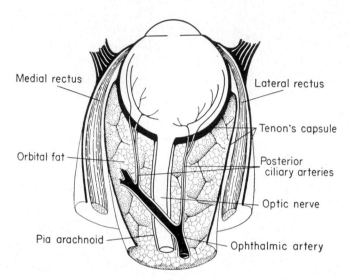

Fig. 113. Horizontal section through the orbit, showing the orbital contents.

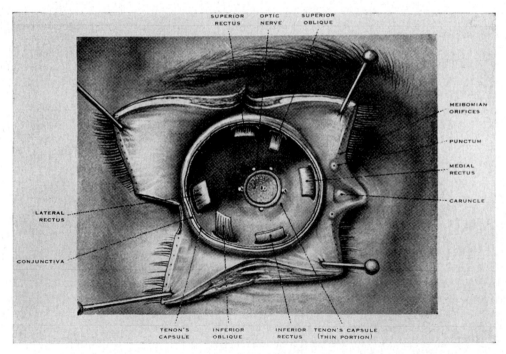

Fig. 114. Dissection to show Tenon's capsule. The (right) eye has been removed. (From Wolff, E.: Anatomy of the eye and orbit, London, H. K. Lewis & Co. Ltd.).

orbital wall where it is firmly attached and forms a check ligament (Figs. 115 and 116). As has been said, these ligamentous expansions are attached to the margin of the orbit so that they fix the eyeball in position and prevent it from being pulled back into the orbit when each rectus muscle contracts or from being pulled forward by contraction of the oblique muscles. The fascial expansions of the medial and lateral rectus muscles are of special clinical importance because these muscles are the ones so frequently operated on in the treatment of strabismus. Their fascial èxpansions form the internal and external check ligaments. They prevent the eyeball from making horizontal rotations beyond 50 degrees from the midline or primary position, as it is called. If the lateral or medial rectus muscles are recessed or advanced from their original positions on the globe, the effect on the corresponding check ligament may be marked, as can be seen in

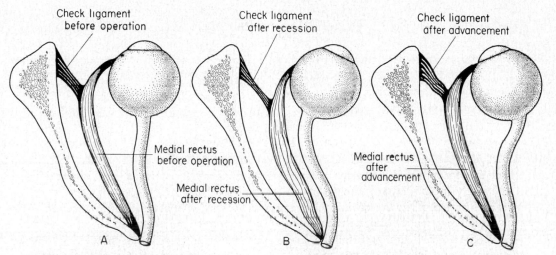

Fig. 115. Diagram showing the effect of recession and advancement of the medial rectus on the check ligament and on the position of the globe.

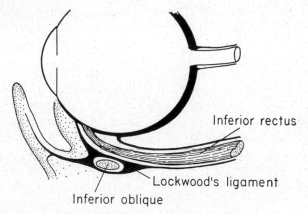

Fig. 116. Vertical longitudinal section through the lower anterior portion of the orbit, showing Lockwood's ligament. (Modified after Maddox.)

Fig. 115. Although advancement of a muscle is seldom performed, resection of a muscle produces much the same effect on the check ligament. When a muscle is recessed, the check ligament is made more taut, with the result that the arc through which the muscle can turn the globe is lessened. This aids in weakening the effectiveness of the muscle. When a muscle is advanced or resected, on the other hand, the check ligament is loosened so that the arc of movement is made greater, and the activity of the muscle is augmented.

The fascia which covers the inferior rectus and inferior oblique muscles fuses where the muscles cross each other to form a dense condensation called the suspensory ligament of Lockwood (Fig. 116). Although this is supposed to have a suspensory function which would prevent the globe from sinking due to the pull of gravity, this action cannot be very effective, for fractures of the floor of the orbit readily permit the globe to sink down and backward in the orbit, and the globe becomes enophthalmic. Because of the fact that this ligament fuses the inferior rectus and inferior oblique muscle, during operations in which the inferior oblique is picked up on a muscle hook care must be exercised that the inferior rectus is not included with it. If this should occur, the inferior rectus might be cut, either along with or in place of the inferior oblique, when a myectomy of the inferior oblique muscle is attempted. The degree of fusion between the inferior oblique and inferior rectus is variable. Because of this, some surgeons claim more consistent results may be obtained in the performance of a recession of an inferior oblique muscle by freeing the muscle from its attachment on the globe and placing its new insertion nearer its origin than to attempt to weaken the activity of the muscle by doing a myectomy in its middle. If the inferior oblique is adherent to the inferior rectus muscle, it can still produce an affect on the globe, even after it has been cut. On the other hand, myectomy of the muscle still has its usefulness and in some patients gives the desired result after a recession of the muscle at its insertion has failed.

MECHANICS OF THE MOVEMENTS OF EACH EYE
Translatory movements

Since the eyeball is firmly fixed in the orbit by the orbital fascia and is held against the rather unyielding orbital fat, only slight movements of the globe are permissible from side to side or from front to back. What slight translatory movements do occur are of minor importance in the normal rotations of the eyes. Forward and backward displacements to a small degree are possible for man but to a much less extent than in the lower animals which possess a sheet of muscle between the insertions of the recti, arising at the apex of the orbit. This is known as the retractor bulbi muscle. When it contracts, the globe is pulled back into the orbit. Its action can be demonstrated easily in dogs with prominent eyes, and its effect must be taken into consideration in experiments performed on the usual laboratory animals. In cats, e.g., stimulation of the cervical sympathetic produces contraction of this muscle which pulls the globe back into the orbit with sufficient force to raise the intraocular pressure considerably. Early experiments showing the effect of sympathetic nerve stimulation on the intraocular pressure did not recognize this factor, and the elevated pressure was assumed to be due to vasodilator fibers to the intraocular blood vessels. The rise in pressure does not occur if this muscle is effectively destroyed before the sympathetic nerves are stimulated.

In rabbits the eyes are so loosely held in the orbit that they can be easily dislocated forward until they are out in front of the lids. In man a demonstrable movement of the globe backward may occur when an object such as a tonometer is placed on the cornea. Even though the eye is anesthetized, some patients attempt to close the lids in a natural defensive reaction when the instrument is brought close to the cornea. At the same time the external ocular muscles may be cocontracted* so that the globe is pulled back into the orbit.

During tonometry when the lids are held apart and the subject is directed to keep his eyes straight ahead, one can sometimes see that the globe is drawn backward 1 to 2 mm. by the cocontraction of the recti muscles. This may compress the globe against the orbital fat and cause an abnormal increase of pressure in the eye. When a tonometer is used to determine the intraocular pressure of a nervous person, care must be exercised that the patient relaxes and does not cocontract his ocular muscles. In young children tonometry must be done under deep general anesthesia for the same reason.

The eye may be displaced backward or forward in the orbit under abnormal conditions. Exophthalmos due to an increase in the volume of the orbital contents and enophthalmos due to herniation of the globe into the antrum following orbital fracture have been described previously. It is possible that a general diminution of the tonus of the four rectus muscles

---

*Cocontraction refers to the simultaneous contraction of muscles which are antagonists and under most circumstances do not contract together, e.g., the lateral and medial recti of the same eye.

may occur in thyrotoxicosis and partially account for the exophthalmos observed in this condition. In paralysis of the ocular muscles, particularly if all four recti are paralyzed, the globe will be exophthalmic 2 to 3 mm. due to loss of tonus of these muscles.

Artificial pressure on the globe from the front through the closed lids forces the globe back in the orbit. The degree of compressibility of the orbital contents under abnormal conditions may tell us something of the character of the orbital contents producing proptosis of a globe. For example, the compressibility of the orbital contents will be considerably reduced in the presence of a solid orbital neoplasm, whereas a vascular tumor such as a hemangioma will show no such increase in resistance. Orbitonometry has been elaborated recently and brought to some clinical significance.[1]

Rotary movements of each globe

The eyeball, supported in the orbit by fascia and ligaments, is rotated by the ocular muscles around a center of rotation

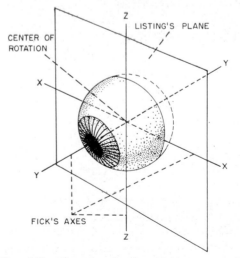

Fig. 117. Diagram showing Fick's axes and Listing's plane.

whose locus is within the globe. Early investigators assumed that this center of rotation was a fixed point, and that the muscles moved the globe by rotating it around one of three axes which run through the center of rotation. These three different axes are called the X, Y, and Z axes of Fick (Fig. 117). Theoretically, the motions produced by contraction of the muscles must be purely rotatory if translatory movements of the globe laterally, vertically, and in or out of the orbit are prevented by the fascia and ligaments attached to the globe. The globe would then rotate around a fixed point which did not move.

It has been shown, however, that translatory movements do take place to some extent, and there is no fixed center of rotation which does not move when the globe rotates.[2, 3] In horizontal movements the point around which the globe rotates

moves in a semicircle in the plane of the rotation. This has been called the space centrode (Fig. 118). A further movement of this point has been termed the body centrode. During a movement of the globe the center of rotation is the point of contact of these two centrodes, which at that time has zero velocity.

Since there is no fixed center of rotation, no analysis of eye movements can be made in exact quantitative terms. Translatory movements do take place to some degree, even in limited eye movements, and under certain conditions these may be considerable, as we have seen described. For practical purposes the approximate center of rotation of the globe lies 13.5 mm. back of the cornea in the average emmetropic adult eye and about 1.6 mm. to the nasal side of the geometric center of the globe.

From a mechanical point of view the globe may be considered to rotate around each of three separate axes: the Z, or vertical axis, rotation around which produces purely horizontal movement; the X, or horizontal axis, producing elevation or depression of the globe, and the Y axis, or anteroposterior axis, rotation around which produces a clockwise or counterclockwise turning of the globe usually spoken of as torsion. One can voluntarily rotate the eyes horizontally around the Z axis and vertically around the X axis, but it is not possible to produce voluntarily movements around the Y axis (Fig. 117).

The X and Z axes lie in the same plane which passes through both the center of rotation and the equator of the eye when it is in the primary position, i.e., looking straight ahead with the eyes held on the horizon. This plane is called the equatorial or Listing's plane. The Y axis runs through the center of rotation at right angles to Listing's plane.

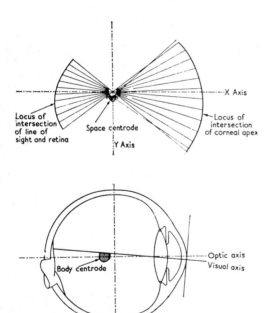

Fig. 118. Position of the space centrode and the body centrode as computed by Park and Park (1953).

Ductions. Rotation of each eye around the X and Z axes are called ductions (Fig. 119), and include the following movements:

1. Rotation around the vertical axis
   (a) Abduction—rotation of each eye temporally
   (b) Adduction—rotation of each eye nasally

2. Rotation around the horizontal axis
   (a) Sursumduction — rotation of each eye upward
   (b) Deosursumduction—rotation of each eye downward

When the eye makes a duction movement from the primary position directly inward, outward, upward or downward, the movement is called a cardinal move-

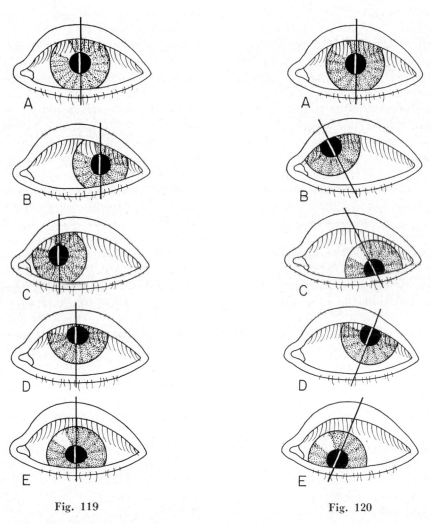

Fig. 119   Fig. 120

Fig. 119. The left eye in primary and secondary positions of gaze. **A,** Primary position; **B,** abduction; **C,** adduction; **D,** sursumduction; **E,** deosursumduction.
Fig. 120. The left eye in primary and tertiary positions of gaze. **A,** Primary position; **B** and **C,** intorsion; **D** and **E,** extorsion.

ment, and the eye is said to have moved from the primary to a secondary position. When the eye moves from the primary position up and to the right or left or down and to the right or left, it is said to have made an oblique movement from the primary to a tertiary position.

It is obvious that when an eye makes a cardinal movement from the primary to a secondary position the movement can be considered to have been made by a rotation around either the X or Z axis. It is not so clear how the eye moves from the primary to a tertiary position. It might move first around the Z axis horizontally and then around the X axis, either up or down to its destined position, or it might move first around the X axis vertically and then around the Z axis horizontally. Finally, it might move obliquely to its destined position around some other axis in Listing's plane intermediate between the X and Z axes. We will return to this after discussing rotations of the eye around its anteroposterior or Y axis.

Torsion. Rotation of the eye around the Y axis produces a clockwise or counterclockwise turning of the globe. If one imagines a perpendicular on the cornea from the 12 to the 6 o'clock position, movement of the 12 o'clock position nasally or temporally is spoken of as torsion. If the 12 o'clock position moves nasally, it is called intorsion, and if it moves temporally, it is called extorsion (Fig. 120). As has been said, an individual cannot voluntarily turn the eyes around the Y axis. It will become apparent in the discussion of the action of the individual ocular muscles that contraction of certain of the muscles working alone and not balanced by the simultaneous contraction of others would produce torsion. This question arises. Does an eye making either cardinal or oblique movements from the primary position undergo rotation around its anteroposterior or Y axis, producing torsion, or is the vertical meridian of the cornea always kept vertical regardless of the final position of the eye?

In Figs. 119 and 121 it is shown that when the eyes are in the primary position the vertical meridians of the corneas are perpendicular, and that they remain so in all secondary positions of gaze; i.e., there is no movement of the 12 o'clock positions on the cornea either clockwise or counterclockwise. However, it is seen in Figs. 120 and 122 that when oblique movements are made from the primary to any tertiary position the 12 o'clock position on the cornea is displaced either nasally or temporally from the objective vertical position determined by a plumb line. It looks as though the eye had actually rotated around its Y axis. This, however, might not be true torsion, which, as defined, is a rotation around the anteroposterior axis of the eye, but might result from the method employed in measuring the deviation of the vertical meridian against the objective vertical or plumb line—in other words, of measuring the change in position of the 12 o'clock point on the cornea with a planar coordinate system, i.e., against vertical and horizontal lines in space. We generally determine changes in position of an object in space by the use of such a system, and when we apply this to the change in position of the vertical meridian of the cornea in oblique movements of gaze, we find that the vertical meridian tilts against the vertical and horizontal lines of the reference background. The direction and amount of this tilt can be predicted on purely mathematical principles. If we use a spherical system of coordinates instead of a planar coordinate system, the vertical meridian of the cornea would line up exactly with the background without any

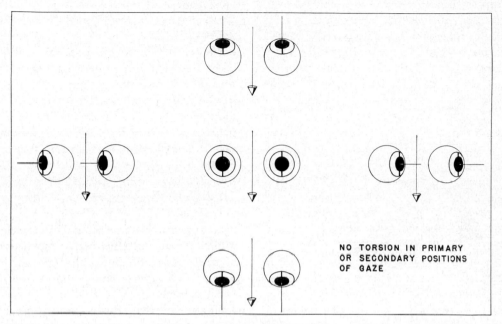

Fig. 121. Diagram of the globe in primary and secondary positions of gaze.

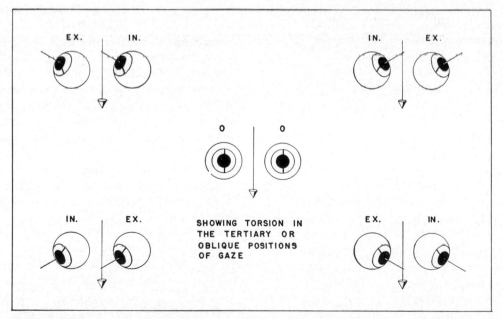

Fig. 122. Diagram of the globe in primary and tertiary positions of gaze.

tilt if no rotation around the anteroposterior axis of the eye had occurred, and by the same token, if it did not line up, it would indicate that such a rotation had actually taken place. The term *false torsion* has been generally employed to indicate the deviation of the vertical meridian of the cornea not due to an actual rotation around the anteroposterior axis of the eye.

It is generally agreed that the vertical meridian of the cornea stays vertical when the eye moves from the primary position of gaze either horizontally or vertically, i.e., to a secondary position. Likewise, it is generally agreed that the vertical meridian tilts when the eye moves from the primary to a tertiary position of gaze. In the first instance there is no torsion, true or false. In the second instance there is still debate whether the observed tilt is or is not entirely false torsion. Table 42 gives the amount of tilting of the cornea as measured by Maddox using a planar coordinate system for an oblique movement of the eye upward and temporally about an axis 45 degrees from the horizontal and vertical axes.

Various methods have been employed

Table 42. *Angle of torsion in oblique gaze according to Maddox*

Degree of rotation	Angle of tilt, 12 o'clock position on limbus temporally
5	6.5″
10	26.0″
15	1°
20	1° 47″
25	2° 49″
30	4° 6″
35	5° 40″
40	7° 33″
45	9° 44″

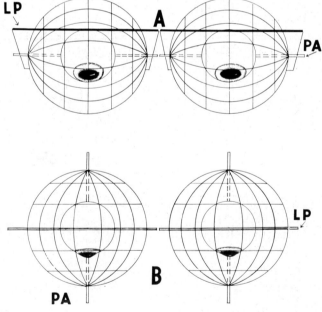

Fig. 123. A, Spherical coordinate system as it should be employed in measuring squint. *PA,* Polar axis; *LP,* Listing's plane. The coordinate system does not move with the eye. **B,** Spherical coordinate system employed to measure rolling. Polar axis is fixed in the primary position. (From Quereau, J. V. D.: Arch. Ophth. **53:**807, 1955.)

to determine whether the tilt in the tertiary positions is false torsion or true rotation of the globe around the Y axis. Quereau[4] measured tilt against a system of spherical coordinates and found that all the tilt could be accounted for on the basis of false torsion when the eye was directed obliquely in the ordinary fields of gaze. In gaze downward and outward,

in the extreme field of gaze there was some true intorsion, and in gaze upward and outward there was extorsion. These findings were confirmed by plotting the blind spots on a spherical coordinate system in oblique movements[5] (Figs. 123 and 124). No true torsion was found in either the extreme superior or inferior nasal field of gaze. This might have been

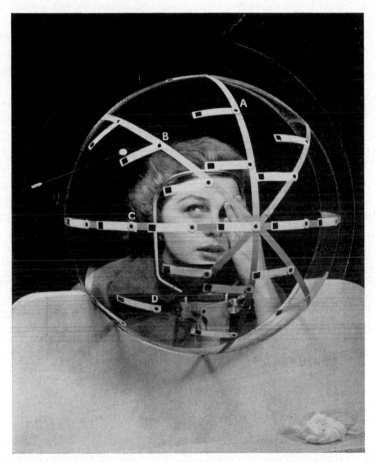

Fig. 124. Projection of retinal horizon for various directions of gaze. Long plastic strips on transparent hemisphere represent meridians of longitude or spherical coordinate system. Polar axis passes through center of rotation of eye and primary position. *Round black dots,* fixation points on meridians of longitude. *Black squares,* positions of blind spot. *Short white strips,* projections of retinal horizon. Points **A, B, C,** and **D** are limits of field of fixation. White strips beyond **A, B, C,** and **D** are hypothetical and only illustrate the nature of compensatory rolling. Test target used is almost as large as the blind spot. (From Quereau, J. V. D.: Arch. Ophth. **53:**807, 1955.)

because of the limitation of the line of sight by the nose before an extreme rotation is reached. Weale,[6] on the other hand, found that true torsion does occur in oblique gaze.

The subject of torsion in oblique gaze has been a controversial one for many years, largely due to the interest the early experimenters had in proposing mechanical systems with mathematical analyses to account for eye movements. An excellent review of this difficult subject has recently been written by Alpern.[7] These systems have had great influence in formulating our ideas of ocular motility. The action of each of the ocular muscles working singly and together with its agonists and antagonists in both health and disease is based on the concept of a fixed center of rotation and fixed axes of rotation. Until now very little has been accomplished to apply physiologic methods to these problems, largely because we have not had the adequate tools to do this. Most of this chapter, therefore, will deal with descriptions and explanations of phenomena based on mechanical models which have not as yet been proved correct. Some recent experimental work which has yielded contrary ideas and

which still needs confirmation will be mentioned, however.

Listing's law. Listing proposed that purely horizontal movements of the eye were performed around a vertical axis in the equatorial plane and vertical movements around a horizontal axis likewise located in the equatorial plane. He also assumed that in all oblique movements the eye reached its destination as though it had rotated around a single axis also in the equatorial plane. This axis would be perpendicular to both the plane containing the initial position of the line of sight and the plane containing the final position of the line of sight (Fig. 125). In making any rotation from the primary to a tertiary position, the line of sight would travel along a meridian and all such meridians would be great circles passing through the occipital point (the occipital point is the point on the globe where an extension of the line of sight backward pierces the globe). On purely geometric grounds all such oblique movements would be associated with a tilt of the vertical meridian of the cornea with the objective vertical at the end of the movement because the angle which the great circle makes with the objective vertical

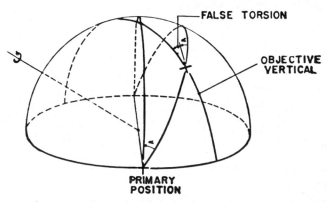

Fig. 125. Simple rotations around axes in Listing's plane induce no cyclorotation with respect to the primary position, although oblique rotations induce false torsion, i.e., cyclorotations with respect to objective verticals. (From Boeder, Paul: Arch. Ophth. **57:**202, 1957.)

varies with the amplitude of the movement along the meridian.

Listing did not state that the eye actually reaches any tertiary position by one route only, but that, regardless of the route it took, it was the equivalent of a rotation around an oblique axis in the equatorial plane. Donders went farther and showed that the angle of false torsion at any tertiary position was the same regardless of how the eye was brought to this position. The eye could move first horizontally and then vertically or first vertically and then horizontally, or could move obliquely directly to its final position, and yet the angle of tilt would remain the same.

Alpern[7] has emphasized that any tertiary position may be fully described by specifying the position of the oblique axis in the equatorial plane about which the rotation may be regarded as occurring and the amplitude of the movement. Only two degrees of freedom are necessary to describe the movement completely. No rotation of the globe around its anteroposterior axis occurs. All other systems of axes of rotation proposed necessitate a rotation of the globe around this axis and therefore require three degrees of freedom of movement. We have seen that at present most of the experimental data verify the predictions of Listing's law, and that in all movements of the globe throughout the ordinary range of gaze there is no rotation of the globe around its anteroposterior axis.

GROSS ANATOMY AND ACTION OF EACH OCULAR MUSCLE
Individual muscles

The ocular muscles, with the exception of the inferior oblique, arise from the back of the orbit and run forward to attach to the globe by means of tendinous expansions. The four recti attach in front of the equator, whereas the superior oblique tendon, after passing through the trochlea, turns backward to attach to the sclera behind the equator, and the inferior oblique, arising from the nasal aspect of the orbit just inside its rim, also passes backward to insert on the globe behind the equator (Fig. 126).

The ocular muscles are paired, each pair having a common muscle plane. The muscle plane is that plane formed by joining the midpoint of the origin of the muscles with the midpoint of their tendinous insertion. These four points establish a plane that runs through the long axis of each of the muscles. The angle formed by this plane with the visual direction or line of fixation depends on the position of the globe. When the line of fixation runs through the muscle plane, the angle is zero. The medial and lateral recti have a common muscle plane lying in the horizontal plane of the globe; the superior and inferior recti lie in a common vertical plane, and their muscle plane makes an angle of 23 degrees with the line of fixation when the eyes are directed straight ahead, i.e., in the primary position. The superior and inferior oblique muscles lie in a common plane, and their muscle plane makes an angle of approximately 51 degrees with the line of fixation when the eyes are in the primary position. The muscle planes of the superior and inferior obliques do not actually coincide, but the difference is negligible for clinical purposes.

Medial rectus. The medial rectus muscle arises from the annulus of Zinn and runs forward to insert on the sclera about 5.5 mm. from the limbus. It is the thickest and most powerful of the ocular muscles and has a very short tendon, slightly under 4 mm. The tendon is about 10 mm. broad where it inserts on the globe. The muscle is supplied by a branch

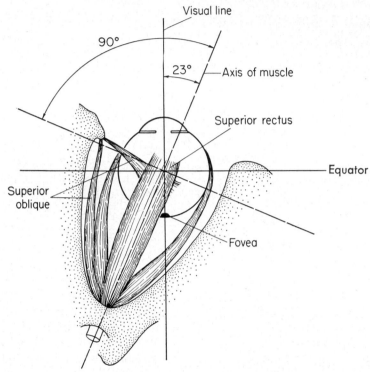

Fig. 126. Diagram of the muscles seen from above, showing the origin and insertion of the superior rectus.

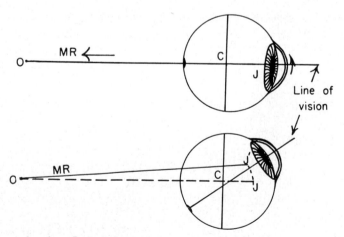

Fig. 127. *Upper drawing,* **J,** insertion of the medial rectus muscle when the eye is in the primary position. *Lower drawing,* when the eye turns up, **J** moves to **J′**.

of the third cranial nerve. The muscle plane is exactly in the horizontal plane of the globe; hence, when the globe is in the primary position, its contraction results in internal rotation only, i.e., adduction. When the visual line is directed above the horizon, contraction of the medial rectus will aid in further elevation, and when the visual line is directed below the horizon, its contraction will further depress the globe (Fig. 127). This muscle has the best-developed check ligament.

Lateral rectus. The lateral rectus muscle arises from the annulus of Zinn and runs forward on the temporal side of the globe to insert approximately 7 mm. from the limbus. It has a very long and relatively thin tendon, approximately 90 mm. in length and the same in breadth. It is supplied by the sixth cranial nerve. The plane of the lateral rectus is the same as that of the medial rectus, and when the eye is in the primary position, contraction of the lateral rectus results in external rotation or abduction alone. Like the medial rectus, when the eyeball is elevated or depressed above the horizon, contraction of the lateral rectus will further elevate or depress the globe. The check ligament of the lateral rectus is not as well developed as that of the medial rectus.

Superior rectus. The superior rectus muscle arises from the annulus of Zinn and runs forward above the globe together with the levator muscle with which it is intimately bound by fascial slips to insert on the globe 7.7 mm. in back of the limbus. As it passes over the equator of the globe, it lies on top of the superior oblique. The superior rectus is supplied by a branch of the third cranial nerve. There is no well-defined check ligament, but the superior rectus and superior oblique muscles are connected by a common fascial sheath which is sometimes well developed.

Because of the fact that this muscle makes an angle of approximately 23 degrees with the visual line when the eye is in the primary position, its contraction when the eye is in the primary position will result in a rotation of the globe around several axes (Fig. 126). This oblique motion is compounded of three separate directions: elevation, nasal rotation or adduction, and rotation around the anteroposterior axis of the globe so that the 12 o'clock position on the limbus turns in toward the nose, i.e., clockwise in the right eye and counterclockwise (intorsion) in the left eye. When the visual line of the eye is directed horizontally outward to 23 degrees from the primary position, contraction of the superior rectus will produce motion of the globe in only one direction, namely, upward. If the eye is moved 67 degrees nasally from the primary position, so that the visual line is at a right angle to the muscle plane, contraction of the muscle will produce adduction and intorsion only. It is evident, therefore, that the effect on the globe of contraction of the superior rectus depends entirely upon the angle its muscle plane makes with the visual line of the eye. In one position (Fig. 128, *B*), its contraction will produce elevation alone. At right angles to this (Fig. 128, *C*) the power of elevation is entirely lost, and a movement of an entirely different character results.

In the primary position the pull of the superior rectus obviously produces more elevation of the globe than adduction or intorsion. Mathematical calculations[8] show that in the primary position the superior rectus is 92.1% effective as an elevator and only 39% effective as an intorter.

Inferior rectus. The inferior rectus muscle also arises from the annulus of Zinn and runs forward underneath the globe to

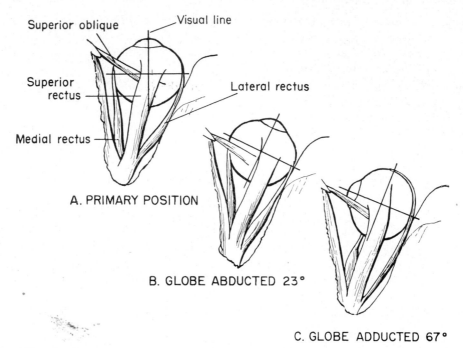

Fig. 128. Globe and ocular muscles viewed from above, demonstrating the effect of contraction of the superior rectus when the globe is in different positions.

attach 6.5 mm. from the limbus. Its tendon is 5.5 mm. long and about 10 mm. wide. It has practically the same muscle plane as the superior rectus. Accordingly, when the eye is in the primary position, contraction of the inferior rectus, like that of the superior rectus, results in a compound movement of the globe consisting of three components. These are depression, adduction, and turning outward of the 12 o'clock position on the limbus (extorsion). When the visual line is turned 23 degrees temporally from the primary position, contraction of the muscle produces depression of the globe alone. When the globe is turned 67 degrees nasally from the primary position, the contraction of the muscle produces adduction and extorsion alone.

Since the inferior rectus has the same muscle plane as the superior rectus, its effectiveness in the primary position is similar. In this position it is 92.1% effective as a depressor and 39% effective as an extorter of the globe.

Superior oblique. The superior oblique muscle arises from the small wing of the sphenoid above the annulus of Zinn and runs forward on the medial side of the eyeball to the trochlear fossa in the frontal bone. A plate of cartilage attached here forms a U-shaped pulley through which the tendon of the muscle passes. It then turns sharply backward over the globe to insert into the sclera just behind the equator. In its course it passes underneath the superior rectus. The superior oblique is supplied by the fourth cranial nerve. The trochlea must be considered to be its physiologic origin, and what is ordinarily the muscle plane in the other ocular muscles is now really the plane of the tendon of the superior oblique, running from the trochlea back to the globe. In its passage backward from the trochlea, the tendon forms an angle of 51 degrees with the visual line when the eye is in the primary position (Fig. 129). In the primary position contraction of the superior oblique produces a compound movement of the globe consisting of three components: depression, intorsion, and abduction. When the eye is turned 51 degrees nasally from the primary position, so that the visual line is parallel to the muscle pull, contraction of the muscle will produce depression of the globe alone. If the eye is turned temporally 39 degrees from the primary position so that the visual line is at right angles to the muscle pull, contraction will produce almost entirely intorsion.

Inferior oblique. The inferior oblique muscle arises from a shallow depression in the anterior floor of the orbit near the lacrimal fossa. It inserts on the globe by passing backward and temporally underneath the inferior rectus to a point just below the insertion of the lateral rectus. In doing so it passes close to the lateral rectus. Care must be taken not to pick up the inferior oblique on the muscle hook when isolating the lateral rectus muscle. The inferior oblique is supplied by a branch of the third cranial nerve. The muscle plane makes an angle of 51 degrees with the visual line when the eye is in the primary position, corresponding to the muscle plane of the superior oblique; hence, when the eye is in the primary position, contraction of the inferior oblique will produce a compound movement of the globe consisting of three components: elevation, extorsion, and ab-

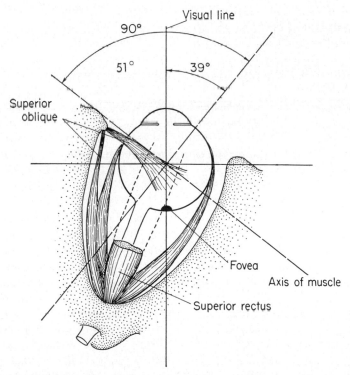

Fig. 129. Diagram showing the origin and insertion of the muscles from above, with the superior rectus cut away. The physiologic origin of the superior oblique is at the trochlea.

duction. When the eye is turned 39 degrees temporally from the primary position, the pull of the inferior oblique produces extorsion and some abduction alone, whereas when the eye is turned 51 degrees nasally from the primary position, the pull of the muscle produces elevation alone. In the primary position of gaze the effectiveness of the inferior oblique is 62.9% as an elevator and 77.7% as an extorter.

The anatomic relations of the inferior oblique to the other ocular muscles and to other structures of the globe are important from a surgical standpoint, particularly the relationship of the insertion of the inferior oblique to certain other structures in this locality, notably the site of the macula, the vortex vein, and the ciliary vessels and nerves. The vortex vein is usually 10 to 12 mm. below the posterior end of the attachment of the inferior oblique and immediately under the posterior border of the muscle. The nerve to the inferior oblique enters the muscle just lateral to the point where this muscle crosses the inferior rectus.

The superior and inferior oblique muscles are antagonistic, but they are quite dissimilar and unequal in power. The superior oblique is the longest of the ocular muscles. The muscular portion of the superior oblique from its origin in the orbit to the trochlea is 40 mm. long, and the tendon from the trochlea to its insertion on the globe is 20 mm. Hence the muscle and tendon together measure about 60 mm. The inferior oblique is the shortest muscle, measuring about 37 mm. from its origin at the anterior orbital margin to its insertion on the globe. The superior oblique has the longest tendon of all of the ocular muscles but no check ligament of any sizable dimensions, whereas the inferior oblique has no tendon, but has the longest and one of the best-developed check ligaments (the suspensory ligament of Lockwood). The superior oblique has a very variable insertion and the shortest arc of contact of any of the ocular muscles, whereas the inferior oblique has the longest arc of contact.

Agonist and antagonist muscles of each eye

When each eye is moved from the primary position to the secondary and tertiary positions of gaze, certain muscles act as agonists, i.e., they aid one another, whereas other muscles act as antagonists, i.e., each acts in the opposite direction. Therefore, if one of these muscles were not inhibited, they would check each other.

Agonists. The superior rectus and the inferior oblique are agonists in that they both elevate the globe. In the primary position of gaze the superior rectus is more effective as an elevator than is the inferior oblique, and, as the eye is abducted, the effectiveness of the superior rectus increases, whereas that of the inferior oblique falls off. When the eye is adducted, on the other hand, the effectiveness of the superior rectus as an elevator falls off and that of the inferior oblique increases.

The inferior rectus and the superior oblique are agonists in that they both depress the globe. In the primary position of gaze it was shown that the inferior rectus is more effective as a depressor than the superior oblique, and the effectiveness of the inferior rectus as a depressor increases as the eye is abducted, whereas that of the superior oblique falls off. When the eye is adducted, however, the inferior rectus loses its power to depress the globe, whereas that of the superior oblique increases.

The superior oblique and the superior rectus are agonists in that they both pro-

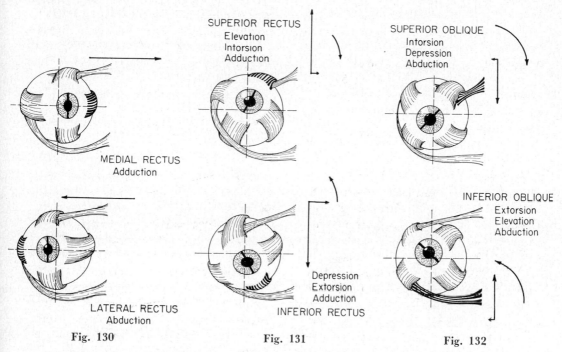

Fig. 130. Diagram illustrating the antagonistic action of the lateral and medial recti.
Fig. 131. Diagram illustrating the antagonistic action of the superior and inferior recti.
Fig. 132. Diagram illustrating the antagonistic action of the superior and inferior obliques.

duce intorsion in the primary position of gaze. The superior oblique is more effective than the superior rectus as an intorter in this position, however, and as the eye is abducted, the power of the superior oblique as an intorter increases, whereas that of the superior rectus falls off. As the eye is adducted, however, the power of the superior oblique as an intorter decreases, whereas that of the superior rectus increases.

The inferior oblique and inferior rectus are agonists in that they both produce extortion in the primary position of gaze. The inferior oblique is more effective than the inferior rectus as an extorter in this position, and its effectiveness increases as the eye is abducted, whereas that of the inferior rectus falls off. When the eye is adducted, however, the effectiveness of

the inferior oblique as an extorter diminishes, while that of the inferior rectus increases.

The lateral rectus and the superior and inferior obliques may be considered agonists in that they all produce some abduction of the globe in the primary position of gaze.* As the eye is abducted, the effectiveness of the obliques increases, and

---

*There are some authors, notably Krewson,[9] who consider the inferior oblique to be an adductor, but the evidence is largely from dissections, and it is very difficult to be sure that the small differences in muscle planes found in these specimens are not artifacts. The whole scheme of ocular rotations works out so perfectly on the assumption that the inferior oblique, like the superior oblique, is an abductor that I feel we should consider it as such until proved one way or the other by physiologic experimentation.

that of the lateral rectus diminishes (p. 367). Similarly, in adduction the effectiveness of the obliques diminishes, while that of the lateral rectus increases.

The medial rectus and the superior and inferior recti may be considered agonists in that they all aid in adduction in the primary position of gaze. The effectiveness of the superior and inferior recti diminishes in abduction, whereas that of the medial rectus increases. Similarly, in adduction the effectiveness of the superior and inferior recti increases, while that of the medial rectus diminishes.

Antagonists. In a similar fashion one may group the various muscles of each eye which act against other muscles or, rather, which would act against other muscles in the same eye if they were not inhibited (Sherrington's law, p. 414). Thus, the medial rectus is the direct antagonist of the lateral rectus, the superior rectus of the inferior rectus, and the superior oblique of the inferior oblique.

The activity of each of the ocular muscles is depicted diagrammatically in Figs. 130 to 132. The eyeball is considered to be in the primary position in all the figures, and in each, one or three arrows are drawn to depict the movements of force each muscle applies to the globe when it contracts with the visual line in the primary position. The direction of the arrow, i.e., right, left, up, down, or curved to depict intorsion or extorsion, gives the direction of the movement. The length of the arrow gives a rough idea of the comparative effectiveness of each of the various components.

MUSCLES CONCERNED IN DUCTIONS

In every movement of the eyes more than one muscle of each eye may aid in rotating the globe in the desired direction. In horizontal movements, i.e., abduction and adduction, five of the six muscles maintain the normal tonus shown in the primary position (p. 374) or actively contract. In elevation and depression of the globe four muscles are active, whereas in oblique movements only three muscles are active. The other muscles show diminution in tonus on the basis of Sherrington's law of reciprocal innervation. At the beginning of a movement, one muscle, which is the chief mover because its position on the globe in respect to the line of sight gives it a mechanical advantage, starts to contract. Other muscles maintain the tonus they had in the primary position of gaze and together aid somewhat in the movement, but since they are not in such a favored mechanical position to bring about the desired movement, their effectiveness is considerably less. However, their chief purpose is to prevent the globe from going out of its course while moving in the desired direction. As the globe moves further in the field of action of the prime mover, this muscle begins to lose its mechanical advantage since its arc of contact becomes shorter, and it now begins to feel the pull of its antagonist which, although relaxed according to Sherrington's law, is becoming stretched around the globe. The other muscles which maintained their normal postural tonus, on the other hand, are now being placed in a position in which they are mechanically more effective in moving the globe, and their aid in the movement becomes more important.

In the monkey Chamberlain[10] found that, when either of the primary rotators was cut from the globe, in no instance was the animal able to abduct or adduct the globe beyond the midline into the field of action of the operated muscle. This indicates that the secondary rotators are not sufficiently innervated in the approximately straight ahead position to produce significant horizontal rotation as long as the opposing primary rotator is intact. If both primary rotators were eliminated, the globe could be rotated through a small amplitude in either direction, although adduction was better than abduction in the operated eye.

If the vertically acting muscles were cut, the primary rotators showed no deficiency in their function within the limits studied. All of these studies would lead one to the conclusion that the so-called secondary adductors and abductors are of minor importance in horizontal rotations as long as the primary rotators are intact. It cannot be denied, however, that the vertical recti are adductors and that the obliques are abductors, for, if the vertical recti are the only muscles left on the globe, Chamberlain found that there is good adduction. If the obliques are the only muscles remaining, there is good abduction.

Abduction. When the eye starts its movement outward from the primary position, the lateral rectus receives a stimulus to contract while the medial rectus is simultaneously inhibited. All of the other muscles maintain their normal postural tonus shown in the primary position throughout the movement. The superior and inferior recti, pulling against one another by this tonus, keep the globe from wobbling up and down as it moves temporally. The torsional actions of these muscles counterbalance each other so that the vertical meridian is held in a vertical position. Both muscles combine to adduct the eye and hence oppose the outward movement to a moderate degree. The superior and inferior obliques keep the vertical meridian of the cornea vertical, preventing wheel rotation throughout the movement since the superior oblique is an intorter and the inferior oblique is an extorter. The globe is also kept from

wobbling up and down since one muscle is an elevator and the other a depressor. Thus, they also act to steady the eye in its course and prevent it from swerving up and down or tilting to right or left. At the same time both these muscles abduct the eye and hence neutralize the adducting action of the superior and inferior recti.

At the beginning of the movement from the primary position their abducting action is small. The net result is that at the beginning of the movement the eye is abducted strongly by the lateral rectus, which at this time is acting at a considerable mechanical advantage, since the muscle then has the longest arc of contact on the globe (Fig. 133). It is simply steadied in its action by the combined tonus of the other four muscles. As the movement progresses, the lateral rectus

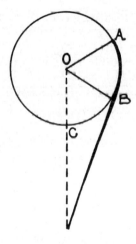

Fig. 133. **A** represents the insertion of the lateral rectus muscle. When the globe is in the primary position, **AB** represents the arc of contact of the tendon. On abduction, the globe rotates around **O**, and **A** moves to **B** where it is now tangent to the globe. Further abduction is possible until eventually **B** moves to **C** which is in direct line between **O** and the origin of the muscle. Further contraction of the muscle would cause the globe to be pulled back into the orbit.

acts at a greater mechanical disadvantage and is now opposed by the increasing passive pull of the lengthening and therefore tightening medial rectus. If these two muscles were acting alone, the outward movement would be slowed up and impeded, but as the power of the lateral rectus diminishes, the abducting action of the obliques becomes more effective since their action as abductors increases as the eye is turned out. Further, the counteracting adduction of the superior and inferior rectus muscles falls off altogether. When the eyeball has turned 23 degrees temporally from the primary position, their adducting action is zero, and when they have turned out beyond this, they probably become abductors. As the eye turns temporally, the job of keeping the eye from wobbling up and down is turned over more and more to the superior and inferior recti, whereas the job of keeping the vertical meridian vertical is turned over to the superior and inferior oblique muscles.

The return of the eye from the abducted position to the midline shows a similar compensating action on the part of the five muscles, while one muscle undergoes inhibition of its tonic activity. At the outset of the return movement the relaxation of the strongly contracted lateral rectus by itself produces a marked effect due to the tension exerted by the stretched medial rectus acting as an elastic cord. Even without this effect the eye would return to the midline by relaxation of the lateral rectus alone, as Sherrington showed in his beautiful experiment demonstrating reciprocal innervation (p. 414). The medial rectus produces an especially marked effect in this position of the globe because the muscle is tense, and its arc of contact on the eyeball is now large. These factors, acting with most efficiency at the outset of the movement, grow less operative as the eye approaches the midline.

Adduction. All of the ocular muscles except the lateral rectus maintain their normal tonus, which diminishes. The medial rectus starts to contract and moves the eye inward strongly since it is acting at a considerable mechanical advantage. Excessive and jerky movement is prevented by the counteracting tonus of the abductors—the superior and inferior obliques. The tonus of the superior and inferior recti aids in adduction and somewhat balances the abducting action of the obliques. They also keep the eye from swerving up or down and by their combined and opposing torsional action keep the vertical meridian of the cornea vertical. The opposing torsional activity of the superior and inferior obliques likewise aids in keeping the corneal meridian vertical. When the eye is well adducted, the medial rectus begins to act at a mechanical disadvantage and is opposed by the passive pull of the stretching lateral rectus. By this time the abducting power of the obliques has become nil, and the adducting effect is steadily reinforced by the increasing effectiveness of the superior and inferior recti. In the adducted position the eye is kept from swerving up and down by the obliques alone, and its vertical meridian is kept vertical by the superior and inferior recti almost entirely.

Based on the length of the arc of contact of the medial rectus muscle, Gordon[11] estimates that the medial rectus alone can produce only 35 degrees of adduction. Internal rotation beyond 35 degrees must be provided by other muscles, and he assumes that this comes from the joint action of the superior and inferior recti cocontracting. The proof of this activity, however, is lacking since electromyographic studies fail to reveal any greater electrical activity in the superior or inferior recti when the eye is adducted than they show in the primary position of gaze.

Elevation. When the eye is moved straight up, the superior oblique and the inferior rectus are inhibited, whereas the other four muscles maintain their normal tonus or contract. The superior rectus and the inferior oblique elevate the eye, the former predominating when the movement starts from the primary position. The abducting and adducting actions of these muscles oppose each other and keep the eye steady in its upward course. The same is true of the lateral and medial recti. The vertical meridian is kept vertical by the counteracting torsional activity of the superior rectus and the inferior oblique. If both of these muscles contracted an equal amount, the globe would be slightly extorted in its final upward position due to the fact that the inferior oblique produces more extorsion than the superior rectus produces intorsion when the eye moves upward in the midline.

We have seen that the vertical meridian of the cornea is not only vertical in the primary position of gaze, but also it stays vertical on upward and downward as well as horizontal gaze. On purely theoretical grounds the vertical meridian of the cornea should be extorted in the primary position of gaze and increasingly so as the eye moves upward if the superior rectus and inferior oblique receive an equal innervation, for the inferior oblique produces more extorsion per unit of muscle pull than the superior rectus produces intorsion.

I have suggested that the superior rectus receives a greater innervation than the inferior oblique by just the right amount to neutralize the extorsion. Alpern[12] has criticized this suggestion on the grounds that if the right superior rectus is more strongly innervated than

the right inferior oblique one should expect an equally increased innervation to the yoke muscle of the superior rectus, the left inferior oblique, on the basis of Hering's law (p. 384). This, of course, would result in no torsion of the right eye but marked extorsion of the left. I do not believe this argument is necessarily valid. Hering's law states that equal and simultaneous innervations are sent to the muscles of both eyes performing a voluntary movement. It is quite conceivable that if the pattern of innervation is set so that the right superior rectus receives greater innervation than the right inferior oblique in the primary position the same is true of the left eye; i.e., the left superior rectus receives greater innervation than the left inferior oblique. There is no reason to assume that a yoke muscle normally receives the same innervation as its agonist, nor does Hering's law state this. At the present time, however, I have to admit that there is no experimental evidence for this explanation of why torsion does not occur in upward and downward gaze from the primary position, and other as yet unproved suggestions are equally plausible, such as unequal innervation of different segments of the same muscle with change in the pattern of this innervation in different directions of gaze.

Depression. All of the ocular muscles are innervated at the start of the movement except the superior rectus and the inferior oblique. These are inhibited. The eye is carried downward by the inferior rectus chiefly, with the superior oblique adding a lesser share. The abducting and adducting actions of these muscles counteract each other, as do the abducting and adducting actions of the lateral and medial recti, so that the eye is kept from swerving to the right or left as it moves down. The torsional action of the inferior rectus and superior oblique nullify each other, and the vertical meridian therefore remains erect. The inferior rectus probably receives more innervation than the superior oblique during the movement; otherwise, intorsion would result due to the fact that the superior oblique in the primary position is a better intorter than the inferior rectus is an extorter.

Oblique movements.

Up and laterally. When the eyes move up and out, the medial rectus, the inferior rectus, and the superior oblique are relaxed, while the remaining three muscles contract. The eye is carried temporally by the lateral rectus, this movement being opposed at first by the superior rectus, but is reinforced by the inferior oblique. As the eye goes farther out and the opposing action of the superior rectus diminishes, the reinforcing action of the inferior oblique increases so that the outward movement is hindered only by the passive pull of the stretching medial rectus. At the beginning of the movement the eye is carried up by both the superior rectus and the inferior oblique, but soon the latter ceases to act as an elevator, and the superior rectus alone lifts the eye. The vertical meridian, which at first was vertical, now becomes tilted outward due to the increasing torsional action of the inferior oblique (an extorter). This is no longer opposed by the superior rectus (an intorter) which in the abducted position of the globe becomes solely an elevator. It will be recalled that no true torsion was found by most investigators until the eye is carried beyond the usual fields of gaze in looking temporally up or down. The suggestion I have made to explain the absence of true torsion in looking straight up or down (p. 375) may also apply here. In looking up and temporally the innervation of the superior rectus may remain greater than that of the inferior oblique and so balance out the extorsional effect

of the inferior oblique in the normal field of gaze. Beyond this point the effort to turn the eye farther upward and outward may change the innervational pattern to greater pull of the inferior oblique and thus produce the true extorsion which has been found. The *change in pattern* would be reflected in the opposite eye, and now in accordance with Hering's law, in that the increase in innervation of the right inferior oblique would flow to the yoke muscle, the left superior rectus. This would produce true intorsion of the left eye looking up and nasally. While this has not been found experimentally, it may be because of the limitation of the field of gaze due to the facial contours.

Up and nasally. The lateral rectus, the inferior rectus, and the superior oblique are relaxed, while the remaining muscles contract. The eye is carried inward by the medial rectus. This movement is opposed by the inferior oblique and is reinforced by the superior rectus. As the eye is adducted, the reinforcing action of the superior rectus increases, and the opposing abducting action of the inferior oblique decreases so that the inward movement is opposed only by the passive pull of the lengthening lateral rectus.

The eye is carried up at first by the superior rectus and the inferior oblique acting together, the action of the former predominating. Later the upward movement results from the inferior oblique alone, for in this position the superior rectus loses its effect as an elevator. In the final position the upper end of the vertical meridian is tilted in, i.e., intorsion, due to the increasing torsional action of the superior rectus (an intorter) which predominates more and more over the decreasing torsional action of the inferior oblique (an extorter).

Down and temporally. The medial rectus, the superior rectus, and the inferior oblique are relaxed, while the other three muscles contract. The eye is carried out by the lateral rectus, assisted more and more by the superior oblique and counteracted to a decreasing extent by the inferior rectus. It is moved down at first by the inferior rectus and superior oblique and later by the inferior rectus alone. The upper end of its vertical meridian is tilted in, i.e., intorsion, by the increasingly predominant torsional action of the superior oblique.

Down and nasally. The lateral rectus, the superior rectus, and the inferior oblique are relaxed. The eye is carried inward by the medial rectus, assisted more and more by the inferior rectus and counteracted to a decreasing extent by the superior oblique. The eye is carried downward at first by both the inferior rectus and the superior oblique and later by the superior oblique alone. The upper end of the vertical meridian is tilted outward by the increasingly predominant torsional action of the inferior rectus.

From a purely mechanical point of view it is possible to predict the action of each of the ocular muscles, with reference to the three axes of rotation, for

the primary position and for any secondary or tertiary position of gaze (Figs. 134 to 139). Using a method of vector analysis, Krewson[8] has made such a study, assuming a fixed center of rotation at the anatomic or geometric center of the globe and using Volkmann's anatomic data of the origins and insertions of the muscles. These calculations give one an excellent idea of how each muscle pulls and how each expends its energy in rotating the globe around these axes when the eye is in a specified position. In general the conclusions arrived at are in agreement with physiologic data already given, with the exception of that for the inferior oblique which considers this muscle to have a component of adduction when the eye is in the adducted position (from 6 degrees outward to 60 degrees inward). It has been pointed out that this concept needs confirmation by physiologic experiment before it can be accepted.

A further mathematical analysis of the cooperative action of the extraocular muscles for several types of rotations has been made by Boeder. His conclusions differ with the views just expressed. This is particularly true of the muscles which effect

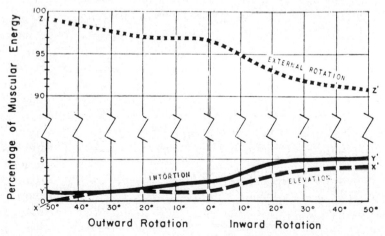

Fig. 134. Action of the lateral rectus muscle. (From Krewson, W.: Tr. Am. Ophth. Soc. 48:443, 1950.)

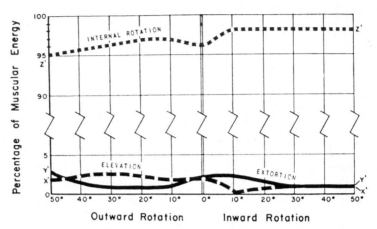

Fig. 135. Action of the medial rectus muscle. (From Krewson, W.: Tr. Am. Ophth. Soc. 48:443, 1950.)

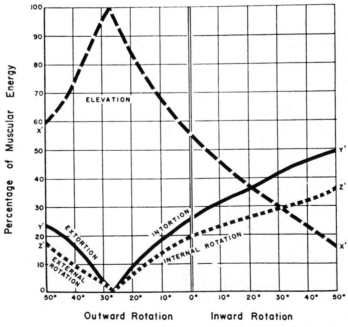

Fig. 136. Action of the superior rectus muscle. (From Krewson, W.: Tr. Am. Ophth. Soc. 48:443, 1950.)

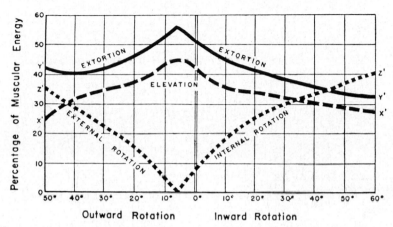

Fig. 137. Action of the inferior oblique muscle. (From Krewson, W.: Tr. Am. Ophth. Soc. **48**:443, 1950.)

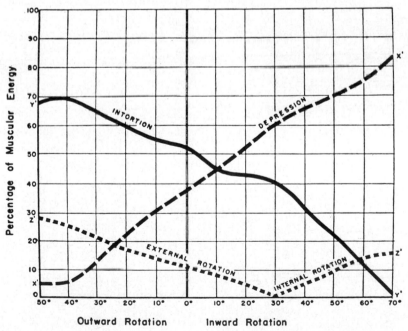

Fig. 138. Action of the superior oblique muscle. (From Krewson, W.: Tr. Am. Ophth. Soc. **48**:443, 1950.)

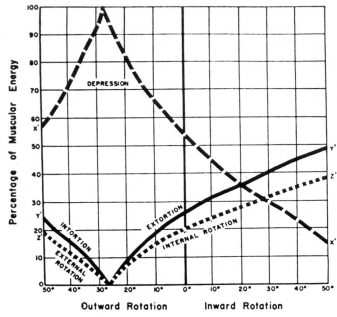

Fig. 139. Action of the inferior rectus muscle. (From Krewson, W.: Tr. Am. Ophth. Soc. 48:443, 1950.)

elevation and depression. According to him the superior rectus contributes more to elevation than does the inferior oblique, even when the eye is in the adducted position. Likewise the inferior rectus contributes more to depression than does the superior oblique, even though the eye is adducted. These conclusions are drawn from mathematical analyses of the anatomic measurements given by Volkmann with certain assumptions whose validity has not been proved. We must admit that at present we can only infer the action of the muscles involved in turning the eyes in any direction of gaze since the experimental proof is inadequate, but what evidence we do have, such as electromyography, does not support Boeder's concepts.[13, 14]

It must be admitted that the action of each of the ocular muscles discussed in this section is based on the assumption of a fixed center of rotation of the globe through which run Fick's axes. Recently Jampel and Bloomgarden[15] have reported the results of animal experimental studies which are quite at variance with our present ideas. They stimulated the oculomotor nerves intracranially in monkeys and observed the movements of the globe after detaching all muscles other than the one being investigated. The results of their studies are shown in Table 43. It can be seen that the superior oblique rotates the globe around an axis whose pole is located at the lateral limbus in order to produce intorsion, and the inferior rectus rotates the globe around an axis whose pole is located at the medial limbus in order to produce extorsion. These axes do not correspond to the anteroposterior axis or Y axis of Fick. Their most surprising finding is the fact that the position of the eye in the horizontal plane has little or no influence on the vector components of the vertical and oblique muscles. In other words, the three components of action of the superior oblique—intorsion, depression, and abduction—were not significantly changed by passively moving the eye into different positions in the horizontal plane. This is so contrary to clinical experience that it cannot be accepted as applying to man until further experimental proof is forthcoming. The characteristic increase in vertical separation of the double images in adduction of the eye with a superior oblique paralysis is diagnostic and is too well established to be denied on this evidence. Further, the finding of these authors that the action

of the inferior rectus changes with the strength of the applied stimulus suggests that different segments of the muscle contract to strong and to weak stimuli. They found that with high voltages the globe was moved straight down in the midline, adducted, and abducted positions, whereas with low voltages extorsion of the globe was produced around an axis pole located on the horizontal corneal meridian at the medial corneal limbus. These components were not influenced by moving the globe passively into different positions in the horizontal plane.

It is not possible at the present time to

Table 43. *Actions of the individual eye muscles of the macaque**

	Superior oblique	Inferior rectus†	Inferior oblique	Superior rectus
Midline position	Intorsion of globe around an axis whose pole is located on horizontal corneal meridian at lateral corneal limbus. Intorsion 25 degrees, depression 16 degrees, abduction 3.5 degrees	Extorsion of globe around an axis whose pole is located on horizontal corneal meridian at medial corneal limbus. Extorsion 22 degrees, depression 16 degrees, adduction 3.5 degrees	Elevation, about 18 degrees	Elevation, about 18 degrees
Adduction about 25 degrees	Intorsion of globe around an axis whose pole is located on horizontal corneal meridian at lateral corneal limbus. Intorsion 25 degrees, depression 16 degrees, abduction 3.5 degrees	Extorsion of globe around an axis whose pole is located on horizontal corneal meridian at medial corneal limbus. Extorsion 22 degrees, depression 16 degrees, adduction 3.5 degrees	Globe moves to midline position before elevating 18 degrees	Elevation, about 18 degrees
Abduction about 25 degrees	Intorsion of globe around an axis whose pole is located on horizontal corneal meridian at lateral corneal limbus. Intorsion 25 degrees, depression 16 degrees, abduction 3.5 degrees	Globe moves to midline position while extorting, etc.	Elevation, about 18 degrees	Elevation, about 18 degrees

*From Jampel, R., and Bloomgarden, C.: Invest. Ophthal. 2:265, 1963.
†The inferior rectus may also act only as a depressor (see text).

explain these radical departures from our contemporary concepts of ocular motility, but if these results are confirmed and are not found to be due to the experimental methods employed, our entire concept of ocular muscle paralysis, i.e., the characteristic angle of strabismus and the characteristic diplopia fields, will have to be revamped.

Tour and Asbury[16] point out the fact that the maximum rotatory effect of any muscle (torque) is developed when the direction of its action lies along the tangent to its point of contact—in other words, when it acts perpendicularly to a radius drawn to the point of contact. If the direction of the force is changed so that it is no longer tangential, there is a corresponding decrease in the amount of torque (Fig. 140, *A* to *D*). The degree

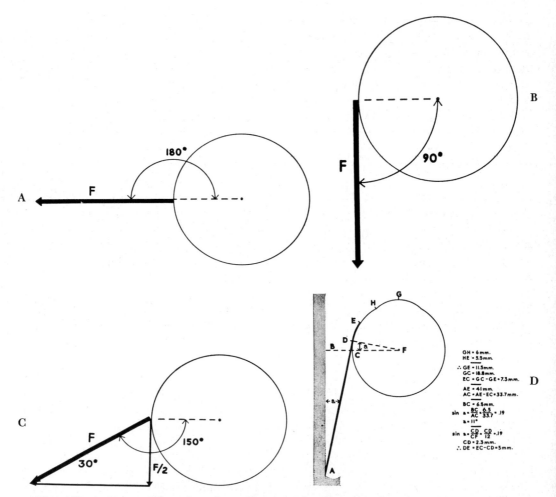

Fig. 140. **A,** Force (*F*) acting along direction of radius to point of contact; no torque. **B,** Force (*F*) acting tangentially at point of contact; maximum torque. **C,** Force (*F*) acting at 30 degrees to direction of radius to point of contact. Resultant torque component is *F/2*. **D,** Scale diagram of relationship of medial rectus to glove. Point of tangential contact (maximum torque) is 2.3 mm. anterior to the equator. Contact arc is 5 mm. (From Tour, R., and Asbury, T.: Tr. Pacific Coast Oto-Ophth. Soc. 145: 1957.)

to which this occurs can be demonstrated by means of vector analysis, the total force being represented as the resultant of two components. One of these components acts tangentially and produces maximum torque; the other acts perpendicularly along the radius to the point of contact and produces no torque. The actual length of the three vectors represents the resultant force of each component, and their respective magnitudes can be computed from elementary trigonometric laws. Because of the wraparound structure of the extraocular muscles with respect to the globe, which results in the placement of their insertions somewhat anteriorly to their point of tangential contact, a relatively small change in the position of the eye following rotation enables the muscles, nevertheless, to act with little or no alteration in their orientation with respect to its center of rotation. However, should their insertions rotate posteriorly to the tangential point of contact, the direction of the applied force begins to change. The muscles no longer act with maximum torque, and they begin to lose mechanical advantage at a progressively rapid rate. The point of contact of the lateral rectus lies somewhat behind the equator. It is perfectly safe, therefore, to recess the lateral rectus to the equator. However, it can be shown that the direction of action of the medial rectus is not parallel to the anteroposterior axis of the eye. Its tangential point of contact, therefore, seems to lie anterior to the equator by almost 2 mm. Consequently its contact arc averages only about 5 mm. instead of 7 mm., as is usually assumed, so that the safely allowable amount of recession that may be accomplished is considerably less than that usually attempted. Therefore, recession of more than 5 mm. does not allow the muscle to act at peak efficiency in adduction, and as we have seen, its efficiency

diminishes at an increasingly rapid rate as greater degrees of inward rotation are attempted. These facts point to the conclusion that the medial rectus muscle should never be recessed more than 4 mm. in order to prevent the development of postoperative exotropia or weakened convergence. It is safer to do small bilateral recessions on the medial recti rather than a large amount on one medial rectus.

BINOCULAR MOVEMENTS

The movements of each single eye from the primary position into the secondary and tertiary positions of gaze are spoken of as ductions. When we speak of the movements of the two eyes together, the term *versions* is used if the movement of the two eyes is in the same direction and the term *vergences* if the movement of the two eyes is in opposite directions. Versions are conjunctive movements, whereas vergences are disjunctive movements.

Versions. The following terms are applied when the two eyes move from the primary position to a secondary position of gaze:

1. Looking to the right: dextroversion
2. Looking to the left: levoversion
3. Looking up: sursumversion
4. Looking down: deosursumversion

When one speaks of movement of the eyes from the primary position into a tertiary position of gaze, combinations of these terms, such as dextrosursumversion (movement of both eyes up and to the right), etc., may be employed. However, these are such cumbersome terms that usually the phrases "up and to the right," "down and to the left," etc., are substituted.

When the two eyes move together not only are some muscles in the same eye working together as agonists and against each other as antagonists, but also certain muscles in the right and left eyes act together in the same fashion. The muscle or muscles which act together in opposite eyes are called yoke muscles. Each muscle in the right eye has a particular yoke muscle in the left eye which works best with it in its field of activity. Since every muscle has a yoke muscle in the opposite eye, there are six pairs, as follows (Table 44).

Table 44. *Yoke muscles of the eyes*

Right eye	Left eye
Medial rectus	Lateral rectus
Lateral rectus	Medial rectus
Superior rectus	Inferior oblique
Inferior rectus	Superior oblique
Superior oblique	Inferior rectus
Inferior oblique	Superior rectus

It should be kept in mind that the list of muscles and their yoke muscles just given indicates only the chief muscle concerned in the desired movement, together with its chief yoke muscle. It has been pointed out previously that in abduction, e.g., the lateral rectus and the superior and inferior oblique in the same eye are agonists, i.e., the lateral rectus together with the two obliques of the right eye produce abduction. The yoke muscles in the left eye which simultaneously produce adduction are the left medial rectus and the superior and inferior recti. In considering the movement of dextroversion, we find that many more muscles are concerned in the movement than merely the right lateral rectus and the left medial rectus, and the same is true for movements of the eyes in all directions of gaze.

Hering's law. In all voluntary movements of the eyes equal and simultaneous innervation flows from the oculogyric centers to the muscles of both eyes concerned in the desired direction of gaze. This is known as Hering's law. It is important to remember that the innervation to both eyes is equal; i.e., under normal conditions the amount of nervous energy required to turn the right eye to the right is sent to the appropriate muscles which turn the left eye to the right. The law does not state that each muscle in the two eyes receives the same amount of innervation. It is possible that to turn the right eye to the right requires that greater innervation be sent to the right lateral rectus than is sent to the left medial rectus because the medial rectus is a larger muscle. Again, more innervation may have to be sent to one muscle than its yoke muscle because of differences in their fascial connections. However, the law does imply that under normal conditions that amount of nervous energy is sent to the muscles of the two eyes which causes the eyes to turn equally in that direction. Further, any abnormal condition in one eye which necessitates greater or lesser than normal innervation in order to turn that eye in one direction will be reflected in a correspondingly greater or lesser innervation sent to the muscles of the fellow eye performing the same function. The application of Hering's law and its effect on movements of the eyes in paralysis of the ocular muscles will be considered in a later section.

Under normal conditions both eyes are fixated on the object of regard in all positions of gaze. If, however, the visual axes are not in alignment, one eye becomes the fixating eye. Under these conditions the amount of innervation sent from the oculogyric centers to the muscles of both eyes concerned in the gaze movement is determined by the muscles of the fixating eye. If these muscles are normal, the innervation sent to both eyes will be normal. If, on the other hand, a muscle in the fixating eye concerned in the gaze movement is weak, excessive innervation will have to be sent to this muscle in order to carry out the desired movement completely. According to Hering's law this excessive innervation will be sent to the yoke muscle of the opposite eye, and this eye will turn too far in the direction of action of this muscle.

If a muscle in the fixating eye is enabled to move the globe in the desired direction with less than a normal amount of contraction of its fibers because, e.g., it is unopposed by the normal tonus of its antagonist (the antagonist muscle being paralyzed), it will receive subnormal innervation. Likewise, a subnormal innervation will be sent to its yoke muscle in the opposite eye.

Proof of the validity of Hering's law has been obtained electromyographically by Breinin (p. 429). In ocular muscle paralysis, if Hering's law is active, it follows that, when the eye with the paralyzed muscle is used for fixation, the angle of strabismus will be greater than when the nonparalyzed eye is used, for when the eye with the paralyzed muscle fixates, excessive innervation is required by the weak muscle to pull the eye in its field of activity. This excessive innervation will go simultaneously to the yoke muscle of the paralyzed muscle, and as a result the eye containing this yoke muscle will be rotated excessively by it. If, e.g., the right superior rectus is paralyzed, the angle of squint will be greater in looking up and to the right (and for that matter even in the primary position) when the right eye is used for fixation than when the left eye is used. When the right eye is fixating, excessive innervation will have to be sent to the right superior rectus in order to rotate the eye up and to the right. According to Hering's law, this excessive innervation will be sent also to the yoke muscle of the right superior rectus, i.e., the left inferior oblique, and this muscle will pull the left eye excessively in its field of action, i.e., up and to the right. When the left eye is used for fixation up and to the right, the left inferior oblique, being normal, will receive normal innervation which will be sent to its yoke muscle, the right superior rectus. This muscle, being weak, will not pull the eye up as far as it should, and the angle of strabismus will depend on how weak the muscle is. When the right eye fixates, the angle of strabismus is compounded of both the amount of deviation due to the weakness of the right superior rectus plus the overaction of its yoke muscle, the left superior oblique. This is the physiologic basis for the law that in patients with paralysis of a muscle the angle of strabismus is greater when the eye with the paralyzed muscle fixates than when the nonparalyzed eye is used to fixate. The law, as generally stated, is as follows: "Secondary deviation (deviation with paralyzed eye fixating) is greater than primary deviation (deviation with nonparalyzed eye fixating) in cases of strabismus due to a paralyzed muscle."

In Fig. 170 (p. 429) is shown the electrical activity in the left inferior oblique muscle in a patient with paralysis of the right superior rectus, as recorded by Breinin. In the upper tracing the first part of the tracing was taken when the nonparalyzed eye was used for fixation. The second part of the tracing shows the activity in the muscle when the right eye (paralyzed) was fixating. These tracings are excellent representations of the increase in innervation sent to the left eye when the right eye with a paralyzed muscle is the fixating eye.

Vergences. When the movement of the two eyes is in opposite directions, the term vergence is applied to the movement. Convergence is a movement of the eyes toward one another, whereas divergence is a movement of the eyes away from one another. Vertical divergence is a term used for a rare condition in which the eyes move vertically in opposite directions. Convergence and divergence will be considered in more detail later (convergence, p. 480; divergence, p. 487).

Comparison of versions and vergences. Although the same muscles may be concerned in carrying out a version movement at one time and a vergence movement at another, e.g., the right medial rectus producing levoversion (adduction

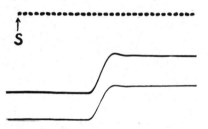

Fig. 141. Typical record of a 20-degree saccadic eye movement. Stimulus presented at S. Time line interrupted every 10 msec. (From Westheimer, F.: Arch. Ophth. **52**:722, 1954.)

of the right eye) and convergence, the neuromuscular mechanism underlying these movements must be quite separate. The characteristics of the two movements are different, and under pathologic conditions one may be lost or impaired while the other remains intact. For example, in internuclear paralysis, the right eye may fail to follow the left on levoversion, which would suggest paralysis of the right medial rectus, but when the patient is asked to converge, both eyes readily take up fixation on a near object. This proves that the right medial rectus muscle is not paralyzed, but that there is an interruption of the impulses to it traveling down the pathways for levoversion so that the impulses never reach this muscle. The impulses for convergence, on the other hand, are not blocked and arrive at both medial recti. The lesion which causes this characteristic syndrome must lie in the medial longitudinal fasciculus between the nuclei of the third and sixth cranial nerves.

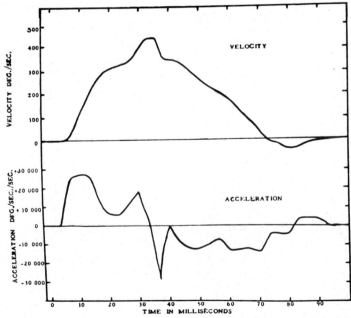

Fig. 142. *Upper tracing,* changes in velocity in saccadic movements of the eye. *Lower tracing,* data calculated as acceleration. (From Westheimer, F.: Arch. Ophth. **52**:722, 1954.)

The condition is called internuclear paralysis.

Versions are very rapid saccadic movements with a velocity up to 400 degrees per second. This is the type of movement which occurs between fixational pauses during reading (p. 510) and in the fast phase of both vestibular and optokinetic nystagmus. It has its basis in the fact that the ocular muscles contract very rapidly and have a very short reaction time (Figs. 141 and 142). Westheimer[17] suggests that saccadic movements represent an instantaneous changeover from one pattern of innervation to another as the eye changes its position, the change in pattern being regulated by a feedback mechanism from the muscle and fascia as tension is built up by the movement.

Vergences, on the other hand, are quite slow—8 to 25 degrees per second. Alpern and Wolter[18] suggest that the difference between these two types of movements may be due to the fact that the final common pathways for saccadic movements are formed by thick somatic nerve fibers, whereas the final common pathways for vergence movements are formed by thin autonomic nerve fibers. While admittedly several different types of nerve fibers are present in the ocular muscles, further proof will have to be forthcoming before this can be accepted as the correct explanation. In favor of this hypothesis are several facts, chief of which is the similarity between the slow movements of convergence and the slow movements of the autonomically innervated intraocular muscles, i.e., the iris and ciliary body. Further, it has been shown that both a saccadic and a vergence movement can occur during a single change in fixation.

Binocular torsions. When torsional movements of the two eyes together occur, the term *cycloversion* is used when the 12 o'clock position on the limbus of each eye moves in the same direction. If both corneal vertical meridians tilt to the right, i.e., the right eye showing extorsion and the left eye intorsion, the eyes are said to have undergone dextrocycloversion. If, however, the right eye and also the left eye undergo intorsion, the eyes are said to have undergone incyclovergence. If both corneal meridians tilt out away from each other, i.e., extort, the condition is called excyclovergence.

In the normal movements of the eyes dextrocycloversion occurs when the eyes are directed up and to the right and down and to the left. Levocycloversion occurs when the eyes are directed up and to the left and down and to the right.

I have already discussed the still unsettled problem of whether the cycloversion in the tertiary positions of gaze is false torsion or a true rotation of the eyes around their anteroposterior axes. It really matters very little whether true torsion occurs or not as long as the tilting of the vertical meridians of the two eyes is in the some direction and to the same degree, so that they remain parallel. The fact that they do remain parallel in normal eyes is important for the preservation of normal binocular vision.

During convergence it is said that the vertical meridians of both eyes extort, i.e., excyclovergence, but this needs confirmation. On purely theoretical grounds if convergence is brought about by contraction of both medial recti and both superior obliques, one would anticipate slight incyclovergence in the convergent position since in this position the superior obliques would still intort each eye slightly.

CHARACTERISTICS OF MUSCLES

The ocular muscles are generally considered to be voluntary muscles, but they have many anatomic and physiologic peculiarities which distinguish them from the rest of the voluntary musculature of the body. In some respects they more nearly resemble smooth muscle in their anatomy and physiology.

Anatomy and physiology of muscle in general

The muscles of the mammalian body may be divided into three groups, based on histologic appearances and physiologic behavior. These groups or types are striated, unstriated, and cardiac muscles.

Striated muscle. All of the skeletal and voluntary muscles of the body are made up of striated fibers, so-called because of the transverse striations visible under the microscope. These muscles are connected directly with the central nervous system and effect voluntary movements of the body. Not all skeletal muscles are alike. They have been divided into two types, red and white, depending upon their relative proportion of red or white fibers. The red fibers contain protein called myoglobin. This substance is chemically related to hemoglobin but has a molecular weight about four times as great, i.e., 68,000. Each molecule of myoglobin can unite with one molecule of oxygen. This combination, therefore, acts as a temporary storehouse of oxygen within the muscle cell. The contraction of red skeletal muscle is relatively sluggish and prolonged when compared with the rapidly contracting white muscle which contains no red fibers.

In the absence of external stimulation or voluntary impulses from the appropriate motor centers, the skeletal muscles are in a resting state. When innervated, they contract rapidly, and the movement is characterized by high speed. Unstriated muscle shows some electrical activity in the resting state and under the influence of certain drugs, such as the cholines and epinephrine, whereas striated muscle only shows such activity after its connections

with the central nervous system have been severed and the nerve fibers have degenerated.

Unstriated muscle. Unstriated muscle is known also as smooth, plain, or involuntary muscle since the fibers show no striations under the microscope, but these muscles do contain some myofibrils. The fibers have long spindle-shaped bodies with a single nucleus in the middle of each cell. They are controlled by the autonomic nervous system, the two components of which, i.e., the sympathetic and parasympathetic systems, form a dual and antagonistic innervation. One system generally brings about muscular contraction, whereas the other system produces muscular relaxation. Unstriated muscle generally shows some degree of spontaneous activity or at least appears to do so in the absence of any external stimulation. This activity is known as tonus and results in permanent partial contraction of the muscle.

The tonus of unstriated muscle may be varied by nervous and chemical controls. The fluctuations in tonus result in frequent periodic changes in length of this type of muscle so that it appears to undergo spontaneous contraction, as just mentioned. The contractions of unstriated muscle are characteristically very slow. Whereas stretching produces an immediate contraction of both striated and unstriated muscle in the living animal, a profound difference in the mechanism of this response is disclosed by comparing the effects of stretching isolated striated and unstriated muscle. Striated muscle contracts when it is stretched, but its response is dependent upon a nervous mechanism which involves nerves passing to and from the central nervous system. Unstriated muscle, on the contrary, responds to stretching with an immediate contraction, even when it is isolated from the central nervous system. The excitability of unstriated muscle varies markedly according to the nature of the stimulus. Most agents which excite skeletal muscle also excite smooth muscle, but the latter is much less sensitive to electrical stimulation and much more sensitive to chemical stimulation.

Cardiac muscle. In many respects, cardiac muscle seems to be intermediate between the two preceding varieties. Its fibers are striated, but they form a network with interlacing crossbars connecting one cell with another, leaving narrow slits between them. The nuclei are in the interior of the fibers, and the myofibrils lie in rather abundant sarcoplasm. They are not under voluntary control, and they cannot maintain contraction. They exhibit spontaneous rhythmic activity, but the speed of their movement is more like striated muscle than unstriated muscle.

Physiologic properties of skeletal muscle

Isotonic and isometric contractions. If a muscle is entirely free to change its length when it is stimulated, its contraction produces what is known as an isotonic contraction. Under physiologic conditions most skeletal muscles contract almost isotonically. If, however, shortening of the muscle is prevented, stimulation of the muscle results in an increase in tension. When this is recorded, it is spoken of as an isometric contraction. In isometric contraction the muscle performs practically no external work, and all the energy of its contraction is converted into heat.

The rapid contraction of skeletal muscle when stimulated makes it difficult to obtain information on the muscle's activity unless it is prevented from shortening; therefore, most of our physiologic knowledge has been based on an analysis of isometric contraction in isolated muscles.

The mechanical response of a muscle to a single induction shock is termed a muscle twitch. The essential features of an isometric twitch are (1) a latent period, which lasts for about 0.05 sec., and (2) following this, an abrupt increase of tension. After reaching a maximum, this gradually declines to its initial value (Fig. 143). The whole twitch is over in about one tenth of a second in the muscles of a frog and in about one thirtieth of a second in mammalian muscles.

The true latent period of the muscle is much shorter when the muscle is stimulated directly than when the muscle is stimulated through its motor nerve. When this is done, time elapses during which the impulse is traveling down the nerve (0.001 second for 3 cm. in the sciatic nerve of a frog). Another delay occurs for the passage of the impulse along the terminal ramifications of the motor nerve into the muscle (0.003 second), and finally there is the true latent period of the muscle itself, which in the frog amounts to 0.002 second. The value for mammalian muscles is much less than this.

The tension developed in an isometric twitch depends upon the length of the muscle at the time it is stimulated. A maximum value is usually obtained when the length of the muscle corresponds to that which it has in the relaxed state in the body with its normal attachments.

Potential changes in muscle. If two electrodes are placed on different parts of a resting uninjured muscle and the external circuit is completed by a sensitive galvanometer, no difference in potential will be found. If the electrodes are placed on injured and uninjured parts of a muscle, however, a difference in potential arises, showing that a constant current is flowing through the galvanometer from

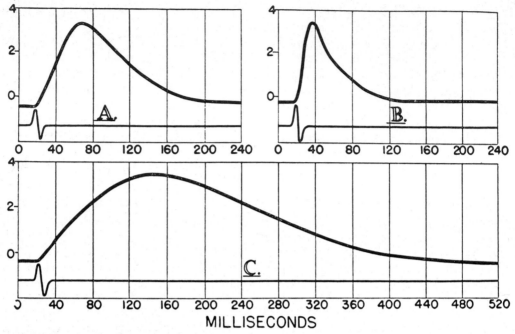

MILLISECONDS

Fig. 143. Form of simple twitch in three muscles. **A,** The mainly white-fibered gastrocnemius. **B,** The wholly white-fibered internal rectus. **C,** The red-fibered soleus. Action potentials are indicated below. (From Amberson, W. R., and Smith, D. C.: Outline of physiology, ed. 2, Baltimore, 1948, Williams & Wilkins Co.)

the uninjured end to the injured end. The current has no physiologic significance but shows that a potential difference always exists between injured and uninjured muscle. If the muscle is stimulated, a momentary decrease in the injury potential occurs due to a transient change of potential at the uninjured surface of the muscle. This is called a negative variation and is a monophasic response.

If two electrodes are placed on an uninjured muscle at different points and the muscle is stimulated, the galvanometer will show a diphasic response. When the change of potential associated with the stimulation, occurs under the first electrode, the current flows from the second electrode to the first, but when later the excitatory process has passed along the muscle as far as the second electrode, the current now passes from the first to the second. This diphasic response is called an action potential (see Fig. 16, p. 74). If the electrical variations in the muscle are recorded at the same time as the mechanical changes, the electrical phenomena will be over almost before the mechanical change begins. The action potential is, therefore, associated with the excitatory process and is not a consequence of the contractile process which it precedes (Fig. 144).

All-or-none property of muscle fibers. When a whole muscle is stimulated with an electric current and the intensity of the electrical stimulus is increased, the response is graded so that there is an increased mechanical response to an increase in the intensity of the stimulus (Fig. 145). This gradation of response

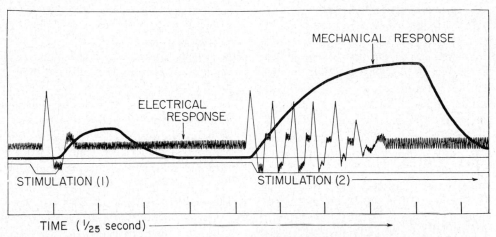

Fig. 144. The relation between the mechanical and electrical responses of a gastrocnemius muscle of a frog with normal circulation to, 1, a single induction shock and, 2, a rapid succession of six shocks. (These six shocks occurred at times indicated by the corresponding action potentials.) In the twitch the electric response is almost over before the mechanical response begins. In the short tetanus there is a discrete electric response to each shock, whereas the mechanical responses are fused. Note the secondary electrical changes complicating the diphasic action potential, which are characteristic of records obtained from muscles in situ or immersed in Ringer's solution. The simple monophasic and diphasic forms of action potential are only obtained from muscles when isolated and suspended in air. (After Fulton.)

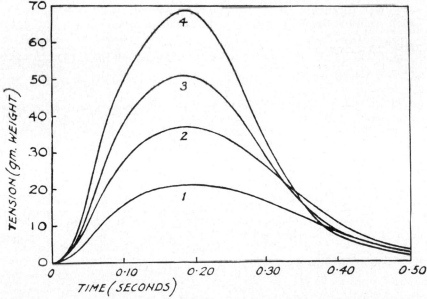

Fig. 145. The influence of increasing the intensity of the stimulus on the tension developed in the isometric twitch of a sartorius muscle isolated from a frog. Curves 1 to 4 represent the responses to progressively greater stimuli. (Based on data given by Hartree and Hill; from Winton and Bayliss: Human physiology, Philadelphia, 1948, The Blakiston Co.)

is not due to a gradation of the tension developed by each individual muscle fiber as the intensity of the electrical stimulus is increased but is due to a variation in the number of fibers contracting. As the stimulus increases in intensity, more fibers contract, and each added fiber contributes to the successive responses.

It can be shown that by stimulating single muscle fibers with minute electrodes each muscle fiber either contracts completely or does not contract at all. There is never any gradation in the response of any single fiber. As the stimulus is increased above the value which excites contraction in a single fiber, the current spreads to an adjacent fiber in sufficient strength to excite it also. As the current increases in strength, therefore, more and more fibers contract, and the summation of these contractions leads to an increase in response of the muscle as a whole. Each single fiber can contract without exciting neighboring fibers, and this insulation provides a finely graded response of the whole muscle which contains many fibers by altering the proportion of fibers which are active.

The property of each fiber either to contract a maximum or not at all is known as the *all-or-none property or law*. The all-or-none principle applies not only to muscle fibers, but also to single nerve fibers as well, and hence to the nerve-muscle preparation. A maximal stimulus is one strong enough to excite all the fibers in a muscle. A minimum or threshold stimulus is one just strong enough to excite the fewest fibers necessary to obtain a demonstrable contraction.

Effects of repeated stimulation. If two maximal stimuli are applied to a muscle, the result depends upon the interval of time between them. If the interval is short enough (less than 0.02 second), the second stimulus has no effect whatever, and the response of the muscle resembles its response to a single stimulus. The period during which the muscle fails to react to a second stimulus is called the *absolute refractory period*. It indicates that the muscle is inexcitable for a brief period following the first stimulus. If the interval between the two stimuli is longer than the absolute refractory period, the muscle responds to the double stimulus by a single response greater and more prolonged than the response to a single shock. The response is not twice as great, however; therefore, the response to the second stimulus must be considerably modified by the first stimulus. As the interval of time between the two stimuli is increased, a stage occurs at which the tension record shows two distinct maxima, and, finally, with still greater separation of the stimuli the muscle responds with two distinct twitches. Responses which are partially or completely superimposed are said to summate (Fig. 146).

When the stimuli are applied in such rapid succession that a sustained contraction is produced, the response is called a *tetanus* and the stimulus which provokes it a tetanic stimulus (Fig. 147).

The most economical frequency of stimulus which produces a tetanus will have an interval between successive stimuli such that each response begins just before the relaxation phase of the preceding contraction is due. In a frog's muscle the frequency is about twenty per second. If the frequency of stimulation is increased, the individual humps in the record disappear, and the responses become completely fused into a continuous sustained contraction. However, the increase of tension produced under such conditions is only slight. In order to produce a maximal tetanic contraction, time is required, and the time necessary depends upon the particular muscle. The

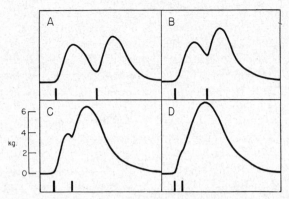

Fig. 146. Mechanical and electrical responses of the median head of the gastrocnemius to double shocks to peroneal nerve. Temperature, 34.5° C. The stimuli were maximal break shocks. Interval between stimuli: **A,** 88σ; **B,** 69σ; **C,** 48σ; **D,** 24σ. (After Cooper S., and Eccles, J.: J. Physiol. **69:**377, 1930.)

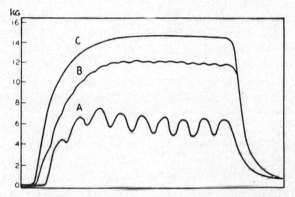

Fig. 147. Mechanical responses of gastrocnemius of the cat to different rates of tetanic stimulation of motor nerve. **A,** 19 shocks per second; **B,** 35 shocks per second; **C,** 115 shocks per second. (From Bard; adapted from Cooper, S., and Eccles, J.: J. Physiol. **69:**377, 1930.)

minimum rate of stimulation for the gastrocnemius muscle of the cat is about fifty per second, and the stimulus must consist of at least ten shocks. On the other hand, the medial rectus muscle of the cat must be stimulated as fast as two hundred and fifty times per second before the response is fused completely, and the stimulus must consist of at least twenty to thirty shocks.

Voluntary contractions of muscles in a living animal are always tetanic contractions since tetanic stimulation is the only means of inducing a muscle to respond with sustained contraction. In the intact animal muscles never contract with the speed observed in a single twitch. If they did, the movements would be hopelessly violent, and the structures to which the muscles were attached might be unable to sustain the stresses set up without injury. In fact, the tensions which may be developed by muscles in good condition when submitted to maximal tetanic stimulation and prevented from shortening are enormous and frequently sufficient to break the tendons. Under ordinary conditions, of course, the contraction is always partially isotonic, and even a small amount of shortening very greatly reduces the tension developed by the muscles. Consequently, such dangerously large tensions are not produced in the living animal ordinarily, even by maximal stimulation.

When voluntary muscles contract under ordinary conditions, the effort does not produce anything like maximum contraction of the muscles because only a fraction of the total number of its fibers are contributing at any one time. During voluntary contraction, the individual fibers are probably contracting intermittently and each at different moments from its neighbors, instead of continuously and all at the same time. The result of the intermittent contraction of these fibers at different frequencies is sustained contraction of the whole muscle. This differs from experimental tetanus in which one set of fibers is thrown into contraction, with a frequency of stimulus great enough to produce complete fusion of their responses, while other fibers remain inactive. Natural tetanus will not result in fatigue so quickly as will experimental tetanus.

Muscular tonus. It has been said that unstriated muscle usually exhibits some degree of spontaneous activity in the absence of external stimulation and that this permanent partial contraction of the muscle without external stimulation represents tonus. Tonus, therefore, may be regarded as sustained submaximal contraction without too obvious a stimulus, and so the meaning of muscular tone or tonus may be extended to include that small permanent state of tension which enables skeletal muscles which are striated when connected with the central nervous system to maintain the postural relations of the body. The longer the muscle in pro-

portion to its sustained tension, the lower its tone.[19]

The tonus of skeletal muscle is probably due to repetitive stimulation, as in tetanic contraction, but tonus differs from tetanic contraction in that tonic contraction affects the individual fibers of the muscle in turn intermittently and asynchronously, whereas tetanic contraction affects a particular set of fibers with regular volleys of stimuli so that they contract continuously and synchronously. As a result of this, during tonus fatigue of any particular muscle fiber is avoided by giving it a rest while its neighboring fibers are contracting.

Striated skeletal muscles possess tonus, made evident by the flaccid paralysis which follows interruption of either the motor neuron or its dorsal roots*; nevertheless, in the normal condition electromyography shows the muscle to be silent in the so-called resting position of the limb to which it is attached. As pointed out (p. 406), this is not the case with ocular muscles, which show marked electrical activity in the primary position of gaze.

This difference in electrical activity is

---

*An older neurologic dictum stated that paralysis of the lower motor neuron produced flaccid paralysis, whereas paralysis of the upper motor neuron caused spastic paralysis. Actually, this is not generally true of all upper motor neurons and is particularly incorrect for the upper motor neurons of the pyramidal tract. This concept is correct only if reference is to the extrapyramidal neurons of the premotor area. These are tied in with the suppressor areas, and lesions involving the premotor area do cause exaggeration of tonus and postural reflexes. After the area of the suppressor strip is removed, the muscles involved become more hypertonic and are said to have suffered spastic paralysis. This paralysis is much more marked when both the premotor and suppressor strip areas are removed.

perhaps not so strange as it might seem. It merely indicates that ocular muscles are under greater tension than are skeletal muscles or are more responsive to the same tension, for even skeletal muscles respond with increased tonus and electrical activity when slighly stretched, and ocular muscles become silent when freed from their insertions.

The great sensitivity of unstriated vertebrate muscle to substances present in the blood, such as epinephrine, suggests that the tonus of these muscles may be due to a direct, continuous chemical action of such substances on the muscle fiber. However, our knowledge of what constitutes tonus is as yet incomplete.

Action of electrolytes on muscular tissue. Experiments on isolated muscles have shown that when muscular tissue is removed from the body it must be bathed in a solution which has chemical and physical properties similar to those of the blood in order to maintain its contractility. For example, Locke, working with isolated mammalian heart muscle, found the concentration of salts which favored the longest survival of the heartbeat to be as follows (Table 45).

Table 45. *Locke's solution*

Salts	Gm. wt.
Sodium chloride	0.9
Potassium chloride	0.42
Calcium chloride (anhydrous)	0.024
Sodium bicarbonate	0.002
Glucose	0.1-2.25
Water	100.0

The action of individual ions on contractile tissue is difficult to assess because various contractile tissues respond in different fashion to an excess or deficiency of any particular ion. In general, however, sodium salts occupy a unique position in all types of muscle in that they must be present in larger amounts than any others. Not more than one half of the amount present in Ringer's solution can be replaced by any other nontoxic substance such as glucose which can bring the osmotic pressure up to the required physiologic value. Calcium and potassium show an interdependence in their relative concentrations. Although the absolute amounts of these salts may vary rather widely, they must be present in about the correct ratio. An excess of potassium salts induces contraction of most muscles, other than those of the heart.

The various anions appear to be relatively unimportant so long as they are nontoxic. The presence of sulfates, bromides, nitrates, carbonates, etc., has very little influence on the survival of isolated muscle. Chlorides are used in most physiologic work since their salts are all freely soluble. The hydrogen ion concentration cannot be removed far from neutrality in order for the muscle to function, and most muscle tissues are favored by a hydrogen ion concentration slightly on the alkaline side of neutrality. Slight acidity produces slowing or arrest of the heartbeat, relaxation of the tone of most unstriated muscles, and phenomena analogous to fatigue in striated muscle.

The electrolyte composition of the muscle cells is quite different from that of the extracellular fluid, and when this relationship is changed, the muscle ceases to function. The normal muscle cell contains potassium ions but practically no sodium ions. The fluid bathing the cell contains sodium and very little potassium. Many cells of the body also contain practically no chloride but much phosphate. These differences in electrolyte composition are maintained in spite of the fact that it is now known that the cell membrane is not entirely impermeable to any kind of ion.

Permeability, both to water and to all substances in solution, is affected by the electrolyte composition of the external fluid. In the absence of calcium, e.g., the permeability of the cell membrane is increased still further. Normal functioning of the muscle cells is possible only in the presence of normal permeability of the cell membrane.

Anatomic characteristics of ocular muscles

Muscle fibers. Ocular muscles are striated fibers similar to ordinary skeletal muscle. Each fiber is finer than the usual skeletal striated muscle fiber, being only from 9 to 11 μ in diameter, and each runs the whole length of the muscle.[20] The muscles also contain an unusually large amount of elastic connective tissue which is distributed between the fibers and develops sometime after birth.[21] Woollard[22]

described two types of muscle fiber, a thick and a thin type, innervated by two distinct types of nerve fibers (Fig. 148). Other authors have not been able to distinguish two distinct sets of muscle fibers based on size.

The large amount of elastic tissue present in the interfascicular septa of the ocular muscles permits passive contraction of the muscle when its tonus is diminished. As it is stretched by its antagonist, the tension in the muscle increases. This makes good the loss of tone which develops when the antagonist starts to contract, according to Sherrington's law, and permits a more delicate regulation of the movements of the eyes. It is possible that this elastic tissue is responsible for producing structural changes in the muscles in strabismus, particularly that caused by paralysis of a muscle. Following paralysis one sometimes sees marked contracture in the antagonist muscle. This does not occur in all patients, however,

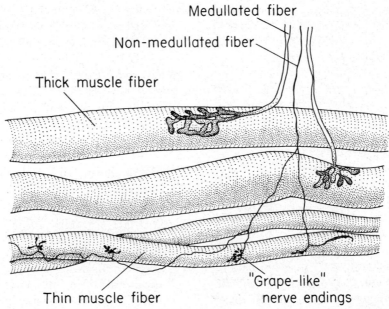

Medullated fiber

Non-medullated fiber

Thick muscle fiber

Thin muscle fiber

"Grape-like" nerve endings

Fig. 148. Methylene blue preparation of the superior rectus of the rabbit, showing the two types of nerve and muscle fibers. (After Woollard.)

and the factors which determine whether shortening of the antagonist muscle will occur are not clear. Even in strabismus not due to muscle paralysis occasionally there are structural changes in the muscle in which marked resistance to passive movement of the eye (the so-called forced duction test) occurs due apparently to contracture of one or more muscles. Again, the causes of these changes are obscure and should be investigated further.

As will be shown later (p. 528), fibrosis may occur in the antagonist of a paralyzed muscle and lead to contracture of that muscle. This is probably the same pathologic change that occurs in a paralyzed skeletal muscle. In addition, fibrosis apparently occurs in ocular muscles as a congenital defect. Laughlin[23] reports patients with strabismus in which muscle tissue removed at operation showed hyalinized collagen enclosed in dense fibrous tissue, and no muscle fibers were present. Adhesions and fibrosis of Tenon's capsule were present, also. This syndrome occurred in four successive generations so that it undoubtedly is an hereditary anomaly of development.

Nerve supply. The nerve fibers from the trunks of the third, fourth, fifth, and sixth cranial nerves enter the ocular muscles at about the junction of the middle and posterior thirds of each muscle. At this point they appear as bundles of coarse medullated fibers and bundles of fine nonmedullated fibers. The former are the more numerous. It has been assumed that the large fibers are ordinary somatic fibers, whereas the thin fibers are autonomic fibers (Fig. 149).

In the extraocular muscles of the rabbit Hines[24] found additional nerve fibers which did not end on the muscles but went to the blood vessels alone. If the oculomotor nerve of the rabbit was cut at the base of the brain, all of the nerves in the motor nerve trunk and all of the nerve endings in the ocular muscles degenerated, leaving the nerve endings to the blood vessels. When the cervical sympathetic trunk alone was cut, the nerve endings on the muscle fibers were undisturbed, but the nerve endings on the blood vessels degenerated. A combination of these two procedures completely denervated the muscle. Therefore, in the rabbit all of the innervation of the muscle fibers originates in the oculomotor nerve, whereas that destined for the blood vessels comes from both the oculomotor nerve and the cervical sympathetic nerve.

Each fiber in the third cranial nerve supplies from five to twenty motor end plates, which are found chiefly in the posterior third of each muscle.[25] The fine nonmedullated fibers seem to be associated either with a peculiar grapelike type of terminal ending or simply naked nerve endings. These endings do not degenerate if either the fifth cranial nerve or its nucleus is destroyed. The cells of origin of the grapelike endings in the muscles have been traced to the motor nuclei supplying the muscles of the eye. It is not possible to decide by this fact alone, however, whether these endings are motor or sensory since Kappers has pointed out the following fact.

". . . [that] cells of the mesencephalic root of the trigeminal lie farther ventralward in most mammals than in lower vertebrates and in man extend to the motor nuclei of the oculomotor and trochlear nerves, and are even intermingled with cells of these nuclei."*

Similar grapelike endings are found in the skeletal muscles of the lower vertebrates, e.g., the frog. This fact, along with others to be mentioned, suggests that the ocular

---

*From Kappers, C., Huber, C., and Crosby, E.: The comparative anatomy of the nervous system of vertebrates, including man, New York, 1936, The Macmillan Co.

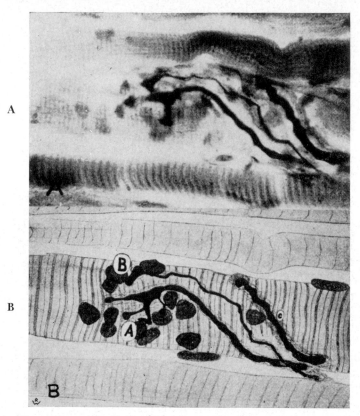

Fig. 149. A, Photomicrograph. B, Drawing of a reconstruction of the double innervation of a large striated muscle fiber of the human eye. *A,* Motor end plate of coarse medullated nerve; *B,* simple looplike ending of delicate nonmedullated nerve on the same muscle fiber; *C,* another nerve fiber which is not related to the end organ here described. (B, Silver carbonate technique of del Rio Hortega; ×800; from Alpern, M., and Wolter, J.: Arch. Ophth. 56:688, 1956.)

muscles represent a more primitive type of muscle than does ordinary skeletal striated muscle.

Daniel[27] was the first to describe in the eye muscles of man a special type of nerve ending which had been looked for in animals in the search for sensory endings serving a proprioceptive function for the ocular muscles. These consist of simple and multiple spirals, as shown in Fig. 150. He found the oculomotor nerves, consisting of thick medullated and thin nonmedullated fibers, to be divided into bundles of decreasing size as they passed along the muscle fibers, and the thick medullated fibers flared out in a fan-shape to terminate at the motor end plates in the middle third of the muscle. In this area many of the medullated fibers are arranged in simple spirals or in complex multiple spirals. The simple spirals are formed by the nerve fiber which makes three to eight spiral turns around each muscle fiber and terminates in fingerlike processes in what resembles the ordinary motor end plate. In the formation of a multiple spiral, a thick medullated fiber approaches the muscle fiber and divides into two or more fibrils, which then encircle the muscle fiber. The fibrils end in fine points alongside the nucleus of each muscle fiber. Neither the simple nor the complex multiple spirals have been found in other somatic muscles, except in the intercostal muscles in the hedgehog.[28] Since they are present in large numbers in the ocular muscles in man, Daniel believes that they probably represent the proprioceptive spindles which Sherrington hoped to find to confirm his hypothesis that spatial perception is visuo-musculo-labyrinthine. The purpose of

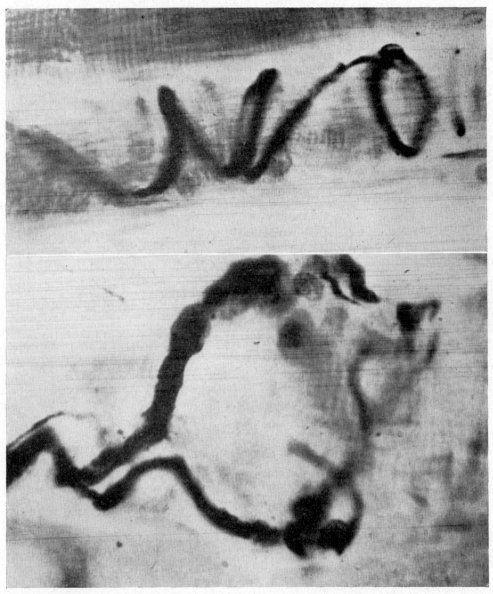

Fig. 150. Muscle spirals described in the ocular muscles of man. (From Daniel, P.: J. Anat. **80:**189, 1946.)

these endings, therefore, would be to record changes in stretch on contraction of
the muscles similar to what is accomplished by the muscle spindles in ordinary
skeletal muscle. The question of proprioceptive mechanisms in ocular muscles will
be considered in more detail in a later
section (p. 418). The presence of these
spirals has been confirmed by Cooper and
Danish[29] and Sunderland[30] who believe
that they are true muscle spindles although they differ in points of detail from
those in other somatic muscles. They are
smaller and more delicate, and each consists of a group of fine cross-striated muscle fibers with a rich nerve supply, and
each is enclosed in a torpedo-shaped very
thin fibrous capsule. They have been
found in all the ocular muscles of man,
the cow, white-tailed gnu, goat, wild and
domestic sheep, pig, giraffe, and chimpanzee, but they are absent in the eye
muscles of the rabbit, cat, dog, bear, and
macaque monkey.

Although the extraocular muscles of the
cat lack muscle spindles, they possess
many sensory endings, some of which can
be activated by passive stretch. Discharges
from these proprioceptors have been recorded in the fibers of the third nerve in
the orbit[31] and have been followed in the
brainstem along the course of the mesencephalic nucleus of the fifth nerve. At
present it is not known just how these
fibers enter the brainstem.[32]

More recently, other types of nerve endings have been described in the eye muscles of man, all of which are thought to be
sensory in function. Wolter[33] recognizes
six different types of endings, type I being
the spiral endings of Daniel. Wolter calls
them "sensory muscle spindles" and points
out that the spindles were first described
by Huber in 1899 in the muscle tendons
of the eye in rabbits. Huber considered
them sensory endings because they were

present in the tendon where they could
serve no useful motor function. On this
same basis Wolter assumes that his five
other types of nerve fiber endings are sensory since they were always found in interstitial connective tissue and not on or
in striated muscle fiber.

The ratio of nerve fibers to muscle
fibers is much less in ocular muscles than
in ordinary skeletal muscles, being approximately one nerve fiber for every five
to ten muscle fibers. In the soleus muscle,
for comparison, the ratio of nerve fibers
to muscle fibers is 1:120. The skill and
precision of the movements performed by
any neuromuscular system vary inversely
with the size of the nerve-muscle unit.
Muscles in which as many as one hundred
and twenty fibers are supplied by one
nerve fiber do not have as fine coordination as muscles in which only five to ten
fibers are supplied by one fiber. This fact
accounts in part for the very precise
gradations in motoility of the eye.

The actual number of fibers present in
each of the nerves supplying the ocular
muscles has been counted with the intent
to compare this number with the number of cells in the nucleus of the corresponding nerve.[34-36] The number of
cells in the nuclei of the fourth and sixth
cranial nerves exceeds the number of
fibers in the nerves themselves. The number of cells in the nucleus of the fourth
cranial nerve was 13% greater than the
number of fibers in the fourth cranial
nerve. The cells in the nucleus of the sixth
cranial nerve averaged 20% more than
the fibers in the sixth cranial nerve. More
fibers were found in the distal portion
than in the proximal portion of each of
these nerves. Measurements of the diameters of the fibers in both the fourth
and sixth cranial nerves suggest that 39%
of the fibers in the fourth cranial nerve
are sensory and 61% are motor, whereas

in the sixth cranial nerve 22% of the fibers are sensory and 78% are motor.[34] The decision as to whether a fiber was motor or sensory was based on the size of the fiber since it has been found that pain fibers are 4 μ or less in size, and motor fibers are larger.[37] Since in the fourth cranial nerve the average ratio of cells in the nucleus to fibers is 1:13, it can be estimated that the ratio of cells in the nucleus to *motor* fibers is 1:85. This indicates that there are about 85% more cells than motor fibers in the nucleus of the fourth cranial nerve nucleus. Similarly, in the sixth cranial nerve the ratio of cells to motor fibers is 1:54 or slightly more than 50% more cells than motor fibers. One may assume, therefore, that the motor nuclei of the fourth and sixth cranial nerves send fibers both peripherally into the fourth and sixth cranial nerves and centrally to other regions, such as the nuclei of other cranial nerves, probably by way of the medial longitudinal bundle. Some of these association fibers may form a mechanism by means of which the activities of the ocular muscles are coordinated. The fact that there are not so many fibers as there are cells gives us good ground for believing that all of the fibers from each of these nerves have their origin entirely within their own nucleus. In other words, there is no indication that part of the fibers in the fourth and sixth cranial nerves have an origin outside of these circumscribed masses of gray matter which are regarded as their respective motor nuclei. When the motor nerves to the ocular muscles of the goat emerge from the brainstem, they are probably purely motor. In the middle of their course in the orbit they are joined by sensory filaments of varying size from branches of the ophthalmic division of the fifth nerve.

Recently Donaldson[38] has made an an-alysis of the size of the fibers in the purely motor segment of the goat's motor nerves. Although there is considerable variation in fiber size, he showed a statistically significant division into two peaks, one of fibers ranging from 11 to 17 μ and the other from 3 to 7 μ. The large fibers are undoubtedly the ordinary fibers supplying the motor end plates on the extrafusal muscle fibers. The smaller fibers are believed to be gamma efferents supplying the intrafusal muscle fibers in the muscle spindles. Physiological evidence for the existence of these gamma efferents will be given later. Donaldson has estimated that there are from eight to eleven gamma efferents available in the inferior oblique muscle of the goat for each muscle spindle.

The ocular muscles, like other skeletal muscles, have more than one end plate per fiber. In some skeletal muscles each individual fiber receives innervation from more than one nerve fiber; i.e., the innervation is polyneural. Recent evidence suggests that the extraocular muscles, while not polyneural, are in fact supplied by multiple endings from the same nerve fiber. They are supplied, therefore, by multiple innervation as opposed to polyneural innervation. This could account for the remarkably short time which elapses before the twitch tension of ocular muscles reaches its peak (7.5 msec. in the cat), for if nerve impulses reach several sites on the muscle fiber simultaneously, the contraction of the fiber as a whole would be facilitated.

On the basis of localization of cholinesterase in the extraocular muscles Kupfer[39] concludes that there are two types of motor nerve endings, gamma efferents with more than one gamma efferent terminating on the same intrafusal fiber and other efferents of larger diameter and faster conduction than the gamma efferents. These may be alpha nerve fibers. According to Kupfer, both the alpha and gamma efferents can innervate some intrafusal fibers while others are innervated by gamma efferent nerves only.

Physiologic characteristics of ocular muscles

The ocular muscles are said to be capable of contraction with shortening like other skeletal muscles (isotonic contraction) or of contraction without shortening (isometric contraction). In the former the globe is rotated around one of its own axes, whereas in the latter the globe is firmly fixed in position while antagonistic muscles contract (cocontraction of antagonists). This latter concept must be accepted with reservations, however. It has not been proved thus far that actual cocontraction of the ocular muscles normally does take place, although antagonistic muscles do maintain the tonus they show in the primary position during version movements of the globe to steady the globe in its course (see discussion of muscles concerned in ductions, p. 359).

The unit element to which activity of ocular muscles may be reduced is the simple twitch. It is the result of a single brief stimulation, either directly to the muscle itself or by a single volley of nerve impulses set up in the motor fibers supplying the muscle. It occurs only in laboratory conditions since all of the discharges in the motor nerves under physiologic conditions produce tetanic contraction. During a simple twitch after a short latent period, the muscle contracts and then promptly relaxes. The twitch lasts from 7.5 to 10 msec. in the medial rectus muscle. Contraction of this muscle is similar to that of muscles performing fine movements elsewhere, such as the extensor digitorum whose twitch lasts 7.5 msec., where-

as muscles performing gross work without delicacy of movement, such as the soleus muscle, have longer twitches—the twitch of the soleus lasts 40 msec.

If a second stimulus is applied during the latent period, no additional response occurs. The muscle is then said to be completely refractory. When the stimulus is applied after the latent period is over, i.e., during the rise of tension, at the height of contraction, or during relaxation, a second response appears. This leads to further development of tension. Thus the tension resulting from two stimuli applied successively at suitable intervals may be considerably greater than that from a single stimulus of the same strength. If a series of stimuli are applied at increasingly shorter intervals, increasingly more complete degrees of summation take place. At rates of from ten to twenty stimuli per second, the mechanical fusion is incomplete, and the muscle gives a tremulous response called a partial tetanus. At higher rates—one hundred to three hundred and fifty stimuli per second—the mechanical fusion is complete, and full tetanus results (Fig. 151). The more complete the tetanus, the greater is the tension exerted by the fibers, and the steadier they pull. With full tetanus it may be impossible to detect the slightest flicker in the mechanical record, although the electrical record shows a series of discrete waves corresponding to the arrival of each nervous impulse.

When an ocular muscle contracts, the behavior of each of its fibers depends upon the character of the discharge from the motor neurons. The rate of discharge varies from very low to high levels. The degree of tetanus resulting will be partial or complete, and the consequent strength and nature of the contraction will vary correspondingly (Fig. 152). The degree of activity of each muscle fiber can thus be

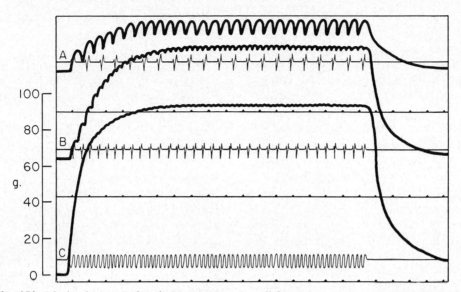

Fig. 151. Mechanical and electrical responses of medial rectus to tetanic stimulation of NIII. Temperature 36° C. Maximal stimuli from neon tube device. Rate of stimulation: *upper record,* 70 shocks a second; *middle record,* 125 shocks a second; *lower record,* 210 shocks a second. (After Cooper, J., and Eccles, J.: J. Physiol. **69**:377, 1930.)

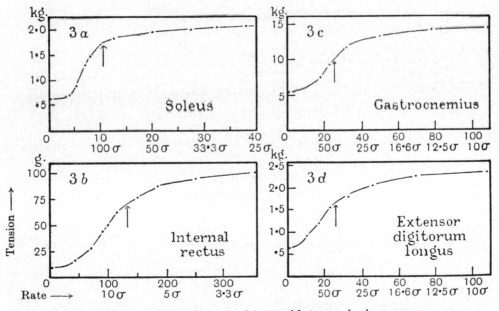

Fig. 152. Curves showing the effect of rate of stimulation of tetanus tension for the four muscles studied. The values under the rates give the interval between stimuli at those rates. The arrow in each case is placed at the interval which equals the contraction time of a single response. (From Cooper, S., and Eccles, J.: J. Physiol. **69**:377, 1930.)

graded. The number of motor cells activated during any excitation may be varied. The larger the number of motor cells activated the greater will be the resulting tension. If the stimulus applied is only of threshold strength, it can excite one motor nerve fiber and its related group of muscle fibers (motor unit). As the strength of the stimulus applied to the nerve is increased, more nerve fibers and, therefore, more nerve-muscle units respond, and the strength of the contraction is correspondingly greater.

Each ocular muscle fiber, like other skeletal muscle fibers, obeys the all-or-none law. If the motor cells discharge out of step and not in unison, the different muscle units will be in different phases of activity at any one moment so that while one group is contracting another is relaxing, and vice versa. Algebraic summation occurs; i.e., the individual variation is evened out, and the muscle reacts with a steady pull. The tension produced in any one cycle is intermediate between contraction and relaxation.

Electromyography of ocular muscles

Contraction of the ocular muscles, as in other skeletal muscles, is accompanied by a change in electrical activity which can be recorded with appropriate apparatus. As early as 1930 Cooper and Eccles[40] studied the mechanical and electrical responses of the medial rectus muscle to tetanic stimulation. Brown and Harvey[20] decerebrated cats and cut the ophthalmic division of the fifth cranial nerve. The nerve to the inferior oblique muscle was laid on electrodes of fine platinum wire. For myographic recording the animal's head was immobilized, and a silk thread was tied to the tendon of the inferior oblique which was fastened to a weak torsion wire myograph. Electrical records were taken from the muscle fibers (Figs. 153 to 155).

The first records of the electrical ac-

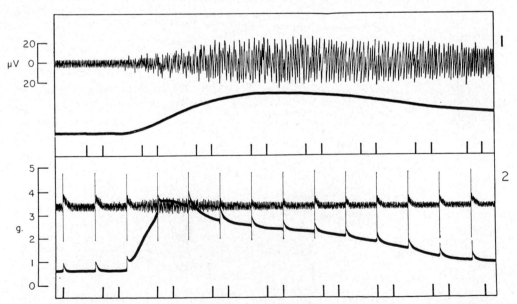

Fig. 153. Myogram and action potentials of inferior oblique. **1,** Response to carotid injection of 100 mg. acetylcholine. **2,** Effect of carotid injection of 50 mg. acetylcholine during excitation of nerve with single maximal shocks. Time, 0.5 second. (After Brown and Harvey.)

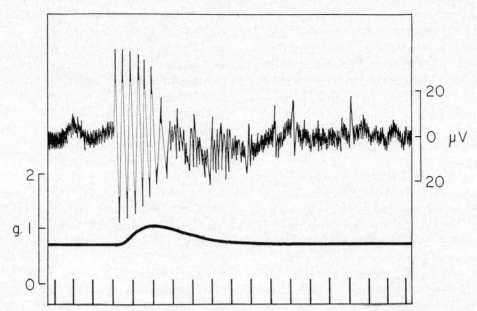

Fig. 154. 3.8 Myogram, 3.8 kg., and action potential (belly tendon) of inferior oblique of the cat, showing spontaneous contraction after intracarotid injection of 0.3 mg. eserine. (After Brown and Harvey.)

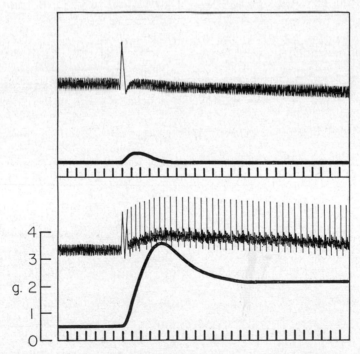

Fig. 155. Myogram and action potential (belly tendon) of inferior oblique, showing response to single maximal nerve volley. **a**, Before eserine; **b**, after eserine. (After Brown and Harvey.)

tivity in human ocular muscles were published by Björk[41] in 1952, and in 1953 Adler and Yasuna[42] recorded the same activity. With the development of better methods of recording muscular activity, Breinin and others have contributed a great deal to our knowledge of the physiology of the ocular muscles, and work still in progress promises to solve many of our present questions.

The normal electromyogram. The electromyogram is a record of the electric discharge of the muscle fibers composing a motor unit. Each motor nerve fiber is connected to several individual muscle fibers, and when an electric impulse sweeps down the motor nerve fiber and strikes the motor end plates in each of the muscle fibers, all of the muscle fibers discharge synchronously. It is the integrated voltage of this discharge which constitutes the electric motor unit which is picked up and recorded by electromyography. The amplitude of the discharge depends on many factors, the chief of which is the distance the recording electrode is from the motor unit. The closer the electrode is to the motor unit, the greater is the amplitude of the discharge. If the muscle fibers composing the motor unit are packed closely together, the amplitude of the discharge will be greater than if they are spread out at a greater distance from one another. When the electrode is in close contact with the motor unit, the discharge is usually in the form of a spike, consisting of a diphasic wave, i.e., with an initial positivity (downward deflection) followed by a negativity (upward deflection).

The electrical activity in the ocular muscles differs in some respects from that found in skeletal muscle. The ocular muscle motor unit has a much lower amplitude, the duration of the discharge is much shorter, and the rate of firing or frequency is very much higher. The individual motor units can also recruit faster than the skeletal motor units. Further, as long as the ocular muscles are attached to the globe in the unanesthetized subject, the motor units are constantly firing, whereas skeletal motor units in the so-called positions of rest (i.e., not actively contracting) are electrically silent. In Table 46 the electrical activity of ocular muscle is compared with that of skeletal muscle.

Table 46. *Electrical activity of ocular muscle compared with that of skeletal muscle*

Characteristics	Ocular muscle	Skeletal muscle
Amplitude at rest	20-150 μv	0
Duration at rest	1-2 msec.	0
Frequency at rest	Up to 150/sec.	0
Amplitude during activity	400-600 μv	100-3000 μv
Duration during activity	1-2 msec.	5-10 msec.
Frequency during activity	Several hundred/sec.	5-30/sec.
Minimal rate of stimulation to produce maximal tetanus	250/sec.	50/sec.
Minimal number of shocks to produce maximal tetanus	20-30/sec.	10/sec.

Since the electromyogram records the activity of only those few fibers with which the electrodes are in contact, it does not tell us what the muscle as a whole is doing. No interpretation of the total activity of the muscle can be made, therefore. A paretic muscle might have more than half of its fibers knocked out and yet the record might appear normal because the electrode happened to lie adjacent to some unaffected motor units. Other sources of error are (1) the possibility of shift of the electrode from one set of motor units to others as the muscle contracts, (2) the accidental pickup of electrical activity in adjacent muscles, e.g., the levator palpebrae in recording from the superior rectus or the inferior rectus in recording from the inferior oblique, (3) irritation of the muscle by the electrodes, causing firing in motor units artificially, and (4) the difficulty in accurately timing the electrical record with shortening of the muscle because of the speed of contraction of the ocular muscles. The difficulties of interpretation of records have been pointed out by Jampolsky.[43]

Activity of muscles in the primary position of gaze. During the waking hours all of the ocular muscles which are not actively inhibited show electrical activity. That is, the so-called position of rest of the ocular muscles—the straight ahead position of the eyes—involves constant contraction of a number of motor units in all of the muscles. It seems probable that certain motor cells discharge out of step so that one group of motor units is contracting while another group is relaxing, and vice versa. Fatigue is prevented in this manner. In the straight ahead position of gaze, electrical activity can be demonstrated in each of the ocular muscles. This is different from skeletal muscles in which no activity can be recorded

while the limb is apparently at rest.

The electrical activity of each of the ocular muscles while at apparent rest is generally the same.

Electrical activity of muscles during version. When the eye turns to the right, e.g., the right lateral rectus and the left medial rectus show an immediate increase in both the number of impulses per second and their amplitude as recorded from each muscle. The antagonist muscles, i.e., the right medial rectus and the left lateral rectus, on the other hand, show an immediate drop in the frequency and amplitude of the impulses normal for the resting position (primary position) of these muscles. The drop in electrical activity in the antagonist muscle is never to zero, except in extreme movement out of the muscle field (Fig. 156). This drop in electrical activity of the antagonist as the agonist contracts follows Sherrington's law of reciprocal innervation, which will be discussed further on p. 414. This is illustrated in Fig. 157.

During horizontal versions the electrical activity of the superior and inferior recti and the superior and inferior obliques shows no change from the resting potential (Fig. 158). There is no evidence, therefore, for the belief that active cocontraction of these pairs of muscles takes place during horizontal versions to aid in either adduction or abduction. It is true, however, as stated in the discussion of muscles concerned in ductions, that these muscles do maintain their normal resting potentials, and in so far as this tenses each muscle, the opposing pairs aid in horizontal movement by preventing the eye from either wobbling up and down or tilting. Further, by their tonic contraction, they do aid in horizontal movement, as explained previously, on a mechanical basis.

During versions in the oblique positions

of gaze electrical activity is increased in three of the six muscles and inhibited in the other three, as would be expected. Thus, in the right eye in gaze up and to the right there is increased activity in the lateral rectus, superior rectus, and inferior oblique, with inhibition in the medial rectus, inferior rectus, and superior oblique.

Electrical activity of muscles during vergences. Convergence is carried out en-

tirely by contraction of both medial recti, without the aid of any other ocular muscles, provided that the eyes converge in the horizontal plane from the primary position. As both medial recti contract to the near point of convergence, the firing in each muscle increases to a maximum and is maintained as long as the eyes are held at the near point. At the same time the activity of both lateral recti decreases to zero. When the eyes are converged in

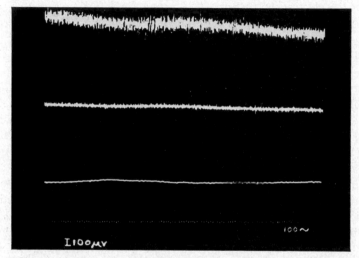

Fig. 156. Lateral rectus, O.D. *Upper tracing,* field of maximum activity (abduction). *Middle tracing,* primary position with rhythmic motor unit activity. *Lower tracing,* inhibition in the adducted position. Time in 100 cycles. (From Breinin, G., and Moldaver, J.: Arch. Ophth. 54:204, 1955.)

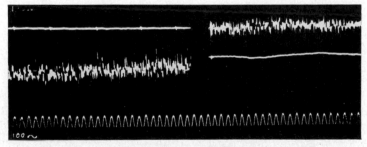

Fig. 157. Reciprocal relationship, lateral recti of the two eyes. *Upper tracing,* O.D.; *lower tracing,* O.S. On extreme gaze right there is marked activity of the lateral rectus O.D., with almost complete inhibition of the left lateral rectus. On extreme gaze left, the left lateral rectus fires maximally, whereas there is complete inhibition of the right lateral rectus. (From Breinin, G., and Moldaver, J.: Arch. Ophth. 54:204, 1955.)

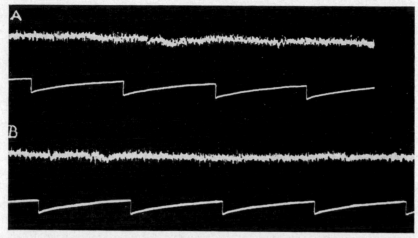

Fig. 158. Electromyogram of left inferior oblique on horizontal versions. **A,** Gaze right, no change. **B,** Gaze left, no change. (From Breinin, G.: Arch. Ophth. **57:**645, 1957.)

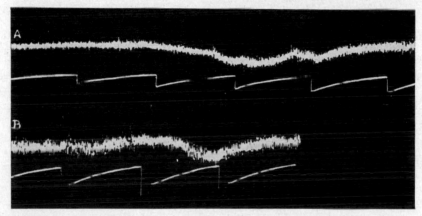

Fig. 159. Electromyogram of left medial rectus. **A,** Convergence up to the near point of convergence. **B,** Dextroversion from the near point of convergence. (From Breinin, G.: Arch. Ophth. **57:**647, 1957.)

the ordinary reading position, the superior obliques are probably increasingly active, but no electromyographic evidence of this has been reported.

When the eyes are converged to the near point, so that no further binocular adduction can be produced, it is still possible to further adduct either the right or the left eye by a version movement to the left or to the right. It has been claimed that this further adduction of one or the other eye was brought about

by increased activity of the superior and inferior recti acting as adductors.[44] Electromyographic records do not show this. The vertical recti show no increase in their activity from that of the resting state during the version. The medial rectus, however, now shows a marked increase in firing over that which was its maximum during convergence (Fig. 159). It would seem that one rate of firing can occur as a maximum during convergence but that this rate can be increased by impulses coming from the oculogyric mechanism controlling versions. This is further evidence that the mechanism for vergences is different from that producing versions.

Also, the pattern of firing in the medial recti is different in convergence and in the adduction of a version movement. Versions are characterized by initial sudden and short discharges of larger motor units followed by a regular pattern of lower amplitude. Convergence, on the other hand, is accompanied by a gradual increment of motor units and is succeeded by a prolonged decrement.[45]

An increase in innervation in the lateral rectus muscle occurs when the eyes move outward from the convergent position to the primary position.[42] This proves that divergence is not a passive affair due solely to the relaxation of convergence and to elastic recoil caused by pull of the stretched lateral recti and their fascia, as claimed by Scobee and others.[46] Further, with the greater sensitivity and freedom from inertia of modern equipment, Breinin[47] has shown that in a patient with intermittent exotropia the lateral rectus, which had been inhibited during convergence, fired large potentials for a period of 20 msec. just before the eye started to diverge and at a time when the medial rectus was still increasing its discharge. Then inhibition of the medial rectus occurred, and the eye diverged. This proves that in this case the lateral rectus actually pulled against the medial rectus, and with cessation of the activity in the medial rectus, the lateral rectus carried the eye out. As Breinin states it, "The concept of divergence based solely on the inhibition of convergence and elasticity of the orbital tissues, fascia and muscles cannot be countenanced any longer."*

---

*From Breinin, G., and Moldaver, J.: Arch. Ophth. 54:206, 1955.

Magee[48] found that the onset of divergence was characterized only by marked variation of the isoelectric line (probably due to movements of the ocular muscles themselves), with no outstanding activity of the motor unit. He conceives of convergence and divergence, as depicted on the electromyogram of the lateral rectus muscle, as oscillating movements of the globe with alternate contraction and relaxation of the muscle until the point of stabilization is reached.

Electrical activity of muscles during combined version and vergence. When a subject transfers his gaze from a distant object situated on his right to a point nearer him, but still on the visual line of the right eye, the right eye does not move, whereas the left eye makes a combined movement of dextroversion and convergence. At first sight this would seem to negate Hering's law (p. 384), which states that in all voluntary movements the innervation goes to the muscles of both eyes concerned with the movement. If the right eye does not move, can Hering's law apply during movements which are combinations of versions and convergences? Hering himself gave the answer to this question by pointing out that two movements occur when a subject converges on a near fixation point lying on the fixation axis of one eye and not in the midline (compared to a fixation point in the midline requiring movement of both eyes to fixate). Under the former conditions both eyes actually converge to the midline and simultaneously perform a version movement to the side of the fixation object. The combination of these two movements cancel each other on one side, but are additive on the other; hence, one eye moves while the other remains stationary. In the instance just mentioned, the right eye performs a movement of convergence to the left and simultaneously a movement of dextroversion. These two movements, being in opposite directions, cancel each other, and the eye remains fixated. The left eye, on the other hand, performs a convergence movement and a movement of dextroversion (also to the right). These two movements are additive, with the result that the left eye does move to the right to take up fixation. Hering's law is still valid, with the implication that somewhere along the neuromuscular pathway the innervations for convergence and dextroversion of the right eye meet each other and cancel out before the muscle is reached, whereas those going to the left eye join together before they reach the muscle.

Breinin has explored this interesting and important fundamental fact in the

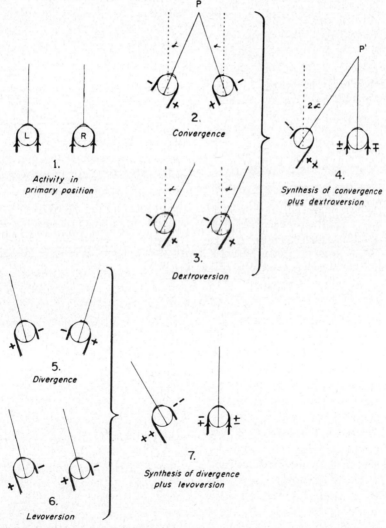

Fig. 160. Scheme of innervations during various movements of the eyes. (From Breinin, G.: Arch. Ophth. 54:408, 1955.)

kinesiology of eye muscles and has found it to be exactly as stated. During convergence, in the midline both medial recti are actively innervated and discharge impulses as they contract, whereas both lateral recti are inhibited, and their potential drops off nearly to zero (Fig. 160, *1* and *2*). When the subject performs dextroversion, the activity of the right lateral rectus increases while the activity of the right medial rectus diminishes (Fig. 160, *3*). In Fig. 160, *4* is shown what happens in the right eye. The innervations cancel each other, and the eye maintains the postural tonus it had in the primary position. The innervations going to the left eye, on the other hand, add up to a double positive innervation in the medial rectus muscle and a double inhibition of the left lateral rectus so that the eye moves to the right. In speaking of the right eye, Breinin states:

". . . for each unit of increased excitation of the medial rectus induced by convergence there is apposed an equal inhibition induced by the version. For each unit of inhibition of the lateral rectus induced by convergence there is apposed an equal excitation induced by the version. The resultant is the exact level of innervation for both muscles that existed before."*

It seems obvious that the innervations going to the ocular muscles are dictated by the retinal images. The sensory apparatus determines what innervations the muscles of the eye shall receive, and somewhere between the visual cortex and the oculomotor nuclei there must be a mechanism which sorts out the desired pattern of excitation and inhibition for each of the muscles and delivers the final product to it. Just where it is we do not know, but it must be close enough to the nuclei

---

*From Breinin, G., and Moldaver, J.: Arch. Ophth. **54:**206, 1955.

so that the messages from both the optomotor and postural mechanisms of the body reach it and influence the final pattern. This could be only in the vicinity of the muscle nuclei and above the level of the vestibular nuclei.

Response of ocular muscles to drugs

The ocular muscles have been used to elucidate some of the more obscure features of the action of substances affecting neurohumoral transmission because their reactions to certain drugs differ from those of the striated skeletal muscles. Skeletal muscles are not sensitive to cholines or nicotine under ordinary conditions. They become so only after their nerve supply has been cut and has degenerated. The ocular muscles, on the other hand, are sensitive to substances with nicotine-like effects, even when in the intact animal they reach ocular muscles through the bloodstream or when applied to the surface of healthy muscle suspended in Locke's solution. In this respect they are similar to human unstriated muscle and to the skeletal muscle of birds. Choline, acetylcholine, and nicotine contract normal striated muscle of birds and frogs and fetal muscles of mammals. Fetal muscle is contracted by these drugs until such time as its motor nerve supply grows out from the central nervous system and reaches the muscle fibers. The sensitivity then ceases. Adult striated muscle reacts to these drugs only after degeneration of its motor nerve supply. This is analogous to the pseudomotor contraction which occurs when the sensory roots are stimulated after degeneration of the motor nerve. Such stimulation probably causes liberation of acetylcholine, which contracts the denervated sensitized muscle.

If a small amount of acetylcholine is injected intra-arterially in an animal, the ocular muscles suddenly contract with a short, sharp twitch. Larger doses result in tetanus (Fig. 153, *1*). Choline and nicotine produce a slow tonic response.[49, 50] It is not known why the ocular muscles react to choline and nicotine in this manner. Duke-Elder suggests two possibilities. First, the anomalous behavior of these muscles seems to be correlated with an anomalous nerve supply. In addition to the motor nerve endings derived from the third, fourth, and sixth cranial nerves, there are an extraordinary number of nerves of the sensory type in ocular muscles. There is some proof[25] that these small fibers belong to the parasympathetic system. Second, their pharmacologic peculiarity may not be neurologic in origin but may be due to some peculiarity in the muscle fibers themselves. The fibers of ocular muscles are extremely thin and delicate, and it is possible that they possess a greater permeability than the fibers of skeletal muscles. Choline may act upon skeletal muscle only after denervation because by this means the permeability of the fiber is increased. On the other hand, ocular muscle fiber, being thin and delicate, may already be sufficiently permeable that choline can penetrate it in its normal state. Opposed to this theory is the fact that some drugs seem to act quantitatively in a similar fashion on both ocular muscles and skeletal muscle. For example, the effects of eserine are in general the same on both skeletal and ocular muscles.

Ocular muscles have a greater sensitivity to curare than do skeletal muscles. Greater spread between dosages is necessary to produce relaxation of ocular muscles and respiratory depression than when the desired effect is for skeletal muscles, which makes the use of curare tolerably safe in ocular surgery.

The enzyme cholinesterase is present in ocular muscles. It hydrolyzes acetylcholine to the almost inert derivative choline. The presence of the enzyme presumably ensures that acetylcholine, normally liberated in response to each nerve impulse (p. 223), produces only a single response of the fibers and does not persist long enough or in sufficient concentration to produce the repetitive responses which occur experimentally. The enzyme is concentrated in the muscle in the region of the motor nerve endings where its presence is most required.

Eserine and Prostigmin are anticholinesterase drugs and thus preserve acetylcholine, which may be liberated in the body or injected into the circulation. After eserine has been injected, the ocular muscle may show spontaneous contraction (Fig. 154). The presence of this drug enhances the contraction of an ocular muscle which is produced by maximal single shocks applied to the motor nerve (Fig. 155). Under these conditions each nerve volley reaching the muscle fibers produces not a simple twitch, but a repetitive response—a short tetanus which, of course, produces greater tension than a twitch. These drugs preserve the acetylcholine naturally liberated at the motor nerve ending long enough for it to elicit repetitive responses similar to those resulting from intra-arterial injection.

Succinylcholine and decamethonium, like acetylcholine, are depolarizing agents[51] and cause the extraocular muscles to contract with lower doses than affect the skeletal muscles, which usually show no effects from these drugs until after denervation. Of considerable interest is the fact that the contraction of the ocular muscle is not necessarily accompanied by an increase in firing. Low doses produce tetanic contraction as evidenced by increased muscle tension and electrical activity, whereas higher doses produce contracture of the muscles with maintenance of tension but loss of electrical activity. The effectiveness of these drugs on the ocular muscles depends on the state of anesthesia.[52] Contracture occurs only in unanesthetized or very lightly anesthetized patients. Under deep general anesthesia succinylcholine appears to have no effect on the muscle.

Because these drugs produce contraction of the ocular muscles the intraocular pressure may be raised. For this reason they should not be used in intraocular surgery unless it is done under deep general anesthesia.

Reciprocal innervation

In the performance of its activity it is essential that a muscle shall not be hampered by an antagonistic muscle working against it. Since early times this fact has been recognized in the case of ocular muscles. In 1662, Descartes (quoted by Fulton[53]) suggested that when the external rectus muscle contracted the medial rectus simultaneously relaxed. This idea was gradually elaborated until Sherrington in his epic work enunciated the law of reciprocal innervation.

At the same time good evidence has accumulated that under certain conditions antagonistic muscles do contract simultaneously, and Tilney and Pike[45] have denied that the law of reciprocal innervation is applicable to the muscles of the eye. However, the evidence is in favor of reciprocal innervation, as against cocontraction, in ocular muscles under most conditions.

It is important to define the term *reciprocal innervation,* which has often been misinterpreted to imply that antagonistic muscles are never simultaneously in a state of contraction. The law, as stated by Sherrington, was enunciated as follows.

"When a decerebrate or spinal preparation executes a muscular movement, augmentation of the contraction never proceeds concurrently in antagonistic muscles, and, similarly, diminution of the contraction in antagonists does not occur concomitantly."*

The law merely states that "increase of contraction (or the converse) does not proceed simultaneously in opposed muscles." As contraction occurs in an extensor muscle, e.g., contractile activity diminishes simultaneously and equally in the antagonistic flexor. Contraction may be present in two antagonistic muscles simultaneously but in a reciprocal relation. This relationship allows steadiness of movement with antagonism.

It must be admitted that under certain conditions antagonistic skeletal muscles do show cocontraction rather than reciprocal innervation. This is certainly true of those voluntary acts in which flexors as well as extensors are simultaneously contracted in an effort to immobilize a joint. When the fist is pronated and supinated, e.g., especially if the grip is kept firm on some object held in the hand, both the biceps and triceps are kept tonically contracted at the same time, forming a support for the elbow. It is not surprising, therefore, that cortical stimulation does not always result in reciprocal innervation, but in cocontraction.

The experiments of Sherrington, which he performed in 1893, proved that under certain conditions the law of reciprocal innervation holds good for the extraocular muscles. Experimenting with the monkey, Sherrington cut the third and fourth cranial nerves on one side intracranially, e.g., on the right side. Several weeks were allowed to elapse for complete degenera-

*From Sherrington, C. S.: Integrative action of the nervous system.

tion of the cut nerves to take place. Examination of the animal then showed complete paralysis of all the extraocular muscles on the right side, except for the lateral rectus muscle innervated by the sixth cranial nerve. The right eyeball was abducted due to the tonus of the lateral rectus muscle being unopposed by the tonus of its antagonist, the paralyzed medial rectus muscle.

When electrodes were placed on the right cerebral cortex in the region which elicits conjugate deviation of the eyes to the left (p. 435). Sherrington found that not only did the left eye turn sharply to the left, due to the pull of the left lateral rectus, but also that the right eyeball moved from its abducted position to the midline. Since all the muscles of the right eye were paralyzed except the right lateral rectus, the movement of this eye inward could be due only to relaxation of the tonus of this muscle. The diminution in tonus of this muscle, in association with an increase in tonic activity of the left lateral rectus, constitutes reciprocal innervation.

The experiments of De Kleyn leave little room for doubt as to the existence of reciprocal innervation in the extraocular muscles of rabbits, and the myograms of McCouch and Adler[54] also prove recipro-

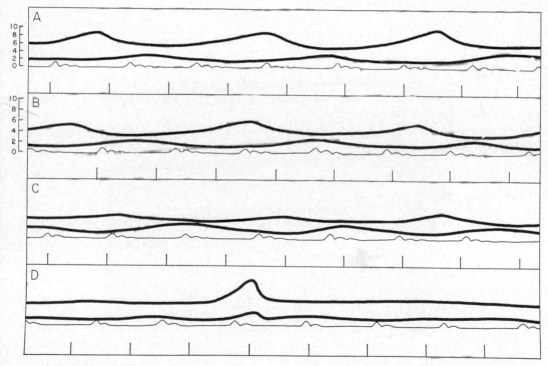

Fig. 161. Spontaneous nystagmus. **A, B,** and **C:** Medial rectus above; lateral rectus below. Standardization for tension of external rectus at left of **A,** for medial rectus at left of **B. D:** Retraction reflex from stimulation of nostril on a background of nystagmus. Internal rectus above; external rectus below. Refractor bulbi is free. The shortening in the external rectus is probably due to tug from the original of retractor and that in the internal rectus chiefly to active contraction. (After McCouch and Adler.)

cal innervation in the ocular muscles of cats during artificially induced nystagmus (Fig. 161). In these experiments the eyeballs in decerebrated animals were removed, and the medial and lateral recti were connected independently from each other with suitable recording levers so that contraction of one would have no influence on the state of tension of the other. Nystagmus was then produced by irrigating the labyrinths with cold water. The records show that when the ipsilateral labyrinth is irrigated lateral nystagmus in which the lateral rectus contracts slowly results, and at the same time the medial rectus relaxes correspondingly until the muscles reach the full extent of their movement. At this point the medial rectus contracts suddenly, and the lateral rectus relaxes with corresponding rapidity.

Electromyographic records from human subjects show reciprocal innervation under normal conditions during versions and vergences (Fig. 157) and in induced nystagmus (Fig. 162). Under abnormal conditions cocontraction may occur. In Fig. 163 is shown cocontraction of the medial and lateral rectus muscles in a patient with retractory nystagmus. This patient had a brain tumor which evidently upset the central mechanism responsible for the normal reciprocity of innervation distributed to antagonistic muscles.

In most patients with complete paralysis of the third and fourth cranial nerves on one side, the eye on the paralyzed side is strongly abducted and when the patient looks toward the opposite side, the paralyzed eye shows no motion toward the midline. This fact has been cited to prove that, in man, reciprocal innervation does not occur in the eye muscles. While the eye under these conditions usually does

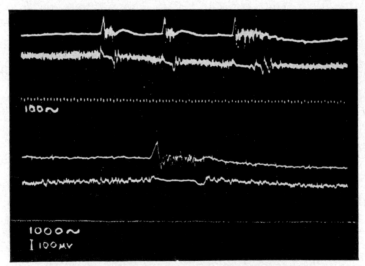

Fig. 162. Caloric nystagmus (cold water in right ear). *Upper tracing,* left lateral rectus. *Lower tracing,* right lateral rectus. (Time, 100 cycles.) In upper tracings extremely rapid nystagmus episodes occur. Note reciprocal relationship between these contralateral antagonists. Base line showed absence of activity in the left lateral rectus, whereas fair activity was present in the right lateral rectus, owing to the gaze being directed to the right. A sudden burst of marked activity in the left lateral rectus corresponded to complete silence of the right lateral rectus. One nystagmus episode is recorded from the same muscle at fast speed. (Time, 1000 cycles.) (From Breinin, G., and Moldaver, J.: Arch. Ophth. **54:**204, 1955.)

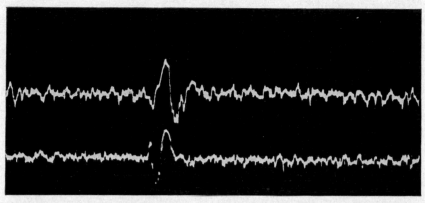

Fig. 163. Simultaneous activity of medial and lateral recti in retractory nystagmus. *Upper tracing,* lateral rectus. *Lower tracing,* medial rectus. (From Breinin, G.: Arch. Ophth. **57:** 175, 1957.)

not move, occasionally one sees a patient in whom paralysis is fresh, and the paralyzed eye does move to the midline merely by reciprocal inhibition of the unparalyzed lateral rectus. The reason most patients do not show this is that contracture of the unparalyzed lateral rectus takes place. This is shown by resistance to passive movement. In these patients, one cannot move the eye to the midline with forceps until the contractured lateral rectus is recessed. A patient with paralysis of both the third and fourth cranial nerves, demonstrating reciprocal innervation, has been reported.[55] If the third and fourth cranial nerves in a monkey are cut and the animal's gaze is directed to the opposite side shortly after the nerve section, the paralyzed eye will move toward the midline.

Most investigators agree that during both versions and vergences electromyographic records show no evidence of cocontraction of antagonistic muscles. Tamler and associates, on the other hand, claim that during saccadic eye movements (voluntary versions from one point to another, as contrasted with following movements elicited by the subject fixating on a moving target) there is increased elec-

trical activity in all of the muscles except the one reciprocally inhibited.[56] Further, they report that in asymetric convergence the medial and lateral rectus of the stationary eye cocontract.[57] Breinin, on the other hand, found no increased activity in the muscles of the stationary eye.[58] Somewhat midway between these opposite reports is that of Miller,[59] who reports that asymmetric convergence is characterized by a saccadic burst of activity in the yoke muscles followed by a convergence pattern in the medial recti. The stationary eye shows similar changes except that the saccade occurs in the lateral rectus and is then followed by a convergence pattern in the medial rectus.

In following movements Tamler and co-workers[60] found cocontraction of antagonistic muscles and subsequently reported that in following horizontal movements when the eyes were above or below the horizontal, the vertical recti were consistently more active in abduction than in adduction, whereas the reverse is true for the oblique muscles.[61]

Both the muscle spindles and the tendon organs discharge impulses up to the brain. The pattern of discharge of the spindle under resting tension shows irregularities comparable to those shown from muscle spindles in the cat's gastrocnemius with an intact motor supply due to the fact that gamma efferents to their intrafusal fibers are constantly affecting the output of the spindle. The effect of this control of the spindle by the gamma efferents may have something to do with the ability of the ocular muscle to contract very rapidly.

We do not know what exact function the sensory discharges from the spindles actually accomplish. There is no evidence that they bring about stretch reflexes or that they supply information to the cerebral cortex, but it is most likely that in some way they ensure smooth and accurate muscle action and serve as sensitive organs for registering the activities of these extremely rapidly acting muscles.[62]

The sensitivity of the primary afferent endings of the muscle spindle to stretch can be increased by stimulation of the gamma efferent fibers to the spindle. This has little or no effect on the threshold of the spindle to stretch.[63]

Proprioception from ocular muscles

It has been known since the early experiments of Sherrington and Mott that voluntary movements of the limbs cannot be carried out normally if the dorsal spinal nerve roots are sectioned. These tracts carry afferent sensory impulses from the muscles into the central nervous system which are essential for the execution of voluntary movements. No disturbance in motility occurs if only the sensory supply from the skin of the limbs is abolished. Sensory impulses from the muscles are necessary for their accurate function. These are called proprioceptive impulses and are due to excitation of specialized end organs in the muscles by the contraction of the muscle fibers. These specialized end organs are called muscle spindles.

By this means the body is kept informed of the position and amount of tension in the various postural muscles, such as those of the limbs. This information modifies the efferent motor impulses in such fashion that any desired movement is carried out smoothly. In the absence of proprioception, the movement may be attempted, but its execution will be awkward, i.e., ataxic.

The muscle spindle may be stimulated by stretch of the muscle or contraction of its fibers. In the tendons of the muscle are sensory structures, similar to muscle spindles, called tendon spindles or organs of Golgi. Several types of sensory nerves with rather complicated endings enter the spindle on each side. It is not known which type of sensory ending is responsible for the discharge of nerve impulses from the muscle (Fig. 164).

Matthews has been able to distinguish three different types of activity in the electric response from muscles. These three types are named A1, A2, and B responses, respectively. About half of the responses obtained are due to the A1 mechanism. The rest are equally divided between the A2 and B mechanisms. In Fig. 165, *A* is shown the A1 type of discharge which occurs when the muscle is stretched. The receptors responsible for the A1 type of discharge fire off as the muscle is stretched, with an initial burst of impulses which dies down as the end organs become adapted. In Fig. 165, *B* is shown the A1 type of discharge which occurs when the muscle is stretched and is then caused to contract against the stretch by stimulation of its motor nerve. It can be seen that the A1 mechanism becomes silent as the muscle contracts but fires again as relaxation begins. The A2 type of discharge occurs if the muscle is made to contract forcibly (Fig. 165, *C*). The B type of response comes from endings which are harder to stimulate than

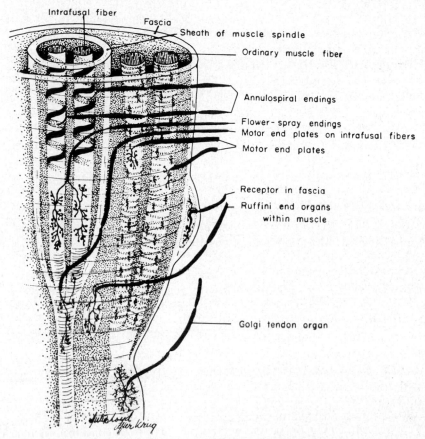

Fig. 164. Muscle spindles in skeletal muscle. (After Amberson, W., and Smith, D.: Outline of physiology, ed. 2, Baltimore, 1948, Williams & Wilkins Co., p, 169.)

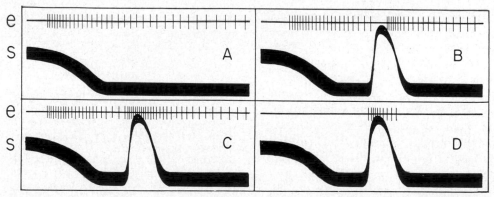

Fig. 165. A, A1 type of discharge when the muscle is stretched. B, A1 type of discharge when the muscle is stretched and then caused to contract against the stretch by stimulation of its motor nerve. C, A2 type of discharge. Stretch and contraction as in B. D, B type of discharge. Stretch and contraction as in B. e, Electrical record; s, stretch and contraction record. (After Amberson, W., and Smith, D.: Outline of physiology, ed. 2, Baltimore, 1948, Williams & Wilkins Co.)

those previously mentioned (Fig. 165, *D*). These endings only fire off when the muscle contracts. Matthews believes that these discharges come from the tendon spindles.

By means of this signaling device the muscles are able to notify the central nervous system at all times concerning their state of stretch or contraction. The number of messages coming into the central nervous system rises and falls as the activity of the muscle waxes and wanes.

In those muscles which show proprioception, specialized end organs can be demonstrated in the muscle fibers, and special fiber tracts that carry these afferent impulses into the brain can be demonstrated in the central nervous system. The muscles which have proprioceptive sense also show stretch reflexes; i.e., in a suitable isolated nerve-muscle preparation when the muscle is put on a stretch, it responds with a contraction.

Proprioception has generally been accepted for the muscles of the limbs, but has been questioned seriously for the ocular muscles. In part the difficulty has been in the marked anatomic differences which occur in different species of animals. The fact that no muscle spindles can be found in the ocular muscles of the cat, rabbit, and dog (the usual laboratory animals) has been interpreted to apply to man. Further, some have stretched the definition of proprioception to include both a vague subconscious awareness of the position of a limb and an accurate localization of the position of the body in space. This has been assumed to account for the fact that we are aware of the position of our eyes in their orbits at all times, even in the dark. This suggests that proprioceptive impulses arise from the ocular muscles themselves and give us information on the position of the eyes in the orbits. The knowledge of the position of the eyes in the orbits does not come from

sensory impulses in the lid or conjunctiva because these can be anesthetized completely without interfering with the sense of the position of the globes.

It has been assumed further that proprioception from the ocular muscles aids in our perception of space. Our awareness of the position of objects in space depends upon a great many different factors, one of which might be a proprioceptive sense from the ocular muscles.

Sherrington devised the following experiment to show the necessity for some such mechanism to modify visual impressions, which would otherwise be incorrect. If a person looks at three dots arranged in a vertical line on a wall straight in front of him, he is aware that the dots are directly in front of him from the correlation of the retinal images and his gravitational sense of position in respect to the ground, i.e., his egocentric localization. He is aware also that the dots are arranged in a vertical line by the fact that their images fall on parts of each retina which, by experience, yield the perception of verticality*; i.e., they are consciously projected in space in a vertical line. If the person now directs his eyes up and to the right to three other dots similarly placed in a vertical line, he maintains the correct impression that these dots are situated up and to the right from the fact that his eyes had to turn up and to the

---

*The relative position of objects in space is made known to us largely because each receptor has a local sign; i.e., when it is stimulated, it gives rise to a sensation of consciousness that the object from which the light rays come has a definite and unchanging location in space. The fovea has the local sign of the straight ahead position when the gaze is straight ahead. All retinal elements on the nasal side of the fovea have local signs of the temporal visual field, and all retinal elements on the temporal side of the fovea have local signs of the nasal visual field.

right to receive the images on their foveas. The dots are still interpreted as being vertical. However, it can be shown now that their images no longer fall on the same retinal receptors as they did formerly because during the movement of the eyes up and to the right into an oblique position of gaze, each globe has undergone a rotation around its anteroposterior axis (torsion.

The images of the dots, therefore, fall on retinal receptors that lie obliquely to those previously stimulated. Since the upper pole of the vertical meridian of each cornea now leans to the right, the image of the dots falling on the retina lies obliquely to the vertical meridian of the retina. This should give rise to a sensation of the dots' being arranged in an oblique line, instead of in a vertical line. Sherrington believed that our correct interpretation of the position of the dots under this condition is due to the fact that proprioceptive impulses from the ocular muscles corrected the retinal impressions. In other words, the local sign of each retinal receptor was somewhat modified due to proprioception from the ocular muscles.

This can be explained in a different way, however. Irvine and Ludvigh[64] point out that the interpretation of retinal images is a very complex affair and that, just because retinal receptors which should produce a sense of obliquity are stimulated, it is not necessary to suppose that they do so, or that some other mechanism alters their local sign. The perceptions yielded by any set of retinal receptors are considerably modified by experience, and under different conditions they may give rise to entirely different perceptions. The situation may be compared to that of a retinal image of a dinner plate which, when seen full face-on, results in a perception of a round object. When viewed tilted at an angle, it still gives the per-

ception of a round plate, in spite of the fact that now the retinal image is not round but an ellipse. In this case, experience has modified the perception of the different forms of the retinal image.

The various criteria just mentioned which are always associated with proprioception and which are present in general voluntary muscles have not been fulfilled in ocular muscles of all species. Muscle spindles have not been found in the ocular muscles of the usual laboratory animals, and no stretch reflexes could be elicited from the ocular muscles of cats.[54] However, as pointed out in the discussion of anatomic characteristics of ocular muscles, typical spindles are present in the ocular muscles of man and certain other animals, and six types of sensory nerve endings have been described, each of which might be considered to relay proprioceptive information from the ocular muscles to the brain. Cooper, Daniel, and Whitteridge,[65] experimenting on the muscles of goats, have recorded the discharges from afferent nerve endings in the inferior oblique muscle from single fibers in the appropriate branch of the oculomotor nerve. They found a spontaneous discharge of low frequency when the muscle was slack. This increased when the muscle was stretched passively. The discharge was completely inhibited during active contraction of the muscle, but there was an increase in frequency during relaxation exactly like that associated with passive stretching. These afferent discharges are thought, therefore, to originate in the muscle spindles.

Later these same authors[66] were able to secure typical stretch discharges in the afferent fibers running in the third, fourth, and sixth cranial nerves via the fifth cranial nerve. Since ocular muscles are flexors and not extensors, one might not expect to find well-developed phasic and static stretch reflexes. Tendon jerk responses, therefore, should not be anticipated. However, this does not rule out some mechanism for signaling changes in muscle tension, which seems to have been proved by the findings just noted.

Further proof of this mechanism has been obtained by Breinin.[67] Constant firing of both the medial and lateral rectus muscles has been found when the eyes are in the primary position. When the medial and lateral rectus muscles are freed from the globe, however, the level of firing decreases radically (Fig. 166). Some firing continues when the fascia supports the muscle and prevents its complete retraction into the position of rest. It would seem that normal firing in the primary position is a consequence of the tension put on the attached muscles. When the muscles are freed from the globe, the spindle mechanism ceases its discharge and thus inhibits motor firing. Breinin was unable to show any increase in the normal firing obtained in the primary position by putting the muscle on the stretch, which suggests that this basic stretch mechanism cannot be augmented beyond a limiting point. While the ocular muscles are on the globe, recipro-

cal innervation is shown, as just stated, with graded augmentation of the agonist and simultaneously graded decrementation of the antagonist. After the muscles are freed from their attachments to the globe, they lose this nicely graded reciprocity. There is an abrupt increase in the agonist, along with silence of the antagonist. When gaze is reversed, the previously active muscle quits before the new agonist commences its abrupt firing (Fig. 167, *A* and *B*). This suggests that the loss in gradation reflects the loss of some afferent mechanism in the muscles which maintains the normal level and gradation of firing.

All of the findings just given prove that some proprioceptive mechanism is present in the ocular muscles of man. However, this does not imply that this mechanism necessarily provides us with a sense of the position of the globe or with an awareness of our position in space.

Some difficulty has been experienced in proving that these afferent impulses are truly sensory and reach the nucleus of the fifth cranial nerve. It has been shown, however, that when the ocular muscles of the goat are stretched central responses can be obtained from an outlying part

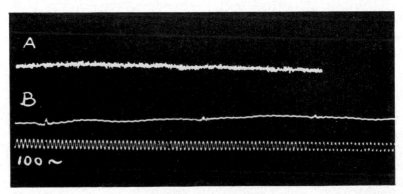

Fig. 166. Electromyogram of a rectus muscle. **A**, Before severance of tendon. **B**, After severance of tendon. Note decreased activity. (Amplitude of time signal, 100 μv.) (From Breinin, G.: Arch. Ophth. **57:**177, 1957.)

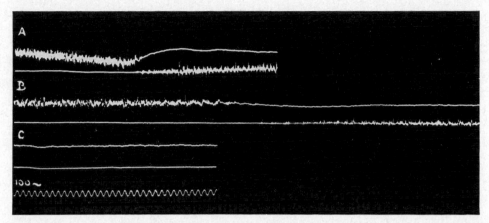

Fig. 167. Electromyogram of the medial and lateral rectus muscles after enucleation. **A,** Reciprocal innervation, rapid. **B,** Reciprocal innervation, slow. **C,** Primary position, no activity. (Amplitude of time signal, 100 μv.) (From Breinin, G.: Arch. Ophth. 57:177, 1957.)

of the mesencephalic nucleus of the fifth cranial nerve just ventral to the posterior commissure, from among the intramedullary fibers of the fifth cranial nerve, and from the region just caudal to the entering fibers of the fifth cranial nerve.[68] Anatomists consider all these sites to be part of the complex of the fifth cranial nerve. Cooper, Daniel, and Whitteridge point out that proprioceptors are an essential factor in all phases of a muscle's activity and that, in the case of the delicate movements performed by the eyes, proprioception is even more necessary than in other types of muscle performing grosser functions. The proprioceptors of the muscles of the eye, they point out, may have a further function, as follows, "associated with the relative speeds with which impulses from the muscles and those from the retina reach the brain."* One of the arguments against the need for proprioceptors in muscles of the eye has been that the retina can supply all the information required by the central nervous system. Yet the responses set up by illumination

of the retina do not reach the brain for an appreciable time due very largely to retinal delay. Creed and Granit[69] found that in the retina of the cat there was a delay of 25 to 80 msec. under various conditions of illumination. When the eye is moved in order to look at an object, the messages from the sensory endings in the muscles must reach the brainstem, with latencies dependent only on their conduction times, i.e., in 1 or 2 msec. Thus, by the time the retinal discharges reach the brain, messages from the muscles in the eye can have been sent to all the centers that may be concerned with the integration of the ocular movement. The neuronal pools of ocular muscles will then be in a state of readiness to control the delicate muscular movements needed for maintaining fixation.[69] This is especially true in making movements of the eyes necessary to follow a rapidly moving object, especially one undergoing rapid changes in direction.

Many of the known facts seem compatible with the hypothesis expressed by Irvine and Ludvigh of an innervational sense, rather than of a true proprioceptive sense, in the ocular muscles. Muscular ac-

*From Cooper, S., Daniel, P., and Whitteridge, D.: J. Physiol. **120**:471, 1953.

tivity, they believe, still forms the basis for the judgment of direction when the eyes are moved, but as they state, this "judgement is not founded on the actual contraction of the muscles, but upon the will to move them."* When the eyes are moved to the right in a dark room, one is conscious of their position, not from proprioceptive sensations from the muscles, but from the conscious effort to turn them.

In support of this hypothesis one can point to the fact that when the eyes are moved reflexly and not volitionally the subject is quite unconscious of their position and in fact of any movement of the eyes at all. During nystagmus due to labyrinthine stimuli, whether resulting from disease artificially induced by rotation in a chair or by douching the ear with cold water, the subject does not know that his eyes are moving, but instead is conscious only of the apparent movement of the room. Everything around him seems to be turning, while he feels certain that neither his eyes nor the rest of his body is moving. The same is true of the movements of the eyes during optokinetic nystagmus. The subject experiences no sensation that his eyes are undergoing constant movement. Pulling the eye from side to side with a pair of forceps produces no conscious sense of a change in position, provided that it is done in a dark room or under such conditions that the subject can obtain no visual clues. Finally, Cornsweet[70] has shown that in the absence of visual control the eyes are incapable of maintaining their fixation. Whatever proprioceptive feedback there is, it does not play a part in the fine corrective movements that serve to maintain ordinary fixation. When our eyes are moved by a conscious effort, we know

that they have moved and can tell exactly what position they occupy in respect to the orbit, but when they are moved by any reflex innervation or passively by mechanical pull, we are not aware of any deviation.

We may conclude that the eyes are without any conscious position sense and that we only know how far we have moved them by judgment of the effort we have made in moving them. The accuracy with which one can position the eyes in the absence of visual clues is about the same as the accuracy of positioning the finger in the absence of visual clues, i.e., ± 1 degree in both horizontal and vertical directions. Likewise, the ability to maintain fixation in the dark is about the same as the ability to hold the hand steady at arm's length. After 5 seconds both show a standard deviation in the horizontal direction of about ± 0.5 degree.[71]

During voluntary movements of the eyes the environment always appears fixed, and we relate the movement to our eyes, whereas during passive reflex motion of the eyes an impression is produced of movement of the environment. It has been argued that active movements of the eyes result in proprioceptive impulses which convey the information that it is the eyes which have moved and not the environment, whereas passive or reflex movement does not excite proprioceptive impulses. Therefore the observer does not realize that his eyes are moving but considers the environment to be moving.[72] This suggests that passive or reflex movements are inadequate to stimulate the proprioceptive mechanism. This is in accord with the idea formerly advanced that the muscle spindles in flexor muscles* respond

---

*From Irvine, S., and Ludvigh, E.: Arch. Ophth. **15:**1037, 1936.

*It must be remembered that the ocular muscles are flexor muscles. Sherrington agreed that the evidence for proprioception was not too secure for flexor muscles.

to active contraction only and not to passive stretch. Even this argument in support of proprioception loses weight since it has been demonstrated that even passive stretch excites muscle spindles to activity and produces stretch reflexes in the muscles of the limbs.[73]

A sensation of movement of the eyes may arise from stimulation of certain areas of the cortex. Penfield and Erickson[74] found that sensation of movement of the eyes (although a rare response) resulted occasionally from electrical stimulation of an area of the frontal cortex, anterior to the fissure of Rolando, in a zone near area 8 (Fig. 168). The sense of the position of the eyes may be akin to the sense of the position of the limbs, i.e., stereognosis. The elements essential for stereognosis are localization of point, discrimination of two points, and a sense of position during movement (muscle-tendon sense). In the hand, e.g., the cortical elements necessary for stereognosis are located in the cortex close to the motor representation for the muscles of the hand.

Proprioceptive sense from the ocular muscles has been invoked to best explain the phenomenon of past-pointing, which occurs in recent paralysis of ocular muscles. When a patient with fresh paralysis or paresis of an ocular muscle, the right lateral rectus, e.g., looks at an object situated in the right motor field, he will point his finger farther to the right of the object when asked to locate its position, provided, of course, that he cannot see where his finger is pointing while he looks at the object. This is called past-pointing and the direction of past-pointing is always in the direction of action of a paretic muscle. Two possible explanations may account for past-pointing. It may be assumed that in order to fixate the object with the paralyzed eye a greater than normal impulse must be sent to the paretic right lateral rectus muscle and that the excessive innervation required, therefore, produces the sensation that the object is farther to the right than it really is.

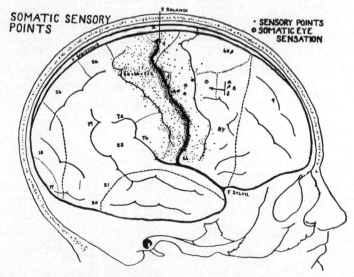

Fig. 168. Diagram of the right motor cortex, showing the points at which stimulation in the conscious subject produces a sensation of movement in the eyes. (From Penfield, W., and Erickson, T.: Epilepsy and cerebral localization, Springfield, Ill., 1941, Charles C Thomas, Publisher.)

Hence, the person past-points to the right. On the other hand, a paretic lateral rectus fails to move the eye its full extent temporally so that an image of an object situated in the temporal part of the visual field does not fall exactly on the fovea. An object in the right temporal field, e.g., does not fall exactly on the fovea but to a point slightly to the nasal side of the fovea of the right eye when that eye has a paretic lateral rectus muscle. Since retinal elements (rods and cones) on the nasal side of the fovea have local signs in the temporal field, the object is interpreted as being farther to the temporal side than it really is. The subject believes that his eyes moved correctly, and this causes him to past-point to the position in space which corresponds to the local sign of the part of the retina stimulated.

This hypothesis has been tested on persons with recent paralysis of a lateral rectus muscle in the following manner.[75] A patient with paresis of a right lateral rectus muscle was seated at a perimeter, and the left eye was covered. A test spot of light was then placed on the arc of the perimeter in the temporal field 30 degrees from fixation. A black cloth was held in such a way that the patient could not see his own arm, and he was asked to point directly to the test spot of light. The difference between the actual position of the spot and the position to which he pointed was then measured. Two types of test objects were used interchangeably: (1) a large white spot of light measuring 15 mm. in diameter and (2) a small letter which had to be identified by the subject. The letter was small enough (2 mm.) that the subject had to move the eye so that its image fell on the fovea before he could identify it. In each trial the letter was changed. It was found that when the large spot of light was used, i.e., target 1, the angle of past-pointing was much larger than when the small spot and letter, target 2, were used. When target 1 was used, the subject did not have to turn his eye so that its image fell on the fovea in order to be seen. The image of the spot, therefore, fell on the nasal side of the fovea and was consciously projected to the temporal side of its true position in the field. When target 2 was used, its image fell on the fovea whose local sign corresponded to the correct position of the test object. No past-pointing occurred, therefore (Fig. 169).

If the angle of past-pointing depended upon false proprioception from the palsied muscle or on excessive innervation sent to this muscle, it would be either the same or greater when target 2 was used than when target 1 was used, for the eye, as stated, had to move farther in order to decipher smaller target 2. It would seem, therefore, that the angle of past-pointing is determined by the position of the image on the retina. When this falls on the fovea, the projection is accurate, but when it falls on some spot other than the fovea, the projection is to the point in space which has the same local sign as the receptor stimulated. It is not necessary, therefore, to account for past-pointing by assuming proprioceptive impulses from the ocular muscles.

Muscle pain

Ordinary naked nerve endings, similar to those known to produce pain in the skin, are found in ordinary muscles, and yet in man or in an animal an exposed muscle may be cut or a needle may be passed through it with little or no pain being felt. Pain in a muscle can be experienced after an injury, during cramps, or if the circulation is interfered with. It is believed that pain in muscle is mediated by some chemical factor and that a diminished flow leads to lack of oxygen so

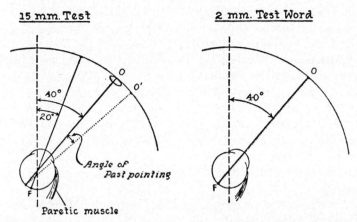

Fig. 169. Right eye of a subject with paresis of the right external rectus muscle. On the arc of a Zeiss perimeter a light, **O**, has been placed at 40 degrees in the temporal field. With the left eye covered, the subject is requested to look at the object and to point with his right hand to it. The right hand is shielded from his view entirely so that he is not conscious of where he is pointing. The angle of past-pointing is then measured. *Left diagram,* the eye does not turn out to 40 degrees to look at a large test object, i.e., a 15 mm. light, but turns out only to 20 degrees, this being sufficient for the subject to see the light. The image, therefore, falls on the nasal side of the fovea and hence is projected into space at **O′**. The subject, therefore, past points at **O′**. *Right diagram* shows what happens when a small test light and word are used, of such a nature that in order to see what the word is the eye must be turned out all the way so that the image falls on the fovea. In this case the projection is correct and there is no past-pointing.

that lactic acid accumulates in sufficient amounts to stimulate the pain nerve endings. Muscle pain is often rather diffuse in character, and is felt not only in the muscle itself, but also in projected or referred to nearby skin areas. A special kind of muscle pain is the so-called cold pain described by Wolfe and Hardy. The phenomenon may be connected with local constriction of blood vessels induced by the cold and can thus be associated with the pain of muscles caused by interruption of their circulation at normal body temperatures. Ocular muscles yield a severe sensation of pain when they are pulled on, however.

Reaction of ocular muscles to disease

We are still quite ignorant of the changes, histologic and physicochemical, which take place in ocular muscles in disease states, but this promises to be a fertile field in the near future, with the application of electrophysiologic techniques to these problems.

Myasthenia gravis. Myasthenia gravis is a disease characterized by great muscular weakness and rapid onset of fatigue, without any histologic changes in the nerves or muscles themselves which can account for this change. The ocular muscles are frequently the first affected. Muscular disability is apparently the result of some disturbance in the normal mechanism of transmission of the nerve impulse from the nerve terminals to the muscle fibers (p. 223). Among the factors which have been examined are (1) insufficient formation of acetylcholine locally, (2) abnormally rapid destruction of acetylcholine due perhaps to excessive local cholinesterase activity, and (3) presence of an abnormal curare-like substance which hampers the access of normally formed acetylcholine to the muscle fibers. There is some evidence that cholinesterase activity is actually lower than normal, but the best available evidence suggests that the last factor (3) is the most probable causative factor. It is noteworthy that the distribution and character of the weakness in myasthenia gravis closely resemble those which occur in man after injection of small doses of curare.

Many drugs which do not antagonize cholinesterase, such as epinephrine, ephedrine, guanidine, and potassium salts, produce some benefit in the treatment of myasthenia gravis. The only common factor in these drugs is their anticurare action. Other potent anticholinesterase agents, such as DFP and eserine, are not so effective as Prostigmin. Di-isopropyl flurophosphate inactivates more cholinesterase than does Prostigmin, without the same beneficial effect, according to Leopold.[76] These observations suggest that in myasthenia gravis some metabolic disorder may lead to the liberation of the curarizing agent. Attention has been directed to the thymus gland as a possible source of the curare-like substance since many patients have benefited from thymectomy. Moreover, it has been found that the blood of patients with myasthenia gravis, when injected into a normal person after exercise, may produce a curare-like effect and that, if a blood pressure cuff is put on the arm of a patient with myasthenia gravis and the arm muscles are thoroughly exercised, myasthenic signs appear elsewhere in the body when the cuff is released.

The muscle weakness may usually be controlled by the use of anticholinesterase or anticurare drugs—neostigmine, edrophonium, etc. The response to these drugs has been of great diagnostic help as well as of therapeutic benefit. This is especially true with the application of electromyography, for the improvement can be detected easily in the electrical responses of the muscle long before the improvement following administration of the drug is sufficient to create a noticeable gross improvement in the function of the muscle. Edrophonium (Tensilon chloride) has proved to be the best drug for this purpose.[77] By means of electromyography it is possible to differentiate between myasthenic paralysis and other types of non-myasthenic paralysis or progressive nuclear ophthalmoplegia.

Paralyses of ocular muscles. Contractures which are likely to occur following paralysis of an ocular muscle have been mentioned previously (p. 396). It must be admitted that there are very few histologic proofs of such contractures, and we do not know whether there is a replacement of muscle fibers by connective tissue or whether the normal content of elastic tissue, which is excessive in ocular muscles, undergoes hypertrophy. The influence of loss of function of one muscle on its agonists, antagonists, yoke muscle, and antagonist of the yoke muscle will be considered in another section (p. 528).

Recently discovered changes in the electrical activity of paralyzed muscles call for comment here. The diagnosis of a neurogenic type of paralysis can be made with confidence, according to Breinin,[77] who has amplified considerably the pioneer work of Björk in this field.[78] The cardinal sign of neurogenic paralysis that involves the lower motor neuron is fibrillation, and characteristic fibrillations have been noted. However, they are not frequent in paralysis of ocular muscles. In fact, not all authors have found them.[79] In moderate paresis of a muscle Breinin has found irregular or spare recruitment, poorly sustained discharge, loss of the interference pattern characteristically seen on effort, occurrences of single-unit discharges in the field of action of a muscle (evidence of the loss of motor units), and denervation fibrillations.

It should always be kept in mind that failure of a muscle to move the eye into its field of action, either completely or not at all, does not prove that this muscle is paralyzed. It is always possible that the restriction of movement is due to structural changes in the antagonist of the muscle, in the fascia of the antagonist, or in the muscle itself which will not permit the muscle to pull the globe into its field of activity. The forced duction test may provide one with an indication that such mechanical hindrances to movement are present, but electromyography proves definitely whether this is the case or not. If a normal level of firing is found in the muscle suspected of being paralyzed, it is certain that failure of the globe to move is due to some mechanical hindrance and not to paralysis of the muscle.

A difference between primary and secondary deviations of the eyes—one of the characteristic signs of early paralysis of an ocular muscle (p. 529)—is shown in records taken from proved cases of paralysis of ocular muscles (Fig. 170). It is well known that this valuable sign of paralysis of a muscle is not always present, and it is generally believed that it disappears with duration of the paralysis. In the early stages of paralysis of a muscle it is always present, but as time goes on, the strabismus becomes more comitant (p. 515), and the angle of squint becomes the same regardless of whether the eye with the paralyzed muscle or the unaffected eye is the fixating eye. With electromyography, it will be interesting to discover in conditions in which the angle of squint has become comitant whether the yoke muscle of a paralyzed muscle fires excessively when the eye with the paralyzed muscle fixates or when the nonparalyzed eye fixates, which should occur theoretically. If this is found to be true, it will indicate that the differences in movement of the eyes, depending upon which one is fixating, is obscured by some other factor; the muscle is firing excessively but cannot increase the angle of strabismus.

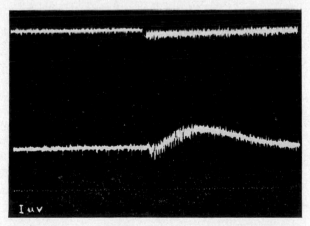

Fig. 170. Left inferior oblique in a patient with paretic right superior rectus. *Upper left tracing,* good eye fixing in primary position—primary deviation. *Upper right tracing,* paretic eye fixing in primary position—secondary deviation. *Lower tracing,* upshoot of inferior oblique. (From Breinin, G.: Arch. Ophth. 54:409, 1955.)

NERVOUS CENTERS AND PATHWAYS FOR VOLUNTARY MOVEMENTS

The eyes, like the arms and legs, are moved by a combination of voluntary and reflex innervations. For purposes of description, the voluntary and the involuntary or reflex movements will be considered individually, but the two mechanisms operate simultaneously and harmoniously and are seldom separated from each other under normal conditions.

Frontal centers for voluntary movements of the eyes

A person may move his eyes voluntarily as the result of a command to do so or of a conscious decision on his part. Whatever the incentive may be to execute a willed movement, the impulse originates in the oculogyric centers in the frontal lobes (Figs. 171 and 172).

In the two most common types of monkey that have been used for experimental purposes *(Macaca* and *Cercopithecus)* frontal cortex from which movements of the eyes can be elicited is situated rostral to the electrically responsive cortex of the precentral gyrus. In the lower part, its caudal boundary is the lower ramus of the arcuate sulcus. Above, the area spreads behind the upper ramus of the arcuate sulcus and in many instances reaches near or to the rostral end of the superior precentral sulcus. Superiorly, the eye field extends over the edge of the hemisphere on to the medial surface as far as the callosomarginal sulcus (sulcus cinguli) (Fig. 3, p. 27).

Destruction of the oculogyric center on one side does not result in lasting paraly-

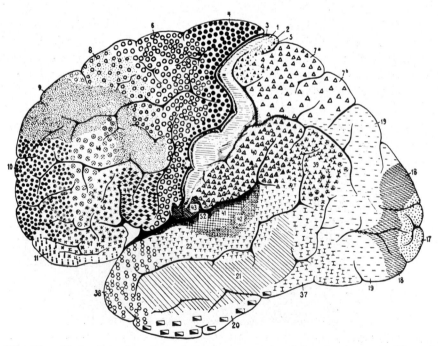

Fig. 171. Map of the lateral surface of the human cortex (after Brodmann). (From Bucy, P. C., editor: The precentral motor cortex, ed. 2, Urbana, Ill., 1949, University of Illinois Press.)

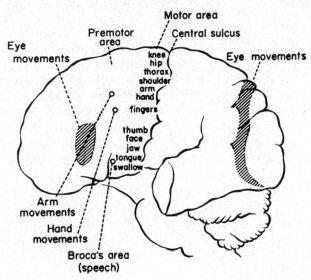

Fig. 172. Motor and premotor areas of the brain.

sis of any of the ocular movements. Inevitably the paralysis of gaze to one side, which ensues on destruction of one oculogyric center, disappears. This has raised doubt as to the importance of the oculogyric centers. Wernicke has suggested that ocular movements to each side may be represented in both frontal lobes, and consequently, as in other bilaterally innervated movements, the effects of a one-sided lesion are compensated by the unaffected side. Bilateral lesions in man produce permanent paralysis of horizontal movements of the eye. In the monkey, removal of both frontal lobes yields no permanent paralysis.

In monkeys, unilateral and bilateral ablation of the oculogyric area is followed by a characteristic syndrome similar to that produced by removal of one frontal lobe. Deviation of the head and eyes toward the side of the lesion occurs. The deviation of the eyes becomes less marked during the first postoperative week, but a tendency to turn the head in this direction persists for a longer time. Coincident with deviation of the head and

eyes are forced purposeless circling movements of the animal.[80, 81] In addition, defects in the visual field contralateral to the lesion are present. Apparently the animal is unable to respond to visual stimuli in the contralateral field of vision. This does not seem to be true hemianopsia, but the animal consistently disregards objects situated in the contralateral field. This defect is transient. When present bilaterally as a result of a bilateral lobectomy, it does not result in blindness; hence, it cannot be due to a block in the afferent visual apparatus similar to true hemianopsia produced by bilateral occipital lobectomy.

Clark and Lashley[82] found that in order for homonymous hemianopsia to be produced in monkeys, the cortical ablation must include more cortex than within the limbs of the arcuate sulcus. The defect in the visual field was not necessarily accompanied by the circling movements or by deviation of the head and eyes, and the hemianopsia could be produced alone by a transverse lesion of the subcortical white substance, which included severance of the superior longitudinal fasciculus. They concluded, therefore, that the visual defect represented a traumatic disorganization of re-entry circuits, producing interaction between the frontal and occipital regions.

The difference between the effects of extirpation of the oculogyric centers in man and in monkey is probably due to the fact that in the monkey the involuntary mechanism, which will be described later, immediately takes over and covers up any deficit in the ocular movements caused by the absence of the relatively unimportant voluntary mechanism. It must be remembered also that symptoms which arise following injury to a part of the central nervous system, such as the oculogyric center on one side, cannot be interpreted as due simply to a loss of function of the injured part. The symptoms which arise as a result of the loss of a part represent a response of the organism to an abnormal situation produced by the lesion and therefore include manifestations of disordered activity of undamaged structures, as Hughlings Jackson pointed out long ago.

Jackson was the first to establish the principle of localization in the motor cortex, and he showed that the quantity of gray matter in the cortex varied in size, depending upon the number of movements usually made by the part innervated, rather than by the size of the muscles of the part. The small muscles of the fingers are represented by much more gray matter than are the voluminous muscles of the upper arm. Greater differentiation of function implies a larger repre-

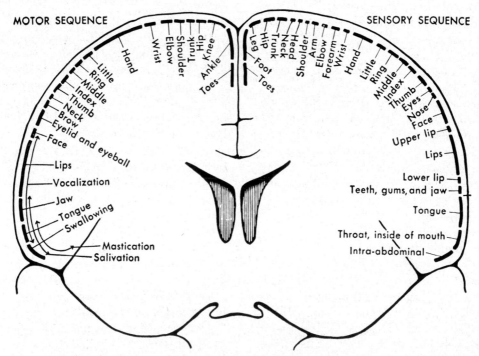

Fig. 173. Cross section of the cerebrum through the sensorimotor region with the motor and sensory sequences indicated. The lengths of the solid bars represent an estimate of the average relative cortical areas from which the corresponding responses were elicited. (From Penfield, W., and Rasmussen, T.: The cerebral cortex of man, New York, 1950, The Macmillan Co.)

sentation in the brain. The representation of the ocular muscles in the oculogyric centers in the frontal lobe is relatively enormous as compared to the size of the ocular muscles, and in that respect it is comparable to the representation of the muscles of the fingers (Fig. 173, left side). Although the muscles of the body have some bilateral representation, the fingers, which are the most differentiated and specialized in their movements, have the least bilateral cortical representation. Muscles which act bilaterally chiefly, such as those of the abdominal wall, have the most pronounced bihemispherical representation. The ocular muscles probably belong in this category. The cortical centers which represent movements of small muscles, e.g., the muscles of the face, the fingers, and the eyes, contain Betz cells which are comparatively small—smaller than the cells that superintend movements of the larger and more voluminous muscles of the limbs and trunk.

Although it has been generally believed that no single ocular muscle is represented in the motor cortex, the muscles for opening and closing the lids are thought to have a separate cortical representation. The general concept that no individual skeletal muscle is represented in the motor cortex has been challenged by Chang, Ruch, and Ward,[83] who isolated eight representative skeletal muscles in a series of monkeys, attaching each muscle to separate myographs. They then explored the responsiveness of these muscles to unipolar stimulation of various foci on the motor area. Using stimuli of minimal intensity, they found that certain points gave "solitary responses," i.e., an isolated reaction of a single muscle unaccompanied by contraction of any other muscles under observation. Not only were individual muscles represented, but also in some instances small portions of a given muscle

could be stimulated in this fashion. Hines[84] comments on these experiments as follows.

"The above study indicates that in the precentral gyrus of the macaque there is a detailed representation of the skeletal muscular system and that the basic plan of this pattern can be analyzed in terms of muscles. Thus, although there is overlapping of cortical fields for peripheral cutaneous areas, individual muscles are represented maximally at particular points on the postcentral gyrus. This does not mean that a particular muscle is the only muscle represented at a specific cortical point, but that it is the one predominantly represented there."*

The maps of muscle foci found by Chang and associates suggested the following to them.

". . . [that] the Betz cells for a particular muscle are distributed over a contiguous area of the cortex with the highest cell concentration located at a particular focus within that area and that the farther from that focus, the more sparsely scattered are the Betz cells devoted to that muscle."†

Compare this with the receptive field of optic nerve fibers in the retinal cortex (pp. 686 to 689).

Horizontal gaze. In man, voluntary movements of the eyes in horizontal gaze occur as a result of stimulation of the cells in the second and, possibly, the third frontal convolution of each hemisphere. Both eyes are moved equally and simultaneously toward the opposite side. According to Penfield and Erickson,[74] in human beings stimulation of the zone centered around Brodmann's area 8, alpha, beta, and gamma (Fig. 174), causes conjugate deviation of the eyes to the opposite side. These movements can be pro-

---

*From Hines, M.: In Bucy, P. C., editor: The precentral motor cortex, Urbana, Ill., 1944, University of Illinois Press.

†From Chang, H., Ruch, T., and Ward, A.: J. Neurophysiol. 10:39, 1947.

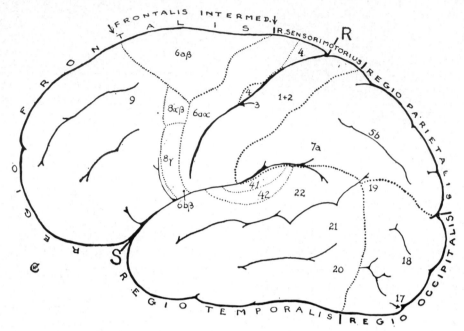

Fig. 174. Surface view of the left motor cortex, slightly tilted to show Vogt's areas 8 alpha, beta, and gamma. These are the areas of voluntary ocular movements to the right and possibly upward. No cortical areas have been discovered where stimulation produces either downward movements or movements of convergence. (From Penfield, W., and Erickson, T.: Epilepsy and cerebral localization, Springfield, Ill., 1941, Charles C Thomas, Publisher.)

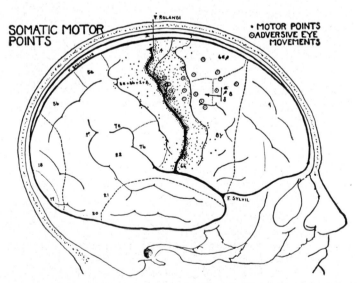

Fig. 175. Surface view of the right motor cortex showing the areas where stimulation in the conscious subject produced conjugate lateral deviation to the left. Occasionally upward movements were observed. (From Penfield, W., and Erickson, T.: Epilepsy and cerebral localization, Springfield, Ill., 1941, Charles C Thomas, Publisher.)

duced by mild electric currents not sufficient to produce any convulsive movements.

Stimulation of the second frontal convolution in the higher mammals usually produces conjugate deviation of both eyes equally and simultaneously to the opposite side, but other movements of gaze occasionally are associated with them. The earlier experiments of Russell and Sherrington showed that after section of the nerve supply of various groups of the ocular muscles stimulation of the oculogyric center on one side might lead to conjugate deviation of the eyes in almost any direction, depending on the combination of the muscles which were made ineffective. They concluded, therefore, that this center was responsible for ocular movements in all directions, laterally and vertically. They argued that, since lateral movements are much more commonly exercised in life, these overshadow the control of other conjugated movements, such as vertical gaze. The earlier reports of Penfield and Erickson indicated that in man stimulation of the oculogyric centers resulted in horizontal movements almost entirely (Fig. 175).

More recently Penfield[85] has shown that another area in which cortical stimulation yields ocular movements is a group

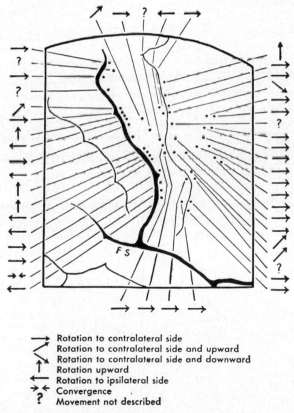

→ Rotation to contralateral side
↗ Rotation to contralateral side and upward
↘ Rotation to contralateral side and downward
↑ Rotation upward
← Rotation to ipsilateral side
→← Convergence
? Movement not described

Fig. 176. Summary chart showing stimulation points of the right visual cortex producing movement of the eyeballs. (From Penfield, W., and Rasmussen, T.: The cerebral cortex of man, New York, 1950, The Macmillan Co.)

of cells of the rolandic lip of the precentral gyrus and a group situated immediately anterior to this. Two thirds of the points (in twenty patients) were situated in the anterior half of the precentral gyrus or caudal portion of the adjacent frontal convolution. Almost all of the responses consisted of rotation to the contralateral side (Fig. 176). The movements of the eyeballs produced here were more varied in character than those produced in the more anteriorly situated stimulation points. Rotation to the ipsilateral side was nearly as frequent as to the contralateral side and rotation upward about half as frequent. Convergence occurred on one occasion. In one third of these stimulations, movement of the eye occurred alone, whereas in the remaining two thirds there was associated movement of the face, lips, brows, or eyelids. The eye-turning mechanism seemed to occupy its expected location in the sensory motor sequence, but extended anteriorly with respect to the rest of the sensory motor strip. Cortical stimulation (in the precentral gyrus chiefly) rarely elicited sensation in the eye. Thus, it would seem that the sensory portion of cortical representation of the eyes is displaced anteriorly likewise with respect to the sensory sequence. Movements of the head were produced less frequently than movements of the eye, but were also localized to cortical areas anterior to the central sulcus. These movements consisted of contraversion and other types of movements such as flexion, extension, and jerking of the head. Movements of the eyelids were produced by stimulation of approximately the same cortical regions as movements of the eye. Two thirds of the loci of movements of the eye were situated anteriorly to the rolandic bank of the precentral gyrus, and only one third of the responses of the eyelids were so located. The remaining two thirds were closely adjacent to the central fissure (Fig. 177). The area mapped out by the points mentioned corresponds in general both in size and position with area 8, alpha, beta, and gamma (Fig. 174). The remainder of the points, however, indicate that the cortical representation of both these movements extends back onto the precentral gyrus as well. It seems clear that conjugate movement of the eyes, although it extends forward out of the sensory motor strip, finds an appropriate place in the motor sequence just above the face and below the thumb (Fig. 173). Sensation of the eye occupies a similar place in the sensory sequence and exhibits rostral migration also, being found almost exclusively in the precentral gyrus. Conjugate turning of the eye and turning of the head and body constitute a response elicited from other areas of the cortex as well.

At the forward margin of the precentral gyrus where there are very few Betz cells is a narrow strip of cortex, forming one of the so-called suppressor bands which when stimulated has a powerful inhibitory effect on the nearby motor area. This inhibition does not come about by transcortical stimulation, but by an elaborate and not altogether understood pathway. In part, the cells in the suppressor area send impulses down to the caudate nucleus. From there the impulses are carried to the thalamus by a pathway which is still not decided. In the thalamus the impulses arriving over this pathway suppress pre-existing activity. This affects everything going on in the motor area of the adjacent cortex—the electrocorticogram being either greatly diminished or disappearing.

Some of the earlier investigators believed that the upper portion of each frontal center represented downward gaze

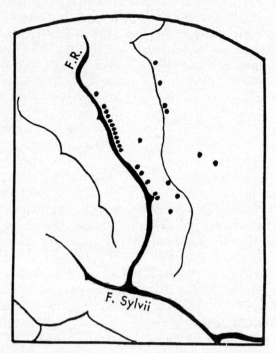

Fig. 177. Summary chart showing stimulation points of the right visual cortex producing eyelid movement. (From Penfield, W., and Rasmussen, T.: The cerebral cortex of man, New York, 1950, The Macmillan Co.)

and the lower portion upward gaze and that, if the upper portion of one side was stimulated, a movement of both eyes to the opposite side and downward resulted. Similarly, stimulation of the lower portion of the center on one side forced the eyes to the opposite side and upward. Most physiologists agree, however, that purely upward or downward movements can be produced on stimulation of the oculogyric centers only (1) by first destroying the horizontally acting muscles or (2) by stimulating the upper or lower portions of the oculogyric center on both sides simultaneously.[86, 87]

The frontal oculogyric centers located in area 8 are separated from the motor cortex supplying the rest of the body musculature by a strip of relatively unexcitable cortex, i.e., area 6a, alpha (Fig. 174). This area also represents motor function,

and isolated movements occur as a result of its stimulation. However, it has a very high threshold, and the effects seem to be mediated through the main motor cortex, area 4. Area 6a, beta, represents mass movements so that the head, eyes, and trunk and also the arm and leg on the opposite side are moved simultaneously.

It will be shown that conjugate movements of the eyes may be produced not only by stimulation of the frontal oculogyric centers, but also by stimulation of centers in the occipital lobe. A rather large area on the lateral surface of the occipital lobe, and a small area on its mesial surface as well, produces ocular movements when stimulated. These are conjugate movements toward the opposite side. These may also have a vertical or convergent component. Electrical stimulation here also produces dilatation of the pupils. One needs even stronger currents to produce ocular movements from stimulation of the occipital region than from stimulation of the frontal centers, and the movements produced by stimulation of the occipital region are generally slower than those originating in the frontal cortex. Occasionally, movements of the eyes from stimulation of the temporal lobe may be observed. These are usually directed to the opposite side also. The temporal center for reflex ocular movements seems to be associated with movements of the eyes produced by acoustical stimuli. Neither the occipital nor temporal cortex is considered a center initiating voluntary ocular movements, however.

A more exact localization of movements produced by stimulation of various portions of the frontal eye fields has been possible in experimental animals than in man. The main region for voluntary control and regulation of eye movements in primates is the same as in man, i.e., areas 8 alpha, 8 beta, and 8 gamma. Area

8 alpha must be intact along with its connections through the corticobulbar system to the oculomotor nuclei in order to produce voluntary movements. The pattern of responses elicited by stimulating various parts of this region has been worked out by Crosby and Henderson as shown in Fig. 178. Stimulation produced the following responses at the sites numbered:

1. To the right and downward
2. Divergence
3. To the right
4. To the right and upward
5. To the right
6. Divergence
7. To the right and downward

Note that stimulation of *5* is a duplication of *3*, *6* duplicates *2*, and *7* duplicates *1*. Crosby suggests this mirror image duplication of pattern serves a dual purpose. The upper of the two patterns is probably the site of origin of corticobulbar fibers, and the lower pattern may be related to the preoccipital and occipital eye fields by intracortical association pathways.

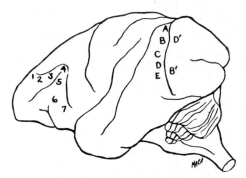

Fig. 178. Left hemisphere of *Macacus mulattus*. Letters **A** through **E** indicate the localization pattern of conjugate movements on the preoccipital eye field (area 19) as follows: **A**, deviation upward; **B**, eyes obliquely upward to right; **C**, eyes to right; **D**, eyes obliquely downward to right; **E**, eyes downward. **D′** and **B′** represent conjugate movements from the occipital eye field (area 18), as follows: **D′**, eyes obliquely downward to right; **B′**, eyes obliquely upward to right. Numbers 1 through 7 represent localization areas on the frontal eye field as follows: **1** and **7**, conjugate ocular deviation obliquely downward to right; **2** and **6**, divergence; **3** and **5**, conjugate right horizontal deviation; **4**, conjugate deviation upward to right. Note duplication of pattern on the frontal eye field. (From Henderson, J., and Crosby, E.: Arch. Ophth. **47:**43, 1952.)

Lemmen and associates[88] believe that there is a similar duplication of pattern in human beings from their observations on stimulation of this region in a patient under local anesthesia (Fig. 179).

Another point of distinction between the duplicate sites in the frontal eye fields is that stimulation of the area below the main fissure (*5, 6,* and *7*) seems to be involved in the mechanism of reciprocal

innervation, whereas the upper area (*1, 2,* and *3*) is not. If the lateral rectus of the right eye and the medial rectus of the left eye are cut, both eyes are turned to the left due to the unopposed tonus of the antagonist muscles. If the left frontal eye field below the main fissure is now stimulated, the eyes will turn to the right as far as the midline due to inhibition of the tonus of the antagonists of the cut

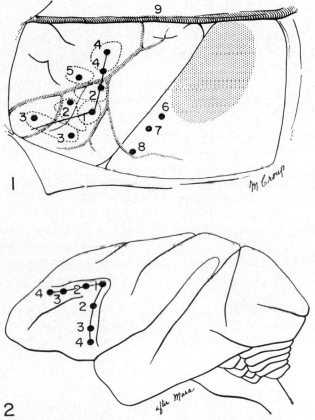

Fig. 179. **1,** Drawing of left frontoparietal area exposed at operation, in which cortical stimulation resulted in movements at the following points: *1,* conjugate deviation of the eyes upward and to the other side; *2,* horizontal conjugate gaze to the other side; *3,* divergence of the eyes; *4,* conjugate deviation of the eyes downward and to the other side; *5,* no response; *6,* hand movement and flexion of the fingers on the right side; *7,* flexion of the right thumb; *8,* retraction of the right lower lip; *9,* longitudinal sinus. **2,** Diagram of the left hemisphere of the macaque showing eye deviations from stimulation of the frontal eye fields at the following points: *1,* eyes up to the right; *2,* horizontal deviation to the right; *3,* divergences; *4,* eyes down to right. (From Lemmen, L. J., Davis, J. S., and Radner, L. L.: J. Comp. Neurol. **112:**163, 1959.)

muscles, i.e., the right medial and the left lateral rectus. If, however, the region above the main fissure is stimulated, no turning of the eyes occurs.[89]

Although there is no direct connection between the frontal center of each side, association fibers connect each frontal oculogyric center with the center in the occipital lobe on the same side. The frontal and occipital centers seem to exert an influence on each other in the intact animal. It has been found that the occipital center exerts an inhibitory effect on the frontal center. Stimulation of the occipital cortex decreases the excitability of the frontal center, and cocainization of the occipital cortex increases its excitability.[90] Association fibers connect the frontal centers with the thalamus, the striatum, and the pons.[91-93] These association fibers form an extensive extrapyramidal system.

Opening the lids is generally associated with upward gaze. Smith[94] stimulated certain portions of the frontal oculogyric centers unilaterally and occasionally obtained an interesting, complex group of movements of the eyes which together simulated awakening and which, therefore, he designated the awakening response. Stimulation of the region around the medial end of the arcuate sulcus resulted in opening of the lids, deviation of the eyes to the contralateral side, dilatation of the pupil, and blinking.

Closure of the eyes in monkeys is not obtained by stimulation of that part of the frontal cortex from which movements of the eyeballs are elicited, but results from excitation of the facial region of the precentral gyrus situated just caudal and inferior to the arc of the arcuate sulcus (Fig. 3, p. 27). If the electrical stimulation in this region is weak, closure of the lids is limited to the opposite side only, but when a stronger stimulus is applied, complete closure of the contralateral eye

and partial closure of the ipsilateral eye result. It appears as though contralateral cortical control of the orbicularis muscle is greater than ipsilateral cortical control.

In man, ptosis or lagophthalmos may result from a lesion in the cortex or in any portion of the oculogyric pathway from the cortex to the nucleus of the third or seventh cranial nerve, respectively. Either ptosis or widening of the palpebral fissure due to retraction of the upper lid can be produced by lesions in the oculogyric pathway.

Course of fibers from frontal oculogyric centers to pontile centers

Horizontal gaze. The fibers which arise from the pyramidal cells in the frontal oculogyric center pass into the corona radiata of the white matter and enter the knee of the internal capsule as part of the corticobulbar system (Fig. 180). They turn into the internal capsule close to the fibers from the cortical representation of the motor innervation of the face and proceed downward into the pons (Fig. 181). In their passage they course through the basal ganglia, occasionally forming synapses. Separate contingents of this tract are given off at different levels, the chief of which is that which has to do with vertical gaze, i.e., the fibers innervating the extraocular muscles of upward and downward gaze, together with the muscles of the upper eyelids and the frontalis muscle. These fibers leave the tract at about the level of the superior colliculi where they probably go to the center for vertical gaze. These will be discussed later. The part of the pyramidal tract which is concerned with lateral gaze leaves the corticobulbar tract as two bundles of fibers in the midbrain and upper pontile region, respectively. Just above the level of the nucleus of the sixth cranial nerve these fibers cross over to the opposite side of the

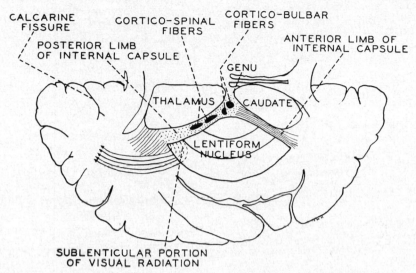

Fig. 180. Horizontal section of the right hemisphere to show the internal capsule. The cortico-bulbar fibers for voluntary eye movement are located in the genu of the internal capsule. (From McCotter, R. E., Fralick, F. B., and Henderson, J. W.: A comprehensive description of the orbit, orbital content, and associated structures, with clinical application, Rochester, Minn., 1949, American Academy of Ophthalmology and Otolaryngology.)

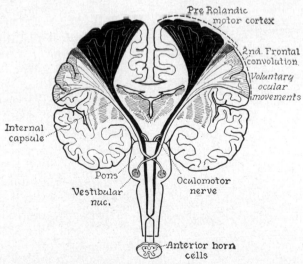

Fig. 181. Diagram of the course of the voluntary oculogyric pathways from the frontal cortex to the pons. The fibers enter the knee of the internal capsule as part of the pyramidal tract. In their course downward separate contingents are given off at different levels, the chief of which is that which concerns vertical gaze, not shown. The remaining fibers cross to the opposite side as shown and probably enter the vestibular nucleus.

pons. From here on, their course is not known definitely.

On the basis of pathologic data most clinicians favor the assumption that the fibers end in a pontile center for lateral gaze, but there is no histologic evidence for the existence of such a center. Patients in whom the nucleus of the sixth cranial nerve on one side has been destroyed show loss of abduction of the homolateral eye, but they retain movement of the contralateral eye toward the side of the lesion. This proves that the nucleus of the sixth cranial nerve cannot itself be the center for lateral conjugate gaze. It suggests that some other group of cells exists outside the nucleus of the sixth cranial nerve which serves as such a center. It is possible, of course, that each fiber conveying oculogyric impulses for lateral gaze merely splits just before reaching the nucleus of the sixth cranial nerve, one branch going to the homolateral sixth nucleus and the other to the nucleus of the third cranial nerve which controls the contralateral medial rectus muscle.

While we are not certain how the fibers from the frontal centers reach the nuclei of origin of the ocular muscles, there is good reason for believing that they get into the medial longitudinal bundle and are distributed from there to the appropriate nuclei of the two sides. Spiegel[95] believes that the impulses from the frontal centers are transmitted to the medial longitudinal bundle by way of the neurons of the vestibular nuclei. In other words, the fibers from the vestibular nuclei in the medial longitudinal bundle carry voluntary oculogyric impulses as well as labyrinthine impulses to be distributed to the various ocular muscles.

Spiegel and Teschler destroyed the vestibular nuclei on both sides and compared the effects of stimulation of the frontal center before and after the injury. The lesion of the vestibular nuclei changed the effects of stimulation. Instead of the normal usually horizontal deviation of the eyes to the opposite side, vertical movements were produced. If only part of the vestibular nuclei had been injured, horizontal or rotary movements to the side of the stimulation occurred. These experiments suggest that the cortical impulses, especially those for horizontal movements of the eyes, are relayed through the cells of the vestibular nuclei before entering the medial longitudinal bundle. The vestibular nuclei send fibers into both sides of the medial longitudinal bundle.

Crosby and Henderson consider the parabducens nucleus (small associative cells in the reticular gray substance adjacent to the abducens nucleus and intermingled with the abducens neurons) the locus at which the oculogyric impulses arrive. From here they are distributed to the abducens nucleus of the same side and the nuclei of the opposite medial rectus. Although at present there is no unanimity of opinion, Cogan recently stated, "Indeed, it may be said with some assurance that those portions of the vestibular nuclei concerned with eye movements are the main centers in the brainstem for conjugate gaze, serving voluntary as well as reflex movements of the eyes."*

Most authors assume a single center lying close to the nucleus of the sixth cranial nerve, probably in front of the nucleus and near the midline, and believe that this so-called pontine center receives all the stimuli which produce horizontal conjugate movements of the eyes, i.e., not only the voluntary movements just described, but also the reflex horizontal movements which will be considered later.

---

*From Cogan, D. G.: Nystagmus: In Strabismus symposium, St. Louis, 1962, The C. V. Mosby Co., p. 114.

On the other hand, the experiments of Hyde[97] indicate that there is no good evidence for assuming a single center which integrates all types of conjugate horizontal movements. She has obtained evidence in cats for at least two "centers for lateral gaze," one subserving impulses arising in the colliculi and another for impulses arising in the occipital cortex.

I have shown that stimulation of the oculogyric center on either side produces movements of the eyes to the opposite side. Occasionally adversive and upward movements are seen, as indicated by the arrows in Fig. 176. In man it has not been possible to obtain solely upward rotation of the eyes by unilateral stimulation of the frontal centers, but in animals

in which this can be done experimentally bilateral stimulation of the lower parts of both centers generally results in upward movement of the eyes, and similarly, stimulation of the upper portion of both centers results in downward gaze.

Vertical gaze. The pathways for vertical movements of the eyes are less well known than those for horizontal movements. Vertical movements may be carried out without the impulses traversing either the vestibular nuclei or the medial longitudinal bundle, according to Spiegel. Fibers in the internal capsule for vertical gaze have never been found. They are first identified experimentally in the region of the superior colliculi. Lesions in this neighborhood are associated frequently with dis-

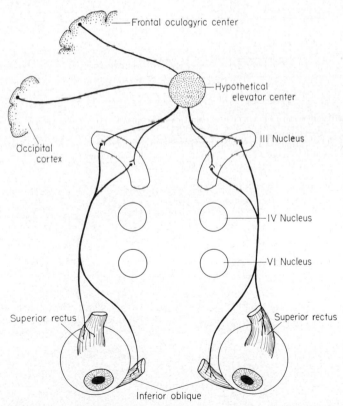

Fig. 182. The central organization for conjugate elevation of the eyes. (Modified after Duke-Elder.)

turbances of vertical gaze along with changes in the position and movement of the lids.

The fibers for vertical gaze, as stated, have eluded detection until they reach the neighborhood of the superior colliculi. The superior colliculus apparently serves as a relay station, or a subcortical center, in the pathway for vertical movements of the eyes similar to the pontile center for lateral gaze. The impulses may reach the medial longitudinal bundle and be distributed through this to those nuclei concerned with upward and downward gaze, but it is fairly certain that they do not first run through the vestibular nuclei. The fibers for upward and downward gaze probably are separate from each other. One frequently sees paralysis of upward gaze alone (Fig. 182). Paralysis of upward gaze may be the initial symptom of a lesion in the neighborhood of the superior colliculus. This may then be followed by paralysis of downward gaze (Fig. 183). Such lesions can be supranuclear rather than involve the nuclei of the muscles concerned with vertical gaze. Although the eyes cannot be turned upward on demand, they will do so if the lesion is supranuclear when the lids are closed voluntarily. This upward movement of the eyeball on closure of the lids is called Bell's phenomenon (p. 27).

In cats, upward movement of the eyes can be produced by placing the stimulating electrode on the roof of the superior

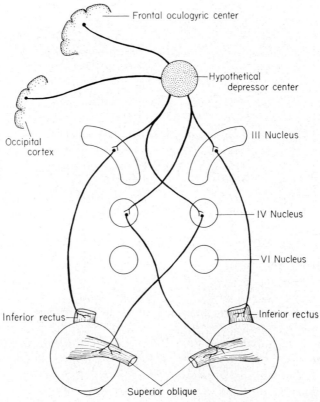

Fig. 183. The central organization for conjugate depression of the eyes. (Modified after Duke-Elder.)

colliculi. Downward movements occur only when the central gray substance beneath or behind the posterior commissure is stimulated.[98] Electrical stimulation of one superior colliculus in cats causes conjugate deviation of both eyes to the opposite side, with a vertical component.[99]

The vertical component is upward when the stimulating current is localized to the medial part of the superior colliculus; the vertical component is downward when the lateral part of the colliculus is stimulated.

It has been demonstrated that in cats the upper contralateral visual field is projected on to the medial part of the superior colliculus and the lower contralateral visual field is projected to the lateral part of the colliculus. This, together with the movements resulting from electrical stimulation of the colliculus, suggested to Apter[99] that the sensory projection of the visual field on the superior colliculus has a motor counterpart. If a small crystal of strychnine is placed on the surface of the superior colliculus, photic stimulation of the retina produces movements of the eyes. Each point on the surface of the superior colliculus is responsible for movement of the eye toward that particular part of the visual field which is projected on that part of the colliculus.

If this arrangement is the same in man, it can explain the usual train of events which occurs in pineal tumors. In most pineal tumors, paralysis of upward gaze occurs first, to be followed by paralysis of downward gaze. Since we now have evidence of a motor counterpart of the sensory localization in the superior colliculus, Apter suggests that the course of events can be explained best by pressure of the enlarging pineal gland first on the medial anterior, then on the lateral anterior, and finally on the posterior part of the colliculus. Paralysis of vertical movements occurs with lesions of other structures besides the superior colliculi so that in man it is impossible to be dogmatic about the exact location of the fibers for vertical gaze.

Occipital lobe control of ocular movements

In the section on optomotor reflexes (p. 470) it will be found that eye movements of a reflex nature arise from oculogyric impulses originating in the occipital lobe. The present section deals with the results of experimentally stimulating the occipital region in animals and the types of eye movements which have been reported.

Stimulation of each occipital lobe in the general region of the calcarine fissure, i.e., areas 17, 18, and 19, produces movements of both eyes to the opposite side. Although there is some variation in the reports of different investigators, the usual pattern of response indicates that the movements follow the representation of the two retinas in the striate cortex. Stimulation above the level of the calcarine fissure produces turning of the eyes down and to the opposite side, whereas stimulation below the fissure turns the eyes up and to the opposite side. This suggests that these movements are induced visually, for the purpose of turning the eyes in the direction of objects attracting attention in any part of the visual field. An object which attracts attention in the upper right visual field stimulates photoreceptors in the lower left-hand quadrant of each retina. The cortical representation of these photoreceptors is in the left occipital lobe below the calcarine fissure. If these visual cells have connections with motor cells which turn the eyes up and to the right, the object of attention would be focused on each fovea.

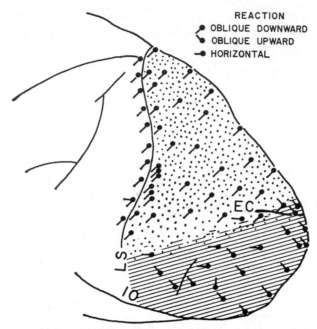

Fig. 184. The direction of eye movements by surface stimulation of the occipital and pre-occipital areas in the macaque. **LS,** Lunate sulcus. (From Wagman, I. H., Krieger, H. P., and Bender, M. B.: J. Comp. Neurol. **109:**169, 1958.)

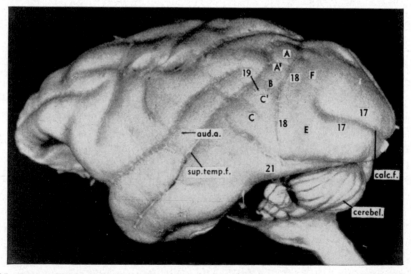

Fig. 185. Photograph of the left side of the brain of Macaca mulatta. Areas 17, 18, 19, and 21 are designated. The various points from which eye movements were elicited are indicated by letters. (From Crosby, E. C., and Henderson, J. W.: J. Comp. Neurol. **88:**79, 1948.)

The cortical map of eye movements found by Wagman and associates is shown in Fig. 184. The main differences between the results of different investigators concerns the exact region or regions from which the motor impulses for adversive eye movements arise. Crosby and Henderson[113] note that in the macaque and probably in man the visual cells of area 17 discharge to the adjoining visual association area in the parastriate cortex, area 18, and that the motor impulses either arise here or relay from this area to area 19 and then go to the nuclei of the oculomotor nerves concerned with the movement. They found that, whereas stimulation of area 18 produced the type of adversive eye movement just described, stimulation of area 19 produced a different pattern of response under light anesthesia and using minimal faradic current, as follows (Fig. 185): stimulation at *A.*, conjugate upward deviation of eyes; at *A'*, oblique movement up and to right; at *B*, horizontal conjugate deviation right; at *C*, conjugate deviation downward; at *C'*, conjugate deviation downward to the right; at *F*, oblique conjugate deviation down to the right; at *E*, oblique conjugate deviation up to the right.

The findings of some of the later investigators are summarized in Table 47. Note that stimulation of area 19 produces exactly the opposite effects to those of stimulation of area 18. This has not been confirmed by Wagman, Krieger, and Bender.

Pathways conducting from visuomotor areas in occipital lobes to brainstem

I have pointed out elsewhere that there is considerable difference between the afferent pathways to the visual cortex in man and those in the lower vertebrates. Many optic fibers apparently serve a visual function going to the superior collicular region in the lower vertebrates, whereas in man all the fibers go to area 17 directly. In the case of the efferent pathways from the visual cortical areas down to the brainstem, on the other hand, the pathways in both man and the lower vertebrates are the same, as far as is known. The fibers for horizontal gaze descend to the pontine level, whereas those for vertical gaze enter the medial longi-

Table 47

Author	Type of movement produced
Walker and Weaver*	Adversive movements, with calcarine fissure dividing lateral surface of occipital lobe in regard to upward and downward vector; division not absolute
Lilly, Hughes, and Galkin†	Adversive eye and head movements on stimulating entire dorsolateral surface
Crosby and Henderson‡	Adversive oblique movements according to usual plan when areas 17 and 18 stimulated, but reverse pattern when area 19 stimulated
Wagman, Krieger, and Bender§	No anatomic landmark dividing upward and downward vector, but in general follow Crosby and Henderson's stimulation of areas 17 and 18; did not confirm findings for area 19

*Walker, E., and Weaver, T.: J. Neurophysiol. 3:353, 1940.
†Lilly, Hughes, and Galkin: Quoted by Wagman, Krieger, and Bender (see below).
‡Crosby, E., and Henderson, J.: J. Comp. Neurol. 88:53, 1948; Crosby, E.: J. Comp. Neurol. 99: 437, 1953.
§Wagman, I., Krieger, H., and Bender, M.: J. Comp. Neurol. 109:169, 1958.

tudinal bundle at midbrain levels. In man lesions in the pons produce horizontal gaze palsies, whereas lesions in the midbrain produce vertical gaze palsies. The two are seldom seen together.

The nucleus of Darkschewitsch is thought to initiate inhibitory impulses by some investigators.[100]

Nuclei of origin of ocular motor nerves

The oculomotor nuclei, from which the fibers of the third cranial nerve originate, are two large masses of cells which are motor cells for the most part, forming a V in the mesencephalon at about the level of the superior colliculi (Fig. 186). At the extreme open end of the V is another paired group of smaller cells called the Edinger-Westphal nuclei. A single group of large motor cells, known as Perlia's nucleus, lies in the middle of the V. The nucleus of Perlia is rudimentary in man and the primates.[101, 102]

The function of these various cell masses is not known entirely. The motor cells forming the V undoubtedly contribute the main mass of fibers in the third cranial nerves, and section of the third

cranial nerves is followed by degeneration of the arms of the V. It must be supposed, therefore, that these cells give rise to the individual fibers which innervate all of the ocular muscles save the superior oblique and the lateral rectus.

The evidence of the exact localization of the cells of origin of each of the muscles supplied by the third nerve is conflicting, however. In fact, the experiments which have been made on transplantation of the ocular muscles in monkeys have been interpreted to indicate that there is no fixed localization of function within the nucleus. Fearing[103] stated that the early experiments of Marina "demonstrate the inadequacy of the traditional theory that function is determined by preexisting neural pathways." Marina cut the tendons of the medial and lateral rectus muscles of one eye, crossed the muscles behind the eyeball, and sewed each to the place on the sclera where the other had been inserted. Similar transpositions were made with the superior oblique and lateral rectus and with the superior rectus and lateral rectus. Within three to four days after operation, movements of the eye were performed in a normal or nearly normal coordinated manner. Since the muscles

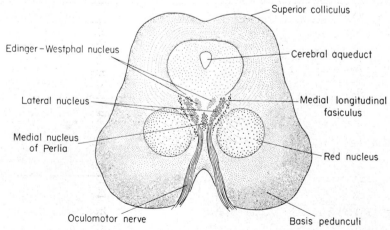

Fig. 186. Nuclei of the third cranial nerve.

were found to adjust themselves to their new situation with such promptness, Marina concluded that conduction pathways had no predetermined function.

Olmsted and associates[104] repeated certain of Marina's experiments with a view to determining whether coordinated movements after operation might not be the result of interaction of the undisturbed muscles, or if transference of function really takes place, whether there is a brief period of readjustment or learning, which would indicate that the original conducting pathways are predetermined and that new ones must be laid down to meet the changed conditions. They found that in cats when the superior rectus muscle was cut eye movements appeared normal in all directions. They then transferred the superior rectus to the site of the lateral rectus, which was removed thoroughly. In all these animals with the lateral rectus removed, outward movement of the eye past the midline was observed.

The authors were well aware of the existence of the retractor bulbi muscles in their experimental animals, and they convinced themselves that the retractor bulbi were not able to rotate the eyeball when the other muscles were cut so that this muscle could not compensate for the lack of a lateral rectus. They, therefore, consider that in their experiments the superior rectus must have taken over the function of the lateral rectus. From this and from experiments on the transplantation of other eye muscles, they believe that readjustment can take place so that the transposed muscles can carry out coordinated movements in directions quite different from their original ones. This readjustment does not take place immediately but involves a short period of training. Elimination of area 8 does not interfere with the adjustment once it is established; therefore, the change from the normal nervous pathway to the newly acquired one involves structures more deeply seated than the cortex. The cortex itself seems to be relatively plastic in its ability to produce movements whose character may vary from time to time or even change completely.

It has been shown that in the motor cortex of monkeys the response from any point is not constant. It may be altered by previous happenings and by other factors and may even be reversed. For instance, a flexor movement may be elicited from a point, the ordinary response of which is extension of the same joint. There is evidence that in man, too, the functions of the motor cortex are modifiable because if, after the flexor and extensor tendons of a joint have been divided, the proximal ends of the flexors are sutured to the distal portions of the extensors and vice versa, the subject may learn to use the joint naturally. To do so he must send messages which produce an extensor movement along paths which normally carry flexor impulses. A certain readjustment of function to meet new conditions has developed. These facts can be interpreted only by assuming that it is function, not anatomic structure, which is represented in the motor cortex and that the functions so represented are to some extent plastic or modifiable.[105]

Leinfelder and Black[106] repeated Olmsted's experiments and obtained evidence that proprioceptive impulses play a part in the recovery of function.

Verhoeff[107] and others have cautioned against accepting such experiments as evidence of the absence of fixed localization within the oculomotor nucleus. The original functions of the muscles may still be performed after transposition by continuation of their pull through the medium of Tenon's capsule.

The Horsley-Clarke stereotactic instrument has been used for localization of the ocular muscles in the nuclei of the third cranial nerve. The scheme of localization which has been accepted for many years is that of Bernheimer. This was based on studies of degeneration made on monkeys and on rather scant clinical evidence. In 1942, Szentagothai[108] showed that the functional organization of the nucleus of the third cranial nerve in cats and dogs was quite different from that pictured by Bernheimer (Fig. 187). In 1943, Bender and Weinstein[109] studied the problem in monkeys. Their results agreed fairly well with those of Szentagothai. According to this work, tracing the cells from the rostral to the caudal end of the nucleus, one finds the following muscles represented: sphincter pupillae (usually giving bilateral responses), inferior rectus, ciliary, inferior oblique, internal rectus, superior rectus,

and levator palpebrum. The fourth cranial nerve supplying the superior oblique (contralateral) lies adjacent to this. They conclude that the individual ocular muscles are functionally represented in the ipsilateral oculomotor nucleus. The superior oblique is governed by the contralateral trochlear nucleus.

The different cell groups are more or less the shape of commas whose tails extend under the head of the next anterior group. This arrangement explains the fact that stimulation at different depths on the same dorsal-ventral axis produces different ocular movements. This type of experiment really does not allow one to determine whether the innervation of the ocular muscles is crossed, direct, or mixed but suggests that the majority of the cells innervate the muscles on the same side.

Danis[110] repeated the experiments of Bender and Weinstein in cats and was able to obtain a definite organization of the nucleus of the third cranial nerve in the anteroposterior direction. Going from the rostral to the caudal end, he found that successive points gave rise to the following movements: depression of the eye (sometimes associated with extorsion), adduction, and elevation of the eye. When the stimulation was carried into the posterior part of the nucleus, the elevation of the eye was accompanied by elevation of the upper lid. An isolated elevation of the upper lid was seen only when the extreme posterior part of the nucleus was stimulated.

These results confirm those of the previous authors in respect to localization in this plane. The main difference is in regard to localization of the inferior oblique. Bender and Weinstein localized the cells of this muscle in the anterior part of the nucleus between the cells for the inferior rectus and those for the medial

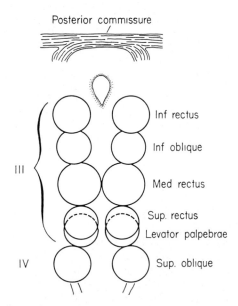

Fig. 187. Functional organization of the nucleus of the third cranial nerve in the cat and the dog, according to Szentagothai. (Modified after Danis).

rectus. They believed that the inferior oblique was localized behind the medial rectus. They assumed that the inferior oblique was localized here since they frequently obtained extorsion by stimulating this region. Danis objected to this reasoning and gives the following plan of organization based on the movements (just described) that he observed: levator palpebrae, inferior oblique, superior rectus, medial rectus, and inferior rectus. These cells are not exactly circumscribed from one another but gradually merge into each other.

These results cannot be applied directly to man, but they are significant. Their main interest hinges around the localization of muscles which have to do with a common direction of movement of the eye. The superior rectus, the inferior oblique, and the levator palpebrae, e.g., are localized together and give an anatomic basis for a single lesion which would produce ptosis and paralysis of upward gaze in both abduction and adduction. Such patients, often without ptosis, are seen frequently and can be accounted for on the basis of small hemorrhages in the nuclear area, if this localization of cells is correct for man.

The same should be true of lesions involving the muscles concerned in downward gaze. The inferior rectus, according to these latter localizations, lies quite separate from the nucleus of the fourth cranial nerve. Hence, the cells for the inferior rectus and the superior oblique could not be caught easily by a small pontine hemorrhage and produce paralysis of downward movement of one eye, both in abduction and adduction. Such cases are seen occasionally, however.

Henderson[111] points out that these latter investigations have been based upon direct electrical stimulation in which presumably the results could be produced by effects gained through the median longitudinal bundle in which the nuclear masses are embedded. He notes that the position of the eyes after destruction of the individual nuclei was not mentioned by these investigators so that the results should not be accepted as final.

It has been shown that in cats the medial portion and sometimes the rostromedial portion of the superior colliculi (p. 440) are concerned with impulses coming from the superior visual fields. Lashley[112] has worked out the same projection patterns in rats. Crosby and Henderson state:

"There is certainly no reason to expect that the pattern would be different in monkeys than in other mammals. Clinical evidence . . . indicates that the frontal portions of the human superior colliculi are concerned with upward conjugate movements of the eyes—the response to stimuli in the superior visual fields. In the monkey, and probably in other primates, the rostral portions of the superior colliculi are connected with the rostral parts of the oculomotor nuclei by tecto-oculomotor fibers and more caudal portions of these colliculi with the more caudal parts of the oculomotor complex."*

As stated, the experimental evidence of most of the early observers and some clinical evidence suggest that the frontal portions of the oculomotor nuclei function in elevating the eyes together with the lids, and that the caudal parts of the nuclei are related to downward movements of the eyes, the midportions of the nuclei being connected with the medial recti and having to do with convergence.

A different approach to the problem was made by Warwick in 1953. He chose to study retrograde chromatolysis in the cells of the third nerve complex after extirpation of each of the ocular muscles

---

*From Crosby, E., and Henderson, J.: J. Comp. Neurol. **88:**53, 1948.

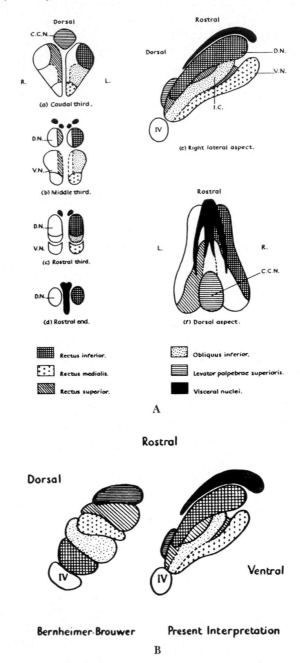

Fig. 188. A, Diagrams showing the representation of the right extraocular muscles in the oculomotor nucleus of the monkey. Transverse sections, at levels as indicated in the complex, are shown in *a* to *d*. D.N., Dorsal nucleus; V.N., ventral nucleus; C.C.N., caudal central nucleus; I.C., intermediate column; IV, trochlear nucleus. B, Diagrams to illustrate the fundamental difference between a rostrocaudal chain of centers, the arrangement common to most schemes of oculomotor organization, including that due to Bernheimer and Brouwer, and the dorsoventrally related rostrocaudal columns described here. In both cases the right lateral aspect is depicted. (From Warwick, R.: J. Comp. Neurol. **98**:499, 1953.)

in monkeys. This technique eliminates many of the objectionable features of direct stimulation of the nucleus. Even with the Horsley-Clarke stereotaxic apparatus it is uncertain whether cells or fibers from other regions are being stimulated, and the introduction of the needle itself may cause stimulation of cells before the final destination is reached. The method of studying chromatolysis is laborious and not without pitfalls. It assumes that no transneuronal degeneration has occurred, which is probably true in this case.

Warwick's reconstruction of the third nucleus is shown in Fig. 188, *A* and *B*. In addition to a rostrocaudal arrangement there is also a dorsoventral arrangement. The levator has only a single midline nucleus that supplies both sides. The medial rectus, inferior rectus, and inferior oblique are innervated directly, whereas the superior rectus is innervated by cells from the opposite side (Table 48).

At the present time it is impossible to account for these widely differing views, and it must be admitted that we have no certain knowledge of the localization of these muscles in the third nerve. The

subject is obviously of great clinical importance and needs more work.

The cells of the Edinger-Westphal nucleus are not typical motor cells. The evidence that they are associated with the nucleus of the third cranial nerve is scant since no fibers have ever been traced from this group of cells into the nucleus of the third cranial nerve. If the ciliary ganglion is removed, however, retrograde degeneration takes place into the Edinger-Westphal nucleus, and by stimulation with the Horsley-Clarke instrument it has been proved that this group of cells is connected with pupillary motor activity.[108] No proof has been given as yet that this nucleus has to do with accommodation, but the nucleus innervating the ciliary muscle should lie close to the center for constriction of the pupil since the two are so closely associated in the near point reaction.

The function of Perlia's nucleus is still more indefinite. There is no evidence that it controls convergence. It degenerates when the third cranial nerve is cut and therefore belongs to the oculomotor nerve. While the axons of the cells which

Table 48

	Bernheimer-Brouwer scheme	*Results of this research*
Mode of representation	Rostrocaudal chain of centers	Rostrocaudally extended columns
Levator	Most rostral center	Caudal central nucleus (confined to caudal third)
	Direct nerve fibers	Bilateral innervation
Rectus superior	Rostral center	Center in caudal two thirds only
	Direct nerve fibers	Nerve fibers all crossed
Rectus medialis	Center in Perlia's nucleus	No
	Direct and crossed (?) nerve fibers	Nerve fibers all direct
Rectus inferior	Nerve fibers all crossed	Nerve fibers all direct
Obliquus inferior	Nerve fibers largely crossed, but some perhaps direct	Nerve fibers all direct

form the nucleus of Perlia leave the midbrain in the oculomotor trunk, they do not go to the medial rectus muscles, at least in the monkey, according to Warwick. He was able to trace the fibers to the superior rectus and in a lesser degree to the inferior oblique so that if they have any function as far as the external ocular muscles is concerned it would seem to be upward gaze.

NERVOUS CENTERS AND PATHWAYS FOR REFLEX ACTIVITY OF MUSCLES OF THE EYE
Necessity for reflex mechanisms

All willed movements of the body have to be coordinated with changes in the posture of the whole body or of its various parts. For example, a movement of the arm made to raise the hand above the head must employ different muscles when the body is in a recumbent position rather than erect. The various muscles concerned in the movement must be called into play in an orderly sequence and by just the right amount in order to produce an even, uninterrupted motion. The great coordinating center which smooths out the muscular activity of the limbs in both time and extent is the cerebellum.

All the willed ocular movements must be coordinated similarly and modified according to the position of the head in space in order to bring about a desired change in the position of the visual axes. The mechanism which exerts these refining influences on the willed ocular movements is to a great extent the vestibular apparatus. There are other sources of tonus of ocular muscles which will be described, and there are probably others not yet discovered.

A few examples will show the necessity for the existence of a mechanism which changes the amount of innervation sent to the ocular muscles when the position of the head is altered during movement of the eyes.

With the head in the erect position, dextroversion of the eyes in the horizontal plane is carried out mainly by the simultaneous contraction of the right lateral rectus and the left medial rectus, together with reciprocal inhibition of their antagonists. (In order to simplify the picture, we need not consider here the activity of all the other muscles which share in movement.) If the head is tilted on the right shoulder, however, contraction of these two muscles alone would not produce dextroversion in the plane of the horizon but would turn the eyes obliquely down and to the right. Other muscles must be brought into play, therefore, to keep the eyes in the plane of the horizon and to turn them to the right under these conditions. Hence, the position of the head in space modifies profoundly the muscles to be activated in order to produce any desired movement of the eyes. To this end, the ocular muscles are kept under a constant state of changing tone through the vestibular nuclei by impulses coming from the muscles of the neck, from the otolith apparatus, and from the semicircular canals.

Further, when the head is tilted on the shoulder, the eyes execute torsional movements around their anteroposterior axes so that as the head tilts the vertical meridians of the corneas tend to stay erect and do not incline with the head. This compensatory torsional movement is brought about by an increase in tonus of those muscles which tend to keep the vertical meridian of the cornea erect as the head is tilted to the right or left. If the head is tilted to the right, e.g., levocycloversion must be produced in both eyes to keep the vertical meridians vertical (Fig. 189). Therefore, an increase in

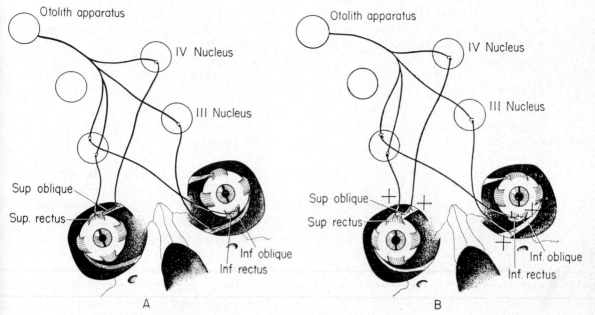

Fig. 189. The effects of head tilting. **A,** The head is tilted toward the right shoulder. In the absence of any compensating mechanism, the vertical meridians of the corneas are tilted to the right. **B,** The otolith apparatus compensates for this and keeps the vertical meridians perpendicular. *Plus marks,* increased tonus of muscles.

tone must be sent to the right superior oblique and the right superior rectus muscles and to the left inferior oblique and the left inferior rectus muscles. These torsional movements are initiated in the otolith apparatus.

All the sense organs of the body send impulses into the central nervous system, modifying at one time or another the state of tonus of the ocular muscles. A sudden loud noise causes the eyes to turn reflexly to the side from which the noise seems to come. A painful stimulus applied to the body causes the eyes to turn involuntarily to the place where the stimulus is located.

The most important source of reflex tonus, other than visual, is that mediated by the vestibular division of the eighth cranial nerve. This complex mechanism serves to correlate changes in posture and movement of the eyes by means of re-

flexes which for the sake of study may be divided into static reflexes, which are caused by changes in position of the head with respect to gravity, and statokinetic reflexes, which occur as a result of movement of the head through space.

Not only do the eyes serve the body well as part of the equipment for the control of the posture and movement of the body, but also changes in posture and movement of the rest of the body exert a large influence on the postural tonus and movements of the eyes themselves, as will be shown. Since all of the reflex activities described in this section have an influence on posture of the eyes, these reflexes will be spoken of as postural reflexes. The known postural mechanisms which cause changes in contractile activity of the ocular muscles are as follows: (1) otolith apparatus, (2) semicircular canals, (3) muscles of the neck,

(4) proprioception from the ocular muscles themselves, and (5) basic tonus of the convergence mechanism (so-called tonic convergence).

Postural eye reflexes

Otolith apparatus. Magnus, to whom we are indebted for most of our knowledge of the postural reactions of the body as a whole, divided postural reflexes into static reactions and statokinetic reactions. The former had to do with the reactions of the body to gravity when it is in a resting state, whereas the latter are observed when the body is moving and are produced by acceleration and deceleration. While many sources of tonus contribute to both these reactions, the chief contribution is made by the two labyrinths. Each labyrinth consists of two parts: the utricle and the saccule and the semicircular canals. The maculae in the utricle and saccule are receptor organs connected to the brain by the vestibular nerve (Fig. 190). Each macula consists of sensory epithelium covered with hair cells and overlaid with a gelatinous membrane in which are embedded small sandlike concretions called otoliths. Changes in position of the head in respect to gravity causes the otoliths to pull on the hair cells of the maculae, and this in turn sets up reflex nervous activity which is relayed to the brain by the vestibular nerves. These messages produce changes in muscular tonus, causing postural changes in the body. The altered tonus persists as long as the new position of the head is maintained. Magnus[114] has shown that the tonic reflexes exerted on the extensor musculature of an animal with changes in posture of the head are evoked from the utricular maculae.

Tonic impulses similar to those sent to the skeletal muscles are sent to the ocular muscles from the otolith apparatus. All of the ocular muscles except the lateral and medial rectus muscles are under the control of the utricular maculae. The lack of control of the horizontally acting muscles is due to the fact that the utricle is not stimulated by changes in the position of the head which take place in the horizontal plane. When the chin is ele-

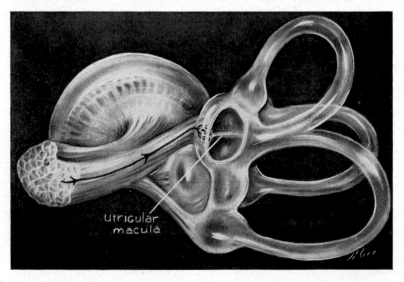

Fig. 190. Labyrinths, otolith apparatus, and semicircular canals.

vated and the head is thrown backward, the impulses from the otolith apparatus send increased tonus to the muscles which depress the eyes, i.e., the inferior recti and superior obliques, with simultaneous inhibition of the elevator muscles. When the chin is depressed on the chest and the head is bent downward, an increased tonus goes to the muscles which elevate the eyes, i.e., the superior recti and inferior obliques, with simultaneous inhibition of the depressors. This activity can be noticed readily in a normal person by asking him to go through the motions of elevating and depressing the chin rapidly and watching the eyes. Unless he is conscious of what is being expected and voluntarily inhibits the activity, it will be seen that the eyes remain more or less in the horizontal plane and do not move up and down with the movements of the chin. This activity is intended to maintain the eyes in their original position on the horizon, in spite of vertical movements

of the head. It has been called the doll's eye phenomenon, from the obvious analogy with the way dolls' eyes are constructed to stay fixed on the horizon when the head is rotated up and down.

If the head is tilted on either shoulder, the change in position of the otoliths sends impulses to the ocular muscles which produce wheel rotation or torsion around the anteroposterior axis. When the head is tilted on the right shoulder, e.g., an increase in tonus is sent to the ocular muscles which produce levocycloversion (Fig. 189), i.e., the right superior rectus and superior oblique (intorsion) and the left inferior rectus and inferior oblique (extorsion). Simultaneously, an inhibitory impulse is sent to the muscles which produce dextrocycloversion, i.e., the right inferior rectus and inferior oblique and the left superior rectus and superior oblique.

The purpose of this change in tonus of the ocular muscles is to maintain as

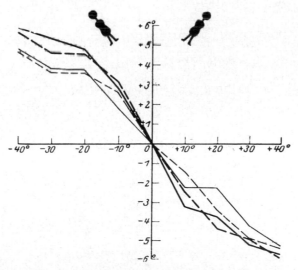

Fig. 191. Torsion of eyes with inclination of body. Abscissa: Inclination of the body $\overset{-}{\leftarrow}$ $\overset{+}{\rightarrow}$ as seen from behind. Ordinates: Torsion + dextrocycloversion − levocycloversion. Instead of the mean, the maxima and minima are given. The heavy solid line is the maximum in the right eye, and the light solid line is the minimum in the right eye. The heavy broken line is the maximum in the left eye, and light broken line is the minimum in the left eye.

nearly as possible the vertical meridians of the cornea in their original primary position, vertical and parallel to each other.

If the body of a person is inclined instead of tilting the head on the shoulder, the same changes in tonus are sent to the ocular muscles from the otolith apparatus. The amount of change in position of the vertical meridians of the corneas is approximately one tenth of the change in position of the body (Fig. 191). The mechanism is effective up to an inclination of the body of about 60 degrees.

In animals with laterally placed eyes the effects of the otolith apparatus are more easily demonstrable than in man.

In the dogfish, e.g., the eyes move independently of each other in the orbits as the head is turned on the trunk by a combination of tonic reflexes from the otolith apparatus and proprioceptive reflexes from the muscles of the neck. If the head is tilted so that the left side is higher than the right side, the left eye is depressed and the right eye is elevated (Fig. 192). Such changes are not determinable in man so readily. The chief importance of the otolith apparatus is to regulate the amount of tonus to each of the muscles concerned in any movement of the eyes while the head changes its position. This is manifest in torsional movements chiefly.

There can be no question that the eyes

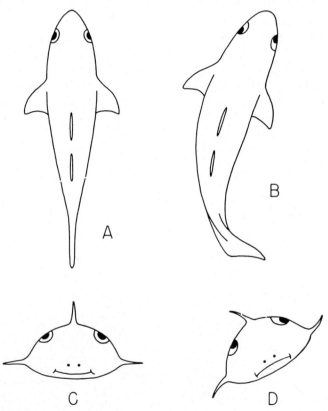

Fig. 192. Compensatory movements of the eyes and fins of the dogfish. **A** and **C**, Position of the fish when at rest. **B**, Compensatory movements of the eyes which occur during swimming or on bending the tail into the position indicated. **D**, Compensatory movements which occur on rotating the fish about its horizontal axis. (After Bard.)

rotate around their anteroposterior axis due to change of position of the body in space. The subject has become of some importance recently because of the possible effects of inertial forces and weightlessness on the eyes. Woellner and Graybiel[115] have compared the torsion produced by tilting the subject with that caused by exposing him to a change in direction of force on a human centrifuge. When the amount of roll is plotted as a function of the incident angles of force, the amount of rolling due to tilt begins to fall off at about 30 degrees, whereas the amount due to g forces is practically linear (Fig. 193). When the amount of roll is plotted as a function of the magnitude of the laterally acting force as the independent variable, a single curve resulted, indicating a straight line relation within the range of one g (Fig. 194).

I have found no published data on the effects of weightlessness, but one would suppose that under this abnormal condition in which the otoliths would obviously be unstimulated by any change in body position, there would be no rolling. Whether this disturbs the astronaut's position sense for which he learns to compensate I do not know.

Semicircular canals. Whenever the head is moved in space, a disturbance is set up in the fluid of the semicircular canals, provided that the movement is carried out with sufficient speed. As a result of this disturbance, the tone of some of the ocular muscles is changed. In the previous section, the mechanism by means of which the eyes were made resistant to change of position of the head with respect to gravity was described. This was the otolith apparatus. In this section, we are dealing with a mechanism which makes the eyes resistant to change in the position of the head when it is moved through space. This is done by the semicircular canals.

The vestibular apparatus is composed

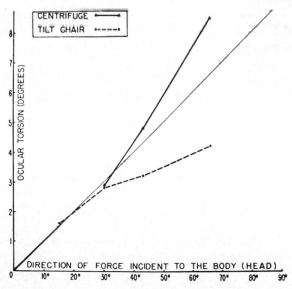

Fig. 193. Comparison of amount of counterroll observed on tilt chair and centrifuge when directions of force incident to the body were the same. (From Woellner, R. C., and Graybiel, A.: J. Appl. Physiol. **14:**633, 1959.)

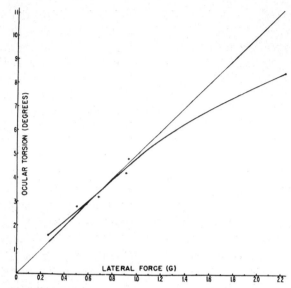

Fig. 194. Degree of counterroll as a function of the magnitude of force acting laterally on the body (head) in tilt chair and centrifuge experiments. (From Woellner, R. C., and Graybiel, A.: J. Appl. Physiol. 14:633, 1959.)

of three semicircular canals firmly imbedded in the petrous bone. Between the bony walls and the membranous canals is a fluid called the perilymph, and filling the canals is another fluid called the endolymph. While the canals are too narrow to permit an actual transfer of fluid, in the sense of a flow of fluid from one end of the canal to the other, changes in pressure in the fluid are set up whenever the head is moved in space, provided that the movement is carried out rapidly enough. The pressure rises at one end and falls at the other end of the canal. This results in a change of pressure on the crista, which is a mound of sensory hair cells imbedded in the bulbous enlargement of each canal (ampulla). The result of this mechanical effect on the crista is thought to be the liberation of a chemical substance which gives rise to an action current in the efferent nerves going to the vestibular nuclei. In this respect, the crista can be looked upon as a sensory

end organ. As in the case of the rods and cones of the retina, an adequate stimulation sets up a chemical reaction which in turn excites a change of potential in the nerve fibers. In the semicircular canals, pressure of the fluid on the crista, which is the adequate stimulus, sets up a chemical reaction that excites a change in potential in the vestibular portion of the eighth cranial nerve.

The adequate stimulus for the hair cells of the crista is an acceleration or deceleration of the endolymph. Movement alone is not sufficient, the effective stimulus being a change in rate. The minimum acceleration for the production of an adequate stimulus is approximately 1 to 3 degrees per second. While it is true that no change in tonus to the muscles of either eye will take place without an adequate stimulus, the semicircular canals must be transmitting constant tonus to all the ocular muscles at all times since extirpation of one labyrinth immediately causes conjugate deviation of the eyes to the same side due to the unopposed action of the intact labyrinth. The influence of the labyrinth on the position of the eyes depends upon the asymmetry of the impulses from the canals of the two sides. If both sets are stimulated equally, no resultant deviation of the eyes occurs, but if one side is stimulated or the other side is depressed, the eyes will be deviated tonically toward the depressed side.

The effect of stimulation of one side is to produce tonic deviation of the eyes away from the side stimulated. Under normal conditions, however, the eyes do not remain long in this position but break away from the tonic impulses which have moved them in that direction and suddenly return to the primary position. Thus, the effect of stimulation of the semicircular canals on one side is to produce a rhythmic movement of the eyes, consisting of a slow deviation away from the side stimulated followed by a quick recovery. This jerklike rhythm is called nystagmus.

Nystagmus. There are various types of nystagmus, each of which will be considered under its appropriate heading. In this section, vestibular nystagmus will be described, i.e., nystagmus due to stimulation of one of the semicircular canals. The usual method employed to elicit vestibular nystagmus is rotation of the subject with the head held in such a position that only one set of the canals is stimulated. Instead, caloric stimulation of one of the canals with hot or cold water may be used. In employing this method, the head is held in such a position that the canal to be stimulated is kept vertical. The effects of convection currents set up by the change in temperature then become effective. Although stimulation of the vertical canal, as well as of the horizontal canals, may be necessary for clinical or experimental purposes, the horizontal canal is the easier to use and will be considered sufficient for the purposes of this section.

The horizontal canal lies in a plane with the anterior end tilted upward 30

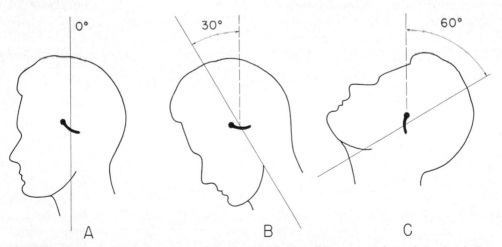

Fig. 195. Plane of the horizontal semicircular canal with different positions of the head. In the erect position of the head, **A**, the horizontal canal is tilted upward approximately 30 degrees but may be made horizontal by tilting the head forward 30 degrees, **B**, or be made vertical by tilting the head backward 60 degrees, **C**. (After Cogan.)

degrees above the horizon (Fig. 195). In order to bring the canal into the horizontal, therefore, the chin must be tilted down on the chest 30 degrees for rotation in the horizontal meridian, or the head must be tilted backward 60 degrees in order to bring the canal vertical when the caloric test is used. The ampulla, containing the crista, is the sensory end of the canal. It is possible that the rest of the canal functions merely to equalize the pressures after stimulation in much the same way that the eustachian tube equalizes the pressures on the two sides of the eardrum. The stimulus is greatest in the case of the horizontal canals when the direction of pressure exerted by the endolymph is toward the ampulla. When

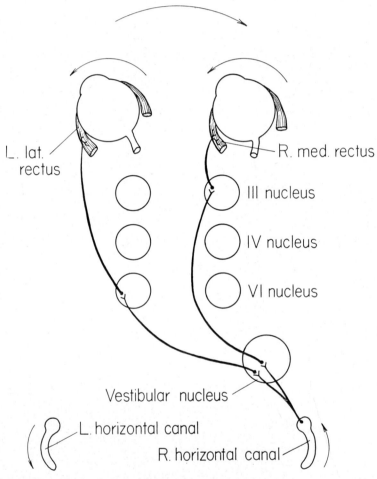

Fig. 196. Deviation of the eyes and displacement of the endolymph with rotation of the head to the right. Rotation of the head to the right results in counterrotation of the endolymph during the rotation and consequent deviation of the eyes (slow phase of vestibular nystagmus) to the left. Since the movement of endolymph is toward the ampulla on the right side and away from the ampulla on the left, the right ampulla will be most strongly stimulated during rotation of the head to the right. The reverse occurs with sudden cessation of rotation (postrotary deviation of the eyes and nystagmus). (Compiled from Cogan and Duke-Elder.)

the head is rotated to the right, the right horizontal canal is stimulated maximally during the rotation and the left canal maximally when the rotation stops (Fig. 196). Rotation of the head to the right causes slow tonic deviation of the eyes to the left followed by a rapid recovery movement of the eyes to the right, until the primary position is again attained. The sequence of events is then repeated. The slow tonic movement constitutes the basis of nystagmus.

It has become customary to name the direction of the nystagmus from the direction the eyes take during the quick phase of nystagmus. When the head is rotated horizontally to the right and the horizontal semicircular canals are stimulated, a stimulus is sent to the muscles producing levoversion so that the eyes move slowly to the left. Following this movement, there is an immediate rapid return of the eyes to the right. The slow

and rapid phases are then repeated. The nystagmus in this case is said to be directed to the right.

Illusion of movement during nystagmus. It has been shown that volitional movements of the eyes give rise to the sensation that the eyes have moved while the visual field remains stationary. If the eyes are moved by reflex activity, as in nystagmus, or by passive motion, the subject is no longer aware that the eyes have moved, but has the illusion that the world about him is in motion. This illusory movement nearly always occurs during vestibular nystagmus. The movement is perceived during the slow phase of the nystagmus but not during the rapid phase. As a result of this, objects in space appear to move continuously in one direction only, opposite to the direction of the slow phase of the nystagmus, i.e., in the direction of the nystagmus (quick component). The fiber connections for the interpretation of movement of the

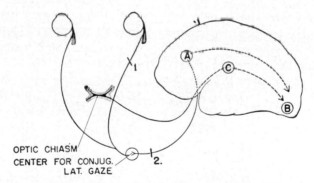

OPTIC CHIASM
CENTER FOR CONJUG. LAT. GAZE

Fig. 197. Diagram illustrating possible connections for the interpretation of movement of the environment. Area **A** represents the frontal center for lateral conjugate gaze. As efferent impulses are sent down to the subcortical center for movement of the eyes, corresponding impulses are sent to area **B**, indicating that a definite amount of image movement on the retina is to be expected. If there is a block at **2** in the efferent pathways (or at **1** in case one eye is used for fixation), the impulses from **A** will get to **B** but the eyes (or eye) will not move and the absence of the expected displacement of the image will result in an illusory movement of the environment in the opposite direction. Similarly when the eyes are moved passively, the displacement of the image on the retina will be transmitted to the visual centers by way of **C**, but since no information has been received from **A** indicating that the eyes have been moved, the image displacement will be interpreted as movement (illusory) of the environment. (From Cogan, D.: Neurology of the ocular muscles, Springfield, Ill.; Charles C Thomas, Publisher.)

environment, according to Cogan, are shown in Fig. 197.

The various characteristics of nystagmus which should be observed are as follows: (1) direction—from the quick component, (2) type—horizontal, vertical, rotatory, or combinations of these, (3) amplitude—coarse or fine, (4) speed—rapid or slow, (5) degree—first, second, or third, and (6) duration—longstanding or recent. The degree of nystagmus may be classified as follows.

1. *First degree.* There is no nystagmus when the eyes are in the primary position, but nystagmus to the right appears on dextroversion, and nystagmus to the left appears on levoversion.
2. *Second degree.* Nystagmus to the right or left occurs when the eyes are in the primary position. This is in addition to nystagmus to the right on dextroversion and nystagmus to the left on levoversion.
3. *Third degree.* Nystagmus is present in all positions of gaze and is always directed to one side, either right or left.

Since the essence of nystagmus is a deviation of the eyes due to an imbalance of the tonus to the ocular muscles, any disturbance in the reflex pathways controlling this tonus may produce nystagmus. Under certain conditions, nystagmus is entirely physiologic. Nystagmus of the first degree occurs in the majority of normal persons when the gaze is carried to the extremes of version. It is then known as end position nystagmus. It also occurs physiologically as fatigue nystagmus. If a normal person keeps looking to one side for some time, horizontal or horizontal-rotary nystagmus may appear after 1 or 2 minutes, along with a disagreeable feeling of fatigue in the eyes.

Nystagmus of first degree may also occur pathologically as labyrinthine nystagmus, as muscle paretic nystagmus, or as gaze paretic nystagmus.

Labyrinthine nystagmus is mixed horizontal and rotary nystagmus. It generally appears immediately when the subjects looks to one side and remains unchanged for some time. However, this diagnosis should be made only if there are additional labyrinthine manifestations, such as vertigo.

Muscle paretic nystagmus occurs in paresis of the external ocular muscles. If the patient looks toward the side of the paretic muscle, the affected eye has a tendency to move back to the primary position because of the weakness of the muscle. New impulses are then sent to the muscle to force the eyes into the desired position. This return to the primary position and the renewed innervation appear as rhythmic nystagmic movements. In this case, the amplitude and the frequency of nystagmus in the paretic eye and in the sound eye are different; therefore, the nystagmus appears more marked in one eye. This is called dissociated nystagmus.

Gaze paretic nystagmus, in association with difficulty in directing the gaze in a particular direction, is due to paresis of conjugate ocular movements. The lesion in such paralyses is always supranuclear.

Nystagmus of second and third degrees is always pathologic and may occur under one of the following conditions. (1) Peripheral labyrinthine nystagmus occurs in disease of the inner ear or of the vestibular nerve. (2) Neurologic nystagmus occurs in disease of the central nervous system, affecting the central part of the vestibular apparatus, i.e., the vestibular nuclei and their connections with the nuclei of the eye muscles. (3) Ocular nystagmus accompanies pathologic changes in the eyes.

Peripheral labyrinthine nystagmus is horizontal rotary nystagmus with an intensity of second or third degree and medium frequency and amplitude. It is always accompanied by typical manifestations of labyrinthine vertigo.

Neurologic nystagmus. The nystagmus may be horizontal, vertical, rotary, or mixed type. It is second or third degree and with moderate frequency and amplitude and is usually in the direction of the diseased side, rarely in the direction of the sound side. There may be only slight vertigo unless the condition is acute, in which case rotary nystagmus or vertigo is pronounced. It results from any lesion in the brainstem that disrupts the normal symmetry of tonus to the muscles of the two eyes arising in the vestibular apparatus. Cogan[116] has called attention to the fact that neurologic nystagmus is actually a manifestation of conjugate gaze palsy. This explains the fact that it is almost always more marked when the subject is asked to direct his gaze toward the side of the lesion.

Ocular nystagmus. Ocular nystagmus is a continuous, wandering, or searching movement of the eyes. The nystagmus occurs in every possible direction, with extremes of amplitude and frequency. It is seldom directed; i.e., it is made up generally of two components which are of about the same rapidity. It occurs in persons who were born with very poor vision due to any cause whatever, but it seldom occurs in persons who are blinded later in life. Since it usually lacks quick and slow components, both movements having an equal time value, frequently it is termed a nystagmoid movement, rather than true nystagmus, or merely pendular nystagmus.

Pathways for vestibular nystagmus. A vast amount of research has been done to determine the afferent and efferent arcs of the nystagmus reflex. The problem of the slow component can be said to be solved in most respects, but we have learned little regarding the quick phase.

Slow phase: The impulses arising in the hair cells of the ampulla are conducted by way of the vestibular branch of the eighth nerve to the vestibular nuclei in the brainstem. The cell bodies of these fibers are found in the ganglion of Scarpa.

Although it was formerly believed that each labyrinth was connected with all of the muscles of each eye, Szentagothai[117] found each to be connected to only three muscles of each eye—namely, the homolateral medial rectus, superior rectus, and superior oblique and the contralateral lateral rectus, inferior rectus, and inferior oblique. The connections of each of the three semicircular canals according to him are shown in Table 49.

Each crista or ampulla sends its impulses to the nucleus of origin of the muscles concerned by a three-neuron arc, two of which are excitatory and one inhibitory, as shown in Fig. 198. Neuron 1 goes from the cells in Scarpa's ganglion

Table 49. *Connections of semicircular canals with ocular muscles according to Szentagothai*

Canal	Homolateral	Contralateral
Horizontal	Medial rectus	Lateral rectus
Superior (vertical)	Superior rectus	Inferior oblique
Posterior	Superior oblique	Inferior rectus

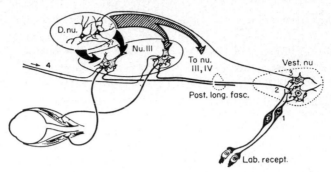

Fig. 198. The nerve pathways that serve as the basis of the reciprocal inhibition in the elementary vestibulo-ocular reflex arc according to Szentagothai and Scháb (1956). (From Alpern, M.: Anatomical aspects. In Davson, H., editor: The eye, New York, 1962, Academic Press, Inc., vol. 3, Muscular mechanisms.)

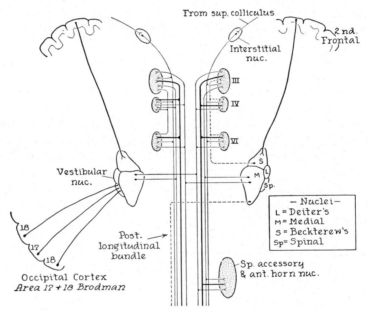

Fig. 199. Diagram of the medial longitudinal bundle, showing the voluntary motor innervation of the ocular muscles on the right side and the reflex innervation from the occipital lobes on the left side. It is not intended to indicate that the fibers end in one or another of the vestibular nuclei since the exact course of these fibers is unknown. The drawing shows a fiber ending in a certain nucleus, e.g., Deiters', merely for convenience.

to one of the vestibular nuclei. Neuron 2 runs from here into the medial longitudinal fasciculus to the nucleus of the ocular muscle actively innervated. Neuron 3 runs from the same vestibular nucleus to the nucleus of Darkschewitsch which in turn supplies inhibition to the antagonist muscle, producing relaxation of this according to the principle of reciprocal innervation.[118] In Fig. 198 the superior and rostral ends of the lateral vestibular nucleus are shown, sending neuron 2 into the homolateral medial longitudinal fasciculus to the nucleus of origin of the superior rectus muscle and neuron 3 by some other path than the medial longitudinal fasciculus (as yet unknown) to the nucleus of Darkschewitsch. The black arrows represent inhibitory impulses from this nucleus to the cells of origin of the antagonistic inferior rectus. By this means as the superior rectus contracts, the inferior rectus is relaxed. The hatched arrows represent other inhibitory impulses from this nucleus to other ocular muscles which may be involved in the movement, e.g., the superior oblique.

As shown in Fig. 199, there are four main cell masses in each vestibular nucleus or cell mass: *L*, Deiter's nucleus or lateral nucleus; *M*, medial nucleus; *S*, Beckterew's or superior nucleus; *Sp*, spinal or inferior nucleus.

What part each of these isolated cell masses play in the innervation of the individual muscles is not definitely known. According to Crosby, the lateral vestibular nucleus sends fibers from its medial and caudal two thirds into the contralateral medial longitudinal fasciculus. These fibers end in cells of the abducens nucleus, supplying the lateral rectus muscle on that side, and also end in cells of the parabducens nucleus from which they make connections with the oculomotor nucleus for contraction of the medial rectus of the opposite eye. In this manner the arc is completed for conjugate deviation of the eyes toward the side of the contracting lateral rectus (Fig. 200).

Rapid phase: The fast component of nystagmus is a corrective movement or

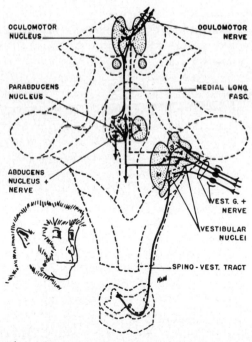

Fig. 200. Diagram showing some connections of the vestibular system related to horizontal conjugate deviation of the eyes. **I,** Inferior vestibular nucleus; **L,** lateral vestibular nucleus; **M,** medial vestibular nucleus; **Medial Long. Fasc.,** medial longitudinal fasciculus; **S,** superior vestibular nucleus; **Spino-Vest. Tract,** spinovestibular tract; **Vest. G. + Nerve,** vestibular ganglion plus vestibular nerve. (From Crosby, E. C.: J. Comp. Neurol. **99:**440, 1953.)

movement of recovery. The eyes, having been turned to one side by the tonic impulses from the semicircular canal, are suddenly released from these impulses and are rapidly brought back to their original position. In rotational nystagmus the speed of the slow component can be changed by the speed of rotation, but the speed of the rapid component is always the same. The slow component has the characteristics of following movements, whereas the rapid component is a saccade.

It is not known as yet where the impulses for the rapid phase originate, other than it is different from the slow component. It is also certain that it does not arise in the muscles themselves, as a stretch reflex. Stretching the isolated muscles during calorically induced nystagmus in cats has no effect on the rhythm.[54] Further, no afferent impulses can be recorded in the oculomotor nerves, which would suggest the presence of such a mechanism for controlling nystagmus.[119, 120] It has been suggested that nystagmus is a rhythmic reflex analogous to the stretch reflex,[122] in which various types of nerve networks set up reverberating circuits which discharge rhythmically.

Quick movements of the body are well compensated for by movements of the eye.[121] If a person is swung from a seat hung from a ball bearing and peers with one eye through the center race of the bearing, the subject rotates around the visual axis of his eye with a half period of about 1 second. Under these conditions, rapid almost complete compensatory movements which are attributable to the effect of the semicircular canals, with a residual compensation due to the otoliths, are performed.

Cogan believes that in man the pathways for the quick component are closely associated with, if not identical to, the voluntary pathways for ocular movements. He has seen patients who have lost the ability to look to one side on command (supranuclear gaze palsy) also show a loss of the quick component of vestibular nystagmus, although they still retained the ability to turn the eyes in this direction by following a moving target (the fixation reflex, p. 474). Also, he records that patients with congenital apraxia show a simultaneous loss of the rapid phase, as well as of the truly command movements, but retain the normal random or quasivoluntary movements. This definitely implicates mechanisms higher than the brainstem in the arc producing the rapid phase, as far as man is concerned, and Cogan believes the impulses are relayed through area 8 in the frontal lobe. This cannot be true of the lower mammals, for labyrinthine nystagmus is not affected by removal of the cerebral hemispheres. The movements of the eyes under these conditions have a component of rolling around the anteroposterior axis.[123]

Proprioception from muscles of the neck. In the lower vertebrates a combination of proprioception from the muscles of the neck and reflexes from the otolith apparatus determine in large measure the position of the eyes with any change in the position of the head in respect to gravity. Rotation of an animal's head after bilateral labyrinthectomy causes an increase in extensor tonus in the forelimb and hind limb on the side toward which the face is turned, with a decrease in tonus on the opposite side. The eyes will be turned in the orbits correspondingly, away from the side toward which the face turned. The fact that these changes in position of the eyes occur in the decerebrate and labyrinthectomized animal proves that they must come from proprioceptive impulses from the neck. While they have been aptly termed tonic neck reflexes, the impulses do not actually arise from the muscles of the neck, for it has been shown[124] that they can still be evoked after bilateral section of all the muscular and cutaneous branches of the first three cervical nerves and denervation of all the muscles in the neck. They actually come from the ligaments in the upper cervical joints, especially the ocipitoatlantal and atlantoaxial joints.

It is questionable whether these reflexes are of much importance in man, but if they are present, they act in the same way that the otolith apparatus does and in addition may exert some influence on the lateral and medial recti muscles.

Proprioception from the ocular muscles. The subject of proprioception from ocular muscles has been discussed previously (p. 418). It has been shown that afferent impulses are sent from the muscle spindles and other sensory endings in the muscles and tendons to the brain along the so-called motor nerves to the eye muscles. It will be recalled that Sherrington and others postulated the existence of such impulses before they were discovered on the theory that it was necessary for the body to have such information of the state of contraction of the eye muscles in order to correct for changes in pattern of the visual receptors stimulated when the eyes move into the tertiary positions of gaze (p. 420). Most psychologists now agree that the corrections which we make for the disparateness of the visual images of the two eyes is not due to information sent into the brain by these afferent impulses, but rather to an awareness of the intensity of impulses sent down the motor nerves to achieve the correct movement of the eyes. Whitteridge has aptly termed Sherrington's idea of proprioception the inflow theory and the idea of awareness of the motor innervation the outflow theory. All of the evidence at present points strongly to this latter idea as the correct one (see discussion of my experiment in past-pointing in ocular muscle paralysis, p. 426).

The proprioceptors in the ocular muscles do not play any part in the conscious appreciation of eye movement and are not responsible for any form of stretch reflex. They probably serve a purpose in the maintenance of exact fixation. Whenever fixation occurs, the discharge of the gamma efferents to the intrafusal fibers in the muscle spindles may be increased, and in this way the sensitivity of the spindles is increased. This would materially aid in the detection of small movements of an object in space, for in a blank field in order to detect a very small movement of a target the body must simultaneously have information that the eye itself has not moved. The minimal detection of a target in a blank field without a fixation point is of the order of 0.5 degree per second. This is about what has been found as the minimum movement which the eye muscles of the goat can signal to the brain.[125]

Basic tonus of the convergence mechanism. This subject will be discussed more fully in the section on convergence (p. 484). All subcortical mechanisms when freed from the influence of cortical control show an increase in activity. Their basic tonus is damped down by the cortex under physiologic conditions. Certain facts indicate that the convergence mechanism is damped down by the cortex and that the basic tonus of the subcortical centers, wherever they may be, is excessive, particularly in infants and very young children. During adolescence this basic tonus becomes weaker, and in adult life the basic tonus may be insufficient even to keep the eyes in parallelism in the absence of visual stimuli.

Optomotor reflexes

We have just discussed reflexes arising from various parts of the body which tended to keep it in status quo with its surroundings. For the most part these were reflexes having to do with the posture of the body as well as with the alignment of the eyes. In a general way one might say that the postural reflexes formed a somewhat crude mechanism by means of which the eyes are kept in alignment with one another, provided of course that anatomically the eyes and the orbits are normal. Given a normal anatomic substratum which permits the eyes to move together in some kind of alignment, the postural reflexes see to it that changes in body posture do not upset this alignment.

For the purposes to which the eyes are put in daily life, however, this degree of alignment might be inadequate. In animals with well-developed foveas it becomes necessary to ensure that the image falls on each fovea at all times. This requires a mechanism with a fine adjustment, far less crude than that provided by the postural reflexes. This mechanism is provided by the eyes themselves, and as will be shown, the marked difference between the acuity at the fovea and that just off the fovea provides a feedback mechanism which automatically directs the eye, like a guided missile, onto the target.

It is well known in general physiology that light exerts tonus on the musculature of the body. It has been shown that in certain flying insects light thrown into the eye affects the tonus of the insect's muscles in such a way as to turn its body in flight toward the light. Under certain circumstances this heliotropic reflex may prove to be the animal's undoing, but under ordinary conditions in nature it is a beneficial mechanism and works for the good of the insect. It is not possible, of course, to demonstrate direct heliotropism in the higher animals, but changes in muscle tonus have been demonstrated in rabbits.

Following reflex. In man the most important source of reflex tonus to the ocular muscles comes from the visual impulses themselves. The importance of this source of tonus increases as one ascends the scale of animal life, and at the same time the effectiveness of the vestibular and neck reflexes diminishes in the same proportion. Thus, we find in the lower vertebrates, such as the rabbit or guinea pig, that the tonic reflexes of the neck and otolith are extremely effective in determining the position of the eyes in their orbits. It is at the same time difficult to demonstrate any change in the position of the eyes of this animal with changing patterns in the animal's visual field. In man, however, the neck reflexes are relatively ineffective, and the eyes show no deviations in response to turning the head on the neck, provided, of course, that the head is turned slowly to avoid stimulation of the semicircular canals. On the other hand, changes in the visual fields, even when of slight attention value, can be shown to produce marked changes in the ocular muscle tonus.

The most marked and common expression of this visual reflex tonus is the behavior of the eyes when a subject looks out of the window of a moving railway carriage at the passing scenery. The eyes will be seen to make a series of movements, consisting of a slow phase in the direction of apparent movement of the scenery and a rapid phase in the opposite direction. The movements continue as long as the subject pays attention to the scenery. The action is purely reflex, and the subject does not know that his eyes are moving. This has been named, most appropriately, railroad nystagmus. It was first studied in the laboratory and was used clinically by Barany. As yet, the exact pathways by means of which the reflexes are mediated are not determined, but many clinicians believe that optokinetic nystagmus, as it is called, can be of considerable importance in the diagnosis of certain cranial lesions.

For clinical testing, it is necessary only to present the subject with a rotating drum on which a series of black and white stripes alternate. It is advisable to have the figures or stripes on the drum provide about eight fixation objects per second for general purposes.[126]

In a normal person when the drum is turned to the right or left or up and down, nystagmus ensues in which the quick phase is opposite to the direction of the movement of the drum. Rotary optokinetic nystagmus is very difficult to elicit in most persons.[127] The width of the stripes is determined partly by the subject's ability to discriminate them, and hence the test can be used as an objective method of measuring visual acuity.[128] For this purpose, optokinetic nystagmus is induced in a subject, using wide alternating stripes on a rotating drum. The width of the stripes is then gradually narrowed until the nystagmus disappears. This occurs when the visual angle subtended by the individual stripes becomes less than the visual acuity of the subject. In this way the acuity of the subject can be determined roughly. The speed of the drum must also be within certain limits. The optimal speed consists of an angular velocity of approximately 40 degrees per second.[129]

Optokinetic nystagmus has been used as a means of measuring the visual acuity of laboratory and other animals, but as Cogan[130] points out, the results cannot be applied directly to man because of the many differences which exist between the ocular apparatus of man and of the lower vertebrates. For example, in man optokinetic nystagmus may be elicited if only a small portion of the visual field is in motion, provided that this portion corresponds to that with the highest visual acuity, i.e., the fovea generally. In animals a comparable effect is elicited only when the whole field is rotated.[131] In man and in the monkey,[132] some part of the visual cortex in the occipital lobe must be present in order to elicit the reflex, but in guinea pigs destruction of the whole visual cortex fails to modify the form, magnitude, or threshold speeds of optokinetic nystagmus.[133] On the other hand, in cats the unilateral destruction of the superior colliculus impairs the reaction to movement of the pattern toward the operated side, and bilateral lesions of the superior colliculi impair or abolish the nystagmus toward both sides. This is another example of the fact that in man the cortex has taken over many of the functions which are served by the subcortical centers in the lower vertebrates.

Visual acuity as determined by the optokinetic response has been correlated with the acuities recorded by the usual Snellen charts, and it has been found that the Snellen visual acuity is nearly always better than that recorded by the rotating drum. This means that one can be certain that an individual whose optokinetic responses indicate a certain level of visual acuity probably has even better than that.[134]

Optokinetic nystagmus is present in newborn infants immediately after birth or at least as soon as measurements can be made—some have been as early as an hour and a half after birth.[135] In ninety-three of one hundred newborn infants 1½ hours to 5 days of age, the infants were found to perceive a pattern which corresponded to a Snellen notation of 20/670.

As has been stated, the centers and pathways for this reflex in man are not known with any certainty. The afferent pathway is, without question, the visual fibers from the retina to the calcarine cortex (Fig. 201). There is no general agreement as to the layer of cells of the visual cortex in which the motor fibers begin. Most authors used to consider the cells of area 17 of Brodmann as the beginning of the efferent arc, but Hines[136] has given some evidence for believing that the optomotor pathway begins in the cells of area 18, the parastriate area, and area 19, the peristriate area, rather than in the striate area itself (Fig. 202).

Each optomotor center is supposed to receive fibers not only from the visual cortex of the same side, but also from that of the opposite side by way of the corpus callosum. The efferent fibers then pass to the deeper aspect of the optic radiation in its posterior part and run forward with it. They part company with the optic radiation at its anterior third, pass into the cerebral peduncle, cross the midline and enter the medial longitudinal bundle of the opposite side, and thence pass on to the center of conjugate gaze for lateral movements in the pons. A lesion anywhere along this pathway will abolish optokinetic nystagmus to the opposite side. If the lesion occurs in that part of the optomotor pathway where it is associated with the optic radiation, i.e., in its posterior two thirds, then the loss of optokinetic nystagmus will be associated with homonymous hemianopsia. If, however, the lesion occurs elsewhere, either in the center itself or farther down

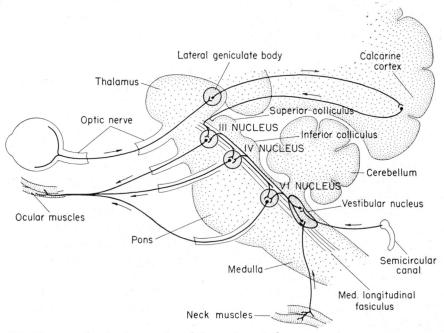

Fig. 201. Diagram of reflex innervation of the ocular muscles.

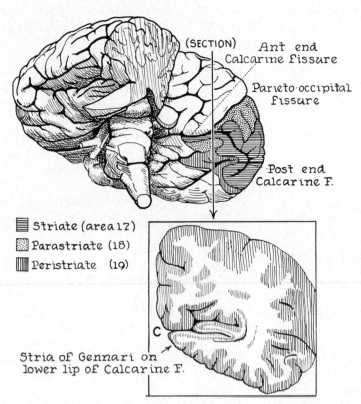

(SECTION)
Ant end
Calcarine fissure

Parieto-occipital
fissure

Post end
Calcarine F.

▤ Striate (area 17)
▨ Parastriate (18)
▥ Peristriate (19)

Stria of Gennari on
lower lip of Calcarine F.

Fig. 202. Diagram of the mesial half of the right occipital cortex, the left occipital lobe having been cut off. The insert shows a transverse section through the calcarine fissure at the level of the arrow. At this level the parieto-occipital fissure joins the calcarine fissure, so that only the lower lip of the calcarine fissure has the white line of Gennari. Some investigators believe that the cells giving rise to the optomotor impulses of the visual fixation reflex arise in the striate area (area 17 of Brodmann), but according to Hines they originate in the cells of areas 18 and 19 of Brodmann.

in the brainstem, then the optokinetic paralysis will occur alone.[137] It has been assumed by some authors that the supratentorial connections fo roptokinetic nystagmus pass to the eye muscles via the superior colliculi[138] by pathways which are entirely separate from the vestibular nuclei and might possibly involve a center of gaze independent of that which subserves vestibular nystagmus. These authors conclude that optokinetic responses to the right and left are subserved by anatomically separate reflex pathways within the brainstem. Each is under the modifying influence of a center in the supramarginal and angular gyri of a particular cerebral hemisphere. The centers of the right hemisphere facilitate optokinetic nystagmus to the left and inhibit it to the right, whereas the opposite effects are exerted by the centers of the left hemisphere. This is similar to the organization which these authors postulate for the neural mechanism of vestibular nystagmus.

In order to develop optokinetic nystagmus, a subject's visual acuity need be only the perception of figures or lines on the revolving drum. As just stated, the acuity must be sufficient to resolve the pattern, which is the essential factor producing the movement. It is not necessary to have central fixation as long as the pattern can be resolved by the periphery of the retina. Patients with large central scotomas still should show normal optokinetic nystagmus to either side. It should be present even though the whole of the peripheral visual field is lost, provided that a small area of central vision is present.[139]

Some authors have postulated that optokinetic nystagmus depends upon an intact cerebral reflex center. This has been located in the oculomotor regions of the occipital lobe,[140] in both occipital and frontal lobes,[141] or in the supramarginal and angular gyri.[142] No evidence for the existence of such an optokinetic center could be found for the monkey by Pasik and co-workers.[132]

In patients who have a lesion in the posterior part of the optic radiation, where the centrifugal fibers for optokinetic nystagmus are in close apposition, homonymous hemianopsia will be combined with loss of optokinetic nystagmus to the side opposite the lesion. For example, a lesion situated on the right side in the posterior third of the optic radiation will produce left homonymous hemianopsia, i.e., blindness in the left half of each visual field, and when the drum is rotated to the patient's right, loss of optokinetic nystagmus to the left (quick recovery movement to the left) will occur. The occurrence of homonymous hemianopsia and loss of optokinetic nystagmus to the same side as the loss of the visual fields are highly suggestive of a lesion in the posterior third of the optic radiation. Optokinetic nystagmus must be present toward the opposite side, however. If the loss of optokinetic nystagmus is bilateral, it has little local-

izing value, as Kestenbaum[138] pointed out.

Optokinetic nystagmus is a somewhat dramatic manifestation of a reflex that is constantly active in daily life, although in a much less obvious form. It has been given various names, such as the following reflex and the fixation reflex.[75] Since the anatomic basis for all of the optomotor reflexes is probably identical, there is little excuse for identifying them by separate names. They all depend upon the fact that the fovea, being the point of greatest visual acuity, must be placed to receive the image of an object looked at in order for it to be distinctly seen. The voluntary movements of the eyes take care of this when there is a conscious need for foveal vision, but nature has further provided us with a mechanism by means of which an image, once it is on the macula, will stay there reflexly or, if it is near the macula, will move the eye reflexly in such a manner that the fovea will receive it. This mechanism is the same that causes the slow phase of optokinetic nystagmus. Whenever the image of an object tends to move off the macula in one direction, an increase in tonus occurs in those muscles which move the eyes in that direction. Thus the eyes are turned reflexly to follow the object (Figs. 203 to 205). There is no recovery or quick phase, as there is in optokinetic nystagmus, probably because the mechanism of the fixation reflex works within only a few degrees of the macula under ordinary circumstances so that there is no need for the eyes to make such a readjustment. The same reflex produces involuntary so-called fusional movements of each eye in an effort to maintain binocular single vision.

While both eyes are turned toward an object which catches our attention by the gross voluntary mechanism, so that its image falls approximately on each fovea, the fixation reflex acts further as a fine adjustment which ensures that identical retinal areas will always be stimulated simultaneously. If anything prevents perfect alignment of the eyes, the fixation reflex steps in to correct the maladjustment, provided, of course, that it does not exceed the limitations of the mechanism. This can be demonstrated readily by the movements the eyes make to

maintain binocular single vision when weak prisms are held up in front of one eye of a person while he looks at a small light 6 M. or more away. If a weak prism (i.e., 1 to 2 $\triangle$) is held in front of the right eye, base in or out, this eye will involuntarily turn to bring the fovea in line with the object of regard. The movement will be made without the subject's awareness, provided that the prism is a

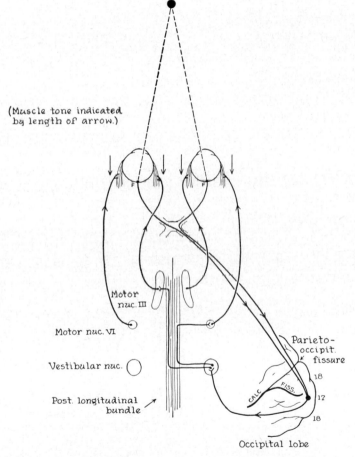

Fig. 203. The image of the dot straight ahead of the eyes falls on the foveas. The impulses are carried up to the extreme tip of the occipital lobe along the calcarine fissure. The optomotor fibers carry impulses from here to the vestibular nuclei, which distribute tone to the ocular muscles (amount of tone indicated by length of arrow in diagram). As long as the images are on the foveas, the tone of the muscles turning the eyes to the right is equal to that of the muscles turning the eyes to the left. The diagram purposely begs the question of bilateral representation of the foveas. It may be imagined that the same stimuli go to the left calcarine cortex, as is shown here to the right.

weak one. If stronger prisms are used, the patient may be conscious of momentary diplopia, and he then *involuntarily* makes an effort at fusion by turning the eye still farther. Eventually, the amount of prism will be too great for the involuntary fusion reflex to overcome, and the subject will experience double images, unless he makes a *voluntary* effort to overcome the diplopia. The prism which breaks up the fixation reflex is the measure of the fusional capacity of the subject. The reflex is demonstrable in both convergence and divergence and to a very slight degree in sursumvergence. Obviously, convergence is much more powerful than the other vergences due no doubt to its constant use.

Torsional movements occur in the interest of maintaining single binocular

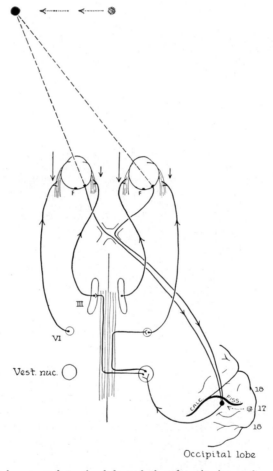

Fig. 204. The spot has moved to the left and therefore its image has moved off the foveas onto the right halves of the two retinas. The visual impulses are carried up to the occipital cortex, to cells which lie farther forward along the calcarine fissure than those which come from the foveas. From these cells an optomotor impulse is sent to the vestibular nuclei which diminishes the tone of the muscles which turn the eyes to the right and increases the tone of those which turn the eyes to the left. The eyes are therefore turned to the left until the image of the spot once more falls on the foveas.

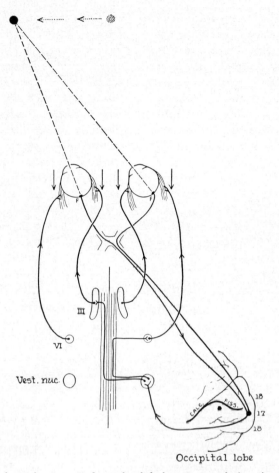

Occipital lobe

Fig. 205. The eyes have been turned to the left by means of the visual fixation reflex to follow the movement of the spot. The images which now fall on the foveas again send their impulses up to the foveal localization of vision in the occipital cortex, and the optomotor impulses once again equalize the tone of the muscles turning the eyes to the right and of those turning the eyes to the left, so that the eyes remain fixed as long as the image of the spot remains stationary.

vision. Experiments show that the muscles of the eye can cooperate to produce cycloversion about the visual axes in the interest of maintaining binocular single vision. The visual axes may remain fixed during the torsional movements. These movements are reflex movements entirely. They take place with any torsional change in the orientation of the visual field. Contours whose images in the two eyes are nearly vertical provide much

stronger stimuli for cyclofusional movements than do those from contours whose images are approximately horizontal.[143]

Fixation reflex. The fixation reflex is, in effect, the same as the following reflex but comes into play after the object of regard has been captured by the fovea by means of the following reflex. The fixation reflex works to maintain the object on the fovea—to keep it from slipping off the region of most acute vision, as it were. Obviously, the attention value of the object of regard determines to a great extent how active this reflex will be. Are there other objects in the field of vision, even though not clearly focused, yet possessing greater attention value? If so, the fixation reflex is inhibited, and the following reflex takes over in the direction of the new stimulus. Perhaps the most effective stimulus to either the following or fixation reflex is movement of the object of regard, but it is evident that contours, color, differences in illumination between object and surroundings, and a host of psychologic factors determine how strong the fixation reflex will be at any moment.

Fusional reflex. The fusional reflex has been described previously, without actual use of the term. It is the force generated by the two foveas working together to maintain a single image focused on receptors having the same visual direction. In this way, only, can the two images be fused into one. As will be shown later, if receptors with different visual directions are simultaneously stimulated by the same object, the object will appear in two different visual directions in space. Diplopia or double vision is then the result.

In order to achieve a single image it is necessary that the eyes move together, not only in versions, but also in vergences, and that their visual lines converge or diverge from moment to moment, as the case requires. A moving object approaching the eyes requires both versions and convergence, and one receding from the eyes requires versions and divergence. The stimulus to these vergences is the same as that for versions, with perhaps added factors, such as change in size of the retinal image and in the amount of ciliary muscle power necessary to accommodate the eyes for the changing distance. At any rate, convergence and divergence are carried out reflexly in the same way that versions are, and the object of regard is held on the two foveas in spite of its change in position away from or closer to a person.

The limits of the fusional reflex are not well known, and it will be necessary to modify somewhat the preceding statement that images must be focused on identical receptors in order to be seen singly. This is not quite true. In fact, when images are focused on slightly disparate retinal receptors, i.e., receptors having slightly different visual directions, the result is stereopsis or depth perception by parallax. This subject is discussed in Chapter 22, Binocular Vision. There is, therefore, a limit to the amplitude of motor fusion, but sensory fusion continues for a time although the images of an object are beyond the limits of identical retinal receptors.

The conception seems to be widely held that fusional movements are induced by diplopia, but this is not true. It can easily be shown that fusional movements occur as a result of the introduction of a very small prism in front of one eye which produces no conscious double vision. How small the disparity has to be in order to elicit a fusional movement and whether this varies in different individuals have never been reported.

It has been postulated that special receptors which induce fusional movements are present in the perimacular area,[144] but this is disproved by the fact that the prism strength can be slowly increased so that the image of the object of regard continues to stimulate each fovea except immediately after the introduction of the increase in prism. Eventually the strength of the prism exceeds the fusional capacity, and the individual has diplopia. Under these conditions the limitation of fusional movement cannot be related to the distribution of fusional receptors in the perimacular region. Prior to the addition of the final prism increment each fovea was stimulated by the object of regard, and the addition of this final increment did not produce any greater disparity than did the addition of the first increment.[145] Further evidence against special receptors in the perimacular area is the fact that fusional movements can be produced by disparity in the periphery of the retinas (see discussion of cyclofusional movements, p. 477).

Fusional movements, like vergences, are slow tonic movements with a maximum velocity of 21.4 degrees per second[146] as compared to 20.2 degrees per second for a lateral vergence movement.[147] This is very much smaller than the speed of saccadic movements.

Under experimental conditions it is possible to determine the effectiveness of peripheral fusional stimuli that cause the eyes to break away from bifoveal fixation. The subject is presented with similar targets which are fixated with both foveas. Targets are then introduced into the peripheral field of each eye which create fusional impulses. In order for these targets to be fused, however, the eyes must break from bifoveal fixation. Thus, an estimate may be obtained of the relative effectiveness of peripheral compared to foveal fusional impulses. Under these experimental conditions, which are never duplicated in nature, it has been found that paramacular targets present a greater stimulus to fusion than do foveal targets, and that it is the retinal locus rather than the area stimulated which determines the effectiveness of the peripheral fusional impulses.[148]

It is of considerable importance to ophthalmologists to know whether the amplitude of fusional movements can or cannot be improved by various training methods. Many orthoptists are of the opinion that it is possible to do so. The evidence for this is not convincing. Sensory fusion is quite a different thing, and there is no question but that individuals can be trained to acquire better sensory fusion in stereoscopic devices. Almost everyone has had the experience that he cannot fuse test targets which have very small disparity if these are looked at first in a stereoscope. If, however, targets with a large disparity are first tried, the knack of fusing more difficult targets is soon learned. This does not mean, however, that one can build up motor fusional abilities, and the evidence to the present time suggests that the amplitude of fusion is fixed in any one individual and cannot be increased beyond that point. Further controlled experiments are needed to decide this.

Accommodative convergence. The basic tonus of the convergence mechanism has been termed tonic convergence. This is the tonus of the convergence mechanism when the eyes are in the primary position. It can be determined best in the intact subject by the potentials discharged from each medial rectus muscle. It will be shown in the discussion on convergence that to this basic tonus must be added several other sources of tonus, all of which add up to total convergence. The effect of accommodation, accommodative convergence, is one of the chief sources of tonus. When an object is brought closer to the eyes, the degree of contraction of the ciliary muscle necessary to change the dioptric power of the eye is accompanied by an increase in innervation of both the convergence mechanism and sphincter pupillae. This combination of accommodation, convergence, and miosis is a synkinesis. All three activities are bound together in a common purpose, but each does not depend on either of the others in the sense of a reflex. The amount of convergence called forth by each unit of accommodation is known as accommodative convergence. This is discussed more fully in the section on convergence. Since convergence issues from a visual stimulus, it is proper to include accommodative convergence among the optomotor reflexes, although admittedly it is not a true reflex. It is obvious that accommodative convergence has a marked influence on the convergence tonus. If because of hyperopia it is necessary for a person to employ an excessive amount of accommodation, the tonus of the convergence mechanism will be excessive in proportion to the excess accommodation. This is the basic pathogenesis of accommodative strabismus.

Vergences

The vergences properly belong in the section on reflex activity of the eyes, although it is possible for most persons to learn to converge the eyes voluntarily. In our daily life convergence movements are brought about almost entirely reflexly. Divergence from parallelism is entirely reflex, and there is no possible control by the will, except in the relaxation from voluntary convergence.

Convergence. The majority of the lower vertebrates have little use for convergence since their eyes are situated laterally in the head, and the visual field directly in front of them is cut off by the snout. The two disjunctive movements of the eyes, convergence and divergence, are of late development in the species, considerably later than versions. Corresponding to this late phylogenetic development, convergence and divergence also appear relatively late in the postnatal development of the human being. Infants show very little convergence un-

til the third month of life. Even in the adult convergence as a purely voluntary act is seldom found without some training. The majority of persons, if asked to converge, cannot do so without having some fixation point in front of them on which to fasten their attention. This brings into play the involuntary part of convergence, which will be considered more fully later on. Because of this need for fixation, care must be exercised in making a diagnosis of paralysis of convergence. Several factors, such as the attention value of the object used for fixation, the patient's cooperation in making the effort to converge, and the vision of each eye and its refractive state, all enter into the final result when a person is asked to converge.

Convergence is always associated with accommodation and miosis, the collective phenomena being called the near point reaction.

Pathways. The near point reaction or near response is limited to man and the primates; the usual laboratory animals have little convergence, although accommodation in some may be well developed. For this reason our knowledge of the pathways which serve this reaction is meager. Convergence can be produced in the primate by simultaneous stimulation of both frontal or both occipital eye fields. In man convergence has been obtained only occasionally by unilateral stimulation of the frontal cortex (see Fig. 176, p. 435, small arrow directed to the right). That the cerebral cortex is involved in the pathway is attested to by the fact that the near response can be voluntarily carried out by man and from the recent findings of Jampel.[149] He was able to produce the near response in the macaque under very light anesthesia by unilateral stimulation of areas 19 and 22, as shown in Fig. 206. He was also able to

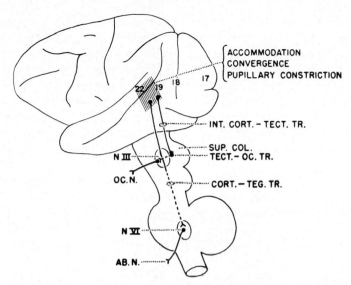

Fig. 206. Diagrammatic representation of the cerebral cortex and brainstem of the *Macaca mulatta* depicting the cortical areas associated with the near response and their neuronal projections into the tectum and tegmentum. **AB. N.,** Abducens nerve; **CORT.-TEG. TR.,** corticotegmental tract; **INT. CORT.-TECT. TR.,** internal corticotectal tract; **NIII.,** oculomotor nucleus; **NVI.,** abducens nucleus; **OC. N.,** oculomotor nerve; **SUP. COL.,** superior colliculus; **TECT.-OC. TR.,** tecto-oculomotor tract; 17, 18, 19, and 20, Brodmann's areas. (From Jampel, R.: Am. J. Ophth. 48:573, 1959.)

trace conducting fibers from areas 18 and 19 to the tectum of the midbrain where they terminated. Other fibers could be traced as far as the level of the inferior colliculi. The latter are assumed to carry inhibitory impulses to the abducens nucleus, producing inhibition of the lateral rectus during convergence. This hypothetical pathway is shown in Fig. 207.

The fiber tracts in man have never been localized, but clinical evidence suggests that they reach the nuclei of the third nerve by way of the anterior brachia and superior colliculi rather than by way of the pons (Fig. 208). Paralysis of convergence is more likely to be associated with paralysis of vertical gaze than with paralysis of horizontal gaze. Patients with large pontine lesions frequently retain convergence, and paralysis of convergence associated with paralysis of upward

gaze occurs frequently with lesions in the neighborhood of the superior colliculi, resulting in so-called Parinaud's syndrome. Pupillary abnormalities are common in this syndrome.

It is apparent from Jampel's findings that the near response is synthesized and controlled at the highest level of nervous activity, the cortex, and is modified at functionally lower levels, the pretectum and tectum of the midbrain. At the cortical level the impulses are probably under many different influences and can be modified by the total activity of the cortex. We will see, e.g., that the effect of accommodation on convergence depends on the effort of accommodation and not on the actual amount of dioptric change in the lens power produced.

Subcortical centers. No subcortical center for convergence has ever been found.

For many years it was assumed that the "so-called" center for convergence was Perlia's nucleus, which consists of an unpaired group of cells lying between the two Edinger-Westphal nuclei (Fig. 186). Perlia's nucleus appears phylogenetically first in animals having the ability to converge. It is not found in the more primitive mammals but only appears in those vertebrates whose eyes assume a frontal position, enabling them to have a binocular field of vision. It has its highest development, with a forward prolongation

in the midline not found in primitive monkeys, in the chimpanzee or in man. This nucleus appears in the human embryo first at a time when the eyes are beginning to swing around from the lateral to the frontal plane. On these facts alone Brouwer and others made the assumption that convergence was mediated by this nucleus. Studies by Warwick (p. 451) have shown that in the monkey the fibers from Perlia's nucleus do not go to the medial rectus muscles at all, but innervate the superior rectus muscles and

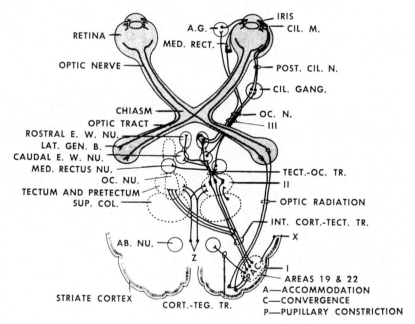

Fig. 207. Diagrammatic neuroanatomic scheme to illustrate the three levels of function in the nervous system involved in the near response. I, Functionally specific area for the near response in the preoccipital cortex. II, Level of the tectum and pretectum. III, Final common pathway for impulses to the ciliary muscle, medial rectus, and iris sphincter. X, Input of nervous activity from the entire cerebral cortex that modifies the output of the functionally specific areas for the near response in the preoccipital cortex. Z, Input of nervous activity from the spinal cord and brainstem which modifies the impulses discharged from the cerebral cortex into the tectum and pretectum. Ag, Accessory ganglion; **Ab. Nu.**, abducens nucleus; **Caudal E. W. Nu.**, caudal Edinger-Westphal nucleus; **Cil. Gang.**, ciliary ganglion; **Cil. M.**, ciliary muscle; **Cort.-Teg. Tr.**, corticotegmental tract; **Int. Cort.-Tect. Tr.**, internal corticotectal tract; **Lat. Gen. B.**, lateral geniculate body; **Med. Ret.**, medial rectus; **Med. Rectus Nu.**, medial rectus nucleus; **Oc. N.**, oculomotor nerve; **Oc. Nu.**, oculomotor nucleus; **Post. Cil. N.**, posterior ciliary nerves; **Rostral E. W. Nu.**, rostral Edinger-Westphal nucleus; **Sup. Col.**, superior colliculus; **Tect.-Oc. Tr.**, tecto-oculomotor tract. (From Jampel, R.: Am. J. Ophth. 48:573, 1959.)

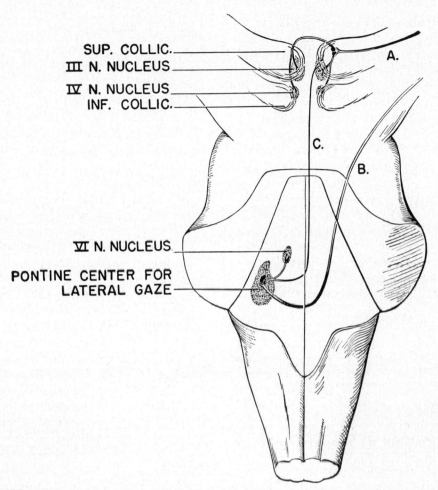

SUP. COLLIC.

III N. NUCLEUS

IV N. NUCLEUS

INF. COLLIC.

A.

C.

B.

VI N. NUCLEUS

PONTINE CENTER FOR
LATERAL GAZE

Fig. 208. Diagrammatic representation of the dorsal surface of the brainstem showing the chief ocular motor centers and their supranuclear connections. The main pathway from the cerebrum for conjugate lateral gaze, **B,** is by way of the cerebral peduncle to the opposite pontine center for lateral gaze and thence to the homolateral sixth cranial nerve and opposite nuclei of the third cranial nerve. The main pathway for conjugate vertical gaze, **A,** and for convergence is by way of the brachium to the superior colliculi and thence to the nuclei of the third and fourth cranial nerves of the same and opposite sides. Thus lesions in the anterior portion of the midbrain will affect primarily conjugate vertical movements and convergence, whereas lesions in the posterior portion will affect primarily conjugate lateral movements. Lesions in between will produce internuclear ophthalmoplegia from involvement of the medial longitudinal fasciculus, **C.** (From Cogan, D.: Neurology of the ocular muscles, Springfield, Ill., Charles C Thomas, Publisher.)

to some degree the inferior oblique muscles. This nucleus must be considered as a possible relay in the pathways for sursumversion, therefore, rather than as having anything to do with convergence.

No collection of cells has ever been found interposed between the fibers descending from the cortex to the third nerve complex, innervating the medial recti muscles. There is no anatomic justification, therefore, for the assumption of any so-called convergence center that relays impulses for binocular adduction to both medial recti (as opposed to the impulses to one medial rectus in a versional movement to the opposite side). And yet, as we will see, the concept is useful in any discussion of strabismus. There can be no doubt that the innervations for versions and vergences are different. This has already been amply shown (p. 440) in the differences between versional and vergence movements, and in the type of paralysis known as internuclear paralysis, in which one or both medial recti fail to respond in versional movements but contract promptly in convergence. Convergence is certainly not dependent on ascending fibers in the medial longitudinal fasciculus, whereas contraction of a medial rectus in a versional movement is. One might suggest that the medial rectus is innervated by two different sets of cells in each third nerve complex. One set innervates a medial rectus in a versional movement to the opposite side, along with simultaneous contraction of the contralateral lateral rectus, and the other set innervates the same medial rectus in a vergence movement, i.e., convergence along with simultaneous contraction of the contralateral medial rectus. While there is no evidence for this, its plausibility is somewhat strengthened by the following fact, according to Jampel.

"There are probably separate cell groups in the oculomotor nucleus for pupillary constriction associated with the light stimulus and for the pupillary constriction associated with the near response and these cells must be in very close proximity."*

Whenever the term *convergence* or *divergence center* is used in this book, it must be understood that I am employing

---

*From Jampel, R.: Am. J. Ophth. **48**:573, 1959.

a concept which has no anatomic reality. Although the term *center* has become unpopular in some circles, I find no embarrassment in continuing its use for didactic purposes.

Physiology of convergence. Binocular vision probably developed in man after the conjugate ocular mechanism had been evolved. With the development of binocular vision, a convergence mechanism had to be created.

In a previous section it was shown that versions in a horizontal plane necessitate the contraction of five muscles in each eye. Some investigators have assumed that several of the extraocular muscles take part in convergence, but Verhoeff[44] does not believe this. He points out that when an eye is directed downward and inward by the conjugate mechanism without the help of convergence it undergoes extorsion. When the eye is directed downward and inward, but the inward direction is produced by the convergence mechanism, the eye undergoes intorsion. According to him, this is proof that convergence is accomplished by innervation to the medial recti alone, together with inhibition of the lateral recti. When the eye is directed downward, contraction of the medial rectus, with relaxation of the lateral rectus, produces not only convergence, but also intorsion.

Two facts support Verhoeff's belief that convergence is accomplished by contraction of the medial recti alone. (1) An eye can be turned considerably farther inward by a conjugate movement than by convergence. For example, the right eye can be turned farther to the left by conjugate deviation of both eyes to the left than by convergence of both eyes. (2) After maximal symmetrical convergence has been obtained by fixation of an object in the midline, one eye at a time can be turned still farther inward by carrying the fixation object to the left, in the case of the right eye, and to the right, in the case of the left eye, while bifixation is still maintained.

Convergence is more restricted, therefore, than conjugate movement. Verhoeff accounted for this as follows. (1) The convergence mechanism has only the medial rectus to turn an eye in, whereas the conjugate mechanism has, in addition, the help of the other ocular muscles, notably the superior and inferior recti. (2) Convergence is primarily an involuntary function. The majority of persons can acquire voluntary control over it more or less, but few actually ever do so without practice. In ordinary use, all movements of convergence are initiated reflexly by the stimulus to fusion of objects approaching or receding from the eyes.

As has been pointed out (p. 407), electromyographic studies have failed to show any active contraction of the superior and inferior recti beyond their so-called resting tonus in either versions or convergence. Breinin could account for the further movement of the adducted eye in versions beyond that possible in convergence on the basis only of further innervation of the medial rectus on the adducted side. At no time did the vertical recti materially cause further adduction of the globe.

Although at first sight convergence would seem to be a relatively simple process, in reality it is quite complex. Tonic convergence has already been mentioned (p. 469). This is the basic tonus of the medial recti with the eyes in the primary position and free from any fusional impulses. Its existence is attested to by the level of firing of the medial recti in electromyography. During sleep and deep anesthesia the muscles are silent. The measure of tonic convergence is,

therefore, the total electrical activity of the medial recti, of which only the few fibers under the electrodes are tapped during electromyography. The total activity probably depends on many different sources, such as those arising in the reticular substance, constant impulses from both labyrinths, and possibly inhibitory impulses from the cortex.

Tonic convergence is present during the waking hours from birth on, is generally excessive in early childhood, and diminishes with age.

In addition to tonic convergence the following other forms of stimuli which effect convergence have been described. These are proximal convergence, accommodative convergence, and fusional convergence.

Proximal convergence is that amount of convergence induced by the sense of nearness of an object. In looking at images in the slide holders of a major stereoscope, e.g., one gets the feeling that the pictures are close at hand even though they may represent distant scenes. This feeling of closeness induces a certain amount of convergence, subconsciously and uncontrollably.

Accommodative convergence has been mentioned previously (p. 479) and was defined as that portion of the total convergence initiated by the stimulus to accommodation. It has always been of interest to determine how closely knit the two functions of accommodation and convergence are. Does every effort of accommodation necessarily carry with it a fixed and unalterable amount of convergence, and does every voluntary or reflex convergence effort similarly evoke an equal and unchangeable amount of accommodation? There are, as Christoferson and Ogle[150] point out, three schools of thought. One school considers the two functions to be largely independent of one another.

but by trial and error are closely associated. The second regards the two functions to be so bound together that they are inseparable and have existed that way since birth. Finally there is a third school which takes an in-between stand, claiming that there is a certain innateness in the association of convergence and accommodation from their development shortly after birth, but that trial and error does play a part in developing plasticity between them. Lord Charnwood[151] expresses the latter view best. He feels that in most of the lower vertebrates the innate relationship between accommodation and convergence is sufficient for the needs of visual acuity of the animal, and consequently there is no acquired change in what then becomes an unalterable relationship. In man and those animals developing greater visual acuity, on the other hand, nature has found it imperative to change this relationship to meet the needs of the moment. Accordingly, on top of the basic unconditioned occipital reflex relationship there has developed in man a conditioned harmonic reflex which permits a certain amount of elasticity between the two functions. This elasticity is not present at birth but comes as a result of trial and error. It is formed and consolidated in childhood by the reward of clearer vision which follows random changes of accommodative innervation. In general Charnwood leans toward accommodation as the determining factor in this relationship. It is the conditioned harmonic reflex with which the orthoptist works in an effort to loosen the link between accommodation and convergence and thus to permit a hyperopic person to accommodate the necessary amount to correct the hyperopia and yet maintain relatively straight visual axes. At the present time no clear-cut evidence for any of these three points of view is forthcoming. Beginning with Maddox, the principle of fixed relationship between accommodation and convergence has been upheld by Ames and Gliddon,[152] Morgan,[153] and Ogle and Prangen.[154] The opposite school, admitting a freely elastic relationship between the two functions, is advocated by Tait[155] and by Duke-Elder.[156]

Accommodative-convergence/Accommodation ratio (A-C/A ratio). In the normal individual any change in accommodation will effect a change in the position of the eyes if they are dissociated sensorially. In other words, a change in accommodation will invariably change the phoria. Since an increase in accommodation always produces an increased tendency for the eyes to converge (increasing esophoria), the effect on the two visual axes is called the accommodative convergence. The magnitude of the change in convergence (esophoria) in prism diopters caused by a given increase in the accommodation measured in diopters is called the A-C/A ratio. It is obviously also true that as the accommodation is diminished the esophoria is lessened.

The simplest way to determine this relationship between accommodative convergence and accommodation is to determine the phoria at a given fixation distance and then add a plus or minus lens before the fixating eye and again measure the phoria. The amount of change in the phoria brought about per diopter change in accommodation gives us the A-C/A ratio.

The A-C/A ratio has been found to be the same for the same individual at all viewing distances and for any change in stimulus to accommodation, provided that the retinal image is not too blurred. The relationship between accommodative convergence and accommodation is linear throughout the entire range of response to changes in the accommodative stimulus in most individuals; i.e., one diopter change in the stimulus to accommodation always produces the same amount of change in the phoria within the entire range of the accommodative response.

Approximately 10% of normal persons have a nonlinear A-C/A ratio, according to Martens and Ogle[158], and a significant nonlinearity was found in a considerable proportion of normal persons by Flom.[157] Martens and Ogle[158] believe that the change in the stimulus to accommodation rather than the actual change in accommodation which has taken place gives rise to the change in accommodative convergence, since the same ratio is found, even when the powers of the lenses used are such that the retinal images are blurred to the point of obscuring the discrimination of the test targets, and from the fact that a linear A-C/A ratio is found in absolute presbyopes within their limited response range. According to them, it is the innervation to the ciliary muscle, rather than any response of the shape of the lens to that innervation, which gives rise to the A-C/A ratio.

Alpern[159] finds that the accommodative vergence follows the changes in accommodative response, rather than the stimulus to accommodation, since he found that the accommodative vergence could be changed even when the accommodative stimulus remained fixed.

In the normal individual the ratio is fairly stable, the mean being 3.5 $\triangle$/D. There may, however, be day-to-day variations around this mean. Cycloplegic drugs increase the ratio dramatically.[150] On the other hand, miotic drugs have little influence.[160] There is little evidence that the A-C/A ratio can be altered by orthoptic training. A statistically significant increase in the calculated A-C/A ratio following orthoptics has been claimed by Flom, amounting to 0.41 $\triangle$/D.[161]

Divergence. There has been no general agreement as to whether divergence is an independent function or is brought about by inhibition of convergence tone alone, the eyes then being moved from a convergent position back to the primary position by the elasticity of the stretched lateral recti and their fascia. No centers or pathways for divergence have been located anatomically in man, and most of the observed phenomena of divergence have been explained on the basis of inhibition of convergence tonus (Fig. 209). On the other hand, divergence paralysis cannot be explained easily without assuming a divergence mechanism. This clinical entity, which is often erroneously diagnosed as bilateral paralysis of the lateral rectus muscles, has such pathognomonic features that the diagnosis should never be missed if these are understood and looked for. At some middistance from the eyes the visual lines can fixate an object, but as the object is withdrawn into the

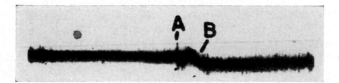

Fig. 209. Electrical activity from the left lateral rectus. A, On the command to diverge, a burst of impulses which precedes the actual movement of the globe is seen. **B,** Movement of the glove is indicated by the downward displacement of the record. (From Adler, F. H.: Arch. Ophth. **50:**19, 1953.)

distance in the midline, the visual axes cannot diverge to maintain fixation; therefore, increasing esotropia develops as the object is removed, with consequent homonymous diplopia. If at any one distance the separation of the double images is measured, and then at this same distance the object being fixated is moved at this distance laterally in the radius of a circle with the patient at the center, the separation of the double images remains the same. When the object is moved to the right or to the left, the separation of the double images remains the same as it was when the object was situated directly in front of him at the same distance. This is the essential point which differentiates this condition from bilateral paralysis of the lateral rectus muscles. Unless this feature is present, the diagnosis of divergence paralysis cannot be made. The great difficulty in making the diagnosis is that late in the course of the disease many patients do develop true palsy of one rectus muscle, in addition to the typical divergence paralysis. If the patient is not seen early before this developed, the diagnosis can only be provisional. The only easy explanation of how divergence paralysis can be produced is by assuming that there is a divergence mechanism, separate from abduction for each lateral rectus, which actively diverges the eyes from the convergent position to the primary position. If such a separate mechanism can be postulated for convergence and adduction in versions, there is no unsurmountable reason why the same should not hold for divergence. The center for divergence must be near the midline in the neighborhood of each nucleus of the sixth cranial nerve, and this explains why late in the disease associated paralysis of one lateral rectus develops as the lesion spreads from the midline toward one or the other side. Several cases

of typical divergence paralysis in which at autopsy the lesion was found in the midline have been reported. From the point of view of pathogenesis, paralysis of divergence could be caused by a lesion anywhere in the supranuclear pathway for divergence from the cortex to the hypothetical subcortical center. For those who denied the existence of a separate divergence mechanism, it was necessary to postulate the cause of divergence paralysis to be a spasm of convergence. This can be ruled out easily since esotropia does not increase as the object comes closer to the patient, and many times these patients show an actual convergence weakness, with crossed diplopia for objects held at the near point of convergence developing.

The various arguments for the presence of a divergence mechanism separate from convergence have been summarized by Bruce.[162] If divergence were a passive function naturally, the position of the eyes during complete muscular relaxation would be divergence to a greater or lesser degree. If the eyes diverge as a result of the elasticity of the external recti solely, divergence should be more rapid at the beginning than at the end of the movement since the lateral recti are then under more tension. Bruce claims, however, that divergence is carried out at a uniform speed, and it must be assumed, therefore, that an active factor enters into the mechanism as a reinforcement. Furthermore, in paralysis of divergence when the patient looks from a near to a distant point, the initial movement is but little affected, whereas the later movement, i.e., that produced as the eyes approach increasingly distant points of fixation, is interfered with increasingly.

It is difficult to believe that of all well-regulated functions divergence alone should be without benefit of a definite innervation. If as Lippmann[163] points out the limit of divergence were identical with the position of rest, brought about by complete relaxation of convergence, every person who loses binocular fusion should manifest divergent strabismus. In reality, only a certain number do so. Bielschowsky[164] has stated that active innervation of divergence is necessary to overcome esophoria, which is a cogent argument if one accepts the idea that esophoria is an excess of innervation of convergence checked by an active opposing innervation as a result of a desire for fusion.

Scobee and Green[46] offered some experimental physiologic evidence against the existence of a separate divergence mechanism. They found a difference in the amount of heterophoria present when measured by the Maddox rod and by a combination of the Maddox rod and screen. They state that if esophoria and exophoria are separate entities one should uncover more esophoria and more exophoria when the screen is used in addition to the Maddox rod than when the Maddox rod is used alone. They argue that if esophoria and exophoria are merely different degrees of a single property, then screening would reveal more of one but less of the other. On normal human subjects their measurements showed that on the average slightly more esophoria and less exophoria were uncovered when screening in addition to the Maddox rod was used.

If there is no active divergence mechanism, pure convergence needs an antagonist in the sense of a mechanism to produce movement in the opposite direction. Some factor of elasticity must be present therefore. Scobee and Green believe this to be the elasticity of the orbital structures. A consideration of the position of the eyes and their relation to each other, taking into account the structure of the orbits and their contents, points to a state of divergence of the visual lines. The medial orbital walls are parallel; the lateral orbital walls make an angle of almost 90 degrees with each other or one of 45 degrees with their respective medial walls. Thus, each orbital axis makes an angle of roughly 23 to 25 degrees with the sagittal plane of the head. The axis of the muscle cone within the orbit coincides just about with the orbital axis, and hence it also makes approximately a 25-degree angle with the sagittal plane of the head. From the standpoint of orbital structure alone, the eyes should assume a position of divergence of the visual lines at all times. They never do this in the absence of pathologic change or narcosis due to the antagonistic force of convergence. Divergence then, according to Scobee and Green, is caused solely by the elastic pull of the orbital structures when convergence tone diminishes. If it is desired to shift the gaze from a near object to a remote one, the degree of convergence is diminished by a proportional decrease in the innervation of convergence. The elastic divergent pull which is constantly present then acts passively and effectively, and the visual lines fixate the more remote object. This takes no cognizance of the fact that the eyes are not in a divergent position during death, as pointed out by Cogan.

It has already been shown that evidence is accumulating that divergence is an active innervation of both lateral rectus muscles and is not due merely to pull of elastic tissues in the absence of active convergence innervation. In Fig. 183 are shown the changes in electrical activity as recorded from the left lateral rectus during divergence from the convergent position, indicating clearly that the lateral rectus during this movement of the globe was actively innervated. The impulses recorded from the muscle fibers actually precede the movement of the globe, showing that they caused the movement and not vice versa. Breinin has given similar evidence with better recording technique.

POSITION OF REST; ORTHOPHORIA AND HETEROPHORIA

The anatomic basis and the neurogenic control of the ocular movements have been outlined in so far as they are known at the present time. There are obvious gaps in our knowledge. In the normal adult this complex mechanism keeps the two eyes associated with one another in all directions of gaze in both versions and vergences so that the two foveas receive the images of the object of regard. When an individual chooses to glance in a particular direction, an equal simultaneous impulse goes to the muscles of both eyes concerned with the movement, according to Hering's law. At the same time an equal simultaneous inhibition is sent to the antagonists of these muscles, according to Sherrington's law of reciprocal innervation. If the eyes are set properly in the orbits, if the orbital fascia and check ligaments are fashioned properly, and if the origin and insertion of the muscles are placed correctly, the eyes will rotate around a theoretical center of rotation into the desired motor field. While the movement progresses, impulses from all parts of the body which affect these movements are pouring into the subcortical machinery constantly. These impulses alter the amount of innervation sent to a particular group of muscles, according to the needs of the moment, such as a change in bodily posture or the appearance in the visual field of an object with high attention value. If the latter should occur, the eyes are turned reflexly in that direction by the following reflex

until the object is imaged on the fovea. The fixation reflex holds it there, and the fusion reflex adjusts the amount of vergence necessary to ensure that both foveas are stimulated simultaneously. During all of this, feedback mechanisms such as changes in pupil size, changes in accommodation (determined largely by the retinal image itself), are effective and have an influence on the tonus of the muscles. Other impulses from the muscles themselves, described as proprioceptive impulses, inform the brain of the amount of tension the various muscles are under. The complexity of this exquisitely developed mechanism is enormous and makes one wonder why it does not break down more often. It would be difficult for an engineer, even with the advantage of electronics, to develop a piece of apparatus which works so well.

Position of rest

The position of absolute rest of the eyes is that assumed when the eyes are freed from all sources of tonus, a condition occurring only during very deep anesthesia, during coma, or in death. Under these conditions the eyes assume the anatomic position of rest. During deep anesthesia there is usually slight divergence and sursumversion (p. 496). It has been believed generally that the eyes assume this same position in death, but Cogan[130] states that the eyes are directed straight ahead or are slightly divergent in death and generally do not assume divergence of the orbital axes when the muscles have lost all their tonus.

During life the position the eyes assume depends to a large extent on which portion of the central nervous system happens to play the dominant role at the time. Thus during profound sleep when the cerebral cortex is inhibited, the eyes assume the position of divergence and upward rotation. In the waking state, too, partial decerebration is a common experience, as in daydreaming. The change from the sleeping to the waking state brings with it activation of the following and fixation reflexes, while a still higher level of cortical control is associated with the functions of convergence and divergence, especially fusional vergences.

It has been shown previously that anatomic features determine the position of the eyes, and that the postural reflexes may alter this position. In addition to this, a finer adjustment of the two eyes to each other is achieved by the optomotor reflexes. It has not been possible or necessary for clinical purposes to investigate the postural reflexes in man. However, it has been advantageous to eliminate to various degrees the optomotor reflexes and to study the effect of their elimination on the posture of the eyes.

The physiologic position of rest—if it is permissible to use this term in this connection—is the position the eyes assume when they are freed from all of the stimuli from the fusional optomotor reflexes. These are the reflexes that direct the two eyes toward the object of attention so that the image of the object falls on each fovea. Eliminating these reflexes eliminates the stimuli for binocular single vision. The position the eyes assume under this condition is sometimes termed the fusion-free position or the dissociated position. Even this is not a very exact term since there are many degrees of freedom from fusion, as will soon be apparent. It is of course, distinctly, not a position of rest, i.e., free of all tonus to the muscles. If, e.g., the subject relaxes his attention and lets his thoughts wander from the objects surrounding him, the position of the eyes may change. In many

normal persons the eyes diverge. If the image of one eye is made poorer than that of the other by placing smoked glasses of increasing density in front of it, the eyes, freed from the fusional impulses, take up a position dictated by the remaining sources of tonus, whatever they may be.

Whenever the vision of one eye interferes with the use of the two eyes together, an attempt may be made by the body to free the eyes from this embarrassment. The new position which the eyes assume will be that which eliminates the embarrassment the best. This new position may not be the same as that assumed by the eyes when they are merely freed of all fusion impulses, as previously described, but may be an entirely different, forced position due to new sources of tonus for the purpose of getting rid of diplopia. The body discovers that, when the two images cannot be fused, they can be separated by deviating the eyes from one another and that this separation helps to avoid the confusion because one of the images may now be suppressed more easily. Hence, the visual axes are turned either in or out to separate the images further.

When a person loses the sight of one eye completely, all impulses to binocular single vision are immediately lost, and the eyes, therefore, assume the fusion-free position. In general, it may be said that if an eye is blinded in childhood, the position most frequently adopted will be that of convergence of the visual axes, whereas in adult life, a blind eye will usually become divergent. This does not mean, however, that divergence is the anatomic position of rest, for frequently the eyes of an adult who has become blind do not diverge.

Divergence in the adult, when only one eye is blinded, is explained by Cogan on the basis that when the stimuli for binocular vision are removed there is a greater loss in tone of convergence than of divergence. As Morrax[165] pointed out, in progressive stupor convergence is one of the first functions to be lost. If both eyes are blinded, convergence and divergence decrease simultaneously and to the same degree so that the visual axes remain approximately straight, as in death.

Fusion-free position or dissociated position

It has become customary for clinical purposes to measure the position the two eyes assume when the fusional impulses are either totally or partially removed by artificial means. If under these conditions the visual axes remain so that the image of the object of regard still falls on the two foveas, a person is said to have orthophoria. If, on the other hand, the images do not fall on the two foveas because the visual axes are either too convergent or too divergent, heterophoria is said to be present. When the visual axes are convergent in the fusion-free position, the subject is said to have esophoria, and when they are divergent, he is said to have exophoria. If the visual axis of one eye rises higher than that of the other, he is said to have right or left hyperphoria, depending upon which eye is the higher. The term *hypophoria,* referring to the lower eye, is seldom used.

The degree of the heterophoria may be measured by the strength of prisms, suitably placed, which just compensates for the new position of the visual axes. In exophoria the strength of the base-in prism, which brings the image on to the fovea with the eye in the divergent position, measures the degree of exophoria. Similarly, in esophoria the strength of the base-out prism, which places the image on the fovea with the eye in the convergent position, is the measure in degrees of esophoria. The same principle applies to hyperphoria.

The implication is made frequently that orthophoria is the normal condition and heterophoria is an abnormal one. This is not true. If this were so, there would be no normal persons. It is true that some persons have orthophoria for distance when measured by the usual Maddox rod test or even by the cover test, but these are few, the majority showing 1 or 2 △ of esophoria or exophoria. The normal condition should be taken to mean an approximate alignment of the visual axes in the fusion-free position. Esophoria of 1 to 2 △ or exophoria of 1 to 4 △ for distance should be considered physiologic. Hyperphoria of either eye of 1 △ nearly always gives rise to symptoms, and hence only 0.5 △ of hyperphoria can be considered within the physiologic range.

The various methods used to dissociate the two eyes will yield different measurements of heterophoria, the amounts depending upon the extent to which the tests eliminate the visual fusional stimuli. Heterophoria determined with the Maddox rod indicates the effectiveness of dissimilar retinal images as compared to the effectiveness of similar retinal images in fusion (the test should be performed in a dark room so that there is no influence from the surroundings). Heterophoria determined with the cover test indicates how effective monocular retinal stimulation is when compared with stimulation of the two retinas simultaneously. Vertical prisms used to determine the lateral phorias indicate what the eyes will do when they are presented with artificially produced double images which, although similar, cannot be fused easily. Under these conditions, the results are probably not a measure of the fusion-free position but are most likely that of some forced position which the eyes assume in order best to avoid the confusion of the double images. Measurements taken with this method are usually smaller than those with either the Maddox rod or the cover test.

As stated, the fusion-free position does not represent a true position of rest. The process of fixation is accompanied by minute rhythmic and voluntary adjusting movements which serve to prevent retinal fatigue by permitting the foveal image to roam over a large number of percipient elements, while at the same time maintaining fixation. Thus, the latter is associated with a state of heightened tonus, affecting all of the extraocular muscles. The fact that prolonged fixation frequently results in symptoms of eye strain bears evidence to the validity of this statement. The closest approach to a position of rest of the eyes during the waking state is a vacant stare into space, no attempt being made to discern any objects.

Tonus-regulating centers control the postural tonus of each eye, without reference to the other. Superimposed upon these are the centers that control binocular innervation, both the tonic and kinetic varieties. In the normal exercise of binocular vision the monocular influences are held in abeyance, being completely inhibited by the higher centers. Hering's law of equal binocular innervation applies only to these latter centers. As Posner[166] has pointed out, two types of eye movements are associated typically with an archaic postural pattern; one is divergence which is reminiscent of the laterally placed eyes in the lower mammals, and the other is an upward deviation which may be considered a protective movement and is still normally present in Bell's phenomenon elicited by closure of the eyelids. All persons have a potential tendency toward upward rotation of the visual axes which increases with any increase in the general tonus of the muscular apparatus. Fixation provides such an increase in muscle tonus. If both eyes are fixating, no movement is possible, of course. However, if one eye for any reason does not participate in the visual act, that eye may manifest the up-drift. The amount of hyperphoria present in the nonfixing eye will depend on the extent to which the binocular innervation is supplanted and inhibited by the more primitive monocular tonus controlling centers and on the degree of dissociation achieved by the clinical method employed. The muscles of the eye are subject to two types of tonus innervation: (1) the tonus derived from the voluntary nerve supply which is invariably bilateral and symmetrical and (2) the reflex postural tonus dependent on such factors as fixation, illumination, and attention. Fluctuations in attention may play a part in the irregular up-and-down movements that are frequently observed in a blind eye while the other eye stares at a fixation object. The spontaneous oscillatory movements reflect the continuous play of tonus-regulating forces upon the entire musculature of the eye. Fixation and illumination tend to heighten the tonic activity of all our muscles.

All persons have a tendency, archaic in origin, as expressed in Bell's phenomenon, for the eyes to turn upward. The greater the muscle tonus, the greater this upward drive becomes. In a large percentage of persons binocular linkage is loose enough to permit a greater or lesser degree of dissociation of the two eyes. When an eye has been blind or amblyopic since childhood, the binocular functions are rudimentary, and the dissociation is quite marked. Hence, fixation by one eye results in a tendency to upward deviation of both eyes, this tendency becoming manifest only in the nonfixating eye and only to the extent that the laxity of binocular innervation permits. Alternating hyperphoria (better termed dissociated alternating sursumduction) and concomitant hypertropia of blind or amblyopic eyes have been interpreted variously as being due to superior rectus paralysis and as a vertical divergence elicited by visual processes. According to Posner's concept, these conditions are looked on as aberrations of the postural tonus mechanism of the extraocular musculature. According to this concept, voluntary binocular control of ocular movements has been superimposed upon an archaic tonus-regulating pattern that does not obey Hering's law and manifests itself to the extent to which any laxity of the binocular linkage will permit dissociation of the two eyes.

Fixation disparity

In some individuals with heterophoria it is possible to demonstrate fusion while the visual axes of the eyes do not actually intersect in the plane of the stimulating target. Such an individual when normally fixating a target will show exact alignment of his visual axes on the target. If now one eye be covered, and let us say that the individual has esophoria of 10 $\triangle$, the covered eye will turn in this amount. When this eye is uncovered, it will slowly turn out to take up fixation with its fellow eye, but at the completion of the fusional movement it will be found that the eye is actually still converged some 3 to 5 $\triangle$ and yet tests will show good sensory fusion with the eyes in this position. The failure of the visual axes to intersect in the plane of the target after the completion of a fusional movement is known as fixation disparity.

Its significance has been questioned by Verhoeff,[167] who points out that the tests used are measuring a deviation due to loss of bifixation. He states that no patient with heterophoria alone, i.e., not manifesting strabismus, has ever complained of diplopia such as might result from fixation disparity, and that many have noted improvement in binocular visual acuity when their heterophoria is corrected prismatically.

Effect of alcohol and anoxia on dissociated position

We do not know at present all of the various sources of tonus which combine to position the eyes when they are freed from the visual fusional impulses. Some of these have been enumerated already, but it is likely that there are others as yet unexplored. At present, none of these can be eliminated experimentally in human beings. Two conditions have been studied which throw some light on involuntary mechanisms such as those of cortical inhibition. These are the effects of alcohol and anoxia. When alcohol is taken in excess, diplopia usually occurs. It has been commonly supposed that this was due to the release of the eyes from visual fusional impulses, similar in a way to the benumbing of all the senses by alcohol. Any heterophoria present before the alcohol was taken would become manifest. If a person had esophoria before he imbibed, it would become manifest under the influence of alcohol and might, if the alcoholic intake had been excessive, lead to a manifest deviation of the visual axes, esotropia. If he had exphoria before drinking, he might then develop exotropia. This has been shown to be incorrect, however, by a number of investigators.

In a series of men and women given alcohol, Powell[168] demonstrated that a definite tendency toward esophoria for distance always developed. This change was constant, gradual, and progressive. Recovery occurred in about 10 hours, and the phoria then returned to its previous level. It made no difference whether the patient was esophoric or exophoric before the alcohol was given; the change was always in the direction of esophoria. The phoria for near vision changed in the direction of progressive exophoria. The angle of convergence (convergence near point) showed a progressive decrease, but the prism divergence was not determined.

Powell explained the progressive esophoria at 6 M. distance on the basis of weakening of the lateral rectus muscles and, in defense of this, called attention to the fact that the abducens nerve is termed the weakling of the cranial contents. He explained the decrease in the power of convergence on the basis of diminished tone and control of the medial recti muscles.

Colson[169] repeated these experiments by giving twenty-one normal adults 2 ounces of rye or Scotch whiskey every half hour and testing their phoria and voluntary ductions for distance. He found that esophoria increased gradually in every patient and in two patients reached a stage of strabismus with diplopia. The minimum change was 2 $\triangle$; the maximum was 11 $\triangle$. It made no difference what the original muscle balance was before the alcohol was taken. Duction tests showed that, according to the usual notation, the abduction was reduced in every case, but if allowance was made for the state of the muscle balance, there was no change in the abduction. The real adduction was decreased in every patient, but in the figures the author gives, this decrease is not striking. Both the conventional and the real adductions were changed hardly at all in two patients and were greatly reduced in only one patient. However, these were the only ones on whom measurements were made. From this observation, one could hardly draw any conclusions regarding duction power.

Brecher[170] and co-workers undertook to study the effect of alcohol on both the motor fusional capacities and sensory fusion. They determined the strength of binocular fusion by measuring the time necessary to accomplish binocular fusion. As a result of their studies they believe that the diplopia that occurs under the influence of alcohol is caused by the progressive impairment of the binocular fusion reflex with rising levels of blood alcohol. This impairment of the fusion reflex occurs regardless of changes in phoria and of the weakening of voluntary convergence. They felt that the decrease in binocular fusion power was due to impairment of the general neuromuscular cordination by alcohol, which at the same time affects the position of the visual axes and diminishes the power of voluntary convergence.

These authors measured the heterophoria and the fusion power at 6 M., 82 cm., and 33 cm. and found that marked esophoria developed progressively at 6 M., only a little amount developed at 82 cm., and marked exophoria appeared at 33 cm. This indicates that the visual axes come to a position of rest at a distance slightly less than 82 cm. with intoxication from strong alcohol. This evidence is further support of the hypothesis that binocular vergence is normally controlled by two different mechanisms, a convergence mechanism and a separate divergence mechanism, since the impairment of these mechanisms by alcohol causes the eyes to assume an intermediate or neutral position. The increase in esophoria and the deterioration of motor fusion reserves have been corroborated recently by Seedorf.[171]

As is apparent from the experiments just cited, it cannot be determined how alcohol induces esophoria for distance.

One might guess that it produces its effect by stimulation of the convergence center. The mechanism may, of course, be the release of inhibition from higher centers on the convergence center so that too great an innervation to the medial recti muscles is set free. It might also be due to weakening of the divergence mechanism. Further pharmacologic investigation is needed before it can be ascertained with certainty where alcohol acts. Since it is generally considered to depress cortical function, it seems more likely that its action is due to loss of cortical inhibition on the convergence center.

It has been found that the eyes act in a similar way under the influence of severe anoxia. Although Wilmer and Berens[172] found that anoxia produced in a low pressure chamber resulted in an increase of any pre-existing heterophoria, Velhagen[173] reported the same kind of changes as those which occur in acute alcoholism, i.e., pronounced development of esophoria. No matter what the subject's muscle balance was to start with, according to this author, the change was always in the direction of esophoria as the atmospheric pressure was reduced. At 3000 M., the results were not conclusive, but at 5000 to 6000 M., the increase in esophoria was considerable. At the near point, there was a change similar to that with alcohol, i.e., a tendency toward increasing exophoria. Curiously, he suggested that the changes he observed were due to alterations in the muscles themselves as a result of changed metabolism due to the anoxia, since he was unable to satisfy himself that there was any increase in convergence tone or hyperexcitability of the convergence center.

The effects of anoxia were investigated by Adler,[174] and Velhagen's results were verified and further amplified. Anoxia produced esophoria for distance and a shift in the range of fusion toward convergence. If severe enough, this resulted in convergent comitant strabismus. The evidence indicated that anoxia acts by depressing the higher centers and that any apparent stimulation results from the "unrestrained activity of lower centers freed from the depression of higher inhibitory control mechanisms," as stated by Goodman and Gilman.[175] These results have been confirmed by Duguet.[176] One may assume, therefore, that the convergence mechanism is normally inhibited by higher centers. Alcohol and anoxia remove this inhibition.

There is a parallel example of this in the case of the pupil. During the third stage of anesthesia induced by ether or chloroform, the pupil constricts, and this constriction is supposed to be due to the abolition of cerebral impulses which normally inhibit the tone of the oculomotor constrictor center, i.e., the Edinger-Westphal nucleus.[175] It has been claimed also that during Plane 3 of the third stage of anesthesia, the eyes are fixed in the convergent position. These forced movements and changes in posture of the eyeballs under general anesthesia have never been studied satisfactorily and should give some clue to the behavior of the mechanism under discussion.

Position of the eyes during sleep and anesthesia

Sir Charles Bell's first communication on the position of the eyes during sleep recorded his observation that during this state the eyes roll upward. Later observers found that, in addition to sursumversion, the eyes were either divergent or convergent. Occasionally a difference in the horizontal level of the two eyes is seen, one eye being above the other. There is thus no one position which can be called the natural position of the eyes during sleep. The usual position of the eyes in the adult after binocular vision has been acquired is either sursumversion with divergence or convergence. In a few persons the eyes may be turned downward. Before binocular vision is established, the eyes are generally found to be horizontal. Skew deviation is not uncommon and may be in any direction. Movements of the eyes frequently continue during sleep, especially in children under 3 years of age.

The position assumed during sleep is believed to be a position of rest. During waking hours the eyes are seldom turned upward, and the fact that more than half of the persons examined showed upward deviation of the eyes during sleep indicates that this posture is assumed to provide relaxation from that taken during the waking hours (see discussion of Posner's concept, p. 494).

Movements of the eyes during anesthesia are frequently used as a guide to the depth of anesthesia. During the early stages the eyeballs make movements from side to side, either in unison or one without the other. One or both eyeballs may also be moved upward or downward eccentrically. All of these movements are slow tonic movements and therefore differ markedly from those of voluntary action. They are of central origin, and as the depth of anesthesia is increased, they gradually cease and the eyes assume the midline position. If the anesthesia is accompanied by anoxia, particularly during the use of anesthetic agents which produce early asphyxial changes such as nitrous oxide and ethylene, the eyeballs are frequently drawn together in a symmetrically convergent and slightly downward position.

Burford[177] made many observations over a period of years on children and adults and concluded that the behavior

of the eyeballs during sleep and anesthesia is the same. During deep sleep the eyeballs are frequently motionless and eccentrically placed when one first raises the lids. After a few seconds, however, slow movements similar to those seen under light anesthesia may resume. Burford believes that these movements are due to an active parasympathetic outflow, which is suggested by the constriction of the pupil at this time. He suggests that the various centers for movements of the eyes should be considered a functional unit and not simply separate isolated nuclei. When this unit is functioning under ordinary stimuli during the waking state, the impulses are sufficient to cause purposeful responses which move the eyes in one fixed direction, equally and simultaneously. When, however, the stimuli are weak, as during sleep, the unit breaks down, producing fractionated responses that are incapable of influencing both sides equally and evenly. The result is that the movements are frequently asymmetrical and purposeless.

In addition to the slow rolling or pendular movements of eyes observed in sleeping children or adults, a rapid, jerky, and binocularly symmetrical movement of eyes is described by Aserinsky and Kleitman.[178] The first appearance of a pattern of rapid, jerky movements occurs approximately 1 hour 45 minutes following sleep. The pattern of motility of the eyes is of variable duration and disappears frequently for a fraction of a minute or for several minutes, only to reappear and disappear a number of times. These eye movements seem to be related to the electroencephalographic pattern and various activities of the autonomic nervous system which were recorded by the authors, and they consider that all these manifestations are due to activity of a particular level of the cortex.

Are there specific differences in the patterns of eye movements associated with different states of anesthesia or of alertness? In order to answer this question the results of stimulation of the motor cortex under varying states of awareness have been compared. In the wakeful state all eye movements produced by stimulation of the motor cortex are conjugate and smooth. In general as consciousness declines, the vertical component of eye movements begins to weaken and then disappear, and this is followed by the horizontal component. With this decrease in those movements having vertical components, the condition known as eye-centering appears. This consists of conjugate movement to the midposition regardless of the prestimulus position of the eyes. With still greater depression of consciousness, the horizontal components fail, eye-centering decreases, and disjugate movements begin to appear. Finally, of course, all spontaneous movements cease, and movements can no longer be elicited by stimulation of the cerebrum.

Other types of patterns of positioning of the eyes occur in certain states of consciousness: (1) upward divergence is often associated with sleep, (2) jerk nystagmus is induced by stimulation of the cerebrum when the alert animal is gazing at a target ipsilateral to a cerebral stimulus at the moment the current is applied, (3) jerk nystagmus with the quick component contralateral to the side of the brain being stimulated and not dependent upon the animal's gaze is often observed in an alert or partially depressed animal, and (4) the speed of eye movements diminishes as the state of consciousness becomes depressed.

From these observations Kreiger[179] and others conclude that the changes in pattern with depression of consciousness indicate that during depression fewer functional units are available for spontaneous or electrically induced responses. The map of cerebral representation of eye movements changes along with the state of consciousness.

Bell's phenomenon

The eyes turn upward not only during sleep and anesthesia, but also whenever the lids are voluntarily closed forcibly against resistance. The upward turning of the eyes with forced closure of the lids is called Bell's phenomenon. It occurs in peripheral facial palsy in which the lids fail to close. When the patient attempts to close the eyes, the lids on the paralyzed side fail to shut, and a slight upward movement of the globe is observed readily. Bell's phenomenon is absent in nuclear lesions of the seventh cranial nerve, which lends support to the theory that the reflex is mediated through lower centers, probably by way of the posterior longitudinal bundle to the nucleus of the third cranial nerve. It is a protective mechanism comparable to the winking reflex, the eyes being turned up when the lids are closed so that they are placed in the position of greatest protection.[180]

PHYSIOLOGY OF COORDINATED MOVEMENTS OF THE EYES
Act of fixation

The visual fixation reflex, which acts as a fine adjustment for keeping the image on the fovea, has been described previously (p. 474). Fixation is a relative term. The eyes are never absolutely still; even under strict laboratory conditions with immobilization of the head, an image cannot be fixed on a single cone in the fovea. During ordinary use the eyes are never entirely at rest, but are continually moving. In this way objects are seen in much the same manner that one feels the character of a surface by touching it with the fingers. When the fingers are moved over the surface, the sensory endings of touch are stimulated and send their tactile messages up to the brain, giving rise to sensations which, interpreted in terms of other sensory phenomena such as sight and influenced by memory, result in a perception of the state of the surface palpated.

Even when the eye is strenuously fixating a stationary cross hair in an optical instrument, which has been found by experiment to be the best test object for securing steady fixation, it is not at rest. When it is steadiest, small trembling movements may be seen on the records obtained photographically[181] (Fig. 210). They probably represent the frequency of vibration of the extraocular muscles. The average movement of a point on the retina, as a result of these fine vibratory movements, is 0.0018 mm. (38 seconds of arc). The diameter of the foveal cones is about 15 seconds of arc. Hence, a point image must move back and forth over several cones. At no time will it come to lie still on a fixed cone pattern.

In addition to these finer movements, the eyes cannot remain fixed for very long on any object, but invariably break from fixation in the form of drifts. During a study of monocular fixation of a stationary object, Ratliff and Riggs[182] found four main types of movement: (1) small rapid motions with a median extent (peak to trough) of about 17.5 seconds angle of rotation and frequencies ranging from 30 to 70 cycles per second, (2) slow motions of irregular frequency and extent, (3) slow drifts in one direction or another upon which the motions just mentioned are superimposed, and (4) rapid jerks with an average extent of about 5.6 minutes of arc, occurring at irregular intervals and at times apparently compensating for the drifts. The total movement due to the combined effects of these motions over a period of 3 to 4 seconds is usually less than 10 minutes of arc. On the basis of these results they conclude that the motions of a retinal image of an object being fixated generally moves over twenty-five to fifty receptors. Slow motions, drifts, and jerks may carry the retinal image across about a dozen receptors. The micronystagmus moves the retinal image across two or three receptors at most. According to these observers the median extent of these motions is so small that the movement of the retinal image under optimal conditions of fixation is not likely to exceed the width of one receptor.

In 1952 Higgins and Stultz[183] recorded the motions of an eye during steady fixa-

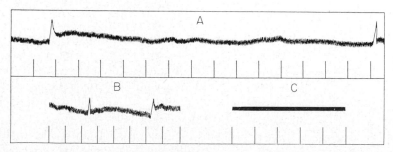

Fig. 210. **A,** Steady fixation of a cross hair. **B,** Another section of the record in the same experiment. **C,** Control record (of an artificial eye) taken before the experiment. The time intervals shown are fifths of seconds.

tion by photographing a blood vessel. They found very rapid motions with a frequency of about fifty per second and an average amplitude of 1.2 minutes of arc. Riggs[184] modified Lord and Wright's method and found the ocular tremor to be in the neighborhood of thirty to ninety vibrations per second with an amplitude of 15 to 20 seconds of arc. Nachmias[185] has been able to record eye movements in both the vertical and horizontal meridians simultaneously.

Micronystagmus has been recorded in cats.[186] The fine tremor varies in frequency from 35 to 65 cycles per second, averaging 50 cycles per second, and in amplitude from 4 to 52 seconds of arc, averaging 22 seconds. Curare decreases and ultimately abolishes all eye movements and the micronystagmus, whereas neostigmine increases them. Micronystagmus is probably mediated by efferent neural stimulation of the eye muscles. The fine ocular tremor probably represents a continuous variation in the total activity of the acting individual motor units of the muscles. The normal tonus of these muscles effectively damps potential pulse movement, and the saccades originate, at least in part, in the binocular motor areas, whereas the fine tremor is entirely peripheral to binocular control.

While both viewpoints have been held that micronystagmus is a useless and undesirable by-product of the ocular motility apparatus,[1] and that it is helpful to vision,[2] recent research indicates that it helps to prevent the fading away of detailed vision which occurs when the retinal image is optically immobilized.[187-189] At the present time there is no positive evidence that micronystagmus is a mechanism devised especially to obtain better performance from an otherwise maximally developed visual discrimination apparatus.

In summary, the involuntary movements of the eye during steady fixation of a target include (1) a high-frequency tremor of amplitude less than 0.5 minute of arc and frequencies up to 150 cycles per second, (2) rapid flicks of up to 50 minutes of arc which occur at irregular intervals, and (3) slow motion drift at the rate of about 1 minute of arc per second in the interflick periods. At the fovea, 1 minute of arc corresponds to a distance of about 5μ. The distance between the centers of adjacent cones, it will be recalled, is about 0.6 minute of arc.

The movements may or may not have any important value in visual perception, and many suggestions have been made as to their influence. By means of stabilizing the retinal image on the retina so that it moves concurrently with any movement of the eye no matter how small, the influence of these involuntary movements has been assessed. When the image is so stabilized, the perception of fine details fails due to sensory adaptation (p. 77). It has been suggested that the impairment of vision when the image is stabilized is due to the loss of some of the information derived from the on-off signals (p. 632).[190] Experiments have been devised which produce an imposed movement of the image on one that had previously been stabilized, so that each component of the natural involuntary eye movements could be separately assessed. It appears from these experiments that annulment of the drift component of involuntary eye movements has very little influence in causing loss of visual perception, but that both the flicks and the micronystagmus do play a part in maintaining constant vision.[191] Contrast discrimination of the eye is considerably reduced when the movements are eliminated.[192, 193]

Patients with pathologic nystagmus

often have poor vision. It might be argued that the nystagmus is the result of the poor vision, which is primarily due to loss of the central visual receptors, and this is undoubtedly true. There is, however, a type of nystagmus known as latent nystagmus, that occurs in some children with strabismus in whom there is no nystagmus when both eyes are open. When either eye is covered and the remaining eye is made to fixate, nystagmus appears. Now, it happens that, if the visual acuity is recorded when both eyes are open and then when one eye is closed, the acuity is always better with both eyes open (it must be kept in mind that the eyes are crossed, and that only one eye at a time is being used to fixate, either when both eyes are open or when one eye is artificially covered). Hence, in these patients the visual acuity of either eye shows a definite deterioration when that eye is showing nystagmus as compared to when it is quiet. This proves that under these conditions the presence of nystagmus is a deterrent to good form perception and not an advantage. Although the small movements of physiologic nystagmus or ocular tremor may help certain retinal functions, they are detrimental to visual acuity.

Motor field

Limits of ocular rotation. Each of the ocular muscles is at least ten times as strong as it need be to rotate the globe fully in the direction of its action. It is never called on to exert itself to the full because the check ligaments halt the rotation before the eye has reached the limits of pull of the muscle. The arc of contact has almost disappeared in the case of most of the muscles by the time this point has been reached. In persons with neurogenic paralysis, it is only when a large number of the muscle fibers have been

knocked out that excessive innervation has to be sent to the muscle in order to recruit enough fibers to fulfill its required function. Very little is known in this field, and many problems await solution.

It should be pointed out here that most of the observations which have been made regarding the function of the ocular muscles have been based on several assumptions which are unexplored as yet. It has been assumed, e.g., that when a muscle is innervated the fibers which are activated at any level of stimulus are distributed equally throughout the whole muscle, and therefore the muscle pulls as a whole. It is conceivable that in a muscle such as the superior rectus only the nasal fibers are activated at low levels of innervation, whereas at higher levels the fibers on the temporal side are called into action. It may be that in certain functions nasal fibers are recruited before temporal ones and vice versa.

Since the muscle power is quite in excess in the case of all of the muscles, the limits of ocular rotation are imposed by the anatomic factors which include the check ligaments. The anatomic peculiarities of the orbits also impose restrictions on ocular movements. A person with deep-set eyes will not have as full a motor field of rotation as one whose eyes are more prominent. Most persons can move each eye through an arc of approximately 50 degrees in every direction. The monocular field of fixation is considerably less than this in some directions, principally toward the nasal side, due to the prominence of the nose which cuts off the fixation target as the eye moves in this direction. The binocular field of fixation, on the other hand, is fully 50 degrees from the primary position in all directions since the opposite eye takes up fixation as the object of regard becomes obscured to one eye by the nose.

It is not always easy to determine whether the fields of fixation in the two eyes are normal. When eye movements are tested monocularly, one must remember that each muscle has many times the power to turn the globe throughout its full range of mobility, and considerable power may be lost before any limitation of movement of the globe becomes manifest. It is much easier to detect slight weakness in a muscle when the binocular movements are examined. Under these conditions, a slight lag in the movement of the eye with the suspected paralyzed muscle may become evident if the subject allows the sound eye to take up fixation, or if the paralyzed eye maintains fixation, overaction of the yoke muscle in the opposite eye may be detected— this eye moves too far in the direction of action of the paralyzed muscle. It is an extremely valuable and telltale sign of paralysis of a muscle, therefore, to have the patient look in the direction of action of the paralyzed muscle and, making sure that the eye with the suspected paralyzed muscle is fixating, to watch the opposite eye while it is intermittently covered and uncovered. Frequently no deviation will be seen while the eye is uncovered because the fusional reflexes will step into the picture and hold this eye in alignment with its fellow, the paralyzed eye. When the normal eye is prevented from fixating by being covered and is watched behind the cover, it will be seen to make an excessive movement in the direction of the action of the paralyzed muscle, and when it is uncovered, it will return to take up binocular fixation. For example, suppose the right superior rectus is suspected of being weak from partially recovered paralysis. When both eyes are uncovered, both eyes move up and to the right to take up fixation quite accurately. Now, if the patient is asked to look up and to the right, and the right eye is made to fix on a target and the left eye is alternately covered and uncovered, the left eye will make a further movement up and to the right when it is covered. When the cover is removed, the left eye will make a movement to redress this excessive movement and will be seen to move down and to the left to take up fixation again with the right eye. This is a pathognomonic sign of partial paralysis of the right superior rectus.

Under normal conditions, the eyes are never moved throughout the full extent of the field of fixation but are moved within a relatively small area around the primary position. Upward gaze normally never exceeds 20 to 30 degrees above the horizon. If the object of regard lies above this, the head is tilted backward. When one looks to the right or left, the eyes are seldom moved beyond 30 degrees without also turning the head. The greatest deviation of the eyes from the primary position is directly downward in the midline. In this direction the eyes may be lowered 60 to 75 degrees without any depression of the chin. The customary field of fixation, therefore, is considerably less than the full extent of possible motility of the eyes. It is important to remember this in considering treatment of patients with paralyzed ocular muscles. This portion of the field must be kept in mind when planning surgical procedures. The most important parts of the field for the average patient are those in the midline and directly downward.

During the act of reading the eyes are moved about 30 degrees above the primary position and approximately 50 degrees downward. Laterally the eyes are seldom carried more than 35 degrees to either side of the midline. It is particularly important to alleviate diplopia in the lower portions of the visual field because of the disturbing effect on reading and walking.

Binocular movements under laboratory experimentation

Voluntary versions. Photographic methods have shown that during willed movement of the eyes from one point to another in space the eyes seldom make the desired movement in a simple, direct fashion. The movement between two points is generally an irregular curve instead of a straight line, and the eyes usually overshoot the mark and have to make a compensatory return movement. The pathway taken by the eyes in following the outline of a circle is shown in Fig. 211.

The velocity of voluntary movements is generally high as compared to those reflexly induced. The average speed may be taken as between 100 and 200 degrees per second if the movements are small and between 200 and 500 degrees per second if the movements cover a large angle. The speed of voluntary movements cannot be varied, except by making pauses. The speed can be accelerated somewhat by fixing one's attention to the

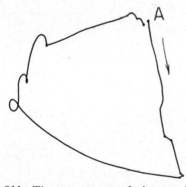

Fig. 211. The movements of the eye in following out a circle. Fixation starts at **A** and runs around in the direction of the arrow. Note the comparative ease and smoothness of the horizontal movements (Stratton). (After Duke-Elder.)

final point of fixation. During reflex movements, on the other hand, the movements are generally slow tonic movements. During the so-called following movements, the speed of the movements depends directly upon the speed of the moving object. If this becomes excessive, of course, the eyes cannot follow, and the reflex is broken. A willed movement may be made then to catch up with the moving object, and again the reflex control will take over.

Voluntary and reflex movements of the eye may, therefore, be described as separate entities, depending upon the stimulus which elicits them. Movements of gaze are elicited optically when an object situated in the visual field at some distance from fixation attracts attention. This may be elicited by the sudden appearance of the object, by a change in its characteristics, and especially by its movement. Movement in the peripheral field is an extremely potent stimulus to reflex versions. Voluntary movements of the eyes can be elicited best by a command. It is incorrect to tell a patient to follow one's moving finger in order to test voluntary versions since this immediately brings into play movements induced by the following reflex.

The type of movement that occurs in voluntary change of the gaze from one point in space to another has been called saccadic. It occurs also in the movements of the eyes during reading, as will be described, and is even found to a certain extent in reflex movements of pursuit following a moving stimulus. Saccadic movements represent a basic pattern of response in the movements of the eyes (p. 387). When two separate targets are presented at a distance from each other and the subject is requested to look from one to the other, there is a latency of 120 to 180 msec., as shown in Fig. 141. The two eyes start to move almost simultaneously and achieve an acceleration that is rapid and maintained over a large part of the movement[17] (Fig. 142). The movement is terminated presumably when the foveas receive the image of the second target by a small overshoot and several small oscillations around the final position. The maximum velocity achieved in a saccadic movement depends on the extent of the movement and, within certain limitations, increases as the distance between the two targets increases (Fig. 212). It can be seen that saccadic movements have characteristics which agree with the physiologic behavior of the ocular muscles. As previously pointed out (p. 402), the ocular muscles have a very short reaction time. The simple twitch lasts from 7.5 to 10 msec., whereas those muscles destined to do grosser work, such as the soleus, have a reaction time of about 40 msec. The rapid acceleration in saccadic movements is probably correlated with a simultaneous burst of discharges in all the muscle fibers inner-

vated; this depends upon the number of motor units activated. It would indicate that whatever units are going to be activated receive their impulses simultaneously. This produces a rapid change of tension in the muscle.

Involuntary pursuit or following movements. Whereas the eyes always move in jumps or saccadic movements when looking from one target to another, they move quite differently when following a moving target. Under these conditions the movement is smooth and not in jumps. Cornsweet[70] investigated movements of pursuit, using a method obviously adequate to pick up extremely small saccadic movements which under conditions of less accurate recording might be interpreted as smooth, but he could find no evidence that any saccadic type of movement occurred. Whenever the eyes follow a moving target, the motion is smooth, and the speed of their movement is generally closely related to the speed of the target. The reaction time of these movements, according to Westheimer,[194] is often less

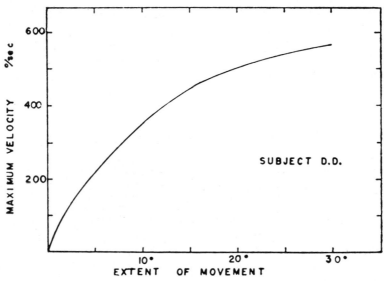

Fig. 212. Relation between maximum velocity and extent of saccadic movements of the eye. (From Westheimer, G.: Arch. Ophth. 52:715, 1954.)

than 200 msec. When the target stops moving or disappears from view, the eyes continue their smooth motion in the same direction for 100 msec. or more. During tracking of the target, however, the eyes seem to adjust to errors in movement by saccadic movements. In general this type of movement is obviously the result of a feedback circuit in which errors modify the performance.

The ability of the eye to fixate a stationary object or to track a moving object is due to a servomechanism in which the retinal image motion serves as a feedback. I have pointed out elsewhere other examples of the use of servomechanisms in ocular physiology, such as control of the pupil size by light and retinal adaptation, focusing of the lens for near vision by the vergence of light rays and the Stiles-Crawford effect, and convergence of the visual axes by retinal disparity.

We have seen that during the most accurate fixation the eye is not immobile but shows a fine tremor (micronystagmus) in addition to slow drifts and sudden changes of direction which have been called flicks. It has now been found that the slow drifts and flicks are motions which enable the eye to track moving objects. When these motions are eliminated by stabilizing the retinal image so that the target moves with every movement of the eye, the eye can still follow a moving target quite faithfully, but the amplitude of the eye motion is changed. It is found that when a target is moved from side to side at a fluctuating velocity to create a sinusoidal stimulus, the amplitude of the eye motion is not as large as that of the target motion when the image is not stabilized on the retina. The drift of the target is followed fairly well by the eye, but from time to time a flick is required for the eye to catch up with the target.

If one compares the curve of the eye motion (after removing certain artifacts called noise from the eye record) with that of the target, the ratio of the two is the gain of the system. In this case the gain is 0.8.[194a] If the image is stabilized on the retina, eliminating drifts and flicks, the gain goes up to 1.8. This confirms the assumption that the retinal image motion constitutes negative feedback since as Fender points out "disconnecting such a feedback loop in an amplifier always results in a considerable increase in gain."

The maximum velocity of a moving target which normal eyes can follow accurately is in the neighborhood of 30 degrees per second. This corresponds to the findings of Ludvigh and Miller[195] who investigated the loss of visual acuity with increasing speeds of a moving target. No significant decrement occurred in visual acuity until the velocity of the target was in the neighborhood of 50 degrees per second.

What decides whether the movement of the eyes is to be saccadic or of the smooth tracking type? Smooth movements seem to occur only when there is a smooth movement of the target over the retina. If the target is stationary and not in the line of sight, the eye always makes saccadic movements in order to achieve fixation. It has therefore been asserted that the movement of the image is the stimulus which evokes smooth tracking. This has been confirmed by Rashbass,[196] who has also shown that the velocity of the smooth movement is linearly related to the velocity of movement of the target, up to 10 degrees per second. A sudden displacement of the target evokes a saccadic response, provided that the displacement is greater than about 0.25 degree. When the displacement is less than this, there is no response. Evidence has also been obtained to indicate that these two types of movement are generated independently of one another.

Vergence movements. Whereas both voluntary versions produced by looking from one target to another and involuntary movements of pursuit produced by tracking a moving target are executed rapidly, vergence movements are carried out relatively slowly. Thus, the average velocity of vergence movements is approximately 8 degrees per second, whereas voluntary and involuntary saccadic movements can exceed 400 degrees per second.

Under ordinary conditions the stimuli which produce vergence movements of the eyes are multiple. Changes in disparity of the images play a major role, but changes in image size, the amount of accommodation required, and various monocular clues all add up to a psychophysic change in the image which experience teaches demands a change in vergence. Under experimental conditions disparity alone is capable of producing an immediate reflex convergence movement.[146] A stimulus requiring only 1.5 degrees of convergence or convergence relaxation produces correspondingly smooth convergence movements in normal subjects. (The term *convergence relaxation* is used to indicate a change from a convergent position of the eyes to one which is less convergent. The term *divergence* is used to indicate a change from parallelism to divergence of the eyes.) Occasionally, relaxation of convergence is not as accurately or as promptly performed. Convergence relaxation is even slower than the movements of convergence, but all vergences resemble the type of movement seen in reflex following or pursuit movements. During vergence movements saccadic conjugate movements of the two eyes occurs occasionally, and the superposition of convergence on a saccadic movement gives rise to the appearance of an unequal movement of the two eyes. If the convergence is factored out in the record, however, the saccadic movements have equal characteristics of time and displacement in the two eyes. This is further evidence to that already given (p. 387) that there are probably two types of innervation to the muscles of the eyes for the two different types of movement, summated at or above the level of the nuclei of the third, fourth, and sixth cranial nerves. The nerves act as the final common pathway for both types of impulses (p. 515).

In experiments in which asymmetric convergence is required, the responses consist of both conjugate saccadic movements and movements of convergence. The two types of movement occur independently and separately in time, as Westheimer and Mitchell state.

"[First, a saccadic movement of the two eyes takes place] to a new direction of conjugate lateral gaze such that the bisector of the angle of convergence actually includes the new fixation point. A convergence movement then takes place, bringing the lines of sight to intersect in the new fixation point. Far from remaining constant in direction throughout the maneuver, the line of sight of the one eye first swings out in unison with that of the other eye and then is brought in again during the response of binocular convergence. It finally assumes exactly the same direction it had at the outset. The two components of the adductive movement of the other eye, viz., that belonging to the conjugate saccadic movement and that belonging to the convergence response, are clearly distinguishable by their different characteristics of time."*

This sequence of movements is schematically illustrated in Fig. 213.

It will be noted that Breinin (p. 411) did not find two separate innervations

_____

*From Westheimer, G., and Mitchell, A.: Arch. Ophth. **55**:848, 1956.

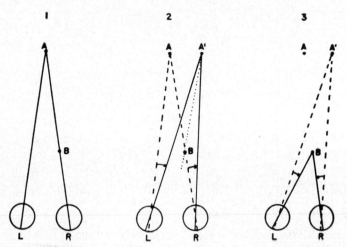

Fig. 213. Schematic diagrams illustrating sequence of movements in changing fixation from **A** to **B. 1,** Binocular fixation of **A. 2,** Conjugate lateral movement without change of convergence to **A'** so that the bisector of the angle of convergence passes through **B. 3,** Convergence movement from **A** to **B.** Steps 2 and 3 are to some extent superimposed, but in view of their characteristics of time, they are easily distinguished. (From Westheimer, G., and Mitchell, A.: Arch. Ophth. **55:**853, 1956.)

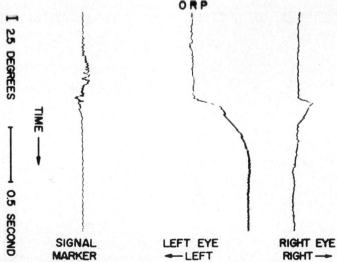

Fig. 214. Binocular refixation from a far (3.4 M.) to a near (0.186 M.) vertical black line on a white background. The near vertical line was carefully aligned on the line of sight of the right eye while it fixated the far vertical line monocularly. (From Alpern, M., and Wolter, J.: Arch. Ophth. **56:**687, 1956.)

electromyographically, and the movement during asymmetric convergence was confined to one eye. No movement of the eye on the side of the fixation object took place, and no change in innervation in either of the horizontal muscles in this eye was found. Alpern and Wolter[18] agree with Westheimer that both eyes of their subject move during asymmetric convergence, and their record shows this movement (Fig. 214).

Obviously, there must be some difference in the conditions under which these two opposing types of response occur. Alpern and Ellen[147] found no movement of the eye on the side of the fixation object when the other eye was occluded, but in the same experiment both eyes showed movement similar to Westheimer's findings when the fixation was carried out binocularly. They point out that there are several explanations to account for the differences in results. It is always possible in electromyographic studies that one cannot record simultaneous responses of all the motor units firing in a muscle, and small movements, such as the small saccadic movement of the eye on the side of the fixation object, could occur without any change in potential being recorded from the needle inserted in the muscle. A more likely explanation is the factor of fixation, as Alpern and Ellen themselves found. The pattern of fixation itself is the determinant of what goes on in the motor system. When one eye is occluded, the fixating eye obviously should not and cannot move *if it maintains fixation*. Under these conditions the opposing motor innervations of version and vergence in the fixating eye cancel each other in the manner described by Breinin. If fixation is allowed binocularly, on the other hand, it is possible that in changing the pattern from far to near there is a momentary slip in fixation from one eye to the other.

This takes place as a result of the disparity of the image which occurs in the nonfixating eye. As the object moves closer to the subject along the line of sight of the right eye, the image moves away from the fovea of the left eye into the temporal retina. This induces a strong impulse to dextroversion, and both eyes then turn to the right. But this now produces a similar situation in the right eye where the image is now on the temporal side of the right fovea. Accordingly, a fusional vergence movement limited to the right eye occurs, and recovery of binocular fixation occurs also.

This does not contradict Hering's law which, as has been stated, is limited to voluntary movements of the eyes and not to reflex activity. The conjugate movements, which are saccadic and (as Alpern and Wolter believe) probably carried out by one type of innervation, constantly obey Hering's law. The vergence movement, in this case fusional convergence which is a slower movement presumably carried out by another type of innervation, probably is not governed by Hering's law, and the amount of innervation due to any one stimulus may not necessarily flow equally to the muscles of the two eyes concerned in the act. In other words, it may be possible to innervate one medial rectus more than the other in fusional convergence. It should be pointed out, however, that I have no experimental confirmation of this possible explanation.

Fusional convergence is an important factor in maintaining the image on both foveas during movements of the object toward or away from a person. The measurement of fusional convergence can be made by inserting prisms which force the eyes to converge in order to maintain bifoveal fixation in front of one or both eyes. The strength of the prism which first causes persistent diplopia is the measure of the fusional convergence, provided that the subject does not use voluntary convergence to bring the eyes into alignment. While it used to be considered imperative to have exact alignment of the image on each fovea, experiments have shown that this is not necessary.[197] The image can fall on the fovea in one eye and slightly off the fovea in the other eye and still be fused. This difference in fixation of the two eyes which will still permit binocular fusion is called the angle of fixation disparity. Ogle was the first to describe this entity adequately.[198] It is also called by various other names in the literature, such as retinal slip[199] and cortical slip.[200] Jampolsky[201] defines it as heterophoria in which there is not exact bifoveal fixation. Heterophoria, as defined previously, is a tendency for the eyes to deviate from each other, being held in check by the fusional mechanism. It is a latent deviation. Hence fixation disparity is an intermediate state in which a very slight deviation does not prevent fusion. Heterophoria is manifest only when fusion is abolished. Jampolsky points out that fixation disparity has the sensory characteristics of heterophoria and the motor characteristics of tropia (p. 514).

It has been already been pointed out that the eyes are never absolutely still because of ocular tremor or micronystagmus (p. 498) so that exact geometric point-to-point imagery in the theoretical center of each fovea is purely fanciful, to start with. The eyes are in constant motion even under the best of conditions with perfect foveal fusion. Further, it will be shown that in a normal person there is no true point-to-point correspondence of the two retinas. A visual receptor in the right eye has more than a single visual receptor in the left eye which has the same visual direction or locus in

space. Instead of speaking of identical retinal points, it is more factual to speak of identical retinal areas. Each cone or group of cones in the right retina has a group of cones in the left retina which under the same conditions has the same visual direction in space. It is doubtful if this is an anatomic group, at least not one entirely limited by anatomic factors, but is physiologic and therefore variable so that the size of the corresponding areas and even their position may vary from time to time.

The areas of the two retinas which are related physiologically by still yielding fusion in spite of different visual directions are called Panum's areas (p. 847). It is obvious that in addition to the lack of exact point-to-point correspondence of the visual lines due to micronystagmus, Panum's areas allow the visual axes further freedom to wander away from point-to-point fixation and still maintain fusion. Hence, in reality everyone has a very small fixation disparity. The size of Panum's areas in the foveas of a normal person have been calculated to be about 6 minutes of arc.[198] In a normal person with an angular separation of more than 6 minutes of arc, images presented simultaneously to each fovea will be seen in two different directions in space, i.e., double, unless the visual axes move. In some persons, especially those with esotropia, this area is enlarged considerably, and the eyes may be several prism diopters out of alignment; yet binocular fusion is possible. These patients are said to have a fixation disparity. While it may not be of any clinical importance to determine whether normal persons have a fixation disparity, it is of importance in patients with esotropia, particularly in operated patients, to realize that the small angle of esotropia remaining after surgery may be due to a fixation disparity. However, from the standpoint of treatment, Jampolsky has stated that "patients with small-degree convergent fixation disparity usually need not be treated."*

Wheel rotations or torsions. Torsional movements occur to maintain single binocular vision. These movements are purely reflex and are responses to torsional changes in the targets presented to a person in a stereoscopic device. It is rare in ordinary life that the images presented to the two eyes could ever be torsionally displaced one to the other except when there has been paralysis of one of the oblique muscles. Torsional diplopia, as will be explained later, is a more disturbing type of diplopia, and the body resents it and makes every effort to correct it when possible by head tilting, by suppression, and by the reflex torsional movements described previously (p. 478). Since these torsional movements are brought about by changes in tonus of the ocular muscles, this type of correction becomes impossible when the disturbance is caused by a weakness of one muscle. Even though more tonic activity were sent to the weak muscle, it could not effect the desired result in most types of paralysis.

Eye movements during reading

During the act of reading, the line of print is fixated by a voluntary act. It might be supposed that the eyes then make a smooth, scanning motion to the right until they reach the end of the line of print. This is not the case, however. Instead, one finds that the eyes make a series of short, jerky fixations called saccadic movements. Between each movement there is a reflex pause, usually lasting between 0.2 and 0.3 second. Each

saccadic movement takes about 0.02 to 0.03 second. Six to eight of these saccadic movements occur in each line of print that is read. The eyes are then brought back to the beginning of the next line of print by a voluntary effort, and the reflex activity starts all over again. These saccadic movements are entirely reflex, and their number and duration cannot be voluntarily controlled. In fact, we are entirely unaware of their presence. The speed of reading is determined largely by the time occupied by the fixation pauses between the saccadic movements. It is during these pauses that the image of the print becomes an effective visual stimulus, for during the saccadic movements, as during all movements of the eyes, the speed is too fast to allow a visual impression (Fig. 215).

During each fixation pause, a number of letters and words are visualized. The length of the line which can be successfully scanned is somewhat a matter of practice, and some persons learn to take in more words than others. Therefore an increase in the speed of reading can be made by increasing one's span of letters at each fixation pause and by cutting down on the time required for each pause.

Many studies have been made on the problems relating to the speed of eye movements during reading and their relation to the so-called poor reader. It is apparent that many psychologic as well as physiologic factors are concerned, and in most slow readers the difficulty cannot be blamed on deficiencies in the oculomotor apparatus.

The ability to read is interfered with seriously in patients with right homonymous hemianopsia. Although such a person generally can fixate the line of print he wishes to read because in most patients the macula is spared (p. 682), it is

---

*From Jampolsky, A.: Am. J. Ophth. **41:** 825, 1956.

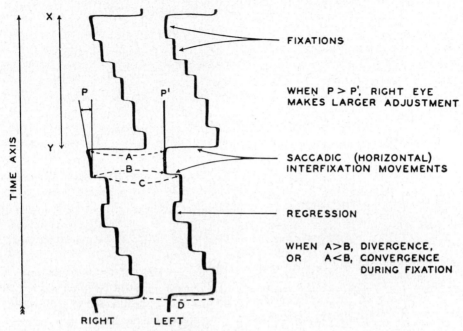

FIXATIONS

WHEN P > P', RIGHT EYE
MAKES LARGER ADJUSTMENT

SACCADIC (HORIZONTAL)
INTERFIXATION MOVEMENTS

REGRESSION

WHEN A>B, DIVERGENCE,
OR   A<B, CONVERGENCE
      DURING FIXATION

Fig. 215. Diagrammatic section of an eye movement photograph. (From MacFarland, R., Knehr, C., and Berens, C.: Am. J. Ophth. **20**:1204, 1937.)

impossible for him to follow the line of print since he is reading into the blind fields. Patients who have left homonymous hemianopsia, on the other hand, may experience some difficulty in fixating the line of print, but can read fairly well since they are reading into the seeing half of the fields. These patients find little difficulty after practice since they learn to place a finger on the beginning of each line of print and direct the eyes in this manner to each new line.

Much of our knowledge of the movements of the eyes is based on recording the movement itself and not on the activity of the individual muscles. We are in need of accurate information regarding the part each muscle plays in movements of the eye, but so far it has been possible to record only the changes in tension or the electrical potential in the ocular muscles of man for purely experimental purposes in a few instances.

If suitable electrodes are placed on the temples and are connected with a sensitive string galvanometer, a galvanometric deflection is produced when the eyes are moved in the same plane as the electrodes. No deflection occurs when the eyes are moved in a plane at right angles to the electrodes. The deflection increases with the degree of the movement and persists as long as a given position of the eyes is maintained. It was thought at one time that these effects were due to the summation of action currents from the muscles, but it is now recognized that the action currents from a contracted intact muscle never summate in such a manner as to produce a potential difference between the muscle as a whole and its antagonist or the surrounding tissue. It is well known that a persistent potential difference normally exists between the

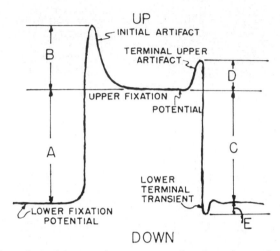

Fig. 216. Idealized vertical electro-oculogram on a time base drawn from a typical tracing to show the dimensions used for measuring artifacts and transients in this report. (From Ford, A.: Arch. Ophth. **61:**899, 1959.)

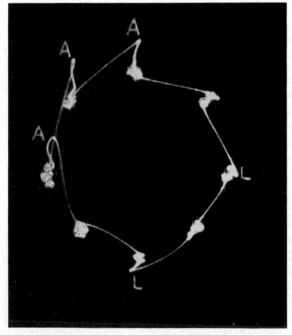

Fig. 217. Two-dimensional electro-oculogram when the subject fixates eight points on a circle in clockwise order in 23-degree steps. Points labeled **A** show the rider artifact; points labeled **L** show small loops which may be terminal corrective transients. (From Ford, A.: Arch. Ophth. **61:**899, 1959.)

front and back surfaces of the eye. The probable explanation of the galvanometric changes produced by eye movements, as just described, is that they are due to changes in the pattern of the electrical field which this potential difference imposes upon the neighboring anatomic structures.

Records taken of the changes in electric potential with eye movements are called electro-oculograms, in contradistinction to electromyograms, which record the changes in potential of individual contracting muscle fibers.* Ford has called attention to certain adventitious potentials which are artifacts when vertical eye movements are being recorded. He believes these so-called rider artifacts are due to action potentials from the superior rectus with some added effect from the superior obliques[202] (Figs. 216 and 217).

The various parameters influencing electro-oculograms have been studied by Shackel[203] who finds a mean potential for a 30-degree horizontal excursion of 580 mv., with a range of 300 to 1000 mv. For excursions up to 30 degrees there is a good linear relationship between the electro-oculogram potential and the excursion of the eyes with an accuracy of about ± 1.35 degrees.

It has been shown that the galvanometric differences in potential are due to this persistent cornea-retinal potential difference, which presumably arises from the high metabolic processes in the retina and the low metabolism of the cornea.[204] Even passive movements of the eyes result in galvanometric deflections comparable in magnitude and polarity to those produced by active voluntary movements of the eyes.[205, 206]

PATHOLOGIC PHYSIOLOGY OF STRABISMUS
Relation of heterotropia to heterophoria

Heterophoria was defined as that condition in which the eyes are unable to maintain bifoveal fixation when the impulses for fusion are broken up. In a person with heterophoria the eyes are in good alignment until the optomotor reflexes are artificially abolished. As soon as this is accomplished by one means or another, the visual axes lose their proper alignment, and the eyes turn in or out or one axis turns higher than the other. Since the optomotor reflexes were holding the eyes straight, the degree of the deviation of the visual axes after fusion has been broken up is a measure of the work constantly being done by the fusion mechanism. It indicates how great a strain this mechanism is under constantly in holding the eyes in alignment for that particular person. The rewards of binocular fusion and the penalties imposed on a person when fusion is prevented and the images presented to the two eyes fall on disparate retinal receptors will be discussed in Chapter 22, Binocular Vision. It is obvious that fusion may be disrupted easier in some persons than in others. Persons with a weak sensory fusional capacity will break earlier than those in whom sensory fusion is strong. When sensory fusion is broken up and the eyes are in the so-called disociated position, they may or may not remain in alignment. They may or may not deviate, depending entirely upon whether the anatomic structure of the eyes and orbits and the postural reflexes are normal, for the optomotor reflexes merely act as a fine adjustment to bring the visual axes

---

*For a history of the development of electro-oculography see Marg, E.: Development of electro-oculography, Arch. Ophth. 45:169, 1951.

into stricter alignment after the anatomic factors and the postural reflexes have aligned them grossly.

In a normal person the anatomic factors, the postural reflexes, and the optomotor reflexes keep the eyes in good alignment in all positions of gaze. Abnormalities in one component may be compensated by the other two normal components. For example, abnormalities in the anatomy, such as unusually prominent eyes and an abnormally wide interpupillary distance, may be compensated by the postural and optomotor reflexes, and the eyes may still be maintained in good alignment in all directions of gaze. If, however, we prevent the optomotor reflexes from functioning in this person, we may find that he has a high degree of exophoria because the anatomic features we have described are conducive to a divergent position of the visual axes. The postural reflexes alone may not be sufficient to overcome this tendency to diverge. Excessive or deficient innervation from any of the postural sources of tonus may be compensated by the optomotor reflexes. For example, the amount of tonic convergence (basic tonus of the convergence mechanism) may be excessive, but the eyes may still be held in good alignment until we break up fusion. Then, such a person has a high degree of esophoria.

The eyes may become dissociated not only by the means employed in the clinic or laboratory to break up fusion, but also as a result of disease. The person just described as having excessive tonic convergence may have straight eyes until the vision of one eye is seriously impaired by disease. This breaks up the fusional reflexes effectively, and from that time on the eyes become dissociated and turn in.

It must be emphasized that just because the optomotor reflexes are broken up the eyes do not lose their proper alignment necessarily. The optomotor fusional reflexes may be absent, e.g., in a person who has had a blind eye since birth; yet his visual axes may remain entirely straight in all positions of gaze due to the combined anatomic features and normal postural reflex activity. Therefore, small changes in one of the three factors may be compensated by the remaining two. On the other hand, a defect may be so marked that it cannot be compensated by the remaining factors. Such a failure results in a manifest deviation of the visual axes in one or more positions of gaze.

When the visual axes are already out of alignment, artificially obliterating the optomotor reflexes, a person is said to have strabismus or heterotropia. Heterotropia is simply manifest heterophoria. It is a pathologic condition in which the optomotor reflexes have been insufficient to maintain alignment. Some defect in the anatomic features or postural reflexes or in both has driven the eyes out of alignment in spite of the optomotor reflexes. Obviously we may have various combinations of abnormality of the anatomy or postural reflexes and fusional capacity. The fusional capacity may be normal or even excessive; yet the force driving the eyes out of alignment may be strong enough to break through these reflexes and turn the eyes out of alignment.

General types of heterotropia or strabismus

Strabismus, heterotropia, or squint (as it is commonly called) is a manifest deviation of the visual axes in one or more positions of gaze. When the visual axes are turned in toward one another, the condition is called esotropia. If the axes are turned away from one another, it is called exotropia; if one axis is higher than the other, it is called right or left hypertropia, depending upon whether the right or left eye is the higher. The term *hypotropia* is more commonly used in connection with strabismus than *hypophoria* is used in speaking of latent deviations (p. 490).

Two main classes of squint are recognized, depending upon whether or not the misalignment of the visual axes remains constant in all directions of gaze. The term *comitant strabismus* is used to denote a manifest deviation of the visual axes in which there is a relatively constant angle of deviation in versions and with either eye fixating. Incomitant strabismus has an angle of deviation which varies in versions and is different when one eye fixates as compared to that when the other eye fixates. In reality few patients have strictly comitant strabismus. Careful measurements, especially in extreme oblique position of gaze, will reveal a vertical incomitant component in otherwise comitant esotropia or exotropia, due to physiologic factors. For practical purposes, however, the strabismus is called comitant if there is no *obvious* difference in the angle of deviation of the visual axes (called the angle of squint) in different versions and regardless of which eye takes up fixation. Whenever there is an obvious difference in the angle of squint when the eyes turn in versions, or whenever the angle of squint is different when the right eye fixates compared to when the left eye fixates, the term *incomitant strabismus* should be applied.

Comparison of comitant and incomitant strabismus with motor abnormalities in the general muscular system of the body

The neuromuscular mechanism which controls movements of the eyes may be compared to that which moves the limbs.

The pathways of each mechanism may be divided into two easily identifiable portions: (1) a supranuclear portion or upper motor neuron and (2) a nuclear infranuclear portion or lower motor neuron. It makes no difference whether the pathways we are considering are transmitting impulses for what, philosophically, we may choose to call willed or voluntary movements or whether they transmit reflex or involuntary activity; each pathway is divisible into these two main portions, and affections of one portion are always different and usually distinguishable from those of the other.

In Fig. 218 are shown the two portions of the corticospinal pathway to the muscles of the arm. The lower motor neuron begins with cells in the ventral horn of the cord. The neurons from these cells to the muscle are spoken of as the final common pathway, a term introduced by Sir Charles Sherrington in 1904. The final common pathway is the sole path by which all impulses, no matter whence they come, must travel if they are to act on the muscle fibers. They constitute a public path common to impulses arising from many different sources in the body.

The upper motor neuron is composed of fibers conducting many different influences to the muscles, each fiber constituting a private path from some special source, such as afferent impulses coming into the central nervous system from the various sense organs, motor impulses originating in the Betz cells of the motor area of the cortex, and modifying impulses from reflex centers such as the vestibular nuclei, all converging on the final common pathway. It is well recognized that lesions of the final common pathway result in restriction of movement of individual muscles, whereas lesions of the upper motor neuron result in complex disturbances usually distributed to groups of muscles serving a common purpose.

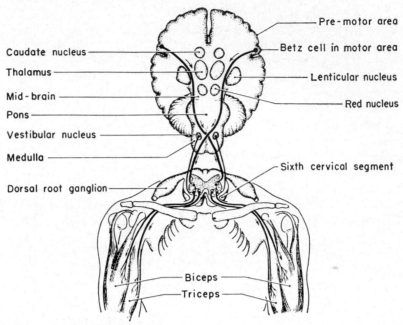

Pre-motor area

Betz cell in motor area

Caudate nucleus

Thalamus

Lenticular nucleus

Mid-brain

Red nucleus

Pons

Vestibular nucleus

Medulla

Sixth cervical segment

Dorsal root ganglion

Biceps

Triceps

Fig. 218. Corticospinal pathway to the muscles of the arm. (From Adler, F.: Arch. Ophth. 50:19, 1953.)

The neuromuscular mechanism which controls movements of the eyes is divisible also into two portions: (1) supranuclear and (2) nuclear and infranuclear. The pathways for dextroversion, both voluntary and reflex, are shown in Fig. 219. The supranuclear portion includes all those pathways, afferent and efferent, lying above the level of the nuclei of the third, fourth, and sixth cranial nerves. It includes both voluntary pathways, serving to turn the eyes in any chosen field of gaze, and the various reflex pathways, which keep the visual axes in strict alignment in the various fields of gaze. The nuclear or infranuclear portion includes the nuclei of origin of the oculomotor nerves, the nerves themselves, the neurohumoral mechanism in the synapses and in the motor end plates, and finally the muscles themselves and their fascia and ligaments.

As has been stated, it has been found useful to divide strabismus into two types, comitant and incomitant.

Incomitant strabismus is always caused by insufficient or excessive activity of one or more of the ocular muscles. The abnormal activity of the muscle or muscles may be due to insufficient or excessive innervation, to faulty anatomic relationships, or to the presence of contractures or fibrous bands. From Fig. 219 it is apparent that any lesion involving the nuclear or infranuclear portion of the pathway for versions will inevitably result in incomitant strabismus since individual muscles will be affected; therefore the angle of deviation of the visual axes will vary, depending upon the field of gaze and upon the fixating eye.

The part played by abnormal check ligaments, muscle footplates, etc., is difficult to evaluate because it is not possible to differentiate between abnormal and normal check ligaments in the usual operative procedures. It seems more plausible to consider any abnormalities of the ligamentous expansions and contractures in muscles to be the result of long-standing strabismus, rather than the cause. Incomitant strabismus should be recognized since treatment for this condition is generally different from that for comitant strabismus. Unfortunately, the diagnosis is not always easy since patients with long-standing paralysis of ocular muscles tend to develop comitance, but a careful examination will usually reveal unmistakable signs of remaining incomitance.

Lesions of the supranuclear pathway for versions will result in a disability of both eyes to move equally and simultaneously in one or more directions of gaze. As indicated in Fig. 219, a supranuclear lesion situated in the pathways for voluntary dextroversion will produce equal embarrassment of the two eyes in willed movements to the right. There will be no strabismus since the muscles of the two eyes which move them equally and simultaneously in one direction will be affected.

In comitant strabismus it is apparent that we are dealing with lesions situated in the supranuclear mechanism having to do with vergences and not with versions; therefore we must look into the vergence mechanisms for the seat of the difficulty.

Comitant strabismus is usually innervational in origin. This is inherent in the

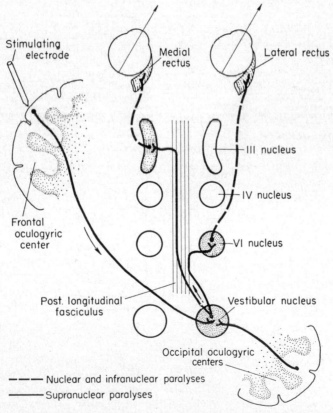

Fig. 219. Motor pathways for dextroversion. (From Adler, F.: Arch. Ophth. **50:**19, 1953.)

very nature of comitance and is proved by the fact that the angle of deviation of the visual axes disappears when the patient is under general anesthesia. Some pathologic process has disturbed the normal vergence mechanism which lies above the level of the nuclei of the oculomotor nerves. It is, therefore, a supranuclear lesion. In convergent comitant strabismus we are dealing with an alteration in the normal amount of convergence innervation. Either the convergence mechanism is sending an excessive innervation to both medial rectus muscles, or the divergence mechanism is sending an insufficient innervation to the lateral rectus muscles for the particular degree of vergence required at that moment.

It has been pointed out that the mechanism or subcortical center (if one chooses to use a term which is in disrepute but still a useful concept) for convergence is unknown. We have had

pathologic evidence (p. 481) of the existence of such a mechanism, whose pathways for binocular adduction (convergence) are different from those innervating each contralateral medial rectus during dextroversion and levoversion. In Fig. 220 is shown the hypothetical convergence mechanism, including pathways for voluntary and reflex activities. The supranuclear part of the mechanism consists of all those pathways which converge on the nucleus of each third cranial nerve, containing the cells of origin of the fibers innervating the medial rectus muscles. The hypothetical divergence mechanism is shown in Fig. 221. The supranuclear part of this pathway includes all those fibers converging on the nuclei of the two sixth cranial nerves, including the hypothetical subcortical center. Evidence has been given previously for the existence of such a mechanism (p. 487).

Any pathologic process which creates

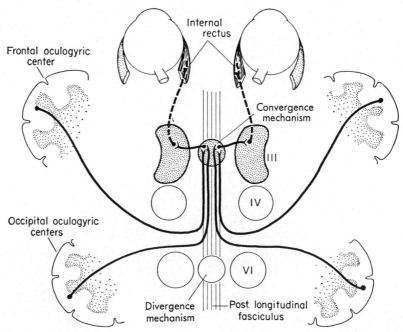

Fig. 220. Mechanism for convergence. *Solid line,* supranuclear pathways. *Broken line,* lower motor neuron. (From Adler, F.: Arch. Ophth. **50:**22, 1953.)

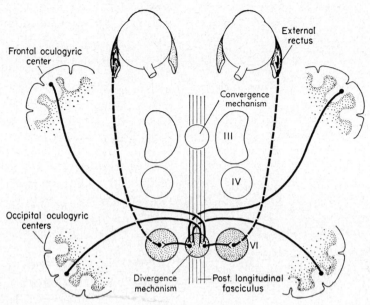

Fig. 221. Mechanism for divergence. *Solid line,* supranuclear pathways. *Broken line,* lower motor neuron. (From Adler, F.: Arch. Ophth. **50:**52, 1953.)

excessive innervation to the two medial recti during binocular adduction or insufficient innervation to the lateral recti during binocular abduction (divergence) will lead to comitant esotropia, unless held in check by the optomotor reflexes. In this case the patient will exhibit a large esophoria. If the process leads to excessive innervation to the lateral recti, the patient will have either divergent strabismus or, if the deviation is kept in check by the optomotor reflexes, large exophoria.

Comitant strabismus

Comitant strabismus is manifest heterophoria. There is no difference between heterophoria and heterotropia, save that heterophoria is a tendency toward deviation which can be detected only by artificially eliminating the fusional component of the optomotor reflexes, whereas in heterotropia the deviation is present already since the fusional reflexes have

already failed to prevent the force that drives the visual axes out of alignment from becoming effective. This concept is fundamental to an understanding of comitant strabismus.

Absence of the fusional reflexes alone will not produce heterotropia. It is common experience to see patients who have no possibility of sensory fusion, with one blind eye, e.g., whose eyes remain in good alignment. Therefore, the pathogenesis of comitant heterotropia must reside in either some abnormality of the anatomic factors or some abnormality in the postural reflexes for vergences.

It has been suggested that some forms of comitant strabismus may be the result of some sort of an abnormal linkage in the brain of the corresponding receptors in the two eyes, as though the wires had gotten crossed, so to speak. If the foveal fibers in the right eye, e.g., were linked in the visual cortex with fibers of receptors from a nasal area of the left retina anatomically prior to birth, it is argued that this would force the visual axis of the left eye to turn in in order for the eyes to be used together. This would produce esotropia. Many different theories have been proposed based on this general premise, but the arguments against such a mechanism are numerous. I need only point out that heterophoria itself is proof against this concept. How can one claim that the eyes turn in in a patient with esophoria because of an abnormal cortical linkage, but are held straight by fusional impulses until these are artificially removed? This concept could more usefully be employed to account for abnormal retinal correspondence, which is considered on pp. 836 to 842.

Comitant strabismus occurs in four different forms: esotropia, exotropia, right hypertropia, and left hypertropia, depending on the direction the visual axes bear toward each other. We know much more about comitant esotropia and exotropia than we do about the comitant vertical tropias. The problem of the pathogenesis of the horizontal comitant tropias resolves itself into a search for the causes of the horizontal phorias, i.e., esophoria and exophoria. What are the factors which favor horizontal misalignment of the visual axes and lead to a tendency for these axes to turn either in or out? These have been discussed previously (pp. 513 and 514).

Sensory and motor disturbances which prevent development of or break up the fusional reflex. Various sensory and motor disturbances may prevent the development of or break up the fusional reflex.

Sensory. During infancy and early childhood the fusion-free position of normal eyes is convergent. In an adult and in aged persons the dissociated position is divergent. Most children have esophoria of low degree, whereas most adults have exophoria of low degree when tested at a 6 M. distance. From this it can be concluded that during infancy the tonus of the vergence mechanisms has a convergence bias; i.e., the basic tonus of the convergence mechanism is excessive, or the tonus of the divergence mechanism is deficient.

The reasons for this change in postural tonus are not known. Many changes occur in the eyes after birth, on both the sensory and motor sides. At birth the eyes function independently to a large extent. The independent function of each eye yields little more than perception of light and motion of objects in the visual field. The foveas are not developed until the third month of postnatal life. At birth the lids will blink when light is thrown into each eye, and the failure of the infant to respond with this protective blink and to retain a blank stare at the light is an ominous sign. However, the eyes may not turn toward a light which is brought into the visual field from the side. At about the second week the infant will respond to light thrown into one eye from the side with a movement of the eyes toward the light, and generally both eyes will move equally and simultaneously toward the light, showing the earliest development of versions. The movement may not be carried out perfectly, however, and not until the first month will the eyes always move together accurately in an attempt to fixate. Vergences develop even later, and not until the third to the sixth month does one find the eyes able to fixate in the convergent position accurately, both straight ahead or with asymmetric convergence. The vergence reflex develops later than the version reflex, therefore.

During the period immediately after birth the eyeball is considerably smaller than it will be in later life. It should, if there were no other factors to change this, be extremely hyperopic. The lens, however, is relatively large and very convex. This in large measure nullifies the hyperopia on the basis of diminished axial length. However, the majority of infants in the United States are hyperopic. In the first four months of life accommodation is not possible, nor is it required, even though the infant may be hyperopic, since the foveas are not fully developed. Accommodation develops only to the degree of the existing visual acuity, which does not approach the adult level until the age of 2 years. During the infant's early development, therefore, accommodation and convergence do not go hand in hand. A more exact accommodation-convergence relationship seems to develop (p. 486), and during this period excessive convergence movements frequently are seen when the normal child looks at near objects. It is the effort of accommodation rather than the actual amount of accommodation which determines the intensity of the associated adduction of each eye.

Since the normal infant has excessive basic convergence tonus, usually some degree of hyperopia, a weak convergence mechanism (which when employed may call forth a greater than normal effort to effect accurate changes in dioptric power of the lens), and a fovea which is just developing, it is no wonder that anything which acts as an obstacle to the development of the fusional reflex will lead to a convergent position of the visual axes. If the fusional reflexes fail to develop to the extent of compensating for these other anatomic and postural deficiencies, then esophoria and finally esotropia are inevitable. Obviously, whether esotropia or merely esophoria will be the outcome depends entirely on how well the child is able to develop the fusional

reflexes as a compensatory mechanism. If the sensory obstacle is slight and the fusional capacities are large, he will retain good alignment of the visual axes. On the other hand, if the sensory obstacle is large and occurs before he has had time to develop good fusional reflexes, then the visual axes are sure to break sooner or later, and periods of esotropia ensue. At first the esotropia is intermittent and occurs only during periods when the child's general state of well-being is at low ebb, such as when he is tired at the end of the day. Generally the deviation occurs during the evening meal or when he is sick or recovering from an illness, i.e., the usual children's diseases. If he has considerable hyperopia, then an additional factor, the accommodative convergence, will be added to the basic tonic convergence, and he is far less likely to escape the downhill path from esophoria to esotropia.

What are the sensory obstacles which may occur to start this abnormal train of events? First and foremost are congenital defects or defects acquired in the very early months of infancy. Any congenital defect which interferes with the clarity of the image presented to the retina of one eye will make it more difficult for an infant to develop fusional reflexes which will associate the two eyes. It need not necessarily be a serious difficulty that destroys the sight on one side, but merely one sufficient that the two images, one good and the other less good, cannot be fused easily. An unclear image makes binocular vision less satisfactory than good monocular vision. Every opthalmologist learns this by experience with adult patients who develop minor visual defects in one eye which interfere more with reading vision than if the offending eye were totally blind. It sometimes becomes advisable to recommend patching an eye with a minor visual defect during the act of reading in order to get rid of the blur this eye causes when open. The type of disease process likely to produce such a disturbance in an infant may range from mild corneal scars and congenital cataracts to serious congenital defects such as microphthalmus, retained primary vitreous, hyaloid artery remnants, colobomas of the macula, etc. Diseases which occur congenitally or very shortly after birth, such as toxoplasmosis and retrolental fibroplasia, will produce the same disturbances. As soon as the fusional reflexes are prevented from developing, whether the visual axes remain straight depends on the other factors, and since in infancy these most frequently cause convergence of the visual axes, esotropia is likely to appear. Occasionally divergence occurs. Whether estropia or exotropia develops depends entirely on whether the sum total of anatomic factors plus the postural convergence tonus favor an in-turning or an out-turning of the visual axes. Convergent strabismus is not always the result. It should be emphasized that there is no fundamental difference between esophoria and exophoria or between esotropia and exotropia, except the obvious one of the visual axes being on different sides of the parallel primary position.

Later in life comitant strabismus, usually esotropia, will develop occasionally from a sensory obstacle—say, in a 1- to 3-year-old child whose eyes have been straight since birth. A retinoblastoma arising in the retina (one of the most malignant tumors of childhood) is heralded frequently by the gradual onset of esotropia at about the age of 3 years, which is the most common time for this dreaded tumor to develop. Pseudotumors, usually metastatic inflammatory conditions reaching the retina via the bloodstream, may show themselves by misalignment of the visual axes, first. The moral is obvious. A careful search for sensory obstacles as the cause should be made in the examination of any infant or child who develops comitant strabismus. This may be difficult in a young infant and will nearly always require dilatation of the pupil and perhaps general anesthesia. It would be useless and impose a great hardship on a young child to insist on patching a good eye in order to break up amblyopia in a squinting eye in which the squint was on a sensory basis, and if a retinoblastoma were the cause, the act would be malpractice.

One of the characteristics by which this type of strabismus may be suspected is that it is always monocular. That is, the eye with the good vision is always the fixating eye; whereas the other eye deviates. A child who develops a squint on a sensory basis never has the dilemma of having to choose between alternating fixation or monocular squinting. As will appear later, one type of strabismus is characterized by being constantly alternating (p. 525) and another type by being either alternating or monocular (p. 523). The sensory type is always monocular.

Motor. There are two ways in which a motor obstacle may prevent the development of or break up the optomotor reflexes and give rise to what appears to be comitant strabismus. In reality the strabismus is not comitant but incomitant, but the incomitance is so slight as to escape detection. Congenital paralysis of one or more of the vertically acting muscles may give rise to vertical separation of the visual axes of the two eyes, at first in the field of action of the paralyzed muscles only but later, through contractures in their antagonists, throughout the entire motor field. As a result of this, the eyes from the very beginning are in vertical misalignment which prevents the development of fusion. The eyes being dissociated are turned either in or out, according to the tonus of the vergence mechanisms, and thus horizontal misalignment is superimposed on the vertical misalignment. Since the horizontal misalignment is always more marked and hence more noticeable than the vertical misalignment, and since the horizontal component is comitant, the vertical component goes unnoticed, and the squint is diagnosed as comitant horizontal strabismus.

The second type of motor obstacle is like the first but appears later in life. Paralyses of muscles after attacks of virus diseases during childhood are reported, and traumatic paralyses are probably not uncommon. The sudden appearance of squint after a fall or a febrile illness is a common history. The squint, which is incomitant at first and causes intolerable diplopia, leads to the suppression of the image in one eye. This self-imposed dissociation permits the vergence mechanisms to take over, and the eyes will be held in the position dictated by their tonus, creating comitant horizontal misalignment. In addition, some authors suggest that the diplopia itself leads to further turning-in of the eyes in an effort to separate the two images further. Hence, diplopiaphobia (the term applied to this condition) may create a marked horizontal angle of squint from a small horizontal or vertical misalignment.

The contracture of the antagonist of a paralyzed muscle has been mentioned previously. This itself leads to the development of a fixed angle of squint, i.e., a comitant element. In some patients with paralysis of a muscle, it is believed that the paralysis itself may recover completely, but that permanent comitant strabismus caused by contracture of the antagonist remains (for further discussion of this point see p. 528).

Refractive errors which influence accommodative convergence. Donders was the first to develop the theory that convergent strabismus was due to hyperopia and divergent strabismus to myopia. He pointed out that a child who was hyperopic needed to accommodate to correct the hyperopia if glasses were not worn, and this accommodation led to excessive convergence innervation. This resulted in a dilemma which the child attempted to solve. Either he chose to get clear images by accommodating, which automatically led to convergence of the visual axes and the development of esotropia, or he accepted blurred retinal images and kept the visual axes straight. In the first choice he was presented with double images at the start, but suppression was soon learned, and one eye, usually the dominant and less hyperopic, accepted the responsibility of fixation while the other turned in by an amount equal to the excessive convergence innervation, and its image was suppressed. In the second choice the child had the benefit of binocular single vision, but the two images were blurred. Obviously binocular single vision would be of little benefit if the images on each fovea were out of focus. Clearly the better choice was to accommodate and squint. Donders found that a large number of children with esotropia also had hyperopia, and the proof of his theory, according to Donders and those who adhered to his school, was the cure of the strabismus in these children by correcting the hyperopia.

In a similar way Donders explained exotropia on the basis of myopia, pointing out that myopic children did not need to employ accommodation for near; therefore, convergence tonus was gradually lost by disuse.

Donders' theory that in childhood comitant convergent strabismus may be caused by hyperopia and comitant divergent strabismus by myopia has never been satisfactorily refuted, although there have been strong opponents to it, and many of the objections have not been satisfactorily answered. It is certain that it is the cause of a number of cases of strabismus but by no means all.

In addition to the excessive tonic convergence of childhood, an infant with hyperopia has the problem of employing an excessive amount of accommodation in focusing on near objects. This occurs at the time of life when the optomotor reflexes are developing. The excessive accommodative effort carries with it excessive accommodative convergence, and the child is in the dilemma of accepting either a blurred single image of the object of regard or a clearly focused double image. Since the optomotor reflexes have little potency at this time and suppression is acquired easily, the excessive accommodative convergence is uninhibited, and the eyes turn in. This can be observed occasionally in normal infants who do not develop strabismus since overconvergence to an accommodative effort frequently occurs in a normal child during the period of development. It is transitory, of course, and a trial-and-error method soon teaches the child the proper amount of convergence to employ. An accommodative squinter persists in the excessive convergence because of the necessity for getting a clear retinal image by accommodation, and the child learns to fixate with one eye and turn the other in. If the eyes are of equal value in the formation of images and there is no strong dominance in either eye, the strabismus may remain alternating, first one eye and then the other being used for fixation. But generally these children become monocular squinters instead of alternators because one eye is more hyperopic or less dominant than its fellow, the one elected to be used. Alternating or monocular fixation depends, therefore, on whether the two eyes are of equal value in seeing.

The arguments just outlined apply equally to infants with either congenital or acquired myopia which, as stated previously, favors exophoria and therefore divergence of the visual axes.

Unknown factors that change the tonus of vergence mechanisms. A large number of patients with strabismus can be proved to have neither a sensory or motor obstacle to fusion nor a refractive error as the cause of the strabismus. Hence, there must be other factors which are instrumental in favoring misalignment of the visual axes and leading to the development of squint. At the present time we do not know much about these; therefore, these patients are sometimes said to have strabismus on the basis of undetermined etiology. While some of these patients may have anatomic anomalies which influence the development of the squint, it would seem that in the majority of them the strabismus is innervational in origin since the deviation disappears during general anesthesia.

It has been shown that when one is under the influence of alcohol or anoxia the convergence tonus increases and, in some persons, can cause temporary comitant esotropia. This may come about as a result of elimination of cortical inhibition, with the release of excessive convergence tonus from the subcortical convergence mechanism, or it may be due to a depressant action on the divergence mechanism. Further studies will be necessary to determine this point. Although it is obvious that neither alcohol nor anoxia has anything to do with the type of squint considered here, the mechanisms involved are probably the same. Failure of development or myelination of these nerve tracts or lesions in either the convergence or divergence mechanism can lead to comitant esotropia and exotropia. Many children afflicted with cerebral palsy have esotropia. Most of these show not only evidence of paralysis of individual ocular muscles, but also signs of gaze palsy, with intensification of end position nystagmus during versions. In other words, there are signs of a combination of supranuclear and nuclear damage.

The following characteristics differentiate this type of strabismus, which is called esotropia of undertermined origin for lack of a more definitive name.

1. The strabismus is either present at birth or develops shortly after birth.
2. The amount of the deviation is generally large, the angle of squint being over 30 $\triangle$.
3. The angle of deviation is more constant than in the accommodative type of squint and measures the same for distance and near.
4. Fixation is generally alternating.
5. The visual acuity is generally normal in each eye; amblyopia is rare.
6. The majority of persons have anomalous retinal correspondence with suppression.
7. The refraction parallels that of the nonstrabismic child in the same age group.
8. Correction of the refractive error has no effect on the angle of squint.
9. Associated motor anomalies, such as latent nystagmus and alternating sursumvergence, are frequent. Some persons have exaggerated end position nystagmus which is more marked on one side than on the other during version, suggestive of recovery from partial gaze palsy. Some have minor motor disabilities, suggestive of a mild form of cerebral palsy, and there is no sharp dividing line between comitant strabismus of unknown etiology and the typical incomitant squint present in children with advanced cerebral diplegia who have other motor defects.

Whether the cause of comitant strabismus is entirely neurogenic or structural is not settled as yet. Cogent arguments can be lined up in favor of each belief. Abnormalities in the supranuclear mechanisms for vergences lead, necessarily, to comitant strabismus. For example, excessive convergence innervation that flows equally to the muscles of both sides, i.e., both medial recti, would lead to an angle of squint which was equal during versions and when either eye took up fixation. Theoretically, of course, such excessive innervation to both medial recti would result in both eyes being overconverged, and this is exactly what happens at first. In the interest of seeing, however, one eye takes up fixation, and the other eye absorbs the excessive innervation and deviates inward. Esotropia on this basis is produced by excessive activity of the convergence mechanism or by deficient activity of the divergence mechanism, and the reverse is true for comitant divergent strabismus. By means of electromyography Breinin has shown this to be true for one type of divergent strabismus, so-called intermittent exotropia. During the outward deviation of one eye the lateral rectus on that side shows a large increment in its electrical activity which precedes diminution in the activity of the ipsilateral medial rectus. The eye which maintains fixation shows no change in its electromyographic activity from that previous to the deviation. The excessive divergence is absorbed by the lateral rectus of the deviating eye alone. The act of fixation shunts this excessive activity to one side entirely. We can now say positively that intermittent exotropia is due to excessive divergence innervation and is not due to diminution in convergence innervation or to structural changes.

It can be said with reasonable assurance that the same must be true for intermittent esotropia, although as yet there is no experimental evidence for this. Breinin's work in electromyography has shown conclusively that whenever an eye moves there is an increase in electrical activity in the muscles which work in that direction of gaze. An eye never moves because of inhibition of an antagonist muscle alone. Inhibition occurs along with increased activity in the antagonist muscle, as predicted by Sherrington. Hence, we can take it for granted that in intermittent esotropia, whenever an eye breaks from fixation and deviates inward, increased electrical activity takes place in the medial rectus of that eye. We can also say that, whenever there is an imbalance in electrical activity between antagonist muscles, the eye will move. This leads at once to an important question.

What is the situation regarding the electrical activity in the muscles in constant esotropia or exotropia? Is there constant excessive innervation in the appropriate muscles that holds the eye in the deviated position? It can be stated categorically that no excessive innervation will be found in the deviated eye in excess of that which exists in the primary position of gaze; otherwise the eye would move because whenever there is excessive innervation in one muscle over and above that in its antagonist, the eye moves. It would be almost unthinkable that under these conditions both the medial and lateral rectus muscles of the deviated eye would show increased electrical activity.

If we postulate that under conditions of *intermittency* there is increased activity when an eye temporarily turns in or out while in *constant* deviations there is no increased activity, we must assume that at some time this increased activity which brought about the deviation disappears. In place of the excessive innervation which originally caused one eye to turn in, some structural change which now holds it there must have occurred.

We may summarize as follows. Intermittency in comitant strabismus is proof that the squint is still in the neurogenic stage. When it has become constant, it has reached the structural or mechanical stage. Most of the disagreement between those who insist on the neurogenic origin of comitant strabismus and those who claim it is due to structural changes can be resolved by assuming that they are looking at different stages of the same disease. This could be due to the fact that the period of intermittency is usually quite short. In accommodative esotropia, e.g., which no one, even the most ardent advocate of the mechanical school, doubts is of neurogenic origin (excessive convergence due to accommodative effort), the squint has become constant by the time most of the children with this disorder are seen. It is rare to see a child in the stage of intermittency. In the stage of intermittency glasses alone will always cure the condition; in the early stages of constant squint they will usually effect a cure, but if the squint has persisted for a long time before treatment is instituted, glasses alone seldom correct the condition. How long is a long time? It varies with different children, but generally squint which has persisted constantly for over a year before glasses are prescribed will have to have surgical intervention.

The structural changes now prevent cure by glasses, and mechanical change in the position of the muscles becomes necessary. In the majority of patients with intermittent exotropia we have to resort to surgery because we do not know what the neurogenic factor precipitating the excessive divergence innervation is. In the early stages of this disease, however, almost all of these children can be cured by retroplacement of the lateral recti. Later, when structural changes have set in, convergence begins to be interfered with because of these structural changes, and the convergence near point becomes remote. A convergence insufficiency is added now to the divergence excess. By this time, retroplacement of the lateral recti muscles will not succeed in curing the squint, and resection of the medial recti muscles will be necessary as well.

What about those forms of comitant strabismus in which the squint is congenital or has set in shortly after birth? It is difficult to tell in many of these patients when the squint actually began. Occasionally the eyes are crossed at birth, but frequently the history indicates that the eyes were straight at birth and began turning a few months later. In these patients we do not know what forced the eyes out of alignment. The increase in esophoria for distance under the influence of anoxia has been described previously (p. 494). Two of our subjects developed temporary comitant esotropia at 18,000 feet for half an hour without oxygen. A number of different workers have confirmed this increase in convergence tonus resulting from the influence of anoxia or alcohol. It cannot be supposed that anoxia is the cause of the esotropia in these children with congenital or early developing esotropia. There are probably many different disturbances during early childhood which, like anoxia, might affect the convergence mechanism, but at present we are entirely ignorant of them. Esotropia occurs quite frequently with cerebral diplegia, as mentioned, and is believed to be due to anoxia occurring at birth or some time prior and not to birth trauma, as believed formerly.

If one grants the possibility that comitant squint is likewise of neurogenic origin of unknown factors, it is conceivable that the structural changes set the squint early because of the early age at which the visual axes are deviated. Surgery is always necessary for these patients, if only for cosmetic reasons, but it is more difficult to achieve a functional cure because the optomotor reflexes have never had a chance to develop in these children. In children whose squint begins later in life, say at the age of 3 years, the optomotor reflexes have developed to the point that if surgical intervention is necessary even a crude alignment of the visual axes is all that is required to secure bifoveal fixation. The fusional reflexes will make good any small deficiency in alignment. If the optomotor reflexes have not developed, the surgery itself must achieve this perfect alignment in order to secure bifoveal fixation, and this fortunate outcome does not always happen.

Scobee, it will be recalled, first assumed that children with congenital comitant esotropia had suffered paralysis of the ocular muscles from which they had partially or completely recovered, leaving them with a comitant angle of squint. Later he changed to the conviction that, in 90% of these patients the condition was caused by primary structural changes in the muscles and fascia. He spoke of abnormal check ligaments, muscle footplates, etc.[207] The structural changes which he pictured as the primary cause of the squint have not been found by most surgeons, although admittedly it is a difficult matter either to confirm or deny such abnormalities in the usual surgical exposure. Scobee's conception of structural changes differs from the conception of structural changes just described in that to him the structural changes were primary. The changes just postulated are secondary and occur as a sequel to a neurogenic disturbance. It must now be asked what these structural changes are and why they cannot be detected at operation.

The structural changes must be of a nature to produce neither a change in electrical activity nor a histologic change in the muscles. To my knowledge, in ordinary comitant strabismus no histologic changes in any muscles have been found on biopsy. There is a condition termed contracture (about which we understand little) in which under certain conditions changes occur in the skeletal muscles of the body. The term as it is used generally is a loose one and implies nothing but shortening of the muscles. The specific term *contracture,* when applied to muscle tissue, is a condition in which tension and shortening develop for a long time, without tetanus, i.e., no summation of the effects of repetitive stimulation. It is a reversible process and therefore differs from cadaveric rigidity due to coagulation of the muscle proteins. During contracture the muscle shows increased metabolism, with heat production above the resting level, with glycosis, and with formation of lactic acid. The muscle fibers during contracture are electronegative in contrast to muscle fibers in the resting state. According to Houssay, a contracture differs from normal contraction in two ways.

"(a) There is no propagated excitatory disturbance with a corresponding spike potential, whether the whole fiber or only part of it is in contracture; (b) the intensity of contracture is graded in respect to the strength of the stimulus; it is not an all-or-nothing phenomenon. Experimental contractures can be produced in isolated or intact muscles in many ways. Repetitive supramaximal stimulation produces a contraction followed by incomplete relaxation, the degree of contracture being dependent on the strength of the stimulus."*

It is obvious that, except for being shortened, a muscle in contracture cannot be distinguished grossly from a normal resting one, so that surgical exposure of the muscle would show nothing wrong with it. Electromyography, likewise, would not show abnormal firing since contracture is not accompanied by a corresponding spike potential. Other ways, such as histochemical examination, will have to be found to determine whether the structural changes just proposed are of this nature. Some method should be worked out to quantitate the resistance of the individual muscles to stretch and in constant squint to see whether these muscles do or do not show contracture.

Incomitant strabismus

When the angle of squint is incomitant, paralysis of a muscle should be suspected. Whenever an ocular muscle is paralyzed, there immediately develops an embarrassment in the movement of that eye in the direction of action of the paralyzed muscle. This produces incomitant squint; i.e., the angle of squint varies with different directions of gaze, becoming greater as the eyes are moved into the field of action of the paralyzed muscle and smaller as they are moved away from that field of activity.

The angle of squint in any one position of gaze will depend upon whether the paralyzed or the nonparalyzed eye is used

---

*From Houssay, B. A.: Human biology, ed. 2, New York, 1955, McGraw-Hill Book Co., Inc.

as the fixating eye. If the nonparalyzed eye is fixating, the angle of squint will be determined by the degree of the paralysis; therefore it will be small if there is slight paresis and large if the muscle is totally paralyzed. The angle of squint is then due solely to the inability of the paralyzed muscle to keep that eye in step with its fellow.

If the paralyzed eye is the fixating eye, another important factor which increases the angle of squint is added. This is the overaction of the yoke muscle in the non-paralyzed eye. As has been stated previously (p. 384), every voluntary impulse for ocular movements arising in the cortex goes equally to the muscles of both eyes concerned in the movement. This is called Hering's law. When one looks to the right, equal innervation is sent simultaneously to the right lateral rectus and to the left medial rectus. The amount of innervation sent down from the motor cortex is determined by the fixating eye.

For example, in a patient with paralysis of the right lateral rectus muscle if the left eye is the fixating eye, the normal amount of innervation will be sent to the muscles on both sides when he looks to the right. Both the left medial rectus and the right lateral rectus will receive the necessary innervation required to move the left eye to the desired position. The right lateral rectus, being paretic, will cause the right eye to lag behind the movement of the left and will thereby create an angle of squint. If, however, the right, paralyzed, eye is the fixating eye, the amount of innervation sent down from the cortex will be determined by the degree to which this muscle is paretic. The weaker it is, the more power it will need from the cortex. This will go equally and simultaneously to the left medial rectus, according to Hering's law. Hence, the left eye will turn too far to the right

and will overshoot the right eye. The left medial rectus is said to overact. The angle of squint will be due to the lagging behind of the right eye plus the excessive movement of the left eye. The angle of squint will now be greater than when the nonparalyzed eye was the fixating eye. This is the principle of secondary deviation, which is always greater than the primary deviation in paralysis of an ocular muscle.

The classic signs of paralysis of an ocular muscle are based on the variations in the action of each of the muscles in the different positions of gaze. It has been demonstrated previously that when the eyes are in the primary position contraction of the superior rectus (e.g.) will effect elevation of the globe mainly. To this must be added a slight degree of intorsion and adduction (Fig. 128, *A*). When the globe is abducted 23 degrees so that the visual line coincides with the muscle plane, its contraction will produce elevation alone (Fig. 128, *B*). If the globe is adducted 67 degrees from the primary position (a degree of adduction never attained normally), contraction of the muscle produces intorsion and adduction (Fig. 128, *C*). The muscle's chief effect on the globe in one position of gaze becomes secondary or disappears altogether in another position, whereas a previous subsidiary effect now becomes predominant. This applies not only to the superior and inferior recti, but also to the two obliques.

It is a simple matter to predict the type of strabismus and the diplopia fields which should be present in paralysis of any particular muscle, based on a knowledge of its action. This picture is based, however, on the effect which this paralyzed muscle has on the movements of this eye alone and does not take into account the fact that its effect is never confined to its own action alone, but in-

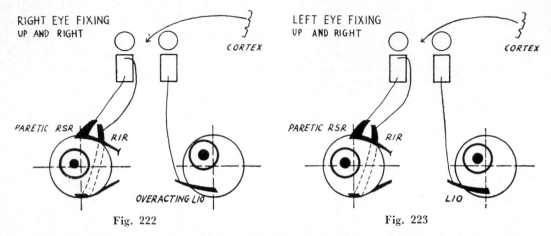

Fig. 222

Fig. 223

Fig. 222. Diagram showing secondary deviation of the left eye on looking up and to the right when the right superior rectus is paralyzed and the right eye is fixing. Excessive innervation is sent down from the cortex to both the right superior rectus and the left inferior oblique, causing overaction of the latter. Compare with Fig. 223, in which is shown the nonparalyzed eye fixing.

Fig. 223. Looking up and to the right when the nonparalyzed left eye is fixing. The primary deviation is less than the secondary deviation shown in Fig. 222.

fluences other muscles in the same eye and under certain conditions other muscles in the opposite eye as well. This is always true when the paralyzed eye is used for fixation, following Hering's law of voluntary movements. To recapitulate, using a vertically acting muscle as an example, when a subject voluntarily moves his eyes up and to the right, equal innervation is sent to the right superior rectus and to the left inferior oblique. Equal inhibition is sent also to the corresponding antagonists of these muscles, according to Sherrington's law of reciprocal innervation. When a muscle is paretic, it requires more nervous energy to effect its movement than if it were normal. In patients with a paralyzed muscle, therefore, excessive innervation is sent not only to the paretic muscle, but also to the yoke muscle in the opposite eye, provided that the paralyzed eye is the fixating eye. If the right superior rectus is paretic and the patient looks up and to the right with the right eye fixating, excessive innervation will be sent to this muscle and to the left inferior oblique. This latter muscle will, therefore, overact so that the left eye will move up too far (Fig. 222). If the left eye is the fixating eye, however, the strabismus will be due entirely to the lag in elevation of the right eye. Under these conditions, the angle of strabismus will be less than when the right eye was fixating (Fig. 223). This is the principle that underlies secondary deviation, which is one of the causes of incomitance in paralytic squint. Incomitance in the angle of squint in paralysis of a muscle is due to two factors: (1) failure of the paralyzed muscle to move the eye in the field of its action and (2) overaction of the yoke muscle when the paralyzed eye fixates.

In all paralyses of sufficient severity to break up binocular vision, i.e., fusion, the eyes become dissociated, and either the paralyzed or the nonparalyzed eye is used for fixation habitually. White[209] stated that in congenital paralysis the paralyzed eye was nearly always the fixating eye.

Many different factors determine which eye will be used to fixate. Visual acuity is sometimes a factor, and the eye with the better acuity may be chosen. This is not always the case, however, and one may see patients in whom the paralyzed eye is used for fixation in spite of the fact that it has poorer vision than the nonparalyzed eye. Fixation with the paralyzed eye increases the strabismus due to secondary deviation. Some authors believe that this is the reason why fixation is carried out by the paralyzed eye so frequently since this increases the distance between the double images and therefore makes them less annoying to the patient.

In addition to the effect on the yoke muscle when the paralyzed eye is used for fixation, the effect on the antagonists of the paralyzed muscle must be considered also. Whenever there is paralysis of a muscle, the antagonist in the same eye is able to move the globe in its direction of action with less effort than it

normally does since it lacks the restraining effect of the normal tonus of the paralyzed muscle. This may seem to deny the existence of reciprocal innervation, but does not do so, actually. The relaxation which a muscle undergoes during contraction of its antagonist is only partial, and considerable tonus is still retained. This is lost, however, when the muscle is actually paralyzed. For example, if the right superior rectus is paralyzed, the right inferior rectus can move the eye down and to the right now with less than normal effort. When a person uses the right eye for fixation down and to the right, the innervation required for the right inferior rectus will be subnormal. A subnormal stimulus is sent, therefore, to the yoke muscle of the right inferior rectus, i.e., the left superior oblique, and this muscle will underact, with the result that the left eye will not be carried down as far as it should be (Fig. 224). When the nonparalyzed left eye is used

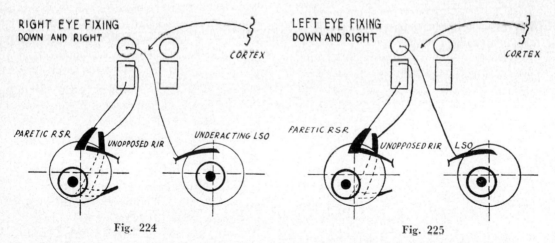

Fig. 224   Fig. 225

Fig. 224. Looking down and to the right. The right superior rectus is paretic and the right eye is fixing. The right inferior rectus moves the eye down with less than the normal amount of innervation since the opposing tonus of the right superior rectus is gone. Less innervation is sent to the left superior oblique, therefore, and the left eye fails to move down and to the right as far as it should. Compare with Fig. 225.

Fig. 225. Looking down and to the right. The nonparalyzed eye is fixing and moves down normally. There is no underaction of the left superior oblique.

to fixate in looking down and to the right, both eyes will move down almost equally well and there will be little strabismus (Fig. 225). Therefore, when the right eye is used to fixate, the left superior oblique will appear to be paralyzed during gaze down and to the right. Chavasse has called this inhibitional palsy of the contralateral antagonist. This term is confusing as well as burdensome. Since the lessened movement depends on the underaction of a muscle (due to the principles embodied in Hering's law) in the same manner that the overaction of a yoke muscle produces excessive movement, it is simpler to call it underaction. This term can hardly be misunderstood.

It is evident that the strabismus that occurs in various positions of gaze will be quite different, depending upon whether the nonparalyzed or the paralyzed eye is habitually used for fixation. A comparison may be made between the strabismus present when the nonparalyzed eye is used to fixate and that present when the paralyzed eye is fixating. Paralysis of the left superior oblique muscle may be used as an example. In Fig. 226 are shown the positions assumed by each eye in the primary and the oblique directions of gaze when the nonparalyzed right

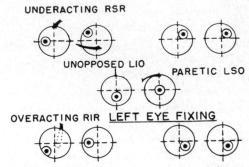

UNDERACTING RSR

UNOPPOSED LIO

PARETIC LSO

OVERACTING RIR LEFT EYE FIXING

Fig. 227. Drawing showing the angle of strabismus in the primary oblique positions of gaze in paralysis of the left superior oblique muscle when the paralyzed left eye is habitually used for fixation. Compare with Fig. 225.

eye is used for fixation. In the primary position, the left eye is too high due to the loss of tonus in the left superior oblique. The greatest vertical separation between the eyes occurs when the gaze is down and to the right due to the weakness of the left superior oblique. In all other oblique positions of gaze, the eyes are in alignment. The strabismus in the various positions of gaze when the left paralyzed eye is used for fixation is shown in Fig. 227. The greatest separation of the visual axes will be in gaze down and to the right, and the angle of squint in this position will be greater than when the nonparalyzed eye was the fixating eye. During gaze up and to the left and down and to the left, the eyes will be in alignment, but when the gaze is directed up and to the right, the strabismus will increase again. The right eye fails to move up as far as it should in this direction while the left eye is fixating. This is due to the fact that the left inferior oblique can move the left eye up and to the right with less innervation than normal since the left superior oblique is paralyzed. A weaker innervation, therefore, goes to the right superior rectus which underacts, and this eye fails to move upward to the

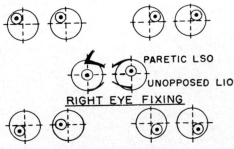

PARETIC LSO

UNOPPOSED LIO

RIGHT EYE FIXING

Fig. 226. Drawing showing the angle of strabismus in the primary and oblique positions of gaze in paralysis of the left superior oblique strabismus in muscle when the nonparalyzed right eye is used for fixation.

full extent. It will lag behind and appear to be paralyzed. If the left eye is covered, the right eye will be able to move up to its full extent, showing that it is not really paretic.

Whenever a superior oblique is paralyzed and this eye is used for fixation, one may expect to find underaction of the superior rectus of the opposite eye. Similarly, if a superior rectus muscle is paralyzed in one eye, one will expect to find the opposite superior oblique underacting when the eye with the paretic superior rectus is used for fixation. One muscle is actually paretic, whereas the other is underacting, according to Hering's law.

The differential diagnosis of which muscle is paralyzed and which one is merely underacting is somewhat beyond the scope of this book. Since some of the differential points are based on physiologic principles, they will be considered briefly.

The most characteristic sign of paralysis of a superior oblique muscle is head tilt. Nearly all these patients carry the head tilted toward one shoulder. Although this occurs to a lesser degree with paralysis of a superior rectus muscle, it is pronounced only in paralysis of one of the oblique muscles. The reason for this may be stated as follows.

When the eyes are in the primary position, paralysis of one of the oblique muscles produces marked tilting of the vertical meridian of the cornea of the affected eye and little up-or-down displacement. It has been shown previously (p. 368) that the superior oblique muscle is 100% effective in depressing the globe only when the eye is adducted 51 degrees. In the primary position, the effectiveness of the superior oblique as a depressor is approximately 43%, whereas its effectiveness as an intorter is 56%. If these values are compared with those for the superior

rectus, it is seen that in the primary position this muscle is 74% effective as an elevator and only 25% effective as an intorter.

Now the response by the body to a paralyzed ocular muscle is to compensate as far as possible for the disturbing effects of the diplopia produced. This can be accomplished either by suppressing the image of one eye or by holding the head in such a position that the diplopia is abolished or at least lessened. The position of the head is determined entirely by the action that the paralyzed muscle has in the primary position of gaze, for that position is the one assumed constantly during waking hours.

In the paralysis of a medial or a lateral rectus, the face is simply turned toward one or the other shoulder in order to overcome the diplopia since these muscles have no other action than horizontal rotation. The head, then, is always turned to the right or to the left so that the eye with the paralyzed muscle will not have to turn into its field of activity. The superior and inferior rectus muscles and the superior and inferior obliques, however, have both vertical action and torsion in the primary position of gaze by the amounts which have just been given. The head must be moved in such a manner as to compensate as far as possible for both these components or at least for that component which is the more important. (A discussion of the abducting and adducting actions of these muscles has been omitted purposely because their consideration would only complicate the understanding of the main problem. The superior rectus, e.g., is called an adductor, which is true in the primary position. As the eye is turned nasalward, the adducting power should increase, but if it is turned temporally and beyond 23 degrees, the action should change to abduction. In addition, the horizontal phorias may so alter the final picture when the eyes become dissociated that it would only confuse the issue to take this into account here.)

The vertical component can be compensated by elevating or depressing the chin. The torsional component must be taken care of by tilting the head toward one or the other shoulder. It has been shown previously (p. 456) that the muscles controlling torsion are under the influence of tonic impulses from the otolith apparatus, and when the head is tilted toward one shoulder, the vertical meridian of the eye on that side is intorted to keep it vertical. The vertical meridian of the opposite eye is extorted to keep it vertical.

If the head is tilted toward the right shoulder, e.g., the muscles which intort the right eye (superior rectus and superior oblique) contract; the muscles which extort the vertical meridian of the left eye (inferior rectus and inferior oblique) contract. The vertical meridians undergo levocycloversion and are kept upright.

If a muscle which produces torsion in the primary position is paralyzed, the vertical meridian of that eye will be tilted and will not be parallel to the vertical meridian of the opposite eye. In order to avoid this tilt, as well as the vertical deviation which occurs (if the superior oblique is paralyzed, the eye will be extorted and higher than the opposite eye, because of the unopposed tone of the inferior oblique and the compensating pull of the superior rectus of the same side), the head will be held in that position which brings the vertical meridian of the normal eye parallel with that of the paralyzed eye. This is accomplished by tilting the head toward the opposite shoulder. In this position the intorters of the paralyzed eye are relaxed; hence, in paralysis of the superior oblique muscle

the vertical meridians are brought into parallelism by tilting the head toward the opposite shoulder, and the up-and-down deviation is kept at a minimum.

Tilting of the head is marked, therefore, and is diagnostic of paralysis of an oblique muscle. It does occur with paralysis of a superior rectus muscle but to a much less extent.

The head is always tilted to the side opposite the paralyzed muscle. For example, in right hypertropia due to paralysis of either the right superior oblique or the left superior rectus if the right superior oblique is at fault, the head will be strongly tilted toward the left shoulder; if the left superior rectus is at fault, the head will be slightly tilted toward the right shoulder.

A third means of differentiation, which is present in both recent and long-standing paralysis of an oblique muscle but never in paralysis of the vertical rectus muscles, is the vertical movement of an eye with a paralyzed oblique muscle when the head is tilted by the examiner toward the shoulder of the *same* side as the paralyzed eye. If the right superior oblique is paralyzed and the head is tilted toward the right shoulder, the right eye will be seen to make a definite upward movement. Bielschowsky[210] called attention to this sign and stressed the subjective phenomenon which accompanies it, i.e., the increase in vertical diplopia. Since the majority of patients with vertical motor paralysis are children who frequently suppress one eye, diplopia fields often cannot be taken, and therefore the objective sign is of much more value.

The pathologic physiology which produces this vertical movement is as follows. Tilting the head toward the right shoulder sends an increase of tonic impulses to those muscles of the right eye which cause intorsion, i.e., the right superior oblique and the right superior rectus. Normally, these two muscles, contracting together by just the right amount, produce nothing but intorsion since their elevating and depressing actions on the globe neutralize one another. If the right superior oblique is paralyzed, the superior rectus works alone and produces some intorsion but also marked elevation of the globe since its upward movement is no longer prevented by the downward pull of the superior oblique muscle.

If the superior rectus is paralyzed and the head is tilted toward the shoulder of the same side, no upward movement of the globe is produced since the muscle which is most effective in producing intorsion is still intact (superior oblique). The necessary amount of intorsion is produced by the superior oblique alone, the superior rectus being contracted simultaneously merely to counterbalance the slight depressing action of the superior oblique as it contracts in the primary position. If any vertical movement of the globe results from this tilting procedure, it will be a slight downward movement of the eye due to the unopposed action of the superior oblique.

On the basis of these facts, one should be able to differentiate between paralysis of the superior oblique and paralysis of the superior rectus of the opposite side by using the following criteria.

1. One eye will be higher than the other when the eyes are in the primary position; i.e., there will be right or left hypertropia. If the paralysis is of the superior oblique muscle, it will be on the side of the higher eye. If the paralysis is of the superior rectus muscle, it will be on the side of the lower eye.

2. If the patient habitually carries the head tilted toward the shoulder of the side of the higher eye, the paralyzed muscle will be the superior rectus of the opposite eye. The tilting of the head will probably not be pronounced. If the head is habitually tilted toward the shoulder of the side of the lower eye, the paralyzed muscle is the opposite superior oblique. The tilting of the head will generally be pronounced.

3. If the examiner, having decided which eye has the paralyzed muscle, tilts the patient's head toward the shoulder of the same side as the paralyzed eye, this eye will be seen to make an upward movement if the superior oblique is paralyzed, but will not move upward if the superior rectus is paralyzed. If any vertical movement occurs, it will be a slight downward movement.

Diplopia

The disability produced by paralysis of an ocular muscle is twofold: (1) disfigurement of the patient by the angle of squint and (2) discomfort from the diplopia. The latter may disappear with the passage of time. This will depend partly upon the age at which the paralysis occurred. The earlier in life, the more likely is the patient to learn suppression of one image. The patient may also compensate partially for his double vision by postural changes of the head. Horizontal diplopia due to paralysis of a horizontally acting muscle is easily overcome by turning the face into the field of action of the paralyzed muscle. Vertical diplopia, caused by paralysis of one of the vertical rectus muscles, is less easily overcome by elevating or depressing the chin. Torsional diplopia due to paralysis of one of the obliques, especially the superior oblique, can be overcome only by tilting the head on the shoulder. This is an uncomfortable posture to maintain. In spite of this, head tilt is such a common accompaniment of superior oblique paralysis that it is almost diagnostic of the condition. The patient adopts a compromise posture, consisting of a tilt of the head to the opposite shoulder (tilt to the right shoulder in paralysis of the left superior oblique and vice versa) plus depression of the chin and some turning of the face away from the eye with the paralyzed muscle.

Torsional diplopia is by far the most annoying of the three kinds of diplopia because the images are seldom sufficiently separated from one another that one can be easily suppressed. Horizontal diplopia is the least annoying, especially if the paralysis is only partial, as the patient can usually maintain single binocular vision by turning the face toward the paralyzed side. If the paralysis is complete, and if contracture of the antagonist has occurred, the double images may be so widely separated that one may be easily ignored.

Interpretation of diplopia fields. Diplopia or double vision is defined as seeing two images of the same object simultaneously, each located in a different direction of space. The sensory factors which produce diplopia are discussed on pp. 847 to 853. In this section we will consider the motor factors which determine the character of the diplopia, the result of which enable us to make a diagnosis of the muscle or muscles paralyzed.

The separation of the double images depends upon the angle of strabismus. When the eyes are turned away from the field of action of a paralyzed muscle and the visual lines intersect at the object of regard so that there is no squint angle, no diplopia will be present. As the eyes are turned into the field of action of the paralyzed muscle and the angle of strabismus increases, the separation of the double images increases. The character of the diplopia field when the eyes are turned in the different directions of gaze is therefore determined by the normal action of the paralyzed muscle, and if we know the normal action of each of the ocular muscles, we should be able to diagnose the paralysis of each. This is not strictly true since other things besides paralysis of a muscle may cause limitation of movement of an eye. For example, contracture of an antagonist muscle such as the inferior rectus will simulate paralysis of a superior rectus. One cannot from

---

Fig. 228. Diplopia fields of paralysis of each of the oculorotary muscles of the right eye. The field in each case is presented as seen by the patient. That is, the right side of each field is the patient's right side, and the left side is the patient's left side. In each field the gray figure is the image from the right eye, and the black figure is the image from the left eye.

A. Paralysis of right lateral rectus. Homonymous horizontal diplopia increases on dextroversion.

B. Paralysis of right medial rectus. Crossed horizontal diplopia increases on levoversion.

C. Paralysis of right inferior oblique. Vertical diplopia increases on looking up. Peripheral image belongs to the right eye. The widest separation occurs on looking up and left.

D. Paralysis of right superior oblique. Vertical diplopia occurs on looking down. Peripheral image belongs to the right eye. Vertical separation is greatest on looking down and left.

E. Paralysis of right superior rectus. Vertical diplopia occurs on looking up. Peripheral image belongs to the right eye. Vertical separation of images increases on looking up and right.

F. Paralysis of right inferior rectus. Vertical diplopia occurs on looking down. Peripheral image belongs to the right eye. Greatest separation of images occurs on looking down and right.

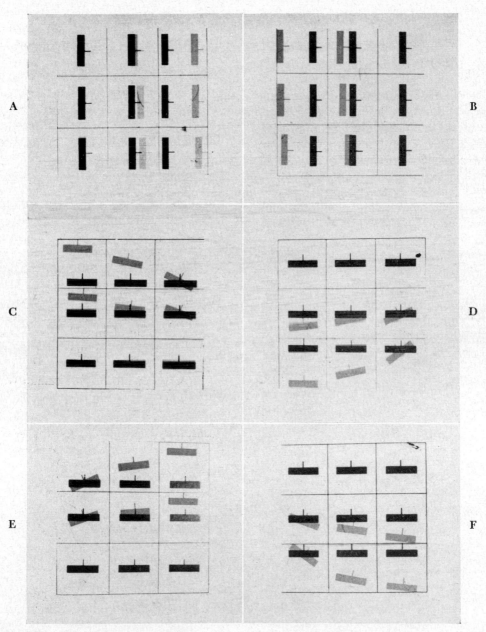

Fig. 228. For legend see opposite page.

a diplopia field alone say that this or that muscle is actually paralyzed, but only that the diplopia field in this particular patient is the kind of field one expects to get in paralysis of that muscle.

The action of each of the ocular muscles has been given, based on vector analyses and clinical experience. Since these are known, or at least are thought to be correctly known, the diplopia fields which one should obtain in paralysis of each of these muscles have been diagrammed as shown in Fig. 228, *A* to *F* and are accepted as standard. The analysis of such a field is a simple matter since the separation of the images increases characteristically when the eyes are moved into the field of gaze where the muscle is mechanically best able to perform rotation of the globe around any fixed axis.

Elevation of the globe is carried out best by the superior rectus when the globe is abducted and best by the inferior oblique when the globe is adducted. Vertical separation of the double images which is greatest in eyes up and right implicates either the right superior rectus or the left inferior oblique. Torsional diplopia that increases in eyes up and right implicates either the right inferior oblique or the left superior rectus.

In practice, however, diplopia fields often do not conform with the theoretical standards. This is particularly true in paralyses of the vertically acting muscles. The diplopia fields from purely horizontally acting muscles are usually those shown in Fig. 228, *A* and *B*. Right lateral rectus paralysis shows horizontal diplopia that increases on looking to the right and is homonymous. Left medial rectus paralysis shows horizontal diplopia that increases on looking to the right and is crossed. Paralyses of the vertically acting muscles frequently yield diplopia fields which do not follow the expected pattern and may

be confusing at first glance (see discussion of atypical diplopia fields, p. 540). In analyzing a diplopia field the following points should be observed.

Practical points in taking diplopia fields. The following factors are of practical consideration.

1. Make sure that the diplopia of which the patient complains is not physiologic diplopia. This always concerns changes in gaze from near to far and vice versa. While looking at a distant object, all other objects closer at hand appear double and vice versa.

2. If the diplopia is not obviously incomitant, it may be merely large heterophoria which has become manifest.

3. If the diplopia is purely horizontal, no difficulty should be encountered. Bilateral lateral rectus paralyses do occur but should not be confusing. Divergence paralysis may cause some confusion. The description of the characteristic diplopia fields begins on p. 536 and they are illustrated in Fig. 228.

4. If there is a combination of vertical and horizontal diplopia, disregard the horizontal element entirely and pay attention only to the vertical element. Paralysis of a vertically acting muscle will dissociate the eyes sensorially so that any pre-existing horizontal phoria will become manifest. This may confuse the picture. For example, in paralysis of a superior oblique there should be uncrossed (homonymous) diplopia as part of the picture, since the superior oblique is an abductor and the eyes should therefore be turned in. However, if the patient happens to have large exophoria, the eyes may be turned out when dissociated, producing crossed horizontal diplopia.

5. The more peripheral image belongs to the eye with the paralyzed or underacting muscle. This makes it easy to spot the eye affected. If both eyes seem to be affected, it is probable that a muscle in one is paralyzed while a muscle in the other is merely underacting.

6. Diplopia fields which suggest ocular muscle paralysis can be produced by other conditions and do not of themselves enable one to state positively that a muscle is paralyzed.

7. If an ocular muscle is only slightly paretic, the fusional reflex may keep the eyes in alignment and either prevent diplopia or mask it. For this reason whenever the diplopia field seems to change while it is being taken, and the patient's responses vary markedly, it is better to keep one eye constantly under cover to dissociate the eyes completely, removing the cover only long enough in each diagnostic position to observe the distance between the two images and then covering again.

Diplopia fields due to paralysis of more than one muscle. The most common diplopia field involving true paralysis of more than one ocular muscle is that due to a third nerve palsy, involving all of the ocular muscles except the lateral rectus and the superior oblique. The next most common is that due to paralysis of upward movement of one eye. In many cases this is due to actual paralysis of both the superior rectus and the inferior oblique muscles, but contracture of an inferior rectus muscle due to the ophthalmopathic type of Graves' disease or chronic orbital myositis may give rise to the same picture. If ptosis is present, the diagnosis is usually easy. Paralysis of downward movement in one eye may also occur due presumably to involvement of the inferior rectus and superior oblique. Although the diplopia fields strongly suggest paralysis of these muscles of either upward or downward gaze, we cannot be sure that the muscles are actually paralyzed. Nor do we have any idea where a single lesion might be placed in order to catch the nerves supplying these muscles. The modern scheme of arrangement of the nuclei of origin of the ocular muscles supplied by the third nerve does not help us in this respect since neither the muscles of upward gaze nor downward gaze in each eye are thought to originate

Table 50. *Comparison of classic representation of ocular muscles supplied by third nerve with modern concept of Warwick*

	Bernheimer-Brouwer scheme	Results of Warwick
Mode of representation	Rostrocaudal chain of centers	Rostrocaudally extended columns
Levator	Most rostral center	Caudal central nucleus (confined to caudal third)
	Direct nerve fibers	Bilateral innervation
Rectus superior	Rostral center	Center in caudal two thirds only
	Direct nerve fibers	Nerve fibers all crossed
Rectus medialis	Center in Perlia's nucleus	No
	Direct and crossed (?) nerve fibers	Nerve fibers all direct
Rectus inferior	Nerve fibers all crossed	Nerve fibers all direct
Obliquus inferior	Nerve fibers largely crossed, but some perhaps direct	Nerve fibers all direct

on the same side. For example, according to Warwick (Table 50) the superior rectus innervation is crossed, whereas the inferior oblique is direct; the inferior rectus is direct, whereas the superior oblique is crossed. Actually, the only certain arrangement is that of the superior oblique whose fibers we know emerge from the back of the brainstem and cross over to the opposite side.

Atypical diplopia fields. The type of diplopia field most commonly met in paralysis of a vertically acting muscle is one in which an elevator of one side and a depressor of the opposite side seem to be paralyzed. It is usually a combination of a superior rectus of one side and a superior oblique of the other side. Whenever this type of diplopia field is encountered, the physician should recognize that probably only one muscle is paralyzed, while the other is underacting because of some changes which take place in muscles other than the one actually paralyzed. This subject has been fully considered on pp. 529 to 533. The diplopia fields naturally follow the changes in squint angle. It should be pointed out that we are not sure just what these changes are due to. According to the theory usually accepted, the underaction of a superior rectus muscle on the right side in a patient with true paralysis of the left superior oblique should only occur when fixation is taken up by the left eye in looking up and to the right. This, however, is not the case. The underaction occurs regardless of which eye fixates. It might be due to contracture of the antagonist of the paralyzed muscle, in this case the inferior oblique. However, it would seem reasonable to expect the contractured left inferior oblique to have some effect on the position of the left eye in both looking up and to the left as well as on looking up and to the right.

We would therefore expect to find the left eye higher than the right in gaze up and left as well as in gaze up and right. This does not occur. Further, I have seen this secondary underaction of a superior rectus develop in the course of a few weeks and have found it already present in a patient with fresh paralysis of a superior oblique of only five days' duration.

The next most commonly seen diplopia field suggests paralysis of an inferior rectus on one side and an inferior oblique on the opposite side. It is much more difficult to tell which of these muscles is primarily paralyzed and which is underacting but not paralyzed than it is in the case of the superior rectus and superior oblique just described. Frequently we have no clue to this.

More complex is the type of diplopia field in which the primary pathologic disorder was probably paralysis of both elevators on one side or both depressors of one side in which the muscles of the other side underact, as just described. In paralysis of the superior rectus and inferior oblique of one side we will then see underaction of the opposite superior oblique and inferior rectus. The diplopia field looks as though four muscles were paralyzed.

The situation of the diplopia, likewise, varies in palsies of different muscles and is more or less annoying, depending upon the muscle affected. In ordinary life the eyes are used in a very limited field of fixation. This seldom extends more than 20 degrees above the horizon, about 30 degrees to either side of the primary position, and downward about 60 degrees below the horizon. When the object of regard lies outside these limits, the head is turned also, rather than the eyes alone. If the paralyzed muscle is one which includes this part of the field of fixation (e.g., the superior oblique which is called

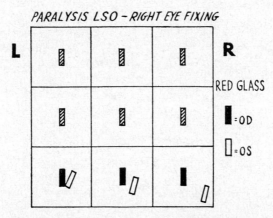

Fig. 229. Simplified diplopia fields of paralysis of the left superior oblique as given in textbooks and found in patients when the nonparalyzed eye is used for fixation. Compare with Fig. 230.

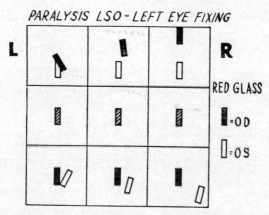

Fig. 230. Simplified diplopia field in paralysis of the left superior oblique muscle found in patients who habitually choose to fix with the paralyzed eye. The fields indicate paralysis of the left superior oblique and paralysis of the right superior rectus.

on especially for all close work of the eyes), the ensuing diplopia will be particularly distressing. A paralyzed inferior oblique or superior rectus, on the other hand, will not cause nearly so much discomfort since their field of action is well above the horizon and away from the important field of fixation.

Corresponding to the differences in the angle of strabismus in various positions of gaze, one finds differences in the diplopia fields, depending on whether the paretic or the nonparetic eye fixates. When the nonparalyzed eye is the fixating eye, the diplopia fields will indicate two paralyzed muscles. In Fig. 229 are shown the diplopia fields when the left superior oblique is paralyzed and the nonparalyzed right eye is the fixating eye. The diplopia fields which are encountered most frequently are shown in Fig. 230, suggesting paralysis of both the left superior oblique and the right superior rectus. The apparent involvement of the right superior rectus is due to underaction of this muscle and not to actual paralysis.

REFERENCES

1. Copper, A.: Introduction to clinical orbitonometry, Leiden, 1948, H. E. Stenfert Kroese.
2. Park, R., and Park, G.: The center of ocular rotation in the horizontal plane, Am. J. Physiol. **104:**545, 1933.
3. Verrijp, C.: Movements of the eyes. In Berens, C., editor: The eye and its diseases, Philadelphia, 1949, W. B. Saunders Co.
4. Quereau, J.: Some aspects of torsion, Arch. Ophth. **51:**783, 1954.
5. Quereau, J.: Rolling of the eye around its visual axis during normal ocular movements, Arch. Ophth. **53:**807, 1955.
6. Weale, R.: The problem of false torsion, Proc. Roy. Soc. Med. **52:**183, 1959.
7. Alpern, M.: Kinematics of the eye. In Davson, H., editor: The eye, vol. 3, New York, 1962, Academic Press, Inc., chap. III, pp. 15-27.
8. Krewson, W.: Action of the extraocular muscles, Tr. Am. Ophth. Soc. **48:**443, 1950.
9. Krewson, W.: Comparison of the oblique extraocular muscles, Arch. Ophth. **32:**204, 1944.
10. Chamberlain, W.: Ocular motility in the horizontal plane, Tr. Am. Ophth. Soc. **52:**800, 1954.
11. Gordon, O.: A study of primary and auxiliary medial ocular rotations, Tr. Am. Acad. Ophth. **58:**553, 1954.
12. Alpern, M.: In Davson, H., editor: The eye, New York, 1962, Academic Press, p. 38.
13. Boeder, P.: The cooperation of the extraocular muscles, Am. J. Ophth. **51:**469, 1961.
14. Boeder, P.: The cooperative action of extraocular muscles, Brit. J. Ophth. **46:**397, 1962.
15. Jampel, R., and Bloomgarden, C.: Individual extraocular muscle function from faradic stimulation of the oculomotor and trochlear nerves of the macaque, Invest. Ophthal. **2:**265, 1963.
16. Tour, R., and Asbury, T.: Overcorrection of esotropia following bilateral 5 mm. medial rectus recession, Tr. Pacific Coast Oto-Ophth. Soc. **38:**145, 1957.
17. Westheimer, G.: Mechanism of saccadic eye movements, Arch. Ophth. **52:**722, 1954.
18. Alpern, M., and Wolter, J.: The relation of horizontal saccadic and vergence movements, Am. J. Ophth. **56:**685, 1956.
19. Winton, F., and Bayliss, L.: Human physiology, ed. 3, Philadelphia, 1948, The Blakiston Division, McGraw-Hill Book Co., Inc., p. 348.
20. Brown, G., and Harvey, A.: Neuromuscular transmission in extrinsic muscles of the eye, J. Physiol. **99:**379, 1941.
21. Kato, T.: Über histologische Untersuchungen der Augenmuskeln von Menschen und Saugetieren, Zentralbl. ges. Ophth. **42:**28, 1939.
22. Woollard, H.: Innervation of ocular muscles, Tr. Ophth. Soc. U. Kingdom **57:** 84, 1937.
23. Laughlin, R.: Congenital fibrosis of the extraocular muscles, Am. J. Ophth. **41:** 432, 1956.
24. Hines, M.: Studies on the innervation of skeletal muscle, Am. J. Anat. **47:**1, 1931.
25. Hirano, N.: Histologische Untersuchungen über die Nervose Innervation der Menschlichen ausseren Augenmuskeln, Arch. Ophth. **142:**560, 1941.
26. Kappers, C., Huber, C., and Crosby, E.: The comparative anatomy of the nervous system of vertebrates, including man, New York, 1936, The Macmillan Co.
27. Daniel, P.: Spiral nerve endings in the extrinsic eye muscles of man, J. Anat. **80:** 189, 1946.
28. Boecke, J.: Nerve endings, motor and sensory. In Penfield, W., editor: Cytology and cellular pathology of the nervous system, vol. 1, New York, 1932, Paul B. Hoeber, Inc., p. 243.
29. Cooper, S., and Danish, P.: Muscle spindles in human extrinsic eye muscles, Brain **72:**1, 1949.
30. Sunderland, S.: A preliminary note on the presence of neuromuscular spindles in extrinsic ocular muscles in man, Anat. Rec. **103:**561, 1949.
31. Cooper, S., and Fillenz, M.: Afferent discharges in response to stretch from the extraocular muscles of the cat and monkey, J. Physiol. **127:**400, 1955.
32. Fillenz, M.: Responses in the brainstem of the cat to stretch of extrinsic ocular muscles, J. Physiol. **128:**182, 1955.
33. Wolter, J.: Morphology of the sensory nerve apparatus in striated muscle of the human eye, Arch. Ophth. **53:**201, 1955.

34. Björkman, A., and Wohlfart, G.: Faser-analyses der Oculomotorious, Tro-chlearis, und Abducens des Menschen und des N. abducens Verschiedener Tiere, Ztschr. mikr.-anat. Forsch. **39**:631, 1936.

35. Maleci, O.: Sul Rapporto Numerico tra le Cellule dei Nuclei di Origine e le fibre di nevri motori encefalici dell'uomo, con osservazioni sulle differenze qualita-tive delle dette fibre, Arch. Ital. anat. e embriol. **35**:559, 1936.

36. Harley, R.: Quantitative study of cells and fibers in nucleus; nerve complexes of fourth and sixth cranial nerves, Am. J. Ophth. **25**:1029, 1942.

37. Zotterman, Y.: Note on relation between conduction rate and fibre size in mam-malian nerves, Skandinav. Arch. Physiol. **77**:123, 1937.

38. Donaldson, G.: The diameter of the nerve fibers to the extrinsic eye muscles of the goat, Quart. J. Exper. Physiol. **45**:25, 1960.

39. Kupfer, C.: Motor innervation of extra-ocular muscle, J. Physiol. **153**:522, 1960.

40. Cooper, S., and Eccles, J.: Isometric responses of mammalian muscles, J. Physiol. **69**:377, 1930.

41. Björk, A.: Electrical activity of human extrinsic eye muscles, Experientia **8**:226, 1952.

42. Adler, F.: Pathologic physiology of stra-bismus, Arch. Ophth. **50**:19, 1953.

43. Jampolsky, A., Tamler, E., and Marg, E.: Artifacts and normal variations in human ocular electromyography, Arch. Ophth. **61**:402, 1959.

44. Verhoeff, F.: Problems concerning con-vergence, Tr. Am. Acad. Ophth. **52**:15, 1947.

45. Miller, J.: The electromyography of ver-gence movements, Arch. Ophth. **62**:790, 1959.

46. Scobee, R., and Green, E.: Center for ocular divergence; does it exist? Am. J. Ophth. **29**:422, 1946.

47. Breinin, G., and Moldaver, J.: Electro-myography of human extraocular mus-cles, Arch. Ophth. **54**:206, 1955.

48. Magee, A.: The electromyogram of the lateral rectus muscle, Am. J. Ophth. **41**: 275, 1956.

49. Duke-Elder, S.: New observations on the physiology of the extraocular muscles,

50. Duke-Elder, S., and Duke-Elder, P.: Contraction of the extrinsic muscles of the eye by choline and nicotine, Proc. Roy. Soc., London, **107B**:332, 1930.

51. Macri, F., and Grimes, P.: The effects of succinylcholine on the extraocular muscles and on the intraocular pressure, Am. J. Ophth. **44**:221, 1957.

52. Lincoff, H., Breinin, G., and DeVoe, A.: The effect of succinylcholine on the ex-traocular muscles, Am. J. Ophth. **43**: 440, 1957.

53. Fulton, J.: Muscular contraction and the reflex control of movement, Baltimore, 1926, Williams & Wilkins Co.

54. McCouch, G., and Adler, F.: Extra-ocular reflexes, Am. J. Physiol. **100**:78, 1932.

55. Adler, F.: Reciprocal innervation of ex-traocular muscles, Arch. Ophth. **3**:318, 1930.

56. Tamler, E., Marg, E., Jampolsky, A., and Nawratzki, I.: Electromyography of human saccadic eye movements, Arch. Ophth. **62**:657, 1959.

57. Tamler, E., Jampolsky, A., and Marg, E.: An electromyographic study of asym-metric convergence, Am. J. Ophth. **46**: 174, 1958.

58. Breinin, G.: The nature of vergence re-vealed by electromyography, Arch. Ophth. **54**:407, 1955.

59. Miller, J.: The electromyography of ver-gence movements, Arch. Ophth. **62**:790, 1959.

60. Tamler, E., Marg, E., and Jampolsky, A.: An electromyographic study of coactivity of human extraocular muscles in follow-ing movements, Arch. Ophth. **61**:270, 1959.

61. Tamler, E., Marg, E., and Jampolsky, A.: Electromyographic study of following movements of the eye between tertiary positions, Arch. Ophth. **62**:804, 1959.

62. Cooper, S., and Daniel, P.: Responses from the stretch receptors of the goat's extrinsic eye muscles with an intact motor innervation, Quart. J. Exper. Physiol. **42**:222, 1957.

63. Whitteridge, D.: The effect of stimula-tion of the intrafusal fibers on sensitivity to stretch of extraocular muscle spindles, Quart. J. Exper. Physiol. **44**:385, 1959.

Tr. Ophth. Soc. U. Kingdom **50**:181, 1930.

64. Irvine, S., and Ludvigh, E.: Is ocular proprioceptive sense concerned in vision? Arch. Ophth. **15**:1037, 1936.

65. Cooper, S., Daniel, P., and Whitteridge, D.: Afferent discharges from extraocular muscles, J. Physiol. **108**:41, 1949.

66. Cooper, S., Daniel, P., and Whitteridge, D.: Muscle spindles and other sensory endings in the extrinsic eye muscles, Brain **78**:564, 1955.

67. Breinin, G.: Electromyographic evidence for ocular muscle proprioception in man, Arch. Ophth. **57**:176, 1957.

68. Cooper, S., Daniel, P., and Whitteridge, D.: Nerve impulses in the brainstem of the goat, J. Physiol. **120**:471, 1953.

69. Creed, R., and Granit, R.: Observations on the retinal action potential with special reference to the response to intermittent stimulation, J. Physiol. **78**:419, 1933.

70. Cornsweet, T.: Determination of the stimuli for involuntary drifts and saccadic eye movements, J. Optic. Soc. America **46**:987, 1956.

71. Merton, P.: The accuracy of directing the eyes and the hand in the dark, J. Physiol. **156**:555, 1961.

72. Kerrer, E., and Stevens, H.: Response of negative after-images to passive motion of eyeball and bearing of these observations on visual perception of motion, Am. J. Physiol. **94**:611, 1930.

73. Mathews, B.: Response of single end organ, J. Physiol. **71**:64, 1931.

74. Penfield, W., and Erickson, T.: Epilepsy and cerebral localization, Springfield, Ill., 1941, Charles C Thomas, Publisher, p. 45.

75. Adler, F.: Pathologic physiology of convergent strabismus, Arch. Ophth. **33**:362, 1945.

76. Leopold, I.: Abstract of conferences delivered at the Academy of Ophthalmology and Otolaryngology (graduate lecture), 1946.

77. Breinin, G.: Electromyography—a tool in ocular and neurologic diagnosis, Arch. Ophth. **57**:161, 1957.

78. Björk, A.: Electromyographic studies of conditions involving mobility of the eye chiefly due to neurogenic paresis, Brit. J. Ophth. **38**:528, 1954.

79. Kamouchi, T.: Electromyogram of the palsied extraocular and levator muscles, Jap. J. Ophth. **1**:30, 1957.

80. Kennard, M., and Ectors, L.: Forced circling in monkeys following lesions of frontal lobes, J. Neurophysiol. **1**:45, 1938.

81. Kennard, M.: Alterations in response to visual stimuli following lesions of frontal lobe in monkeys, Arch. Neurol. & Psychiat. **41**:153, 1939.

82. Clark, G., and Lashley, K.: Visual disturbances following frontal ablations in monkey, Anat. Rec. **97**(supp. 10): 1947.

83. Chang, H., Ruch, T., and Ward, A.: Topographical representation of muscles in motor cortex of monkeys, J. Neurophysiol. **10**:39, 1947.

84. Hines, M.: In Bucy, P., editor: The precentral motor cortex, Urbana, Ill., 1944, University of Illinois Press.

85. Penfield, W., and Rasmussen, T.: The cerebral cortex of man, New York, 1950, The Macmillan Co., p. 75.

86. Spiegel, E.: Der Einfluss Labyrinthaner und Corticaler Reizung auf die Augenstelling nack Durchschneidung des hinteren Langsbundels, Zentralbl. ges. Ophth. **25**:406, 1931.

87. Spiegel, E.: Role of vestibular nuclei in cortical innervation of eye muscles, Arch. Neurol. & Psychiat. **29**:1084, 1933.

88. Lemmen, L., Davis, J., and Radner, L.: Observations on stimulation of the human frontal eye field, J. Comp. Neurol. **112**: 163, 1959.

89. Crosby, E. C.: Relations of brain centers to normal and abnormal eye movements in horizontal plane, J. Comp. Neurol. **99**: 468, 1953.

90. Claess, E.: Contribution a l'etude physiologique de la fonction visuelle; etude des centers oculomoteurs corticaux chez le chat non anesthesie, Arch. internat. physiol. **48**:238, 1939.

91. Hirasawa, D., and Kato, K.: Uber die Fasern, Insbesondere die Conticaler extrapyramidalen aus den Area 8 und 9 der Grosshirnride beim Affen, Folia anat. Japon. **13**:189, 1935.

92. Godolowski, W.: The subcortical centers for gaze and associated movements of the eyes, Prav. clin. Mal. Merv., Cracovia, 1936.

93. Sunderland, S.: The projection of the cerebral cortex on the pons and cerebellum in the macaque monkey, J. Anat. **74**: 201, 1940.

94. Smith, W.: In Bucy, P., editor: The precentral motor cortex, ed. 2, Urbana,

Ill., 1949, University of Illinois Press, p. 317.

95. Spiegel, E.: Physiopathology of voluntary and reflex innervation of ocular movements, Arch. Ophth. **8:**738, 1932.

96. Cogan, D. G.: Nystagmus. In Strabismus symposium, St. Louis, 1962, The C. V. Mosby Co., p. 114.

97. Hyde, J.: Effect of hindbrain lesions on conjugate horizontal eye movements in cats, Exper. Eye Res. **1:**206, 1962.

98. Spiegel, E., and Scala, N.: Ocular disturbances associated with experimental lesions of the mesencephalic central gray matter, with special reference to vertical ocular movements, Arch. Ophth. **18:** 614, 1937.

99. Apter, J.: Eye movements following strychnization of the superior colliculus of cats, J. Neurophysiol. **9:**73, 1946.

100. Szentagothai, J., and Schab, R.: A midbrain inhibitory mechanism of oculomotor activity, Acta Physiol. Acad. Sc. Hung. **9:**89, 1956.

101. Crosby, E., and Woodburne, R.: The nuclear pattern of the nontectal portions of the midbrain and isthmus in primates, J. Comp. Neurol. **99:**437, 1943.

102. Warwick, R.: The so-called nucleus of convergence, Brain **78:**92, 1955.

103. Fearing, F.: Reflex action, Baltimore, 1930, Williams & Wilkins Co.

104. Olmsted, J., Margutti, M., and Yanagisawa, K.: Adaptation to transposition of eye muscles, Am. J. Physiol. **116:**245, 1936.

105. Holmes, G.: The organization of the visual cortex in man, Proc. Roy. Soc., London, **132B:**348, 1945.

106. Leinfelder, P., and Black, N.: Experimental transposition of extraocular muscles in monkeys, Am. J. Ophth. **24:** 1115, 1941; Am. J. Ophth. **25:**974, 1942.

107. Verhoeff, F.: Transposition of extraocular muscles (letter to editor), Am. J. Ophth. **25:**227, 1942.

108. Szentagothai, J.: Die innere Gliederung des Oculomotorius Kernes, Arch. Psychiat. **115:**127, 1942.

109. Bender, M., and Weinstein, E.: Functional representation in oculomotor and trochlear nuclei, Arch. Neurol. & Psychiat. **49:**98, 1943.

110. Danis, P.: The functional organization of the third nerve nucleus in the cat, Am. J. Ophth. **31:**1122, 1948.

111. Henderson, J.: The anatomic basis for certain reflex and automatic eye movements, Am. J. Ophth. **32:**232, 1949.

112. Lashley, K.: The projection of the retina upon the primary optic centers in the rat, J. Comp. Neurol. **59:**341, 1934.

113. Crosby, E., and Henderson, J.: Mammalian and isthmus regions; fiber connections of the superior colliculus; pathways concerned in automatic eye movements, J. Comp. Neurol. **88:**53, 1948.

114. Magnus, R.: Physiology of posture, Lancet **2:**531, 1926.

115. Woellner, R., and Graybiel, A.: Counterrolling of the eyes and its dependence on the magnitude of gravitational or inertial force acting laterally on the body, J. Appl. Physiol. **14:**632, 1959.

116. Cogan, D.: Nystagmus. In Strabismus symposium, St. Louis, 1962, The C. V. Mosby Co., p. 116.

117. Szentagothai, J.: The elementary vestibulo-ocular reflex arc, J. Neurophysiol. **13:**395, 1950.

118. Szentagothai, J., and Schab, R.: A midbrain inhibitory mechanism of oculomotor activity, Acta Physiol. Acad. Sc. Hung. **9:**98, 1956.

119. DeKleyn, A.: Some remarks on vestibular nystagmus, Confinia., neurol. **2:**257, 1939.

120. McIntyre, A.: Quick component of nystagmus, J. Physiol. **97:**8, 1939.

121. Merton, P.: Compensatory rolling movements of the eye, Proceedings of the Physiology Society, Mar. 20, 1956, J. Physiol. **132:**25, 1956.

122. Lorente de No, R.: Vestibulo-ocular reflex arc, Arch. Neurol. & Psychiat. **30:** 245, 1933.

123. Davies, T., and Merton, P.: Recording compensatory rolling of the eyes, J. Physiol. **140:**27, 1958.

124. McCouch, G., Deering, I., and Ling, T.: Location of receptors for tonic neck reflexes, J. Neurophysiol. **14:**191, 1951.

125. Cooper, S., Daniel, P., and Whitteridge, D.: Afferent impulses in oculomotor nerve, from extrinsic eye muscles, J. Physiol. **113:**463, 1951. (See Whitteridge, D.: Central control of eye movements, Handbook of physiology, sect. 1, vol. II, p. 1107.)

126. Roelofs, C., and van der Bend, J.: Betrachtungen und Untersuchungen über

den Optokinetischen Nystagmus, Arch. Augenh. **102**:551, 1930.

127. Brecher, G.: Die Optokinetische Auslosung von Augenrollung und Rotatorischen Nystagmus, Arch. ges. Physiol. **234**:13, 1934.

128. Goldmann, H.: Objektive Sehscharfenbestimmung, Ophthalmologica **105**:240, 1943.

129. Dodge, R., Travers, R., and Fox, J.: Optic nystagmus, Arch. Neurol. & Psychiat. **24**:21, 1930.

130. Cogan, D.: Neurology of the ocular muscles, ed. 2, Springfield, Ill., 1956, Charles C Thomas, Publisher, p. 138.

131. Brecher, G.: Optisch ausgeloste Augenund Körperreflexe am Kaninchen, Z. vergl. Physiol. **23**:374, 1936.

132. Pasik, P., Pasik, T., and Krieger, H.: Effect of cerebral lesions upon optokinetic nystagmus in monkeys, J. Neurophysiol. **22**:297, 1959.

133. Smith, K.: The neural centers concerned in optic nystagmus, Am. J. Physiol. **126**:631, 1939.

134. Reinecke, R., and Cogan, D.: Standardization of objective visual acuity measurements, Arch. Ophth. **60**:418, 1958.

135. Gorman, J., Cogan, D., and Gellis, S.: An apparatus for grading the visual acuity of infants on the basis of optokinetic nystagmus, Pediatrics **19**:1088, 1957.

136. Hines, M.: Recent contributions to localization of vision in central nervous system, Arch. Ophth. **28**:913, 1942.

137. Carmichael, E., Dix, M., and Hallpike, C.: Lesions of the cerebral hemispheres and their effects upon optokinetic nystagmus and caloric nystagmus, Brain **77**:23, 1954.

138. Kestenbaum, A.: Clinical methods of neuro-ophthalmologic examination, New York, 1946, Grune & Stratton, Inc.

139. McDonald, P.: Bilateral thrombosis of posterior calcarine arteries with sparing of macular vision, Arch. Ophth. **29**:92, 1943.

140. Spiegel, E., and Somer, I.: Neurology of the eye, ear, nose and throat, New York, 1944, Grune & Stratton, Inc.

141. Crosby, E., and Henderson, J.: Mammalian midbrain and isthmus regions; fiber connections of superior colliculus; pathways concerned in automatic eye movements, J. Comp. Neurol. **88**:53, 1948.

142. Carmichael, E., Dix, M., and Hallpike, C.: Lesions of the cerebral hemispheres and their effect upon optokinetic and caloric nystagmus, Brain **77**:345, 1954.

143. Ogle, K., and Ellerbrock, V.: Cyclofusional movements, Arch. Ophth. **36**:700, 1946.

144. Tait, E.: Fusional vergence, Am. J. Ophth. **32**:1223, 1949.

145. Alpern, M.: In Davson, H., editor: The eye, vol. III, New York, 1962, Academic Press, Inc., p. 100.

146. Westheimer, G., and Mitchell, A.: Eye movement responses to convergence stimuli, Arch. Ophth. **55**:848, 1956.

147. Alpern, M., and Ellen, P.: A quantitative analysis of the horizontal movements of the eyes in the experiment of Johannes Mueller, Am. J. Ophth. **42**:(pt. 2) 296, 1956.

148. Nauheim, J.: A preliminary investigation of retinal locus as a factor in fusion, Arch. Ophth. **58**:122, 1957.

149. Jampel, R.: Representation of the near response on the cerebral cortex of the macaque, Am. J. Ophth. **48**:(pt. 2) 573, 1959.

150. Christoferson, K., and Ogle, K.: The effect of homatropine on the accommodation-convergence association, Arch. Ophth. **55**:779, 1956.

151. Charnwood, J.: An essay on binocular vision, London, 1950, Hatton Press, Ltd.

152. Ames, A., and Gliddon, G.: Ocular measurements, Tr. Sect. Ophth. A.M.A. p. 102, 1928.

153. Morgan, M.: Accommodation and its relationship to convergence, Arch. Ophth. **47**:745, 1952.

154. Ogle, K., and Prangen, A.: Further considerations of fixation disparity and the binocular fusion process, Am. J. Ophth. **34**:57, 1951.

155. Tait, E.: Textbook of refraction, Philadelphia, 1951, W. B. Saunders Co., p. 147.

156. Duke-Elder, S.: Textbook of ophthalmology, vol. IV: The neurology of vision, motor and optical anomalies, St. Louis, 1949, The C. V. Mosby Co., p. 3982.

157. Flom, M.: On the relationship between accommodation and accommodative

convergence, Am. J. Optom. **37:**517, 1960.

158. Martens, T., and Ogle, K.: Observations on accommodative convergence, Am. J. Ophth. **47:**455, 1959.

159. Alpern, M.: Vergence and accommodation. II: Is accommodative vergence related merely to the accommodative stimulus? Arch. Ophth. **60:**358, 1958.

160. Ogle, K., and Sabin, F.: The accommodation-convergence association; effects of neosynephrine, pilocarpine and physostigmine, Quoted in Christoferson, K., and Ogle, K.: The effect of homatropine on the accommodation convergence association, Arch. Ophth. **55:**779, 1956.

161. Flom, M.: On the relationship between accommodation and accommodative convergence, Am. J. Optom. **37:**619, 1960.

162. Bruce, G.: Ocular divergence, its physiology and pathology, Arch. Ophth. **13:** 639, 1935.

163. Lippmann, O.: Paralysis of divergence due to cerebellar tumors, Arch. Ophth. **31:**299, 1944.

164. Bielschowsky, A.: Paralysis of conjugate movements of the eyes, Arch. Ophth. **13:** 569, 1935.

165. Morrax, P.: Paralysis of associated movements of the eyes, Ann. ocul. **176:** 337, 1939.

166. Posner, A.: Non-comitant hyperphorias, Am. J. Ophth. **27:** 1275, 1944.

167. Verhoeff, F.: Fixation disparity, Am. J. Ophth. **48:**339, 1949.

168. Powell, W.: Ocular manifestations of alcohol and consideration of individual variations in seven cases studied, J. Aviation Med. **9:** 97, 1938.

169. Colson, Z.: Effect of alcohol on vision; experimental investigation, J. A. M. A. **115:**1525, 1940.

170. Brecher, G., Hartman, A., and Leonard, D.: Effect of alcohol on binocular vision, Am. J. Ophth. **39:**44, 1955.

171. Seedorf, H.: Effect of alcohol on the motor fusion reserves and stereopsis as well as on the tendency to nystagmus, Acta ophth. **34:**271, 1956.

172. Wilmer, W., and Berens, C.: The effect of altitude on ocular function, J. A. M. A. **71:**1394, 1918.

173. Velhagen, K.: Heterophoria, Unter der Bedingungen des Hohenfluges, Luftfahrtmed. Abhandl. **1:**344, 1937.

174. Adler, F.: Effect of anoxia on heterophoria and its analogy with convergent comitant squint, Arch. Ophth. **34:**227, 1945.

175. Goodman, L., and Gilman, A.: The pharmacological basis of therapeutics, New York, 1941, The Macmillan Co.

176. Duguet, J.: Etude des effets de l'anoxemie sur les heterophories, Soc. ophth. Paris **20:**12, 1947.

177. Burford, G.: Involuntary eyeball motion during anesthesia and sleep; relationship to cortical rhythmic potentials, Anesth. & Analg. **20:** 191, 1941.

178. Aserinsky, E., and Kleitman, N.: Regularly occurring periods of eye motility and concomitant phenomena during sleep, Science **118:**273, 1953.

179. Krieger, H., Wagman, I., and Bender, M.: Changes in state of consciousness and patterns of eye movements, J. Neurophysiol. **21:**224, 1958.

180. Abraham, S.: Bell's phenomenon and the fallacy of occlusion test, Am. J. Ophth. **14:**656, 1931.

181. Adler, F., and Fliegelman, M.: Influence of fixation on the visual acuity, Arch. Ophth. **12:**475, 1934.

182. Ratliff, F., and Riggs, L.: Involuntary motions of the eye during monocular fixation, Nature, London **162:**25, 1948.

183. Higgins, J., and Stultz, K.: Frequency and amplitude of ocular tremor, J. Optic. Soc. America **42:**872, 1952.

184. Riggs, L.: Measurement of normal ocular tremor by corneal reflection, J. Optic. Soc. America **42:**287, 1952.

185. Nachmias, J.: Two dimensional motion of the retinal image during monocular fixation, J. Optic. Soc. America **49:** 901, 1959.

186. Hebard, F., and Marg, E.: Physiological nystagmus in the cat, J. Optic. Soc. America **50:** 151, 1960.

187. Riggs, L., and Ratliff, F.: J. Optic. Soc. America **42:**872, 1952.

188. Ditchburn, R., and Ginsborg, B.: Vision with stabilized retinal image, Nature, London **170:**36, 1952.

189. Cornsweet, T., and Cornsweet, J.: J. Optic. Soc. America **43:**495, 1953.

190. Dichtburn, R.: Eye movements in relation to retinal action, Optica Acta **1:** 171, 1955.

191. Dichtburn, R., Fender, D., and Mayne,

S.: Vision with controlled movements of the retinal image, J. Physiol. **145:** 98, 1959.

192. Dichtburn, R., and Ginsborg, B.: Vision with a stabilized retinal image, Nature, London **170:**36, 1952.

193. Ginsborg, B.: Small involuntary movements of the eye, Brit. J. Ophth. **37:**746, 1953.

194. Westheimer, G.: Eye movement responses to a horizontally moving visual stimulus, Arch. Ophth. **52:**932, 1954.

194a. Fender, D.: Control mechanisms of the eyes, Scient. Am., July, p. 24, 1964.

195. Ludvigh, E., and Miller, J.: Study of dynamic visual acuity, U. S. Naval School of Aviation Med., Pensacola, Fla., March, 1933. Project No. NM-001-067. 01-01, Rep. No. 1.

196. Rashbass, C.: The relationship between saccadic and smooth tracking eye movements, J. Physiol. **159:**326, 1961.

197. Ogle, K.: Researches in binocular vision, Philadelphia, 1950, W. B. Saunders Co.

198. Ogle, K., et al.: Fixation disparity and the fusional process in binocular single vision, Am. J. Ophth. **32:**1069, 1949.

199. Ames, A., and Gliddon, G.: Ocular measurements, Tr. Sect. Ophth. A. M. A., 1928, p. 102.

200. Walls, G.: The vertebrate eye, Cranbrook Institute of Science, Bloomfield Hills, Mich., 1942, Cranbrook Press.

201. Jampolsky, A.: Esotropia and convergent fixation disparity, Am. J. Ophth. **41:** 825, 1956.

202. Ford, J.: A significance of terminal transients in electro-oculographic recordings, Arch. Ophth. **61:**899, 1959.

203. Shackel, B.: Pilot study in electro-oculography, Brit. J. Ophth. **44:**89, 1960.

204. Mower, O., Ruch, T., and Miller, N.: The corneo-retinal potential difference as the basis of galvanometric method of recording eye movements, J. Physiol. **114:**423, 1935.

205. Fenn, W., and Hursh, J.: Movements of the eyes when the lids are closed, J. Physiol. **118:**8, 1937.

206. Mower, O.: Some neglected factors which influence duration of post-rotational nystagmus, Acta oto-laryng. **22:**1, 1935.

207. Scobee, R.: Anatomic factors in the etiology of heterotropia, Am. J. Ophth. **31:** 781, 1948.

208. Houssay, B.: Human physiology, ed. 2, New York, 1955, McGraw-Hill Book Co., Inc., p. 804.

209. White, J.: Paralysis of the superior rectus muscle, Tr. Am. Ophth. Soc. **31:** 551, 1933.

210. Bielschowsky, A.: Lectures on motor anomalies, Dartmouth College Publication, Hanover, N. H., 1940.

CHAPTER 11

LIGHT

NATURE AND ORIGIN OF LIGHT

Light may be defined as that group of wavelengths of the energy spectrum capable of stimulating the photoreceptors of the human retina and producing thereby a conscious sensation called sight. This definition may be amplified to include that part of the energy spectrum capable of producing motor reactions in the lower animals, since they cannot communicate with us regarding their sensations. In the case of those lower organisms which show simple motor phenomena in response to light we speak of the reactions as phototropic behavior. The wavelengths capable of initiating vision in man and phototropic reactions in the lower organisms are almost identical; the retina in man can be stimulated by only a relatively small segment of the known energy spectrum, and only this same segment can produce phototropic reactions in other living creatures. The bee, it is true, has been found to be perceptive to shorter wavelengths than the human eye can see (i.e., the ultraviolet) and to be insensitive to the longer wavelengths which we see as red. This is unlike the sense of hearing in which the range of audible sound for man is quite different from that of other animals. The dog, e.g., can hear whistles of a high pitch which is entirely inaudible to man. It would seem that the primary reaction of all living creatures to the visible portion of the energy spectrum is a motor one, and that conscious vision has been a further development in the higher forms, dependent entirely upon the acquisition of an increasingly complex cerebrum.

Energy spectrum. Radiant energy is energy that can travel through space without any apparent vehicle to transport it. For a long time in history the portion of the energy spectrum capable of producing sight was the only one known. The science which formulated the laws governing this part of the physical universe was called optics. Other forms of radiant energy have been discovered or produced in the last century having similar properties of light energy. Today there is a vast range of radiation known to exist in nature which quite dwarfs the small band known as light. The sun, e.g., radiates many forms of energy besides light—heat, ultraviolet, etc. This energy travels to the earth through a vacuum and expresses itself as energy only after absorption by appropriate matter. The portion which represents light energy only becomes known to us when it is absorbed by a retina or some similar photoreceptor; heat energy becomes heat when it is absorbed by the air or by our skin and is transformed into heat. One form of radiant energy has been produced by means of various oscillating electrical circuits. This is used in radio and radar transmission. By shooting high-speed electrons at metal targets in a vacuum, other radiations, the x-rays, have been produced, which have great power of penetrance through solid objects, and by using an apparatus called a betatron an enormous velocity can be given to electrons, producing still another type of radiation. Other forms of radiation are produced in nature from radioactive substances, and most recently still others known as cosmic rays, reaching the earth from outer space, have been discovered.

All of these forms of radiant energy are alike except in their wavelengths and frequencies. The emission of all radiant energy is periodic with respect to both time and space. The emission is not continuous. Light, e.g., is emitted in pulses having the same value a large number of times per second; the exact number is called the frequency. The emission travels with a certain speed through space, and the intervals in space which fall between each emission or pulse are called the wavelengths. The velocity (c) is equal to the product of the frequency (v) and the wavelength (λ) since during each pulse the wave advances a distance equal to one wavelength. Hence, the wavelength, lambda (λ) equals the velocity (c) divided by the frequency (v). Thus

1. $\lambda = \dfrac{c}{v}$

The velocity of light is constant and is roughly 186,000 miles per second. The accepted value is $c = 2.99790 \times 10^{10}$ cm./sec. when light is travelling in a vacuum.* In any other medium the velocity is reduced by a factor equal to 1/n where n is the refractive index of the medium.

That portion of the energy spectrum called light is composed of a series of emissions having different wavelengths and hence different frequencies. Since the speed of light is constant and the wavelength is equal to the speed divided by the frequency, it follows that the frequency varies inversely as the wavelength.

In Fig. 231 is shown the whole of the energy spectrum and what each part is best known for is indicated. All parts of the spectrum are identical in their electromagnetic nature, but each has its characteristic wavelengths and frequencies. That portion of the energy spectrum which is known as x-rays is identical to the portion known as visible rays, except that the x-rays are considerably shorter than the visible rays and are emitted at a greater frequency. In the same fashion the visible rays differ from the hertzian waves which are picked up by radio only in being considerably shorter than the hertzian waves and of greater frequency.

The energy spectrum is propagated as a series of electromagnetic vibrations or waves that are released as separate units or packets which are not divisible. These are called quanta. Just as matter is composed of ultimate particles which apparently cannot be further subdivided, such as the electron, so radiation exists in the universe in the form of discrete particles. At present, the tendency is to consider matter and energy different forms or expressions of the same entity, but further

*The accepted speed of light at present is $c = 2.99790 \times 10^{10}$/sec. (From Essen, L.: Nature **167:**258, 1951.)

one would have to suppose that the hypothetical ether was at least semisolid. The idea of such a hypothetical ether has finally been abandoned. Further, Fresnel has shown that light does consist of transverse and not longitudinal vibrations.

An important step in the development of Young's theory came in 1873 when Clerk-Maxwell published his electromagnetic theory of light which explained the known facts more completely than any previous theory had been able to do. He supposed that light consisted of alternating electric and magnetic waves, and by an advanced mathematical treatment he was able to prove that these waves are transverse and travel with the known velocity of light. Instead of describing the energy of radiation in terms of the potential and kinetic energy of a mechanical ether, Maxwell described it in terms of electrostatic and electromagnetic energy, i.e., the electromagnetic field. It is now certain that light and all radiant energy is propagated by electromagnetic waves.

The electromagnetic wave theory of light explains all the phenomena connected with the propagation of energy, but fails to explain what happens whenever matter is concerned with the production or the destruction of radiation. In dealing with the emission or absorption of radiant energy, it has been shown that the exchanges of energy take place in discrete units. In any exchange the amount of energy involved is always an exact multiple of these fundamental units. Planck called these units of energy quanta. The fundamental unit of energy is the quantum (e). The value of e is given by the equation

$$e = h \, v$$

where v is the frequency of radiation, and h is a universal constant. The accepted value of h, called Planck's constant, is 6.55×10^{-27} erg. sec.

In the case of the portion of the energy spectrum called light the unit of radiation is called the photon.

As soon as it became necessary to regard radiant energy as being propagated in discrete units and to accept the fact that light energy comes to us in that form and not as a continuum, physicists attempted to combine the corpuscular theory with the wave theory of light. At present they think in terms of wave mechanics and regard energy and matter as different expressions of the same entity.

From the formula e = h v, it is apparent that all parts of the spectrum producing vision do not have the same energy content. As stated in the formula given previously

1. $\lambda = \dfrac{c}{\lambda}$

Hence

2. $v = \dfrac{c}{v}$

The energy of the photon from different portions of the visible spectrum may be calculated as follows

3. $e = \dfrac{c}{\lambda}$

Thus it is apparent that the energy varies with the wavelength.

Pirenne[2] has given a good illustration of the different energy values of photons which emanate from different parts of the spectrum. A metal such as sodium will emit electrons if light from the violet end of the spectrum is played on it. The number of electrons emitted depends, however, on the wavelength of the light acting on the sodium. The shorter this is, the higher the energy of each quantum will be; therefore the light need be less intense in order to produce an emission of electrons. As the wavelength is increased, it becomes increasingly necessary to step up the energy in the light used because each quantum has less energy until finally no emission of electrons takes place, no matter how intense the light is.

"As a certain definite amount of energy is necessary to expel an electron, the light quantum interacting with the metal . . . must have sufficient energy. . . . If the wave length is longer than the critical value, none of the quanta will have the requisite energy to expel an electron. Each quantum acts independently on the metal."*

Since the magnitude of the quantum of radiation is inversely proportional to the wavelengths, the energy of the quantum of violet light of wavelength 400 mμ is twice as large as that of the quantum of red light of wavelength 800 mμ. The energy of a quantum of light of wavelength 500 mμ, e.g., can be calculated by means of formula 3.

$$e = \frac{hc}{\lambda}$$
$$h = 6.55 \times 10^{-27} \text{ erg.} \times \text{sec.}$$
$$c = 3 \times 10^{10} \text{ cm./sec.}$$

If the wavelength of light under consideration is 500 mμ, then the following calculation can be made:

$$\lambda = 500 \text{ m}\mu = 5 \times 10^{-5} \text{ cm.}$$
$$e = \frac{(6.55 \times 10^{-27} \text{ erg. sec.}) \ (3 \times 10^{10} \text{ cm./sec.})}{5 \times 10^{-5} \text{ cm.}}$$
$$e = 3.93 \times 10^{-12} \text{ erg.}$$

If light of 700 mμ is used instead, the value of e would be 2.80×10^{-12} erg. We will have occasion elsewhere to return to this when we inquire into the minimal amount of light energy able to stimulate the human dark-adapted rods.

From a practical standpoint when dealing with quantities as minute as 1 or

*From Pirenne, M.: Vision and the eye, London, 1948, The Pilot Press, p. 80.

2 photons, it is not always physically possible to produce or to deliver to some predetermined spot the exact number desired. It is physically impossible to set up a source of light which can always emit a constant number of photons in a unit of time. It is possible to make a light source which delivers accurately several thousand photons per millisecond with a relatively small variability in this number on a percentage basis, but, when a light source which will deliver exactly 6 photons per millisecond is desired, the variability of this number on a percentage basis will be relatively enormous, necessarily. At one time the source may deliver exactly 6 photons, at another 3 photons, and at still another 8 photons. This must be kept in mind in dealing with experiments in which the eye is exposed to minimal quantities of light for the purpose of determining its threshold.

TRANSMISSION OF LIGHT BY THE OCULAR MEDIA

When light passes from a medium of one optical density to another it undergoes one or more of the following changes in varying degrees: (1) it may be reflected, (2) it may be absorbed, or (3) it may be transmitted.

All three of these changes generally occur at all optical surfaces in nature. Those parts of the human eye such as the cornea and lens which are intended to act as optical surfaces and change the direction of incident pencils of light without stopping their passage must have excellent transmissibility and therefore should reflect and absorb light energy to a minimum degree. On the other hand, that part of the eye intended to transform the light energy into a nerve impulse such as the retina should absorb all the visible rays and reflect or transmit them to a minimum degree, for only those rays which are absorbed can bring about photochemical reactions.

Although the cornea and lens should transmit the visible rays (those whose wavelength is from 400 to 800 mμ) maximally, they should prevent the passage of longer and shorter wavelengths, especially those known to be harmful to biologic systems.

The cornea is practically opaque to all wavelengths shorter than 293 mμ.[3] As the wavelength increases, transmission begins in increasing quantity until at about 315 mμ most of the longer ultraviolet waves are getting through. Visibility begins at about 400 mμ, and transmission is almost perfect from here to 1250 mμ, which is well above the limits of visibility. From 1250 mμ on, transmission takes place at several bands. One band is at about 1400 mμ, one at 1650 mμ, and another between 2000 and 3000 mμ, where most of the rays pass through the cornea. Practically all of the harmful ultraviolet rays are filtered out by the cornea before they enter the eye. The infrared rays, on the other hand, can penetrate the cornea in sufficient amounts to be harmful to the retina if the light source is intense enough. Exposure to ultraviolet rays may damage the anterior segment of the eye and frequently does so, e.g., in snow blindness, which is a severe conjunctivitis caused by ultraviolet rays. If the conjunctivitis is severe enough, the lids may be closed and cannot be opened because of intense swelling, giving rise to the impression that the person is blind. The cornea itself may be affected also. These rays cannot be considered to reach the lens or retina in sufficient concentration to be damaging to these structures under ordinary circumstances.

Apart from the absorption of ultraviolet by the cornea, the vitreous itself strongly absorbs wavelengths shorter than 300 mμ. Cattle vitreous with a pH between 5.0 and 10.0 shows an absorption band with a maximum at 265 mμ which Balazs attributes to ascorbic acid. In dialyzed vitreous an absorption band at 277 mμ is due to the proteins. In addition to ascorbic acid other substances probably contribute to the absorption between 200 and 300 mμ, chief of which is hyaluronic acid.[4]

The amount of any wavelength which succeeds in reaching the retina, therefore, depends on the transmission of the various ocular media (chiefly on that of the cornea and lens) as well as on the intensity of the light.

Before the light reaches the photoreceptors, it must pass through not only the cornea, aqueous humor, lens, and vitreous, but also a large segment of the retina since the photoreceptors lie next to the pigment epithelium. The effect of the absorption of light by the retinal tissue through which the light has to pass before reaching the rods and cones is minimal and is of little significance in our usual measurements of retinal function— i.e., the absolute threshold of vision, the equality of brightness of different spectral regions, or the determination of the flicker fusion frequency. Under certain conditions, however, it has been found that the foveal photopic spectral sensitivity curve is not smooth, as it should be after allowing for the effect of absorption by the media in front of the retina. If the angular subtense of the experimental light is reduced below one degree, inflections occur which can only be explained by selective absorption on the part of the retina anterior to the rods and cones, and perhaps also to partial enhancement of the spectral sensitivity by the photoreceptors themselves, which of these is more important cannot be decided at present.[5]

The intensity of the light incident upon

the eye depends upon its distance from the light source and upon the angle of incidence of the light at the corneal surface. Light travels outward from its source in straight lines in all directions. Its energy falls off proportionally to the square of the distance from the object receiving it. Thus, an eye situated at 10 feet from a light source receives only one hundredth of the amount of light energy which it will receive if situated 1 foot away. The intensity varies directly with the cosine of the angle of incidence. This loss of energy due to the angle of incidence of the rays at the surface is due to reflection from the surface. This is at a minimum when the light rays enter along the normal (perpendicular) to the surface. At an angle of 60 degrees the incident ray has lost 50% of its effective energy. These two features, i.e., the distance and the angle of incidence of light, are of importance in considering injuries to the eye due to exposure to intense flashes of visible light or to harmful radiation of infrared or ultraviolet light. Another important factor is the concentration of the rays after they have passed through the ocular media.

In this respect, it is of interest that Stafford[6] reported that the threshold of absolute light of baby chicks was raised by previous exposure to radiant energy of wavelengths in the neighborhood of 360 mμ. He inferred that these results might apply to human beings. If radiation of 360 mμ is actually harmful to the human retina, the wearing of sunglasses out of doors would certainly be indicated because ultraviolet radiation of wavelengths around 360 mμ are present in the sunlight which penetrates the earth's atmosphere.

In order to test whether such deleterious effects could be demonstrated in human beings, Ludvigh and Kinsey[7] ex-posed a series of persons to radiations from a 1000 watt mercury-vapor arc from which most of the visible rays and all of the ultraviolet radiations shorter than 320 mμ were filtered. Fixation was made for 5 minutes at a distance of 30 cm. The difference in foveal sensitivity to light (p. 712) and the critical fusion frequency (p. 747) of both eyes of these persons had been determined previously. Retesting was done 5 minutes and 1 hour after exposure to the arc. There was no difference in the results between the two eyes of the normal observers or between the measurements of any one eye before and after irradiation. One can conclude, therefore, that ultraviolet radiations longer than 320 mμ encountered in nature are without any deleterious effect on these two important functions of the normal human eye.

Conditions are quite different, as stated, in the case of infrared radiation. Considerable infrared radiation can pass through the cornea and cause damage. These rays, especially when concentrated by the refraction of the cornea, frequently cause cataracts in workmen who are exposed constantly. Since this type of cataract occurs commonly in glass blowers, it is called glass blower's cataract. Workmen, such as puddlers, tin-plate workers and mill rollers, who work in industries in which there is constant exposure to infrared rays frequently develop this type of cataract.[8] The cataract develops after long exposure, generally over a period of three years, and usually progresses very slowly. The lens fibers have the property of absorbing these rays, which denature the proteins or enzyme systems responsible for the normal metabolism of the lens. The lens then becomes opaque. In addition, heating the aqueous humor and the iris and ciliary body may alter the metabolism of the lens.

The infrared rays are in great concentration when the eye is exposed to direct sunlight. This is especially true when the light is concentrated by the lens systems of a telescope (such as in viewing an eclipse of the sun by the moon), and the retina may suffer damage. The resultant condition is called eclipse blindness because of the frequency with which such accidents occur among the general population at times of eclipses. The effects of electric currents, lightning, x-rays, and gamma radiation are beyond the scope of this book.

The question sometimes arises whether the amount of light used in photographic flash bulbs, especially electronic flashes, could harm the eye. Theoretically, there is insufficient ultraviolet or infrared radiation from the standard electronic discharge tube ordinarily used to be harmful to either the exterior or the interior of the eye, even when the gaze is directed on the light source. No ophthalmoscopic or microscopic changes have been shown in the eyes of rabbits by exposures of more than 2000 lumen seconds from a discharge tube at a distance of 3 inches, nor have any cases of injury been reported in humans. This is of some practical importance in view of the frequency with which photographs are taken of patients, even infants, with the pupils fully dilated. It is conceivable that amblyopia discovered later in life might be attributed by the child's family to the flash used in taking the infant's picture.

REFERENCES

1. Deller, J.: The nature of light. In Sorsby, A., editor: Modern trends in ophthalmology, vol. 2, New York, 1947, Paul B. Hoeber, Inc.
2. Pirenne, M.: Vision and the eye, London, 1948, The Pilot Press, p. 80.
3. Duke-Elder, S.: Textbook of ophthalmology, vol. IV: The neurology of vision; motor and optical anomalies, St. Louis, 1949, The C. V. Mosby Co., p. 281.
4. Balazs, E.: Studies on the structure of the vitreous body, Am. J. Ophth. **38:**21, 1954.
5. Weale, R.: Spectral sensitivity curves and the absorption of light by the ocular media, Brit. J. Ophth. **37:**148, 1953.
6. Stafford, J.: Disinfection of schoolroom air by ultraviolet light, Science supp. **14:**102, 1945.
7. Ludvigh, E., and Kinsey, V.: Effect of long ultraviolet radiation on the human eye, Science **104:**246, 1946.
8. Kutscher, C.: Ocular effects of radiant energy, Tr. Am. Acad. Ophth. **50:**230, 1946.

CHAPTER 12

METABOLISM OF
THE RETINA

GENERAL CONSIDERATIONS

As pointed out recently,* in the last decade two separate fields of interest in medicine have been gradually approaching one another, until now they have merged forces with a common objective. The study of anatomy began with a description of organs and tissues as they appeared to the naked eye. This was followed by a more minute examination of the individual cells composing these structures. Cell biologists then began examining cell structure under increasing magnification until, with the advent of electronmicroscopy, their descriptions are approaching molecular dimensions. The study of chemistry began with investigations of the fundamental reactions of molecules, but biochemists found themselves dealing with chemical systems of ever-increasing size and complexity, until now they are investigating the behavior of the whole living cell. The anatomist and biochemist have now joined hands, and as a result we are witness to a marvelous development of cell physiology. No field of physiology has benefited more by this unification of effort than that of retinal physiology, in which the function of the photoreceptors and their complicated neuronic pathways are being analyzed in terms of their submicroscopic structure and enzyme systems. It can be safely predicted that this will shortly open new approaches to the study of ocular diseases that affect the retina. We already have evidence, e.g., that pigmentary degeneration of the retina is due to the absence or disappearance of an enzyme system in the rods necessary for their viability, the enzyme of which is part of the gene and therefore accounts for the familial and hereditary nature of this disease.

Before the problems of the highly specialized photoreceptors, the rods and cones, are approached, it will be well to review briefly a description of the average body cell as it is known today and how it maintains its metabolism.

---

*An excellent review of the biology of the living cell will be found in the September 1961 issue of *Scientific American,* the entire issue being devoted to this subject.

THE CELL MEMBRANE

Each cell is surrounded by a membrane which delimits it from its neighboring cells and from their milieu. This membrane is one of the chief components of those cells concerned with movement, such as muscle cells, of cells which deal with communication within the body, such as nerve cells, and of cells concerned with the reception of messages from the environment outside the cell, such as sensory cells. Although only about 10 mμ in thickness, the cell membrane has a structure that is resolvable into finer details by the electronmicroscope. The cell membrane has selective permeability by means of which substances of certain molecular size and electric charge are permitted to pass through the membrane while others are held out. This selective permeability depends upon the nature of the membrane itself and may change from time to time, depending on factors operating within and without the cell. Substances may also enter the cell by another process known as pinocytosis, in which microvesicles form by adsorption of particles, molecules, or ions on the cell membrane. The loaded membrane then flows into the cell and discharges its contents. When vesicles form which can be visualized microscopically, the process is usually called phagocytosis.

The membrane also has the property of active transport of ions across it. This helps potassium ions get into the cell interior and removes sodium ions from the cell. The mechanism which achieves this is not merely one of semipermeability, but of active ion transport necessitating the presence of complex enzyme systems in the cell. Substances enter and leave the cell, therefore, by two processes. Active transport involves the movement of substances across the membrane by forces which are manufactured by the cell; passive transport involves the passage of substances across the membrane by chemical and electrical forces supplied by the cell environment, the passage being regulated by the differential permeability of the membrane. These passive forces in the environment consist of a concentration gradient between the two sides of the membrane, the difference in electrical potential between the two sides of the membrane, the physical size of the molecules or particles to be transported across the membrane, and in the case of certain cells in which there is a bulk flow of solute, the process known as solute drag. Here solute particles diffusing in the direction of flow are speeded up while those diffusing in the opposite direction are slowed down.

What do we know about the nature of the membrane which allows these forces of passive transport to take place? Since substances soluble in lipid solvents penetrate cell membranes easily, it seems probable that the cell membrane must contain a layer of lipids. Since water-soluble substances can also penetrate cell membranes, there must be dehiscences or pores in this layer of lipids through which these substances can penetrate. Finally, a protein layer must be present to account for the low surface tension of cell membranes and other characteristics which preclude a purely fatty composition.

The most recent and generally accepted model of such a membrane has been proposed by Danielli, as shown in Fig. 232. This consists of a double layer of lipid molecules oriented parallel to one another at right angles to the plane of the membrane. The nonpolar ends of the lipid molecules point toward one another, and the polar groups point toward the two surfaces of the membrane. Covering these two layers of lipid molecules is a single layer of protein, adsorbed to the

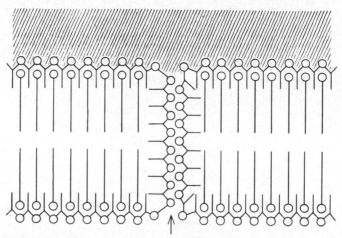

Fig. 232. Model of cell membrane as proposed by Danielli. (From Holter, H.: Scient. Am. 205:171, 1961. Reprinted with permission. Copyright © 1961 by Scientific American, Inc. All rights reserved.)

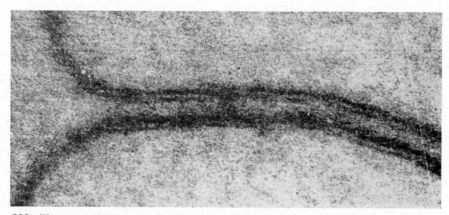

Fig. 233. Electron micrograph of membranes of two cells in a mouse nerve fiber enlarged 400,000 diameters. Each membrane is approximately 75 Å thick and consists of two dense lines each 20 Å wide separated by a light area 35 Å across. The gap between the cells is nearly 150 Å. The two dense lines of each membrane correspond to Danielli's protein component. The light area between them may be the lipid region. (Electron micrograph courtesy J. David Robertson, Harvard Medical School; from Holter, H.: Scient. Am. 205:171, 1961. Reprinted with permission. Copyright © 1961 by Scientific American, Inc. All rights reserved.)

polar ends of the lipid molecules. In places these protein molecules turn at right angles to form pores through the entire thickness of the membrane.

The lipid layers account for the passage of lipid-soluble substances, whereas water-soluble substances are supposed to enter through the pores. The protein monomolecular layer gives mechanical resistance and elasticity to the membrane and accounts for its low surface tension. Danielli calculated the thickness of the lipid molecule to be about 3 mμ and the protein layer to be about 1 mμ thick. Hence the total membrane should be about 8 mμ in thickness.

This model has been beautifully supported by electronmicroscopic evidence. In Fig. 233 are shown the membranes of two cells in a mouse nerve fiber. Each membrane is about 7.5 mμ thick. Each consists of two dark lines of 2 mμ thickness, which correspond to Danielli's protein layer, with a light area between of 3.5 mμ thickness, which may be the lipid molecules. The total thickness in the electronmicroscope is therefore 7.5 mμ. This corresponds quite well to Danielli's model after allowing some shrinkage due to methods of preparation for electronmicroscopy. So far, no pores have been shown by electronmicroscopy, but this is not surprising since the pores are thought to be spaced relatively far apart.

It seems likely that the cell membrane may not be homogeneous throughout, but that patches of the membrane may have different chemical composition, in order to account for the high selectivity in the passage of certain substances which many cells exhibit. Enzymes have been localized on the surfaces of cells which convert substances otherwise insoluble, so that they are able to penetrate the cell membrane.

Pinocytosis and phagocytosis are essentially the same process. Phagocytosis was originally observed in white blood cells and consisted of the active ingestion of whole bacteria by the cell, visible with the microscope. Pinocytosis is essentially the submicroscopic correlative of phagocytosis, detected by electronmicroscopy. It is a subject of considerable interest, and much work is being done on its mechanism and significance to the cell.

The story of active transport of substances across the cell membrane is only in its beginnings. Electrical potential differences between the inside and the outside of the cell have been known for a long time, and their influence on the active transport of ions across the membrane has been suspected. Recently it has been shown that these electric potential differences are themselves set up by the active transport of ions across the cell membrane and are maintained by some metabolic processes going on within the cell. It has been well established that more potassium is found within the living cell than in its normal milieu and less sodium. Blood plasma contains twenty times more sodium than potassium, whereas the red blood cell contains twenty times more potassium than sodium. The cell membrane is passively permeable to both sodium and potassium ions, and both ions have the same electric charge and are about the same size. If passive permeability were the only mechanism present, eventually sodium would leak into the red blood cell and potassium would leak out, and their concentrations inside and outside the cell would be equal. The cell must, therefore, have some mechanism which maintains this different ionic concentration between it and its surrounding plasma, constantly extruding sodium and accumulating potassium against an aggregate fiftyfold concentration gradient.

At the present time various mechanisms involving enzyme systems have been proposed. One such mechanism for the nerve fiber cell is described on p. 617.

THE CELL INTERIOR

Our conception of the interior of the cell has changed considerably from the earliest description of a jellylike blob of cytoplasm containing a nucleus. The details of the submicroscopic structures in the cell and their chemical functions constitute one of the most exciting developments in cell physiology. In addition to a nucleus containing a nucleolus and chromosomes, many other structures are now recognized to be of great importance.

The cytoplasm is not a uniform blob of jelly but has a definite structure, a cytoskeleton only visible under the electronmicroscope. This varies considerably in different cells, but is especially well developed in those cells which specialize in the production of proteins, such as the liver and pancreas. Porter of the Rockefeller Institute has given it the name of endoplasmic reticulum. When well developed, it forms a network of canaliculi through the cell. Some observers consider it continuous with the cell membrane that lines the cell, forming a vastly increased surface area across which substances can diffuse throughout the cell. It is supposed to be continuously produced, and Palade of the Rockefeller Institute thinks this is the function of the Golgi bodies, which seem to be continuous with the endoplasmic reticulum.

Some of the membranes of the reticulum are studded with granules, and these are definitely connected with the production of protein. They are rich in ribonucleic acid (RNA) and are now called ribosomes.

Embedded within the cytoplasm are other organelles that appear as mere granules in the ordinary microscope. Chief of these in the animal cell are the mitochondria. In plants which contain chlorophyll, chloroplasts are found which are the homologue of the mitochondria. The chloroplasts utilize the energy of the sunlight to form adenosine triphosphate (ATP) from which the cell extracts energy for its metabolic needs. The mitochondrium is the power plant of the animal cell, extracting energy from the chemical bonds in the nutrients of the cell by oxidation and respiration and, like the chloroplasts, making ATP available to the cell for its metabolic needs.

Another organelle, distinguishable from the mitochondrium, is the lysosome, containing digestive enzymes that break down fats, proteins, and nucleic acids into smaller constituents that can be oxidized by the oxidative enzymes of the mitochondria. The centrosomes form the poles of the spindle apparatus that divides the chromosomes during mitosis.

The cell nucleus is surrounded by a membrane—a double membrane as seen with the electronmicroscope—with holes in the outer layer open to the cytoplasm. These may be pores through which large molecules pass into and out of the nucleus. Inside the nucleus is the chromatin material in which the cell's complement of deoxyribonucleic acid (DNA) is entirely localized. The principal constituent of the chromosomes is DNA, and one of the most important questions for the cell geneticist is to discover how genetic information is encoded in the structure of this macromolecule. I have already spoken of ribonucleic acid (RNA) found in the ribosomes on the endoplasmic reticulum as the substance which the cell uses to arrange amino acids into their proper sequence for linkage into protein chains. Deoxyribonucleic acid presides at the synthesis of RNA which, unlike DNA, is found in both the nucleus and the cytoplasm; DNA is therefore indirectly concerned with protein synthesis.

When the cell is in the resting state, the chromatin material and hence the DNA is diffusely distributed in the nucleus. Thus the DNA can make surface contact with much of the material in the nucleus from which it pieces together the molecules of RNA and replicates itself. In preparation for cell division the chromatin coils up tightly to form the chromosomes.

The nucleoli inside the nucleus of the cell are probably also active centers of protein and RNA synthesis, for they are rich in RNA.

THE RETINA AS A WHOLE

Interest in the metabolism of the retina centers largely on the changes produced in it by light since the metabolic changes that occur with illumination should tell us something of the visual process. The photochemical changes that occur in the retinal pigments under the influence of light will be reviewed in Chapter 13. This chapter is concerned with the chemical and physical changes which constitute the metabolism of the whole retina and in particular the photoreceptors and the pigment epithelium.

The changes in energy which can be detected may be compounded of many different metabolisms—e.g., the basal metabolism of the cells of the retina, the breakdown of the visual pigments and their re-formation, the active transport of metabolites from one part of the retina to another, and the transmission of the nerve impulses through the synaptic layers of the retina.

CARBOHYDRATE METABOLISM

It has been generally claimed that the glucose metabolized by the retina was largely supplied by the bloodstream. Glycogen, the most readily demonstrable of the substrates for glycolysis, until recently has not been shown to be present in human retinas in any considerable quantity.[1] A moderate amount has been demonstrated recently in human retinas, localized in Müller's cells and fibers, by Kuwabara and Cogan.[2] Glycogen was found in large amounts in guinea pig and rabbit retinas and in very small amounts in rat and mouse retinas. The variations in amounts of glycogen in different species is interpreted by these authors to be correlated with the availability or un-

availability of substrates from the bloodstream, for the largest amounts of glycogen are found in retinas in which blood vessels are either absent or least able to supply substrates to the retinas.

Not only is the glycogen present in the retinas largely localized in Müller's fibers, but glycolytic enzymes are also chiefly localized there, such as lactic acid dehydrogenase. The retina is able to synthesize glycogen from glucose but from no other substrate. These findings throw a new light on the functions of glial cells, such as Müller's cells and fibers and in some species horizontal cells, which have formerly been looked on as purely supportive structures. It is now apparent that they also serve for the synthesis and storage of glycogen and for the major enzyme activity involved in glycolysis.

Injury to the retina, which is followed by gliosis, increases the amount of glycogen in the retina, most of which is concentrated in Müller's fibers and other glial cells. The retina has the highest rate of respiration of any tissue in the body and in common with embryonic tissues and tumor tissue can accumulate lactic acid both aerobically and anaerobically. The breakdown of glucose to lactic acid takes place by the usual series of phosphorylative reactions known as the Embden-Meyerhof cycle. Large amounts of adenosine triphosphate (ATP) and creatine phosphate (CRP) are found in the retina, along with the enzyme creatine phosphokinase. The oxidation of lactate and pyruvate is probably through the citric acid cycle, and many of the enzymes active in this cycle such as citric acid dehydrogenase have been found. Noell pictures the presently known pathways for the breakdown of the glucose molecule in the simplified diagram shown in Fig. 234.

The brain cortex has about half the rate of respiration and produces lactic

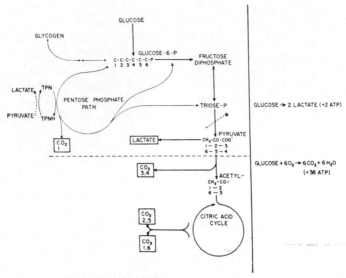

Fig. 234. Pathways of glucose metabolism. *Heavy arrows,* pathway of the Embden-Meyerhof and the citric acid cycle. *Asterisk,* main site of iodoacetate inhibition (triose-phosphate dehydrogenase). *Boxes,* end products. Reactions below the dashed horizontal line require oxygen. (From Noell, W.: Am. J. Ophth. 48:348, 1959.)

acid aerobically at best only 15% and anaerobically 35% of that of the adult retina. The oxygen consumption of the brain exceeds aerobic lactic acid production by a factor of two, whereas the reverse is true of the retina. On the basis of his own work and that of Lowry,[3] Noell calculates that half of the in vitro respiration and half of the aerobic lactic acid production of the adult rabbit's retina is contributed by the photoreceptors, whereas anaerobically about two thirds of the lactic acid comes from the inner retinal layers. There seems to be considerable difference in the distribution of glycolytic enzymes in the retina in different species, which may be related to the differences in the blood supply of the different retinal layers. In the rabbit there are no capillaries throughout the retina, and all oxygen must diffuse into the retina from the choriocapillaris. In this animal the inner layers are relatively high in glycolytic enzymes and low in

enzymes of the citric acid cycle. In the monkey and presumably in man, however, the reverse is true. The distribution of the enzymes in the photoreceptors is considered on pp. 570 to 574.

Following the original discovery of the high glycolytic rate of the retina by Warburg, a number of investigators have reported changes in metabolism due to the influence of light.[4] Nakashima and Hayashi[5] reported that in the retina of a frog the oxidation-reduction potential of suspensions or extracts in Ringer's solution rises when the preparation is exposed to light and falls again when the light is removed. On the other hand, others[6, 7] found an increased oxygen uptake in the posterior segment of frogs' eyes when they were kept in the dark and attributed this increased metabolism in the dark to the re-formation of visual purple. Chase and Smith[8] were unable to find that light or darkness had any influence on the oxygen uptake in the retina.

These contradictory results indicate that probably the changes attributed to the influence of variations in illumination are artifacts due to the methods employed or to factors which are difficult to control in measuring the metabolic rate. This is borne out by the report of Lindeman,[9] who found no consistent difference in the rate of oxygen consumption in the dark or in the light with the use of the Warburg apparatus but obtained a slight increase in oxygen consumption for approximately 10 minutes after the light-adapted retina was exposed to the dark when the Fenn manometer method was used. If light causes any change in the oxygen consumption of the retina, it is difficult to demonstrate. The mean QO_2 for the retina is 3.22, according to Lindeman (the QO_2 of the cornea is discussed on p. 48).

Although the studies on increased carbohydrate metabolism of the retina exposed to light are equivocal, evidence is accumulating that an increase in metabolic activity of the enzyme succinic dehydrogenase does occur in the light-adapted retina as compared to the dark-adapted retina. The activity of this enzyme can be roughly quantitated by histochemical staining methods. The activity is particularly marked in the portion of the inner segments of the rods and cones known as the ellipsoid. As will be shown in a later section (p. 569), the ellipsoid is particularly rich in mitochondria so that one would expect this region of the inner segment to be active metabolically.[10] Recent studies have suggested that the rate of metabolism of the ellipsoid is increased when it is exposed to light.[11]

There is some evidence that the cones are less susceptible to artificially produced anoxia than are the rods. When a subject is exposed to centrifugal forces which produce blackout, loss of peripheral vision occurs earlier than loss of central vision, and, under conditions of oxygen deficiency, obliteration of the peripheral fields with the preservation of central visual acuity occurs. It will be recalled that the area of the retina in which the cone population is maximal is supplied least with blood vessels and that in the fovea the central retinal artery supply is lacking entirely. Since it is unlikely that the oxygen needs of the fovea are really less than those of the rest of the retina, it has been suggested that the yellow pigment of the macula may be concerned with the oxidation requirement of this region.[12]

When the retina degenerates, its utilization of glucose diminishes. For example, in cats after section of the optic nerve with subsequent optic atrophy on one side, a comparison of the utilization of glucose by the two retinas shows almost no glycolysis on the side of the optic atrophy. The glucose utilization of the retina seems to be dependent on the integrity of its cells, probably the ganglion cells, since it has been shown that trituration of the retina in a tissue grinder abolishes its utilization of glucose entirely, whereas if the retina is merely cut into a number of pieces by scissors, the utilization of glucose is not appreciably different from that in the intact retina.[13]

The metabolism of the brain and retina is unique in that it is accompanied by the formation of ammonia. It has been claimed that the amount of ammonia produced is greater during aerobic glycolysis than during anaerobic glycolysis and that the light-adapted retina gives off more ammonia than the dark-adapted retina. The source of the ammonia is not known, although it may be liberated from adenosine phosphate. The oxidation deaminization of adenine is one of the steps in the breakdown of the purine bases, and the deaminization of amino acids in the retina may account for the production of ammonia. Some breakdown of urea in the kidney occurs with the formation of ammonia. The significance of the production of ammonia in the retina is not known, but if its formation is accelerated by light, it would indicate that during illumination the products of the breakdown of the visual pigments stimulate metabolism.

EFFECT OF GAMMA AMINOBUTYRIC ACID AND GLUTAMIC ACID

The transmission of the nerve impulse throughout the body is mediated by acetylcholine (pp. 223 to 225). It would not be surprising, therefore, if this substance and its enzymatic inhibitor cholinesterase were present in the retina. Koelle and Friedenwald[14] presented evidence (confirmed by Noell[15]) that in the retina acetylcholine is the transmitter substance at the synapse between the bipolar and the ganglion cell. Studies on the chick embryo have shown that the acetylcholine and cholinesterase of the retina closely parallel the development of the function of the eyes. Cholinesterase has been found in greatest concentration in the synaptic layers of the retina.

Some information about the source of energy for the visual processes may be obtained from a study of the phosphoric acid and phosphoric acid esters in the retina because of their importance in intermediate carbohydrate metabolism. Two types of organic phosphate which liberate inorganic phosphate on illumination have been found in the retina, one of which appears to be phosphocreatine and the other to be a soluble phosphate ester.[16] It has been thought that the phosphoric acid content of the retina arose from the splitting of phosphocreatine, similar to the manner of its formation in muscle,[17, 18] but others have found that isolated retinas of frogs and rats produce

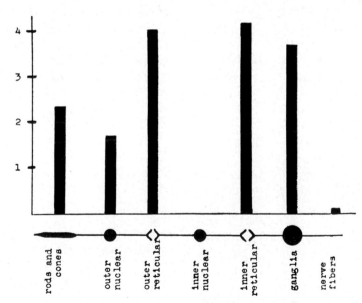

Fig. 235. Distribution of diphosphopyridine nucleotide in the bovine retina. Calculated for nerve fiber tissue from the data of Sym, Nillson, and von Euler. (From Anfinsen: J. Biol. Chem. **152:**279, 1944.)

phosphoric acid in Ringer's solution even in the dark, probably as a result of autolysis. Von Studnitz[19] believed that light decomposes the cone substance, with the production of phosphoric acid, expansion of the pigment, and contraction of the cones. As proof of this he showed that the injection of phosphoric acid into the dark-adapted retina produced configuration of the cones and pigments similar to that in the light-adapted retina, whereas injection of alkali into the light-adapted retina resulted in the type of configuration present in the dark-adapted state. It is questionable whether the acid reaction to illumination is due to the production of phosphoric acid or to the production of lactic acid caused by glycolysis.

Since the retina possesses extremely high rates of respiration and glycolysis, it would not be surprising to find that it contained appreciable amounts of diphosphopyridine nucleotide (DPN). Using a manometric method by means of which 0.001 to 0.006 gamma of DPN could be determined with an error of less than 5%, Anfinsen[20] was able to measure the concentration of DPN in various layers of the retina. In Fig. 235 it is demonstrated that the concentration is highest in the two synaptic layers. The layer of ganglion cells also contains considerable quantities, whereas the rods and outer nuclear layer contain relatively small amounts of this coenzyme.

HYDROGEN ION CONCENTRATION

The pH of the dark-adapted retina has been found to be 7.3 and that of the light-adapted retina to be 7.0.[21] This change is thought to be related to the activity of the visual cells rather than to that of the nerve fibers since it varies with the type of cell. It has been claimed that the retina of the guinea pig, which is almost entirely a rod retina, shows no changes in pH with illumination, whereas the retina of the cat and fish, which contains many cones, shows a shift to the acid side.[22] The acidity increases with the time, corresponding to the regeneration of the visual pigments, and also in direct relation to the intensity of illumination. As just stated, Von Studnitz believed that it was the acidification of the retina which led to contraction of the cones and expansion of the retinal pigment.

The retina has a high metabolic rate, as described, and the energy so liberated may be stored in part in the high-energy phosphate bonds of adenosine triphosphate and creatine phosphate, both of which are present. Some of this energy is probably reused in the synthesis of acetylcholine. Since the enzyme diphosphopyridine nucleotide (DPN) is involved in the production of high-energy phosphate radicals, some significance may be attached to the fact that DPN is highly concentrated at the synapses in the retina. The high-energy phosphate bonds are also a likely source of energy for the resynthesis of rhodopsin; however, these compounds are not likely to be involved in the breakdown of rhodopsin.[23]

By selective staining of the ganglion cells of the retina, Bech[24] was able to show that when the eye was exposed to light and was therefore undergoing physiologic activity the same type of metabolism of nucleic acid occurs in the ganglion cells as occurred in the dark, but of a far greater magnitude.

EFFECT OF GAMMA AMINOBUTYRIC ACID AND GLUTAMIC ACID

Certain amino acids have profound effects on the activity of spinal neurons.[25] Noell has found similar effects of these amino acids on the responses of the retina to light. In Fig. 236 is shown the effect

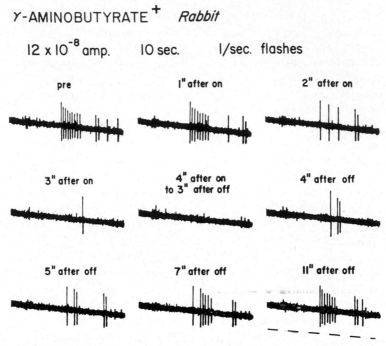

Fig. 236. The effect of γ-aminobutyrate on the response of the ganglion cell to repetitive light flashes. (From Noell, W.: Am. J. Ophth. 48:348, 1959.)

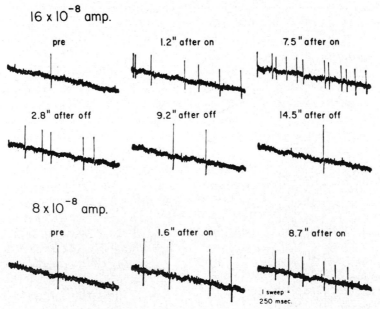

Fig. 237. The effect of glutamate on the responses of the ganglion cell to repetitive light flashes. (From Noell, W.: Am. J. Ophth. 48:348, 1959.)

of the electrophoretically administered amino acid γ-aminobutyrate on the response of the ganglion cell to repetitive light flashes. This substance immediately depresses the responses of the ganglion cell. In Fig. 237 is shown the effect of glutamate similarly administered, which is exactly the opposite. This amino acid enhances the spontaneous activity of the ganglion cell. Although these findings are not immediately informative as to the mechanism of the visual function, studies of this sort will inevitably lead to important clues and eventually may even be useful therapeutically.

THE PHOTORECEPTORS

Electronmicroscopic analysis of the photoreceptors has considerably increased our knowledge of the structure and function of these sensory cells.* Only those items of morphology which are of physiologic interest in connection with retinal metabolism will be mentioned here.

The structure of the rod cell of the rabbit is shown in Fig. 238, and in Fig. 239 are shown the guinea pig rods according to Sjostrand. In the guinea pig each outer segment consists of a pile of disks 14 mμ thick, each disk consisting of two layers 3 mμ in thickness separated by an interspace 7 to 8 mμ wide. It is believed that these disks are produced by infoldings of the cell membrane as the rod develops, as shown in Figs. 240 and 241, in the same way that the concentric rings in myelinated nerve fibers arise from infolding of their cell walls (Fig. 245). Since the dimensions of the disks are within the range of macromolecules,

---

*For a detailed account consult Smelser, G., editor: The structure of the eye, New York, 1961, Academic Press, Inc., and Cohen, A.: The fine structure of the extrafoveal receptors of the rhesus monkey, Exper. Eye Res. 1:128, 1962.

Sjostrand has deduced a model showing the arrangement of the molecular architecture based on the proposed models of cell membranes as depicted on p. 000 (Fig. 242). The metabolic enzymes are thought to be contained in the protein layers. It is certain that all of the rhodopsin resides in the outer segments of the rods, and Sjostrand believes that it is localized in the middle of the disks.

The outer segments of the rods and cones are connected with the inner segments by a thin stalklike connection resembling a cilium. In the guinea pig this connection consists of nine filaments which pass for a distance into the inner segment and then it forms a structure which appears like a basal body. A filamentous structure continues from this basal body through the inner segment. The cilia-like filaments either may be purely structural, giving support to the outer and inner segments of each rod, or they may represent the conducting path by which the electrical activity originating in the outer segment by the breakdown of visual pigments is conducted into the inner segment of each rod.

The inner segment is characterized chiefly by the accumulation of mitochondria; in fact, there seem to be no mitochondria present in the outer segments, although they are present in the pigment epithelial cells. The Golgi apparatus is also found in the inner segments. The mitochondria in the inner segments probably serve the function of amplifying the electric discharge that originates in the outer segment, building it up in much the same way as an electrical signal is amplified in a vacuum tube, the energy coming from oxidative sources in the mitochondria.

The rod or cone fiber as it emerges from the inner segments of the photo-

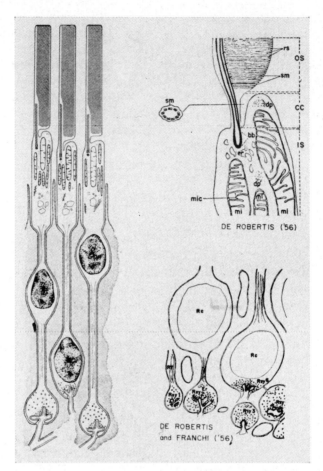

DE ROBERTIS ('56)

DE ROBERTIS
and FRANCHI ('56)

Fig. 238. Schematic representation of the fine structure of the rod cell of the rabbit. OS, Outer segment; **cc,** connecting cilium; IS, inner segment; **mic,** mitochondrion; **bb,** basal body of connecting cilium. *Shaded areas* in the drawing on the left represent Müller cell cytoplasm. Processes of the Müller cells extend into the spaces between the innerlimbs. (From Noell, W.: Am. J. Ophth. **48:**348, 1959.)

receptors is surrounded by the glial element of the retina, the Müller's cells. As the fiber passes through the external limiting membrane of the retina, the peripheral region of the cytoplasm and the plasma membranes, as well as the Müller's cells, are especially well differentiated. The rod fibers show many morphologic features characteristic of nonmyelinated nerve fibers, and the Müller's cells show a relationship to the rod fibers similar to that of the Schwann cells to nonmyelinated nerve fibers. The glia and modified glial cells, known as Müller's cells, have always been considered supporting elements in the retina, but the findings of Cogan and Kuwabara[2, 26] show that they serve an important metabolic role. They are a storage facility for glycogen and contain many of the oxidative enzymes which we have seen are necessary for the mitochondria in their role of amplifying the responses of the outer limbs of the rods. The glia and

Müller cells pack the space between the neurons to the extent that the retina has no true extracellular space, and where the Müller fibers come in contact with the rods and cones, these glial cells are connected with one another by desmosomes or terminal bars to form the external limiting membrane of the retina.

The rod or cone fiber eventually synapses with the neurons in the layer of bipolar cells. This synapse is unlike the usual ones found in the central nervous system. The visual cell fiber expands into a spherule into which the dendrites of the bipolar cell penetrate and branch.[27] Sjostrand recognizes two types of receptor cells in the guinea pig retina, one called the a-cells which have a shape and structure of the synaptic body characteristic of rod cells, and receptor cells, called b-cells, which are characterized by synaptic bodies showing the conical shape and higher degree of complexity characteristic of cone cells. In the synaptic connections not less than four b-cells make contact with one a-cell (Fig. 243).

Small vesicles are scattered all over the cytoplasm of the synaptic body. Noell

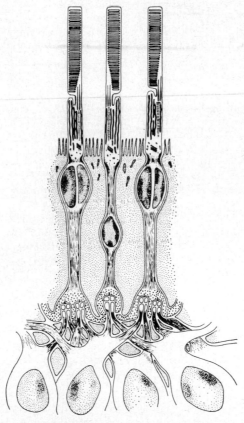

Fig. 239. Schematic drawing of retinal receptors (rods) in the guinea pig retina. One a receptor in the middle is flanked by two b receptors. Interceptor contacts as well as the synaptic connections between receptor cells and the neurons of the layer of bipolars are represented schematically. (From Sjöstrand, F.: In Smelser, G., editor: The structure of the eye, New York, 1961, Academic Press, Inc.)

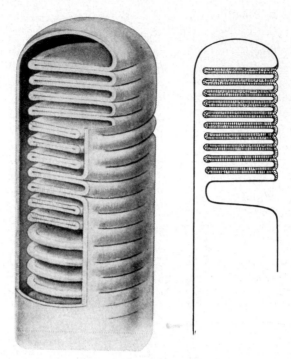

Fig. 240. Schematic drawings showing the arrangement of the outer segment discs in perch cones. The discs extend as folds from the plasma membrane across the whole diameter of the outer segment. (From Sjöstrand, F.: In Smelser, G., editor: The structure of the eye, New York, 1961, Academic Press, Inc.)

Fig. 241. Schematic drawing showing the formation of the outer segment discs infoldings of the plasma membrane. (From Sjöstrand, F.: In Smelser, G., editor: The structure of the eye, New York, 1961, Academic Press, Inc.)

considers that these vesicles should contain a transmitter substance which would be released from the vesicle at the synaptic membrane at the time of excitation. This substance diffusing across the gap would effect a change at the membrane of the bipolar cell which would produce postsynaptic excitation. Sjostrand is not convinced that these vesicles would contain transmitter substance, however.

Attempts have been made to localize various metabolic enzymes in the layers of the retina, starting with the work of Kuwabara and Cogan,[28] who studied the oxidative enzymes of the mammalian retina. The work of Lowry has been mentioned previously (p. 564). Pearse[29] finds that while the highest oxidative activity is achieved by glycolytic pathways (lactate dehydrogenase), malate, glutamate,

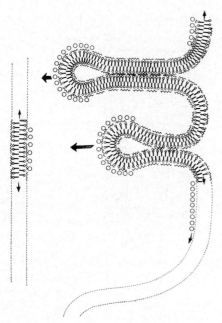

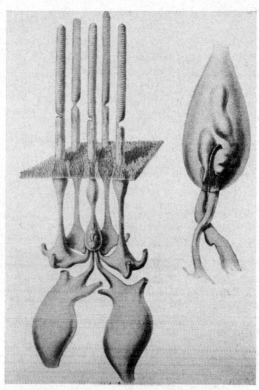

Fig. 242. Schematic drawing illustrating the proposed model for the molecular architecture of the discs of the outer segments of rod and cone cells with the differentiation of these discs in an edge zone and a central zone. According to the proposed hypothesis, the edge zone would interfere with the formation of the rest of the disc and would represent the region from which the disc grows. The edge zone appears as a part of the plasma membrane which has been dislocated through the growth of a fold which represents the first step in the development of the disc. The molecular architecture of the main part of the disc is proposed to be represented by four double layers of lipid molecules, each double layer being sandwiched between thin layers of protein. The edge zone is pictured to correspond to the complete membrane model proposed for the plasma membrane with a layer of globular proteins associated with a double layer of lipids sandwiched between two thin layers of proteins with extended peptide chains. *Small open circle attached to bar,* lipid molecule with the polar end indicated by the open circle. *Jagged lines,* protein molecules with peptide chain stretched. *Large open circles,* globular protein molecules. (From Sjöstrand, F.: In Smelser, G., editor: The structure of the eye, New York, 1961, Academic Press, Inc.)

Fig. 243. Schematic drawing illustrating the interceptor contacts in the guinea pig retina. Four receptors of the B type enter into roving contact relation with one a receptor. On the right side is a slightly simplified drawing of the synaptic body of an a-cell. (From Sjöstrand, F.: In Smelser, G., editor: The structure of the eye, New York, 1961, Academic Press, Inc.)

and DPN-linked and TPN-linked isocitrate dehydrogenases are nearly as important (Fig. 244). The citric acid cycle plays a relatively minor role in retinal metabolism (Fig. 234).

It was noted that mitochondria were absent from the outer segments of the photoreceptors. There are likewise none in the rod fiber or in the cytoplasm surrounding the nucleus. The various respiratory enzymes and electron carriers are an integral part of the mitochondrial structure so that the whole respiratory

ZONES OF OXIDATIVE ENZYME ACTIVITY IN CHICK AND RAT RETINA

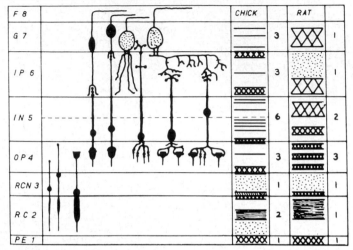

Fig. 244. First column: **F,** fiber zone; **G,** ganglion cell layer; **IP,** inner plexiform layer; **IN,** inner nuclear layer; **OP,** outer plexiform layer; **RCN,** rod and cone cell nuclei; **RC,** rod and cone body layer; **PE,** pigment epithelium. Second column: diagrammatic representation of cell bodies, axons, dendrites, and synapses in a composite retina, indicating their general arrangement within the numbered zones of classic histologic practice. Numbers in right-hand columns indicate the number of layers (of formazan pigment) visible with the light microscope or in photomicrographs taken with suitable filters. The other indications in the right-hand columns have the following significance: *single lines,* clearly separated thin lines of activity; *two lines with crosses,* much stronger activity in band form; *parallel lines,* very strong activity; *diffuse dots,* background diffuse activity of greater than normal amount; *clear areas,* low background activity or absence of activity. (From Pearse, A.: In Smelser, G., editor: The structure of the eye, New York, 1961, Academic Press, Inc.)

capacity of the visual cells seems to reside solely in the inner segments. Those parts where such enzymes are lacking must make use of nonrespiratory mechanisms for their metabolic needs, and it has been shown that in the rabbit and monkey the outer plexiform layer is rich in glycolytic enzymes.

THE PIGMENT EPITHELIUM

There is little doubt that the pigment epithelium is of critical importance in vision, but little is known about the functions of this important tissue, although recent studies have shed some light on its ultramicroscopic structure.[30, 31]

The epithelium is firmly bound down to the choroid by Bruch's membrane on its outer surface. On its inner surface it is in intimate contact with the photoreceptor cells, although up to now it has been generally believed that there was a potential space between the epithelium and the rods and cones, representing the space between the two layers of neural epithelium due to the invagination of the primary optic vesicle. It is here that separation of the retina occurs. From some electronmicroscopic studies,[31] however, it now appears that the outer segments of the rods at least are imbedded in the pigment epithelial cells which seem to form an anchor for the photoreceptors. Others question the intimacy of the association of the outer rod segments with the microvilli of the pigment epithelial cells and feel that the membranes of these two cellular structures are simply closely approximated by the forces that normally operate between closely applied cell membranes.[32]

The differences between these two points of view may be due to the time at which the contact between the pigment epithelial cells and the photoreceptors is examined. It has now been shown that prior to the fifteenth day of embryonic life the pigment epithelium and the neural retina must be free to slip over one another. This is attested to by the fact that they readily separate from each other in freshly dissected eyes prior to the fifteenth day. After that the processes of the pigment epithelial cells begin to appear, interdigitating with the developing rods and cones until soon it becomes impossible to separate these two layers without doing damage to one or both layers.[33]

The development of the pigment epithelium is determined by the intraocular pressure which begins to build up in the eye after closure of the choroidal fissure due to the growth of the vitreous. As a result of this the pigment epithelial cells undergo true hypertrophy.

The nutrition of the outer segments of the photoreceptors throughout the entire retina and all of the retinal structures in the fovea must come from the choriocapillaris through the epithelial cells, since no capillaries from the central retinal artery reach the fovea. The pigment epithelium is probably of some influence on the passage of metabolites to and from the photoreceptors, but at present we know nothing specific about this function.

Melanin granules are found as cytoplasmic inclusions in the epithelial cells. Some investigators believe that these granules are a lipofuscin rather than the melanin found in the choroid. The origin of these granules is not definitely known, but some evidence points to their origin in the Golgi apparatus. Moyer[34] believes that they form in intracisternal dilatations of the endoplasmic reticulum and are gene-induced. It is interesting in this respect to recall the poor vision of albinos, who have a gene-induced chemical abnormality that makes it impossible for them to produce melanin. Whether the poor vision in albinos is due directly to the reflection of light back from the white choroid in an irregular fashion so as to interfere with a proper gradient of contrast on the photoreceptors (p. 770) or to some more subtle effect of the absence of pigment on the excitatory process in the retina is not known.

Large numbers of mitochondria are found along with large spherical granules.[35] The fine structure of the epithelial cells underlying the peripheral portions of the retina in the ora serrata is quite different from that where photoreceptors are present. This suggests that the pigment epithelial cell may have considerable to do with the processes of visual excitation. It is well known that regeneration of rhodopsin does not take place in the retina unless the retina is in contact with the pigment epithelium. Wald[36] has made the ingenious suggestion that the pigment epithelium may represent the sheath of Schwann of the retina, and that its relationship with the outer segments of the photoreceptors is comparable to the intimate relationship of the Schwann cells with the nerve axons (p. 576) (Fig. 245).

Noell in 1952 discovered that the intravenous injection of sodium azide produced a rapid transitory change in the demarcation potential across the eye amounting to about 20 mv., as shown in Fig. 246. This occurred in either the dark or the light and persisted in animals in

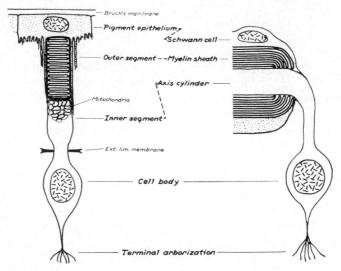

Fig. 245. Structural relations between a retinal rod and a peripheral nerve cell. The pigment epithelium of the retina, with its long protoplasmic processes in which the outer segments of the visual receptors are embedded, bears much the same intimate relation to the outer segment of a rod as does the Schwann cell to a nerve axon. Both tissues are neuroglial. The outer segment is comparable in structure with the myelin sheath, both being composed of double layers. The inner segment of the rod is comparable with the axis cylinder of nerve. Both cells possess comparable cell bodies with nuclei, and both end in aborizations which make synaptic contact with other nerve cells. (From Wald, 1958.)

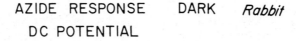

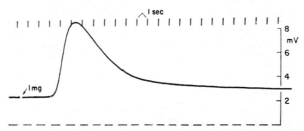

Fig. 246. Response of demarcation potential, **DC,** across the eye to fast intravenous injection of sodium azide, 1 mg. in 2 ml. (From Noell, W.: Am. J. Ophth. 48:348, 1959.)

which the photoreceptors had been completely degenerated by a previous administration of sodium iodoacetate. This change in potential could not have been due to the visual cells, therefore. If, however, a previous injection of iodate was given, the change in the demarcation potential across the eye failed to appear, although there was no change detectable in either the a or the b waves of the electroretinogram. The c wave of the electroretinogram, however, was abolished along with the change in the demarcation potential. From these and other reasons, Noell came to the conclusion that the effect of the azide injection was on the pigment epithelium, and in support of this belief he showed that the histologic effect of iodate is preferentially and primarily damage to the pigment epithelium. In addition, it has been shown that when the c wave is eliminated from the electroretinogram by iodate a potential of opposite polarity appears. This is a slow cornea-negative potential, which in contrast to the c wave, is insensitive to azide and has therefore been termed the azide-insensitive slow potential by Noell. Noell assumes that this azide-insensitive potential reflects the original ionic changes that occur in the retina in response to illumination, and that the pigment epithelium attempts by means of active ion transport to restore its ionic equilibrium at the visual cell border, the c wave being the reflection of this ion transport. After prolonged illumination similar results occur when the illumination is cut off. After sudden cessation of illumination, a slow potential change in the opposite direction of the c wave appears. If the animal is poisoned by iodate and azide sensitivity is thus eliminated, the c wave is replaced by the azide-insensitive cornea-negative potential,

whereas the normal cornea-negative "off" wave is replaced by a cornea-positive azide-insensitive reaction. These two changes, the "on" and "off" changes, have similar forms and amplitudes. Noell believes they indicate an ionic imbalance of one sign in reaction to the "on" and of the opposite sign to the "off" of illumination. In effect, this potential change comes from the nonneuronal pigment epithelial cells as a direct result of ionic changes that occur in the neighboring neuronal cells when they are stimulated by light. It obviously implicates the pigment epithelium in the mechanism of vision. Further work will have to be done before we can adequately assess the importance of this function.

A substance which stimulates the regeneration of rhodopsin[37] and an enzyme which promotes selective esterification of 11-cis vitamin A have been extracted from the pigment epithelium. Krinsky[38] suggests that this enzyme diffuses from the epithelium into the outer rod segments where hydrolysis and synthesis of rhodopsin occur. This may account for the well-known fact that patients with retinal detachment see much better in the morning on awakening from sleep than later in the day after they have been in

Table 51. *Partition of phosphorus compounds in pigment epithelium and retina**

Fraction†	Pigment epithelium		Retina	
	μg P/mg. protein	% total P	μg P/mg. protein	% total P
Total P‡	15.5		21.3	
Acid-soluble P§ (inorganic and organic)	3.9	30	2.1	10
Phospholipid P	7.8	60	9.9	47
Nucleic acid P	2.6	20	8.5	41
Protein P	—		—	

*From Glockin, V., and Potts, A.: Invest. Ophthal. 1:111, 1962.
†Fractionation by method of Schneider.
‡P determined by method of Weil-Malherbe and Green, after acid digestion.
§Inorganic P was less than 5% of total acid-soluble P.

an erect posture. During the night the retina falls back in contact with the pigment epithelium where this diffusion can more readily take place into the rod outer segments. A comparison of the partition of phosphorus compounds in the pigment epithelium and the rest of the retina has been made by Glockin and Potts,[39] as shown in Table 51.

PIGMENTARY DEGENERATION OF THE RETINA

To the present time, this familial and often hereditary disease has been included in the group of conditions called abiotrophies. By definition these are conditions in which tissues that have attained full maturity undergo progressive degeneration. Although not all clinicians accept the theory, most pathologists believe that the pigmentary degeneration starts as a primary selective degeneration of the photoreceptors, particularly the rods, and that the constriction of the retinal arteries and the pigment dissemination are secondary.

In recent years much light has been shed on pigmentary degeneration of the retina. It is discussed here because investigation of the condition has inadvertently yielded some information of value in retinal physiology. In 1929 Riehm reported a series of patients who suffered severe loss of vision along with the typical retinal changes of pigmentary degeneration as a result of the intravenous injections of an iodine-containing antiseptic solution Septoiodine. Following this, similar results were obtained in experimental animals. Sorsby obtained a similar picture in rabbits with injections of sodium iodate, one of the principal constituents of Septoiodine, and Noell and co-workers found that functional impairment of the retina could be demonstrated in animals before any histologic changes

in the retina were visible. With injections of sodium iodoacetate Noell found marked depression of the electroretinogram with recovery if the dose was small, but the depression was irreversible when larger doses were injected. Visual cell death was found in inverse relationship to the degree of recovery of the electroretinogram, with markedly selective effects on the rods. This was particularly true in the rhesus monkey, paralleling the histopathology in human beings.

As a result of his studies, Noell suggested that the effect of iodoacetate was primarily interference with anaerobic glycolysis. Iodoacetate has been known for a long time to be an effective inhibitor of the triose phosphate dehydrogenase of the Embden-Meyerhoff pathway in glycolysis. The probable site of the interference is indicated by the asterisk in Fig. 234. The visual cells and especially the rods seem to be uniquely sensitive to iodoacetate, indicating that they are extraordinarily dependent upon glycolysis as a process distinct from total cell respiration as a source of phosphate-bond energy.

In 1938 Bourne and others found a typical picture of pigmentary degeneration in a breed of rats which was inheritable. This colony and subsequently others have been used to great advantage in research on pigmentary degeneration, on the assumption that if it is not identical the condition is similar to that occurring in man. In these rats the degeneration of the photoreceptors can be shown to have already begun before the differentiation of the retina has been completed. Histologic changes occur in the photoreceptors as early as fifteen days before the visual cells have completely differentiated.[40, 41] This evidence immediately lifts pigmentary degeneration of the retina out of the category of abiotrophies, which are

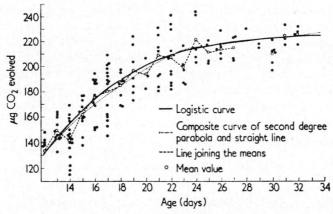

Fig. 247. Graph of the rate of anaerobic glycolysis against age for retinas from control rats. (From Brotherton, J.: Exper. Eye Res. 1:234, 1962.)

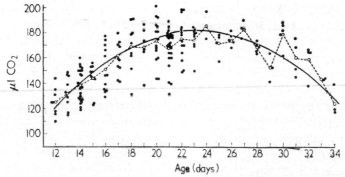

Fig. 248. Graph of the rate of anaerobic glycolysis age for retinas from affected rats. (From Brotherton, J.: Exper. Eye Res. 1:234, 1962.)

limited by definition to those tissues which have already matured. This, plus other evidence, strongly suggests that this disease is due to an inborn error of metabolism and is probably gene-determined.

A considerable diminution in the amount of retinal anaerobic glycolysis was demonstrated by Walters in affected rats before the visual cells began to show signs of dissolution.[42] This has been confirmed in rats even as young as 12 days of age, i.e., before the visual cells are fully differentiated, by Brotherton.[43] A comparison between the rates of anaerobic glycolysis of control rats and rats affected with pigmentary degeneration

is given in Figs. 247 and 248. The fall in the rate of glycolysis with age suggests that in the process one of the end products is inhibiting the main reaction, and Brotherton suggests, "In affected rats such an inhibitor could be produced in larger amounts and could cause the metabolic activity of the cells gradually to cease."*

Other changes in the chemical composition of the retinas of these affected rats have been found. The normal rat retina contains large amounts of a free amino

---

*From Brotherton, J.: Exper. Eye. Res. 1: 234, 1962.

acid, taurine, which is markedly deficient in affected rats. There are likewise a decrease in β-aminoisobutyric acid and an increase in aspartic acid and glycine.

It is beginning to look more and more as if this disease is due to the deficiency of an enzyme, and that the degeneration of the visual cells is caused by reduced resistance to the harmful effects of some normal constituent. One enzyme, triosephosphatedehydrogenase, which depends on its sulphydryl groups for activity, may possibly be implicated, for the changes in free amino acids just cited indicate that the sulphydryl groups in the retina are not acting in their normal manner.

Some investigators have pointed out that the retinotoxic effect of substances such as iodate and iodoacetate cannot depend on generalized sulphhydryl inhibition or upon inhibition of glycolysis per se,[44] for other compounds having similar inhibitory properties on metabolism are not retinotoxic. Certain substances seem to have protective effects against the retinotoxic action of iodate and iodoacetate, but no clear-cut picture of the exact mode of action of either the retinotoxic drugs or of the protective agents has yet been presented. Cysteine, e.g., has a protective action against the retinotoxic effects of sodium iodate but not against the effects of iodoacetate. As Sorsby and Harding point out:

"For the present the position is paradoxical in that the retinal degeneration produced by iodoacetate, a known inhibitor of −SH enzymes, is not prevented by the −SH-containing protectors recorded here, whilst the preventable retinotoxic effect of iodate is not known to be due to inhibition of −SH enzyme activity."*

Many other substances have been discovered which have retinotoxic effects

*From Sorsby, A., and Harding, R.: Vision Res. 2:147, 1962.

which may prove of great interest in experimentation. The diaminophenoxyalkanes used in the treatment of schistosomiasis given to cats cause histologic changes which are limited initially to the pigment epithelium.[46] In frogs these compounds decrease the rate and extent of regeneration of rhodopsin during dark adaptation[47] and in rabbits produce changes in the electroretinogram. It seems probable that these drugs act primarily as specific poisons in some stage of the rhodopsin cycle.[48]

In addition to the strain of rats showing pigmentary degeneration, various other strains of mice have been found which develop other types of retinal anomalies which seem to be based on enzymatic disorders of retinal cell metabolism. A strain was reported by Keeler, called rodless, in which the retina fails to develop the outer layers of the retina during early postnatal development. A strain known as the C3H mice has been reported by Dunn (1954) and Noell (1958) in which in the normally developed retina pyknosis and lysis of the visual cells occur.[49, 50]

VITAMIN A DEFICIENCY

The part vitamin A plays in the synthesis of rhodopsin is considered in Chapter 13. The effects of vitamin A deficiency on the fine structure of the photoreceptors will be discussed here. It has been known for a long time that vitamin A starvation in man and animals will lead to severe histologic degeneration of the retina. If the deprivation is continued long enough, xerosis of the conjunctiva and other mucous membranes, xerophthalmia, and finally death ensue.

Dowling and Wald[51] found that rats deprived of vitamin A could be kept alive and healthy if vitamin A acid was added

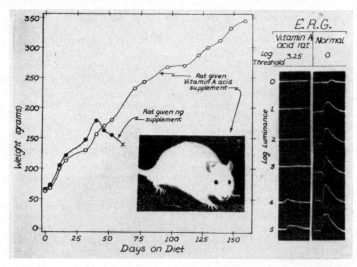

Fig. 249. Biological activity of vitamin A acid. Litter mates were placed on vitamin A-deficient diet. The animal receiving no supplement grew until vitamin A stores were exhausted, then lost weight rapidly, and died on the fifty-seventh day of the experiment. The animal given vitamin A acid grew throughout the experiment (five months) and remained in good condition. The picture of this animal was taken at the end of the experiment, as were the electroretinograms shown at the right, compared with those of a normal animal. They show that this rat is highly night blind: it has a visual threshold 3.25 $\log_{10}$ units above normal, corresponding to loss of 96 to 98% of the rhodopsin from the eye. (From Dowling, J., and Wald, G.: Proc. Nat. Acad. Sc. **46:**587, 1960.)

to the diet, but these animals developed night blindness and degeneration of the retina just the same (Fig. 249). This offered the opportunity for a study of the effects of vitamin A deficiency on the retina alone, uncomplicated by other changes in the body. It also gave them the opportunity to correlate the progressive changes in the retina with the simultaneous changes in retinal function and biochemical changes in the retina.

REFERENCES

1. Crane, R., and Ball, E.: Relationship of $C^{14}O_2$ fixation to carbohydrate metabolism in retina, J. Biol. Chem. **189:**269, 1951.
2. Kuwabara, T., and Cogan, D.: Retinal glycogen, Arch. Ophth. **66:**680, 1961.
3. Lowry, O., Roberts, N., and Lewis, C.: The quantitative histochemistry of the retina, J. Biol. Chem. **220:**879, 1956.
4. Takano, H.: Über die Gewebsatmung der Netzhaut, Acta Soc. Ophth. Jap. **38:**1307, 1934.
5. Nakashima, M., and Hayashi, K.: Sur le potentiel d'oxydo-reduction de la retine, J. Biochem. **17:**315, 1933.
6. Jongbloed, J., and Noyons, A.: Sauerstoffverbrauch und Kohlendioxydeproduktion der Froschretina bei Dunkelheit und bei Licht, Ztschr. Biol. **97:**399, 1936.
7. Ikemune, I.: Studien über den Ruhestrom und Aktionsstrom des Auges, Jap. J. M. Sc., III, Biophysics **5:**18, 1938.
8. Chase, A., and Smith, E.: Regeneration of visual purple in solution, J. Gen. Physiol. **23:**21, 1939.
9. Lindeman, V.: The respiratory metabolism of the frog retina, Physiol. Zool. **13:**411, 1940.
10. Berkow, J., and Patz, A.: Histochemistry of the retina, Arch. Ophth. **65:**820, 828, 1961.
11. Enoch, J.: The use of tetrazolium to distinguish between retinal receptors ex-

posed and not exposed to light, Invest. Ophthal. **2**:16, 1963.

12. Dartnall, H., and Thomson, L.: Retinal oxygen supply and macular pigmentation, Nature, London **165**:876, 1949.

13. Kornblueth, W., et al.: Glucose utilization of the retina, Arch. Ophth. **50**:45, 1953.

14. Koelle, G., and Friedenwald, J.: A Histochemical method for localizing cholinesterase activity, Proc. Soc. Exper. Biol. & Med. **70**:617, 1949.

15. Noell, W., and Lasansky, A.: Effects of electrophoretically applied drugs and electrical currents on the ganglion cell of the retina, Fed. Proc. **18**:115, 1959.

16. Tarawa, M.: The effect of light upon the phosphoric acid fraction of the retina, Acta Soc. Ophth. Jap. **42**:1503, 1938.

17. Tahamatsu, T.: Photochemische Studien der Netzhaut, Acta Soc. Ophth. Jap. **38**:1035, 1934.

18. Nakashima, M., and Arata, Y.: Azotometrie der Netzhaut, Acta Soc. Ophth. Jap. **40**:1586, 1936.

19. Von Studnitz, G.: Vom Energieumsatz in der Netzhaut, Naturwissenschaften **22**:193, 1934.

20. Anfinsen, C.: The distribution of diphosphopyridine nucleotide in the bovine retina, J. Biol. Chem. **152**:279, 1944.

21. Nakashima, M.: Beitrage sur Kenntnis des Sehpurpur, Zentralbl. ges. Ophth. **22**:772, 1930.

22. Von Studnitz, G.: Die Retinale Sauerbildung, Arch. ges. Physiol. **238**:802, 1937.

23. Swan, K.: Lectures to graduate students, Boston, 1949.

24. Bech, K.: Physiological activity changes in the retinal ganglion cells, Danish M. Bull. **5**:72, 1958.

25. Curtis, D., Phillis, J., and Watkins, J.: The depression of spinal neurones by a-amino-n. butyric acid and beta-alanine, J. Physiol. **146**:185, 1959.

26. Cogan, D.: Retinal architecture and pathophysiology, Am. J. Ophth. **54**:347, 1962.

27. Ladman, A.: The fine structure of the rod-bipolar cell in the retina of the albino rat, J. Physiol. & Biochem. Cytol. **4**:459, 1958.

28. Kuwabara, T., and Cogan, D.: Tetrazolium studies on the retina. I. Introduc-tion and technique, J. Histochem. **7**:329, 1959.

29. Pearse, A.: Localization of oxidative enzymes in rat and chick retina in various physiological conditions. In Smelser, G., editor: Structure of the eye, New York, 1961, Academic Press Inc.

30. Yamada, E.: The fine structure of the pigment epithelium in the turtle eye. In Smelser, G., editor: Structure of the eye, New York, 1961, Academic Press Inc., p. 73.

31. Bernstein, M.: Functional architecture of the retinal epithelium. In Smelser, G., editor: Structure of the eye, New York, 1961, Academic Press Inc., p. 139.

32. Cohen, A.: The fine structure of the extrafoveal receptors of the rhesus monkey, Exper. Eye Res. **1**:133, 1961.

33. Coulombre, A., Steinberg, S., and Coulombre, J.: The role of intraocular pressure in the development of the chick eye, Invest. Ophthal. **2**:83, 1963.

34. Moyer, F.: Electronmicroscope observations on the origin, development and genetic control of melanin granules in the mouse eye. In Smelser, G., editor: Structure of the eye, New York, 1961, Academic Press Inc., p. 469.

35. Bernstein, M., and Pease, D.: J. Biophys. & Biochem. Cytol. **5**:35, 1959.

36. Wald, G.: Discussion of retinal structure in relation to the visual process. In Smelser, G., editor: Structure of the eye, New York, 1961, Academic Press Inc., p. 101.

37. Bliss, A.: Properties of the pigment layer factor in the regeneration of rhodopsin, J. Biol. Chem. **193**:525, 1951.

38. Krinsky, N.: The enzymatic esterification of vitamin A, J. Biol. Chem. **232**:881, 1958.

39. Glockin, V., and Potts, A.: The metabolism of retinal pigment cell epithelium, Invest. Ophthal. **1**:111, 1962.

40. Lucas, D.: Exper. Zool. **126**:537, 1954.

41. Lucas, D., Attfield, M., and Davey, J.: Retinal dystrophy in the rat, J. Path. & Bact. **70**:469, 1955.

42. Walters, P.: Anaerobic glycolysis in rats affected with retinitis pigmentosa, Brit. J. Ophth. **43**:686, 1959.

43. Brotherton, J.: Studies on the metabolism of the rat retina with special references to retinitis pigmentosa. I. Anaerobic

glycolysis, Exper. Eye Res. **1:**234, 1962.

44. Sorsby, A., and Nakajima, A.: Experimental degeneration of the retina. III, Brit. J. Ophth. **42:**558, 1958.
45. Sorsby, A., and Harding, R.: Experimental degeneration of the retina. VII, Vision Res. **2:**147, 1962.
46. Ashton, N.: Degeneration of the retina due to 1:5 (p-aminophenoxyl)-pentane dihydrochloride, J. Path. & Bact. **74:**103, 1957.
47. Goodwin, L.: The toxicity of diaminophenoxyalkalanes, Brit. J. Pharmacol. **12:**468, 1957.
48. Arden, G., and Fojas, M.: The mode of action of diaminophenoxyalkanes and related compounds on the retina, Vision Res. **2:**173, 1962.
49. Noell, W.: Differentiation, metabolic organization and viability of the visual cell. Arch. Ophth. **60:**702, 1958.
50. Dipaolo, J., and Noell, W.: Some genetic aspects of visual cell degeneration in mice, Exper. Eye Res. **1:**215, 1962.
51. Dowling, J., and Wald, G.: Proc. Nat. Acad. Sc. **46:**587, 1960.

CHAPTER 13

PHOTOCHEMISTRY
OF VISION

ABSORPTION OF LIGHT

As discussed in Chapter 11, the wave-lengths of the energy spectrum between 400 and 800 mμ stimulate the retina and give rise to visual sensations. Just how the energy in light is transduced to electrical energy in the photoreceptors is not clear at present, but the first step in the process must be a photochemical one; i.e., the light energy breaks down some substance in the retina which is light sensitive. One of the products of this breakdown then changes the electrical potential of the transmitting neurons so that a coded message in the form of a repetitive discharge is sent to the visual centers in the brain. In order to effect a breakdown of any substance by light, the light must be absorbed by the substance. A transparent substance cannot be chemically affected by light since it does not absorb the light. This is a fundamental law of photochemistry.

Photosensitive pigments

Substances which have the property of absorbing parts of the visible spectrum are called pigments. Their color is due to the reflection of those wave-lengths which are not absorbed back to the eye of the observer. Black, e.g., is a pigment which absorbs all the visible wavelengths so that none are reflected back. A red pigment is one which absorbs all wavelengths except those from the red end of the spectrum, around 700 mμ, which are reflected back. Any substance in the retina which absorbs portions of the visible spectrum must belong to the general class of pigments. Not only the human eye but also the photoreceptors in all forms of life possess one or more such pigments capable of selectively absorbing different portions of the visible spectrum. Most of these photosensitive substances are not limited in their absorption to one small band of wavelengths, but absorb some wavelengths better than others, with a peak of absorptive ability at one particular wavelength. This peak of absorption is called the absorption maximum (abbreviated to lambda max.) of the particular pigment. The curve representing this differential absorptive property to different wavelengths is called the absorption spectrum of the pigment. If a particular photoreceptor is found to be especially sensitive to one part of the spectrum and not to others, it is certain that it will contain a pigment or pigments whose absorption spectrum will match its characteristic sensitivity.

Pigments present in lower animals and plants. The pigments which are found in all the photosynthetic cells of plants and in the photosensitive cells of animals belong to the general chemical class of carotenoids, which are unsaturated hydrocarbons, soluble in fatty substances. One of the carotenoids, beta-carotene, discovered in the carrot, is an aldehyde which can be readily converted to the corresponding alcohol, which is vitamin A (see formula at bottom of page).

The beta-carotene in the retina has been termed retinene. Other carotenoids are found in the retina, substances derived from carotene, e.g., carotene glycol or xanthophyll, which constitutes the yellow pigment found in the macula of man and the higher mammals.

The light which stimulates photokinetic responses in plant structures is absorbed by these carotenes and xanthophylls in the plant cells. These same pigments are concentrated in the eyespots of certain Protista (unicellular organisms midway between plants and animals). The active role of light absorption in the image-forming eyes of mollusks and arthropods is assumed by rhodopsin, a combination of the carotene, retinene, and a protein. In the freshwater vertebrates a slightly different chemical form of retinene (retinene$_2$) exists which combined with a protein is called porphyropsin. In most species of animals examined this form of carotene is closely associated with freshwater existence. The marine fishes and the terrestrial vertebrates, having evolved from the freshwater vertebrates, would be expected to have porphyropsin as a photosensitive pigment, but instead they seem to have reverted to rhodopsin found in mollusks and arthropods. Interpolated between the freshwater and the marine fishes are euryhaline forms which spawn in either fresh or salt water. The salmon and the eel, as is well known, spend part of their lives in fresh water, where they lay their eggs, and the rest of the time in salt water. These euryhaline fishes possess both rhodopsin and porphyropsin in mixtures but always predominantly the one associated with the environment in which the fish spawns. In the Amphibia, which are similarly interpolated between the freshwater fishes and the permanently terrestrial vertebrates, both systems appear again, although the factors which determine their distribution are still obscure. In Fig. 250 are shown various classes of plants and animals and the form of the carotenoid present, as deter-

Vitamin A

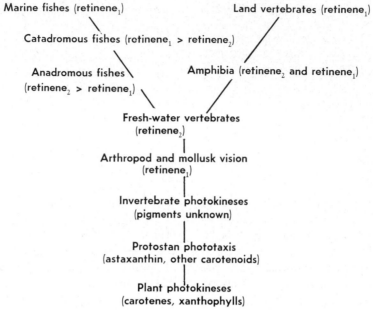

Marine fishes (retinene$_1$)

Catadromous fishes (retinene$_1$ > retinene$_2$)

Land vertebrates (retinene$_1$)

Anadromous fishes
(retinene$_2$ > retinene$_1$)

Amphibia (retinene$_2$ and retinene$_1$)

Fresh-water vertebrates
(retinene$_2$)

Arthropod and mollusk vision
(retinene$_1$)

Invertebrate photokineses
(pigments unknown)

Protostan phototaxis
(astaxanthin, other carotenoids)

Plant photokineses
(carotenes, xanthophylls)

Fig. 250. Relation of photosensitive pigments to various classes of plants and animals. (After Wald.)

mined by Wald. As just stated, the form of retinine which when combined with a protein gives rise to rhodopsin is called retinene$_1$, whereas that which gives rise to porphyropsin is called retinene$_2$. The structural formula of retinene$_1$ as compared to retinene$_2$, is shown as follows.

Retinene$_1$

Retinene$_2$

Pigments present in the vertebrates.
The first pigment to be extracted from the
retina of vertebrates was rhodopsin, first
called visual purple by Boll in 1876. He
noted that the retina of a frog kept in
the dark showed a purplish color which
rapidly faded out when the eye was exposed to light. When the eye was put
back in the dark again, the purplish color
returned. Since the discovery of rhodopsin, many other visual pigments have been
found. All of these pigments are combinations of either retinene$_1$ or retinene$_2$ with a
protein known as opsin. If the pigment
is located in rods, which are the receptors
that function in the dark-adapted state,
the protein is called scotopsin. If the pigment is located in cones, which function
only in daylight illumination, the pigment is called photopsin. At present four
pigments with sufficiently different characteristics for identification have been
isolated. Wald believes that they can
account for all the requirements for light
absorption in animals' retinas. Two of
these pigments are found only in rods
and have already been mentioned, i.e.,
rhodopsin and porphyropsin. Rhodopsin
is retinene$_1$ combined with scotopsin,
whereas porphyropsin is retinene$_2$ combined with scotopsin. In 1937 the first
light-sensitive pigment to be found in
cones was discovered by Wald in the
chicken eye, which is almost entirely a
cone retina. He gave this pigment the
name iodopsin and found that it was
composed of retinene$_1$ combined with
the protein photopsin. Reasoning by analogy from the combinations of scotopsin with retinene$_1$ and retinene$_2$, Wald
proposed that a fourth pigment would be
discovered in cones in those animals
which had retinene$_2$ instead of retinene$_1$.
He thereupon set out to synthesize this
pigment and was able to do so, giving it
the name of cyanopsin. As yet this pig-

ment has not actually been extracted
from any animal's eye, but there is suggestive evidence that it is present in the
retina of the European tortoise *Testudo
graeca* and is the pigment of cone vision
in these animals.

In summary, four pigments are recognized as entities by Wald, as follows:
1. *Rhodopsin*—retinene$_1$ combined with
   scotopsin; found in rods
2. *Porphyropsin*—retinene$_2$ combined
   with scotopsin; found in rods
3. *Iodopsin*—retinene$_1$ combined with
   photopsin; found in cones
4. *Cyanopsin*—retinene$_2$ combined with
   photopsin; found in cones

Wald has consistently held the following opinion.

". . . [that] in the rods of vertebrates there is
substantial evidence for the existence of only
two visual pigments, rhodopsin and porphyropsin. The distribution of these pigments has
been explored to the point at which it begins
to seem probable that there are no others."[*]

This may be an oversimplification since
a number of similar pigments having
slightly different chemical and physical
properties have now been isolated. Porphyropsin extracted from different species
of fish have been found to have absorption
maxima ranging from 524 to 532 mμ. In
the human being and in the rat rhodopsin
has an absorption maxima (λ max.) at
497 mμ. Some of these pigments and their
absorption maxima are shown in Fig. 251
and the λ max. of pigments from various
vertebrates in Fig. 252. Retinene$_1$ and
retinine$_2$ exist in a number of different cis-
trans forms and combine with opsins to
form photosensitive pigments of somewhat
different properties. Dartnall[2] therefore
prefers to use the term *rhodopsin* as the
generic name for all rod pigments based

[*]From Wald, G.: Ann. Rev. Biochem. **22:**
497, 1953.

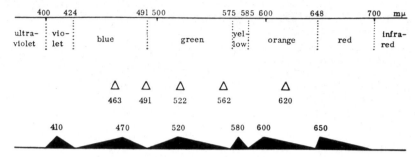

Fig. 251. Absorption maxima of extracted and synthesized photosensory pigments range across much of the spectral range visible to man. Commonly accepted boundaries (top) and representative centers (bottom) of appropriate wavelengths of light are shown for each hue sensation. Photosensory pigments include: 463, euphausiopsin (Kampa, 1955); 491, rhodopsin (Kuhne, 1877) and cephalopsin (Bliss, 1948); 522, porphyropsin (Wald, 1937); 562, iodopsin (Wald, 1937); and 620, cyanopsin (Wald, 1953). (From Milne, L., and Milne, M.: In Handbook of physiology. Neurophysiology. Washington, D. C.: Am. Physiol. Soc., 1959, sect. 1, vol. I, chap. 26, pp. 621-645.)

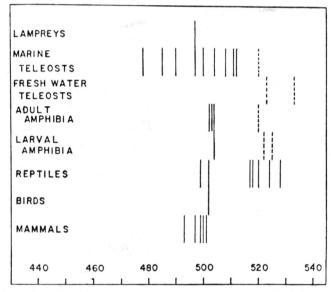

Fig. 252. Wavelengths of maximum absorption of retinal photolabile pigments from various vertebrates, as inferred from their hydroxylamine difference spectrums. *Solid lines,* retinene₁ pigments; *dotted lines,* retinene₂ pigments. For all the pigments shown, Dartnell's generalization holds, at least approximately. (From Crescitelli, F.: Ann. New York Acad. Sc. 74:230, 1958.)

on retinene rather than as a name for a specific pigment. In referring to individual pigments he uses the absorption maximum to identify each. Thus, λ max. 497 mμ is used to indicate human or rat rhodopsin. Only one pigment has been extracted from

cones, but as we shall see, there is evidence for the existence of at least two photolabile pigments in the human fovea, which is rod-free (p. 599).

Since rhodopsin is the photosensitive pigment about which we have any considerable knowledge, this chapter will deal largely with its properties. Much of our knowledge of photoreception is based on the behavior of rhodopsin, but it seems probable that the kinetics of bleaching and re-formation of the cone pigments are similar to those of rhodopsin.

RHODOPSIN

Rhodopsin is a magenta-colored pigment in the dark which under the influence of light rapidly bleaches to a mixture of the yellow carotenoid retinene$_1$ and the colorless protein scotopsin after passing through intermediary products colored orange. Under certain conditions, which will be defined later, this yellow solution of retinene$_1$ and scotopsin gradually becomes colorless, and an analysis of this colorless solution reveals that most of the retinene$_1$ has been changed to vitamin A. It has been shown that retinene is the aldhehyde of vitamin A. The structural formulas for retinene and vitamin A are given on pp. 586 and 585.

The conversion of retinene to vitamin A occurs slowly and best in the dark and consists in the reduction of retinene by the enzyme alcohol dehydrogenase together with the coenzyme DPN. In Fig. 253 is shown the breakdown of rhodopsin to vitamin A and scotopsin, passing through retinene$_1$ and scotopsin. It will be emphasized later that light is concerned in this breakdown only in the early stages, the others being thermal reactions.

If we take a closer look at the effect of light on rhodopsin, various intermediate products can be identified between the rhodopsin molecule and retinene$_1$. In Fig. 253 it is shown that the first effect of light is a very rapid conversion of rhodopsin to the orange-red intermediate product called lumirhodopsin. Not only is this the first effect of light in breaking down rhodopsin, but it is also the only direct effect of the light energy. What follows is independent of the presence of light, i.e., reactions which proceed equally well in light or darkness. Several inter-

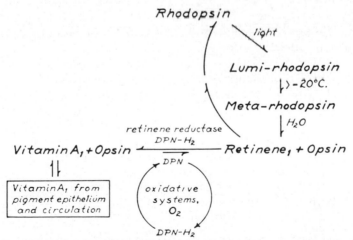

Fig. 253. Known components of the rhodopsin system. The intermediate steps in the bleaching of rhodopsin may not all be retraced when retinene$_1$ and opsin recombine to form rhodopsin. The bulk of the rhodopsin system lies within the outer segments of the retinal rods, but it is supplemented with vitamin A$_1$, respiratory factors, and oxygen itself from the pigment epithelium and the blood circulation. (From Hubbard, R., and Wald, G.: Proc. Nat. Acad. Sc. **37**:69, 1951.)

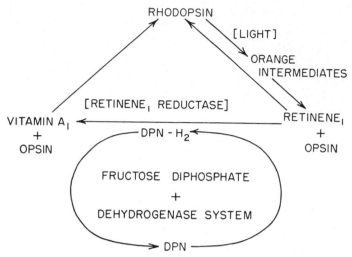

Fig. 254. Breakdown and resynthesis of rhodopsin according to Wald.

mediates have been isolated by different authors by differences in absorption spectrum. One of these, called metarhodopsin, is the next step, according to Wald, in the conversion of lumirhodopsin to retinene₁.*

The re-formation of rhodopsin from its breakdown products takes place by two routes. While retinene₁ is being formed under the initial influence of light through the steps of lumirhodopsin and metarhodopsin, an immediate reconversion of retinene₁ and scotopsin back to rhodopsin is also taking place. This breakdown and reconversion forms a steady state, the amount of rhodopsin present depending upon the intensity of the light. In the dark there is a further spontaneous combination of retinene₁ and scotopsin to form rhodopsin which requires no enzyme nor any external source of energy. Like all spontaneous reactions, it yields energy, and this energy is applied to oxidize vitamin A back to its aldehyde, retinene₁. In Figs. 253 and 254 it was shown that retinene was converted to vitamin A through alcohol dehydrogenase and DPN, involving the transfer of hydrogen from reduced DPN to the aldehyde group of retinene. Similarly, vitamin A is oxidized to retinene. This again is a two-way street, and as some retinene₁ is being reduced to vitamin A, likewise some Vitamin A is being oxidized back to retinene₁. However, the equilibrium between vitamin A and retinene₁ lies far over toward the side of reduction toward vitamin A. It requires work, therefore, to force vitamin A back to retinene₁ and scotopsin in the dark. Scotopsin traps retinene₁ in the dark, removing it to form rhodopsin, and this displaces the equilibrium of the vitamin A-retinene₁

---

*Not all authors agree on the primary products that result from the exposure of rhodopsin to light. Lumirhodopsin and metarhodopsin have been defined to include only that fraction of the initial photoproduct that is unstable in the dark,[3] but according to Wulff[4] this unstable fraction seems to be a mixture of pigment molecules that have different properties. It still remains valid that whatever the product of bleaching is that effects the initial stimulus to rod excitation it must be formed within the first few milliseconds of the exposure of rhodopsin to light since the latent period of vision is of this same order.

steady state in the oxidative direction. Thus the trapping of retinene$_1$ by opsin in the dark forces vitamin A back to retinene$_1$ and thence to rhodopsin. The basic mechanism of rhodopsin synthesis is therefore as Wald puts it, "the energy-demanding oxidation of vitamin A to retinene, coupled with the energy-yielding condensation of retinene and opsin to form rhodopsin."* This reaction is self-limiting. Vitamin A is oxidized to retinene only as long as scotopsin is present to trap retinene. When all the scotopsin in the rods has been converted to rhodopsin, the conversion of vitamin A to retinene$_1$ stops.

It would seem that all that is required to form rhodopsin is a suitable mixture of scotopsin, obtained from the outer segments of the rods (p. 569), vitamin A, alcohol dehydrogenase, and DPN. This in fact is true, but only if a special form of vitamin A is used. Vitamin A occurs in a number of different molecular shapes, cis-trans isomeres of one another. The predominant form found in the blood and the liver is all-trans vitamin A (Fig. 255). In vitro it has been found that this form of vitamin A will not form rhodopsin. The all-trans form will oxidize to retinene but will not combine with scotopsin to form rhodopsin. However, another form, the 11-cis form, will combine with scotopsin, and the retina must possess some mechanism which isomerizes the all-trans form to this 11-cis form which Wald has termed neo-b (Fig. 256). The oxidation of neo-b vitamin A to neo-b retinene permits its union with scotopsin to form rhodopsin. It is not entirely clear at present just what this mechanism is, but an enzyme, retinene

*From Wald, G.: In Handbook of physiology. Neurophysiology. Washington, D. C.: Am. Physiol. Soc., 1959, sect. 1, vol. I, chap. 28, pp. 671-692.)

isomerase, has been isolated from eye tissues which specifically catalyzes the interconversion of all-trans and neo-b retinene and which is also light-sensitive.

To summarize, light energy entering the rhodopsin molecule immediately changes it to lumirhodopsin. The effect of light probably stops here. The lumirhodopsin much more slowly is converted to metarhodopsin, and this breaks down to retinene and scotopsin. Even though the light is still on, some of this retinene and scotopsin automatically combine again to re-form rhodopsin, establishing a steady

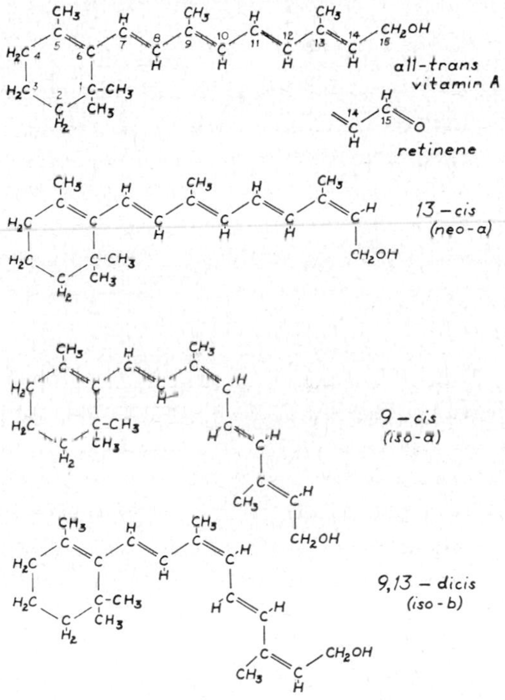

Fig. 255. Unhindered geometric isomers of vitamin A. This molecule can assume the cis configuration only at double bonds 9 and 13 without encountering serious steric hindrance. At the other double bonds, groups come into conflict, and the cis configuration not only bends but also twists the molecule. (Modified from Hubbard and Wald, 1951; from Wald, G.: In Handbook of physiology. Neurophysiology. Washington, D. C.: Am. Physiol. Soc., 1959, sect. 1, vol. I, chap. 28, pp. 671-692.)

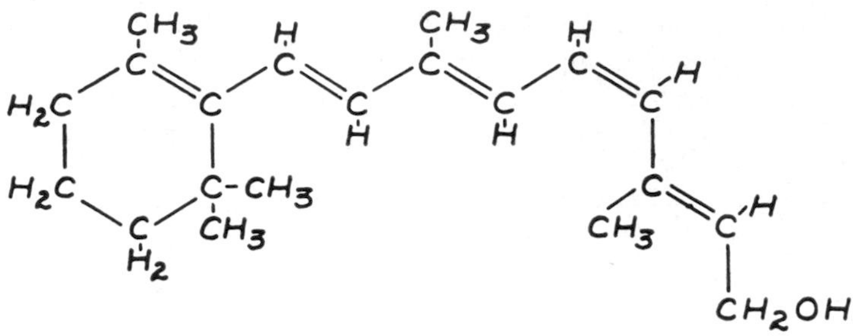

11-cis (neo-b)

Fig. 256. The sterically hindered neo-b (11-cis) isomer of vitamin A, the precursor of rhodopsin and iodopsin.

state, determined by the intensity of the illumination; the brighter the light the more rhodopsin is decomposed and the more retinene and scotopsin are present. In the dark, the retinene is gradually converted to vitamin A by the alcohol dehydrogenase-DPN system, and some of this newly formed vitamin A is forced back to retinene by the energy released when retinene and scotopsin automatically combine to re-form rhodopsin.

As the vitamin A is used up in this process, it must be replaced from stores in the blood and liver, but the form of vitamin A found in these reservoirs must undergo isomerization in the retina from the all-trans to the 11-cis isomer before it can catalyze rhodopsin. If, as postulated, the breakdown of rhodopsin by light releases energy which is transduced into an excitatory stimulus to the rods, what is the nature of this stimulus and what part of the breakdown products release it? It is most probable that the stimulus consists in a change in electrical polarization of part of the rod structure which engenders a flow of current. This, altered no doubt by many local phenomena, is eventually conducted up the nerve fiber in the form of trains of nerve impulses that constitute the sensory message to the higher visual centers. As to

what produces this change in electrical polarization we are at present largely ignorant, but certain possibilities have been suggested which have sufficient experimental backing to be intriguing.

The effect of light itself seems to go no further than to initiate the conversion of rhodopsin to lumirhodopsin or possibly to metarhodopsin. This effect is an almost instantaneous one and therefore fits in well with the observed facts that vision is almost an instantaneous affair; the perception of light occurs within milliseconds following exposure (p. 733). The further breakdown to retinene takes far too long, and, further, retinene is a bland relatively inert substance, hardly capable of acting as a stimulus. Rhodopsin has a large molecular weight, from 30,000 to 40,000, and contains one molecule of retinene. While it is true that the color changes in rhodopsin on exposure to light represent the changes in the prosthetic group, retinene, and therefore attract our attention, it is probable that the effect on the protein part of the rhodopsin rather than on the prosthetic group is the important element in vision. The rhodopsin molecule is largely protein. Scotopsin is probably a lipoprotein,[6] and a change in the scotopsin at the time of conversion to lumirhodopsin seems to be a plausible mechanism for

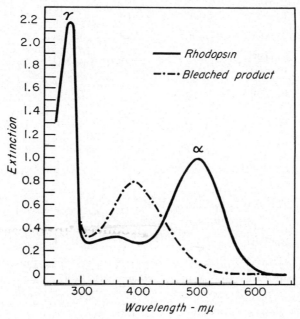

Fig. 257. Spectrums of rhodopsin and of the product of its bleaching in aqueous solution. Bullfrog rhodopsin in solution in 2% aqueous digitonin at pH 5.55. The spectrum of rhodopsin consists of three absorption bands. On bleaching, the alpha and beta bands of the carotenoid prosthetic group are replaced by the spectrum of retinene$_1$, with an absorption maximum at about 385 mμ. The protein gamma band remains unchanged. (From Wald, G.: J. Optic. Soc. America 41:949, 1951.)

excitation. This change may have something to do with the presence of free sulfhydryl (–SH) groups on scotopsin, and Wald has constructed two model systems, both based on the fact that light exposes ion-binding groups on scotopsin—sulfhydryl groups in one case and an acid-binding group in the other.

We have described elsewhere the ultrastructure of the rod outer segment (p. 572) composed largely of stacks of disks like a stack of coins, amounting to several hundred to several thousand layers, apparently of protein, each about 4 to 6 mμ thick. This protein is largely scotopsin, for 60% of the nonlipid dry weight of a frog rod and 22% of a cattle rod is accounted for by the rhodopsin present. The rhodopsin is found entirely in the outer segment of the rod, and it is likely that the light

energy is transduced into nervous energy here by the ionic shifts set up in the scotopsin of the disks.

Absorption spectrum of rhodopsin. When light falls on a solution of rhodopsin, it like all pigments absorbs some wavelengths to a greater extent than others. The curve representing this relative absorption to different wavelengths is known as the absorption spectrum. The relative absorption spectrum of frog rhodopsin, expressed as the coefficient of extinction,* is shown in Fig. 257. The curve shows three maxima of absorption to the wavelengths to which the solution was exposed: maximally between 200 and

---

*For this technique see Weale, R.: The eye and its function, London, 1960, Hatton Press, Ltd., p. 40.

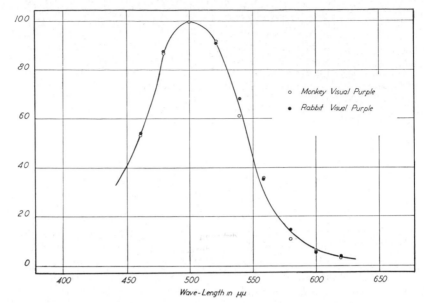

Fig. 258. Absorption spectrum of rhodopsin of rabbit and monkey. Ordinates represent relative absorption. (After Hecht and Williams.)

300 mμ, which is well below the range of visible light (p. 551), a small rise at about 340 mμ, and a sharp rise with a peak at around 500 mμ. The dotted line in Fig. 257 indicates that after bleaching there is a marked shift in the curve, the peak of absorption in the visible spectrum being shifted to around 400 mμ. Of chief interest to us is the alpha band. In Fig. 258 are shown the alpha bands of rhodopsin of the rabbit and monkey, and it can be seen that both are alike. Since the middle regions of the visible spectrum are almost entirely absorbed by rhodopsin and the other wavelengths are reflected back, the color of a solution of rhodopsin is a mixture of the red and blue ends of the spectrum or magenta (although rhodopsin was first called visual purple, the color is not true purple, but magenta).

Resemblance of the absorption spectrum of rhodopsin to the scotopic luminosity curve. It will be pointed out in the discussion of dark adaptation (p. 711) that the rods are the photoreceptors with

a very low light threshold. They respond to light intensities which are way below those necessary to stimulate the cones. The rods, therefore, are preeminently the mechanism for seeing when the eye is dark-adapted. We have seen that rhodopsin is present in the outer limbs of the rods only, from which one can infer that rhodopsin is the visual pigment whose breakdown by light is part of that mechanism for vision in dim illumination. We have seen that rhodopsin, like all pigments, absorbs some parts of the visible spectrum better than others and has a peak of absorption or lambda max. at 500 mμ. We would expect to find, therefore, that the dark-adapted eye would have its greatest sensitivity to light of 500 mμ, and that the curve of its sensitivity to different wavelengths would match that of the absorption spectrum of rhodopsin.

It has been found that the curve of sensitivity of the dark-adapted individual does match the absorption spectrum of rhodopsin, with a peak of sensitivity at

500 mμ, if certain corrections are made so that the two can be justifiably compared. The curve of sensitivity of the eye to different wavelengths is called the visibility or luminosity curve. That taken in the dark is called the scotopic luminosity curve, and that taken when the eye is light-adapted the photopic luminosity curve. The dark-adapted eye is color-blind, so that when a dark-adapted individual is being tested with different parts of the visible spectrum he sees no different colors but merely different intensities of gray. He will invariably pick the 500 mμ wavelengths as the brightest. The light-adapted person, on the other hand, appreciates the different colors of the different wavelengths, and his photopic luminosity curve is quite different from his scotopic luminosity curve, with a peak of 550 mμ. From this it can be concluded that some other pigment is present in the cones, and that its absorption spectrum must match that of the photopic luminosity curve. The peak of sensitivity in the scotopic luminosity curve at 500 mμ represents the blue-green part of the spectrum, whereas the peak of sensitivity of the photopic luminosity curve at 550 mμ represents the yellow-green part. This interesting change in the sensitivity of the human eye under conditions of light and dark adaptation was first described by Purkinje in 1825 and is known as the Purkinje shift. It proves beyond doubt that the human eye is a duplex sensory organ, having two different types of photoreceptors and at least two different visual pigments, one mechanism being effective at very low light intensities and the other at high intensities. This is what has been known as the duplicity theory.

In Fig. 259 are shown such spectral sensitivity curves for both the cone mechanism in the light-adapted eye and for

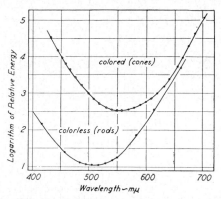

Fig. 259. Luminosity curves showing minimal amount of energy just perceptible to both dark-adapted and light-adapted subject in different portions of the spectrum. (After Hecht.)

the rod sensitivity curve in the dark-adapted eye. In this figure the wavelengths of light are plotted against the logarithm of relative energy necessary to produce a response. In the case of the cones, in the light-adapted eye the response is that of a colored light of varying hue. In the rod curve the retina was dark-adapted, and therefore the light perceived was colorless. The Purkinje shift shows nicely that the lowest energy capable of stimulating the cones is found at 550 mμ, whereas that of the rods is at 500 mμ. If instead of plotting the graph in this form, the reciprocal of the logarithm of relative energy is used, and the corresponding figures are used as percentages, from zero to 100%, the result is shown in Fig. 260. This, as can be seen, is strikingly similar to that of the absorption spectrum of rhodopsin, the visibility curve of the dark-adapted eye practically overlapping that of the absorption spectrum of rhodopsin.

It was this discovery which led physiologists to suggest that rhodopsin and the rod mechanism together were responsible for scotopic vision. Further, it was found

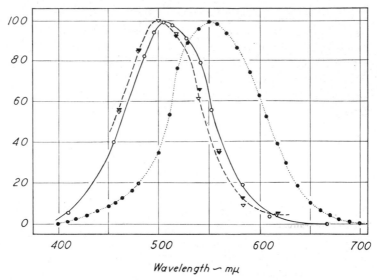

Fig. 260. Visibility curves and absorption spectrum of rhodopsin. *Open circles and continuous line,* recording of the relative effectiveness of the spectrum at the lowest intensities which are the reciprocals of the energies recorded in Fig. 259 arranged so that the maximum effectivement is 100. *Filled circles and broken line,* recording of the effectiveness of the spectrum at high intensities of illumination. (After Hecht.)

that animals who had had their rhodopsin destroyed by vitamin A deprivation lost their ability to become dark-adapted. When they were kept in the dark after exposure to bright light, their retinal action potentials disappeared, showing that rods without rhodopsin cannot function.

Close scrutiny of the curves of the scotopic luminosity and the absorption spectrum of rhodopsin shows that the fit is not perfect. The maximum luminosity of the dark-adapted eye is actually at 510 mμ, whereas the lambda max. of rhodopsin is at 497 mμ. This discrepancy is considerable and must be explained before the curves can be considered to be matched sufficiently to prove that rhodopsin is the photosensitive pigment whose breakdown activates the rods in dim illumination. The proof now seems complete, however, due to the work of Dartnall and Goodeve[7] and of Wald.[8] Wald pointed

out that in order for light rays to reach the retina they first have to traverse the ocular media. The transmission of light through the cornea and lens filters out some of the wavelengths selectively (p. 554). The cornea, aqueous humor, and vitreous humor absorb some light in the violet and ultraviolet regions of the spectrum. The lens, in addition, causes quite marked changes in the transmission of light, depending largely upon the age of the subject. In older persons as the lens becomes denser, the total amount of light transmitted is diminished, and the quality of the light transmitted is affected by the pigment which accumulates in the lens with age. Not only does this vary with age, but it also differs widely among people of the same age. Most of the accumulation of pigment, which is yellowish, occurs in the lens nucleus. This produces considerable interference with the formation of a clear retinal image if the accumulation is marked, forming what is known as a nuclear cataract. Another factor which changes the character of the light before it actually reaches the photoreceptors of the retina is the pigment found in the macula, referred to previously as xanthophyll.

The absorption spectrum of rhodopsin must, therefore, be matched with a visibility curve which is corrected for these factors. The luminosity curve must also be quantized; i.e., it must be expressed in terms of the actual quanta or photons of light which reach the retina. Generally what is measured is the relative energy at each wavelength needed to evoke a constant response. The reciprocal of this is the relative sensitivity, and this divided by the wavelength is the sensitivity in terms of relative numbers of incident photons. Also, corrections have to be made in the absorption spectrum of the visual pigment, in this case rhodopsin. In Fig. 261 are shown the absorption spectrum of rhodopsin and the human scotopic luminosity curve with these corrections made, showing an excellent fit of the curves. Also shown in Fig. 261 are the human photopic luminosity curve and the curve of iodopsin, a visual pigment extracted from the chicken eye. Iodopsin and cone vision will be referred to later.

Rhodopsin has been detected as early as six days after birth in rat eyes.[9] However, the mere presence of rhodopsin does not lead to the establishment of electrophysiologic events until organized retinal structure is laid down. The bipolar cell layer is not well delineated until the sixth day after birth, and Bonting and associates[9] found that the electroretinogram was not present until the twelfth day, which coincided with stacking of the rod discs in the outer segments.

IODOPSIN

We have seen that if the scotopic visibility curve is computed on the basis of the relative number of quanta which reach the retina at any wavelength, there

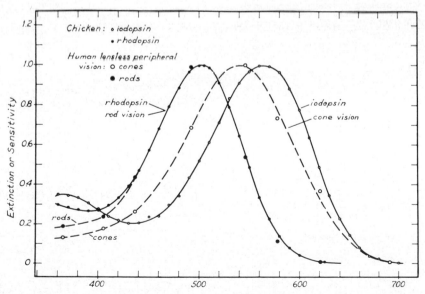

Fig. 261. Comparison of absorption spectrum or rhodopsin and iodopsin and photopic luminosity curve. (From Wald, G., Brown, P., and Smith, P.: J. Gen. Physiol. **38:**623, 1955.)

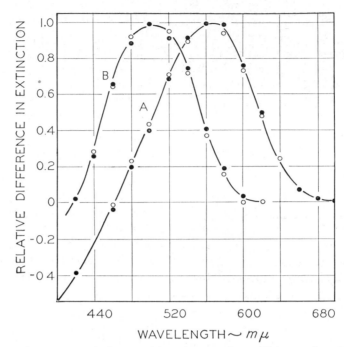

Fig. 262. Absorption spectra of photosensitive pigments from chicken retina. **A,** Change due to red light. **B,** Change due to white light after bleaching with red light. (After Bliss.)

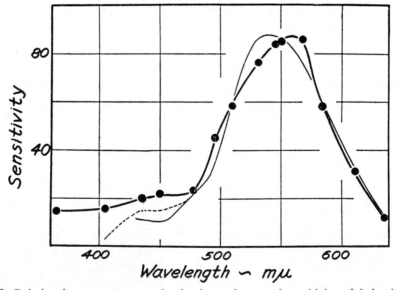

Fig. 263. Relation between spectrum luminosity and spectral sensitivity of iodopsin. *Heavy line,* spectral photosensitivity of iodopsin. *Light line,* spectral sensitivity of human cone vision according to Gibson and Tyndall. *Dotted line,* spectral sensitivity of human cone according to Stiles. (From Bliss, A.: The Chemistry of Daylight Vision, J. Gen. Physiol. **29:**277, 1946.)

is good agreement with the absorption spectrum of rhodopsin, but that the photopic visibility curve does not coincide with this. If photopic vision is also a photochemical process, some pigment must be present in the cones whose absorption spectrum fits the photopic visibility curve.

No photosensitive pigments have been extracted from the fovea of man, but Wald[11] has extracted a photosensitive pigment from the retina of the chicken, which has almost all cones. This red pigment bleaches in the light to form a yellow product, and has been given the name iodopsin by Wald. Its absorption bears a rough resemblance to the visibility curve of the light-adapted chicken. The absorption spectrum of this pigment[11] is shown in Fig. 262.

Iodopsin resembles rhodopsin in many of its chemical characteristics but has a lambda max. at 540 mμ (Fig. 263). Like rhodopsin, iodopsin is a carotenoid protein whose bleaching yields an inactive isomer of retinene$_1$, apparently the all-trans isomer. The carotenoids of the rhodopsin and iodopsin systems are identical; only the proteins are different.[12] In the case of iodopsin the protein in the cones is photopsin and in rhodopsin the protein is scotopsin in the rods.

VISUAL PIGMENTS IN HUMAN CONES

Although to date no visual pigments have been extracted from the eyes of man or the primates, the existence of at least two pigments in human cones has been established by the ingenious experiments of Rushton and co-workers. The method they employed, in essence, is to throw light onto the fovea and observe the intensity of the light reflected back. The reflected light has obviously made two passages through the cones (there are no rods in the fovea), once on the way in and again after reflection by the pigment epithelium. If a photosensitive pigment is present in these cones, some of the light will be trapped, changing the intensity of the reflected light. The intensity of the reflected light can be accurately determined as it is received by a photomultiplier cell. This method was first used by Rushton to measure the rate of bleaching of rhodopsin in the human eye, and these experiments will be referred to in the discussion of the nature of the photoreceptor process (p. 601). The existence of two different pigments in the normal human fovea could be clearly established, one pigment which is red-sensitive and one that is green-sensitive. Examination of the fovea of a protanope who was red-blind showed the existence of the green-sensitive pigment only. The curve of bleaching and regeneration of cone pigment measured upon the fovea of this subject is shown in Fig. 264. It can be seen that after bleaching with a white light regeneration takes place in about 8 minutes, which matches very well the recovery time of the fovea to attain full sensitivity after exposure to a bright light (p. 709). If this individual had both red-sensitive and green-sensitive pigment in his cones, we would expect to get quite different results by partial bleaching with red light and with green light instead of using white light, for the red light would bleach chiefly the red-sensitive pigment and the green light the green-sensitive. In Fig. 265 is shown the difference spectrum resulting from a partial bleach with red light and with green light in this subject. The results are the same. This proves that the protanope lacks entirely the red-sensitive pigment in his cones and has the green-sensitive pigment only. Measurements made on individuals with normal color vision, on the other hand, show a

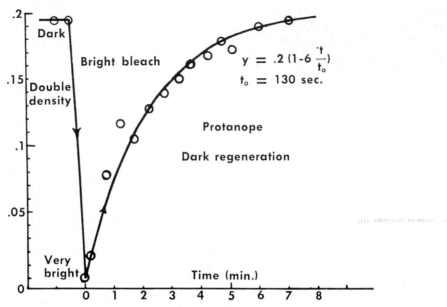

Fig. 264. Bleaching and regeneration of cone pigment measured upon the fovea of the protanope. (From Rushton, W.: Visual pigments in man, Liverpool, 1962, Liverpool University Press.)

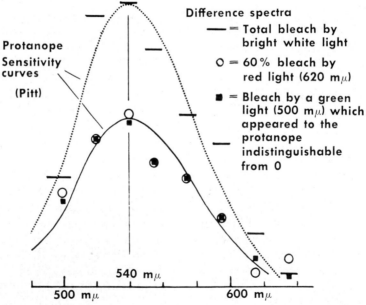

Fig. 265. Difference spectrum of foveal pigment of the protanope on partial bleaching by red or green light. (From Rushton, W.: Visual pigments in man, Liverpool, 1962, Liverpool University Press.)

marked difference in the difference spectrum with deep red bleach and with bright white bleach after all the red pigment had been removed by bleaching. This proves that in the normal color-sensitive fovea at least two pigments are present, one the pigment present in the fovea of the protanope and another pigment in addition. The green-sensitive pigment, present alone in the protanope, Rushton has called chlorolabe (green-catching), and the red-sensitive pigment present in normal individuals along with chlorolabe he has called erythrolabe (red-catching). A blue-sensitive pigment must also be present in order to account for the normal trichromacy of color vision (p. 804), but so far this has not been detected. Rushton calls this as yet undiscovered pigment cyanolabe. The pigment in both normal and protanope retinas has a λ max. at about 540 mμ (chlorolabe). The second pigment found only in normal foveas has a λ max. at about 590 mμ (erythrolabe).

NATURE OF THE PHOTORECEPTOR PROCESS

It has been shown that pigments which absorb light are necessary for the function of the retina, and the action of light on these pigments is to break them down into one or more active products which are thought to stimulate the photoreceptors. These then discharge an impulse in the optic nerve fibers. The constant breakdown of these pigments in the light and their equally constant re-formation in the dark establish a steady state, depending upon the degree of the illumination. This steady state, which is produced as a result of a balance between catalysis and synthesis, exists as long as the illumination remains unchanged. Such a steady state requires a constant supply of photosensitive material which is gradually being used up in the process.

At present little is known of the actual products of the breakdown of rhodopsin or iodopsin which change the retinal potential and thereby produce the electroretinogram, which will be described in Chapter 14. The bleaching of rhodopsin, at least as far as metarhodopsin, requires energy, and this is afforded by the light which is absorbed. The synthesis of rhodopsin from retinene$_1$ and scotopsin is a spontaneous reaction and requires no external source of energy. Whenever these two substances are present together in the dark, they form rhodopsin and yield energy spontaneously. However, the synthesis of rhodopsin from vitamin A$_1$ and scotopsin requires energy again. The equilibrium between retinene$_1$ and vitamin A$_1$, as stated, lies far over toward the side of reduction, i.e., toward vitamin A$_1$. In the dark, scotopsin traps retinene, removing it to form rhodopsin and hence displacing the equilibrium in the oxidative direction.

"The basic mechanism of rhodopsin synthesis, therefore, is the energy-demanding oxidation of vitamin A to retinene, coupled with the energy-yielding condensation of retinene and opsin to form rhodopsin."*

When rhodopsin is bleached, not only is the carotenoid split off from the protein scotopsin, but also profound changes occur in the configuration of the scotopsin itself, which in turn must be reversed when rhodopsin is synthesized. Wald points out that the changes taking place in the configuration of the protein are equally important or more significant in the mechanism of visual excitation.

There is evidence that after the initial breakdown of the visual pigment other processes occur which finally excite the

*From Wald, G.: Am. J. Ophth. **40**:18, 1955.

axon. It has been shown in the case of *Limulus*[13] that the excitator effects in the photoreceptor are not limited to the period during which light energy is being absorbed and active photolysis is taking place. After a short flash of fixed intensity, the latent period decreases with increasing duration of flash, up to a certain critical value beyond which continuation of the exposure has no further effect on the time of appearance of the first impulse in the nerve preparation. The processes that determine the beginning of the response are completed at the end of the critical duration, even though the impulses themselves do not appear until some time later. The excitatory effects in the photoreceptor take time to develop and suggest the concept of a photochemical stimulus distinct from some subsequent reactions that finally excite the axon. These other processes limit the speed with which a photoreceptor can respond to a change in stimulus.

It has been suggested that the generator potentials arise as a consequence of a change in permeability of the cell's membrane brought about by the action of some chemical substance liberated by the photoreceptor during illumination.[14]

Whatever the end products of bleaching that stimulate the firing of the photoreceptors may be, there is a definite relationship between their concentration and the state of excitation of the visual apparatus. In the dark, the concentration of rhodopsin builds up to a maximum, and as will be shown later, the sensitivity of the retina is at a maximum. This is the state of dark adaptation or scotopic vision. Under these conditions the sensitivity of the eye is more than ten thousand times as great as when the eye is light-adapted. When light is admitted to the retina of an eye which is completely dark-adapted, the breakdown of rhodopsin

takes place, and if the illumination is steady, a steady state level is reached. Depending upon the amount of light admitted, this steady state level will shift toward the side of greatest degradation of rhodopsin into its end products, and the further the shift is in this direction, the more the eye becomes light-adapted, i.e., in the photopic state, and the less is its sensitivity. In other words, the more rhodopsin and the less end product of rhodopsin breakdown present in the retina, the greater is its sensitivity; the less rhodopsin and the greater the breakdown products present, the less is the retinal sensitivity. The relationship between the amount of rhodopsin present and retinal sensitivity is not a simple linear one, however. The bleaching of the first few molecules of rhodopsin has a relatively enormous effect on the sensitivity of the retina and results in a large fall. Wald[15] has shown that bleaching of 0.6% of the rhodopsin present lowers the sensitivity of the retina 3300 times. Conversely, the resynthesis of the last small fraction of rhodopsin must raise the sensitivity greatly. Much of light and dark adaptation involves the first and last small portions of rhodopsin that is bleached and resynthesized. Wald has suggested that this is due to the fact that the rods are compartmented structures, each of which contains a large quantity of rhodopsin, one molecule of which is discharged by the absorption of a first quantum of light. The residual rhodopsin continues to absorb light and to bleach, but this does not contribute to excitation further. A rod is rendered wholly inexcitable when each of its compartments has absorbed one quantum of light which has bleached one molecule of rhodopsin. The bleaching of the rest of the rhodopsin takes place but does not enter into excitation. In this way the bleaching of a small quantity of rhodopsin can lead to a high state of light adaptation.

Within the last few years an ingenious method has been developed of measuring the bleaching of visual pigments in the living eye and the kinetics of their re-synthesis.[16-21] The method consists in comparing the light reflected from the retina with that of an entering beam. Since the reflected light will have been altered by absorption by the visual pigments present, it will be slightly different from that which entered the eye, and the differences can be analyzed in terms of the amount and character of the visual pigment present. A blue-green light is absorbed strongly by rhodopsin, whereas an orange light is absorbed scarcely at all. If such a light is thrown into the fovea of the eye of an animal or human being, no change in the reflected light takes place since the fovea contains no rhodopsin. If it is thrown into a region of the retina containing rods and rhodopsin, however, the light reflected is changed by being absorbed by the rhodopsin, and as the rhodopsin bleaches, this is indicated by the character of the reflected light. Rushton and co-workers[19, 20] have shown that the concentration of rhodopsin falls to a steady state level in about 5 minutes, which is in good agreement with the time required for complete light adaptation of the human rods, and that the concentration of rhodopsin reaches a maximum in about 30 minutes, again in good agreement with the time required for the human retina to become practically dark-adapted. The course of bleaching and re-synthesis of rhodopsin in the human retina is not a direct linear relationship but correlates with the logarithm of the retinal sensitivity as it rises from light adaptation to dark adaptation. This is in agreement with Wald's theory of the rhodopsin being contained in compartments in the rods, as just stated.

REFERENCES

1. Wald, G.: The biochemistry of vision, Ann. Rev. Biochem. **22**:497, 1953.
2. Dartnall, H.: The visual pigments, London, 1957, Methuen and Co., p. 41.
3. Hubbard, R., and Kropf, A.: The effect of light on rhodopsin, Proc. Nat. Acad. Sc. **44**:130, 1958.
4. Wulff, V., and Adams, R.: Effect of flash illumination on rhodopsin in solution, Ann. New York Acad. Sc. **74**:281, 1958.
5. Wald, G.: In Field, J., editor: Handbook of physiology, vol. I, Baltimore, 1959, Williams & Wilkins Co., p. 673.
6. Krinsky, N.: The lipoprotein nature of rhodopsin, Arch. Ophth. **60**:688, 1958.
7. Dartnall, H., and Goodeve, C.: Scotopic luminosity curve and absorption spectrum of visual purple, Nature, London **139**: 409, 1937.
8. Wald, G.: Human vision and spectrum, Science **101**:653, 1945.
9. Bonting, S., Caraveggio, L., and Gouras, P.: The rhodopsin cycle in the developing vertebrate retina, Exper. Eye Res. **1**:14, 1961.
10. Bliss, A.: The chemistry of daylight vision, J. Gen. Physiol. **29**:277, 1946.
11. Wald, G., Brown, P., and Smith, P.: Iodopsin, J. Gen. Physiol. **38**:623, 1955.
12. Wald, G.: The photoreceptor process in vision, Am. J. Ophth. **40**:18, 1955.
13. Hartline, H., Wagner, H., and MacNichol, E.: The peripheral origin of nervous activity in the visual system, Cold Spring Harbor Symposica Quant. Biol. **17**:125, 1952.
14. Fuortes, M.: Initiation of impulses in visual cells of limulus, J. Physiol. **148**:14, 1959.
15. Wald, G.: On the mechanism of the visual threshold and visual adaptation, Science **119**:887, 1954.
16. Weale, R.: Tapetal reflection and its influence on some visual functions of the cat, J. Physiol. **118**:43, 1952. (Oral communication.)
17. Brindley, G., and Willmer, E.: The re-

flection of light from the macular and peripheral fundus oculi in man, J. Physiol. **116:**350, 1952.

18. Rushton, W.: Apparatus for analysing the light reflected from the eye of the cat, J. physiol. **117:**47, 1952. (Oral communication.)

19. Rushton, W., Campbell, F., Hagins, W., and Brindley, G.: The bleaching and regeneration of rhodopsin in the living eye of the albino rabbit and of man, Optica Acta **1:**183, 1955.

20. Rushton, W., and Campbell, F.: Measurement of rhodopsin in the living human eye. Nature, London **174:**1096, 1954.

21. Campbell, F., and Rushton, W.: Measurement of the scotopic pigment in the living human eye, J. Physiol. **130:**131, 1955.

CHAPTER 14

ELECTRICAL PHENOMENA IN THE EYE

THE ELECTRO-OCULOGRAM

The demarcation current or current of injury was discussed on p. 73. This phenomenon, which occurs in cut muscle, is also found in the eye if electrodes are placed on the cornea and the cut optic nerve after enucleation. Electrodes connected between the cornea and the back of the intact eye also show a difference of potential with the cornea positive. Similarly, electrodes connected between the front and the back of the retina disclose a potential difference with the front of the retina positive. It is not known exactly what produces this difference of potential. Since it occurs in the intact eye, it cannot be the usual current of injury, but represents a physiologic change in potential between different parts of the uninjured eye. In vertebrates, as mentioned, the cornea is positive relative to the retina, but in invertebrates the reverse is true, the cornea being negative. This corresponds to the difference in orientation of the retinas of these two groups, the visual cells pointing outward in the vertebrates and inward in the invertebrates. Evidence has been offered that a Donnan membrane equilibrium at the blood-aqueous barrier is responsible for the potential gradient, but it seems much more likely that it is due to the orientation of the photoreceptor cells, which because of metabolic processes have become negative in relation to their surroundings. As a result of this they become what has been aptly termed a *sink* for positive current. An electrode placed at some distance from the sink thus becomes positive and is known as the *source*. The current then flows from the source into the sink. The actual polarity, however, will change as one places the electrodes very close to the cell so that the electrode becomes negative when the cell does and positive as it becomes positive.

Whatever the source of this resting potential, which is present in the dark, it has been used successfully to measure eye movements, for if electrodes are suitably placed at the inner and outer canthi, the eye behaves like a dipole oriented along its anteroposterior axis, and any movement of the eye will cause changes of the standing potential. This is the basis of electro-oculography. The records indicating movements of the eyes obtained by this means are called electro-oculograms or the EOG (p. 513).

THE ELECTRORETINOGRAM

While the resting potential in the eye remains at a relatively constant level in the dark, i.e., about 1 mv., the admission of light to the retina results in marked changes. These changes in potential under the influence of light were discovered simultaneously by Holmgren in Sweden and Dewar and McKendrick at the University of Edinburgh. Even with the crude apparatus of that day they were able to describe some of the electrical changes which take place when the retina is exposed to light. However, the complexity of the response from the vertebrate eye soon turned workers to investigate invertebrate material. The most suitable was found to be the eye of *Limulus,* the king crab, and the eye of the water beetle, a member of the genus *Dytiscus.* With the development of better methods of recording, the response of the retina to light

could be seen to be complex and to consist of a number of different sources of potential change. During the past few years considerable effort and ingenuity have been expended in attempting to analyze the various component parts of the record and to localize in the retina where they are generated.

The electroretinogram of the invertebrate

In Fig. 266 is shown the electroretinogram of *Limulus* together with the electrical discharges from the optic nerve fibers. The electroretinogram of this eye is very simple and consists of a positive potential change of 20 mv., after a latent period of 0.02 second. Following the appearance of this potential change in the retina, the optic nerve fibers discharge. There is little evidence in the electroretinogram of *Limulus* of the three components seen so clearly in the electroretinogram of the vertebrate and no evidence of the "off" effect (p. 608). As seen in Fig. 266, *A,* the record from the whole

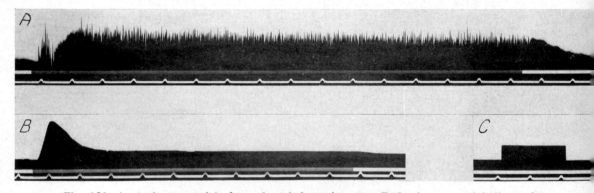

Fig. 266. A, Action potentials from the whole optic nerve. Deflection upward indicates increasing negativity of lead next to the eye. (Height of maximum rise, 0.4 mv.) Lower white line indicates time in fifths of seconds. Line above time record signals the onset and cessation of illumination. **B,** Retinal action potential. Deflection upward indicates increasing negativity of the cornea with respect to the back of the eye. (Height of maximal rise, 1.35 mv.) Time record and signal as in **A. C,** Record of a calibrating potential of 0.16 mv. applied to the amplifier input; sensitivity as in **A.** Time in fifths of seconds. (From Hartline, H., and Graham, C.: J. Cell. & Comp. Physiol. **1:**277, 1932.)

optic nerve shows the presence of a slow potential upon which the individual spikes of the optic nerve impulses are superimposed. The nearer the electrode is to the point of entry of the optic nerve into the eye, the larger is the slow potential; so that it appears that the retinal effects are being transmitted into the optic nerve. It has been suggested that it is this electrotonic potential which actually excites the autorhythmic mechanism of the optic nerve fibers and produces the succession of spikes.

The electroretinogram of the vertebrate

The vertebrate retina is a complex arrangement of neurons. Three separate layers of nerve cells are recognized—the rod and cone layer, the bipolar layer, and the ganglion cell layer. These cells are joined to one another in a variety of combinations of cross-connections by means of the horizontal and amacrine cells. The intimate histologic picture of these various unions is given elsewhere (p. 658). The retina is a true nervous center, no less complex than other parts of the central nervous system. One would expect, therefore, that its physiologic reactions would be quite complicated and likely to show the same phenomena which characterize the central nervous system in general. This complexity makes the process of unraveling the component parts difficult, but more fascinating.

When the electroretinogram in vertebrates is recorded, one electrode may be placed on the cornea and the other on the exposed optic nerve, on the other eye, or in a small incision in the skin.[1] In man, one electrode may be placed on the forehead while the other is fastened into a plastic contact glass fitted over the cornea of the eye being recorded. The electroretinogram varies in different animals and

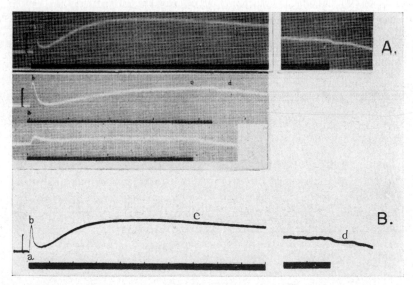

Fig. 267. Electroretinogram from the cat. **A,** Actual galvanometer records with a stimulus of 14 millilamberts reflected from an area of 1661 sq.mm. (top record) and 370 mm. (middle record) and a stimulus of 0.14 ml. at 70 mm. (bottom record). **B,** Top record drawn with a, b, c, and d waves marked; vertical line, 0.05 mv. (From Granit, R.: J. Physiol. **77:**207, 1933.)

under different conditions. Its general form is shown in Fig. 267 which is the electroretinogram of the cat. The main features are (1) the a wave, an initial negative wave which occurs after a latent period following the onset of the illumination, (2) the positive b wave, a positive potential of short duration, (3) the c wave, a slow rise of potential which continues with a still slower fall, and (4) the d wave or "off" effect which occurs when the light is turned off and is followed by a fall in potential until the resting potential is gradually reached.

The electroretinogram or ERG depends upon the existence of intact receptor cells, for it disappears from the retina of a certain species of mouse[2] which has a rod-free retina after the cones have degenerated. Also the electroretinogram disappears from the retinas of persons with advanced pigmentary degeneration[3] and in response to certain toxic agents which cause selective damage to retinal receptor cells.

The electroretinogram does not depend upon the ganglion cells being intact, according to Auerbach and Burian,[5] since it can be obtained in eyes blinded from glaucoma in which there is deterioration of the ganglion cell layer.

Early analyses of the electroretinogram

The form of the electroretinogram, like that of the electrocardiogram, is a composite curve because of the presence of several superimposed events. Several separate events are taking place simultaneously, each of which contributes to its final form. Various analyses of the electroretinogram have been made, one of the most rewarding being that of Granit. For comparison with his more complicated analysis, the early diagram of Einthoven and Jolly, made in 1908, is given (Fig.

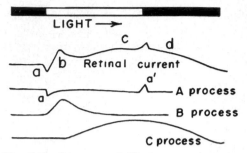

Fig. 268. Diagram of Einthoven and Jolly's analysis of the retinal response into three components, **A, B,** and **C.** (After Adrian, E., and Matthews, R.: J. Physiol. **63:**378, 1927.)

268). According to Einthoven and Jolly, the following reactions take place in the frog's eye when a light is turned on. There is first of all a negative deflection, a, in which the current passes through the external circuit from the back of the eye to the cornea (the A process). This is followed by a positive deflection, b (caused by the B process), that decreases under steady illumination, but may increase again because of the development of the slower C process which causes the c wave. When the light is turned off, there is a rapid positive deflection, a', and finally a slow return to the resting condition (a' is the same as the d wave).

They considered the initial negative deflection, a, and the rapid positive deflection on darkening, a', to be caused by the same process, the A process. The positive deflection, b, which succeeds a, is caused by the B process and is seen best with feeble illumination. Finally, the C process is a very much slower change which may remain for many seconds after the light is turned off[6] and produces the wave c.

As a result of his own and other findings, Piper in 1911 modified this scheme to that shown in Fig. 269. Since this time the development of suitable apparatus has brought out many changes in the various components of the electroretinogram.

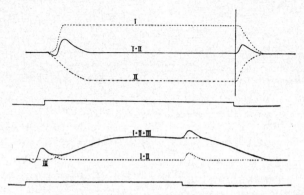

Fig. 269. Piper's original analysis of the electroretinogram. **I,** Cephalopod eye. **II,** From Waller's work on the frog. **III,** Slow potential responsible for the c wave. (From Granit, R.: Sensory mechanisms of the retina, London, 1947, Oxford University Press.)

Granit's analysis of the electroretinogram

A new attack on the problem was made by Granit, who narcotized animals in an attempt to remove the separate components of the electroretinogram one at a time. His scheme is shown in Fig. 270. According to him, there are three components or processes in the electroretinogram (as suggested by Einthoven and Jolly) which he calls the P I, P II, and P III, in the order of their disappearance from the records when the subject is under ether anesthesia. P I accounts for the c wave, P II for the b wave, and P III for the initial a wave.

The d wave or "off" effect is an interference phenomenon. These three processes and the way in which their combination produces the electroretinogram at two intensities of light are shown in Fig. 271.

The chief characteristics of each of these processes and the probable location in the retina where they occur according to Granit are as follows.

P I. The P I process accounts for the positive c wave. It is the first to disappear from the electroretinogram of the cat during ether anesthesia. It is absent in the cone retinas of certain cold-blooded vertebrates and disappears in all eyes in the light-adapted state. It is associated with the rod mechanism since the c wave is absent from the electroretinogram of the frog if the stimulating light is selected far enough in the red end of the spectrum that it does not stimulate the rods. The process responsible for the c wave seems to have the same spectral sensitivities to different wavelengths as the rods. It has a variable latent period of from 2 to 6 seconds in the frog and about 0.5 second in the cat. P I is probably not connected with the discharges of the optic nerve since no impulse frequency referable to this part of the electroretinogram can be noticed,[7] and P I is not transmitted electronically into the nerve.

Granit is not certain in exactly what part of the retina P I has its origin, but it appears to be localized chiefly, if not exclusively, in the rod pathways. It has a sensitizing effect on P II; hence it must arise either at the same time as the latter or before. The rods themselves cannot be excluded as the source of P I, and it appears early in the chain of events initiated by stimulation of the rod receptors (p. 614).

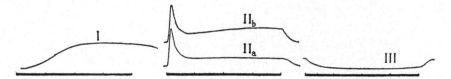

Fig. 270. Components of the electroretinogram. Two alternatives are given for P II. If **IIa** is used, **III** should be drawn with the gradual rise shown in **IIb** to fit those patients in whom the combination of P II and P III shows a secondary rise after removal of P I with ether. (From Granit, R.: Sensory mechanisms of the retina, London, 1947, Oxford University Press.)

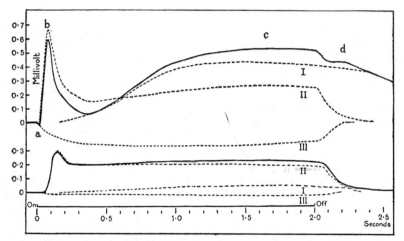

Fig. 271. Analysis of the electroretinogram at two intensities. *Upper tracing,* 14 ml. *Lower tracing,* 0.14 ml., as shown in Fig. 267. The a wave has been broadened slightly out of proportion to demonstrate its derivation more clearly. (From Granit, R.: The sensory mechanisms of the retina, London, 1947, Oxford University Press.)

P II. P II accounts for the positive b wave. Since the b wave shows rather marked variations in response, especially at low intensities of illumination in which occasionally in the dark-adapted eye it shows a staircase effect, Granit suggests that the retinal elements yielding P II do not all behave alike. The P II component, therefore, probably represents the total of a number of processes with different latent periods and rates of appearance, producing different amounts of positive potential. P II is affected in the same way as the discharges in the optic nerve, and anything which affects the discharge of the optic nerve affects P II. Augmenta-

tion of the discharge of the optic nerve is associated generally with an increase in P II and vice versa. A slow late b wave in the electroretinogram corresponds to a slowly rising delayed discharge in the nerve, but since the b wave is the average result of the activity of several P II processes, this correspondence holds only for the over-all action of the optic nerve and is not true necessarily for the responses of single fibers.

The size of the P II response roughly produces the intensity or quantity of the effect which is carried to the brain as a sensory message. P II is removed usually from the electroretinogram by ether directly after P I. It is also removed by asphyxia and, in fact, so selectively that P II may be removed before P I, leaving a pure curve of P I and P III. The application of glucose increases the b wave rapidly for light of 450 mμ. Since glucose does not increase the rate of regeneration of rhodopsin, its effect must be either on P II or on some intermediate process which makes the eye sensitive to the breakdown of rhodopsin. Since P II is very sensitive to a lack of oxygen, one can understand why any interference with the retina is likely to lead to a secondary diminution in the size of its positive potential changes.

Granit suggests that P II originates somewhere in the neural pathways between the receptors and the ganglion cells —perhaps in the bipolar cells—and is the electrical manifestation of excitation in these pathways. For some reason as yet unknown, the rod pathways are much more efficient generators of P II than are those of the cones because P II is reduced greatly by light adaptation, and in the eyes of cold-blooded vertebrates it is larger in mixed retinas than in pure cone retinas.

I have called attention to the fact that P I is able to sensitize P II.[8] This must be of great visual importance at the moment of transition from dark adaptation to light adaptation. The effect of the large potential of the b wave produced by a light strong enough to light-adapt the dark-adapted retina is to leave a long refractory period. We all know this from our own experience, for we are temporarily blinded when we are dark-adapted and come out into a strong light. As Granit[9] has stated:

"PI can, to some extent, compensate for this refractoriness of the visual apparatus and thereby render the eye capable of seeing well sooner than would otherwise have been possible. In eyes which are already light-adapted, so that all reactions are faster, the refractory period resulting from a strong stimulus is much shorter, and in addition there is a vigorous off effect which signals any darkening of the visual field and so contributes to the differentiation of light and shade. A sensitizing process like PI would not, therefore, be nearly so significant in the light-adapted state. Nevertheless it is, apparently, present in the light-adapted bird retina although never in a pure cone eye."*

The influence of certain drugs on P II has been tested. Strychnine enhances the b wave, and the general excitatory state is followed by a depression of P II activity. Eserine and acetylcholine have a depressing effect although with eserine this is occasionally preceded by transient excitation. Atropine greatly increases the size of the b wave when light of short wavelength is used but never has much effect on the d wave. This suggests that atropine excites the rods but not the cones.

P III. P III is responsible for the initial negative a wave and the d wave. It is the last to disappear under ether anesthesia. Like P I, it is small at low intensities of light. The latent period of P III is identical with that of the a wave of the electroretinogram.

P III is associated with inhibition. It is always larger in the light-adapted eye than in the dark-adapted eye and increases, as stated, both with increased intensity of illumination and with increase in duration of the exposure to a constant light. Alcohol is the only substance known to have a selective depressant effect on P III, and all the evidence points to P III being more resistant to the action of external agents

*From Granit, R.: Sensory mechanisms of the retina, London, 1947, Oxford University Press.

than either of the other processes. The end result of any interference with the eye is to leave P III and make the responses of the electroretinogram more negative.

The belief that P III is connected with inhibition has been completely confirmed, according to Granit, by the alcohol test, which cuts down the activity of P III selectively and always results in decreased inhibition.

The d wave (off effect). It will be recalled that when the light is turned off a further positive potential, called the d wave or "off" effect, may develop in the typical electroretinogram. This is believed to be the result of interference between the positive potentials developed in the b and c waves and the negative potential developed in the a wave. With the cessation of illumination, the negative a wave rebounds, and if this has been an especially large negative potential, the rebound may produce a positive deflection or d wave which is carried into the optic nerve fiber as a burst of impulses at off. Granit has postulated that the P III negative component of the electroretinogram is a "preparation for an off effect" during illumination, and that the "off" effect is a kind of release from inhibition due to the return of P III to the base line.

In the frog retina, Hartline was able to identify certain nerve fibers which he called c fibers whose only response to illumination was at off (p. 632). These fibers can be inhibited by reillumination, and their activity can be governed by the amount and character of the illumination to which their receptors are exposed. The property of responding to darkness is the result of their preparation by the light, and all the evidence points to P III as the mechanism by means of which this is accomplished.

Relation of the electroretinogram to discharge of the optic nerve

The various excitatory and inhibitory processes going on in the retina under the stimulus of light are of interest to us largely in so far as they can be shown to be determinants of the responses conducted to the brain by the optic nerve fibers. What we want to know is whether the whole electroretinogram or any part of it is transmitted electrotonically into the optic nerve fibers. This can best be done by investigating to what extent the impulses in the optic nerve fibers follow changes in the electroretinogram.

The b wave, or P II process of Granit, is the only part of the electroretinogram which directly influences the optic nerve responses and is probably the only part of the electroretinogram transmitted into the optic nerve. This potential must be closely related to the discharge of impulses in the optic nerve fiber because these impulses disappear as soon as the b wave has been eliminated by experimental means. The frequency of the optic nerve impulses seems to depend on the height of this potential. Neither P I nor P III can be directly related to discharge of the optic nerve.

The initial a wave seems to be the only part of the electroretinogram whose origin can be ascribed to the physical presence of the photoreceptors. In order for the b wave to exist, it is necessary to have the intermediate cell layers present. The ganglion cells themselves need not be present in order to obtain an electroretinogram. This is apparent from experiments in which ganglion cell degeneration was produced by optic nerve section with maintenance of a normal electroretinogram.

Most of the recent evidence used in ascribing the seat of origin of the different components of the electroretinogram to different portions of the retina has been derived from selective degeneration experiments, using interruption of the blood supply and toxic drugs which have a selective affinity for isolated retinal structures.[10]

The electroretinogram recorded with microelectrodes

Great advances in electroretinography have been made recently by the use of intraretinal microelectrodes. If the responses are recorded from a microelectrode inserted at different depths in the retina while the whole retina is exposed to uniform illumination, the amplitude of the response suddenly diminishes greatly in passing from a depth of 200 μ to 300 μ. The steady potential decreases by 10 to 30 mv. This and other evidence suggests that somewhere at about this depth in the retina the microelectrode has suddenly penetrated a membrane of high electrical resistance and capacity. This phenomenon was first discovered by Tomita,[11] and subsequent work showed that it is always present if the eye is in good condition, particularly if the blood supply is intact. In eyes devoid of a blood supply the pattern found by Tomita disappears very rapidly, and a pattern found by Ottoson and Svaetichin[12] is substituted. Brindley[13] also found a marked change in electrical response as the electrode passed from one level to a deeper one in the retina, postulated the existence of such a membrane, and called it the R membrane. While at first he inclined to the belief that this membrane was identical with the external limiting membrane of the retina, he later changed this concept on the basis of other evidence to Bruch's membrane, and most investigators are now in agreement that the site of this sudden change in potential is actually Bruch's membrane.

As the microelectrode is advanced through the retina, the zone of greatest change of response with distance corresponds approximately with the layer of bipolar cells, and Brindley adopts the hypothesis provisionally that the bipolar cells are the only structures which contribute substantially to the generation of the electroretinogram. Since Bruch's membrane is extraretinal, lying between the pigmented epithelium and the choriocapillaris, the rods and cones cannot be the sole source of the electroretinogram.

The use of microelectrode techniques gives us much more information regarding the exact origins of the various components of the electroretinogram than do older techniques, but since the slow potentials generated from the retinal area near the microelectrode show distinct differences as well as similarities to those picked up in the conventionally recorded electroretinogram, a large amount of work had to be done before one type of message could be related with the other. The work of Brown and Wiesel[14-16] has demonstrated that the ERG obtained by conventional methods and records obtained by microelectrodes, called the *local* electroretinogram or LERG, are fundamentally the same potentials, and that the local electroretinogram is more promising in affording us information of the origin and physiologic significance of the various components of the potential changes.

According to these authors, the c wave originates in the pigment epithelium (Fig. 272). This was first suggested by Noell[17] on the basis that the c wave disappeared in rabbits after poisoning with sodium iodate, whereas the other components of the electroretinogram were not disturbed. Since iodate poisoning selectively destroys the pigment epithelium, Noell concluded

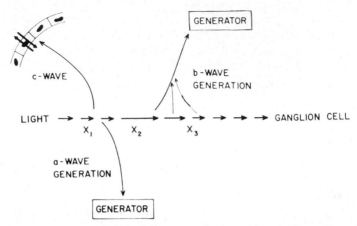

Fig. 272. Schematic presentation of retinal pathway and origin of a, b, and c waves. Generator indicates the unknown structures or boundaries which produce a and b waves. The generator for c waves is the pigment epithelium. (From Noell, W.: Am. J. Ophth. **48**:362, 1959.)

that this structure is concerned primarily with the elaboration of the c wave. Brindley[18] points out that either the rods and cones or the rods themselves must provoke the pigment epithelium to respond, for the spectral sensitivity of the c wave in the frog and rabbit corresponds to the absorption spectrum of rhodopsin and not to that of melanin. In spite of this argument, Brown and Wiesel suggest that the pigmented epithelial cell may itself be light-sensitive, and they call attention to the presence of intracellular organelles having structural similarities to light-sensitive organs which have been described in the retinal pigment cells of the frog[19] and the bat.[20] They admit, however, that the c wave has never been recorded from isolated pigmented epithelial cells.

The a wave probably arises in the outer segments of the photoreceptors. It has its origin in some structure close to the vitreal side of Bruch's membrane, probably the outer segments of the rods and cones.[21]

The b wave is localized by Brown and Wiesel distal to the inner nuclear layer, whereas Tomita and associates[22] locate it in the inner nuclear layer.*

Clinical electroretinography

During the last few years electroretinography has been utilized in the clinic, and electroretinograms have been recorded for many different diseases of the retina and optic nerve. It is still too early to assess the value of this method of studying retinal function, but the continued increase in the number of contributions in the literature attest to the interest being shown it.

When stimuli of short duration are used, the electroretinogram consists of an a wave and a b wave when the eye is dark-adapted, as shown in Fig. 273. The scotopic electroretinogram is much larger than one taken when the eye is light-adapted and hence decreases the relative magnitude of error in measuring

*Reviews of experimental work on the electroretinogram are found in the following: Brindley, G.: Physiology of the retina and the visual pathway, Edward Arnold, London, 1960, (Publishers), Ltd. and Crescitelli, F.: Physiology of vision, Ann. Rev. Physiol. **22**:525, 1960.

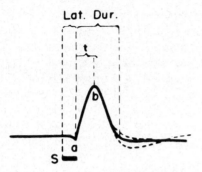

Lat. Dur.

S   a   b

Fig. 273. Diagram of a scotopic electroretinogram of a human being in response to a flash, **S. a,** a wave; **b,** b wave; **Lat.,** latency; **Dur.,** duration of b wave; **t,** culmination time. Alternatives for changes in succeeding b waves are marked in the illustration. (Adapted from Karpe; from Bounds, G. W., Jr.: A. Arch. Ophth. **49:**81, 1953.)

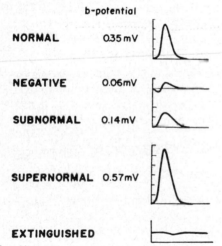

b-potential

NORMAL	0.35 mV
NEGATIVE	0.06 mV
SUBNORMAL	0.14 mV
SUPERNORMAL	0.57 mV
EXTINGUISHED	

Fig. 274. Diagram of the normal and pathologic types of electroretinograms. (Adapted in part from Henkes; from Bounds, G. W., Jr.: Arch. Ophth. **49:**81, 1953.)

the potentials. The changes in the electroretinogram have now been recorded with most of the various parameters of the stimulus controlled for investigation—the intensity, size, duration, retinal location, wavelength, and state of adaptation have been generally assessed. Karpe[23] and Henkes[24] have described four types of abnormal electroretinogram. These consist of the following: (1) the subnormal electroretinogram, which is of subnormal size, (2) the negative electroretinogram, which is a more or less pure negative response, (3) the extinguished electroretinogram, and (4) the supernormal electroretinogram, which is of supernormal size. These are diagrammed in Fig. 274.

Zetterstrom[25] has followed the development of the electroretinogram in healthy children from birth to the age of 1 year. During the first two or three days of life she found that either no electroretinogram was demonstrable or only a very slight rise in the base line was present. During the first half year of life there is a distinct increase of the b potential. The electroretinogram of the infant is a different type from that of the adult and is characterized by the absence of P III, i.e., of the negative component of the electroretinogram or a wave. This author does not advance any theory to explain both the absence of the electroretinogram in infants and its different appearance during the first half year after it arises. Since the electroretinogram can be recorded after a few days, she suggests that light may be the factor responsible for its appearance. It is conceivable that the rods are incapable of being stimulated at birth because rhodopsin is not present in a functionally active form.

Except for the macula, the retina in the newborn human infant is well developed, and one would expect the electroretinogram to be present. In animals whose retinas are not fully differentiated at birth the electroretinogram was found to be absent by Noell.[26] In rabbits he found the electroretinogram made its first appearance at about the eighth day when miniature sensory organelles had developed in the central region. Following this the sensory organelle rapidly approached the adult appearance, and simultaneously the electroretinogram became quite definite.

These findings have been challenged by Horsten and Winkelman.[27] They find that if adequate dark adaptation be given and light of high intensity be used, an electroretinogram can be recorded in the human newborn infant and even in premature infants. Unlike Noell, they were unable to correlate the appearance of the electroretinogram with any stages of histologic development of the retina in newborn animals (dogs).

Slow potentials and spikes

Two kinds of electrical activity can be recorded from the retina—slow potentials and spike discharges. The classic electroretinogram is a representative of the slow potentials and one of the most extensively studied phenomena. The significance of these slow potentials depends upon whether they are reflected in the discharge pattern of the retinal ganglion cells, i.e., whether they appear in the activity of the optic nerves. The unitary spike discharge can also be picked up in the retina with microelectrodes. The relation of the slow potentials to the spike discharges is not exactly known at present.[28]

The slow potential changes occur when light is turned on the retina and persist as long as the light continues. They cease when the light is turned off. Their magnitude varies with the light intensity. There has been considerable difference of opinion concerning where these potentials arise. At one time they were thought to come from the cones themselves.[29] It was found, however, that the same potentials could be recorded when the tips of the recording electrodes were separated by as much as 50 μ. No cells of this size have

ever been found in the retina by ordinary staining techniques. Either the potentials are produced by large cells which cannot be demonstrated by ordinary stains or in the large spaces between cells. The ramifications of special glial cells called Müller's fibers fit into this category.[30] Other slow potentials have been identified as originating in the horizontal cells.[31]

Until now we have been dealing with electrical events that occur in the retina itself. We have seen that many different types of potentials can be recorded, but of these only the b wave of the electroretinogram seems to be transmitted into the optic nerve fibers. We will now study the activity of these fibers and find out what differences occur in the message sent to the brain when the various parameters of the visual stimulus are experimentally altered. Some of this material has already been considered in the discussion of corneal sensation (p. 76). Before we consider the optic nerve responses, a review of conduction in nerve fibers in general may be helpful.

Function of nerves in general

The typical nerve cell consists of a cell body with a nucleus and a long prolongation or axon which conducts messages to some outlying part of the body such as a motor end plate in muscle. Connecting with the cell body are numerous twigs or dendrites which conduct messages into the cell body either from sensory organs or from other axons.

Each axon consists of a nerve fiber surrounded by a fatty substance or myelin sheath. Surrounding this in most nerve fibers is an envelope or sheath of Schwann, containing scattered nuclei along the course of the axon. At intervals the sheath of Schwann runs into the myelin up to the nerve fiber, forming segments of the axon. These junctions are known as the nodes of Ranvier. Each myelin segment is produced by the nucleated Schwann cells that wind their cytoplasm in a spiral envelope around the surface of the axon. The Schwann sheath is somehow concerned with regeneration of the nerve fiber following injury or disease. Without the cell body, the nerve fiber cannot exist for any long period. Separation of the axon from its cell body invariably results in degeneration.

Analysis of the chemical composition of the fluid inside the Schwann sheath and on its outside surface shows a marked difference between electrolytes. Outside the giant axon of the squid 90% of the ions are sodium (positively charged) and chloride (negatively charged). Inside the membrane these ions account for only 10% of the solutes. Here, the principal positive ion is potassium, and the negative ions consist of organic particles too large to diffuse easily through the membrane. As in most body cells (p. 561) the concentration of sodium is about ten times higher outside the cell membrane and the concentration of potassium is about thirty times higher inside the membrane. The membrane is not impermeable to these ions, but potassium and chloride can move through the membrane much more easily than sodium and the large organic ions can. This results in a voltage drop across the membrane of 60 to 90 mv., with the inside of the cell being negative with respect to the outside.

Since these ions can diffuse through the cell membrane, the difference in ionic composition which we have called attention to must be maintained by some mechanism which forces sodium ions uphill and outward through the cell membrane as fast as they leak in. However, the leak inward due to the slight permeability to sodium is relatively small when the nerve fiber is in the resting

state, and the work required by this pumping mechanism amounts to only a fraction of the energy that is continuously being made available by the metabolism of the cell.

The mechanism which maintains this electrical potential difference is thought to be a kind of sodium pump (p. 135) which trades sodium and potassium ions. Numerous models to explain how this sodium pump works have been proposed. That of T. J. Shaw proposed in 1954 suggests that the movement of potassium and sodium ions is due to lipoid-soluble carriers (X and Y) that are specific for the two ions. The compounds formed (KX and NaY) can move across the membrane by diffusion, whereas the free carriers themselves cannot. At the outside surface of the cell membrane the sodium carriers are converted to potassium carriers, losing energy in the process. At the inside surface the potassium carriers are reconverted to sodium carriers by the metabolism of the cell, which furnishes energy-rich phosphate compounds for this purpose. Thus the metabolism of the cell maintains constant active transport of ions in either direction across the cell membrane, assuring a negative potential on the inside of the membrane of approximately 80 mv.

Although many cell membranes show this difference in potential between the two surfaces, the nerve cell membrane is distinctive in that its permeability in turn is regulated by the voltage difference across the membrane. When the voltage difference across the membrane is lowered, the membrane becomes more permeable to sodium ions. As the sodium ions leak into the cell, they cancel out locally a portion of the negatively charged ions, which reduces the potential difference between the two sides of the membrane, and as this potential difference falls, the membrane becomes even more permeable to the penetration of still more sodium ions. In other words, the flow of some sodium ions through the membrane makes it easier for others to follow. Eventually, the difference in potential is changed to the reverse of that found in the resting nerve, the inside becoming positive to the outside of the membrane. This change creates a positive action potential discharged down the nerve fiber as an electric impulse and shows up on the oscilloscope as a spike potential (p. 75). As this spike potential passes down the fiber, it sets up the same changes in permeability of the membrane directly ahead of it, repeating the whole process until the spike has travelled down the whole length of the fiber. Immediately after the peak of the wave, the sodium gates, which had opened during the rise of the peak, are closed again, and the potassium gates are opened briefly. This produces a rapid outpouring of the positive potassium ions through the membrane, restoring the original negative charge to the inside of the membrane. This process repeats itself down the nerve fiber. Immediately after the appearance of the spike potential it becomes difficult to displace the voltage and set up another impulse. This constitutes the refractory period of the nerve during which it is impossible to set off another impulse, no matter how strong the stimulus.

It can be seen from this that a stimulus applied to a nerve sufficiently strong to produce a spike potential sets off a continuous change in the potential difference between the two sides of the membrane. It is this which is propagated down the fiber and not the original stimulus itself. A stimulus insufficient to produce a spike potential in a fiber soon dies out and is not propagated.

The change in electrical potential travelling down the fiber is of very short duration and travels down the fiber with great rapidity. The velocity of conduction varies directly with the diameter of the fiber. The fastest fibers, called the A group, consist of large myelinated fibers which conduct at rates varying from 10 to 120 M. per second. The B group, consisting of small myelinated fibers found only in the autonomic system, conducts at 7 to 15 M. per second, whereas the C group made up of unmyelinated fibers conducts at 15 to 20 M. per second. In the nerves of frogs the maximum velocity is about 30 M. per second, which is about a mile a minute.

The refractory period in A fibers is about 0.4 to 0.5 msec. It can be seen that the refractory period sets a limit to the number of impulses which a nerve can conduct per second. In the largest mammalian fibers the limit is 2000 impulses per second, but no fibers can conduct more than a few impulses at such a frequency. An isolated nerve in the presence of an adequate supply of oxygen can conduct at the rate of 50 to 100 impulses per second for many hours. It may be said therefore that a nerve fiber is indefatigable. If a nerve is deprived of oxygen, however, it soon stops conducting.

A fibers cease to conduct after 30 to 40 minutes. B fibers show changes after 2 to 3 minutes, whereas C fibers can tolerate about 2 hours of complete asphyxia before they fail. Compression of a nerve blocks conduction. This occurs earlier in the larger myelinated fibers than in the smaller myelinated fibers and last of all in the unmyelinated fibers. Anesthetics such as cocaine block the C fibers first and the largest myelinated fibers last.

Even in the resting state, nerves consume oxygen and produce carbon dioxide. Respiration is increased slightly during activity, but this increase is exceedingly small. In the resting state, a small amount of heat is produced by the metabolic processes going on in the nerve fiber, and when stimulated, a further rise in temperature occurs. This is exceedingly small however when compared to the heat produced by the contracting muscle fiber.

The discharge in all sensory fibers is approximately the same, whether the fiber is conducting pain impulses, the sensation of touch, hearing, or seeing. It consists of a burst of spikes which appear after a short latent period following the adequate stimulus. The frequency of the spikes and their duration vary with the parameters of the stimulus, but the amplitude of each spike, i.e., its voltage, never varies in each fiber. If the fiber responds at all, it gives its all. This is the well-known all-or-nothing law. In the following sections we shall see how the individual message carried by each optic nerve fiber changes with changes in the stimulus. This is a coded message which has to be decoded by the cells in the cortex. The change in consciousness which we refer to in terms of sensation, such as feeling pain, touch, hearing, or seeing, is not inherent in this message but depends entirely upon the portion of the cortex to which the message is sent. If it were possible to transplant the optic radiations carrying the final coded message of vision to some other portion of the cortex than the striate area, e.g., the part of the cortex normally giving rise to audition, we would hear the visual world, and vice versa, we would see sounds if the auditory radiation were transplanted successfully into the visual cortex.

The optic nerve discharge

The changes in the retinal potential which occur under the influence of light have been described. These changes in some way not as yet entirely clear to us

finally excite the ganglion cells to discharge a volley or burst of spikes into each nerve fiber. It is these discharge patterns that we are now going to explore. It would be impossible to obtain much information regarding the message which the optic nerve fibers send up to the brain if all of the fibers in the nerve were tapped simultaneously. The electroretinogram of *Limulus* and a simultaneous record of all of the fibers in the optic nerve from this eye were shown in Fig. 266. The record shows a jumbled array of spikes from which any analysis of the parameters of the stimulus could not be obtained. It is very much like trying to make out a conversation between two persons at a cocktail party where the level of noise is great because everyone is talking at once and each is saying something different. Were all talking in unison, what they were saying would be quite clear. It is, therefore, necessary to isolate individual fibers in the optic nerve and tap the message each is delivering. In order to do this the lateral eye of *Limulus* has been employed and studied extensively by Hartline, to whom we owe much of our knowledge of the fundamental character of the messages which the eye sends to the brain.

ACTION POTENTIALS FROM THE OPTIC NERVE OF INVERTEBRATES

In *Limulus* the eye is a primitive faceted structure made up of a number of units called ommatidia, placed side by side. Each ommatidium is composed of several retinula cells clustered around a laminated structure called the rhabdom, together with a large eccentric cell. These cells give off fibers which join a plexus just below the ommatidium which then runs into the central ganglion. Light falls on an ommatidium after passing through a transparent cuticular layer.[32]

Such a structure is quite suitable for recording electrical potentials since it is relatively easy to split each nerve from an ommatidium into its component fourteen to sixteen nerve fibers, from each one of which records can be taken. In this way the difficulties encountered with the very complex system of neurons presented by the vertebrate eye can be avoided. But even in this simple eye it can be shown that there is interplay between neighboring parts of the eye, and that single retinula cells are influenced by others surrounding it.

Responses from a single photoreceptor

In Fig. 275 are shown the action potentials in a single optic fiber in response to steady illumination of the eye. The changes in potential, appearing as individual spikes in the record, are all of the same height and follow each other with great regularity. The eye had been exposed to a constant light for some time so that by the time this record was taken the sensory receptor had become fully adapted (p. 707). As long as the intensity of a light is kept steady, the response of this fiber will be an uninterrupted series of rhythmic impulses travelling up the nerve at a rate about twenty-five per second.

Signaling changes in intensity of the stimulus. When the illumination is increased, as shown in Fig. 276, the number of responses per second is markedly increased, whereas the individual impulses are not graded in size. This is in accordance with the all-or-none principle of nerve fibers. After the initial burst of impulses, the fiber becomes adapted to the steady illumination, and the number of impulses per second falls to a steady level (p. 77). The relation between the frequency of impulses and the logarithm of intensity of the stimulating light is shown in Fig. 277. A comparison of curves *A* and *B* shows that adaptation serves to extend the range of intensities which a single receptor can mediate. Curve *A* gives the values for the initial maxima of the discharges, and curve *B* gives the values of the frequencies after

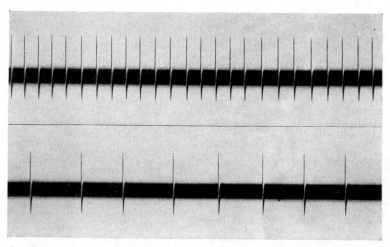

Fig. 275. Oscillogram of the amplified action potentials in a single optic nerve fiber in the eye of *Limulus* in response to steady illumination of the eye. Magnitude of deflection about 1 mv. Full length of record equals 1 second. (From Hartline, H.: The Harvey Lectures, 1941 to 1942.)

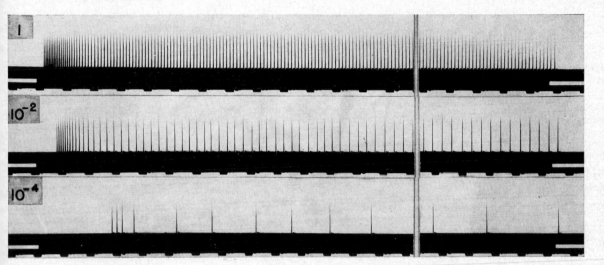

Fig. 276. Discharge of impulses in an optic nerve fiber in the eye of *Limulus* In response to illumination of the eye at three different intensities. Relative values are given at the left. The eye was partially light-adapted. Signal of exposure to light blacks out the white line above the time marker. Time is marked in one fifth seconds. (From Hartline, H.: The Harvey Lectures, 1941 to 1942.)

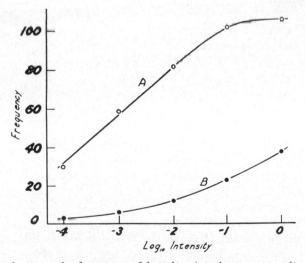

Fig. 277. Relation between the frequency of impulses (number per record) and the logarithm of intensity of stimulating light for the discharge in a single optic nerve fiber in the eye of *Limulus*. A, Frequency of initial maximal discharge. B, Frequency of discharge 3.5 seconds after onset of illumination. (From Hartline, H.: The Harvey Lectures, 1941 to 1942.)

3 seconds of continuous illumination, which has allowed time for adaptation to take place. At high intensities curve *A* flattens out and will ultimately be limited by the inability of the receptor to generate such high frequencies or of the nerve fiber to follow them. After adaptation to these high frequencies has taken place, on the other hand, the receptor is able to give a significant variation of frequency with intensity. Thus each individual sense cell combines high sensitivity with wide range of response.

Responses to different portions of the spectrum (the visibility curve). It has already been shown that the first step in the mechanism whereby light energy is translated by the receptor cell into a nerve message is a photochemical one and that only those rays which are absorbed by some photosensitive pigment or pigments present in the eye can be expected to produce this message. Therefore, we should find that the electrical responses in the optic nerve fiber are dependent primarily on the absorption of light by the visual pigments present. In other words, one should be able to construct a so-called visibility curve from the responses of the photoreceptor to light of different wavelengths. In Fig. 278 are shown the records of the activity of a single receptor in *Limulus,* stimulated by brief flashes of light of various wavelengths. It was found that the different spectral lights were not equally effective, and in order to produce equal responses of the sense cell (measured in terms of number of impulses discharged per second in its fiber), it was necessary to adjust the relative energies of the flashes of different wavelengths to the values given in Fig. 278. The receptor was less sensitive to red and violet lights than to green light. The visibility curve plotted in Fig. 279 may be interpreted as the absorption

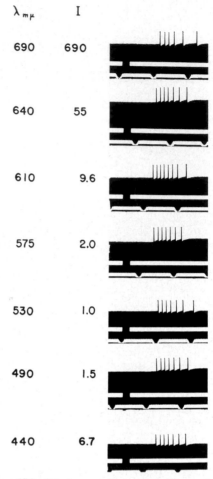

$\lambda_{m\mu}$	I
690	690
640	55
610	9.6
575	2.0
530	1.0
490	1.5
440	6.7

Fig. 278. Discharges of impulses in a single optic nerve fiber in the eye of *Limulus* in response to lights of different wavelengths λ, showing that responses can be made practically identical by suitable adjustment of the incident intensities, **I,** Values of **I** (thermopile determinations) are given relative to its value at λ equals 530 mμ. Duration of stimulus flash equals 0.04 second, signaled in the white line above the marker. Time is in one fifth seconds. (From Hartline, H.: The Harvey Lectures, 1941 to 1942.)

spectrum of the photosensitive pigment of the eye of *Limulus.* In Fig. 280 this is compared with the curve of scotopic luminosity in the human eye.

The reciprocity law of Bunsen and

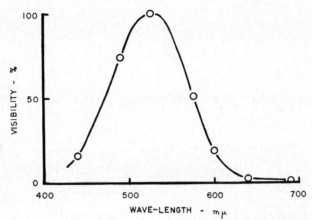

Fig. 279. Visibility curve for a single visual sense cell in the eye of *Limulus.* Visibility at each wavelength is the reciprocal of the relative intensity necessary to produce a specified burst of impulses (see Fig. 278). (From Hartline, H.: The Harvey Lectures, 1941 to 1942.)

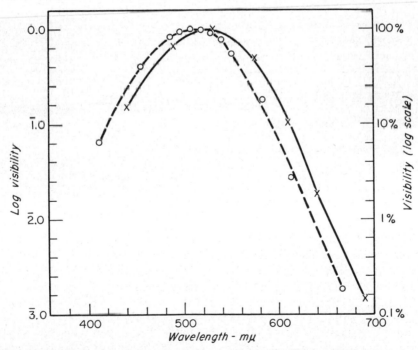

Fig. 280. *Broken line with circles,* curve of scotopic luminosity in the human being (after Hecht and Williams). *Continuous line with crosses,* response of optic nerve fibers in the eye of *Limulus* to changes in wavelength. The correspondence between the two curves is striking. (Courtesy of Dr. H. K. Hartline.)

DURATION

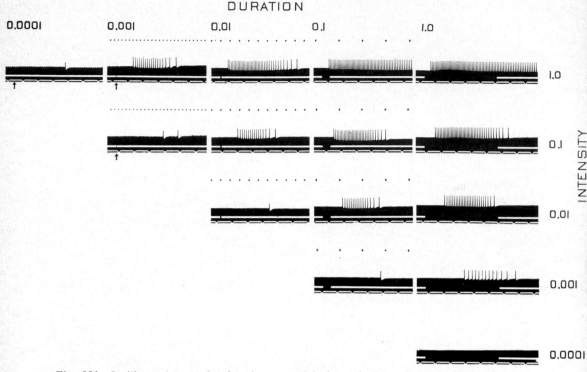

Fig. 281. Oscillograph records of action potentials from single optic nerve fibers in the eye of *Limulus* in response to illumination of the eye by flashes of light of various intensities and durations. Horizontal rows contain responses to flashes of constant intensity and varying duration. Vertical columns contain responses to flashes of constant duration and varying intensity. Values of intensity of flash (in arbitrary units: 1 arbitrary unit = 3.0×10^6 meter-candles on the surface of the eye) given at the right, opposite the respective rows. Values of duration of flash (in seconds) given at the top, above the respective columns. In any given record the lower white line marks fifths of seconds. Above this is a white line containing the light signal recording the interval during which the eye is illuminated. For very short flashes this signal does not reproduce clearly. Its position is shown by the arrows. The black edge records electric potential between two points on the nerve fiber. At the top of each record is a row of black dots giving the speed of rotation of the shutter disk. (From Hartline, H.: J. Cell. & Comp. Physiol. 5:229, 1934.)

Roscoe obeyed in responses of the single fiber. Within limits, the phototropic responses of light-sensitive organisms follow the reciprocity law of Bunsen and Roscoe ($I \times t = k$). Therefore, it would be reasonable to expect that the electrical responses in the optic nerve of *Limulus,* if produced by photochemical activity, would also show that the rate of discharge of impulses is dependent on the energy of the stimulus (product of inten-

sity and duration). In Fig. 281 is shown an array of records of the responses in a single optic nerve fiber, illustrating that both intensity and duration of the stimulating light affect the latency of the response of the sense cell, the number of impulses discharged, and the frequency of the discharge. Intensity and duration affect the sense cell to the same degree quantitatively. Therefore, it can be said that if the exposure to illumination is brief the higher the intensity of a flash of given duration, the shorter is the latent period of the response, the higher is the frequency of the discharge, and the greater is the number of impulses produced.

The effect of changing the duration is the same as changing the intensity if the flashes are of brief duration. The greater the duration of a short flash of given intensity, the stronger is the response of the sense cell. As shown in Fig. 281, the responses standing in a given diagonal, for which energy of flash is constant, are practically identical in all respects, pro- vided that short flashes only (duration of 1.0 sec.) are considered. This is true for each diagonal, ranging from an energy value just slightly above the threshold to one a hundred times as great, in which the response is quite vigorous.

Apparently, the photochemical reactions which initiate the nerve impulse in the eye of *Limulus* are sufficiently simple that the Bunsen-Roscoe law applies to them, provided that only short durations of ex- posure are considered.

Dark adaptation of the single photo- receptor. The ability of the photoreceptor

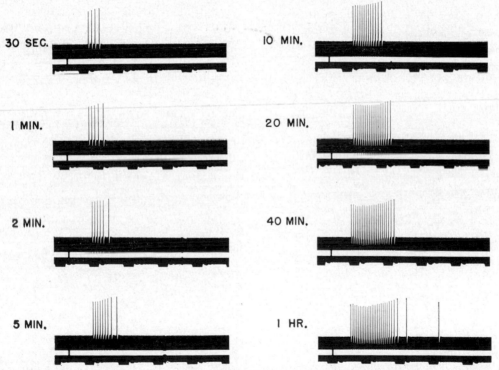

Fig. 282. Dark adaptation of a single visual receptor in the eye of *Limulus*. Oscillograms of the amplified action potentials of a single optic nerve fiber, showing the discharge of impulses in response to a test flash of light of fixed intensity applied to the eye at various times in the dark (given at the left of each record) following a period of light adaptation. In each record deflections of the upper black edge are the amplified action potential spikes of a single active fiber in a small bundle dissected from the rest of the optic nerve and slung across electrodes connected to the input of a vacuum tube amplifier. On the lower black edge are time marks (one half second). The white band just above contains the signal of the test flash (narrow black stripe near the left hand edge; flash duration 0.008 second). (From Hartline, H., and McDonald, P. R.: J. Cell. & Comp. Physiol. **30**:230, 1947.)

to adapt itself to changes in illumination has been mentioned previously. It has been shown that when associated with rhodopsin the rods can increase their sensitivity in the dark many thousand times. Records of the action potentials in the optic nerve fibers of *Limulus* show that the photoreceptors in this eye also undergo dark adaptation to a high degree.

After initial exposure to a light of known intensity, the sensitivity of the eye of *Limulus* may be measured by recording the number of impulses discharged up the nerve in response to a test flash of constant intensity thrown upon the eye at various times after the preadapting exposure. The records from such an experiment are shown in Fig. 282. Thirty seconds after the preadapting light, the test flash succeeded in producing a response of only four spikes. After 5 minutes of dark adaptation, the same test flash produced nine spikes, and after 1 hour spent in the dark, the number of spikes had increased to a maximum, showing that the receptor had recovered its original sensitivity.

In Fig. 283 is shown the course of dark adaptation of a single receptor following periods of light adaptation of various durations. Each one of the curves shows the same general time course of dark adaptation as that indicated in Fig. 282; i.e., there is a rapid recovery of sensitivity at the beginning which proceeds with a steadily diminishing rate to approach the final dark-adapted level asymptotically. The greater is the initial loss of sensitivity, and the longer is the time required for complete recovery.

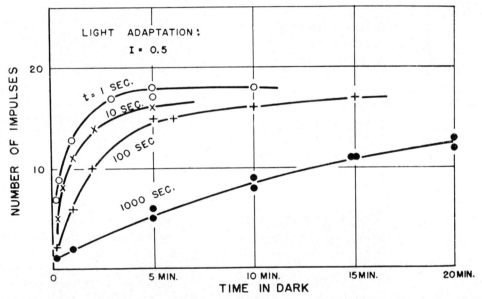

Fig. 283. Dark adaptation of a single receptor following periods of light adaptation. Ordinates: number of impulses elicited by a test flash of constant intensity (5 arbitrary units) and duration (0.010 second). Abscissae: time in the dark (in minutes, linear scale) following the end of the period of light adaptation. I, Intensity of light-adapting exposures (0.5 arbitrary unit); t, duration of light-adapting exposures on respective curves. (From Hartline, H., and McDonald, P. R.: J. Cell. & Comp. Physiol. 30:237, 1947.)

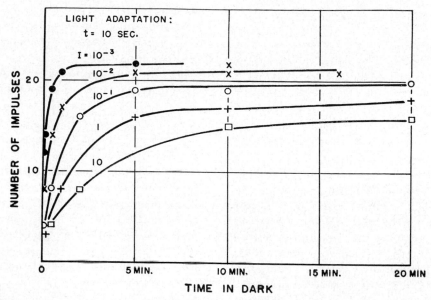

Fig. 284. Dark adaptation of a single receptor following periods of adaptation to light of various intensities. Ordinates: number of impulses elicited by a test flash of constant intensity (1 arbitrary unit) and duration (0.010 second). Abscissae: time in the dark (in minutes, linear scale). t, Duration of light-adapting exposures (10 seconds); I, intensity of light-adapting exposures given on respective curves in arbitrary units. (From Hartline, H., and McDonald, P. R.: J. Cell. & Comp. Physiol. 30:238, 1947.)

In Fig. 284 is shown the dark adaptation of a single receptor following periods of adaptation to light of various intensities, each of which was of 10 seconds' duration. The greater the intensity of the preadapting exposure, the greater is the initial loss of sensitivity, and the longer is the time required for recovery.

These effects of intensity and duration of the preadapting exposure of light on the subsequent course of dark adaptation of the photoreceptors in *Limulus* closely parallel the changes observed in dark adaptation in huan beings (p. 713). It would seem that the fundamental properties of the simple photoreceptor cells in *Limulus* are sufficient to account for all of the changes that occur in more complex retinas during light and dark adaptation and that it is not necessary to postulate activities other than those which re-

side in such simple units. It has been suggested, e.g., that other components in the vertebrate retina such as the complex system of synapsing neurons participate in and partially account for the changes that take place during light and dark adaptation. Schouten and Ornstein[33] have postulated the spread of electric influences over the retina during indirect adaptation which they believe has its seat in the retinal synapses, and Lythgoe[34] has suggested changes in the functional connections of the receptor elements to explain the progressive deterioration of the final visual judgments during dark adaptation. Hartline and McDonald point out, however, that their own experiments on *Limulus* do not exclude the possibility of additional effects in the vertebrate retina, nor can the comparison between the receptor unit in *Limulus* and the vertebrate rod or cone be made without reservation.

Résumé of responses from a single photoreceptor. Up to this point we have been considering the type of response a single sensory cell transmits to its nerve fiber as a result of stimulation. In résumé, it has been shown that as soon as a light of threshold intensity is turned on such a photoreceptor it responds after a short latent period with a burst of impulses. These gradually die down in frequency but remain at the same height (voltage) until a steady state has been reached, after which they may keep on firing impulses at this constant rate continuously for as long as the stimulus is kept constant. If the illumination is increased, the number and frequency of impulses increase, and this within limits (short exposures) follows the reciprocity law in that the product of intensity and duration is constant. Light of different wavelengths produces the same rate of discharge if the relative energies of the flashes of different wavelengths are suitably adjusted. From this, a curve which represents the visibility curve to light of different wavelengths can be drawn. This in all probability is the absorption spectrum of the photosensitive pigment contained in this animal's eye. This eye shows the properties of becoming dark-adapted, i.e., increasing its sensitivity by a stay in the dark. The course of this dark adaptation and the effects of the character of the preadaptation light on it resemble strongly the course of dark adaptation in human beings.

Although the lateral eye of *Limulus* is composed of independent receptors whose excitation elicits activity in each independent optic nerve fiber, there is also a crude form of functional organization in this retina of such a nature that activity in any one optic nerve fiber may be affected by the illumination of other receptors in the same eye. The influence exerted upon a single receptor unit by the activity of its neighbors is inhibitory solely.[35] It is of interest to find inhibitory interaction in such a simple retina as that of *Limulus*. Inhibitory interaction can achieve important visual effects in more complicated vertebrate eyes; e.g., one of its consequences is enhancement of visual contrast. Under normal conditions the pattern of the image on the retina consists of regions of unequal illumination coming from different parts of the visual field. The more intensely illuminated receptor units in the retina exert stronger inhibition upon the less intensely illuminated units than the latter exert upon the former, especially if they lie close together. As a result of this, differences in activity from differently lighted retinal regions are exaggerated, and contrast is enhanced.[36]

Simultaneous responses from more than one photoreceptor

It is obvious that the message sent to the brain in response to the stimulus is more than the firing off of one receptor, even in the case of *Limulus,* and, therefore, we must examine records in which two or more fibers are active at the same time. The receptors of *Limulus* probably differ somewhat in their individual properties and in their thresholds of stimulation with the character of the light to which they are exposed. It is, therefore, the aggregate of these responses from all of the receptor elements which constitutes the visual message.

By careful dissection of the bundle of nerve fibers in the nerve, it is possible to secure a specimen in which only a few fibers are left to function. The action potentials from a nerve containing several active fibers are shown in Fig. 285, *A* to *C*. It can be seen that the responses in *A*

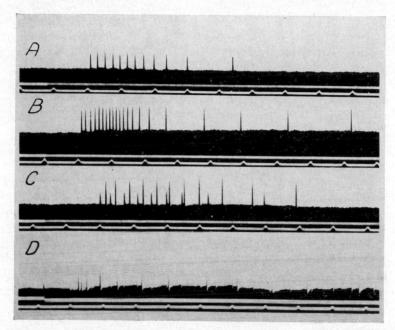

Fig. 285. Action potentials from nerve strands containing several active fibers. **A** to **C,** From bundle containing two active fibers. **A** and **B,** Stimulation of respective end organs separately (intensity, 0.1). **C,** Stimulation of both end organs simultaneously (intensity, 0.03). **D,** Record showing discharge in three active fibers. Record as shown in Fig. 266. (From Hartline, H., and Graham, C.: J. Cell. & Comp. Physiol. 1:277, 1932.)

differ in size from those in *B.* In *C* both receptors were simultaneously and equally illuminated and were firing off simultaneously. There is no difficulty in recognizing the small impulses from *A* and the large impulses from *B.* In Fig. 285, *D* is still another example, taken from another preparation, of several fibers with different voltages and different rhythms firing off simultaneously. Now, it can be visualized easily why the record taken from the whole optic nerve (Fig. 266) with the entire eye illuminated is such a complicated pattern of spikes.

From this complex pattern, which represents the message sent from the eye to the brain, an animal can recognize the distribution of light and shade in the retinal image, and those animals possessing color vision can visualize the various colors of the outside world. There is nothing in

the discharge of the impulses from one individual sense cell to distinguish what wavelength excites it. In order for one to discriminate between different qualities of stimuli, the response of more than one receptor cell is a necessity. It is the aggregate of these responses from several sensory cells which allows us to interpret differences in color.

It must be supposed that different receptor cells possess different spectral distributions of sensitivity in order to furnish the organism with the necessary basis for color perception. Hartline and Graham[37] have investigated the responses of different individual cells to light of different wavelengths. They found that if several active fibers in the same eye were isolated and illuminated independently the cells responded differently to lights of different wavelengths. The responses from two sense cells in the same eye to three different wavelengths are shown in Fig. 286. The two active fibers are readily identifiable by the differences in the size and form of their impulses. The intensities of the different spectral lights have been adjusted so that the response in the fiber giving the large impulses is constant for all wavelengths. It is seen that these intensities do not constitute a match for the fiber giving the small impulses, but that this fiber gives a stronger response with the red light. In passing from the green to the violet light, the latent period increases progressively and the number of impulses decreases. Therefore, the visibility for this sense cell must be lower in the violet light and higher in the red light than the visibility for the cell giving the larger impulses.

In about 50% of the fibers the visibilities differ from each other by significant amounts. Although no single cell can distinguish differences in wavelength, the two sense cells whose responses are given in Fig. 286 can distinguish red from violet light. The presence of differential sensitivity to wavelength in the various photoreceptors, therefore, may be considered a peripheral mechanism for color discrimination. To make use of this sensory information the animal obviously must possess adequate central mechanisms for integrating this kind of pattern of nerve fiber activity. It will be shown later that the photoreceptors of animals known

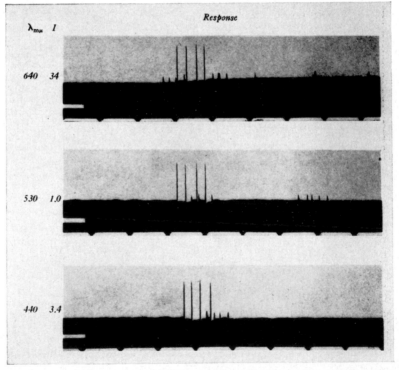

Fig. 286. Oscillographic records of responses from two sense cells in the same eye to three different wavelengths. The relative intensities have been adjusted so that the responses of one sense cell (large impulses) are approximately matched. (From Hartline, H., and Graham, C.: J. Gen. Physiol. **18:**917, 1935.)

to possess a sense of color show differential sensitivity to light of different wavelengths.

It was emphasized on p. 620 that by recording from a simple eye such as *Limulus* the message sent to the brain from each separate unit could more easily be analyzed in terms of alterations in the light stimulus. From this it might be inferred that what occurred in each photoreceptor was entirely independent of the state of activity of the surrounding photoreceptors. This, however, is not the case. It has been shown[38] that each photoreceptor is profoundly influenced by the activity of other photoreceptors lying within a distance of several millimeters of it. When the discharge of one receptor is recorded with light of a fixed intensity falling on it alone and simultaneously another receptor is stimulated, the effect is to inhibit the activity of the first receptor. The threshold to light of the first receptor is raised, and the frequency of the discharge that it can maintain in response to suprathreshold illumination is decreased. This inhibitory action is exerted reciprocally between any two receptors that are separated by no more than a few millimeters. The anatomic basis for this inhibitory interaction is a plexus of nerve fibers lying just back of the layer of ommatidia, connecting them together.

If only two ommatidia are illuminated, the magnitude of the inhibition of each one depends only on the degree of activity of the other; the activity of each, in turn, is the resultant of the excitation from its respective light stimulus and the inhibition exerted on it by the other.

When more than two receptors are simultaneously stimulated, so that the additional receptors are illuminated in the vicinity of an interacting pair too far from one receptor to affect it directly, but near enough to the second to inhibit it,

the frequency of discharge of the first increases as it is partially released from the inhibition exerted on it by the second.

It is quite evident that even in the simple *Limulus* eye the reaction of any receptor in the retina is considerably influenced by inhibition from other receptors simultaneously stimulated.

ACTION POTENTIALS IN THE OPTIC NERVES OF VERTEBRATES

The discharge of impulses in the vertebrate eye was studied first by Adrian and Matthews. Since then, these investigations have been carried on and elaborated by many different physiologists, particularly by Hartline and by Granit and co-workers. In cold-blooded vertebrates, such as the frog, the eye may be removed and the posterior segment cut away, exposing the retina. The optic nerve fibers form a thin layer on the surface of the retina, and small bundles of them may be dissected from the retina in the region where they converge to enter the optic disc. Such a bundle, split up until only a very few active fibers remain, may be placed on electrodes, and its electrical activity may be recorded in the usual manner. Then, the retina is explored with a small spot of light to determine the region which must be illuminated in order to elicit a discharge of impulses in these fibers. This technique has been elaborated by Granit, who uses microelectrodes which record the activity of very few or even single elements.[9]

Different types of fibers in the optic nerves of vertebrates

The most striking difference between the responses of the optic nerve in the frog's eye, as compared to those of the invertebrate eye, is the marked diversity of the responses of different fibers in the eye of the frog. Hartline found three quite distinct types of response in the optic nerve of the frog, indicating that there are three different types of fibers present.

The three different types of response from three separate fibers are recorded in Fig. 287. In *A,* the fiber responds with a rapid burst of impulses when the light is turned on. Although the light is kept constant, this soon dies down to a steady, slower discharge similar to that in the response of the photoreceptors in *Limulus.* There is no response to cessation of illumination of this fiber. This is called the "on" fiber. In *B,* a different fiber responds as the previous one does, but the impulses stop completely although the light is kept on. In addition, this fiber shows a burst of impulses when the light is turned off. This never occurs in records from any fibers of the invertebrate eye. This is termed the "on-off" fiber. Still more striking is the record shown in *C,* in which still another fiber gives no response whatever when the light is turned on or throughout the entire duration of illumination, but when the light is turned off,

there is a rapid burst of impulses. This is called the "off" fiber. Each of these three kinds of responses is peculiar to a particular fiber which never gives any other kind of response, regardless of the conditions of stimulation or adaptation of the retina.

These same three types of responses are seen in all cold-blooded vertebrates and have also been reported in the retinas of mammals.[39, 40] Since the invertebrate eye which contains no synapses shows only the *A* type of response, it is natural to assume that the *B* and *C* types are due to the complex ganglionic structures of the vertebrate retina, interposed between the sensory receptors and the axons of the retinal ganglion cells. It will be recalled that there are several neurons in the vertebrate retina, of which the axon of the ganglion cell forming the optic nerve is the last. It is known that ganglionic cells modify the responses from photoreceptors because leads taken from the optic ganglion of *Limulus* with microelectrodes have recorded a discharge of

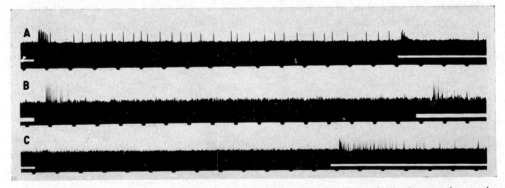

Fig. 287. Oscillographic records of the action potentials in three single intraocular optic nerve fibers of the frog's eye, showing three characteristic response types. A, Response to illumination of the retina consisting of an initial burst of impulses followed by a maintained discharge lasting throughout illumination. There is no response to cessation of illumination in this fiber (the "off" response in this record is partly due to retinal potential and partly to another fiber which discharged several small impulses). B, Response only to onset and cessation of light. C, Response only to cessation of illumination. In this record, the time is marked in one fifth seconds, and the signal marking the period of illumination fills the white line immediately above the time marker. (From Hartline, H.: Am. J. Physiol. 121:400, 1938.)

impulses in response to cessation of illumination upon the eye.[41]

The responses of each of these three kinds of fibers, *A, B,* and *C,* are subject to the same factors which determine the responses of the visual cells in the eye of *Limulus.* An increase in illumination produces an increase in the frequency of discharge, and the sensitivity of the retina is diminished by light adaptation and increased by dark adaptation. In addition, certain new properties are found. The *B* fibers respond to very slight changes in intensity; the greater the change, the more marked is the response. These fibers are also extremely sensitive to any movement of the retinal image, whether it be a spot of light or a small shadow on the uniformly illuminated retina (Fig. 288). The higher the intensity and the more rapid and extensive the movement, the greater is the number of impulses discharged per unit time. This type of response is obviously of great importance to the animal in its search for food and escape from enemies. The response in the *C* fibers to

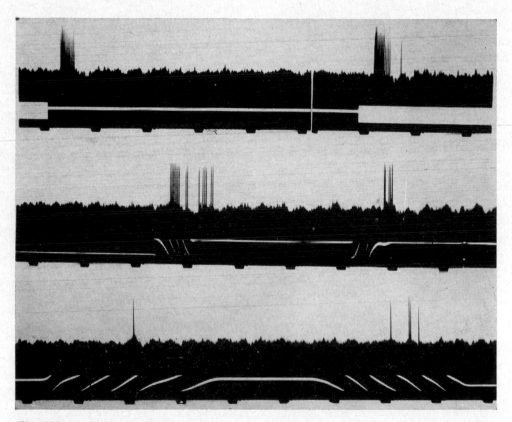

Fig. 288. Oscillograms of action potentials in a single optic nerve fiber of the frog, showing responses to slight movements of small spot of light (50 μ in diameter) on the retina. Fiber responded only to "on" and "off"; there is no discharge during steady illumination if stimulus spot was stationary (*upper record,* signal marking period of illumination blackens the white strip above time marker). Slight movements of stimulus spot on retina are signaled by narrow white lines appearing above time marker. These are shadows of spokes attached to head of micrometer screw controlling position of stimulus spot. Each spoke corresponds to 7 μ on the retina. Time in one fifth seconds. (From Hartline, H.: Am. J. Physiol. **130**:690, 1940.)

turning off of the light usually subsides in a few seconds, and the intensity of the preceding illumination determines the initial frequency and the duration of the discharge. Although the ganglion cells which probably produce this discharge are not active throughout the whole time the stimulus acts, something must be happening in the cells to determine the character of the final discharge. As a matter of fact, the discharge in these fibers can be abruptly suppressed at any time merely by reillumination of the retina. The discharge of impulses in the *C* fibers, signaling cessation of stimulation, must not be held to imply that the fiber is actually responding to darkness or the absence of light. Some process which would seem to be identical with inhibition must be developing in the retina during illumination, stopping the discharge in these fibers upon reillumination. When the stimulus is removed, impulses to fibers connected with receptors giving the "off" effect are set free. In other words, these receptors must be prepared for this response by the effect of the light stimulus because only if they are prepared previously by the stimulus can they function when it is removed.

The nature of this inhibitory process is unknown, but its potential is negative compared to the other excitatory processes, which have a positive potential. Thus, in the visual system there are neurons whose activity is governed by inhibitory as well as by excitatory influences, and the interplay of excitation and inhibition, characteristic of the activity of the central nervous system, is demonstrable in the functions of the retina.

The receptive field

Another feature which recordings from the vertebrate eye have revealed is that the discharge from a single fiber in the optic nerve is not limited to the illumination of a single spot on the retina. It is well known that the receptor cells in the vertebrate retina far outnumber the ganglion cells. Each ganglion cell must, therefore, be connected with several receptors. The area of the retina which supplies any one ganglion cell with action potentials may be considerable. Hartline found that a single ganglion cell in the periphery of the frog retina could be stimulated by a small light falling within an area of a millimeter, which must comprise many receptor elements (Fig. 289). This proves that a retinal ganglion cell can receive excitatory influences over many convergent pathways and that its axon is the final common path for nervous activity originating in many sensory elements. This furnishes us with the functional basis for the spatial effects observed in the peripheral retina of man (pp. 730 to 732).

The area of the retina, throughout which spot illumination will continue to yield a response in a particular optic nerve fiber, is termed the receptive field of that fiber. The location of the receptive field on the retina is fixed, but its extent depends upon the intensity and the area of the exploring spot and on the state of adaptation of the eye. It is smallest with threshold stimulation, being then usually 0.25 to 0.50 mm. in diameter. With intensities one hundred to one thousand times the threshold, it may be twice this size. The larger the area of the spot of illumination falling within the receptive field, the greater will be the response of the fiber.[42]

The sensitivity of the area so determined is not the same throughout, but like the whole visual field in the eye of a human being, it has a central region of greatest acuity (lowest threshold) surrounded by an area of diminishing acuity (increasingly high threshold), as shown in

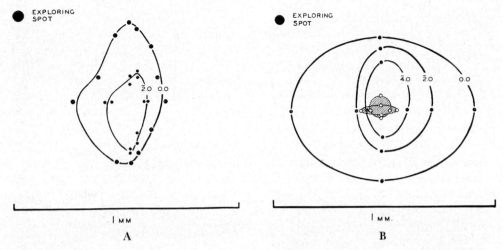

Fig. 289. Charts of the retinal regions supplying single optic nerve fibers in the eye of the frog. **A,** Determination of the contours of the receptive field of a fiber at two levels of intensity of exploring spot. Dots mark positions at which exploring spot (50 μ in diameter) would just elicit discharges of impulses, at the intensity whose logarithm is given on the respective curve (unit intensity $= 2.10^4$ meter-candles). No responses at log I $= -3.0$, for any location of exploring spot. This fiber responded only to "on" and "off". **B,** Contours (determined by four points on perpendicular diameters) of receptive field of a fiber at three levels of intensity (value of log I given on respective contours). In this fiber steady illumination (log I $= 0.0$ and -2.0) produced a maintained discharge of impulses for locations of exploring spot within central shaded area. Elsewhere discharge subsided in 1 to 2 seconds. No maintained discharge in response to intensities less than log I $= -2.0$. No responses at all to an intensity log I $= -4.6$. (From Hartline, H.: Am. J. Physiol. **130:**690, 1940.)

Fig. 289. The sensitivity to light for a particular ganglion cell is not distributed uniformly over the whole area of the retina it supplies. The region of maximal sensitivity is usually several tenths of a millimeter in diameter, but responses to light can be elicited over a considerably larger area; appreciable sensitivity generally extends over an area of approximately one square millimeter.

In the case of the *C* fibers, whose response is the "off" effect, it is found that the inhibitory impulses also converge on each ganglion cell from a considerable area of the retina, just as the excitatory influences do on the other types of fibers.

Whenever there is interaction between neurons, it is not surprising to find spatial summation. For example, let us suppose that we have two photoreceptors connected to the same ganglion cell. Electrodes on the optic nerve fiber, which is the final common pathway for the two receptors, record potential changes. If a subliminal (under the threshold) stimulus is applied to one receptor only, no activity occurs in the nerve fiber, but if subliminal stimuli are applied to both receptors simultaneously, the nerve fiber will fire off.

In Fig. 290 are shown the responses to illumination of the retina, with patches of light of various sizes falling well within the limits of the fiber's receptive field. The larger the area illuminated by a stimulus patch of fixed intensity, the shorter is the latency of the response, and, for moderate degrees of stimulation,

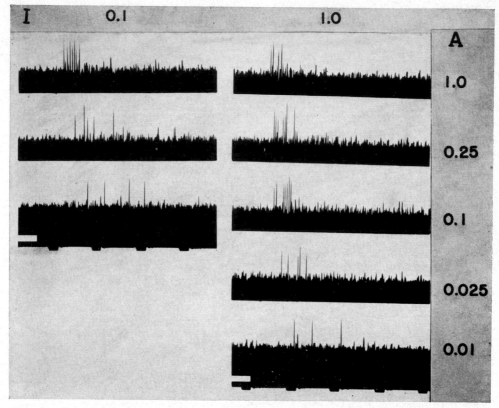

Fig. 290. Oscillograms of action potentials in a single optic nerve fiber from a frog's retina, showing effect of size of stimulus patch upon the discharge of impulses. Retina illuminated with circular patches of light, centered on receptive field of the fiber. **A,** Relative areas given on right (**A** = 1 corresponds to 0.006 mm.²). For the responses in the left-hand column the intensity of illumination was one tenth that used for the right-hand column (**I** = 1 equivalent to 3.10⁵ meter-candles). Fiber was one responding with bursts of impulses at "on" and "off," with no impulses discharged during steady illumination. Only "on" burst shown here. Signal of illumination blackens white line above the marker (only shown in bottom records). Time in one fifth seconds. (From Hartline, H.: Am. J. Physiol. **130:**690, 1940.)

the higher is the frequency and the greater is the number of impulses in the discharge. These effects are similar to those obtained by increasing the intensity of a patch of light of fixed area, as may be seen from a comparison of the responses in the two columns of Fig. 290. The response of the ganglion cell is determined solely by the total amount of the luminous flux (area times intensity). This relation holds only if the area illuminated does not include the less sensitive margins

of the receptive field of the fiber, which can contribute only a little to the excitation of the ganglion cell. With large areas which exceed the size of the receptive field, only the intensity of illumination determines the response.

The activity of a fiber representing a unit or receptive field can be influenced by what is going on in other receptive fields adjoining its own. Illumination of some parts of the receptive field of a retinal ganglion cell may inhibit responses generated by illuminating other parts of the same receptive field, and the responses of a retinal ganglion cell may be inhibited by illumination of retinal regions entirely outside its receptive field.

Receptive fields in mammalian retinas

Studies of the receptive fields of mammalian retinas have shown a number of new features in their patterns of organization compared to those of lower vertebrates.[43, 44] While the responses of the mammalian retina are also in the form of receptive fields, two different types are found. One type gives "on" discharges when the center is stimulated by light and "off" discharges to illumination of the periphery of the receptive field. The other type shows the reverse arrangement, with "off" responses in the center and "on" responses from the surrounding area. In the mammalian retina a constant background of firing of the ganglion cells takes place, even with no illumination. The cells with "on" centers show a marked increase in firing when the centers are illuminated, whereas the periphery of the field shows inhibition in this background firing when a spot of light is shone on it, and when the light is turned off the firing becomes quite marked. A diagram of these two types of ganglion cells with different types of receptive fields is given in Fig. 291. In general, the responses from the central region of a receptive field is the opposite of that obtained from the periphery. The character of each ganglion cell cannot be changed by altering any of the parameters of illumination. That is, an "on" center ganglion cell cannot be converted into an

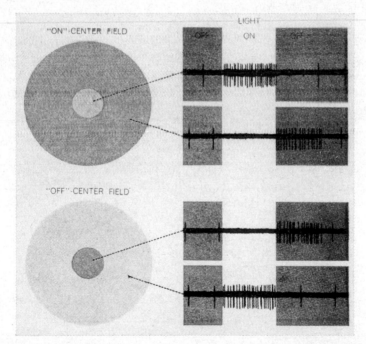

Fig. 291. Concentric fields are characteristic of retinal ganglion cells. *Top,* Oscilloscope recording shows strong firing by an "on" center type of cell when a spot of light strikes the field center. If the spot hits an "off" area, the firing is suppressed until the light goes off. *Bottom,* Responses of a cell of the "off" center type. (From Hubel, D.: Scient. Am. **209:**57, 1963. Reprinted with permission. Copyright © 1963 by Scientific American, Inc. All rights reserved.)

"off" center cell. Further, the center and the surrounding regions of each field are functionally opposed, each tending to suppress the other. In this manner each ganglion cell connected with the photoreceptors which comprise its receptive field is subject to multiple influences from its various receptors. What it finally discharges into the optic nerve fiber (its axon) will be the resultant of these various influences. In other words, its discharge pattern will express the balance between these opposing and interacting contributions. It may well be, therefore, that what Hartline termed different types of optic nerve fiber in the frog retina (pp. 631 to 634) are really an expression of the characteristics of different types of receptive fields. Whether a particular fiber gives an "on," an "off," or an "on-off" response may be due to the influences of the receptors that make up each receptive field and not to any fundamental characteristic of the optic nerve fiber itself.

Monkeys, which have well-defined foveas, likewise show the same pattern in their receptive fields, the central and peripheral portions of each field being mutually antagonistic.[45] The receptive fields vary in size considerably. Those nearest the fovea (4 degrees from the fovea) are the smallest, with a diameter of 4 minutes of arc (20μ on the retina). The size increases as one goes out into the periphery. The largest have a diameter of 2 degrees. The difference between the great acuity of the fovea and the poor acuity of the periphery of the retina in man may be related to this difference in size of the receptive fields in the two regions.

It is quite evident that the coded message sent up each optic nerve fiber is the result of many different events going on in the retina after a light stimulus reaches it. The capture of a sufficient number of quanta of light energy by a photopigment in a rod or cone outer segment results in a change in the molecular structure of this complex lipoprotein, with the release of electrical energy, i.e., a change in polarity of the outer segment. This is transmitted to the inner segment where it is probably amplified and is sent on its course to the bipolar cell. Groups of receptors which form the receptive field of a single ganglion cell react to the light stimulus in various ways. Some augment the stimulus to the ganglion cell; others inhibit it. Unquestionably, interaction takes place between groups of receptive fields, and ganglion cells are probably linked together by impulses distributed laterally in the retina by amacrine cells and horizontal cells. The final message arrives at the lateral geniculate ganglion, the first and only stop on its way to the cells of the visual cortex. The electrical activity of these two regions is described in the chapter devoted to the visual pathways (pp. 676 and 686).

The message transmitted by the optic nerve is not a replica of the differences in light intensity falling on the photoreceptors, nor does it necessarily faithfully mimic the temporal pattern of retinal stimulation. In other words, the pattern of nervous activity which reaches the brain is by no means a direct copy of the pattern of radiant energy incident on the retina. Two distinct mechanisms which have recently received considerable study play important roles in the detection and signaling of information to the cortex about contours. I have already described how in *Limulus* the simultaneous stimulation of ommatidia in the vicinity of a single receptor whose responses are being recorded immediately inhibits the response of that receptor to any particular light stimulus. The closer these ommatidia are to the receptor being tested, the greater is the inhibitory effect. Even a single photoreceptor stimulated in the vicinity of the photoreceptor being studied will affect its responses, and they mutually interact in that the more intensely illuminated retinal receptor exerts a stronger inhibition on the less intensely illuminated one. In an animal's normal environment different receptors of the eye are usually subjected to unequal intensities of illumination from different parts of the visual field. As a result of this inhibition of one portion of the retina on another, differences in neural activity from differently lighted retinal regions become exaggerated; in this way, contrast is enhanced. This may be called a static inhibitory mechanism that serves to exaggerate information about spatial differences in intensity.[46]

A second dynamic mechanism is present which serves to signal information about temporal changes in intensity. Both these mechanisms may be closely related. This second mechanism was described previously for human vision in the discussion of the effects of stabilization of the retinal image (p. 760). The stimulation of those retinal elements which respond only to "on" and to "off" of the stimulus is immediately blocked if the retinal image is stabilized, i.e., if the normal micronystagmus and flicks are abolished artificially. All contours and discontinuities in the image gradually fade out under these conditions, and the visual field appears blank until movement of the object in respect to the retinal receptors is re-established.

We have evidence, therefore, that neural mechanisms are present in the retina which modify the responses of the rods and cones in such a way that contours are enhanced while other information is discarded. Just as an artist may convey the complete image of a face with a single line as a contour, leaving to the imagina-

tion the filling in of all details, so the optic nerve response may emphasize certain features of the scene it transmits to the brain and omit other details. The myriad interconnections in the retina afford by their interplay excitatory and inhibitory influences which eventuate in an optic nerve message quite different from the primary response of the photoreceptors.

The message sent to the visual cortex is quite different from any replica of the retinal image. Even at the retinal level the differences in light and shade of the retinal image can only be crudely signaled to the optic nerve fibers since only a small number of the receptors stimulated can send a separate message to the brain. The concept that the array of photoreceptors is equivalent to the grain of a photographic emulsion is untenable. Actually the retina is more a filter than a film. It is quite likely that the retina discriminates and sends on to the brain only what it considers, so to speak, the most useful information. Discrimination is probably also practiced by the lateral geniculate body and by the cortical cells themselves. Muntz[47] has recently offered evidence that the retina in frogs may respond only to small moving objects such as bugs and not to larger objects or to stationary objects in the field of vision. This filtering out of information is of value in the ordinary life of a frog but is possibly disadvantageous under unusual conditions. A frog might well starve to death when surrounded by dead flies. As Muntz has said:

"The eye . . . is a biological instrument adapted to meet the animal's needs; to understand the function of the frog's eye it is necessary to consider the frog's point of view."*

---

*From Muntz, W.: Scient. Am. **211**:111, 1964. Reprinted with permission. Copyright © 1964 by Scientific American, Inc. All rights reserved.

Muntz found that certain fibers in the frog's optic nerve respond mainly to blue light, and that this represents genuine hue discrimination. The frog apparently utilizes this information, and its behavior is dominated by this response or preference for blue. The function of this blue-sensitive system (the basic factor is the presence of so-called green rods in the frog retina; the responses are conducted up the optic nerve to the dorsal thalamus by "on" fibers) is to enable a frightened frog to jump in such a way that it will leap into the water to escape its predators and not into the grass where it could be caught. Green is particularly ineffective in stimulating the frog's blue-sensitive system, so that light from any other source will be more effective than the green light from the vegetation.

REFERENCES

1. Karpe, G.: The basis of clinical electroretinography, Acta ophth. 24 (supp.):1, 1945.
2. Keeler, C., Sutliffe, E., and Chaffee, E.: Normal and rodless retinae of the house mouse with respect to the electromotive force generated through stimulation by light, Proc. Nat. Acad. Sc. 14:477, 1928.
3. Keeler, C.: Hereditary blindness in the house mouse with special reference to its linkage relationships, Bulletin no. 3, Howe Laboratory of Ophthalmology, January 1, 1930.
4. Noell, W.: Studies on the electrophysiology and metabolism of the retina, Randolph Field, Texas, 1953, USAF School of Aviation Medicine.
5. Auerbach, E., and Burian, H.: Studies on photopic-scotopic relationships in human electroretinogram, Am. J. Ophth. 40:42, 1955.
6. Adrian, E., and Matthews, R.: Action of light on the eye; discharge of impulses in the optic nerve and its relation to electrical changes in the retina, J. Physiol. 63:378, 1927.
7. Granit, R., and Therman, P.: Excitation and inhibition in the retina and in the optic nerve, J. Physiol. 83:359, 1935.
8. Therman, P.: The neurophysiology of the retina in the light of the chemical methods of modifying its excitability, Acta Soc. sc. fenn. 11:1, 1938.
9. Granit, R.: Sensory mechanisms of the retina, London, 1947, Oxford University Press.
10. Potts, A., Modrell, R., and Kingsbury, C.: Permanent fractionation of the electroretinogram by sodium glutamate, Am. J. Ophth. 50:900, 1960.
11. Tomita, T.: Studies on the intraretinal potential, Jap. J. Physiol. 1:110, 1950.
12. Ottoson, D., and Svaetichin, G.: Electrophysiological investigations of origin of ERG of frog retina, Acta physiol. scandinav. 29(supp. 106):538, 1953.
13. Brindley, G.: The passive electrical properties of the frog's retina, choroid and sclera for radial fields and currents, J. Physiol. 134:339, 1956.
14. Brown, K., and Wiesel, T.: Analysis of the intraretinal electroretinogram in the intact cat eye. J. Physiol. 158:229, 1961.
15. Brown, K., and Wiesel, T.: Localization of origins of electroretinogram components by intraretinal recording in the intact cat eye, J. Physiol. 158:257, 1961.
16. Brown, K., and Tasaki, K.: Localization of electrical activity in the cat retina by an electrode marking method, J. Physiol. 158:281, 1961.
17. Noell, W.: The origin of the electroretinogram, Am. J. Ophth. 38:78, 1954.
18. Brindley, G.: Physiology of the retina and visual pathway, Baltimore, 1960, Williams & Wilkins Co., p. 61.
19. Porter, K.: The submicroscopic morphology of protoplasm, Harvey Lect. 51:175, 1955-56.
20. Yamanda, E. A.: A peculiar laminated body observed in the cells of the pigmented epithelium of the bat, J. Biophys. Chem. Cytol. 4:329, 1958.
21. Brown, K., and Wiesel, T.: Intraretinal recording in the unopened cat's eye, Am. J. Ophth. 46:91, 1958.
22. Tomita, T., Murakami, M., and Hashimoto, Y.: On the R membrane in the frog's eye; its localization and relation to the retinal action potential, J. Gen. Physiol. 43:81, 1960.
23. Karpe, G.: Apparatus and method for

clinical recording of the electroretinogram, Docum. ophth. **2**:268, 1948.

24. Henkes, H.: Use of electroretinography in disturbances of the retinal and choroidal circulation, Proceedings of the Sixteenth International Congress of Ophthalmology, London **2**:596, 1950.

25. Zetterstrom, B.: The clinical electroretinogram; the electroretinogram in children during the first year of life, Acta ophth. **29**:295, 1951.

26. Noell, W.: Differentiation, metabolic organization, and viability of the visual cell, Arch. Ophth. **60**:702, 1958.

27. Horsten, G., and Winkelman, J.: Development of the ERG in relation to histological differentiation of the retina in man and animals, Arch. Ophth. **63**:232, 1960.

28. Motokawa, K., Yamashita, E., and Ogawa, T.: Slow potentials and spike activity of retina, J. Neurophysiol. **24**:101, 1961.

29. Svaetchin, G.: Cone action potential, Acta physiol. scandinav. **29**(supp. 106): 565, 1953.

30. Rushton, W.: The retinal organization of vision in vertebrates, Symposia of the Society for Experimental Biology no. 16. London, 1962, Cambridge University Press, p. 28.

31. Tikawa, T., Ogawa, T., and Motokawa, K.: Origin of so-called cone action potential, J. Neurophysiol. **22**:102, 1959.

32. Hartline, H., Wagner, H., and McNichol, E.: Cold Spring Harbor Symposia Quant. Biol. **17**:125, 1952.

33. Schouten, J. F., and Ornstein, L. S.: Measurements on direct and indirect adaptation by means of binocular method, J. Optic. Soc. America **29**:168, 1939.

34. Lythgoe, R.: The mechanism of dark-adaptation, Brit. J. Ophth. **24**:21, 1940.

35. Hartline, H., Wagner, H., and Ratliff, F.:

Inhibition in the eye of limulus, J. Gen. Physiol. **39**:651, 1956.

36. Hartline, H.: Inhibition of activity of visual receptors by illuminating nearby retinal areas in the limulus eye, Fed. Proc. **8**:69, 1949.

37. Hartline, H., and Graham, C.: The response of single visual sense cells to lights of different wave length, J. Gen. Physiol. **18**:917, 1935.

38. Hartline, H., and Ratliff, F.: Inhibitory interaction of receptor units in the eye of limulus, J. Gen. Physiol. **40**:357, 1956-57.

39. Granit, R.: Isolation of colour-sensitive elements in mammalian retina, Acta physiol. scandinav. **2**:93, 1941.

40. Wilska, A.: Untersuchungen über das Richtungshören, Acta Soc. med. fenn. duodecim **21**:1, 1938.

41. Wilska, A., and Hartline, H.: The origin of "off-response" in the optic pathway, Am. J. Physiol. **133**:491, 1941.

42. Hartline, H.: The receptive fields of optic nerve fibers, Am. J. Physiol. **130**:690, 1940.

43. Kuffler, S.: Discharge patterns and functional organization of mammalian retina, J. Neurophysiol. **16**:62, 1953.

44. Wiesel, T.: Receptive fields of ganglion cells in the cat's retina, J. Physiol. **153**: 583, 1960.

45. Hubel, D., and Wiesel, T.: Receptive fields of optic nerve fibers in the spider monkey, J. Physiol. **154**:572, 1960.

46. Ratliff, F., Miller, W., and Hartline, K.: Neural interaction in the eye and the integration of receptor activity, Ann. New York Acad. Sc. **74**:210, 1958.

47. Muntz, W.: Vision in frogs, Scient. Am. **211**:111, 1964.

CHAPTER 15

THE OPTIC NERVE

COMPARISON OF THE OPTIC NERVE WITH TRUE SENSORY NERVES

The optic nerve fibers are derived from the retina. When the embryo is 4 mm. long, the optic stalk is an open tube that connects the optic vesicle to the fore-brain. At this stage, the ganglion cells begin to send their processes into this open tube, and as they grow, they ascend to the brain where they eventually connect with cells which form the lateral geniculate body. The nerve fibers are, therefore, part of a tract of the central nervous system since the retina has developed from the optic vesicle which is an outpouching of the original neural tube. They do not have the same origin as the fibers of ordinary sensory nerves which grow into the cerebrospinal axis from structures outside the primitive neural tube.

The essential part of every nerve fiber in the body is a delicate threadlike axon. The most obvious difference between nerve fibers is the nature of the covering of the axon. Most axons are covered with a thick fatty sheath of myelin and hence are called myelinated fibers. When this sheath is absent, the fiber is unmyelinated. Outside of this myelin sheath nearly all sensory nerves have a second sheath, a thin delicate membranous covering termed the neurilemma or sheath of Schwann. This latter sheath is important in the regeneration of nerve fibers.

The optic nerve fibers are composed of the usual axons and the myelin sheath but lack a neurilemmal sheath entirely. They are not separated from one another by neurilemmal sheaths, as are other sensory nerves. Instead, neuroglial cells are scattered between them, separating them. In this respect, the optic nerve fibers again resemble the fiber tracts of the brain and spinal cord. Thus, while all of the nerves attached to the brain and spinal medulla, with the exception of the olfactory and optic nerves, are covered with a myelin and a neurilemmal sheath, the entire mass of the white substance of the brain and spinal cord and the fibers of the optic nerve are formed of myelinated fibers, devoid of any neurilemmal sheath. The olfactory nerve fibers have a neurilemmal sheath, but are unmyelinated. Therefore, the optic nerve fibers are histologically unlike other sensory nerves in the body, but resemble the fibers of the central nervous system.

Myelination of the optic nerve fibers begins very late. All nerve fibers are unmyelinated when first formed, but most sensory fibers, with the exception of those of the olfactory nerves, soon acquire a myelin coating. The fibers which form the white substance of the cerebrospinal axis do not acquire their myelin until the fifth month of fetal life. Although myelination of the optic nerve fibers begins at about this time, it is generally not until the seventh month of fetal life that this has progressed down the nerve as far as the lamina cribrosa. The deposit of myelin usually stops at this point, but occasionally it extends beyond the lamina, and the nerve fibers in the retina then appear as semiopaque white sheaths in one or more quadrants adjacent to the optic disc. This constitutes the condition known as re-

tained medullated nerve sheaths or myelinated fibers.

It is evident that the optic nerve is not a true peripheral nerve. It is one neuron, or link, in the chain of fibers which runs from the rods and cones to the occipital cortex. One may compare the neurons in the pathway for the sense of sight with those of touch or pressure. The pathway of this sensation is composed of three neurons. End organs present in the skin, the so-called corpuscles of Meissner, connect with each sensory nerve ending, recording the sense of touch or pressure from the skin (Fig. 292, *A*). The first neuron in this pathway connects the sensory end organ to a cell in the posterior horn of the spinal cord. Thus, this first neuron may run all the way from the sole of the foot, up the leg, and into the dorsal region of the spinal cord. The cell body which governs its nutrition is near its point of entrance in the cord. These cells form the posterior root ganglia. The second neuron starts in the posterior column of the cord and ascends to the

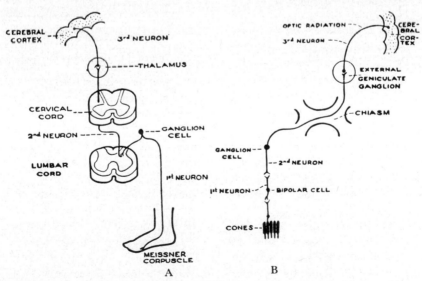

Fig. 292. A, Neurons in the pathway of common sensation. B, Neurons in the visual pathway. (From Adler, F.: Ann. Surg. **101**:1, 1935.)

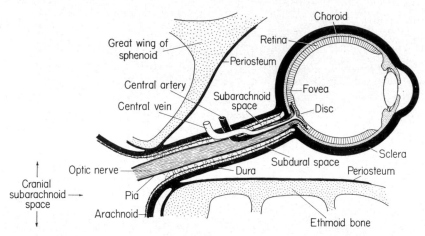

Fig. 293. Diagram showing the continuity between the sheaths of the optic nerve and the sheaths of the brain and the continuity between the cranial subarachnoid space and that around the optic nerve. Note how the central vessels cross the space and may be compressed, if the intracranial pressure is raised and thus produce papilledema.

thalamus. As this fiber passes up the cord, it crosses over to the opposite side and comes to lie in the opposite anterolateral column. The third and last neuron begins with a cell in the thalamus—the fiber running from this point to its appropriate cell station in the temporal lobe of the brain.

In the case of the optic nerve and tracts, three similar neurons are linked together, extending from the retina to the occipital cortex (Fig. 292, *B*). The sensory end organs that respond to the adequate stimulus, light, are the rods and cones. The first neuron begins in the outer plexiform layer and ends in the inner plexiform layer. The cell body governing the nutrition of this fiber is the bipolar cell, the cells of which form the inner nuclear layer. This neuron, although extremely short, is the true optic nerve in the physiologic sense and corresponds to the long fiber which runs from the sole of the foot into the spinal cord. The second neuron in the retina begins in the inner nuclear layer and runs from here to the lateral geniculate body. A part of this is the anatomic optic nerve. The cell

governing the nutrition of this fiber is the ganglion cell. As these fibers ascend to the lateral geniculate body, most of them cross over to the opposite side. In the more primitive mammalians, all the fibers cross over, similarly to the crossing, described previously, for the second neuron for the sensation of pressure. In man, only about 75 to 85% of the fibers cross. The crossing takes place in the chiasm. The third neuron runs from the lateral geniculate body by way of the optic radiation to the occipital cortex. It is to be expected that the anatomic optic nerve, which actually is a second-order neuron, or a tract in the path of conduction, and not a true sensory nerve should suffer from diseases which commonly affect second-order neurons in the central nervous system and not sensory nerves. Likewise, the reactions of the anatomic optic nerve to injury and disease should be those peculiar to second-order neurons in the central nervous system.

A further point of difference between the optic nerve and other sensory nerves in the body is the fact that the optic nerve is surrounded by prolongations of the sheaths which encase the brain, i.e., the dura mater, pia mater, and arachnoid (Fig. 293). At the entrance of the optic nerve into the orbit the dural sheath splits into two layers; one lines the orbit as the periosteum, whereas the other adheres closely to the optic nerve itself and finally becomes indistinguishable from the outer layers of the sclera where the nerve enters the eyeball. In other sensory nerves these sheaths begin only where the fiber enters the cerebrospinal axis. The presence of these layers and the spaces between them and the nerve account for many of the pathologic reactions of the optic nerve. The sheaths surrounding the optic nerve are supplied with many sensory nerves. These give rise to pain in inflammatory conditions of the nerve in the orbit, such as occurs in retrobulbar neuritis in the acute stage. The fact that patients with choked discs suffer no pain, although the nerve head itself is edematous and the fibers are pressed upon, proves that the pain in retrobulbar neuritis arises from the sheaths and not from the nerve fibers themselves. The subarachnoid and subdural spaces are in direct communication with those of the brain. The significance of this will be pointed out in the discussion of papilledema (p. 649).

The optic nerve is supplied by the vascular network of the pia mater throughout its entire intraorbital course. Capillaries from the blood vessels in the pia mater penetrate the optic nerve throughout its length.

Whereas the existence of the central retinal artery is accepted without question, considerable controversy has arisen recently over its importance in supplying the optic nerve itself with blood. The existence of a separate artery whose chief function is to supply the optic nerve with blood has been described by several different authors, who have given it differ-

ent names. François[1] and co-workers call this artery the central optic nerve artery and describe its origin in most cases as from the ophthalmic artery, although they state that it may sometimes be a branch of the first part of the central retinal artery.[2] These authors claim that the central retinal artery may branch within the optic nerve, but that any such branches are not distributed to the tissues of the optic nerve, and that the true blood supply of the optic nerve comes from the vessel that they call the central optic nerve artery. In fact they describe a syndrome of occlusion of this central optic nerve artery which must be differentiated from occlusion of the central retinal artery and acute papillitis.

The evidence presented by François has been challenged by Hayreh[3, 4] and by Blunt[5] who maintain that the so-called central artery of the optic nerve is merely one of the numerous intraneural branches of the central retinal artery. They believe that François' inability to demonstrate an intraneural distribution of the branches of the central retinal artery is due to the inadequacy of his technique of injection. Unless further evidence should be presented, it would seem wise to adhere to the long-established idea that the nutrition of the optic nerve is primarily supplied by the central retinal artery and its branches.

The distribution of the fibers in the nerve as they arise from various portions of the retina is described in Chapter 16, Visual Pathways. The action currents in the nerves when the retina is exposed to light are considered in Chapter 14, Electrical Phenomena in the Eye.

Conduction in the optic nerve

The optic nerve behaves like other sensory nerves in the body and conducts stimuli in one direction only, i.e., up to the primary optic centers. The adequate stimulus consists of impulses generated in the receptor organs in the retina. Either these impulses are accompanied by changes in electrical potential or are the electrical changes which we can record. When they originate at one end of the nerve fiber, they are transmitted at a very rapid rate and with no loss of energy to the cells in the next synapse or cell station. Little is known about the rate of conduction in the mammalian optic nerve. The presence of oxygen is required for constant functioning of the optic nerve, and interference with the circulation results in an immediate block of the impulses.

Localized pressure causes a block in conduction of the optic nerve impulses. This has been well termed physiologic block by Cushing. A tumor pressing on the optic nerve may prevent conduction to the point of blindness. When the pressure is removed, the nerve may recover its powers of conduction immediately, showing that the block was only functional. Long-continued pressure on nerve fibers, probably by interfering with the blood supply, results in degeneration of the fibers.

RESPIRATION OF OPTIC NERVES

Gerard and Hartline[6] dissected the eye of *Limulus* with its optic nerve and measured the oxygen consumption and carbon dioxide production when light was thrown into the eye (Fig. 294). In such a preparation when light is thrown into the eye, the oxygen consumption immediately rises. When the light is turned off, the rate does not fall immediately to the old resting level. It takes about half an hour for the effects of the stimulation to disappear. This is evidence of a long recovery phase in the activity of nerves. Additional oxygen is utilized during the time that the afterpotential persists and the recovery heat is being generated.

The all-or-none principle applies to the optic nerve fibers as well as to the other sensory nerves. The intensity of a light stimulus will be signaled to the brain by an increase in the rate of impulses delivered by each optic nerve fiber and by

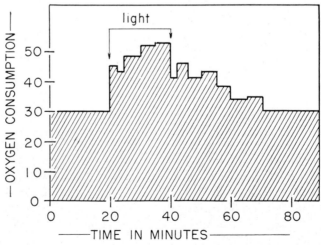

Fig. 294. Rate of oxygen consumption by the optic nerve in the eye of *Limulus*, before, during, and after illumination of the eye. (From Amberson, W., and Smith, D. C.: Outline of physiology, ed. 2, Baltimore, 1948, Williams & Wilkins Co.)

the number of fibers in action at any one time. An intense stimulus calls into play more fibers than a weak one. On this basis, the range of intensities in the sensation of light should include at least as many steps as the total number of fibers present. There are no satisfactory figures which give the limits of visibility for white light, but the eye exhibits an amazing degree of sensitivity. When fully dark-adapted, a very minute amount of light may be detected, and from this point up to the limits of dazzling brightness small differences in illumination may be detected.

DEGENERATION OF FIBERS
Degeneration in ordinary sensory fibers and in the optic nerve

When a nerve fiber is cut, the portion peripheral to the point of section is separated from the body of its nutritive cell. It, therefore, undergoes degenerative changes. The degenerative process does not start at the point of section and progress to the periphery but involves all parts of the fiber simultaneously, even to the finest terminals. The whole fiber degenerates, including the myelin sheath, and eventually all that remains is an empty neurilemmal tube or sheath of Schwann. These changes are called wallerian degeneration. On the proximal side of the section, retrograde degeneration also takes place. The nerve fiber shows changes similar in nature to those just described as far centrally as the first node of Ranvier. Atrophy of the cell body may result ultimately.

In all peripheral nerves regeneration of the fiber may take place. This is accomplished by downgrowth of the neurofibrils from the proximal segment of the cut nerve. These enter the empty neurilemmal sheath at the distal segment and in time may traverse the entire length of the nerve. The sheath of Schwann is a requisite, however, for regeneration to take place. Apparently the cells of the neurilemma form a protoplasmic matrix for the sprouting neurofibrils. If the sheath of motor nerves is divided, the conditions for regeneration may give rise to bizarre functional results.

The ganglionic sympathetic fibers regenerate with great rapidity, as has been demonstrated by Haimovici and Hodes.[7] They excised large sections of the sympathetic chain. As early as fifty-four days after operation, stimulation of the cephlic end of the cervical sympathetic stump caused pupillary dilatation and retraction of the nictitating membrane.

The nutritive cells for the optic nerve fibers are the ganglion cells in the retina. If the optic nerve is cut through, the portion central to the point of section soon degenerates, i.e., up to the lateral geniculate body. The same is true if the ganglion cell itself is damaged. Occasionally cells farther up the pathway in the central nervous system exhibit chromatolysis, and their fibers degenerate. This has been designated transneuronal degeneration. Degeneration occurs in the lateral geniculate body when lesions in the retina are made, but the degeneration does not stop here and may proceed up to the cells in the calcarine cortex.

Toxic agents such as quinine and methyl alcohol damage the ganglion cells, and optic atrophy with blindness may ensue. The toxic agent in methanol poisoning probably is formaldehyde.[8]

Since the optic nerve is part of the central nervous system and has no neurilemmal sheaths, theoretically regeneration is impossible. Experiments designed to prove regeneration and recovery of function in the optic nerve after transection have not been successful in mammals so far. It has been claimed that eyes have been transplanted and that restoration of visual function occurred. In certain mammals on which these experiments have been made, chiefly the spotted rat, it is very difficult to tell by the animal's behavior whether the eyes are functioning or not since vision is subservient to the sense of smell in these animals. Most of their activity is performed in the dark, and when deprived of their eyes, they show little difference in behavior from normal rats. Although regeneration of cut axons in the brain or spinal cord in most laboratory animals does not occur, Sugar and Gerard[9] have adduced evidence of spinal cord regeneration in the rat.

PRODUCTION OF CUPPING IN THE OPTIC NERVE

In its passage into the interior of the eye, the optic nerve has to pass through the scleral foramen, which is in reality a short canal. The outer layers of the sclera are reflected back onto the nerve so as to form its outermost sheath, whereas the inner layers of the sclera stretch over the foramen and are perforated by openings through which various bundles of fibers make their way into the interior of the globe. This perforated layer of tissue forms the so-called lamina cribrosa.

It was formerly believed that the so-called glaucomatous cupping that occurs in chronic simple glaucoma of the open-angle type was due solely to the elevated intraocular pressure which pushed back the lamina cribrosa. It was reasoned that this was the weakest spot in the tunics of the eye so that it was the first to yield to the elevated intraocular pressure. According to this view, glaucomatous cupping was the direct result of the raised intraocular pressure. It is generally recognized, however, that there is no direct relationship between the degree of elevation of the pressure and the amount of the cupping.

Goldmann[10] has pointed out that, in reality, the cupping is not due to the increased pressure primarily, but to the changes which occur simultaneously with the rise of pressure in the posterior segment of eyes in chronic open-angle simple glaucoma. Measurements of the distance between the retinal surface and the lamina cribrosa in normal patients and in patients with chronic simple glaucoma who have a fully developed glaucomatous excavation but still retain visual function show no differences. If anything, the distance is less in patients with glaucoma. This indicates that the glaucomatous cupping is not caused by the lamina cribrosa bending backward, which is really a late effect and occurs frequently in patients with absolute glaucoma. The cupping, according to Goldmann, is due to the changes which occur behind the lamina cribrosa—a fact which was pointed out by Schnabel first and confirmed by Elschnig and Fuchs. For a long period the lamina cribrosa does not participate in the glaucomatous excavation, but the cupping is caused by the disappearance of the nerve and supporting glial tissue due to a peculiar type of change which Schnabel called cavernous optic atrophy. Therefore, the cause of glaucomatous excavation is the disappearance of the supporting glial tissue. In primary atrophy, on the contrary, this supporting tissue remains practically unchanged so that no cup is produced.

The duration of the pressure, rather than the height of the pressure, is the chief factor in determining the extent of the cupping. An acute rise of pressure, lasting a week or more, seldom gives rise to any cupping of the optic disc, whereas pressure slightly above normal that continues for months and years eventually gives rise to a deep glaucomatous cup and atrophy of the nerve fibers.

PRODUCTION OF CHOKED DISC (PAPILLEDEMA)

When the pressure of the spinal fluid in the skull is increased, the intraocular end of the optic nerve becomes congested and swollen, forming a so-called choked disc or papilledema. Von Graefe was the first to note the relation between elevation of intracranial pressure and the production of swelling of the nerve head. His first theory of the causation of choked disc was that the tumor pressed either directly or indirectly upon the cavernous sinus and blocked off the return venous circulation from the eye. This produced stasis of blood in the veins, edema of the nerve, and hemorrhages. Shortly after this, it was demonstrated that free anastomosis between the angular branch of the facial vein and the ophthalmic vein exists so that the return circulation of blood from the eye would not necessarily be interfered with, even if the cavernous sinus were blocked. This led von Graefe to abandon his original theory and to focus his attention on the continuity between the subarachnoid space inside the skull and around the optic nerve.

It is probable that papilledema is produced by fluid being forced into the subarachnoid space around the optic nerve as a result of raised intracranial pressure, together with venous stasis. The primary factor is local increase in the pressure of the cerebrospinal fluid. Mechanical factors alone are sufficient to account for the production of papilledema. The space between the optic nerve sheath and the optic nerve is continuous with the space between the sheaths of the brain and the brain substance. The intracranial subarachnoid space is in free communication, therefore, with the corresponding space of the optic nerve sheath. The intracranial pressure can be transmitted directly through the cerebrospinal fluid to the intravaginal space of the optic nerve as far as the lamina cribrosa. The central vein of the retina with its companion artery traverses this space and makes an almost right-angle bend as it leaves the optic nerve and, crossing the intravaginal space, pierces the arachnoid and dura mater a short distance behind the eyeball. In its passage the vein traverses a rather long section of the subarachnoid space where it is exposed to the pressure of the cerebrospinal fluid in this space (Fig. 293). Any elevation of intracranial pressure distends the sheath and tends to compress the vein in its course across the intravaginal space, thereby impeding the return flow of blood. There is very little effect of this pressure on the flow of blood in the artery since its walls are not easily compressible. As a consequence of this, the venous pressure of the eye rises, and the intraocular part of the vein and its branches becomes engorged. Therefore papilledema results. It has been shown that the intraocular pressure determines the amount of papilledema to some degree. Animals on which a trephine opening in one eye has been made and whose intracranial pressure has been elevated artificially show papilledema in the eye with the lower tension first.

EFFERENT FIBERS IN THE OPTIC NERVE

Histologic evidence for the existence of fibers in the optic nerve which conduct impulses from the brain to the retina has been offered by many different authors, including Polyak.[11] Recently Granit[12] has produced physiologic evidence of these fibers by being able either to inhibit or facilitate spontaneous induced retinal potentials on stimulating the mesencephalic reticular substance. Hartline and co-workers[13] and Motokawa and Ebe[14] have shown antidromic activity also. Finally, Barany and Hallden[15] have shown that alcohol and the barbiturates, both central nervous system depressants, affect retinal interrelationships.

On the other hand, Brindley and Hamasaki[16] showed that in cats lightly anesthetized with pentobarbital or in conscious but resting and drowsy cats section of the optic nerve on one side is entirely without effect on the electro-retinograms. No evidence that the electro-retinogram was modified by impulses passing to the eye along the optic nerve could be shown. The earlier experiments of Jacobson and Gestring[17] suggested that retinal activity was controlled through efferent impulses from a center in the brain via the optic nerves, but more recent experiments by Jacobson[17a] and others have shown such a lack of uniformity in experimental results due probably to the variability of the effects of pentobarbital upon the electroretinogram. It must be concluded that the existence of a centrifugal inhibitory

pathway is at present only conjectural.

Three groups of fibers in the optic nerve and tract of the cat conduct at velocities of 70 M., 30 M., and 17 M. per second, respectively.[18, 19] The first and third peaks are more prominent in responses of the crossed fibers by superficial stimulation of the tract, whereas the first and second peaks were more prominent on deep stimulation. Of the uncrossed fibers, the second peak was greater than the first on superficial stimulation, and the first peak was greater than the second on deep stimulation. The third peak was not detectable in the uncrossed pathway.

This suggests that there are three groups of fibers in the primary optic pathway of the cat, having different sizes. This is borne out by histologic studies. Although fibers of all sizes can be found in almost every sector of the tract, the general tendency of distribution seems to be that the most medial sector of the tract is occupied predominantly by medium and small fibers and the central and lateral portions of the tract mostly by large fibers.

REFERENCES

1. François, J., and Neetens, A.: Vascularization of the optic pathway; lamina cribrosa and optic nerve, Brit. J. Ophth. **38:** 472, 1954.
2. François, J., and Neetens, A.: Central retinal artery and central optic nerve artery, Brit. J. Ophth. **47:**21, 1963.
3. Hayreh, S.: The ophthalmic artery. III. Branches, Brit. J. Ophth. **46:**212, 1962.
4. Hayreh, S.: The central artery of the retina; its role in the blood supply of the optic nerve, Brit. J. Ophth. **47:**651, 1963.
5. Blunt, M.: Intraneural branches of the central retinal artery, Brit. J. Ophth. **47:** 664, 1963.
6. Gerard, R., and Hartline, H.: Respiration due to natural nerve impulses. Method for measuring respiration, J. Cell. & Comp. Physiol. **4:**141, 1934.

7. Haimovici, H., and Hodes, R.: Preganglionic nerve regeneration in completely sympathectomized cats, Am. J. Physiol. **128:**463, 1940.
8. Potts, A., and Johnson, L.: Studies on visual toxicity of methanol, Am. J. Ophth. **35:**107, 1952.
9. Sugar, O., and Gerard, R.: Spinal cord regeneration in the rat, J. Neurophysiol. **3:**1, 1940.
10. Goldmann, H.: The glaucoma problem. In Newell, F., editor: Glaucoma, Transactions of the Second Conference, New York, 1957, Josiah Macy, Jr., Foundation, p. 137.
11. Polyak, S.: The vertebrate visual system, Chicago, 1957, University of Chicago Press, pp. 246-255, 579, 589.
12. Granit, R.: Centrifugal and antidromic

effects on ganglion cells of the retina, J. Neurophysiol. **18:**388, 1955.

13. Hartline, H., et al.: Mutual inhibition among the receptors of the eye of limulus, Proceedings of the Sixteenth International Physiological Congress, Montreal, 1953, p. 441.

14. Motokawa, K., and Ebe, M.: Antidromic stimulation of the optic nerve and photosensitivity of the cat retina, J. Neurophysiol. **17:**364, 1954.

15. Barany, E., and Hallden, U.: The influence of some central nervous system depressants on the reciprocal inhibition between the two retinae as manifested in retinal rivalry, Acta physiol. scandinav. **14:**296, 1947.

16. Brindley, G., and Hamasaki, D.: Evidence that the cat's electroretinogram is not influenced by impulses passing to the eye along the optic nerve, J. Physiol. **163:**558, 1962.

17. Jacobson, J., and Gestring, G.: Centrifugal influence upon the electroretinogram, Arch. Ophth. **60:**295, 1958.

17a. Jacobson, J.: Personal communication.

18. Chang, H.: Fiber groups in the optic pathway of the cat, J. Neurophysiol. **19:**224, 1956.

19. Lenox, M.: Single fiber responses to electrical stimulation in cat's optic tract, J. Neurophysiol. **21:**62, 1958.

CHAPTER 16

VISUAL PATHWAYS

It is easy to show that a real inverted image of an object in space is formed on the retina. If a window is cut in the sclera at the posterior pole of an enucleated eye and the eyeball is held in a cardboard tube to eliminate extraneous light, an image of a candle flame held at a distance of a few feet in front of the pupil will be sharply focused on the retina, as on the ground-glass plate of a camera. This image is real and inverted. It is the function of those parts of the eye which refract the rays of light to form a sharp image on the retina. This image is the adequate stimulus which excites the sensory receptors. The differences in light intensity of the image produce different steady state levels of pigment breakdown to which the photoreceptors respond correspondingly. They transform the energy of the stimulus into a nerve impulse which is conducted by the optic nerve fibers to appropriate cell stations in the brain. This chapter deals with the mechanism which conducts the visual impulses from the photoreceptors to the visual centers in the occipital cortex.

The visual receptors in the retina are the rods and cones. The existence of the normal blind spot proves that the optic nerve fibers themselves cannot be stimulated directly. In the fovea, where vision is most perfect for details of form and color, there are no rods and most of the layers of the retina are thinned out so that only cones remain, showing the importance of these structures. Since all of the retinal structures are transparent, the rays of light pass through them until they reach the outermost opaque layer of pigment epithelium. Immediately in front of this layer lie the outer segments of the rods and cones, containing photochemical pigments, and it is here that the light energy is absorbed and converted into the nerve impulse. Since this receptive layer in the mammalian retina lies furthest away from the object in space, the light rays must traverse all of the other layers of the retina in order to reach it. It is imperative, therefore, that all of the retinal structures in front of the rods and cones be as transparent as possible. In order to insure this transparency in the macular region, no large blood vessels run into the macula (Fig. 295), and in the fovea where vision is most acute even the capillaries of the central retinal artery are absent. The fovea must receive its nutrition largely from the underlying choriocapillaries.

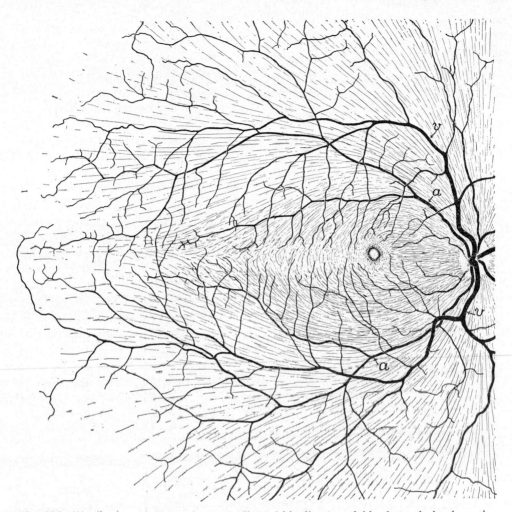

Fig. 295. Distribution of the optic nerve fibers (thin lines) and blood vessels in the retina of an adult rhesus monkey as seen in a whole-mount preparation stained with methylene dye during life. **a,** Arteries. **v,** Veins. The white elliptical papilla or disc of the optic nerve at the right margin of the figure is the center from which emerge large arteries and veins. These, by dividing, are gradually distributed over the retinal surface, the larger branches avoiding the central area and fovea (small round stippled area free from blood vessels). The transparent round center of the central fovea is its flat floor, surrounded by the darker wall or slope, where the nerve cells are present in great numbers. The optic nerve fibers, arising as axis cylinders from the retinal ganglion cells collected in bundles, converge from all points of the retinal surface toward the papilla where they leave the eyeball and form the optic nerve. In the nasal half (right in the illustration; only partly visible) the course of the fibers is radial. In the temporal half of the retina (left) the fibers pass above and below the central area in order to leave the central fovea free. The line along which the fibers passing above separate from those passing below, called the raphe or seam, corresponds to the horizontal meridian. Some of the nerve fibers arising from the fovea and central area pass in a straight course to the papilla; others describe arches above and below the foveal depression (the so-called papillomacula bundle). (From Polyak, S.: The retina, Chicago, 1941, University of Chicago Press.)

THE RETINA

A knowledge of the cellular structure of the retina is necessary in order to trace the impulses originating in the photoreceptors as they pass through the retina and up the optic nerve fibers on their way to the brain. In the past much of the function of the retina had to be inferred from its structure. With the development of electrical recording by microelectrodes which can sample what is going on at different depths in the retina, we are getting physiologic information of the organization of the retina as a nervous center. Fortunately most of what was previously surmised is now being confirmed.

The retina is not a simple sensory receptor but an extremely complex layer of nervous tissue composed of many different types of cells and fibers through which the impulses set up in the rods and cones are modified as they pass on their way to the optic nerve. Its very complexity predicts the enormous variations in the quality and quantity of the sensory responses of which we find the eye to be capable.

Neurons in the visual pathway

The retina, like all nervous tissue, is made up of a series of histologic units, each nerve cell synapsing with another to form a series of neurons. Each neuron is made up of a cell body containing a nucleus and projecting from one side of the cell a number of fine expansions called dendrites. From the opposite side of the cell an axis cylinder or axon emerges, with its terminal ramifications called teledendrons. The dendrites receive the nerve message from the teledendrons of other cells with which they synapse. The message is transmitted through the cell body and is discharged by way of the axon through its teledendrons to the next receiving neuron (Fig. 296).

The basic functioning unit of the central nervous system and therefore of the retina, which is part of the brain, is the

---

Fig. 296. Diagram illustrating the basic facts of the structural and functional organization of the nervous system. First, a few of the many types of varieties of the histologic units or nerve cells—the neurons—which compose the nervous tissue are shown, each neuron made up of a body or perikaryon, with a nucleus, dendritic expansions or mychodendron, an axis cylinder or axon, and its terminal ramification or teledendron. Second, the dynamic or functional polarity of a neuron is demonstrated, wherein the dendrites perform a receptive function, the body and the axis cylinders serve as the transmission cable, and the teledendric termination serves as the discharging apparatus. Finally, the connections of the neurons with one another, called synapses, and the principal varieties of synaptical relationship are illustrated. **A,** d variety of the bipolar cells of the primate retina with a relatively wide dendritic treetop (above) synaptically related to a group of both rods and cones, whence it receives impulses which it transmits by means of a teledendron to a group of ganglion cells (below, only one shown here)—a polysynaptic common path. **B,** h variety of bipolar cells of the primate retina, with very restricted terminations both of the dendritic (above) and of the axonal expansions (below), related to a single cone and to a single, small ganglion cell—a monosynaptic individual path. **C,** Several h bipolars, each related to a single cone cell (above), but all synaptically connected with a single ganglion cell of the n variety with a relatively wide dendritic treetop (below)—a simple collector pathway. Each of the three basic mechanisms of the simian and human retinas is capable of different selection, combination, and distribution of the nervous impulses received from the same photoreceptors, the rods and cones, where such impulses are generated by the physical agent, visible light. (From Polyak, S.: The retina, Chicago, 1941, University of Chicago Press.)

ganglion cell. Most of the basic principles of neurophysiology which apply to the ganglion cells of the brain and cord also apply to the ganglion cells of the retina. A brief description of these is in order for a better understanding of retinal neurophysiology.

The dendrites or terminal nerve fibrils which arrive at the ganglion cells from the axons of the bipolar cells and horizontal cells in the retina penetrate the ganglion cell and end in small knoblike structures called terminal knobs. The impulses traveling along these fibrils control

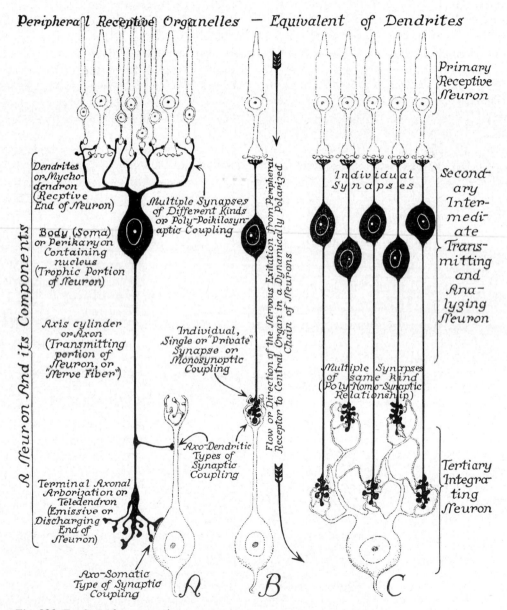

Fig. 296. For legend see opposite page.

the degree of activity of the ganglion cell, probably by secreting hormones which either excite the ganglion cell or inhibit it. The fibrils that cause excitation are probably different from those that cause inhibition, and the substances they secrete are probably different chemically. At present little is known about these substances. Since acetylcholine is the chemical substance which mediates transmission from the nerve fiber to the muscle cell, it has been suggested that this is also responsible for excitation of ganglion cells in the central nervous system, but some facts are against this hypothesis, and for the present it is probably best to refer to this substance simply as the *excitatory hormone*. Similarly, the substance produced by those fibrils which inhibit the ganglion cell is best referred to as the *inhibitory hormone*. The relative number of excitatory and inhibitory fibrils which supply the ganglion cell varies considerably from cell to cell. Further, the fibrils ending on each ganglion cell may originate from either a single bipolar cell or come from many different bipolar or other cells in the retina.

Excitation of a ganglion cell takes place when a sufficient number of excitatory fibrils produce sufficient excitatory hormone to exceed the threshold of that particular ganglion cell. Usually many excitatory terminal knobs must be stimulated simultaneously in order to stimulate a ganglion cell. However, if inhibitory terminal knobs are simultaneously stimulated, the production of inhibitory hormone neutralizes the excitatory hormone produced so that it is possible to have both excitatory knobs and inhibitory knobs stimulated simultaneously and yet the ganglion cell remains quiescent. Even though it fails to discharge, it can be shown that such stimulation of excitatory

and inhibitory knobs may change the resting state of the ganglion cell.

It is generally believed that the release of the excitatory hormone inside the ganglion cell increases the permeability of the ganglion cell membrane so that negative charges leak to the outside. When a sufficient number of these charges spreads laterally over the outside of the cell membrane, an action potential is set up which then discharges through the axon of the ganglion cell. Transmission is always a one-way affair. The ganglion cell always discharges through its axon as a result of excitation coming into it from the dendrites. It never discharges backward through the dendrites. It is not known just how the inhibitory hormone affects the cell, but in some way it blocks the effects of the excitatory hormone.

When the excitatory knobs entering a ganglion cell have secreted some excitatory hormone, the negative charges collect on the outside of the ganglion cell membrane and build up an electric potential which is called the *synaptic potential*. When this synaptic potential reaches the level of the threshold of excitation of the ganglion cell, it in turn fires. Even though the synaptic potential may not be sufficient to cause the ganglion cell to fire, it affects the ganglion cell, making it more ready to fire by any succeeding impulses from other excitatory knobs. This state is known as facilitation.

The firing of a ganglion cell consists in the release of a series of repetitive impulses along the axon. The number of impulses per unit of time depends upon the individual ganglion cell and upon the amount of excitatory hormone produced or, if both excitatory and inhibitory hormones are being produced simultaneously, upon the excess of excitatory over inhibitory hormone produced. The greater the amount of excitatory hormone, the more impulses per unit time are discharged along the axon.

In most parts of the central nervous system and probably in the retina the ganglion cells are congregated into pools, and the connections of the nerve fibers in these pools are different for different pools. In any ganglionic pool one nerve fiber connects in such a way with a number of ganglion cells that excitation of this nerve fiber always causes all of these ganglion cells to fire. However, the same fiber may also connect with other surrounding ganglion cells, but with too few excitatory knobs to each of these cells, so that instead of firing these cells remain silent but in the facilitated state. These cells may then fire when another nerve fiber connected with them sends in an impulse which by itself alone would not have been sufficient to cause the cells to fire. Various types of connections are found between ganglion cell pools of such a nature that they have the ability to continue firing for prolonged periods of time after an input stimulus reaches the pool. This effect is known as *after-discharge*. It permits a single incoming stimulus to produce a response from the ganglion cells lasting for various periods of time which otherwise would last no more than a few milliseconds.

In the mammalian visual pathway we find three separate links or neurons interposed between the photoreceptors and the visual cortex. Two of these neurons are in the retina itself. The first neuron is formed by the bipolar cells whose dendrites connect with the photoreceptors and whose axons synapse with the dendrites of the ganglion cells. The second neuron is formed by the ganglion cells, connecting as just stated with the bipolar cells on the one hand and the axons ending in a synapse with the cells of the

lateral geniculate body. A comparison of the visual pathway with that of pressure sensation has been given on p. 643.

The photoreceptors—rods and cones

The rods get their name from their outer segment which is rodlike (Fig. 297). The rod proper is about 60 μ long and 2 μ thick, lying next to the pigment epithelium. It terminates in the so-called ellipsoid. Anterior or internal to this is the inner segment which terminates in a thin fiber that makes connections with the dendrites of the biopolar cells by means of a knob. The cell nuclei of the rods lie together with those of the cones, forming the external nuclear layer. The dendrites of the rods and cones connecting with the bipolar cells form the external plexiform layer. The swelling at the vitreal end of the inner rod fiber, found in the plexiform layer, is called the terminal rod spherule and is the equivalent of a teledendron of a neuron elsewhere. There are about 120 million rods in the primate retina.

The cones derive their name from their shape which resembles a flask with a narrow neck, corresponding to the outer segment, and a plump inner segment (Fig. 297). The cones are slightly shorter than the rods, averaging 51 μ in length, but their thickness is in reverse proportion to their length. The transition between the inner and outer segments is marked by an indentation or waistline, which marks the place where the cone fits into the neuroglial ring that surrounds the opening in the outer limiting membrane. This latter keeps the cone fixed in its place. The cell body and nucleus are found just inside the outer limiting membrane in the outer nuclear layer. From this structure the cone fiber runs inward to terminate in the cone pedicle. This is the homologue of the teledendron

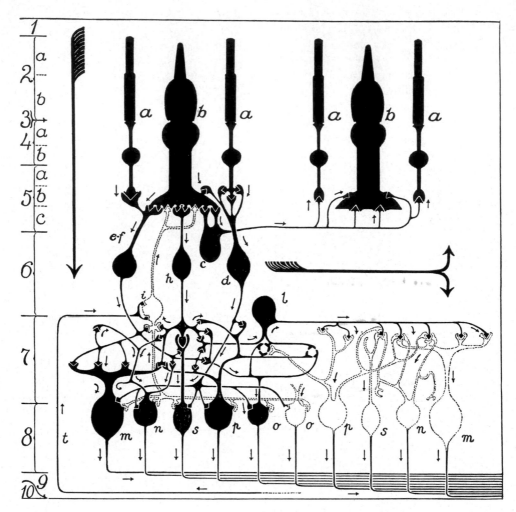

Fig. 297. Structure of the primate retina reduced to its essentials, including the synopsis of the propagation of the retinal impulses from the photoreceptors to other parts of the retina, to the brain, and from the brain back to the retina (direction indicated by arrows). The marking of the layers and the zones the same as in Fig. 286. Labeling of the cells: **a** and **b** rods and cones or the photoreceptors where the nervous impulses are generated by physical light (in the scheme only the left group of the photoreceptors is assumed to be stimulated by light); **c,** horizontal cells by means of which the impulses are transmitted to the surrounding rods and cones; **d, e, f,** and **h,** centripetal bipolar cells of the mop, brush, flat, and midget varieties, which transmit the impulses from the photoreceptors to the ganglion cells, the bipolars serving as analyzers; **i,** centrifugal bipolar cell, a variety of amacrine cells, which probably receives the impulses from the centripetal bipolars, from the ganglion cells, and also from the brain by way of the centrifugal or efferent fibers, **t,** and transmits them back upon the photoreceptors, **a** and **b**); **l,** an amacrine cell which possibly intercepts a part of the bipolar impulses and spreads them over the surrounding territory; **m, n, o, p,** and **s,** ganglion cells which receive impulses from the centripetal bipolars and transmit them to the brain along their axons celled optic nerve fibers. (From Polyak, S.: The retina, Chicago, 1941, University of Chicago Press.)

of neurons in other parts of the nervous system. The cone pedicles are all placed in the middle zone of the outer plexiform layer (Fig. 298). In general, the cone pedicles are much broader than the terminal rod spherule, with the exception of those in the foveal region. There are approximately 6 million cones in the retina.

The outer segments of both the rods and cones are the true photoreceptor organelles. The inner segments are, however, indispensable. In addition to the photoreceptors, the retina contains many

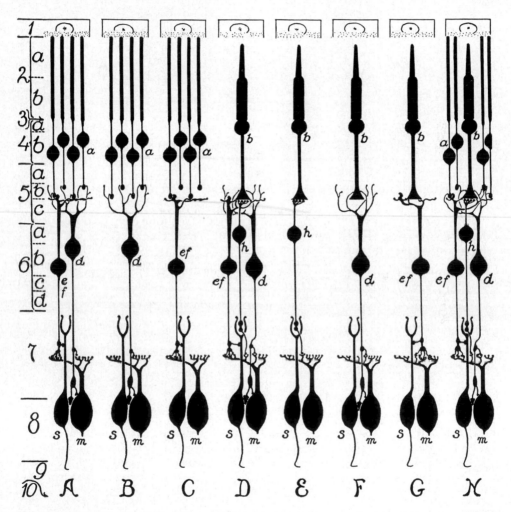

Fig. 298. Grouping of the neurons of the primate retina into functional systems: **A,** Rod system. **B,** Rod system with only one intermediate constituent, the mop bipolar, *d.* **C,** Rod system with only the brush, *e,* or the flat bipolar, *f,* as the constituent. **D,** Cone system. **E,** Pure cone system. **F,** Cone system with the mop bipolar, *d,* as the constituent. **G,** Cone system with either the brush, *e,* or the flat bipolar, *f,* as the constituent. **H,** Mixed or common rod and cone system. The parasol ganglion cell, *m,* is being used as a symbol for the entire category of the diffuse or polysynaptical ganglion cells, *m, n, o, p,* and *r.* (From Polyak, S.: The retina, Chicago, 1941, University of Chicago Press.)

different types of cells concerned with the propagation of the nerve impulse, both into the optic nerve fiber and laterally in the retinas. Several different types of bipolar cells act as relay stations between the light receptors and the optic nerve fibers. These are divided into individual or cone types of bipolar cells and diffuse bipolar cells. The pedicle of each cone, particularly of those in the fovea, touches the dendritic tuft of a single individual bipolar cell. In the case of the diffuse bipolar cell, each is related to several cones.

Connections of rods and cones. The main types of connections between the rods and cones and the optic nerve fibers are shown in Fig. 298. In *E* is shown a single cone, *b*, connected to a ganglion cell, *s*, and optic nerve fiber through a bipolar cell, *h*, which makes no connection with other rods and cones. This cone has a single line connection as far as the lateral geniculate body. As stated, most of the cones of the fovea have this type of connection.

The arrangement of the rods is quite different (Fig. 298, *B*), several rods being connected to the same bipolar cell so that their stimulation converges on the same nerve fiber.

A horizontal cell (Fig. 299), with its cell body in the inner nuclear layer, connects a cone with surrounding cones or rods, and so-called centrifugal bipolar type cells transmit impulses from the higher centers or from the ganglion cells or bipolar cells down to the rods and cones. The horizontal cells are especially numerous in the macula. Each cell may bring one group of cones into reciprocal relationship (up to fifteen in number in the macula) with another and larger group of cones and possibly with a group of rods also. As has been shown previously (p. 634), Hartline found that

the receptive field of an optic nerve fiber covers an area of approximately 1 mm. Therefore, a ganglion cell can receive excitatory or inhibitory influences over many convergent pathways. The axon of a ganglion cell is simply the final common path for nervous activity that originates in many sensory elements. Lateral conduction is mediated by the horizontal and amacrine cells.

Ganglion cells. Two types of ganglion cells are recognized—diffuse (Fig. 298, *m*) and individual (Fig. 298, *s*). The individual ganglion cell is called a midget ganglion cell because of its small size. It effects a synaptic contact with a single individual or cone bipolar cell and is related therefore to a single cone. Some midget ganglion cells may be in synaptic contact with bipolar cells of the diffuse type. The diffuse ganglion cells have relatively long and numerous dendrites, with considerable reciprocal overlapping of the territories of adjacent cells.

From the minute structure of the retina, it is evident that some of the optic nerve fibers are connected to single cones, whereas others which act as units are connected to very large groups of rods. Intermediary types of connections (Fig. 298, *H*), in which both rods and cones are connected to the same nerve fiber, exist also.

In man there are approximately 1 million optic nerve fibers, 120 million rods, and 6 million cones. Only a very small proportion of the cones, therefore, can be connected by a single fiber to the higher centers. It is likely that both rods and cones in the greater portion of the retina are connected in groups to each fiber.

The plexiform layers. Two layers of the retina are identified by being synaptic layers where contact is made between the cells of two adjoining layers. These are

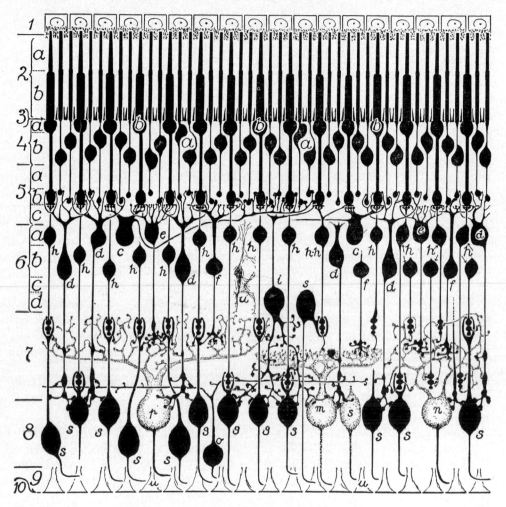

Fig. 299. Scheme of the structures of the primate retina as revealed by the method of Golgi. Layers and cones are indicated as follows. 1, Pigment layer; 2a, outer zone; 2b, inner zone of the rod and cone layer; 3, outer limiting membrane; 4a, outer zone; 4b, inner zone of the outer nuclear layer; 5a, outer zone; 5b, middle zone; 5c, inner zone of the outer plexiform layer; 6, inner nuclear layer with its four zones; 7, inner plexiform layer; 8, layer of the ganglion cells; 9, layer of the optic nerve fibers; 10, inner limiting membrane. Nerve cells are indicated as follows. a, Rods; b, cones; c, horizontal cells; d, e, f, and h, bipolar cells; i and l, so-called amacrine cells; m, n, o, p, and s, ganglion cells; u, radial fibers of Müller. In this scheme the nervous elements are reduced to their essentials with, however, the characteristic features of each variety preserved—the location of the bodies, the size, the shape, and the spreading of the dendrites and of the axis cylinders—and with the synaptical contacts presented accurately. (From Polyak, S.: The retina, Chicago, 1941, University of Chicago Press.)

the external plexiform layer, where contact is made between the photoreceptors and the bipolars, and the internal plexiform layer, which is the synapse between the bipolar and ganglion cells. In addition we find horizontal cells at the feet of the photoreceptors and the amacrine cells between the bipolar and ganglion cells.

Interaction between various parts of the retina takes place in these plexiform layers. As a result, what goes on in one particular region of the retina influences other regions, either facilitating or inhibiting the bipolar and ganglion cells in these parts (p. 730). The horizontal cells end in dendritic baskets that connect cones to larger groups of rods and cones. The amacrine cells have dendrites which spread across the internal plexiform layer for distances up to a millimeter and are probably inhibitory in nature.

Regional differences in the retina

In man and the higher mammals, the central region or macula differs considerably in histology from that of the surrounding retina. Accordingly, there are marked differences in its physiologic properties. The differences in function between the central and peripheral regions have led to the recognition that the retina is in reality two sense organs thrown into one. The duplicity theory of retinal function rests primarily on this foundation.

The center of the macula, i.e., the fovea centralis, contains only cones and no rods, and the cones in this region are quite different in shape from those in the surrounding retina since they resemble rods more nearly. In fact, the cones in the fovea are so rodlike that they can best be distinguished by their different type of synapse with the bipolar cells; the rod synapse is in the form of a knob, whereas that of the cone is in the

form of a pedicle. The rod-free area of the retina measures about 0.25 to 0.3 mm. in diameter, which corresponds to a visual angle of about 1 degree. One minute of arc equals 4.85 μ. Therefore the rod-free area subtends a visual angle of 54 minutes.

Pirenne[1] has measured the number of rods and cones per unit area throughout the entire retina. A flat section of a region of the human fovea is shown in Fig. 300. The section has cut the inner segments of the rods and cones. Except in the center, the cones appear as circles which are much larger than those corresponding to the rods. In this particular retina the most central rod appears at a distance of about 0.13 mm. from the center of the fovea. The number of rods and cones along a complete meridian of the retina are given in Fig. 301. The number of cones decreases rapidly from the center, falling to a low value in the periphery, but rises again slightly at the ora serrata. Outside the rod-free area the number of rods increases rapidly, reaching a maximum of about 160,000 rods per square millimeter in a region 5 to 6 mm. from the center. In more peripheral regions the number of rods decreases, but it remains considerably higher than the number of cones. The highest density of cones occurs in the fovea centralis, where they number about 147,000 per square millimeter. In the exact center of the fovea there are only a few hundred of the very thinnest cones, resembling rods. These are used for the discrimination of fine details (pp. 783 to 788).

The distance between the centers of any two adjacent cones in this region of most acute vision generally measures 0.0020 to 0.0025 mm. Fig. 302 is a graph of the distribution of rods and cones in and near the fovea. The first rods appear

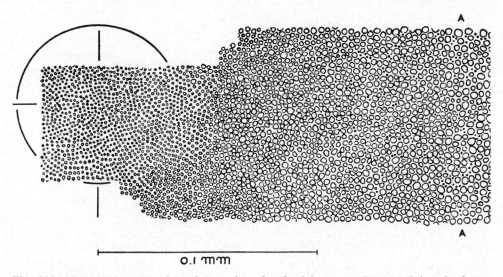

Fig. 300. Horizontal section through a region of a fixed human retina containing the fovea. The scale refers to the retina in the fixed state. Multiply by 1.31 to allow for the shrinkage due to fixation. The center of the fovea (on the left, top drawing) is defined by the intersection of the three straight lines or by the center of the circle. The section has cut through the inner segments or bodies of the rods and cones. In the center of the fovea, the cones are represented by small circles. These become progressively larger as one goes toward the parafovea. In this region the rods, appearing as small circles, are seen in between the broad inner segments of the cones. The first rod is seen in the preparation near the middle of the drawing above the right end of the scale. It is situated at a distance of 0.13 mm. from the foveal center. Flat sections such as this are more likely to reveal the presence of rods near the foveal center than vertical sections such as that shown in Fig. 303 since sections of the latter kind obviously may fall in between the most centrally placed rods and miss them. This may explain why the rod-free area, as measured on the latter preparation, has a considerably larger radius than on the present preparation. But the possibility of individual variations from retina to retina must also be borne in mind. (After Osterberg; from Pirenne, M.: Vision and the eye, London, 1948, The Pilot Press.)

at about 0.3 degree. The number of rods per unit area increases, whereas the number of cones decreases, their proportion being equal at about 1 degree from the center of the fovea.

Polyak has further divided the retina into seven regions. Region I is the central fovea (also called the foveola). In Fig. 303 is shown the central fovea of the human eye, characterized by a small depression caused by the bending away of all the layers of the retina other than the photoreceptors and the outer nuclear and plexiform layers—the latter two are actually thickened. From edge to edge

it measures approximately 1500 μ across and subtends a visual angle of about 5 degrees. The floor of the pit is about 400 μ across. In this region the cones are longer and thinner than elsewhere in the retina, measuring 70 μ in length and 1.5 μ in thickness. The area of the fovea containing cones only is a little larger than this pit, measuring about 500 to 600 μ across and containing about 34,000 cones. In the whole region of the fovea, measuring about 1500 μ across, there are about 115,000 cones. Regions II and III are called the parafoveal and perifoveal regions, respectively. The former measures

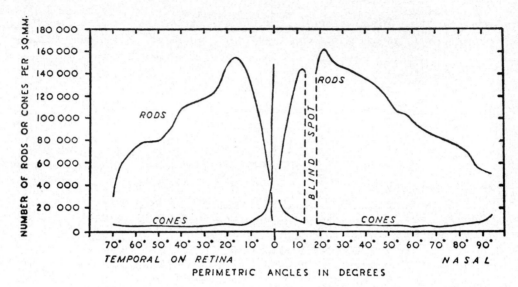

Fig. 301. Distribution of the rods and cones in the human retina. Instead of retinal distances, Osterberg's values for the corresponding perimetric angles are given. Although approximate, only, especially at the higher angles, such values are more useful in practice than the distances in millimeters on the retina. Note that the distribution of rods and cones on the nasal side in and near the fovea is not given on this graph. It would be approximately the same as the distribution on the temporal side of the retina—which is seen on the left of the vertical passing through 0° on the angle scale. (After Osterberg; from Pirenne, M.: Vision and the eye, London, 1948, The Pilot Press.)

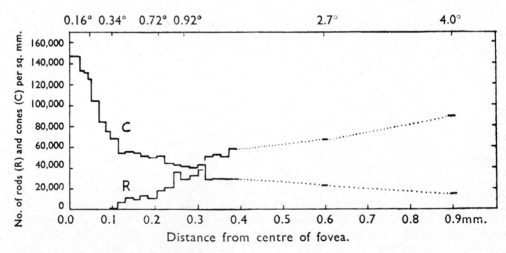

Fig. 302. Distribution of rods and cones in the center of a human retina. The distances in millimeters are uncorrected for shrinkage of the preparation (multiply by 1.31 to obtain the real distances). The corresponding distances in perimetric degrees have been calculated by Osterberg. (From Pirenne, M.: Vision and the eye, London, 1948, The Pilot Press.)

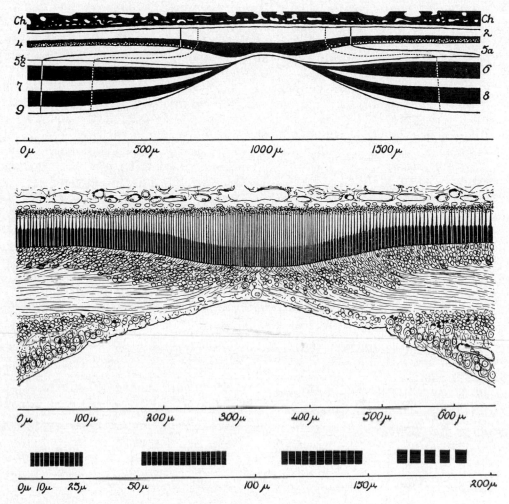

Fig. 303. Central fovea of the adult human eye. *Upper drawing,* semidiagrammatic representation of changes in the relative thickness and position of the retinal layers brought about by the foveal excavation. It also shows peculiar topical functional relationships of the photoreceptor layer, 2, and the deeper layers, 4 to 9, caused by the latter's displacement owing to the formation of the fovea. *Broken lines,* the rodless territory of the bacillary layer and the portion of the foveal pit functionally related to it. *Solid lines,* the territory of the thickened portion of the bacillary layer, the outer fovea, and the extent of the inner layers functionally related to it. *White dots in layer 4,* rod nuclei. *Ch,* portion of the choroid membrane. *Middle drawing,* the outer fovea filled with thin elongated cones. The most centrally located rods in the bacillary layer correspond with the most central rod nuclei in the outer nuclear layer, *shaded area.* Note the thinning of the mentioned layer and the practical disappearance of the remaining inner layers in the foveal center. *Solid black area,* Müller's nuclei in the inner nuclear layer. *Lower drawing,* samples from four localities showing relative size and number of cones (inner segments), beginning from the left: center of the outer fovea, slope of the same, edge of the same, and periphery of the central area or region III. (Upper sketch ×80; middle sketch ×250; lower sketch ×700; actual sizes in microns on the accompanying scales; from Polyak, S.: The retina, Chicago, 1941, University of Chicago Press.)

about 2500 μ across and the latter 5500 μ across. In region III the number of cones has diminished and the number of rods has increased so that there are only about 12 cones per 100 μ (compared with 50 per 100 μ in region I), and approximately 2 rods are interposed between each pair of cones. Regions IV to VII lie outside these central regions and extend out to the ora serrata.

Arrangement of nerve fibers in the retina

There are about 1 million nerve fibers in the human optic nerve, most of which arise from ganglion cells in the retina. In the higher primates and in man, these fibers have a characteristic arrangement as they run from the ganglion cells in the retina into the optic disc on their way up to the chiasm (Fig. 304). Each retina may be divided into two halves by dropping a perpendicular line through the center of the optic disc. In this manner a temporal half and a nasal half of each retina are formed through the center of the bouquet of central cones of the fovea. The fibers which come from

ganglion cells in the nasal half of each retina run directly into the disc in a straight line from their point of origin, forming a figure like the spokes of a wheel. The fibers entering the disc from the temporal half of each retina, on the other hand, do not take such a direct course. Due to the presence of the fovea in this temporal portion of the retina, the fibers coming from the temporal quadrants take an arcuate course to reach the disc and thus skirt the macula and the macular nerve fibers. These fibers from the macula go directly into the temporal aspect of the optic disc and are called the papillomacular bundle.

The fibers which come from the ganglion cells above the horizontal meredian of the retina swing above the macula, whereas those coming from the ganglion cells below the horizontal meridian swing down below the macula. They thus enter the disc in compact bundles at the upper and lower temporal margins, respectively.

It is evident that a lesion at the disc margin, such as a knife cut, on the nasal side of the disc (Fig. 304, *A*), would result in interference with nerve fibers

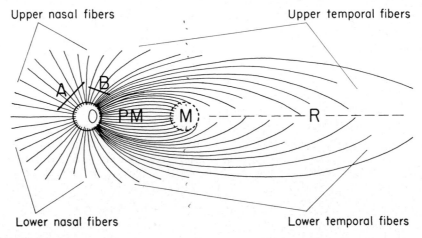

Upper nasal fibers | Upper temporal fibers

Lower nasal fibers | Lower temporal fibers

Fig. 304. Schematized distribution of the left retinal nerve fibers. **PM,** Papillomacular bundle. **M,** Macula. **R,** Raphe formed by meeting of the fibers from the upper and lower temporal quadrants. **A,** Lesion of upper nasal fibers. **B,** Lesion of upper temporal fibers.

entering the disc in the form of a fan.
Such a lesion would therefore produce a
fan-shaped scotoma or blind area in the
field of vision (Fig. 305, *A*). A similar
lesion on the temporal side of the disc
above the horizontal meridian would
catch a bundle of fibers spread out in the
form of a scimitar (Fig. 404, *B*) and
would therefore produce a scimitar-
shaped scotoma in the visual field (Fig.
305, *B*). The fibers which come from
ganglion cells above the horizontal meridian never go below it in their course to
the disc, and those arising below the
meridian never rise about it. For this
reason a horizontal raphe is formed from
the fovea out into the temporal periphery
(Fig. 304, *R*).

Another and equally important division of the nerve fibers in the retina can
be made. The retina may be divided into
two halves by dropping a perpendicular
line through the fovea. A temporal half
and a nasal half are produced thereby,
the nasal area being much the larger of
the two. All of the nerve fibers arising
from the temporal half remain on the
same side of the pathway in their course
through the chiasm, optic tract, and
radiations up to the occipital cortex. On
the other hand, all of the fibers arising
from ganglion cells situated in the nasal
half of the retina cross in the chiasm to
enter the optic tract on the opposite
side, and they remain on this side of the
pathway up to the cortex. It is obvious
that there must be many more crossing
than noncrossing fibers, and in man the
proportion has been estimated to be
about 75%.

The uniocular visual field is the field
which includes all of space perceptible
to an eye which is fixed while the head
is held stationary. Its limits are imposed
by the orbital rims and the nose and the
depth to which the eye is sunk in the

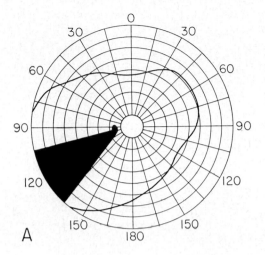

A

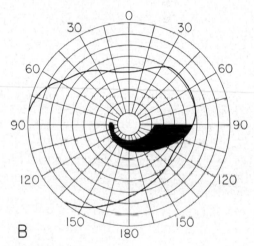

B

Fig. 305. A, Fan-shaped scotoma resulting from
a lesion of the upper nasal fibers. **B,** Scimitar-
shaped scotoma resulting from a lesion of the
upper temporal fibers.

orbit. A prominent eye will have, naturally, a larger field than one which is
deeply sunk in the orbit, other things
being equal. A prominent nose will cause
greater constriction of the nasal field
than will a small one.

The theoretic limits of the field have
been determined for the schematic eye
in which the radius of curvature of the
cornea is 8 mm. and the plane of the

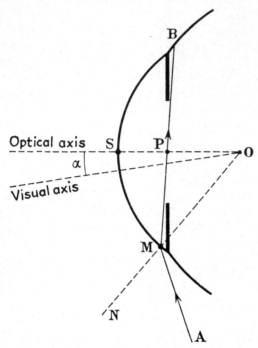

Fig. 306. Theoretical limit of the visual field. (From LeGrand, Y.: Light, colour and vision, New York, 1957, John Wiley & Sons, Inc., p. 51.)

iris is 3.6 mm. in back of the cornea. In Fig. 306 is shown the theoretic limits of the visual field as calculated by LeGrand. The extreme incident ray, *AM,* which can enter the eye is refracted along *MB,* passing through the center of the pupil, P, close to the plane of the iris. It is nearly at right angles to the optic axis (if *0* is the center of curvature of the cornea, the angle *OPM* is obtuse but almost a right angle).

Since cos $MOP = OP/OM = 4.4/8 =$ 0.55 (approximately, the angle *MOP* is 56 degrees, 38 minutes). The sine of the angle of refraction, *PMO,* has the same value, and consequently sine $AMN = 0.55 \times 1.336 = 0.735$ so that the angle of incidence, *AMN,* is 47 degrees, 17 minutes. Therefore, the angle between the incident ray and the optic axis is about 104 degrees. Since the eccentricity is measured from the visual axis, which on the average is an angle of 5 degrees with the optic axis, the theoretic limit of the visual field corresponds to an angle, *n,* of about 109 degrees on the temporal side.

The extent of the visual field taken with colors can be determined in two ways: (1) when the test object is just perceived or (2) when the true color of the test object is recognized. If the latter method is adopted, the extent of the field will differ considerably with different colors, depending on their chromatic interval. Blue, e.g., is recognized as blue from almost the first moment it is perceived entering the visual field, whereas red is perceived as a white or colorless object long before it is seen as red. Between recognition as white or as a colorless object and red, it passes through various shades of yellow and orange.

When the visual fields are determined with colors and the isopters are recorded at which the test object is just perceived, the critical factor which determines the field size is the absolute energy of the light which reaches the retina. The color, i.e., its specific wavelength, has no influence per se on the field size. Under ordinary testing conditions, however, the different colored test objects either reflect or transmit to the eye being tested light of different energy. Hence one would expect to find the size of the field smaller with those colors which yield less light energy to the eye than those of greater energy. It has been shown experimentally[2] that if absolute light energies are carefully controlled the fields for blue and green are identical. Red fields are smaller, but this may be due to technical difficulties inherent in the standardization of the red light.

Macular fibers in the retina

The macular fibers form a separate group from those of the rest of the retina. They run directly from the fovea to the disc in a compact bundle and enter the temporal side of the disc, spreading the rest of the fibers from the temporal retina to the upper and lower poles of the disc. Damage to these macular fibers results in a central scotoma (Fig. 307, *A*) or a cecocentral scotoma from the optic disc to the fovea (Fig. 307, *B*). If the damage leads to atrophy of these fibers, pallor of the temporal side of the disc, limited to the papillomacular bundle, occurs. This is called papillomacular atrophy. The macular fibers themselves, since they lie on both sides of the perpendicular line through the fovea, are both crossed and uncrossed fibers.

It has been proposed that the nerve fibers arising between the fovea and the optic disc approach the optic nerve by a different course—namely, that the fibers arising from ganglion cells in the

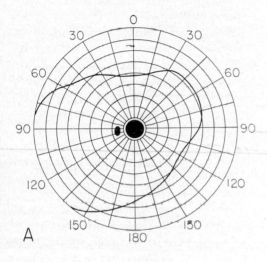

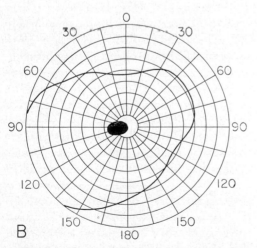

Fig. 307. A, Central scotoma. **B,** Cecocentral scotoma, resulting from a lesion of the macular fibers.

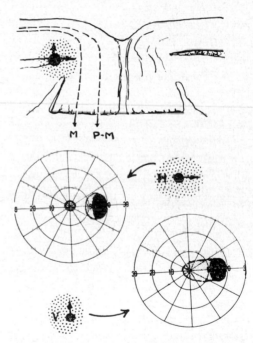

Fig. 308. Mechanism for production of visual field defects produced by choroidal or chorioretinal lesions at the temporal margin of the optic disc. If the lesion *(stippled area)* involves principally macular fibers, **M,** by spreading horizontally, the visual field defect indicated by **H** in the diagram, results. If the lesion spreads along the course of the vertical arrow and interrupts both macular, **M,** and papillomacular area fibers, **P-M,** a cecocentral scotoma, **V,** results. (From Hoyt, W. F., and Tudor, R.: Arch. Ophth. **69:**503, 1963.)

papillomacular area arch away from the horizontal meridian to enter the optic nerve nasally at its superior and inferior margins, and that these fibers do not pass directly into the temporal side of the optic nerve with the macular fibers.[3] This has not been supported by recent studies in primates which indicate that axons arising from the zone of the retina between the macula and the optic disc pass directly into the optic nerve on its temporal side adjacent to the central core vessels (Fig. 308).[4]

Comparison of the rod and cone systems

As we have said previously, two distinct mechanisms seem to be present in the retina (Fig. 297).

1. The first consists of a reception and transmission apparatus composed of chains made up of three successive links of neurons. These are rods, *a*, and cones, *b*, the centripetal bipolar cells, *d, e, f,* and *h*, and ganglion cells, *m, n, o, p,* and *s*.

2. The second is the association or integrating apparatus whose function is to regulate the transmission of the message through the retina and weld this membrane into a functional organ. This is composed of horizontal cells, *c*, of amacrine cells that have an axis cylinder terminating with the photoreceptors, *i*, centrifugal bipolar cells, and some amacrine cells possessing horizontal axons, which Polyak terms internal association cells.

The reception and transmission apparatus is composed of two different sets of neurons, one belonging to the rods and hence called the rod system and the other belonging to the cones and called the cone system.

The rod system is composed of the following three neurons (Fig. 297): the rods, *a,* all of the mop bipolar cells, *d,* some of the brush bipolar cells, *e,* and *f,* and probably all of the ganglion cells, *m, n, o, p, r,* and *s*. Therefore, the rods are connected to the ganglion cells by diffuse bipolar cells only.

The cone system is composed of the following three neurons: the cones, *b,* all varieties of the centripetal bipolar cells, *d, e, f,* and *h,* and all varieties of ganglion cells, *m, n, o, p, r* and *s*. The cone impulses may be transmitted to the ganglion cells by one, two, three, or possibly four bipolar varieties, therefore.

In the area of the retina which is made up entirely of cones, i.e., in the fovea itself, the so-called pure cone system is made up of the following three links (Fig. 298): The cones, *b,* the midget bipolar cells, *h,* and the midget ganglion cells, *s*. In this area each cone is synaptically related to a single midget bipolar which, in turn, is synaptically connected to a single midget ganglion cell. Each of these units seems to function quite differently from that of the rod system in which several rods are connected to the same bipolar cell. The pure cone system cannot have spatial summation, whereas in the rod system a large faint patch of light may stimulate a group of rods by adding their individual responses together until they reach the threshold necessary to fire an impulse through one nerve fiber. This system can respond to light of lower intensity than can the cone system, even though the sensitivity of the single rods might be assumed to be no greater than that of the single cone. However, this increase in sensitivity, as a result of summation, is at the cost of a loss in accuracy of detail since the individual elements which detect light are not single rods but groups of rods belonging to a single nerve fiber. Obviously, such a group will be much larger in area than a single foveal cone. Those areas which have single receptors connected to one nerve fiber have great discrimination of detail, whereas the areas in which there is considerable spatial summation have lower thresholds for the detection of light and are especially useful for the detection of movement of objects in the visual field.

Further differentiation of the rod and cone systems, as will be pointed out in Chapter 20, Color Vision, is that the cone system, functioning in good illumination (photopic vision), is chiefly concerned in the discrimination of colors, i.e., differentiation of the various wavelengths in the visible spectrum. This does not deny the possibility that the rods are concerned also in color vision, which is still a debatable point. Finally, it has been found that when dissimilar images that cannot be fused into a single percept mentally are presented to the two foveas, the result is retinal rivalry (p. 855). This consists of alternate suppression of one or the other image. On the other hand, when dissimilar images are presented to the retinal periphery of each eye, fusional movements of the two eyes frequently occur (p. 478).[5]

THE OPTIC NERVE

Most of the physiology of the optic nerve has been considered in a separate chapter (Chapter 15, The Optic Nerve). In this section, the course of the fibers from the various quadrants of the retina on their way up to the chiasm will be described (Fig. 309).

It has been shown that the fibers from the upper half of each retina enter the disc above the horizontal meridian, and those from each lower half enter below the horizontal meridian. The upper quadrants of each retina are represented in the upper half of the nerve, and those from the lower quadrants in the lower half of the nerve. This arrangement persists throughout the entire course of the visual pathways through the optic nerve, chiasm, tracts, and optic radiations.

Experiments have shown[6] that the fibers from the periphery of the retina lie peripherally in the optic nerve. Evidence that this is also true in man has been obtained from patients with solitary chorioretinitis. Therefore, it is probable that in the human being, as well as in the monkey and the rabbit, the nerve fibers from the periphery of the retina lie deep in the retinal nerve fiber layer and enter the disc in the peripheral portions of the optic nerve head.

The macular fibers are found just back of the entrance of the optic nerve on the outer or temporal aspect of the nerve (Fig. 309, *B*). The extramacular temporal fibers lie above and below these, and the nasal fibers are pushed over to the nasal side of the nerve, occupying a position comparable to the macular fibers on the temporal side. Farther back in the nerve, the macular fibers lie more centrally (Fig. 309, *C*), and just before reaching the chiasm they are found in the exact center of each nerve. If one examines cross sections of the optic nerve in its course from the eyeball to the optic chiasm, the arrangement of the bundles of fibers, representing the various quadrants of the retina, are seen to undergo rotation. The right optic nerve, apparently, has undergone a clockwise rotation of 45 degrees, whereas the left optic nerve has undergone a similar 45-degree rotation, counterclockwise. Because of this rotation the inferior nasal bundle which lay on the nasal side of the disc just below the midline as the nerve left the globe comes to lie in the lower half of the nerve as it enters the chiasm (Fig. 309, *D*.)

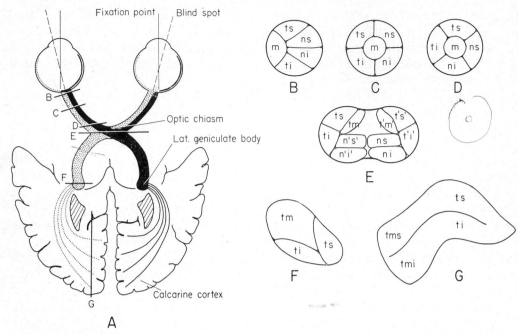

Fig. 309. Diagram of the visual nerve paths and representative cross sections showing distribution of the nerve fiber bundles at different levels of the pathway. **A,** Visual pathways. **B,** Optic nerve behind the eye. **C,** Optic nerve behind the entrance of the central vessels into the nerve. **D,** Optic nerve in front of its entrance into the chiasm. **E,** Optic chiasm. **F,** Lateral geniculate body. **G,** Calcarine cortex. *ts,* Fibers from the temporal superior quadrant of the extramacular retina. *t's',* Fibers from the temporal superior quadrant of the extramacular retina of the other eye. *ti,* Fibers from the temporal inferior quadrant of the extramacular retina. *t'i',* Fibers from the temporal inferior quadrant of the extramacular retina of the other eye. *ns,* Fibers from the nasal superior quadrant of the extramacular retina. *n's',* Fibers from the nasal superior quadrant of the extramacular retina of the other eye. *ni,* Fibers from the nasal inferior quadrant of the extramacular retina. *n'i',* Fibers from the nasal inferior quadrant of the extramacular retina of the other eye. *m,* Fibers from the macula. *tm,* Fibers from the temporal half of the macula. *tms,* Fibers from the temporal superior quadrant of the macula. *tmi,* Fibers from the temporal inferior quadrant of the macula.

Angioscotoma

The emergence of the large blood vessels from the optic disc must necessarily cause some interference with the visual receptors in this region. It is possible to map out the vessels in the visual field by the use of small test objects. The resulting defects in the field are called angioscotomas, and their significance and clinical use have been explored thoroughly by Evans.[7]

Caution must be exercised in attributing significance to the angioscotomas produced by the smaller branches of the central retinal artery since artifacts may be produced with ease, merely by the method of examination. If, e.g., a small test object is used in mapping out a suspected scotoma, and the object is held stationary instead of being kept in motion, it will disappear; when it is moved again, it will reappear, and so on. The reason for this is the well-known phenomenon of sensory adaptation, which is discussed on p. 77.

It can readily be seen that small angioscotomas or for that matter any small scotoma in the field of vision may be produced artificially by this means. Since the central regions of the retina show much less adaptation than the peripheral areas, artifacts due to adaptation are produced much more easily in the peripheral parts of the fields.

It has been suggested that the arcuate scotomas that occur in glaucoma are angioscotomas due to an arrest of the precapillary circulation. It has been found[8] that the circulation in the superior and inferior parts of the temporal half of each retina are not independent, but that the two circulations anastomose intimately through a rich capillary network which is well marked in both the perimacular region and the more peripheral regions. This would indicate that arcuate scotomas are in reality neuroscotomas and are not dependent on the anatomic peculiarities of the retinal circulation. However, arguments in favor of vascular rather than primary neurogenic origin of glaucomatous field changes have been summarized by Harrington,[9] who concludes that they are the result of circulatory insufficiency in the anterior portion of the optic nerve. The insufficiency results from an imbalance between the intraocular pressure and the arterial and capillary pressure in the nerve and may be produced by either an abnormally high intraocular pressure or an abnormally low arterial pressure or both acting together.

THE CHIASM

In the lower mammals, almost all of the optic nerve fibers cross to the opposite side, but in no mammal is the decussation complete. In the opposum only 20% of the retinal fibers remain uncrossed, and in the ferret about one third are uncrossed. In the monkey about 40% of the fibers remain uncrossed, whereas in man 25 to 30% are uncrossed.

Fibers from the upper half of each retina occupy the upper half of each optic nerve and run into the upper or dorsal part of the chiasm (Figs. 308, *E,* and 310). Similarly, the fibers from the lower half of each retina are found in the lower half of each optic nerve and enter the lower or ventral part of the chiasm. The chiasm may be considered to consist of three layers of fibers: a lower or ventral layer, a middle layer, and finally an upper or dorsal layer.

The uncrossed temporal fibers remain on the outside or temporal aspect of the chiasm. The uncrossed fibers from each inferior temporal retinal quadrant run on the extreme outside or lateral edge of the chiasm and occupy the middle layer. The uncrossed fibers from each upper temporal retinal quadrant run nearer the midline and almost entirely in the upper or dorsal layer. The crossing fibers from the inferior nasal retinal quadrant are found almost entirely in the lower or most ventral layer. These fibers lie in the anterior portion of the chiasm, and the most anterior of these swing into the opposite optic nerve as they cross to the opposite side to form the anterior knee. The fibers from the upper nasal retinal quadrant run backward almost into the optic tract on the same side, forming a posterior knee before swinging across the chiasm into the opposite optic tract. They skirt the posterior surface of the chiasm and eventually lie on the mesial side of the tract near its surface. They comprise the middle and uppermost layers of fibers.

From this description (Fig. 311), it is obvious that the lower layer of the chiasm is formed almost entirely of the crossing fibers from each inferior nasal retinal quadrant. These are the fibers which form the anterior knee in each optic nerve.

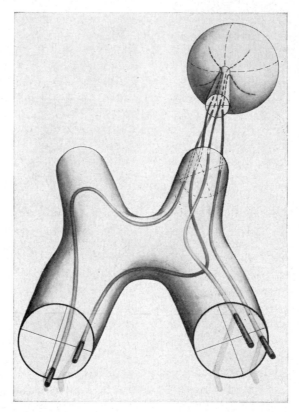

Fig. 310. Stereogram showing the course of the fibers in the chiasm. The back of the right retina is pictured. The chiasm is seen as a transparency from above.

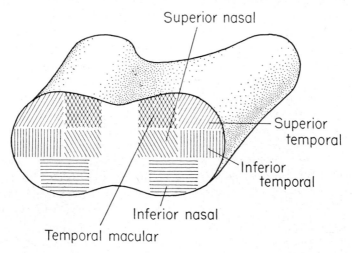

Fig. 311. Stereogram showing the distribution of nerve fiber bundles in the optic chiasm.

The middle layer of the chiasm contains both crossing and noncrossing fibers, i.e., the crossing fibers from each superior nasal retinal quadrant and the noncrossing fibers from each inferior temporal retinal quadrant. The upper layer is formed by both crossing and noncrossing fibers, i.e., those from the superior nasal retinal quadrant and those from the superior temporal retinal quadrant. Although this relationship may seem to be complex, Kestenbaum[10] has pointed out that the result is, in general, what would be expected from the rotation of the optic nerve around its anteroposterior axis 45 degrees toward each nasal side.

The macular fibers form a separate bundle in the chiasm, coming from the middle of the optic nerve as they enter the chiasm. The uncrossed temporal fibers go directly down the side of the chiasm, about equidistant from its lateral surface, to enter the tract on the same side at about its middle. The crossing macular fibers go to the posterior part of the chiasm before they cross to the opposite side so that the actual crossing lies close to the posterior edge of the chiasm. In this situation they are in close vicinity to the third ventricle and are separated from it only by Gudden's commissure.

The course of the fibers as outlined here is based largely on the work of Wilbrand. There has been little recent experimental work which throws any further light on the arrangement of the fibers in the chiasm. Most of the evidence within recent years has come from an evaluation of clinical material. As Clark pointed out:

". . . The intimate topographical relation between the optic chiasm and certain hypothalamic commissures in this region make it very difficult in normal preparations to decipher the precise course of the retinal fibers here. . . . For one thing, the fibers of the supraoptic commissure (which probably have nothing to do with visual functions) are not always distinguishable from retinal fibers. Also, in the chiasma the decussating fibers may run an aberrant course which can be very misleading to the casual observer."*

The chiasm is supplied chiefly by branches of the internal carotid and the anterior cerebral and anterior communicating arteries. The chiasm is invaded partly by the arteriolar and capillary networks of the optic nerve as it enters the chiasm and partly by the optic tract as it leaves the chiasm; hence, there is a very rich blood supply for this whole general area.[12]

THE OPTIC TRACT

The same general arrangement of fibers in the chiasm holds for the optic tract. The fibers in the upper portion of the tract come from the upper quadrants of the two retinas, whereas the fibers in the lower portion come from the lower retinal quadrants of the two retinas. The homolateral and crossed fibers, from corresponding areas of the two retinas, are intimately and evenly mixed with each other in the optic tract. There is no stratification such as is found in the lateral geniculate body. Crossed and uncrossed fibers become disentangled and separated from each other inside the lateral geniculate body, only.

In the lower mammals large numbers of retinal fibers run to the superior colliculus, and in these animals the superior colliculli provide an integrating mechanism of considerable complexity in relation to visual impulses.

In the cat Apter[13] found a complex pattern of projection of the optic tract on the superior colliculi. This may not be concerned with vision in the usual sense

*From Clark, W. E. L.: Physiol. Rev. **22:** 205, 1942.

of the word. Retinal impulses call forth many reflex activities which never reach the level of consciousness, especially in the lower vertebrate forms. In man none of the visual fibers run into the superior colliculus. So far as is known, all these fibers end in the lateral geniculate body.

The optic tract fibers are not all the same size. In the cat, e.g., the fibers range in size from less than 1μ to 11μ. These fibers have different conduction velocities, and the question arises whether this is just a random size difference, with random conduction velocities, or whether these fibers belong to separate groups perhaps with different functions. Some authors maintain there are two main groups[14]; others recognize three[15] and even six[16] groups. The most recent evidence is in favor of the existence of three separate groups with conduction velocities of 52, 37, and 16 M. per second.[17] We cannot at present assign different functions to these different groups, although Lennox[18] has found some correlation between conduction velocity and the differential response to blue and red light. The slow fibers responded more actively to blue than to red by a mean of 2.5 times. Fast fibers responded more actively to red than to blue light by a mean of 1.04 times. This is suggestive evidence that the final message received by the brain to different wavelengths of light is not determined by what goes on in the retina alone but concerns central nervous mechanisms also.

Lateral geniculate body

The lateral geniculate body of man and the primates is composed of a dorsal nucleus and a pregeniculate nucleus. The latter is the ventral nucleus of the lower vertebrates. While it contains small-fiber visual projections in the primates, it is not exactly known what role it plays in the transmission of the visual impulses

to the cortex. It may be concerned with the pupillary light reflex.[19] It is the dorsal nucleus which is of chief interest to us.

In man and the higher primates the lateral geniculate body or LGB is composed of six distinct clearly demarcated cell laminae separated by intervening layers of white matter. The laminae have been numbered 1 to 6, from the surface inward. The crossed fibers of the optic tract terminate in cells of laminae 1, 4, and 6. The uncrossed fibers end in laminae 2, 3, and 5. Hence, if one optic nerve in a monkey is sectioned, the cells of layers 2, 3, and 5 of the lateral geniculate body of the same side will be found to have atrophied, and likewise the cells in layers 1, 4, and 6 of the opposite lateral geniculate body will be atrophied.

The projection onto the lateral geniculate body of corresponding photoreceptors in the two eyes is shown in Fig. 312. The mode of termination of the optic nerve fibers in the lateral geniculate body differs in different animals. In the monkey and man each optic nerve fiber is terminally related to as many as thirty lateral geniculate body cells. There is no overlap of the terminals of different fibers. In the cat, on the other hand, one finds a profusion of synaptic contacts in the lateral geniculate body and an overlap of many different optic nerve fibers. This provides the anatomic basis for a high degree of sensitivity to light and movement, even at low intensities of illumination, but a low visual acuity in this animal.

The retinal projection onto the lateral geniculate body is quite precise in man and approximates a point-to-point representation. Optic nerve fibers from ganglion cells lying close to one another synapse with lateral geniculate body cells close together. The upper retinal quadrants terminate in the medial segment of the dorsal nucleus and the lower retinal

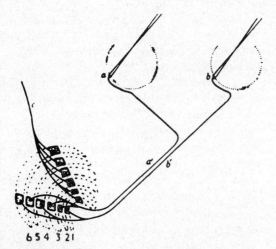

Fig. 312. Representation of the retina on the lateral geniculate body of the primate. Impulses from corresponding points (**a** and **b**) in the two retinas pass up the optic tract. Uncrossed impulses (**a′**) terminate in laminae 2, 3, and 5. Crossed impulses (**b′**) terminate in laminae 1, 4, and 6. These fibers terminate in a reception unit in the lateral geniculate body which forms a band of cells radiating from the hilum. The projection unit from the lateral geniculate body (**c**) to the visual cortex forms a band of cells involving all the laminae (after Le Gros Clark). (From Le Gros Clark, W.; Tr. Ophth. Soc. U. Kingdom **62**:237, 1942.)

quadrants in the lateral segments, whereas the fibers coming from the macula terminate in the large intermediate segment (Fig. 309, *F*). This medial segment containing the macular fibers widens at the posterior extremity until it covers the entire width of the lateral geniculate body.[11]

The projection of each part of the retina onto the lateral geniculate body is quite precise even in cats. Bishop and others[20, 21] created lesions in various parts of the retina and recorded from the various portions of the lateral geniculate body. They were able to establish a topographic map of the projection of each retinal locus onto the geniculate.

The lamination in the lateral geniculate body suggests that this provides the

anatomic basis for fusion of crossed and uncrossed retinal impulses. The fact that in the lower vertebrates which do not possess a binocular field and hence cannot have fusion no lamination of the lateral geniculate body occurs tends to support this concept. The evidence is conflicting. The earlier workers found no evidence of facilitation which suggests fusion of retinal images at the level of the lateral geniculate body,[22] whereas some overlap of fibers has been found by Hayhow,[23] and Bishop and others[24] have found some cells in the lateral geniculate body whose discharge can be altered by stimulation of the opposite retina.

Although the lateral geniculate body is a way station for the visual impulses on their way to the cortex, it is probably much more than that. There is evidence that impulses arrive at the lateral geniculate body other than those coming from the retina. Some evidence suggests that inhibitory activity reaches the lateral geniculate body from the cortex which modifies the response of the lateral geniculate body cells to impulses from the retina. In other words, the lateral geniculate body adds its own counterpart to the messages it receives from the retina and transmits this in altered form to the cortex.

The electrical discharges in response to stimulation of the retina can be picked up in the lateral geniculate body. Four different types of response have been recorded.[25] These consist of "on" discharges, "off" discharges, "on-off" discharges and a decrease in the frequency of spontaneous discharges during illumination. The lowest threshold of response, i.e., the minimum amount of light energy which causes a perceptible discharge, is about three times greater than the threshold of response of the unanesthetized cat as determined by behavioural methods.[26]

The receptive fields of the retina have been described (p. 637), e.g., the retinal area containing visual receptors linked with a single optic nerve fiber. The receptive fields in the lateral geniculate body have also been explored,[27] and it has been found that these correspond in most details with those found in the retina. Thus, in both the retina and the lateral geniculate body the receptive fields are concentric, with an "on" center surrounded by an "off" periphery or the reverse. Further, as stated, there is minimal binocular interaction at the lateral geniculate level, whereas most of the visual cells in the striate cortex are influenced by stimulation of receptors in both retinas. Another point of differentiation is that the lateral geniculate body cells respond briskly to diffuse retinal illumination, whereas the cortical cells seldom do. And movement of the light source across the retina causes firing of geniculate cells regardless of the direction of movement, whereas at the cortical level the response is often conditioned by the direction of the movement[28] (p. 686).

Under certain conditions recording from the ganglion cells in the dorsal nucleus of the lateral geniculate ganglion shows repetitive firing; i.e., as many as ten distinct secondary spikes may be observed from the ganglion cell being recorded following a single optic nerve stimulus. So-called repetitive firing or afterdischarge (p. 657) has been found in other parts of the central nervous system, i.e., in sympathetic ganglia and in motor neuron pools. The repetitive firing from the lateral geniculate body is unlike that described in sympathetic ganglia and appears to be analogous to that observed in motoneuron pools, in which there exists simple reverberating circuits involving short axon cells. From this Bishop and co-workers[29] conclude that the dor-

sal ganglion of the lateral geniculate body may function as an integrating center in addition to its role as a relay and redistribution center.

Each geniculate cell has its own receptive field similar to those of the ganglion cells of the retina. There are some differences in the responses of the geniculate cells compared to those in the retina. The geniculate cell has a greatly enhanced capacity in the periphery of its receptive field to cancel the effects of the center. Hubel interprets this as meaning the following:

". . . [the geniculate cell] must be even more specialized than retinal ganglion cells in responding to spatial differences in retinal illumination rather than to the illumination itself. The lateral geniculate body, in short, has the function of increasing the disparity— already present in retinal ganglion cells—between responses to a small centered spot and to diffuse light."*

OPTIC RADIATION

In man, the lateral geniculate body is the exclusive source of the fibers in the optic radiation. The cells of the geniculate body, as described, give rise to new fibers, forming the third neuron in the optic pathway. This proceeds through the optic radiation to the cells in the striate area of the calcarine cortex.

After emerging from the lateral geniculate body, the fibers pass through the posterior part of the internal capsule, behind the sensory fibers and internal to the auditory bundle. This so-called optic peduncle spreads out to form a large flat fan that sweeps around the lateral wall and the posterior horn of the lateral ventricle (Fig. 313). This fan or medullary optic lamina bends downward and for-

---

*From Hubel, D.: Scient. Am. **209**:58, 1963. Reprinted with permission. Copyright © by Scientific American, Inc. All rights reserved.

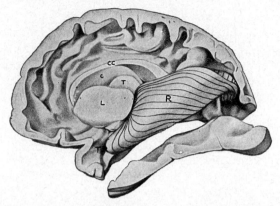

Fig. 313. Upper visual path. The left hemisphere is seen from within, showing the internal surface of the gray matter, the basal ganglia, and the geniculocalcarine pathway (after Pfeifer). **C,** Caudate nucleus. **CC,** Corpus callosum. **L,** Lentiform nucleus. **R,** Medullary optic lamina. **T,** Optic thalamus. **Tr,** Anterior genu of the medullary optic lamina. (From Duke-Elder, S.: Text-book of ophthalmology, St. Louis, 1946, The C. V. Mosby Co., vol. 1.)

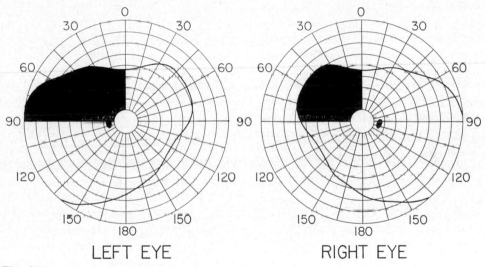

LEFT EYE   **RIGHT EYE**

Fig. 314. Left superior quadrantanopia caused by a temporal lobe tumor on the right side.

ward into the temporal lobe, forming the so-called temporal loop or Meyer's loop, which contains the fibers from the lower temporal quadrant of the retina of the same side, together with the fibers from the lower nasal retinal quadrant of the opposite eye. A lesion in this situation, such as a tumor of the temporal lobe, can easily catch these fibers from the lower retinal quadrants alone, while sparing the fibers from the upper retinal

quadrants, thus producing contralateral superior quadrantanopsia (Fig. 314).

All of the fibers then turn backward toward the calcarine fissure. At this point, the fibers from the upper and lower retinal quadrants again become separated from each other since the fibers from above the horizontal meridians of the retina enter the calcarine cortex above the fissure. Throughout their course in the optic radiation the fibers remain segregated in bundles, in accordance with the site of their origin from the lateral geniculate body.

THE VISUAL CORTEX

In man all of the visual fibers end in the so-called striate area of the cortex. This area of the cortex is characterized by the fact that lamina 4, the internal granular area, is highly developed. Moreover, it is split into two strata of cells, lamina 4A and 4C, separated by a fiber layer, lamina 4B. Of the two granular cell layers, the deeper 4C is by far the more conspicuous, and some difficulty is experienced in distinguishing lamina 4A from the superjacent pyramidal cell layer, lamina 3, in histologic sections. The intricate plexus of fibers found in lamina 4B forms a white band in the fresh brain, usually visible to the naked eye, which is termed the stria of Gennari. Hence the visual cortex is often spoken of as the striate area (Fig. 202, p. 473). It is limited closely to the area around the calcarine fissure on the mesial aspect of each hemisphere but spreads backward to the extreme posterior tip of the occipital lobe and somewhat over onto its lateral aspect, in man. The striate area is also known as area 17 of Brodmann. In the monkey much of area 17 is found on the lateral surface of the occipital lobes.

Localization of the retina in the cortex

There is a precise localization of corresponding areas of the two retinas in each striate area. Fibers from the corresponding upper retinal quadrants end in cells above the calcarine fissure, and fibers from corresponding lower retinal quadrants end in cells below the fissure. The macula is represented in a large posterior portion of area 17 (Fig. 315). The areas outside of the macula are represented along the calcarine fissure. Those retinal areas close to the macula are found at the extreme posterior tip of the fissure, and the more peripheral the retinal area, the farther away from the occipital pole will its representation be found. At the extreme anterior end of the calcarine fissure is the representation of the most peripheral nasal retina of the opposite side. Since the nose cuts off the corresponding temporal retina of the other eye from simultaneous usage, this results in an unpaired temporal crescent in each visual field.

The temporal half-moon, as the area in each field which corresponds to this isolated peripheral nasal retinal segment is called, is located in the most ventral portion of the lateral geniculate body. It is not known where these fibers are located after they leave the lateral geniculate body until they reach the cortex where they end, as stated, in the cells in the anterior end of the calcarine fissure. We have no evidence as to which portion of the area striata represents the upper half and which the lower half of the temporal half-moon. Lesions of the visual radiation occasionally produce isolated loss of the temporal half-moon, and this is produced usually by a lesion that encroaches on the radiation from the convex surface of the brain.[31] In patients in whom loss of the temporal half-moon on one side is of localizing value, the ventromedial portion of the radiations in the parietal, temporoparietal, and parieto-occipital lobes are usually involved.[32]

Lesions of the posterior portion of the optic radiations and lesions of the occipital cortex are likely to produce either homonymous quadrantic defects or homonymous hemianopic defects, with so-called sparing of the macula. Lesions situated in the anterior portion of the visual pathways, back of the chiasm, usu-

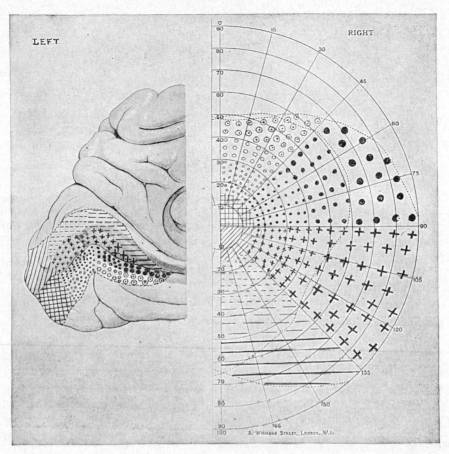

Fig. 315. Cortical retina. The calcarine fissure is represented as widely opened. The macular area is relatively large; the peripheral area is relatively small. The areas of the visual field are marked correspondingly to their areas of cortical projection. (From Duke-Elder, S.: Text-book of ophthalmology, St. Louis, 1946, The C. V. Mosby Co., vol. 1.)

ally result in homonymous hemianopia, and the line of demarcation between the seeing and the nonseeing portion of the fields runs directly through the point of fixation. In such patients, visual acuity is usually affected, and the macula is said not to have been spared. On the other hand, in posterior lesions, i.e., lesions involving the optic radiations and especially the cortex, it is common to find sparing of the macula, the line of demarcation between seeing and nonseeing halves of each field skirting the macula by as much as 5 degrees and leaving the visual acuity unimpaired. This has given rise to the belief that there is bilateral representation of each macula, and that the entire macular representation on one side of the cortex could be destroyed without interfering with the function of either macula. This necessitated postulating the existence of some pathway anterior to the visual cortex by means of which the macular fibers could be distributed to both sides. It was assumed that the macular fibers cross in the corpus callosum,[33] but neuroanatomic investigations[34] and clinical studies[35] do not bear this out.

It has been shown in carefully controlled experiments that occipital lobectomy in man may be associated with either sparing or nonsparing of the macula.[36] The whole problem of macular sparing is still to be solved, but the evidence for bilateral representation is insufficient at present to accept this as the explanation. Macular sparing appears to be either a mere phase of developing hemianopia or a sign of readjustment to a defect which actually splits the macular region.[37]

One of the explanations of sparing of the macula in lesions of the occipital lobe is based on the double blood supply to the macula. The frequency of sparing of the macula in lesions of the occipital lobe is explained by the fact that practically all such lesions are due to vascular accidents.

Numerous other theories, such as Verhoeff's, have been proposed to solve this perplexing problem.[38] He regards macular sparing, after complete destruction of one occipital lobe as only apparent and to be due partly to instability of fixation and partly to the establishment of an eccentric fixation point. The theory, in brief, is that apparent sparing results from loss of necessary cortical integration and that this loss may be produced by unilateral cortical injury but not by unilateral interruption of the lower visual pathways. He argues that central fixation is not controlled by the high visual acuity of the fovea but must be controlled by integration and correlation of a wide central region with the oculomotor mechanism. Some of the integration may take place in the retina itself, but obviously some of it, the final part, must take place in the cerebral cortex, and an essential part of the corresponding oculomotor coordination must take place here. He assumes that there is some area in the brain, which

he terms the conscious visual area, that has not as yet been identified. This is not a closely circumscribed area. It is at this level that the theory of replacement (Verhoeff) assumes that corresponding retinal points are represented by a single unit. The center is probably unilateral and, in the case of right-handed persons, probably in the left cerebral hemisphere. When one occipital lobe is destroyed, loss of integration between the seeing field and the blind field in the conscious visual cortical area occurs. As a result of this loss, an eccentric retinal point is employed for fixation, and slipping of fixation then occurs easily. The original macular field is actually split through the center, but in field tests it appears to be more or less spared. When one optic tract is interrupted, the integration in question is not disturbed, and splitting of the macula is found, therefore. Even after complete destruction or removal of one occipital lobe, macular splitting may be found by such tests if integration in the conscious visual area in use is not disturbed too greatly. These conditions would be obtained most likely when the lobe destroyed was on the side opposite to that of the conscious visual area.

Whether bilateral macular representation exists or not, the fact remains that sparing or nonsparing of the macula is of clinical importance in helping to locate a particular lesion which gives rise to homonymous hemianopia. In hemianopia without sparing, the lesion is nearly always in an optic tract. In hemianopia with sparing of the macula, the lesion is nearly always in an optic radiation or in the cortex.

There is still much to be learned about the function of so-called cerebral centers. It has been pointed out that in man there is no adequate clinical evidence for the precise and exclusive localization of function in any part of the cerebral cortex. It seems that the loss of function which results from local ablation of any part of the cortex is due to blocking of the nervous paths entering or emerging from it. Local cortical ablation will produce no loss of function, provided that there is a free alternative path to and from the cortex; it will give rise to temporary loss of function if a secondary path is available, but permanent loss of function will result only if no other path is available. In the case of those functions for which alternative paths are available, their facilitation is more rapid in animals in which differentiation is less advanced and in children in whom neuroblastic development is active (Duke-Elder).

The visual functions belong to the category wherein no alternative path is possible. In lesions of the visual cortex, the absence of recovery is probably explained by the fact that there is but one solitary afferent visual path which is blocked out by a lesion at its termination. The path is more important than its whereabouts in the cortex. It is obvious that those regions of the cortex wherein a systematized path ends will be of peculiar functional importance in relation to the activities of that path. It is probable also that those regions of the cortex immediately adjoining will share in this interest. It is only in this sense that we can speak of centers.

Caution must be exercised in drawing conclusions as to the exact localization of the retina on the higher centers, based on disturbances of function which follow lesions of the cortex. It can be said with certainty that the striate area or area 17 is the visuosensory area in man and forms an anatomic, functional entity. Outside area 17 and closely following its contours are two other areas which, as we have seen (p. 447), are concerned with visual

reactions also. These have been termed the parastriate area or area 18 and the peristriate area or area 19. They are present in all grades of primates. Area 18 has been considered the visuomotor field (p. 472) and area 19 the visuopsychic field. The anatomic boundaries of these areas are not exact, and not only their function but also their location and extent have been disputed. This is due partly to differences in various species. In man, e.g., area 18 plus area 19 (7,838 mm.^{2}) is almost three times as large as area 17. In the orangutan area 18 plus area 19 (2,864 mm.^{2}) is not even twice the size of area 17, and in the monkey area 18 plus area 19 (1,334 mm.^{2}) is still somewhat smaller in relation to area 17.[39]

It is possible to define these areas physiologically by flashing a small light in known relation to the point of fixation in front of an animal's eye while recording from electrodes in fixed positions on the occipital lobe. In this way the area of the cortex which responds to stimulation of the retina by light can be determined fairly accurately. In the primate, the "on" and "off" responses are restricted sharply to area 17.[40] The area so determined corresponds very well with the visual area as outlined by anatomic evidence, i.e., coincides with the striate area.[41] Small angular displacements from the fixation point are recorded at relatively large distances from its representation, but as the light is thrown on the retina at distances from the fovea in equal steps, the displacement of its representation is less per step on the cortex. The projection, in other words, is not uniform in the sense that each portion of the cortex corresponds to a proportionately equal segment of the retina. The cortical representation of the more highly involved specialized macula, which subserves central vision, e.g., occupies a relatively greater portion of the striate area than the peripheral parts.[42]* It has been shown also that in the cat the area of the cortex which receives the macular fibers, like that in the monkey, is much larger than that which responds to stimulation of the periphery of the retina.

Talbot and Marshall[43] found that the cortical map which represents the fovea shows great magnification of the pattern. Thus, the messages from a small illuminated point on the fovea are distributed to a cortical area ten thousand times as large as the area stimulated.

The map of visual events in the cortex is on a scale of quite different order from that used for tactile events. In the pig's snout, for instance, the sensory surface is about ten times as large as the cortical area connected with it. For the human fingertip, the relation of sensory surface to receiving area is of the same order. For the basilar membrane of the ear of the dog, the ratio is nearer equality, whereas for the region of most distinct vision in the retina, the cortical area is ten thousand times larger than the sensory surface.

There is divergence of the foveal pathways on the way to the visual cortex instead of convergence. At first sight it is difficult to see what advantage can be gained by expanding the map in this way. Nothing is gained by magnifying the dots in a halftone picture in a newspaper. To magnify the retinal mosaic of active and inactive cones would seem to do no more, but the analogy is not a good one. To begin with, the visual pattern on the cones is in constant movement. The eye is never held quite steady, and the image

of a line on the retina will be constantly shifting from one cone to another (p. 498). The effect of this shifting on the cortex will be a ridge of maximum activity shading away on either side, and Talbot and Marshall have pointed out that the cortical image could be sharpened by suppressing all but the peak of the ridge. Probably, contrasts are enhanced, and the details are brought out by similar processes occurring somewhere between the rods and cones and the cerebral cortex.[44]

Another reason for the expansion of the cortical map is the extreme concentration of the receptor organs in the central part of the retina. The cones there are packed far more closely than are the nerve cells in the striate area; therefore, in any case, the peaks and troughs of activity could not be reproduced on as fine a scale. Also expansion of the interconnections of cortical cells become necessary, because if there are to be two distinct peaks of excitation in the cortex, they must probably be separated by far more than the distance between one nerve cell and another.

Another method of investigation which has been found useful in the determination of the function of various cortical areas and their relation to one another is the use of strychnine locally as a chemical stimulant. There is reason to believe that strychnine poisons an acetylcholine esterase, so that acetylcholine is permitted to accumulate, whence the cells are discharged so easily that the electrical impulses of any cell excite all the strychninized cells. Strychnine acts on nerve cells only where synapses are present and produces disturbances propagated only in the ordinary direction of conduction. Applied to the occipital cortex locally, strychninization of area 17 causes area 17 to fire and also fires area 18. Similar strychnini-

---

*Compare this with the same phenomenon on the motor side; see discussion of cortical representation of ocular muscles (p. 433).

zation of area 18 fires an adjacent sector of area 17, fires almost all parts of area 18 of that hemisphere and the corresponding points in area 18 of the opposite hemisphere, and fires much of area 19 ipsilaterally. Thus, area 17, which receives impulses in a relatively discrete fashion, normally keeps them so within itself, but relays them to a larger fraction of area 18. This feeds excitation back into the original segment of area 17 and forward into area 19.[40]

If one stimulates areas 17, 18, and 19 directly with electrodes under appropriate conditions, deviation of the eyes is produced in a direction and manner dependent upon the exact site of stimulation. With ordinary 60-cycle current sustained deviation of the eyes is obtained from stimulation of any point in area 17. This turns the eyes in such manner as to bring the fovea to bear on the corresponding point in the visual field (p. 473). This form of stimulation is less effective in area 18, and the response is transient. Stimulation of area 19 produces suppression of motor functions. This suppression of electrical activity, like the suppression of motor function, can be elicited from several areas which, therefore, are called suppressor areas. All such areas, except area 19, have been shown to project to the nucleus caudatus. This may prove subsequently to be true of area 19.[40]

More than one cortical receptive area for different sensations has been found in various laboratory animals. In 1940 Adrian first demonstrated a second somatic receiving area in the cat, and in 1942 a second visual area was mapped out by Talbot. Following these discoveries a second auditory area was found in the cat. The significance of this duplication is not known, but recent studies have suggested that the second visual area in the rabbit may be homologous to area 18 in primates.[45]

Recently it has been found possible to record single neuron activity in the visual cortex in animals with chronically implanted electrodes, thus eliminating the effects of anesthetics and other acute experimental procedures which often suppress or alter the true picture. Since the animal is in the normal state, it is possible to correlate the electrical events in the cortex with such variables as the waking state, attention, learning, and motor activity.[46] As would be expected, maintained background activity in most of the cortical cells is found, comparable and perhaps induced by the maintained activity in the retina observed by Kuffler.[47] The receptive fields as mapped out in the cortex differ from those of the retina and lateral geniculate body (p. 678) in being of much greater variety and in not having the concentric circularly symmetrical pattern found at the lower levels. Further, binocular interaction is an almost constant feature of cortical cells, most of which can be influenced by stimulation of receptors in both eyes instead of just one as generally found in the lateral geniculate body.

Diffuse illumination of the retina produces little or no response in most cortical cells, whereas a stationary 2-degree spot illumination produces responses in most cortical units. The ineffectiveness of diffuse illumination is explained by Hubel by supposing that the response from the restricted region is inhibited by illumination of the surrounding field. This same antagonism between the center and the surrounding parts of the receptive field has been verified many times for the retinal ganglion cells.[48, 49]

Movement of the spot source of light across the retina is especially effective in producing cortical cell activity. Many units are much more sensitive to a moving stimulus as opposed to a stationary one, and in some units the activity is much greater when the light source is moved in one direction than in another. Further, movement activates a unit over a relatively large region of the visual field (5 mm. on the retina) which suggests that convergence from a large retinal field must occur on some cortical units. In other words, the cortex does not represent a point-to-point end station for retinal receptors entirely, but what occurs at the cortical level can be changed by the type of retinal stimulation as well as by its location, namely, movement asymmetries.

The receptive fields of the visual cortical cells are not concentric. Further, there seem to be many different types of cortical cells, but in general they may be classified by function into two groups. One of these Hubel calls simple cells and the other complex cells. The function of simple cells is to respond to line stimuli—such shapes as slits, dark bars, and edges between light and dark regions. Each simple cell will respond only when the stimulus is presented to the retina in a particular position of the receptive field and in a particular orientation. For example, a bar shone vertically on the receptive field may activate a given cell, whereas if the bar is displaced to one side or oriented appreciably away from the vertical, no response will occur[30] (Figs. 316 and 317).

Complex cells also respond best to bars, slits, or edges, and as with the simple cells these must be properly oriented. However, complex cells are not so discriminating as to the exact position of

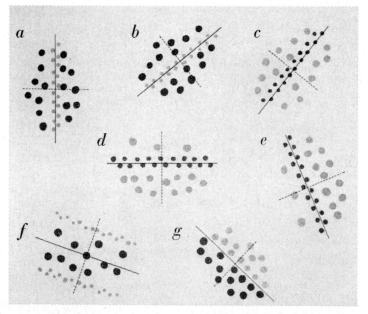

Fig. 316. Simple cortical cells have receptive fields of various types. In all of them the "on" and "off" areas, represented by black and gray dots, respectively, are separated by straight boundaries. Orientations vary, as indicated particularly at **a** and **b**. In the cat's visual system such fields are generally 1 mm. or less in diameter. (From Hubel, D.: Scient. Am. **209**:58, 1963. Reprinted with permission. Copyright © 1963 by Scientific American, Inc. All rights reserved.)

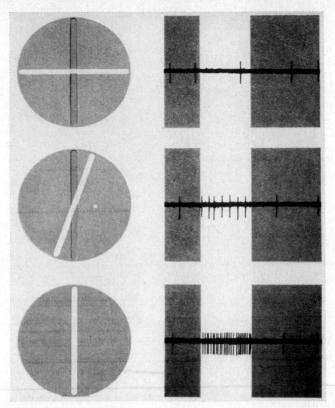

Fig. 317. Importance of orientation to simple cortical cells is indicated by varying responses to a slit of light from a cell preferring a vertical orientation. Horizontal slit (top) produces no response; slight tilt, a weak response; vertical tilt, a vigorous response. (From Hubel, D.: Scient. Am. **209**:58, 1963. Reprinted with permission. Copyright © 1963 by Scientific American, Inc. All rights reserved.)

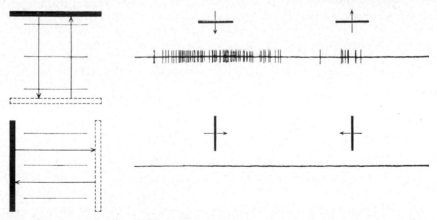

Fig. 318. Complex cortical cell responded to slow downward movement of a dark horizontal bar. Upward movement of the bar produced a weak response, and horizontal movement of a vertical bar produced no response. For other shapes, orientations, and movements there are other complex cells showing maximum response. Such cells may figure in perception of form and movement. (From Hubel, D.: Scient. Am. **209**:58, 1963. Reprinted with permission. Copyright © 1963 by Scientific American, Inc. All rights reserved.)

the stimulus in the receptive field, and unlike simple cells, complex cells respond with sustained firing to moving lines (Figs. 318 and 319). Hubel considers that the geniculate fibers end in simple cells, and that the complex cell receives its input from a large number of simple cells, all of which are of the same general type and have the same field orientation as the complex cell.

"A complex cell responding to vertical edges, for example, would thus receive fibers from simple cells that have vertically oriented receptive fields. All such a scheme needs to have added is the requirement that the retinal positions of these simple fields be arranged throughout the area occupied by the complex field."*

This scheme preposes an enormous degree of cortical organization. A vast network of connections is needed if "a single complex cell is to receive fibers from just the right simple cells, all with the appropriate field arrangements, tilts, and positions."* However, Hubel has evidence which points strongly to such being the case. He found that the cortical cells are not arranged in haphazard fashion but with a high degree of order. The cortex is divided into tiny columns like a beehive, each segment extending from the surface to the white matter. The cells contained in each column all have the same receptive-field orientation (Fig. 320). The columns are irregular in cross-sectional shape and average about a half a millimeter across. In each column are the cells one should expect to find in order to be interconnected, i.e., cells whose fields have the same orientation and the same general retinal position. There are rich intercommunications between neighboring cells, mainly in a vertical direction, so that each column of cells

*From Hubel, D.: Scient. Am. **209**:58, 1963. Reprinted with permission. Copyright © by Scientific American, Inc. All rights reserved.

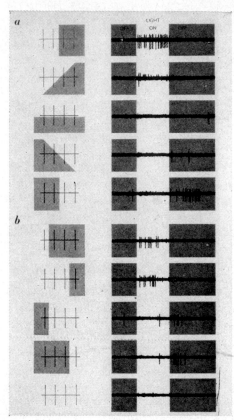

Fig. 319. Single complex cell showed varying responses to an edge projected on the cell's receptive field in the retina. In group **a** the stimulus was presented in differing orientations. In group **b** all the edges were vertical, and all but the last evoked responses regardless of where in the receptive field the light struck. When a large rectangle of light covered the entire receptive field, however, as shown at bottom, the cell failed to respond. (From Hubel, D.: Scient. Am. **209**:58, 1963. Reprinted with permission. Copyright © by Scientific American, Inc. All rights reserved.)

can be looked on as an independent functional unit of the cortex in which the simple cells receive connections from the lateral geniculate cells and send projections to the complex cells. The result is that the visual cortex rearranges the input from the lateral geniculate body in a way that makes lines and contours the most important stimuli.

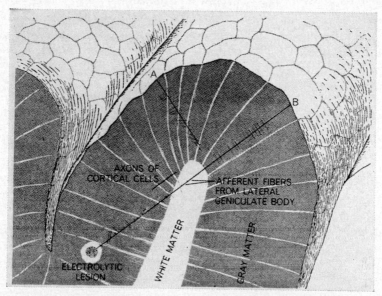

Fig. 320. Functional arrangement of cells in the visual cortex resembled columns, although columnar structure is not apparent under a microscope. Lines **A** and **B** show paths of two microelectrode penetrations. Hatched black lines show receptive field orientations encountered. Cells in a single column had same orientation. Change of orientation showed new column. (From Hubel, D.: Scient. Am. **209**:58, 1963. Reprinted with permission. Copyright © 1963 by Scientific American, Inc. All rights reserved.)

The electroencephalogram

In 1929 Berger discovered that a regular oscillation of electrical potential could be recorded from metal electrodes fixed to the scalp due to the activity of cells in the brain. The discharges had a frequency of 9 to 10 per second in normal human beings and were much slower than the discharges commonly found in cortical centers. These oscillations, now known as the alpha rhythm or electroencephalogram, when suitably recorded represent a very small change in potential about 50 μv, and accordingly indicate a very small ebb and flow of current in the cerebral cortex. As Adrian[50] points out, there is nothing unexpected in the fact that brain cells show constant changes in electrical potential, as all active cells do, but the unexpected thing in Berger's discovery is the regularity of the rhythm, which indicates that a large number of brain cells must be working in unison at the same rate.

The alpha rhythm comes from large areas of the occipital region and, when suitable leads are used, to some extent from the frontal cortex. The potential change is not found at its maximum over areas known to be sensory receptive areas but over the silent or association areas. In the occipital cortex the rhythm is at its maximal potential over areas 18 and 19 and not over area 17.

In man, in order for rhythm to be produced, the eyes must be closed and the attention must be relaxed so that vision is excluded as far as possible. In animals in which vision does not play such an important part in the animal's activity, the alpha waves may be present with the eyes open as long as there is relative inattention to objects in the field of vision. Any movement or change in contour likely to attract the animal's conscious attention immediately breaks up the rhythm. In man, even trying to see in a dark room breaks up the waves; therefore it is evident that the rhythm depends on the absence of attention to the visual field and not on actual excitation of the retina by light. The rhythm is an activity which appears when the attention is not directed to vision and disappears when it is; it is a rhythm of inattention. It is not the basic rhythm of unstimulated nerve cells, and some kind of competition must exist between the messages from the eyes and from the source of the alpha rhythm to decide which shall control the cortical areas.

The work of Adrian and others indicates that the decision as to whether the alpha rhythm or the electrical discharges from the cortical centers shall dominate the picture is made by some deep-seated part of the brain—a relatively small region, probably in the neighborhood of the thalamus and near the main incoming pathways. It is from here that the alpha rhythm is controlled, and Adrian suggests that it is the sudden disturbance of this region which causes loss of consciousness

after a blow on the head. The exact source of the alpha rhythm has not been determined accurately. According to Case,[51] an interruption anywhere in the geniculocalcarine pathway interferes with the alpha rhythm on that side. The interruption of the alpha rhythm by any method involving attention to the stimulus—visual, auditory, touch, or merely mental activity—is known as blocking of the rhythm, a good example of which is shown in Fig. 321 from van Balen and Henkes.[52] Of more interest than the blocking reaction is that known as driving. The alpha waves can be changed or driven by exposing the eye to flickering lights. At a certain rate of flicker the alpha rhythm changes from its original rhythm to that of the flickering light. In monkeys this is accomplished at frequencies of 2 to 4 cycles per second. Studies have been made of the dependency of driving on such factors as intensity of the flickering light and its wavelength. The greatest driving for variations in intensity is obtained with flashes of 80 footcandles. At this intensity, the flickering light is twice as effective in producing driving as flashes of 4 foot-

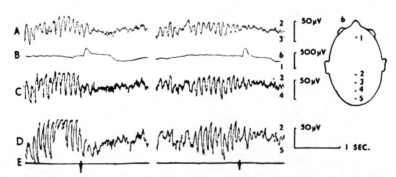

Fig. 321. Blocking of alpha rhythm in electroencephalogram recordings (tracings **A**, **C**, and **D**) by light stimulus (tracing **E**). Channel **B** records the scotopic electroretinogram of the left eye. Channels **A**, **C**, and **D** record the electroencephalogram using electrodes placed in the midline of the occipital region. Indifferent electrode (no. 1) was placed on forehead. Contact lens electrode is shown at no. 6. (Time constant, 0.7 sec.) (From van Balen, A., and Henkes, H.: Brit. J. Ophth. 44:449, 1960.)

candles. Monochromatic light is relatively more effective in producing driving than white light of the same luminous energy, and the blue region of the spectrum is considerably more effective than that of the red region.[58]

Alpha rhythms similar to those obtained with leads from the cortex can be recorded with leads from deeper structures, such as the geniculate body and optic radiation. At an intensity of 10 footcandles the optic nerve and lateral geniculate body can be driven at a maximum rate of 62 and 59 cycles per second, respectively. This rate is considerably above the maximum critical fusion frequency (p. 740) for man and probably for the monkey. The cortex of the striate area can be driven to a maximum rate of 34 cycles per second.

If the alpha rhythm is recorded and brief light flashes are presented to an eye, the changes in the rhythm are known as the specific or evoked response. Unfortunately it is only possible to demonstrate these evoked responses in a small number of individuals because of technical difficulties. Recently van Balen and Henkes[52] have made use of a method devised by Dawson[53] which involves estimating the mathematical average of a large number of records by means of an electronic toposcope, with an electronic stroboscope as a light source. Unlike the alpha rhythm generally, which can be recorded from almost any region of the cortex, the evoked response is limited mainly to the occipital cortex. Although the evoked response is composed of several different waves, only two of these have been clearly identified with light stimulation. These can be fairly constantly produced in all individuals and are known as the c^1 and c^2 components. The c^1 component is identified with the phototopic mechanism, whereas the c^2 component correlates with

the activity of the scotopic mechanism. Since photopic and scotopic mechanisms relate to the physiology of the retina, i.e., foveal cones and peripheral groups of rods together with cones, this suggests that the occipital response actually reflects the presence of these two separate mechanisms.

Further analyses of the changes in the c^1 and c^2 response with attention and without attention were made by van Balen and Henkes.[54] They showed that both c waves appear in the attentive state when low-intensity light flashes are used, but in the nonattentive state when the same intensity of light flash is used, the c^2 response only is produced. In responses to high-intensity stimuli in the attentive state, the c^1 wave exceeds the c^2 wave to a greater extent than in responses in the nonattentive state. Attention seems to favor the development of the c^1 response, as it should if this represents the activity of the foveal (cone; photopic) mechanism.

It may seem strange that functional differentiation between fovea and peripheral retina should be evident in the cortex, but we can recall that the anatomic representation of these two parts of the retina are separate in the cortex, the fovea being localized strictly to the extreme tip of the calcarine fissure. Further, the two mechanisms are separated in all parts of the visual pathway from the fovea up to the cortex. Further, in most subjects the c^1 wave could be led off only from the extreme occipital pole, location 3 in Fig. 322.

What is the anatomic substratum for the so-called attention factor? The influence of attention on sensory responses has been dealt with by many different investigators, and it is believed that this influence is mediated by way of the reticular formation in the brainstem. An

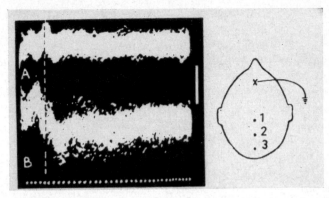

Fig. 322. Recording of normal human occipital electroencephalogram after light stimulation by Dawson's superimposition technique. (From van Balen, A., and Henkes, H.: Brit. J. Ophth. **46:**13, 1962.)

Energy of stimulator flash: 4/3 Joule
Distance from eye to stimulator: 24 cm.
Background illumination: 100 Lux.
Time calibration: 50 cycles per second.

Voltage calibration: 20 μV.
Vertical dotted line: at 100 msec. after stimulus.
A: Leading off between electrodes 1 and 2.
B: Leading off between electrodes 2 and 3.

influence of the reticular formation on the tonus of the extraocular muscles has been previously suggested by Breinin.

Electroencephalograms of subjects with various types of visual field defects have been studied extensively, but it is still uncertain how valuable they are as a guide to the type or localization of disease. Subjects with hemianopic defects due to involvement of the optic radiations are said to show a substantial difference in the alpha waves recorded from the two sides of the brain. The changes observed in amblyopia of strabismus are dealt with on p. 874.

Blocking of the occipital alpha rhythm cannot be considered the specific response of the retina arriving at the cortex since it begins so late following the stimulus.[55] The time relations between the arrival of the specific retinal response, the cortical time, the blocking time, and the motor reaction time of man are shown in Fig. 323.

Considerable work has been done in recording the electroencephalogram from the occipital lobe of animals under various experimental conditions, but it is difficult to assess this as a whole and to fit the extensive material into a unified story that tells much about the function of the visual apparatus. Various rhythms that range from 2 to 4 per second, considered analogous to the alpha rhythm of man, have been found in various optic structures of the cat.[56] In the rabbit the intrinsic rhythm of the visual pathway has been identified with the 5-per-second alpha rhythm.[57]

Not all observers agree that the alpha rhythm can be driven by flicker at frequencies other than its natural period of 8 to 13 per second.[58] Toman[59] concludes from a study of normal persons that flicker-following (driving) is a succession of overlapping "on" responses, comparable to the slowest components of the cortical response to optic nerve stimulation found in the cat and rabbit.[60]

It is known that the mammalian visual

system has a high resolving power in space but a low resolving power in time (p. 740). The range of frequencies at which man can distinguish intermittent light from steady light is 4 to 5 cycles per second at low intensities and 35 cycles per second at high intensities.[61] Since sensory nerves can transmit discrete impulses at rates above this limit, it has been generally assumed that the limiting factor in temporal resolving power is the retina. Retinal lag or persistence has been made the basis for many visual phenomena, from the fusion of motion pictures when projected at 15 to 20 cycles per second to chromatic afterimages. It can be supposed, as a working hypothesis, that the primary phenomena of fusion are dependent upon the maximum rate at which the slowest element in the visual system can be reactivated from the periphery. Applying the findings just given, Walker and co-workers[62] reached the conclusion that the mechanism that limits the temporal resolving power of the primate visual system is a fusion

mechanism in the cortex and not the retina itself.

The conduction rate from the retina to the visual cortex has been estimated by measurements of the interval between the appearance of the b wave in the electroretinogram (p. 612) and the inhibition of the alpha rhythm, which signifies the arrival of the retinal action current in area 17. This averages 124 msec., which is about three times the duration of the latent period of the action current in the retina. The rate of conduction of the impulses from the retina to the cortex is not altered by changing the intensity of the stimulus although the latent period of the retinal action current is considerably shortened by increasing the intensity of the light stimulus (p. 733).

Encephalographic studies in a variety of purely ocular conditions have been conducted, and it is believed by some that the results throw light on the site and type of lesion present.[63]

Dyer and Bierman[64] reported a dis-

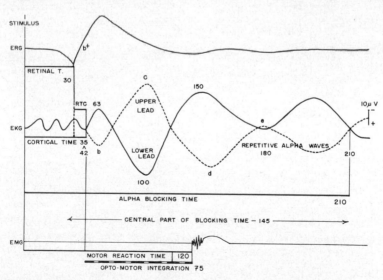

Fig. 323. Time relations of retinal, cortical, and motor responses to a light flash in man. (Redrawn after Monier, M.: J. Neurophysiol. **15:**469, 1952.)

turbance in the alpha rhythm in a patient with amblyopia ex anopsia. However, previously Callahan and Redlich[65] had found no difference from the normal in the electroencephalograms of ten subjects with amblyopia ex anopsia, and similar negative results have been reported by Stillerman, Gibbs, and Perlstein[66] and by White and Schlaegel.[67]

Effect of stimulating the occipital cortex on conscious human subjects

Penfield[68] found rather marked variations in the type of visual hallucination produced by stimulating different portions of the occipital cortex of epileptic patients in the conscious state. The subject's responses could be recorded while various portions of the exposed cortex were stimulated electrically. The brain tissue itself is insensitive. The results of electrical stimulation of the occipital cortex in three-hundred and thirty operations are summarized in Fig. 324. The subjects said that they saw various types of colored lights, wheels, flickering lights and shadows, radiating gray spots, etc., when different regions of the occipital pole were stimulated. Formed percepts were never produced. Stimulation of the cortex at a

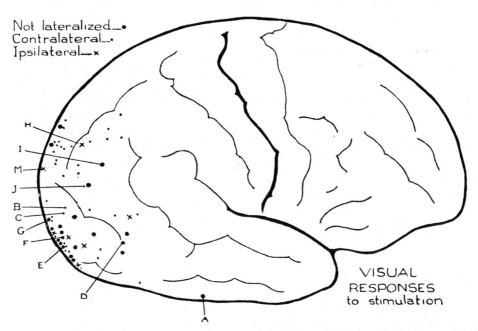

Not lateralized—•
Contralateral—.
Ipsilateral—x

VISUAL
RESPONSES
to stimulation

Fig. 324. Visual responses collected from a 17-year-old operative period (330 operations). When point **E** was stimulated, the patient saw colors which whirled in a counterclockwise direction. The point was restimulated twice with exactly the same result. On the other hand, when point **B** was stimulated, another patient said she saw something "pink and blue" in the contralateral field. Later the same point was restimulated. This time she reported "stars with spokes" directly in front of her. This illustrates the fact that there is at times variability in the response from a single occipital point. Only one visual response came from a point well out of the occipital lobe. This followed stimulation at **A** when the patient stated that he had seen brown squares followed by light before his eyes. It is possible that the electric current reached the optic radiations in this case and that it is therefore not a cortical response. (From Penfield, W.: Proc. Roy. Soc. London s.B **134**:329, 1947.)

distance from the occipital pole was more likely to produce a contralateral image. Stimulation at the posterior pole produced an unlateralized image.

As Penfield points out:

"What we call the visual cortex forms a station in the afferent stream of visual impulses on their way from peripheral sense organs to the level of consciousness. If the station and its subcortical connections are left intact, wide areas of surrounding cerebral cortex can be removed without depriving the patient of sight."*

THE CONSCIOUS LEVEL OF VISION

Up to this point we have been considering the transmission of the visual stimulus to the visuosensory cortex in the brain. Physiologists are agreed that vision, as man experiences it, is a function of still higher parts of the brain or perhaps of the brain as a whole. It has been impossible, naturally, to experiment with man by removing various portions of the cortex or tracts in order to determine their relative importance, but the experiments performed in the study of disease show clearly that only the crudest visual sensations result from stimulation of any part of the visual paths or occipital cortex. Thus, stimulation of the retina by trauma gives rise to a sensation of bright points of light—the subject says he sees stars. Mechanical stimulation of the optic nerve or of the tracts up to and including the occipital cortex as a result of trauma, by the growth of tumors, or from vascular spasm may also cause the subject to have flashes of light, colored or uncolored. Electrical stimulation of the human optic nerve in the conscious subject results in a sensation of light, often accompanied by colors. Formed objects are also perceived

_____

*From Penfield, W.: Proc. Roy. Soc., London, s.B **134**:329, 1947.

in various portions of the visual field.[69] The various forms of scintillating scotoma which frequently occur in migraine are thought to be due to spasm of blood vessels in the occipital cortex. Patients never complain of any recognizable forms or figures. This is in accord with the findings of Penfield, described previously. Visual hallucinations that take some recognizable shape are described by patients with tumors of the temporal lobe. This has led to the belief that the association pathways connected with the percepts of form must be in this region.

The message which is relayed to the visual cortical area (area 17) enables one only to see. It does not enable a person to recognize what he sees nor to recall things which have been seen. It merely makes possible the perception of form and color of the animate and inanimate worlds as well as of written and printed symbols of language. The actual processes by means of which a person obtains conscious vision with the ability to recall is a function of other parts of the brain. In order to understand the alterations in function which come about as the result of disease processes in these cortical areas, one will find it useful to review the facts which are known about the cortical functions of speech. In the normal person these are called (1) euphasia, the ability to speak, (2) eugnosia, the ability to recognize, identify, and understand the significance of objects, and (3) eupraxia, the ability to perform simple or complex purposive movements.[70] Specific cortical areas serve the functions of euphasia, eugnosia, and eupraxia, but these areas are so interrelated that a disturbance in one will nearly always result in a disturbance in the others.

In the development of the infant, certain areas known as primary sensory receptive cortical areas are set apart. These are the first cortical areas to mature in the infant. They are (1) the primary visual receptive area, which we have seen is localized in area 17, (2) the primary somatesthetic area, localized in the post-central convolution of the parietal lobe, (3) the primary olfactory area on the medial surface of the hemisphere near the tip of the temporal lobe in the uncus, and (4) the primary gustatory area, located on the insula. Of the various primary sensory cortical areas, three play significant roles in psychic processes. These are the visual, auditory, and somatesthetic areas. The impulses which reach these primary sensory cortical areas must be intact, but by themselves they are inadequate to yield recognition or to form memory patterns. In order for this level of consciousness to be achieved, so-called secondary sensory cortical areas must develop. These areas are activated by the nearby primary areas. The primary sensory areas function in sensory perception, as stated, but the secondary sensory areas have two important functions to perform. (1) They are essential for the interpretation of the sensation during the process of observation and recognition. (2) They make possible the recall of the memory of previous sensory experiences by voluntary effort or by thought association.

We have seen that the primary visual cortical area is area 17. In order for one to interpret the message which reaches area 17 and to be able to recall the memory of previous sensory experiences, the message must be sent on to the two secondary visual areas, areas 18 and 19, which surround the primary visual area (Fig. 202). Area 18 is concerned exclusively with the recognition of objects, animate or inanimate, but is not concerned with the recognition of written or printed symbols of language; hence it is not concerned directly with speech. Area 19 is concerned with the recall of visual memory relating to objects but not to language symbols. Visual agnosia is a disturbance of recognition of objects by sight and results from a lesion of area 18. The agnosia is for animate or inanimate objects only, and there is no interference with the recognition of language symbols since the memory of these is stored in another cortical area, the angular gyrus. In visual agnosia, the patient can see and recall the features of objects or persons, but he cannot recognize them when he is confronted with them. While he is not blind, he behaves as though he were. Although he cannot identify a watch by sight, he can identify and recognize it by some other sense—e.g., by hearing it tick or by feeling it when the watch is placed in his hands. The subject has no difficulty in reading and writing.

A lesion in area 19, on the other hand, is not associated with difficulty in recognition of objects but in the recall of the physical aspects of things seen. For example, while a patient can recognize a watch promptly when he looks at it, he cannot describe the features of a watch by mere recall. Combined lesions of areas 18 and 19 are particularly debilitating since the patient can neither recognize by sight nor recall the visual memory of his belongings, friends, home, and environment. Therefore, he cannot orient himself in space.

Whereas the primary visual centers (area 17) show no cerebral dominance or very little evidence of dominance, areas 18 and 19 show very definite cerebral dominance, particularly area 19. On the other hand, the dominance shown by areas 18 and 19 is not enduring since the minor secondary area can be retrained with little difficulty, as a rule, if the dominant is ablated.

It has just been stated that areas 18 and 19 are not concerned with the recognition of written and printed symbols of language since the engrams for these are stored in another cortical area, the angular gyrus. This is the area of recognition and recall of visual speech and contains the memory pattern of symbols of written or printed language. Such engrams are essential for reading and writing. The angular gyrus is not concerned with the recognition and recall of animate or inanimate objects, but only with the visual symbols for them as found in reading and writing. In addition, the angular gyrus is concerned not only with their recognition, but also with the interpretation of written or printed letters, symbols, and words. In some persons, interpretation of visual language symbols by the angular gyrus depends greatly on its connection with the area of Wernicke, which is the secondary auditory sensory area occupying the posterior part of the first temporal convolution on the lateral surface of the hemisphere. In these persons, auditory memories are essential to interpretation of written and printed words. There is considerable dominance in the angular gyrus, and the major angular gyrus is intimately linked with the major area 19. Hence, function of the major angular gyrus in the recognition of visual language symbols suffers when lesions of the major area 19 are present. The handwriting center is situated in the middle frontal convolution in line with the arm center of the true motor cortex. This area contains the kinetic engrams of movements used in writing. This is not an automatic writing center since it depends for its normal function on the visual language symbols stored in the angular gyrus, on the verbal speech symbols stored in the area of Wernicke, and finally on the area of language formula-tion. It is only when these cortical areas and their connections with the handwriting center are intact that the latter can function properly in writing. The area containing the visual engrams for mathematical figures is situated in the posterior part of the angular gyrus and extends somewhat into the occipital lobe. Lesions of the major handwriting center result in inability to express thoughts in written language. Agraphia may result from a lesion of the handwriting center as the result of loss of engrams of the kinetic movements used in writing or may be due to loss of engrams of visual speech symbols from a lesion of the angular gyrus.

The functions of areas 18 and 19 in controlling movement of the eyes have been described in Chapter 10, Ocular Motility. These areas are called the occipital oculogyric centers and are concerned with the optomotor reflexes. The fact that areas 18 and 19 are now thought to be intimately concerned with the complex functions of writing and reading may lead to a better understanding of the difficulties which many children with comitant strabismus have. Often, it is found that these children show so-called mirror writing and reversals in speech. They write *ton* for *not, nac* for *can,* etc. In a similar fashion, they read words backward. This suggests that this type of strabismus may be due primarily to some lack of development of these cortical areas, which would explain both the motor defects and the psychologic disturbances that are frequently associated. More work needs to be done along these lines.

In contrast to visual sensations, psychologic processes such as visual percepts are so complex that they defy immediate analysis, but continued study of the elementary physiologic processes may lead eventually to a better understanding of the more complex phenomena.

It has always been assumed that the complex functions of the human brain, such as insight, reasoning, and generalization, are built up of more elementary processes by a combination of the activities of many sensory fields. This combining of simpler processes into a complex one is supposed to be brought about by transcortical association pathways and to be controlled by the activities of higher coordinating centers.

Lashley[71] attacks this problem of generalization as a synthesis of simple processes into a complex one from a unique point of view. He considers generalization to be one of the primitive basic functions of organized nervous tissue and not built up from elementary processes. He points out that when an animal is trained to choose the larger or brighter of two objects and is then confronted with a still larger or brighter one he chooses on the basis of relative size or brightness.

Such generalizations are universal, from the insects to the primates. In the rat they persist after total destruction of the striate cortex[72] and thus may be looked upon as primitive, as is discrimination. The explanation of perceptual generalization is to be sought in the primitive organization of nervous tissue, rather than in any elaborate construction of transcortical associative connections or of higher coordinating centers. Visual reactions, according to Lashley, are determined by relations that subsist within the stimulus complex and not by association of a reaction with any definite group of receptor cells. In the recognition of every visual object, visual fixation is held accurately for only a moment, and yet, in spite of changes in direction of gaze, the object remains the same object. An in-

definite number of combinations of retinal cells and afferent paths are equivalent in perception and in the reaction which they produce. This is the problem of stimulus equivalents. Neurologically, the problem is clear enough. As shown in Fig. 325, first, experience of a stimulus, *bc f* excites a certain number of neurons in a definite pattern. An associated reaction, *y,* is formed as a result of this stimulation. Thereafter, the excitation of any similar pattern of neurons, *ce k,* will elicit the associated reaction. The latter stimulation need not—in fact, it never does—involve the original combination of sensory cells. It preserves only certain proportions or relations among the elements of a stimulus pattern.

Adrian[73] has described and analyzed the same problem as it involves hearing. A tune is recognized, not because it affects the same receptors and therefore the same cells in the auditory cortex, but because of the relationship of the stimulus pattern. It is the proportion or relation among the elements of the stimulus pattern which must be preserved. The first stimulation leaves some trace in the nervous system which determines the subsequent reactions.

The difficulty for neurologic theory arises when an attempt to localize this trace is made. It cannot be restricted to the neurons originally excited or to their immediate connections because they need not be reactivated in order to elicit the reaction again. It cannot be in any other restricted group of cells because after a single experience any part of the macular field can mediate the reaction. The memory trace somehow becomes a property of the whole system. The dilemma is that nerve impulses are transmitted over definite restricted paths in the sensory and motor nerves and in the central nervous system from cell to cell through

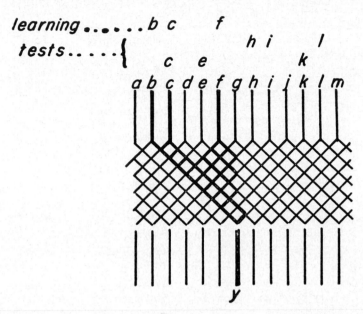

Fig. 325. Diagram to illustrate the problem of stimulus equivalence. An association is formed with **y** by stimulation of receptor cells, **bc-f.** Thereafter any similar pattern of receptors, **ce-k,** will excite reaction, **y.** A fixed trace, indicated by the heavy lines, fails to account for such equivalence. (From Lashley, K.: Biol. Symposia 7:301, 1942.)

definite intercellular connections; yet all behavior seems to be determined by masses of excitation by the form or relations or proportions of excitation within general fields of activity, without regard to particular nerve cells. It is the pattern and not the element that counts.

Lashley believes that in cortical activity there must be postulated a persistent substratum of tonic innervation upon which are superimposed fluctuating patterns, resulting from current stimulation, in the same way that the innervation of voluntary movement is superimposed upon the spinal pattern of postural tonus.

Basing his experiment on Wiener's work in electronics,[74] Hoagland[75] has made an interesting attempt to visualize the processes of translating visual stimuli into conscious vision, with all of its psychological attributes including visual memory. Wiener worked out the principles for a computer for the solution of partial differential equations with more than one variable and made interesting comparisons of this machine with the brain.

Data are fed to the machine which then performs a complicated series of logical operations at a rapid rate of electronic switching devices. The computations are based on a scale of two, after the algorithms of Boolian algebra, rather than on a scale of ten, and electronic relays which give an On-Off or a Yes-No answer are the switching devices employed. The machine processes all the data in accordance with the rules of logic and number in sets of choices between two alternatives, and all the operations on the data take the form of making a set of new choices, depending on a set of earlier choices. The operations are timed by a central clocking device. This clocking may be performed by an actual clock, or its equivalent may be performed by not permitting a process to take place until its antecedents have occurred. There is no human interference with the process from the time the machine is supplied with its initial information until the end of the calculations. Thousands of ordered operations take place at an extremely rapid rate, condensing into minutes processes that would require days to complete with ordinary methods of computation. The machine has devices to retain impulses until it is time for the appropriate circuit to act and relate them to other events in the processes of computation. This may be done by systems of reverberating circuits and by electronic scanning devices, such as are used in television, and also by magnetization patterns of the molecules in iron wire, after the manner of the well-known wire recorder. Thus, information can be stored until ready for use. The machine quite literally possesses a functional memory in the form of patterns of dynamic electrical configurations or of molecular patterns which may be called upon to furnish information by appropriate stimuli, arriving as time pulses, from other circuits in the apparatus. It is important to realize that this memory need not be lodged in any one locus in the machine but belongs to its function as a whole. To ignore this is to commit the fallacy of Descartes of locating the action of the mind on matter in the pineal gland.

A basic controlling principle in the integration of patterns of activity in the machine is that of negative feedback. This principle is utilized by many of our ordinary devices. The thermostatically controlled heating system in a house is a common example of negative feedback because, as the temperature rises, the thermostat shuts off the heater, and when the house cools off, it turns on the furnace again. Other examples are the robot-controlled plane and the proximity fuse which detonates the shell as it approaches the target by the return of electromagnetic waves broadcast from the shell and reflected back to it.

The nervous system is replete with examples of negative feedback. Increasing blood pressure excites stretch receptors in the carotid sinus which send impulses to the vasomotor center, causing a fall in blood pressure. In general homeostatic mechanisms that regulate our internal environment use the principles of negative feedback. Lorente de Nó has demonstrated the action of what he calls "reverberating chains of neurons," so arranged in closed paths in the central nervous system that each neuron excites the next around a loop, the last finally re-exciting the first. With 10 billion neurons in the human central nervous system, an appalling number of interacting neuron loops are possible. Action, once started in such reverberating circuits, can continue indefinitely as long as metabolism supplies the requisite energy. Voluntary acts by their nature exemplify negative feedback. Thus, when we pick up an object from a table, we do not command the specific sequence of muscular acts. Rather, as Weiner suggests, the controlling factor in the act is the degree to which the act has not been completed. The object may be picked up with either the right or left hand or even by the mouth if the hands are tied. The action ceases when the purpose is realized, after the manner in which servomechanisms control actions and bring them to a stop.

Pitts and McCulloch[76] present anatomic diagrams based on cortical neuroanatomy and a mathematical analysis indicating how a scanning mechanism, consisting of waves of impulses sweeping up and down over interlacing nonspecific and dissociated afferent fibers of the cortex, can furnish a basis for the perception and recognition of form when specific afferent stimuli arrive over sensory pathways. In this type of nerve network, form is independent of size or position in the field, and it is independent of any particular neuron or small neuron group. Pitts and McCulloch write:

"It is to the nonspecific afferents that modern physiology attributes the well-known rhythmic sweep of a sheet of negativity up and down through the cortex—the Alpha rhythm. If our model fits the facts, this Alpha rhythm performs a temporal scanning of the cortex which thereby gains at the cost of time the equivalent of another spatial dimension."*

According to this, memory traces are more or less stable resonance patterns that are extensively reduplicated all over the cortex ready to respond to incoming signals which fit the pattern of response.

Adrian has pointed out that it is difficult to see how memories can survive great changes in the over-all patterns of activity in the brain, such as occur during normal sleep or anesthesia. However, Hoagland suggests by analogy that the storage of information in the wire recorder modifies the wire at a molecular level but not within optically observable microscopic dimensions, and information fed by such a wire to scanning circuits can reappear in its original form after a shutdown of the apparatus when its circuits are reactivated later. Both the brain and the machine operate in relation to internal master clocks. In the case of the brain, steady state enzyme kinetics appear to regulate our time sense.

Under the general heading of temporal and spatial summation I have described how visual stimuli set up changes in the retina which influence successive responses to further stimulation. Afterimages, e.g.,

are the result of chemical changes in the retina which alter the perception of subsequent visual stimuli. In addition to the purely local retinal effects of visual stimuli it has now been shown that visual stimuli also cause changes in the visual cortex which modify the perception of successive stimuli. These aftereffects have been demonstrated mainly through the work of Kohler and Wallach. Many of the so-called optical illusions are now believed to depend on these cortical aftereffects rather than on retinal changes. The following are cited by Prentice.[77]

In Fig. 326 the open square when first looked at may appear to present the bottom face tilted upward toward the observer, or the top face may appear tilted slightly down and seen by the observer from above. In either case if one gazes steadily at the figure, these two possibilities will present themselves to consciousness, and the observer will become aware that first he sees the figure one way and then suddenly the other way. Al-

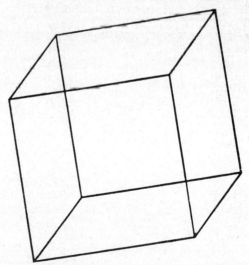

Fig. 326. Figure showing multiple visual interpretations. (From Prentice, W.: Scient. Am. **206**:1, 1962. Reprinted with permission. Copyright © 1962 by Scientific American, Inc. All rights reserved.)

*From Pitts, W., and McCulloch, W.: Bull. Math. Biophysics **9**:127, 1947.

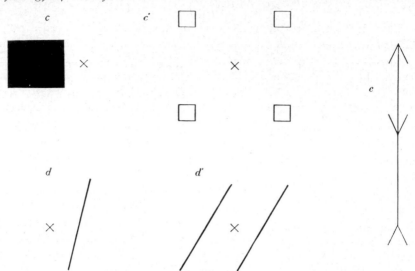

Fig. 327. Drawings **c, c', d,** and **d'** demonstrate cortical aftereffects, according to Kohler and Wallach. Prolonged viewing of cross in **c** causes apparent vertical displacement of left-hand squares when gaze is shifted to cross in **c'**. Similarly, prolonged inspection of cross in **d** causes apparent displacement of right-hand line in **d'** when gaze is shifted to cross between parallel lines. Drawing **e** is the Müller-Lyer illusion, in which the upper half of the line appears shorter than the lower. Brief inspection of this figure, repeated over a period of days, can reverse the original illusion. (From Prentice, W.: Scient. Am. **206**:1, 1962. Reprinted with permission. Copyright © 1962 by Scientific American, Inc. All rights reserved.)

ternation seems to be without rhyme or reason.

Similarly if one looks at the X in Fig. 327 situated between the four squares, the distances between the squares will appear equal, as they are in reality drawn. If, however, one gazes for a minute or two at the X in Fig. 327 alongside of the black rectangle and then transfers the gaze back to the first X, the distance between the upper and lower squares on the left will appear to be greater than that between the upper and lower squares on the right. These illusions according to Kohler as stated by Prentice are due to changes in the electrical activity of the cells of the cortex.

"[When the electrical message from localized retinal stimulation reaches the appropriate portion of the visual cortex, the cortical cells] generate direct currents through and around the tissue. This current must in turn rapidly induce a state of polarization at cell interfaces that increases the resistance of the tissue to the flow of the current. As a result the conductivity and polarizability of the tissue are changed, and new impulses from later stimulation behave differently.

"In visual perception such currents would be set up especially by the electrical imbalance resulting from the contrasting pattern of stimulation produced by a simple figure. The density of current would be greater in that section of the cerebral cortex associated with the retinal image of the figure's edge or contour. As resistance builds up, the flow of this current would be displaced to sections of the visual cortex in which the tissues offer less resistance —sections that correspond to the periphery rather than to the interior of the object. If the image of a new object now falls on the same place on the retina, the corresponding section of the visual cortex, having been already satiated, will no longer be able to react as it did initially. The object under inspection will accordingly appear distorted or displaced from its former location."*

---

*From Prentice, W.: Scient. Am. **206**:44, 1962. Reprinted with permission. Copyright © 1962 by Scientific American, Inc. All rights reserved.

It can easily be proved that the effects of widening the distance between the left-hand squares compared to the right-hand squares is not retinal. The X beside the black rectangle in Fig. 327 may be looked at with the right eye only, and then the left eye only is used to gaze at the X between the squares. The result is the same. Further experiments will have to be done to prove the validity of Kohler's hypothesis that changes in resistance to current flow in the cortex account for the observed phenomena.[78]

The chief value of attempts such as these to analyze the activities of the brain from which arise alterations in the state of our consciousness is to demonstrate their complexity. It is the interactions of the brain as a whole, or at least of large portions of it, from which visual percepts must emerge. The memory of past experiences is almost as important in the seeing of an object as the correct stimulation of a pattern of retinal cells and the message which they send to the visual cortex. It may be that some day we will be more able to grasp the meaning of things which now seem hopelessly complex. In the meantime the urge to discover what consciousness is must be satisfied first with a more complete understanding of the message which the visual cortex—the first station on the road to conscious vision—receives.

REFERENCES

1. Pirenne, M.: Vision and the eye, London, 1945, The Pilot Press.
2. Berk, M.: A critical evaluation of color perimetry, Arch. Ophth. **63**:966, 1960.
3. Posner, A., and Schlossman, A.: Development of changes in visual fields associated with glaucoma, Arch. Ophth. **39**:623, 1948.
4. Hoyt, W., and Tudor, R.: The course of parapapillary temporal retinal axons through the anterior optic nerve, Arch. Ophth. **69**:503, 1963.
5. Winkelman, J.: Central and peripheral fusion, Arch. Ophth. **50**:179, 1953.
6. Wolff, E., and Penman, G.: The position occupied by the peripheral retinal fibers in the nerve fiber layer and at the nerve head, International Congress of Ophthalmology, Tr. Ophth. Soc. U. Kingdom **70**:35, 1951.
7. Evans, J.: Present status of angioscotometry, Am. J. Ophth. **25**:861, 1942.
8. François, J.: Anatomical study of the retinal circulation, Brit. J. Ophth. **66**:37, 1952.
9. Harrington, D.: The pathogenesis of the glaucoma field, Am. J. Ophth. **47**:177, 1959.
10. Kestenbaum, A.: Clinical methods of neuro-ophthalmologic examination, New York, 1946, Grune & Stratton, Inc.
11. Clark, W. E. L.: Visual centers of the brain and their connexion, Physiol. Rev. **22**:205, 1942.
12. François, J., Neetens, A., and Collette, J.: Vascularization of optic pathway; optic tract and external geniculate body, Brit. J. Ophth. **40**:341, 1956.
13. Apter, J.: Projection of the retina on the superior colliculus of cats, J. Neurophysiol. **8**:123, 1945.
14. Bishop, P., Jeremy, D., and Lance, J.: The optic nerve. Properties of a central tract, J. Physiol. **121**:415, 1953.
15. Chang, H.: Fiber groups in primary optic pathway of cat, J. Neurophysiol. **19**:224, 1956.
16. Bishop, G., and Clarke, M.: Organization and distribution of fibers in the optic tract of the cat, J. Comp. Neurol. **103**:269, 1955.
17. Lennox, M.: Single fiber responses to electrical stimulation in cat's optic tract, J. Neurophysiol. **21**:62, 1958.
18. Lennox, M.: The on responses to colored flash in single optic tract fibers of cat; correlation with conduction velocity, J. Neurophysiol. **21**:70, 1958.
19. Polyak, S.: The vertebrate visual system, Chicago, 1957, University of Chicago Press.
20. Bishop, P., Kozak, W., and Vakkur, G.: Some quantitative aspects of the cat's eye; axis and plane of reference, visual field coordinates and optics, J. Physiol. **163**:466, 1962.
21. Bishop, P., Kozak, W., Levick, W., and Vakkur, G.: The determination of the

projection of the visual field on the lateral geniculate nucleus in the cat, J. Physiol. **163**:503, 1962.

22. Marshall, W. H., and Talbot, S. A.: The recovery cycle of the lateral geniculate of the nembulatized cat, Am. J. Physiol. **129**:417, 1940.

23. Hayhow, W.: The cytoarchitecture of the lateral geniculate body in the cat in relation to the distribution of crossed and uncrossed optic fibers, J. Comp. Neurol. **110**:1, 1958.

24. Bishop, P., Burke, W., and Davis, R.: Activation of single lateral geniculate cells by stimulation of either optic nerve, Science **130**:506, 1959.

25. Marriott, F., Morris, V., and Pirenne, M.: The absolute visual threshold recorded from the lateral geniculate body of the cat, J. Physiol. **146**:179, 1959.

26. Gunter, R.: The absolute threshold for vision in the cat, J. Physiol. **114**:8, 1951.

27. Hubel, D., and Wiesel, T.: Integrative action in the cat's lateral geniculate body, J. Physiol. **155**:385, 1961.

28. Hubel, D.: Single unit activity in lateral geniculate body and optic tract of unrestrained cats, J. Physiol. **150**:91, 1960.

29. Bishop, P., Jeremy, D., and McLeod, J.: Phenomena of repetitive firing in lateral geniculate of cat, J. Neurophysiol. **16**:437, 1953.

30. Hubel, D.: The visual cortex of the brain, Scient. Am. **209**:58, 1963.

31. Kronfeld, P.: The temporal half-moon, Tr. Am. Ophth. Soc. **30**:341, 1932.

32. Shenkin, H., and Leopold, I.: Localizing value of temporal crescent defects in visual fields, Arch. Neurol. & Psychiat. **54**:97, 1945.

33. Penfield, W., Evans, J. P., and MacMillan, J.: Visual pathways in man with particular reference to macular representation, Arch. Neurol. & Psychiat. **33**:816, 1935.

34. Polyak, S.: Projection of the retina upon the cerebral cortex based upon experiments with monkeys, Arch. Res. Nerv. & Ment. Dis. **13**:535, 1934.

35. Hyndman, O.: The central visual system, Arch. Neurol. & Psychiat. **42**:735, 1939.

36. Halstead, W., Walter, A., and Bucy, P.: Sparing and non-sparing of "macular" vision associated with occipital lobectomy in man, Arch. Ophth. **24**:948, 1940.

37. Bender, M., and Kanzer, M.: Dynamics of homonymous hemianopias and preservation of central vision, Brain **62**:404, 1939.

38. Verhoeff, F.: A new answer to the question of macular sparing, Arch. Ophth. **30**:421, 1943.

39. Filimonoff, I.: Über die Variabilität der Grosshirnrindenstruktur; Regio occipitalis bei den höheren und niederen Affen, J. Psychol. u. Neurol. **45**:69, 1933.

40. McCulloch, W.: The functional organization of the cerebral cortex, Physiol. Rev. **24**:390, 1944.

41. Von Bonin, G., Garol, H., and McCulloch, W.: The functional organization of the occipital lobe, Biol. Symposia **7**:165, 1942.

42. Holmes, G.: Ferrier Lecture; the organization of the visual cortex in man, Proc. Roy. Soc. London, s.B **132**:348, 1945.

43. Talbot, S. A., and Marshall, W. H.: Physiological studies in neural mechanisms of visual localization and discrimination, Am. J. Ophth. **24**:1255, 1941.

44. Adrian, E.: The physical background of perception, Oxford, 1947, Clarendon Press.

45. Thompson, J., Woolsey, C., and Talbot, S. A.: Visual areas 1 and 11 of the cerebral cortex of the rabbit, J. Neurophysiol. **13**:276, 1950.

46. Hubel, D.: Single unit activity in striate cortex of unrestrained cats, J. Physiol. **147**:226, 1959.

47. Kuffler, S.: Discharge patterns and functional organization of mammalian retina, J. Neurophysiol. **16**:37, 1953.

48. Kuffler, S., FitzHugh, R., and Barlow, H.: Maintained activity in the cat's retina in light and darkness, J. Gen. Physiol. **40**:683, 1957.

49. Wiesel, T., and Brown, K.: Analysis of receptive fields in the cat's retina, Ann. New York Acad. Sc. **74**:405, 1958.

50. Adrian, E.: Brain rhythms, Nature, London **153**:360, 1944.

51. Case, T. J.: The alpha waves in relations to structures involved in vision, Biol. Symposia **7**:107, 1942.

52. van Balen, A., and Henkes, H.: Recording of the occipital lobe response in man after light stimulation, Brit. J. Ophth. **44**:449, 1960.

53. Dawson, G.: Cerebral responses to nerve stimulation in man, Brit. M. Bull. **6**:326, 1950.

54. van Balen, A., and Henkes, H.: Attention

and amblyopia, Brit. J. Ophth. **46**:46, 1962.

55. Monnier, M.: Retinal, cortical and motor responses to photic stimulation in man, J. Neurophysiol. **15**:469, 1952.
56. Gerard, R., Marshall, W. H., and Saul, L.: Electrical activity in cat's brain, Arch. Neurol. & Psychiat. **36**:675, 1936.
57. Bartly, S.: Some factors in brightness discrimination, Psychol. Rev. **46**:337, 1939.
58. Jasper, H. H.: Electrical signs of cortical activity, Psychol. Bull. **34**:411, 1937.
59. Toman, J.: Flicker potentials and the alpha rhythm in man, J. Neurophysiol. **4**:51, 1941.
60. Bishop, G., and O'Leary, J.: Potential records from the optic cortex of the cat, J. Neurophysiol. **1**:391, 1938.
61. Hecht, S., and Verrijp, C.: Intermittent stimulation by light; the relation between intensity and critical fusion frequency for different retinal locations, J. Gen. Physiol. **17**:251, 1933.
62. Walker, A., Woolf, J., Halstead, W., and Case, T. J.: Mechanism of temporal fusion effect of photic stimulation on electrical activity of visual structures, J. Neurophysiol. **6**:213, 1943.
63. Watanabe, T.: Electroencephalogram induced by flicker illumination, Acta Soc. Ophth. Jap. **59**:873, 1955.
64. Dyer, D., and Bierman, O.: Cortical potential changes in amblyopia ex anopsia, Am. J. Ophth. **33**:1095, 1950.
65. Callahan, A., and Redlich, F.: Electroencephalography and ophthalmology, Am. J. Ophth. **29**:1522, 1946.
66. Stillerman, M., Gibbs, E., and Perlstein, M.: Electroencephalographic changes in strabismus, Am. J. Ophth. **35**:44, 1952.
67. White, P., and Schlaegel, T., Jr.: Some observations on the relationships of electroencephalographic changes to neuro-ocular disease, Am. J. Ophth. **41**:1070, 1956.
68. Penfield, W.: Ferrier Lecture; some observations on the cerebral cortex of man, Proc. Roy. Soc. London, s.B **134**:329, 1947.
69. Nakagawa, J.: Experimental study on visual sensation by electric stimulation of the optic nerve in man, Brit. J. Ophth. **46**:592, 1962.
70. Solnitsky, O.: Disturbances of language formulation and expression, GP **14**:83, 1956.
71. Lashley, K.: The problem of cerebral organization in vision, Biol. Symposia **7**:301, 1942.
72. Hebb, D.: Innate organization of visual activity; discrimination of brightness after removal of striate cortex in the rat, J. Comp. Psychol. **25**:427, 1938.
73. Adrian, E.: The basis of sensation, New York, 1928, W. W. Norton & Co.
74. Wiener, N.: Cybernetics, New York, 1949, John Wiley & Sons, Inc.
75. Hoagland, H.: Rhythmic behavior of the nervous system, Science **109**:157, 1949.
76. Pitts, W., and McCulloch, W.: How we know universals; the perception of auditory and visual forms, Bull. Math. Biophysics **9**:127, 1947.
77. Prentice, W.: After effects in perception, Scient. Am. **206**:44, 1962.
78. Kohler, W., Held, R., and O'Connell, D.: Proceedings of the American Philosophical Society. vol. 96, no. 3, June, 1952, pp. 290-330.

CHAPTER 17

ADAPTATION

The retina is unlike a photographic plate in that its properties are not fixed. The sensitivity of a photographic plate cannot be altered immediately to meet the requirements of different intensities of illumination, whereas the retina within a relatively short time can adapt itself to changes in the level of brightness. Another quality of the retina in which it differs from a photographic plate is the property whereby each region is affected by what is going on in surrounding areas so that the effects of stimulation are not strictly localized in extent. Therefore, the activity of the retina depends upon changes due to previous stimulation and upon activities taking place in other regions of the retina at the time of stimulation. These effects are called temporal and spatial induction, or adaptation.

TEMPORAL INDUCTION

The chief manifestation of temporal induction is the change in sensitivity of the retina by means of which it automatically accommodates itself to changes in light intensity. By means of this change, the eye comes into sensory equilibrium with a new set of conditions; it adjusts itself to a change in the level of brightness.

When a person comes from a dark room into brilliant sunlight, the eyes are temporarily blinded, but within a very short period of time they adapt themselves to the intense light and vision returns. This is not accomplished entirely by a change in the size of the pupil, which also occurs, for if the size of the pupil is kept constant by artificial means, adaptation still occurs although not as thoroughly. The contraction of the pupil is helpful. If the pupils are dilated, the intensity of the light may be so great that, even with retinal adaptation taking place, the eye is unable to withstand the brightness.

After the eyes have been adapted to bright illumination and the light is then reduced considerably, dimly illuminated objects cannot be seen at first. Gradually these objects become visible, without any change in the illumination taking place.

Photopic and scotopic vision

The process whereby the retina adapts itself to bright light is called light adaptation, and that by which it adapts itself to dim illumination is called dark adaptation. When the eye is light-adapted, vision is said to be photopic, and when the eye is dark-adapted, vision is called scotopic.

It is obvious that these terms refer to any change in illumination to which the eye is exposed. Starting with any level of illumination, an increase calls on the processes of light adaptation, whereas a decrease calls into play the processes of dark adaptation.

The terms *light adaptation* and *dark adaptation* are relative and indicate the change in sensitivity which the retina is making, rather than any static condition. For example, if the illumination in a room is that of moderate daylight and a person goes out into the sunshine, the retina undergoes light adaptation. If the person goes from this same room into a dark closet, the retina undergoes dark adaptation. The change which takes place is always that which best enables the retina to function under the new condition. In general parlance, however, during photopic vision the eye is adapted to intensities of illumination commonly met with in good daylight or good artificial illumination. Dark adaptation begins at about the level of twilight illumination. Light adaptation is a very rapid process and is generally complete within a minute or two, whereas dark adaptation is much slower and is not complete for nearly an hour.

The lowest level of illumination at which scotopic vision may be said to commence for practical purposes is around 3 log units micromicrolamberts. This corresponds roughly to night ground luminance when the sky is completely overcast without the moon. Scotopic vision is in effect with increasing illumination up to 5.5 log units micromicrolamberts. Above this, vision is mesopic to approximately 8.5 log units micromicrolamberts, and above this the eye may be said to be photopic or light-adapted. The mesopic range begins at approximately that of night ground luminance with a clear sky

and full moon and runs up to that of sky luminance on a cloudless day a quarter of an hour after sunset.

At all levels of illumination between complete light adaptation and complete dark adaptation, the retina makes an effort to come into equilibrium with any change in illumination. Below the level of a 0.1 meter-candle, the rods alone function. Above this level, the cones begin to function. It is possible that, as the illumination increases still further, complete bleaching of rhodopsin stops rod function entirely and that vision at high levels of illumination is due solely to cone function. At intermediate levels it seems likely that both cones and rods are active. The chemical nature of these processes has been discussed in a different section (pp. 589 to 593). The sensory phenomena connected with adaptation will now be considered.

Light adaptation

When the eye is dark-adapted, its sensitivity to light energy is at a maximum. It will respond to almost the smallest amount of light energy which can be released in nature, i.e., several photons (p. 553). When such a dark-adapted eye is exposed to light of moderate intensity, its sensitivity immediately falls. Light adaptation develops so quickly that it is difficult to follow the changes which take place. Within 20 seconds the sensitivity has fallen considerably, and during the next minute or two it may fall slightly further to reach a level which is then maintained.

Wright[1] and others found that exposure of an eye to light immediately diminishes its sensitivity. The fall in sensitivity plotted against the time of exposure of the eye to the adapting light is shown in Fig. 328. The sensitivity falls rapidly to a constant level in about 50 seconds. If

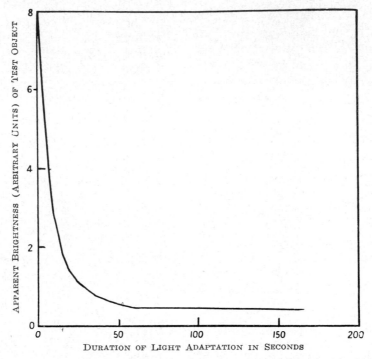

Fig. 328. Development of photochemical adaptation (beta adaptation) with increasing exposure to adapting radiation. (From Wright, W. D.: Proc. Roy. Soc. London s.B **115**:49, 1934.)

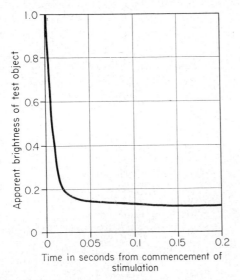

Fig. 329. Reduction of sensitivity of the fovea immediately the eye is stimulated; the so-called alpha adaptation. (After Wright.)

measurements are taken immediately after stimulating with the adapting light, it will be found that the reduction in sensitivity begins at once. In Fig. 329 is shown the very rapid reduction in sensitivity of the fovea following stimulation of the eye with light. This fall in sensitivity is practically over in 0.05 second; therefore, it was believed to be due to a different process than that which Wright measured, which took almost 1 minute for completion.

Alpha and beta adaptations. Because of this, the term *alpha adaptation* has been applied to the rapid phase of adaptation and the term *beta adaptation* to the later, slower one. Further differentiation of these two processes was made by showing that alpha adaptation applies to the whole retina, even though only a small part is stimulated, whereas beta adaptation is confined exactly to the region stimulated. Because of this, it was considered that the alpha process represents a nervous mechanism, whereas the beta process is photochemical in origin.

Both alpha and beta adaptations are reversible (Fig. 330). Following alpha adaptation, beta adaptation begins. The first effect of the adapting light (alpha adaptation), the immediate depression of its brightness, is complete in a fraction of

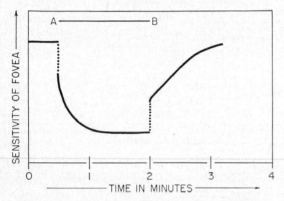

Fig. 330. Schematic representation of alpha and beta adaptation. **A-B,** Interval of exposure of the eye to light; *dotted lines,* decrease in alpha adaptation and increase in sensitivity which are virtually instantaneous. (After Wright.)

a second and is independent of whether the adapting light falls directly on the part of the retina used to view the test light or somewhere in its neighborhood. This effect was thought to be due to the P III component of the electroretinogram, as illustrated in Fig. 331, i.e., the a wave.

This suppression effect on cone vision is similar to that demonstrated for rod vision in eyes like the cat's. It has been shown that if successive flashes of light are presented, the b wave of the electroretinogram produced by the second flash is smaller than the first. This suppressive effect could be due to either photochemical or neural mechanisms, but the evidence at present is in favor of the latter.[2]

Since the first description of alpha adaptation by Schouten and Ornstein,[3] it has been found that the effect is not produced by retinal interaction, as they supposed, but by the scattering of light from the glare source.[4] Alpha adaptation like beta adaptation is, therefore, probably of photochemical origin, and the effect merely demonstrates how rapidly the breakdown of rhodopsin diminishes retinal sensitivity.

Beta adaptation, which is complete in

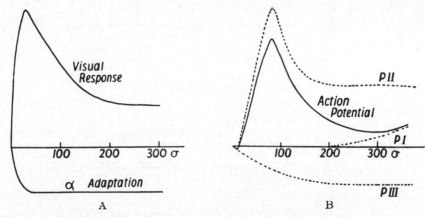

Fig. 331. A, Development of visual response and alpha adaptation. **B,** Development of retinal action potential and its subdivision into components. (From Wright, W. D., and Granit, R.: Brit. J. Ophth., supp. 9, pp. 7-80, 1938.)

about a minute, is, as previously stated, of photochemical origin and represents the reactions which lead to a steady state between the amount of photochemical substance being broken down and the amount being re-formed. This can be correlated further with the optic nerve discharge, which shows a fall in frequency of impulses as the light is kept at a steady level (Fig. 332).

Effect of light adaptation on photopic vision. What is the effect of light adaptation on photopic vision? The eyes adapt to changes in illumination so that new levels of brightness are soon lost to consciousness. When a person enters a brightly lighted room, the immediate effect is a conscious increase in the intensity of illumination, but this sensation rapidly disappears. If the person then enters a room still more brightly illuminated, once more the sensation of an increase in the level of brightness occurs and then disappears. The conscious level of illumination is inversely proportional to the intensity of this illumination. If B is the brightness of the light to which the eye is exposed and S the final sensitivity of the eye after it has become completely adapted to this level of illumination, then the following formula applies:

$$B \times S = k$$

It is found that as B increases, S decreases so that over a fairly wide range of illumination the product is the same.

The region in which this relationship holds, by experiment, is about the same as that throughout which the Weber law holds. This law, which has validity so far as visual phenomena are concerned only within a relatively narrow range of illumination, was formulated from the original work of Weber on the sensation of pressure. Weber found that the smallest difference between two weights which could be detected was a constant fraction of the weights used. The least detectable

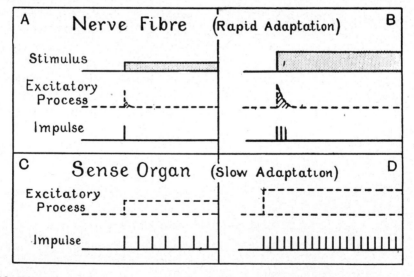

Fig. 332. Diagram to show effect of continued stimulus of a nerve fiber and a sense organ. In the nerve fiber the excitatory process declines almost instantaneously, and only one impulse is set up unless the stimulus is very strong. In the sense organ adaptation is much slower, and a succession of impulses is produced. (From Adrian, E.: The basis of sensation, New York, 1928, W. W. Norton & Co.)

difference in weights amounted to 1:30. That is, if the original weight was 30 Gm., the smallest increase which could be discriminated was 31 Gm. The law[5] is usually stated as follows:

$$\frac{\triangle W}{W} = k$$

In man, the validity of the law as it relates to vision with high illuminations has been questioned.[6] For moderate intensities of light under constant experimental conditions, Weber's law seems to apply to intensity discrimination, and it is found that the least perceptible difference of illumination bears a constant relation to the total illumination. At moderate intensities (Fig. 333) the relationship is constant and the curve relating intensity difference, $\frac{\triangle I}{I}$, to the log intensity of the light is a straight line. At high intensities, however, there is a marked upward trend of the curve, denoting a deviation from the law.

Smith[7] was able to eliminate the rise in the curve with high illumination by surrounding the test field with a large field of about the same brightness and by adapting the eye to this brightness. When this is done, no rise in the curve of $\frac{\triangle I}{I}$ occurs. Hecht has shown that the behavior of the curve for human discrimination of brightness is due to the duplex nature of the retina and that the break occurs at the junction of the illumination intensities where the rods cease functioning or at least lose their importance due to the preponderance of cone function. The fact that no such break occurs in the curve for intensity discrimination of the invertebrate eye is due to the presence of only one kind of receptor.

Dark adaptation

When one goes out of doors on a clear starlit night, after having been in a brightly lighted room, the sky looks black at first, and not even the brightest stars can be seen. Very soon, however, stars of the first magnitude appear. As the eyes become accustomed to the dim illumination, i.e., become dark-adapted, the fainter stars become visible. The sensitivity of the retina gradually increases until finally even stars of the sixth magnitude can be distinguished. Fainter stars than these can be seen if the observer is placed in a dark room having only a small opening through which to see a portion of the sky. In this way, the general illumination of the sky, caused by the whole galaxy of stars, is eliminated. This light, though faint, is sufficient to reduce the sensitivity of the retina somewhat, i.e., prevent the development of complete dark adaptation. Under ideal conditions stars of 8.5 magnitude can be seen after complete dark adaptation. The amount of illumination from a star of this magnitude is about 10^{-14} that produced by the sun, i.e., one quadrillionth of the illumination per unit area

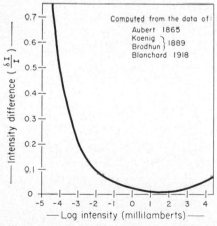

Fig. 333. Curve of the intensity discrimination of light. Blanchard's data are in their original units. Those of the other observers were converted to these units. (After Hecht.)

which we receive from sunlight.[8] When maximum dark adaptation has been attained, the sensitivity of the eye to light is one hundred thousand times greater than at the onset of dark adaptation. This is an enormous range of sensitivity. The increase in sensitivity of the eyes of some animals may even be greater. Using a method of behavioral discrimination in cats, it has been found that the threshold values for the perception of light in the dark-adapted cat is between 6.32×10^{-8} millilamberts and 12.21×10^{-8} millilamberts. Under the same conditions two human subjects had thresholds of 5.47×10^{-7} millilamberts. The absolute threshold of the cat is lower than that of human subjects by a factor of almost 6. This may be due in part to the effect of the tapetum in the cat's retina which considerably increases the illumination by reflection.

The process of dark adaptation is the transition through which a retina goes in passing from the light-adapted or photopic state to that of the dark-adapted or scotopic state. As the eye becomes dark-adapted, its sensitivity to light increases, and as it becomes light-adapted, it loses its sensitivity to light. This may appear strange, at first sight. We are accustomed to think of the eye functioning at its best under conditions of strong light. It will be shown (p. 775) that visual acuity increases with an increase in light intensity up to a maximum. From this we would be tempted to conclude that light increases the sensitivity of the retina, and yet the reverse is what actually occurs. Visual acuity is a measurement of the ability of the eye to resolve patterns. The maximum resolution of patterns occurs at the fovea. It might be assumed that the fovea acts differently from the rest of the retina and does not gain in sensitivity as the illumination becomes dim, i.e., that the fovea does not become dark-adapted along with

the rest of the retina. This is not true, however. The fovea, like the periphery of the retina, does dark-adapt, and does increase in sensitivity as the illumination decreases, and does lose sensitivity as the illumination increases. The explanation of why visual acuity increases with greater illumination is a problem which will be discussd more fully later on (p. 780). It will suffice here to say that the reasons are not at present entirely understood, but that it is certainly not due to an increase in retinal sensitivity to light energy. The fovea gains in resolving power with an increase in illumination in spite of the fact that the cones become less sensitive to light. On the other hand, the fovea and the periphery of the retina differ markedly in their ability to dark-adapt and the manner in which this takes place.

In testing dark adaptation in human beings we obtain data in terms of sensation. It is difficult to measure changes in sensation, e.g., to determine when one light is exactly twice or three times as bright as another. It is easier to determine the threshold of the minimum amount of light which can just be detected, and this is the method generally employed. The eye is first exposed to a standard bright light in order to bring the retina into the full light-adapted or photopic state. The light is then turned off, and a very small faint test light is then turned on for a brief exposure on a fixed and predetermined region of the retina. The region selected is usually about 20 degrees off the fovea, for reasons which will appear later.

The intensity of this first test flash is purposely made so low that it cannot be detected, but the intensity is increased on each successive exposure until the subject becomes aware of it. This illumination, usually expressed in micromillilamberts, is the threshold of sensitivity of that region of the retina at that moment. As the eye is kept in the dark between the test flashes, the sensitivity of the retina increases, and accordingly the threshold becomes lower. If one records the time in the dark when the successive test flashes are seen, and plots this on a chart against the intensities of the test flashes, a curve is produced which shows the gradual increase in sensitivity of the retina due to dark adaptation. In Fig. 334 is shown such a record of the course of dark adaptation in 110 normal individuals, the shaded area representing the mean of dark adaptation in these subjects.

The process of dark-adapting takes a considerable time. It takes at least 30 minutes before the retina approaches its greatest sensitivity; in fact, the maximum is only achieved after one hour's stay in the dark. It will be seen from Fig. 334 that time is recorded on the abscissa in linear units, whereas the intensity of the test light is expressed in log units on the ordinates. This is done in order to reduce the spread of the data so that it can be printed on a page, for the range in sensitivity is so great that were linear units used for the changes in light intensity they would make a chart several yards tall.

Variables influencing dark adaptation. In order to obtain comparable data on different subjects or on the same subject examined on different occasions, standard conditions of examination must be adhered to. The various instruments used in the laboratories and those now on sale for clinical use are made to control a number of variables, each of which

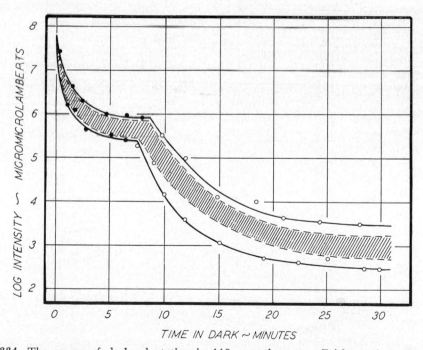

Fig. 334. The course of dark adaptation in 110 normal persons. Fairly marked differences in the final state of dark adaptation are seen. *Upper and lower curves,* the extremes of dark adaptation in the subjects. *Shaded area,* the mean of dark adaptation in the subjects. (After Hecht and Mandelbaum.)

influences the curve of dark adaptation. The following variables must be controlled: (1) the region of the retina from which the measurements of change in retinal sensitivity are recorded, (2) the intensity, duration, and wavelength of the light used to preadapt the eye prior to making the measurements, i.e., one must secure a completely light-adapted condition of the whole retina prior to making the measurements of dark adaptation, and (3) the duration of the test light and its wavelength.

Region of the retina from which the measurements are made. It can be seen in Fig. 334 that the curve of dark adaptation in the normal subject is composed of two distinct parts. After an initial fall in the intensity of the test flash, the curve flattens out for the first 5 to 7 minutes, and this is followed by a further fall which is continued for over 30 minutes. It has been shown that this division of the curve into two segments is due to the different behavior of the cones and rods in the retina. Dark adaptation of the cones begins very quickly and is completed in approximately 7 minutes, whereas dark adaptation of the rods is much slower in onset and continues for a much longer time. Whereas cones do show a definite increase in sensitivity in the absence of light, this increase is not nearly so marked as the increase in sensitivity of the rods, which is at least a thousand times greater than that of the cones. The type of curve

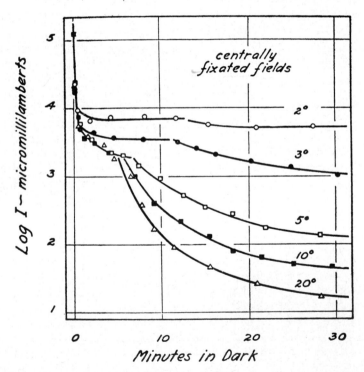

Fig. 335. Threshold during dark adaptation for centrally fixated areas of different size. The primary and secondary portions of the dark adaptation curves have been separated by a slight gap since it is uncertain whether the transition between them is sharp or rounded; most likely it is rounded. (From Hecht, S., Haig, C., and Wald, G.: J. Gen. Physiol. **19:**321, 1935.)

of dark adaptation obtained will, therefore, depend upon the varying proportion of cones and rods in the region of the retina selected for testing.

The thresholds for centrally fixated areas of different size during dark adaptation are shown in Fig. 335. It will be noted that the curve for a centrally fixated area of 2 degrees is quite different from that involving a 20-degree field. In the 20-degree field there are two obvious segments of the curve, representing the functions of both cones and rods. The first part of the curve is steep and is completed in about 6 minutes. It resembles the 2-degree curve. Following this, a second segment, much less steep, begins and is not completed for over 30 minutes. This second segment does not appear in the 2-degree curve. All the curves were made with the subject using his fovea as the area tested, and since there are only

cones in the fovea, the dark adaptation of cones only was being measured in the test flash covering 2 degrees. In the 20-degree curve, on the other hand, the region around the fovea as well as the fovea was being tested, and this region contained rods as well as cones.

It might be argued that the difference in these two curves was due to the different sizes of the areas tested and not to the fact that one contained cones only while the other contained both rods and cones. This is made unlikely from the fact that the curves representing dark adaptation for centrally fixated areas that range between 2 and 20 degrees show gradual transition from one to the other, as would be expected from the change in proportion of the rod-cone population in these regions. At about the 3-degree area enough rods are present to become effective in altering the curve as their

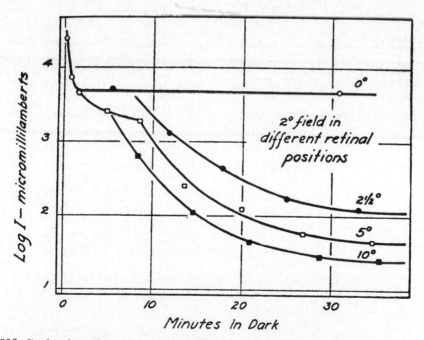

Fig. 336. Dark adaptation as measured with a 2-degree field placed at different distances from the center. Compare this with Fig. 335 for centrally fixated fields of different sizes. (From Hecht, S., Haig, C., and Wald, G.: J. Gen. Physiol. **19:**321, 1935.)

threshold falls below that of the cones. In the 5-degree area the number of rods is much greater; hence their thresholds appear sooner and the sensitivity of the region increases markedly.

Positive proof that the difference in the response between the 2-degree and 20-degree curves is actually due to the difference in the type of photoreceptor present and not to the difference in the size of the area tested is obtained by measuring the dark adaptation of a 2-degree area of the retina in the same subject using different regions of the retina. In Fig. 336 are shown the curves of dark adaptation measured in the same subject using a 2-degree test field placed at different distances from the fovea as well as on the fovea. The 2-degree field using the fovea yields the same type of curve as the 2-degree field shown in the previous illustration (Fig. 335). The 2-degree field, taken 2.5 degrees from the fovea, now corresponds to the 5-degree field in Fig. 335, and the 2-degree field, taken 5 degrees from the fovea, corresponds to the 19-degree field in Fig. 335. Hence, it can be stated with certainty that the dark adaptation curve varies in its characteristics with the region of the retina tested. Since the fundamental difference between different regions of the retina is the change in type of photoreceptor present, it is likely that the different response is due to this. Additional proof of this is shown by the different responses obtained using test lights of different wavelengths, as will be shown later (p. 719).

Character of the preadapting light. The intensity, duration, and wavelength of the preadapting light influence the course of dark adaptation. The effect of increasing both the intensity and duration of the preadapting light is shown in Fig. 337. Either of these variables produces the same effect over a wide range, whether the increase in the degree of light adaptation is produced by increasing the intensity or prolonging the period of exposure to the preadapting light.

The spectral quality of the preadapting light is also a factor in changing the curve of dark adaptation. The sensitivity of the retina is diminished not only by the amount of light to which it is exposed but also to a different degree by different wave lengths of light. This is of great practical as well as of theoretical importance. Unfortunately, from the theoretical point of view the subject is still not entirely clear. It has been shown experimentally that dark adaptation is much faster following a preadaptation to red light than to white light. In order to produce the same degree of dark adaptation in the same time, the pre-exposure to red light must be thirty times as bright as to

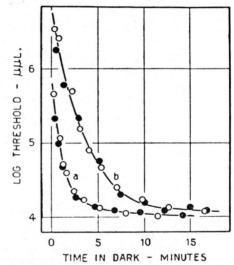

Fig. 337. Dark adaptation measurements showing the effect of increasing both the intensity and duration of the preadapting illumination. Light adaptation: **a,** *filled circles,* 4 minutes × 20 millilamberts; *open circles,* 0.2 minute × 447 milliliters. **b,** *filled circles,* 4 minutes × 110 milliliters; *open circles,* 1 minute × 447 milliliters. (From Haig, C.: J. Gen. Physiol. **24:**735, 1941.)

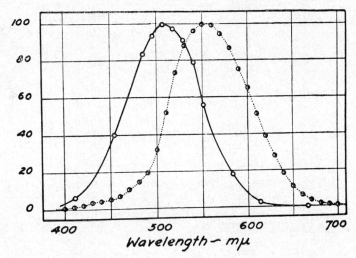

Fig. 338. Luminosity curves for scotopic (rod) vision and photopic (cone) vision. The scotopic data are the measurements of Hecht and Williams. The photopic data are those of Gibson and Tyndall. Since the maxima are arbitrarily set at 100, these curves give no information about the relative sensitivity of rods and cones for red or for any other part of the spectrum. (From Hecht, S., and Hsia, Y.: J. Optic. Soc. America 35:261, 1945.)

white light.[9] When the use of red light to achieve dark adaptation is advised, it is usually explained that the rods are practically insensitive to red light by comparison with the cones which mediate photopic vision, and as evidence of this, reference is generally made to photopic and scotopic luminosity curves, as shown in Fig. 338. Although this conclusion might at first glance seem reasonable, Hecht has pointed out that this is incorrect since the luminosities of the two systems are not given because the maximum of each curve has been arbitrarily put at 100. It is not true that the rods are practically insensitive to red light as compared with the cones. This becomes clear from a comparison of two luminosity curves on a real energy basis as is shown in Fig. 339. The rods and cones have practically identical sensibilities for red light. It has been shown that from the fovea to the extreme periphery the sensitivity of the retina to red light remains practically constant.[10]

From the practical point of view it has been customary to use red goggles on individuals who wish to keep their eyes in the dark-adapted state and yet go about in full daylight or semidaylight. During the last war all personnel engaged in night flying, in which dark adaptation was of great importance, wore red goggles whenever they were exposed to lights bright enough to interfere with their dark adaptation. Similarly, radiologists customarily wear red goggles when they go out of the fluoroscopic room into daylight in order to preserve their state of dark adaptation. A plausible explanation of the effect of red goggles is that their use prevents the short waves of the spectrum from reaching the rods, and only the rods are affected by the blue end of the spectrum under conditions of dim illumination. In order that the sensitivity of the rod mechanism be preserved, the blue end of the spectrum must be eliminated.

A further practical application of this principle is the use of blue lights as markers for streets, entrances, exits, etc., during

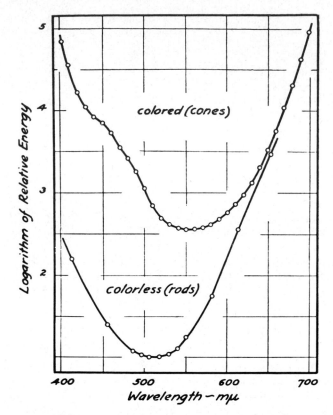

Fig. 339. Spectrum sensibility curves for rod and cone vision on a real energy basis. The data for the separate curves are from the same sources as given in Fig. 338. The position of the two curves on the ordinates corresponds to the fact that after complete dark adaptation, any region of the retina outside the fovea sees red light of 650 mμ as colorless at the threshold, and as colored only above the threshold. The precise energy increment above the threshold for the appearance of color (cone function) varies for different parts of the retina; in the parafovea it lies between 0.1 and 1.0 log unit. (From Hecht, S., and Hsia, Y.: J. Optic. Soc. America **35**:261, 1945.)

blackouts. These can be seen most easily because the rods in the dark-adapted retina are sensitive to blue. Since they are small lights and low in intensity, they do not destroy the scotopic state of the rods. It must be pointed out, however, that by the same token they could be detected most easily by enemy pilots, who are naturally also dark-adapted.

We have seen that the spectral sensitivity of the rods differs from that of the cones (p. 716). Only the rods are sensitive to light of very short wavelength, i.e., the blue end of the spectrum. Both rods and cones are relatively insensitive to light of long wavelength, i.e., the red end of the spectrum. Therefore, measurements of dark adaptation should vary with the character of the light used for the test flash as well as for the preadapting light.

Duration of the test flash and its wavelength. The duration of the test flash is a variable which must be controlled. With short exposures the retina obeys Ricco's law which states that the duration of the exposure times the intensity remains constant. The wavelength of the test flash is of importance, particularly in respect to the character of the curve of adaptation of the cones. Since only the rods are sensitive to light of short wavelengths and both rods and cones are relatively insensitive to light of long wavelengths, measurements of dark adaptation should vary with the character of the light used to test the thresholds, and this variation should be found to depend on the region of the retina tested, i.e., whether cones or rods predominate. These variations are shown in Fig. 340. For most colors there are two distinct parts of the curve of dark adaptation. The first part corresponds to cone adaptation and is nearly the same for all colors. With light of moderate intensity the cones do not adapt at all to blue light, but if the intensity of the preadapting light is made high enough,

some cone adaptation does occur.[11]

We have seen that the retina has a built-in feedback mechanism whereby every change in light intensity produces an alteration in the sensitivity of the cones and the rods to light. Lowering the light intensity increases the retinal sensitivity, and raising the light intensity lowers retinal sensitivity. This mechanism is effective at all illuminations and is constantly active. The response of the pupil to changes in light intensity is likewise constantly active, but the effect is in the opposite direction to that of the changes in retinal sensitivity. As the illumination diminishes, the pupil widens, letting in more light; the retina increases its sensitivity as the illumination is diminished, and as the pupil dilates and lets in more light, the retinal sensitivity falls. These two mechanisms, retinal adaptation and pupil response, act together to maintain

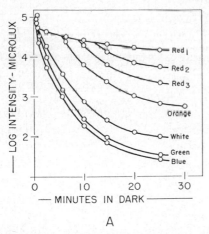

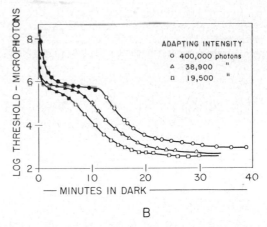

A   B

Fig. 340. A, Dark adaptation of an area 1 degree in diameter situated 5 degrees above the fovea (after Kohlrausch). Red_1 is the only color which limits the measurements of the cones. The other two reds let more orange light through and show up rod adaptation. With blue light, cone adaptation is barely evident. **B,** Dark adaptation of a 5-degree field situated 30 degrees nasally (after Hecht and Haig). Though measured with extreme violet light, the course of adaptation shows two distinct sections due to the high light adaptation preceding the measurements. Note that the secondary rod adaptation appears later, the higher the intensity of preadaptation. The filled-in symbols indicate that a violet color is apparent at the threshold during the measurements. Open symbols indicate that no color can be recognized at the threshold. (After Hecht.)

as nearly as possible a constant status quo of the retina.

We have seen that the central region of the retina, the fovea, does undergo dark adaptation but to a much lesser degree than the surrounding retina. By comparison the enormous increase in retinal sensitivity of the peripheral retina at the end of dark adaptation makes foveal vision seem very poor. It has been said that under conditions of dark adaptation the fovea becomes another physiologic blind spot. I have called attention to this fact by citing the well-known experience that if one looks at a group of very faint stars after the eyes have become thoroughly dark-adapted fainter stars can be seen than before complete dark adaptation occurs. If a group of stars is singled out, such as the Pleiades, four or five stars can be distinguished after complete dark adaptation has had time to occur when one gazes directly at the group, i.e., using foveal fixation. If now the gaze is directed slightly to one side so that the images of the stars falls just off the fovea, at least six or seven of the group can be visualized. With a little practice it is easy to demonstrate the comparative blindness of the fovea under these conditions by shifting the gaze back and forth as described. The region of the retina which seems to be the most sensitive under these conditions lies about 7 degrees from the fovea on the nasal side. One should theoretically therefore, direct the gaze about 7 degrees to the left of the group of stars when fixating with the right eye alone.

However, the exact part of the retina employed for fixation under such conditions is a subject of some controversy. Some experimenters conclude that no preferred area exists, the location chosen by any individual depending on many variables. Others have found a consistent region chosen. Jayle and Aubert[12] find that pilots during dark adaptation fixate 20 degrees below the object of regard. Pickard[13] found no constancy in the area chosen, but generally it was about 10 degrees from the fovea and usually below it. Recently von Noorden[14] finds that in all instances the area chosen is supramacular, the distance from the fovea varying somewhat but always decreasing with increasing light intensity of the fixation target.

Physiologic mechanism concerned in dark adaptation. What brings about this remarkable change in retinal sensitivity with changes in light intensity? The evidence seems overwhelming that photochemical mechanisms are chiefly concerned, but there is increasing evidence that neurophysiologic mechanisms also play a part. It seems certain that all of the mechanisms concerned reside in the retina. The extra retinal neural mechanisms concerned with vision, the lateral geniculate ganglia and the occipital cortex, are not involved.

The photochemistry of vision has been discussed in Chapter 13. It was pointed out that the curve of the absorption spectrum of rhodopsin exactly fits the curve of the visibility of the completely dark-adapted eye, provided that certain justifiable corrections are made. Since rhodopsin is concentrated in the rods and is not found in the cones, it seems certain that the bleaching of rhodopsin accounts for the loss of sensitivity of the rods, and its re-formation restores this sensitivity. It takes about an hour for a bleached solution of rhodopsin to return to its original state, and this corresponds well with the time required for a human subject to regain maximal rod sensitivity after a preexposure to intense light. Many of the phenomena of vision of the scotopic eye can be related to the photochemistry of rhodopsin and are dealt with in this book in the sections on the optic nerve response, the electroretinogram, and the flicker fusion frequency. The fact that vitamin A is concerned in the re-formation of rhodopsin and that lack of vitamin A leads to a breakdown in this resynthesis and also to night blindness in human beings and experimental animals all prove beyond question that at least one of the important steps in rod dark adaptation is the re-formation of rhodopsin in the dark. On the other hand there have been many objections to the photochemical theory of dark adaptation. These are largely centered around the fact that there is no linear relationship between the degree of dark adaptation and the amount of rhodopsin present in the retina. For example, Rushton and Cohen (1954) have shown that retinal sensitivity is lowered from ten to sixty times its full capability by a loss of only 2% of the rhodopsin by bleaching, and this loss is not the same if either the area of the retina or the duration of the light exposure is changed separately. From this it can be concluded that the concentration of unbleached rhodopsin present is not the sole factor which determines retinal sensitivity in the scotopic state. It would appear that it is the first small fraction of rhodopsin destroyed which plays the most important part in dark adaptation and the last small fraction which is re-formed which counts in light adaptation. This has led to various hypotheses which consider the rods to be divided into small compartments, isolated from each other. Light falling on these compartments provokes luminous excitation by one photon affecting one molecule of rhodopsin. The first few molecules bleached set off the process. The bleaching of other molecules by further photons occurs, but this does not enter into the excitatory effect.

It would seem probable that neural mechanisms, both excitatory and inhibitory, play some role in retinal sensitivity along with photochemical changes. Much work needs to be done before complete understanding of this phenomenon will be reached.

It goes without saying that the problems of cone adaptation must be similar to those of rod adaptation. We are even further away from a complete analysis of the problem of cone adaptation since as yet no one has identified the cone pigment in the human retina. It is assumed that it is comparable to iodopsin, isolated from the cone retina of the chicken, and that changes in cone sensitivity are due primarily to the bleaching and re-formation of some pigment closely related chemically to iodopsin.

Using the method of retinal densitometry with which he has so beautifully demonstrated the rates of bleaching and regeneration of visual pigments in the living human subject (p. 599), Rushton[15] has found that no matter how much rhodopsin is bleached by the pre-exposure light the beginning of rod adaptation always occurs at the moment when 92% of the rhodopsin has been resynthesized. The establishment of the beginning of rod adaptation from an area of the retina containing a population of cones as well as of rods has always been difficult and somewhat uncertain, but by a unique method this transition point (seen in the usual curve of dark adaptation as a kink in the curve) was established with great accuracy (Fig. 334). In Fig. 341 are shown three runs in the same subject in which the pre-exposure light bleached all of the rhodopsin, 35% of it, and 25% of it. In all cases the rods first responded when exactly 92% of the rhodopsin had been re-formed. The threshold for rods is just below the dark-adapted cone threshold and 1.9 log units above absolute

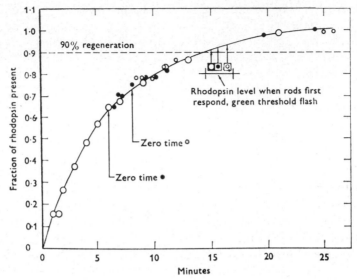

Fig. 341. Regeneration of rhodopsin in the dark. The curve is an exponential of time constant 6 mm. All black circles are displaced to the right so that zero lies at the point indicated. Small white circles are similarly dispaced, but further. For each run the cone-rod transition of the dark adaptation curve lay where shown by the arrow. Small white circle, 25%; black circle, 35%; large white circle, total bleach. (From Rushton, W.: J. Physiol. **156:**166, 1961.)

rod threshold at the time when 92% of the rhodopsin in the rods has regenerated. Rushton suggests that this indicates there is a fixed relation between threshold and the fraction of opsin still uncombined. The cones are the first to regain their sensitivity in the dark and within a very few minutes reach their peak. The curve of rod recovery is, so to speak, covered by the cone curve, and there is no way we can tell from the curve whether or not the rods are regaining their sensitivity during these first few minutes. We can only measure the rod mechanism below the cone threshold. As Fuertes and co-workers aptly state, "We are left wondering what course the rod branch may take after it disappears behind the cone branch."* These authors had the opportunity to examine the increment thresholds in a rod

monochromat whose retinal function was limited entirely to that of rods. On the basis of this and the work of Aguilar and Stiles[17] they conclude that above a certain level of illumination the rods do not function, and that the abolition of rod function by a bright background is not due to inhibition of rods by cones. It appears that the signal generated by each rod in response to light increases with illumination up to a fixed limit at which the rod becomes saturated. This is a property of the light transducer mechanism of the rod itself and will probably be explainable in the future in terms of its ultramicroscopic structure.

Dark adaptation under abnormal and pathologic states. Keeping in mind the fact that temporal adaptation of the retina concerns the sensitivity of the retina to changes in light intensity, we would expect to find deficiencies in this function under certain abnormal conditions and

*From Fuertes, M., Gunkel, R., and Rushton, W.: J. Physiol. **156:**179, 1961.

disease states. This is, indeed, true. However, these changes are not as conspicuous or as easily determined as are changes in central visual acuity, which is a function of the fovea (and therefore of cones only). Slight deficiencies of dark adaptation often go unnoticed by a patient and are only discovered by testing with instruments not always available in ordinary practice. Since dark adaptation is largely a function of the rod-rhodopsin mechanism, it is probably always affected to some degree in any abnormal state which affects the periphery of the retina. The conditions in which abnormal dark adaptation have been chiefly investigated are considered in the discussion that follows.

Hypoxia. Oxygen deprivation results in a disturbance of many different ocular functions. The peripheral visual fields contract after long exposures to oxygen pressures equivalent to 10,000 feet above sea level,[18] and the central field shows changes during marked oxygen deprivation.[19] The effects on the ocular muscles have been considered on p. 494. The course of dark adaptation is also changed.[20] (Figs. 342 to 344.) After inhalation of 10 vol.% oxygen, about half the normal amount, the thresholds of both the rods and cones are raised. This is due to the effect of anoxia on the neural elements of both the retina and the central nervous system and not to changes in the photochemical reactions in the retina. The principal effect seems to be on conduction in the neural elements of the retina, which are adversely affected by lack of oxygen.

Vitamin A deficiency. It has been known for many years that night blindness may be associated with poor nutritional states of the body. The underlying cause of the night blindness was eventually shown to be a lack of vitamin A in the diet. This was subsequently proved experimentally in rats kept on a diet adequate in all respects other than vitamin A. While other factors are apparently also concerned, it is generally agreed that vitamin A deficiency, if extreme and persistent over a long period of time, results in some degree of night blindness in both experimental animals and man. Up to 45 years of age men are more susceptible

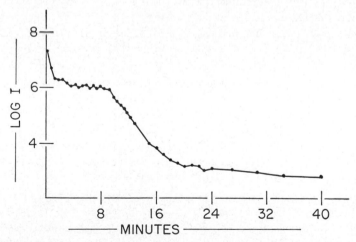

Fig. 342. Normal dark adaptation curve of observer's right eye. The preadapting intensity was 4900 millilamberts and the time exposure was 3 minutes. The unit of threshold intensity is the micromicrolambert and is the same for all experiments. The test flash was exposed for one fifth second.

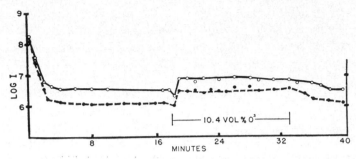

Fig. 343. Dark adaptation curves of subject's right eye showing the final cone threshold, with the use of a red filter ($\lambda = 680$ mμ). The preadapting intensity was 4900 millilamberts. *Solid circles,* normal curve and effect of hypoxemia. *Open circles,* effect of vitamin A deficiency and hypoxemia.

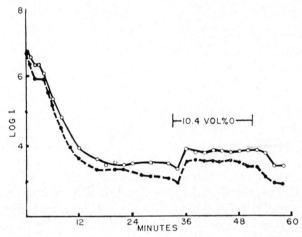

Fig. 344. Dark adaptation curves with preadapting intensity of 510 millilamberts, showing the effect of hypoxemia on the final rod threshold. *Solid circles,* normal curve and effect of hypoxemia. *Open circles,* effect of vitamin A deficiency and hypoxemia.

than women, but this difference disappears in older age groups. The reason is unknown. Some people are much more susceptible than others, and not all human subjects deprived of vitamin A show changes in dark adaptation, even though the deprivation is carried to the point at which characteristic changes in the skin appear.[21, 22] Generally after two weeks' deprivation of vitamin A from the diet most subjects show dark adaptation thresholds above any values normally found, and the thresholds continue to rise as long as the diet is adhered to until the subject is quite night blind. The return to a normal diet, with or without supplementary vitamin A, usually results in an immediate drop in the threshold until normal values are again reached. It has been reported, however, that this return may be alarmingly slow and may even never be complete, so that such experiments are not without some risk.[20] There is no evidence that the threshold of dark adaptation can be lowered in normal individuals by additional vitamin A administered either by mouth or parenterally. Even huge doses of vitamin A fail to lower the thresholds in normal individuals. Patients frequently ask whether taking vitamin A or eating foods rich in vitamins will improve their vision. Neither their central visual acuity or their dark adaptation thresholds can be improved by this means. It must not be forgotten, however, that many people who think they are on an adequate healthy diet in reality may not be getting adequate amounts of vitamins, especially vitamin A. The office worker who gulps a cup of black coffee and some cereal with skim milk and sugar for breakfast and partakes of a 5-minute drugstore lunch and dinner served mostly out of cans may be in a chronic state of vitamin A deficiency. The addition of vitamin A in pill form to such a diet would obviously be wise.

The loss of dark adaptation when vitamin A is withheld from the diet is readily understood from our knowledge of the chemistry of the re-formation of rhodopsin. This has been described in detail on pp. 580 to 581. Even after most of the vitamin A has disappeared from the retina, the liver may be a source of supply of rhodopsin for a long time, as large quantities of vitamin A are stored in the liver. Differences in the amounts stored in the liver of different individuals may explain the marked differences in susceptibility of different subjects to dietary experiments. It is also possible that vitamin B_2 and vitamin E are in some way linked with

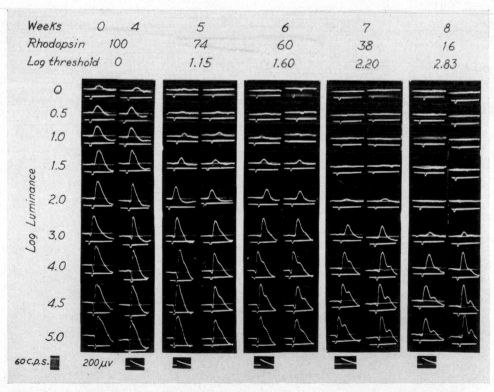

Fig. 345. Electroretinograms from vitamin A–starved rat. Observations were made over a period of eight weeks. (From Dowling, J.: Am. J. Ophth. **50:**875, 1960.)

night blindness due to vitamin A deficiency, but the exact role they play is still debated. Dowling[23] has recently correlated the effects of vitamin A starvation with the loss of dark adaptation and the reduction of the rhodopsin concentration in the retina. He made measurements of dark adaptation, the vitamin A level of the liver and blood, and the concentration of rhodopsin in the retinas of normal and vitamin A-starved rats. The thresholds of dark adaptation were determined by the lowest luminance needed to evoke a perceptible electroretinogram (p. 725; Fig. 345). The histology of the retinas was also studied at various periods to correlate the changes produced with the rhodopsin levels. No changes appear during the first three to four weeks except a steady fall in the vitamin A content of the livers. By the fifth week the livers are depleted, and the blood vitamin A level

falls suddenly. Simultaneously the rhodopsin content of the retina begins to fall, and with this there first appear changes in the dark adaptation thresholds. The rhodopsin content continues to fall throughout the experiment. At the seventh week the animals begin to show general bodily signs of vitamin A deficiency, which continues to their death at about eight to nine weeks.

When approximately 26% of the rhodopsin has disappeared from the retinas, the threshold of the electroretinogram is raised 1.15 log units or about 14 times. By the time 84% has disappeared the threshold has been raised to 2.83 log units or about 680 times. The course of rhodopsin loss and increase in log thresholds is shown graphically in Fig. 346. In addition to the increase in threshold values, the form of the electroretinogram changes also. The a wave is more severely sup-

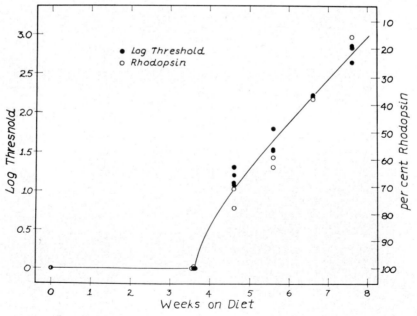

Fig. 346. Loss of rhodopsin correlated with rise in dark adaptation threshold in vitamin A–starved rats. (From Dowling, J.: Am. J. Ophth. **50**:875, 1960.)

pressed than the b wave and disappears at a time when the b wave is still of considerable size. The b wave separates into two positive peaks, and the secondary peak eventually separates off as a second wave. Dowling believes this second wave appearance is characteristic of vitamin A deficiency and is not seen in the rat under other circumstances. Noell (in discussion of Dowling's paper) has seen this double b wave in normal eyes, however, and believes it may be due to the effect of Nembutal when it is used as the anesthetic. This needs further confirmation.

During light adaptation, the concentration of rhodopsin falls in the retina, as we have already seen, and Dowling compared the changes in the electroretinogram thresholds with this fall in rhodopsin. As in vitamin A deprivation, the electroretinogram thresholds are elevated by light adaptation, but the changes in the form of the electroretinograms which Dowling believes are pathognomonic of

vitamin A deficiency are not seen. Both a and b waves are depressed in the early stages of light adaptation, and the b wave remains a single peak.

Of considerable theoretical interest is the fact that the course of dark adaptation follows the concentration of rhodopsin in the retina in a linear fashion; the logarithm of the visual threshold rises linearly as the concentration of visual pigment falls. This is shown in Fig. 347. We have already pointed out that other authors have not found this relationship and have drawn the conclusion that the course of dark adaptation cannot be accounted for on photochemical changes alone.

In addition to dietary deficiencies, in which usually large groups or populations are affected, individuals suffering from a variety of diseases may at some time in the disease suffer from night blindness on the basis of vitamin A deficiency. Most of these diseases concern the liver, and

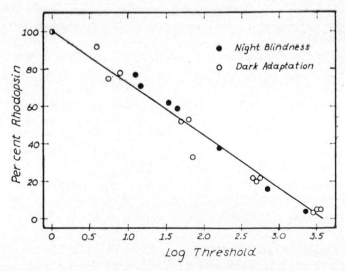

Fig. 347. Relation between rhodopsin content of the retina and the visual threshold in animals night-blind due to vitamin A deficiency and in normal animals dark-adapting after exposure to bright light. In both instances the same relationship is observed: the log threshold rises linearly with fall in rhodopsin concentration. (From Dowling, J.: Am. J. Ophth. 50:875, 1960.)

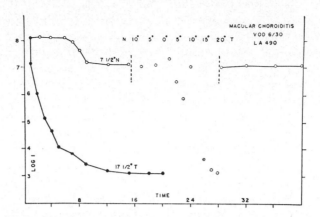

Fig. 348. Light adaptation at 490 millilamberts. At this intensity of light adaptation, cone adaptation is not marked. *Open circles,* curve showing the course of dark adaptation of a patient with macular choroiditis, measured 7½ degrees to the nasal side of the fovea. *Individual open circles* (inserted in center), threshold readings at various points taken on the nasal and temporal sides of the fovea. *Closed circles,* curve showing the course of dark adaptation taken with the test flash falling 17½ degrees to the temporal side of the fovea.

since this is the body's largest storehouse of vitamin A it is understandable that night blindness may follow liver destruction from any type of pathologic condition.

Diseases of the eye. It is to be expected that dark adaptation would be affected adversely in many eye diseases, in particular those conditions in which the rod-rhodopsin mechanism is the chief site of the disease. Dark adaptation thresholds, but not the course of dark adaptation, naturally would be raised in all conditions in which the amount of illumination reaching the retina was diminished. The transparency of the ocular media determines the amount of light energy reaching the retina so that in all conditions in which the transparency is reduced the thresholds are raised. It makes no difference whether the loss of transparency is due to corneal, lenticular, or vitreous opacification.

On the same principle, uncorrected refractive errors reduce the concentration of light energy at the retina, since the focus of light falls either in front of or behind the retina in the ametropic eye. In addition to this it has been found that many myopic persons have poor dark adaptation even when correcting glasses are worn. The myopia may be only slight, and the loss of dark adaptation does not depend on the presence of myopic degeneration of the retina. No satisfactory explanation for this has been found.

Defects in the visual field will obviously produce areas of depressed dark adaptation that correspond to the field damage. Tests taken from the blind halves of the retina in patients with hemianopic field defects fail to elicit any threshold until the intensity of the test flash is raised sufficiently to allow spread of the stimulus into the seeing halves of the fields. Patients with glaucoma may show deficient dark adaptation when the test flash is confined to areas of the retina which correspond to depressed areas of the visual field, such as Bjerrum scotomas. Dark adaptation in patients with glaucoma is normal as long as the fields are normal.

Whenever the areas of the retinas selected for tests of dark adaptation are diseased, it is reasonable to expect that the thresholds will be raised. The regions of the retina which are not diseased will have normal thresholds. The course of dark adaptation measured from different regions of the retina in a patient who had macular choroiditis is shown in Fig. 348. The measurements, made in the usual manner at 7.5 degrees on the nasal side of the fovea, showed that there was practically no cone adaptation, and this was followed by poor rod adaptation. At 15 to 20 degrees from the fovea on the temporal side, the thresholds for dark adaptation were within normal limits.

Night blindness is the most important and the earliest symptom of tapetoretinal degeneration, such as pigmentary degeneration of the retina in all its forms, choroideremia, gyrate atrophy of the retina, and choroidal sclerosis. The night blindness depends on damage to the rod mechanism, which occurs first in all these diseases, due apparently to loss of some enzyme in the rods which is gene-determined.

Contribution of rods versus cones in different stages of adaptation

We have seen that a light of very low intensity is capable of stimulating the rods if sufficient time is allowed for them to achieve maximum sensitivity by the accumulation of rhodopsin. The cones on the other hand never achieve sensitivity sufficient for them to function at such low levels of illumination. As the intensity of the light is increased, the brightness finally exceeds the threshold necessary to activate the cones. Thereafter, the responses of the rods and cones merge together, and the combined response continues to grow as the light intensity is steadily increased. It is unlikely, however, that at high inten-

sities both the rods and cones continue to act in tandem. Some authors believe that in some way the response of the rods is suppressed at the higher levels of luminance by the cones. It would appear that we have three physiologic levels of activity in the retina as we increase illumination from a very low level in the completely dark-adapted eye up to the level of full daylight: (1) a very low intensity level in which only rods are activated, called the scotopic level, (2) an intermediate level within which both rods and cones are acting simultaneously, known as the mesopic level, and (3) a high intensity level at which the cones alone respond, the photopic level. There is still some uncertainty as to whether the rods are completely inactive or whether they, too, contribute to the response in the third level of physiologic activity. There is no question that as the intensity of the light is increased the cone activity becomes relatively greater and the rod activity relatively less. The exact nature of the mechanism by which this changeover from a preponderant rod activity to a preponderant cone activity occurs is not known. It is likely that both photochemical processes and purely neurophysiologic reactions are combined.

The question of whether the rods continue to function when the intensity of the light is raised above the scotopic level cannot be directly determined from the graphic presentation of the course of dark adaptation during the first few minutes because during this time the cones have a greater sensitivity to light and take over the function of light perception. The rod curve makes its appearance only when the retina has recovered sufficient sensitivity so that the intensities below the cone threshold can be recorded. During this time, however, it is certain that rod adaptation has been going on, for when the curve first appears, it is already proceeding with a well-established slope. Only by recording the dark adaptation curve in individuals with complete color blindness, in which there is presumably no cone function, can this part of rod dark adaptation be mapped out.

Mandelbaum[24] has measured the loss of rod activity as cone activity takes over with increasing illumination by an ingenious method. This is based on a previous observation of the change in saturation of violet light during mesopic vision. He previously noted that the saturation of violet light differed to an observer, depending upon whether the eyes had been previously light-adapted or dark-adapted, when the saturation of the violet light was estimated at low levels of light intensity. Such saturation matches are difficult to determine accurately, and Mandelbaum was unable to make precise quantitative measurements. He did establish the fact, however, that rods still predominate when the level of light intensity has been increased to 10 times the threshold of the cones; at 100 times this level, rod activity is still dominant. Not until 1000 times the threshold of cone activity do rods and cones play an equal part in the total brightness sensation, and at 10,000 times this threshold cones dominate the picture for the first time.

The practical aspects of dark adaptation are obvious. Specific information about the levels of illumination at which scotopic vision gives way to mesopic vision and this in turn to photopic vision is useful in our daily lives. In certain occupations it becomes of paramount importance. How bright should the sidewalks be lighted at night or the turnpikes for high-speed driving? What illumination is advisable for the aisles in motion-picture theatres? What effect does a day on the beach in full sunshine have on the dark adaptation of the automobile driver when he drives home that night? These are some of the many practical questions to which a knowledge of retinal physiology must be applied.*

SPATIAL INDUCTION

Examples of spatial summation have been cited from time to time in other chapters of this book. The effects of irradiation will be considered in relation to the apparent size of white objects on a black background as compared to black on a white background—a white object on a black background always looks smaller (Fig. 361, p. 757). In the same manner a patch of gray on a white background looks darker than the same patch on a black background. Colors, as well, are affected by their juxtaposition to other colors or backgrounds, the differences in hue being greatly enhanced by being placed alongside each other. Similarly, a neutral gray takes on the complementary color when it is placed next to a colored surface. It would appear that in the case of black and white a white background depresses the sensitivity of the whole retina so that the gray test patch, superimposed on it, looks darker. A black background, on the other hand, enhances the sensitivity of the retina so that the same gray test patch appears brighter. In the case of colors, spatial summation enhances the sensitivity of the retina to the complementary color of the test patch. If the colored stimulus is red, the sensitivity of the surrounding retina to green is enhanced.

---

*A complete discussion of these questions and those which relate to special occupations in which vision is employed under dim illumination can be found in the following excellent English text: Jayle, G. E., and others: Night vision (translated by Baisinger and Holmes), Springfield, Ill., 1959, Charles C Thomas, Publisher.

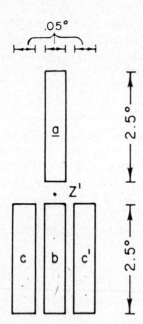

Fig. 349. Stimulus pattern used in experiments by Alpern. **a** is seen always by the left eye and c-c′ always by the right eye. **b** is seen by the right eye except in the experiment illustrated in Fig. 350 by the solid circles. **Z′** is the fixation point viewed binocularly. (From Alpern, M.: Invest. Ophthal. 2:47, 1963.)

Early investigators in the field of retinal physiology assigned the effects of spatial summation to psychologic mechanisms mainly. Hering was one of the earliest to voice the opinion that physiologic mechanisms were concerned chiefly, but the earliest experimental evidence was given by Sherrington, who showed that interaction among the neurons of the retina took place in the same way as in those of the central nervous system. The recent work of Hartline, Granit, and others (referred to in Chapter 14, Electrical Phenomena in the Eye) brings conclusive proof that interaction occurs among the retinal neurons and that many of the phenomena of vision are to be attributed to these effects. In fact, it is doubtful whether any of the individual photoreceptors, other than the cones in the fovea, have a direct line to the primary optic

centers, all of the other receptors being linked together through complicated internuncial paths. The activity of each receptor thereby influences the activity of many surrounding receptors. These effects are undoubtedly the underlying cause of spatial summation.

An experiment by Alpern[25] demonstrates that simultaneous brightness contrast is due to retinal effects rather than to more complex psychological processes. In Fig. 349 *a* is a bright field (the comparison standard) maintained at a standard level, *b* is a similar field (the test patch), and Z′ is the fixation point. The luminance of *b* (B_b) can be changed to match the luminance of *a*; *c* and *c′* are

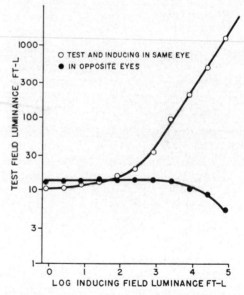

Fig. 350. Simultaneous brightness contrast compared when the test was seen by the right eye *(open circles)* and when the test patch was seen by the left eye *(solid circles)*. In each case the inducing patch was seen by the right eye. The ordinate is the luminance of b (B_b) necessary to establish a match to the standard which was always viewed by the left eye. The value of the luminance of the standard (B_a) for the open circles was 126 FL.; for the solid circles it was 13.9 FL. (From Alpern, M.: Invest. Ophthal. 2:47, 1963.)

two similar patches (the contrast inducing patches) whose luminance can likewise be changed within a wide range.

If both b and c-c' are seen by the right eye only and a by the left eye, then as soon as the inducing patches (c-c') become very bright they make the test patch appear much dimmer and its luminance must consequently be greatly increased in order to re-establish a match with a. This is shown in Fig. 350 in the curve of the open circles. On the other hand, if the inducing patches (c-c') are seen by the right eye only and the test patch, b, is seen by the left eye, no such effect occurs at all. In fact when the inducing patch becomes very bright, the test patch actually increases slightly in brightness. This proves that simultaneous brightness contrast requires the test and inducing patches to be exposed to the same eye. This is strong evidence that the mechanisms concerned to produce the effect are retinal and not cerebral.

REFERENCES

1. Wright, W.: The perception of light, New York, 1939, Chemical Publishing Co., Inc.
2. Arden, G., Granit, R., and Ponte, F.: Phase of suppression following each retinal b-wave in flicker, J. Neurophysiol. 23:305, 1960.
3. Schouten, J., and Ornstein, L.: Measurements on direct and indirect adaptation by means of a binocular method, J. Optic. Soc. America 29:168, 1939.
4. Fry, G., and Alpern, M.: The effect of a peripheral glare source upon the apparent brightness of an object, J. Optic. Soc. America 43:189, 1953.
5. von Bekesy, G.: Physik, Ztschr. 30:115, 1929.
6. Hecht, S., and Wald, G.: Visual acuity an intensity discrimination of drosophila, J. Gen. Physiol. 17:517, 1934.
7. Smith, J.: Spatial and binocular effects in human intensity discrimination, J. Gen. Psychol. 14:318, 1936.
8. Pirenne, M.: Vision and the eye, London, 1948, The Pilot Press.
9. Hecht, S., and Hsia, Y.: Dark adaptation following light adaptation to red and white lights, J. Optic. Soc. America 35: 261, 1945.
10. Mandelbaum, J.: Dark adaptation, Arch. Ophth. 26:203, 1941.
11. Hecht, S., and Haig, C.: Dark adaptation as influenced by intensity of light adaptation, J. Optic. Soc. America 26:304, 1936.
12. Jayle, G., and Aubert, L.: La vision nocturne, Rev. Chibret 53:3, 1959.
13. Pickard, R.: A study of the central and peripheral light and dark adaptation with varying backgrounds, Brit. J. Ophth. 19: 481, 1935.
14. von Noorden, G.: Peripheral viewing in scotopic vision, Arch. Ophth. 69:547, 1963.
15. Rushton, W.: Dark adaptation and the regeneration of rhodopsin, J. Physiol. 156: 166, 1961.
16. Fuertes, M., Gunkel, R., and Rushton, W.: Increment thresholds in a subject deficient in cone vision, J. Physiol. 156: 1179, 1961.
17. Aguilar, M., and Stiles, W.: Acta ophth. 1:59, 1954.
18. Halstead, W.: Chronic intermittent anoxia and impairment of peripheral vision, Science 101:615, 1945.
19. Evans, J., and MacFarland, R.: Effects of oxygen deprivation on the central visual field, Am. J. Ophth. 21:968, 1938.
20. McDonald, R., and Adler, F.: Effects of anoxia on the dark adaptation of the normal and of the vitamin A deficient subject, Arch. Ophth. 22:980, 1939.
21. Steffins, L., Bair, H., and Sheard, C.: Dark adaptation and dietary deficiency in vitamin A, Am. J. Ophth. 23:1325, 1940.
22. Brenner, S., and Roberts, L.: Effects of vitamin A depletion in young adults, Arch. Int. Med. 71:474, 1943.
23. Dowling, J.: Night blindness, dark-adaptation, and the electroretinogram, Am. J. Ophth. 50:875, 1960.
24. Mandelbaum, J.: Rod activity at photopic intensities, Arch. Ophth. 63:402, 1960.
25. Alpern, M.: Simultaneous brightness contrast for flashes of light of different duration, Invest. Ophthal. 2:47, 1963.

CHAPTER 18

SENSORY RESPONSE

SENSORY RESPONSE TO A SINGLE STIMULUS

When the eye is exposed to a single brief flash of light of fairly high intensity, the resulting sensation is complex. It has been subjected to analysis by many different investigators. A latent period follows the turning on of the light before any actual sensation of light begins. The length of the latent period depends upon a number of factors (which will be described). Following the latent period an initial sensation, called the primary image, rises rapidly in intensity to a maximum and as quickly falls to a sustained level, which then gradually dies away. During the phase of the primary image, several fluctuations in intensity take place if the stimulus is not too prolonged, i.e., beyond the so-called action time. This is the least time during which light of a chosen intensity must act in order to produce a maximal response. If the stimulus is prolonged beyond this value, the fluctuations or pulses do not appear. They are referred to sometimes as Charpentier's bands. After the disappearance of the primary image, recurring sensations, called afterimages, make their appearance if the conditions for observation are suitable.

Latent period. The latent period before the appearance of the primary image varies with the region of the retina stimulated, with the subjective intensity of the light, with its wavelength, and with the stage of adaptation of the retina (Fig. 351). The latent period is longer when the fovea is stimulated than when the peripheral areas of the retina are stimulated. As the intensity of the illumination is increased, the latent period is shortened. The latent period is shortest when light from the blue end of the spectrum is employed. The duration of the latent period at various stages of light adaptation and dark adaptation depends on the intensity and duration of the preadapting light used and probably on other factors which have not been controlled adequately. With ordinary intensities and durations of exposure to white light the latent period varies from 50 to 200 msec. The latent period of the electroretinogram is about 40 msec., and the conduction rate from the retina to the visual cortex is approximately 124 msec., making a total of 164 msec., which is comparable to the values of the subjective latent period just given. The latent period of the electroretinogram varies inversely with the intensity of the illumination, being

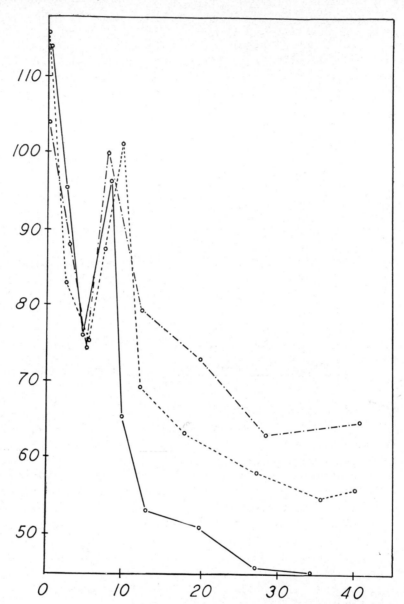

Fig. 351. This curve shows the change in the latent period of the sensation in the course of dark adaptation. The ordinates are the latent period in milliseconds. The abscissae are the period of adaptation in minutes. Constant stimulus of 1 NK (neue kerze). (After Kovacs.)

shorter the stronger the intensity of the flash. Likewise, the latent period of the visual sensation is shortened by increasing the apparent brightness of the light.

Primary image. The primary image ap-

pears after the latent period and lasts for a variable period of time. The duration of the primary image, like the latent period, varies from 50 to 200 msec., depending upon the region of the retina

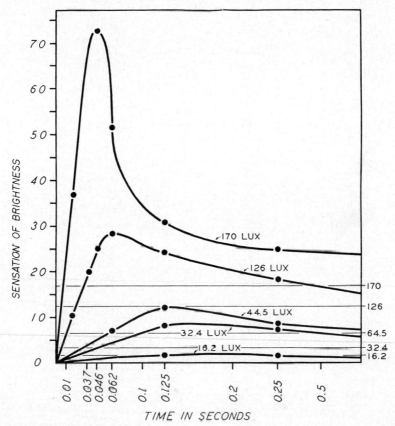

Fig. 352. Sensation curves in response to light of various intensities. Each curve represents the primary image measured in arbitrary units of brightness. Note that the duration of the primary image varies inversely with the intensity of the stimulating light. (After Broca and Sulzer.)

stimulated and the nature of the stimulating light. The duration is less when the periphery is stimulated than when the fovea is the seat of stimulation.

The duration of the primary image varies inversely with the brightness of the stimulating light (Fig. 352). This relationship might at first seem surprising since vision has been described as primarily a photochemical process. From this point of view the primary image, being caused by the breakdown of a photochemical substance, should last longer the more substance produced, and this should vary directly with the intensity of the light. The response of the eye to illumination cannot be described in terms of photochemical processes alone, however, and it seems certain that the relationship between the intensity of the light and the duration of the primary image is determined by nervous mechanisms, rather than by chemical mechanisms. As the sensitivity of the retina increases with dark adaptation, the duration of the primary image describes a curve, increasing up to approximately 10 minutes of dark adaptation and then falling off again (Fig. 353).

The intensity of the sensation and its

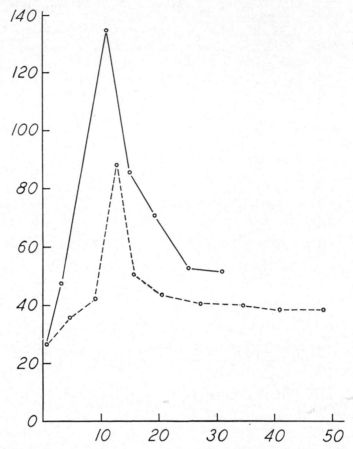

Fig. 353. Curve shows the effect of dark adaptation on the duration of the primary image. The two curves are observations on two separate individuals from a peripheral retinal area 4 to 8 degrees from the fovea. The ordinates are the duration of the primary image in milliseconds, and the abscissae represent the period of dark adaptation in minutes. Constant stimulus of 0.6 NK. (After Kovacs.)

time course depend on the intensity of the flash and its duration and also on its wavelength when monochromatic light is used (Fig. 352). The height of the sensation varies directly with the intensity of the flash and with its duration, provided that it is less than the action time.

In an analysis of the electroretinogram it was shown (p. 607) that after a latent period an initial negative deflection occurred, called the a wave. Granit attributed the a wave to the P III process. The negative P III is always associated with cone activity, and the evidence suggests that it is associated with inhibition, rather than with excitation. Granit regards the P III component as a mechanism by means of which the eye rids itself of the effects of a previous stimulation. It wipes the slate clean, so to speak, before any new impressions are made. Hence, he speaks of the effect of the P III process as pre-excitatory inhibition. The first effect of stimulation is an inhibitory one, therefore. The stronger the light stimulus, the more rapid will be the appearance of this component of the electroretinogram and the more effective it is in inhibiting the sensation of light which remains from a previous stimulation.

It is apparent from this that the primary image will be cut short by the P III or a wave and that, the stronger the illumination, the shorter will be the duration of the primary image. This offers an explanation of the fact that the duration of the primary image varies inversely with the brightness of the stimulating light.

Afterimages. After the primary image has faded out, a remarkable succession of fluctuating sensations, called afterimages may occur, whose nature depends on the manner in which the eye is stimulated. If the retina is stimulated momentarily by a bright white light and then the eyes are closed or turned toward a *dark* background, an image of the light will appear gradually. After several fluctuations in intensity, this fades out and finally disappears. In the same manner, if the light used for stimulation is colored, the afterimage will have the same color as the stimulating light. These are known as positive afterimages.

On the other hand, if after the original stimulation the eyes are directed to a *brightly lighted* surface instead of a dark surface, the afterimage will appear dark on the bright background but will have the same contour as the original stimulating light. If the first stimulus is colored, then the afterimage on the bright background will have the same form but will be of the complementary color. Afterimages seen on a bright background are called negative afterimages. The bright background is, in effect, a second stimulation of the retina. The exposures necessary to produce both positive and negative afterimages are much longer than those required to produce fusion of successively presented light stimuli.

What physiologic significance do afterimages have? Can they throw any light on retinal function, and can they be explained by what is known of the processes which go on in the retina under the influence of light? The appearance and reappearance of visual sensation following momentary stimulation of the retina prove that the processes going on in the retina have persistence. These processes are not only excitatory, but also inhibitory, for it has been pointed out that a single stimulus, sufficient to produce a positive afterimage, imparts to the retina an inhibition which affects all subsequent visual processes of a like nature. At the same time it encourages visual processes of an opposite kind so that a second stimulus falling on the same area gives rise to a negative afterimage. When a white light is fixated and a positive afterimage is made to appear on a black background, the region of the retina stimulated is now made relatively resistant to further stimulation by white light. Hence, if the subject fixates a white wall (forming a second stimulation to the retina), the afterimage appears dark because this area of the retina is now inhibited while the surrounding retina is stimulated. By contrast, therefore, the afterimage is dark on a white field. This phenomenon is often called successive contrast.

If the primary and secondary stimuli are the same, the negative afterimage will be changed merely in luminosity. If the two stimuli are of the same color, not only a change in luminosity of the negative afterimage results, but also a diminution in its saturation and in some cases a slight change in its hue. If the primary stimulus is a color and the second stimulus (the wall) is white and falls on the retina during the period of the positive afterimage, the afterimage has the complementary color. If, e.g., the eye fixates a red light, the negative afterimage will be green-blue; if orange, the afterimage will be blue; if yellow, it will be indigo blue; etc.

Both positive and negative afterimages undergo rapid changes, and even with white light the succession of sensations which follow one another is quite complex and consists of a number of different phases following each other in rapid succession. It is possible to select a second stimulus of the proper intensity which will prevent the appearance of any afterimage, positive or negative.

Afterimages may arise from either photochemical or electrical processes in the retina. Craik[1] confirmed the view generally held that the positive afterimage is due to retinal afterdischarge, and negative afterimages are due to local reduction of retinal sensitivity. By an original experiment, he found it possible to produce afterimages by exposing an eye to a stimulating light but at the same time preventing any impulses from traveling up its optic nerve by pressure on the globe sufficient to produce anoxia. In spite of the fact that during the time of stimulation the eye was "blind" ordinary afterimages could be produced readily, demonstrating that they originate in the retina rather than in higher centers. Since anoxia does not prevent the formation of afterimages, it is not likely that they arise from purely neural processes but are photochemical in origin. Central processes may exert inhibitory influences on afterimages, but it seems certain that they do not take their origin in the higher centers. It has not been possible so far to identify any afterimage as being of purely nervous origin, but it is certain that some afterimages can arise *purely* from photochemical reactions. To determine this Brindley[2-4] and others have made use of the basic law of photochemistry, the Bunsen-Roscoe law, which states that the photochemical effects on any two light stimuli are identical if the products of their strength and the length of time they operate are equal. According to this law, if two bright flashes of light, one lasting a second and the other lasting one one-hundredth of a second, but being one hundred times brighter than the first, were compared by an eye, they would be indistinguishable. This, however, is not the case. The eye easily establishes that the first flash is longer and the second is brighter. One must conclude that the two flashes must have different effects on at least some part of the nerve cells along the visual pathway. When Brindley and co-workers examined the negative afterimages of these two flashes, they found that during the first 15 seconds the afterimages differed in color and strength, but that after 15 seconds they were absolutely indistinguishable. The Bunsen-Roscoe law is, therefore, valid for the late afterimage since two flashes consisting of the same total amount of light produce identical late afterimages. This suggests that the late negative afterimage of a brief bright stimulus must depend only on its photochemical effects and not at all on its immediate effects on nerve cells.

Attempts have been made to study afterimages quantitatively—an obviously difficult procedure. By matching the brightness sensation of the afterimage in one eye with variable illumination of the other eye, Padgham obtained consistent results that showed that the sensation of brightness and duration of the afterimage increased up to 4 seconds exposure.[5, 6] Afterimages of high-luminance stimuli are probably of cone origin. This is borne out by experiments[7] with afterimages produced by stimuli of different angular size, covering different areas of the retina.

Afterimages showed marked differences in character when the area stimulated was confined to the rod-free area than when rods were also stimulated.

The persistence and intensity of some afterimages are such as to make one question why they do not become bothersome in ordinary vision. The failure of the afterimage to intrude itself on consciousness during ordinary life is due to some extent to the continual shifting of the eyes from one point of fixation to another so that the image on the macula is changing constantly. This is well demonstrated by an experiment of Hartridge in which, after fixation of an object for a period of time sufficient to produce an afterimage in outline on the retina, the gaze is quickly turned to a second fixation mark placed some distance from the first. After this is done, it is found that when the gaze is returned to the first mark some time has to elapse before the appearance of the object in outline is observed again. In fact, the time required is not very different from that required to reach this stage at the beginning of a new experiment. The second impression effects almost complete removal of the afterimage of the first impression, so that when the gaze returns to the first again, the slate has been wiped clean, and the first impression acts as though it were a new one. This is in keeping with what was stated regarding the effect of stimulation of the retina by light, i.e., that it leaves the retina for a certain period of time less sensitive to a second stimulus similar in kind to the first but more sensitive to a different kind. The afterimage takes place during this period.

As a result of simultaneous contrast, the contrasts between contours, luminosity, and hue of different objects are intensified, and as a result of successive contrast, the confusion which would result from the persistence of images falling successively on the same region of the retina is prevented. At each new impression the retina is momentarily less sensitive to a similar impression but is made more sensitive to a different stimulus.

The duration of afterimages also suggests that their origin is most likely a chemical one. Some electrophysiologic phenomena are probably concerned with the formation of afterimages—e.g., the appearance of an "off" effect in the retinal and optic nerve action currents at the cessation of illumination and the tendency of the impulses during the "off" effect to become synchronized just as afterimages are known to fluctuate. Both the "off" effect and afterimage show periodicity, which in the case of the "off" effect is due to the synchronization of groups of impulses. On the other hand, there can be little doubt that the higher centers also contribute to the periodicity of the afterimages, and a number of investigators have found that the cessation of illumination signaled to the visual cortex is in the form of alterations in the cortical potentials—the electroencephalogram.[8]

INTERMITTENT STIMULI

If intermittent lights are presented to the eye, they are perceived as separate as long as the rate at which they are presented is below a certain value. When the rate is very slow, the light merely seems to be turned on and off. During the light period the brightness is maximal, and during the dark period, it is zero. When the rate of presentation of light is increased, the light appears to stay on but shows rapid alternations of intensity, producing a sensation which has been called flicker. In other words, the sensations of light and dark become less sharply delimited in time and less clearly separated in intensity. The light period loses its brightness, and the dark period gains in brightness. The more frequent the alternations, the less is the difference between the successive sensations, and when the frequency is sufficiently high, the difference between the successive sensations vanishes. Therefore, the sensation of flicker persists as the rate is increased up to a certain critical* rate at which it ceases suddenly. The sensation of flickering is so striking, and the cessation of flicker has such a sharp end point when the rate of intermittency of the light reaches a critical value, that the phenomenon is used for the estimation of retinal function under many different conditions.

Critical fusion frequency

The critical fusion frequency† (abbreviated c.f.f.) is the rate or frequency per second at which an intermittent light loses its flicker and appears to shine steadily. It has a stable, repeatable end point as long as conditions are kept constant. It is easy to elicit in children or in adults who have had no training in observation. It can be used as a subjective test, but it is reproduced also in the alternations of the alpha rhythm in man. It can be shown also in the electroretinogram and the electroencephalogram of animals.[9]

Mechanism of fusion

Why are lights fused when the rate of their presentation to the eye is sufficiently rapid? The answer to this question has already been suggested in the section in which the sensory responses of the eye to a single flash of light were described. It was shown that, if a flash of light acts long enough to produce a maximal response and no more, after a short latent period the resulting sensation rises rapidly to a maximum. This is known as the primary image. After several rapid fluctuations, this gradually dies away. The latent period averages from 50 to 200 msec., depending on the nature of the stimulus and the region and state of adaptation of the retina stimulated. The duration of the primary images also varies from 50 to 200 msec., depending on the same factors which influence the latent period. If the stimuli used are of equal subjective brightness, the duration of the primary image is less when the periphery is stimulated than when the central regions are tested, and the latent period is diminished.

As the brightness of the stimulating light is increased, the duration of the primary image decreases, i.e., the duration of the sensation varies inversely with the intensity of the stimulating light, but the curve expressing this relationship shows a sharp break in passing from low to moderate illumination (passing from rod thresholds to cone thresholds) (Fig. 354). The primary image lasts for a considerably longer time for the rods than for the cones. It is apparent that the latent period and the duration of the primary image are similarly affected by most changes in the stimulating light, as shown in Table 52.

The fusion of successive stimuli occurs when the primary image of the first stimulus lasts until the primary image of the next appears.

Fusion depends on the duration of the primary image of each stimulus, therefore. The factors which diminish the duration

---

*As pointed out by Landis: "*Critical* is used in the physical sense of a transition point of change from one state to another; for example, the physicist speaks of the critical temperature where ice becomes water." (From Landis, C.: Physiol. Rev. **34:**259, 1954.)

†Flicker fusion frequency (f.f.f.) is also used by some authors, but the term *critical fusion frequency* emphasizes the fact that it is a critical threshold.

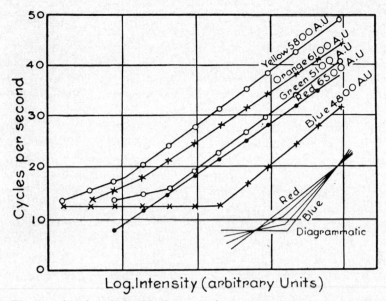

Fig. 354. The logarithmic relationship between the critical frequency and the illumination. Note the break in each curve, representing the point at which cone function is added to or replaces rod function. This break is sharpest with light of short wavelength. (After Ives; from Duke-Elder, S.: Textbook of ophthalmology, St. Louis, 1946, The C. V. Mosby Co., vol. 1.)

Table 52. *Comparison of changes in latent period and primary image with changes in stimulus*

Stimulus	Latent period	Primary image
Increasing intensity	Shortened	Decreased duration
Foveal stimulation	Lengthened	Lengthened duration
Peripheral stimulation	Shortened	Decreased duration
Effect of wave length		
(a) Red end of spectrum	Shortest	Shortest with yellow (590) when light-adapted, but shifts to (567) in
(b) Blue end of spectrum	Longest	scotopic vision

of the primary image should therefore raise the critical fusion frequency (since each sensation dies away quicker, more stimuli per unit time have to be used to produce a continuous effect.

Since the primary image may last as long as 200 msec. under conditions most favorable for its maintenance, it is possible to have continuous sensation of light when periodic stimuli are presented to the eye within that period of time. On the other hand, the primary image is never shorter than 50 msec. so that when the primary image disappears as rapidly as possible continuous sensation can occur if the stimuli follow one another within 50 msec. Therefore, the values of the critical fusion frequency possible for the human eye should be found to vary from 5 to 20 cycles per second, depending upon the conditions under which the critical fusion frequency is tested.

Where does fusion take place?

There are three possible locations where fusion of intermittent stimuli might take place—namely, in the retina, in the conducting pathways, and in the brain. The conducting pathways may be ruled out immediately, for it has been shown that the optic nerve can maintain the separation of intermittent impulses even at a frequency of 50 cycles per second. In other words, intermittent stimuli presented to the conducting pathways stay intermittent and are not fused. In flicker, however, the optic nerve receives no such sharply limited alternation of phases. For a frequency of intermittent illumination as small as 5 cycles per second at low intensities and three times as frequent at higher illuminations the impulses along the optic nerve of the eel show no periodic changes.[10] The brain may be responsible for part of the transformation of intermittent stimulation into continuous sensation, but it is certain from the analysis of the electroretinogram that most of the change occurs in the retina itself.

The negative component of the electroretinogram, the inhibitory P III, plays a large part in the response of the retina to flicker. It will be remembered that P III comes on rapidly after exposure to light and is responsible for the initial a wave in the electroretinogram. Since the electroretinogram of the cat exhibits only a low-grade type of flicker with a low critical fusion frequency and has a very poor P III component, Granit feels this is evidence that the P III determines the phenomenon of flicker. On the other hand, retinas such as the pigeon's are almost exclusively cone retinas, show well-marked flicker, and have a high critical fusion frequency. It has been found that in the light-adapted frog, in which the cones are predominantly active, there is marked flicker and a high critical fusion frequency,

whereas in the dark-adapted frog the behavior is similar to the retina of the cat, rat, and guinea pig.

The critical fusion frequency is determined by the size of the a wave; the greater the intensity of the light stimulus, the greater and more rapid is the appearance of this negative component which inhibits the sensation of light remaining from each stimulus (primary image). In order to produce fusion of intermittent stimuli, it is necessary to present the separate stimuli to the eye in rapid succession since the inhibition of the primary image cuts down the period of time each one lasts. Hence, in retinas with a large P III component, the critical fusion frequency will be large.

In retinas that have negligible P III components the sensation of flicker depends on the b wave's dying down sufficiently to allow the next stimulus to evoke a new b wave. In these retinas no inhibitory a wave cuts short the duration of the primary image; therefore a considerable period of time will elapse before the sensation finally dies down. The critical fusion frequency is very low, therefore. The effect of increasing the intensity of the stimulus on the critical fusion frequency will depend on the degree to which the b wave is affected by the increase in intensity.

There is some evidence that the fusion of intermittent stimuli takes place in the ganglion cells and is determined largely by the rate at which these ganglion cells can be made to fire by receptors and interneurons.[11]

Factors which influence the critical fusion frequency

The chief determinants of the critical fusion frequency are the following.

1. Luminance of the intermittent light, including the intensity of the light and the wavelengths employed

2. Influence of the region tested and the area stimulated
3. State of adaptation of the retina
4. Size of the pupil, which determines the intensity of the stimulus reaching the retina and the area of the retina stimulated
5. Spatial summation
6. Monocular and binocular presentations
7. Age, physique, diurnal variations, fatigue, and probably psychologic factors
8. Oxygen and carbon dioxide
9. Drugs
10. Integrity of the visual apparatus

Influence of the stimulating light. The luminance of the stimulating light, including its intensity and wavelength, influences the critical fusion frequency.

Intensity. Since the duration of the primary image is shortened as the luminosity of the stimulating light is increased, the rate of stimulation must be more rapid in order to produce fusion. Therefore, the critical fusion frequency is higher, the brighter the stimulating light. The relationship between intensity of stimulating light and the critical fusion frequency has been stated in the Ferry-Porter law, as follows:

$$\text{c.f.f.} = \text{k. log I} + \text{k}'$$
$$\text{I} = \text{the intensity of illumination}$$
$$\text{k. and k}' = \text{constants}$$

The first constant involves the relationship between the critical fusion frequency and the area of the retina exposed. The second constant involves the quantity of energy in the light and the state of adaptation of the retina.

This law holds good for a wide range of illuminations above 0.25 meter-candles, but below this level it breaks down. Its validity has been proved not only by subjective testing, but also from an analysis

of flicker in the electroretinogram of the frog (Fig. 355). It can be seen in this illustration that when the frequency of stimulation is increased beyond a certain point the rhythm established in the electroretinogram is eliminated suddenly; i.e., the responses to each individual stimulus are fused.

The law as formulated by Porter stated that the critical fusion frequency was proportional to the logarithm of the illumination intensity. However, Porter subsequently found that when the critical fusion frequency was plotted against the logarithm of the intensity the data fell on two straight lines instead of one. The two lines intersected at an illumination of about 0.25 meter-candles, and the slope of the lower was 1.56, whereas that of the upper was 12.4. These peculiarities are difficult to reconcile with the obvious interpretation of Porter's data, which are generally given in terms of the duplicity theory, i.e., that the lower limb describes the functions of the rods and the upper limb describes the functions of the cones.

In order to clarify this seeming discrepancy, Hecht and co-workers[12-13] studied the phenomena of flicker and measured the critical fusion frequency for different portions of the retina, for different types of adaptation, for different colors, and for as large a range of illumination as possible in order to render the data reproducible and definitive. They found that when white light is used and the rod-free area of the fovea is stimulated (cones only), there is a single sigmoid relation between the critical fusion frequency and the logarithm of I (Fig. 356).

Measurements made in a similar fashion with a retinal area 5 degrees away from fixation, which contains both rods and cones, show a relation possessing two clearly separated sections (Fig. 357). The

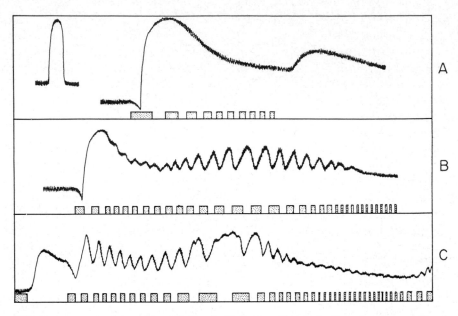

Fig. 355. Responses to intermittent light. **A,** Retinal action potential of a thoroughly dark-adapted eye (4 hours in a dark room). It is noticeable that despite the considerable potential developed and the rapidity of its development there are nevertheless at the most only traces of intermittent waves during the course of interrupted stimulation. The eye was then illuminated for 5 minutes and after the "off" effect had disappeared, record **B** was obtained. The briskness of the waves that now appear is striking and again indicates a fundamental change in the reaction of the retina. The string in both cases is at the same tension, as shown by the calibration to the left of **A** (0.67 mv.). The fusion frequency in **B** is at about 14 flashes per second. With less thoroughly dark-adapted eyes than the one responsible for curve **A,** values between 6 and 8 flashes per second may be obtained. The response **C** begins with the "off" effect after some minutes of light adaptation. Then intermittent stimulation follows before the "off" effect has had time to drop. Several features in this record should be noticed. (1) The first effect of the first flash upon the "off" effect is to cause a large negative dip followed by a spontaneous rise before the next flash appears. (2) As the rate of intermittent stimulation increases, the whole curve swings downward and again swings upward at the end of the curve when the stimuli are spaced farther apart. (3) The peaks of the up-spokes are very sharp. (4) Small ripples are superimposed upon the rounded tops of two long flashes in the middle of the curve. The fusion frequency is at about 18 flashes per second. (After Granit and Riddell.)

high-intensity section resembles the one obtained for the fovea, but the low-intensity section is new. The two sections are separated by a horizontal limb at about 10 cycles per second, maintained for 1.25 log units of intensity. These two sections of the data represent the functions of the rods at low intensities and of the cones at high intensities. This is borne out by measurements made with retinal areas 15

and 20 degrees from the fovea where the ratio of rods to cones is anatomically greater than at 5 degrees off center. As a result, the two sections of the data become separated still further than at 5 degrees off center.

Wavelength. Measurements made using different portions of the spectrum further confirm the rod-cone character of the peripheral data. Following the established

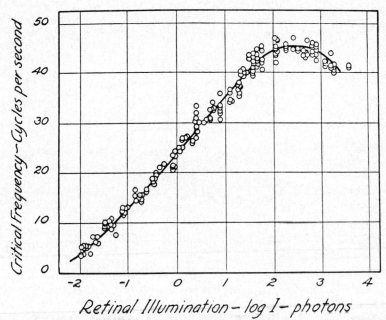

Fig. 356. Critical frequency function of the rod-free fovea as influenced by illumination. Data of Selig Hecht recording 176 separate measurements. (From Hecht, S., and Verrijp, C.: J. Gen. Physiol. **17:**237, 1933.)

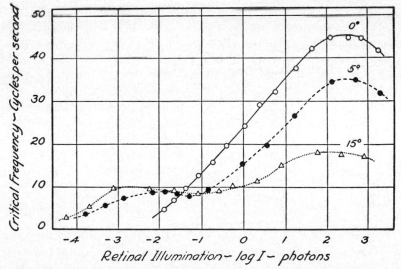

Fig. 357. Data of Selig Hecht showing relation between critical frequency and log I for white light for three different retinal locations. *Open circles*, at the fovea; *closed circles*, 5 degrees above the fovea; *triangles*, 15 degrees above the fovea. (From Hecht, S., and Verrijp, C.: J. Gen. Physiol. **17:**251, 1933.)

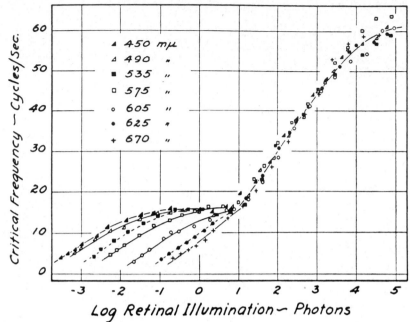

Fig. 358. Data of Selig Hecht showing the relation of critical frequency to log I for the different spectral regions shown. (From Hecht, S., and Shlaer, S.: J. Gen. Physiol. **19:**965, 1936.)

variations in relative sensibility of the rods and cones at different wavelengths (the cones being relatively insensitive to blue light), the two sections of the data show corresponding separation along the intensity axis for different wavelengths. The separation is greatest in the violet part of the spectrum and least in the red.[15, 16]

The curves that describe the relation between the various portions of the spectrum and the critical fusion frequency may be interpreted as made by two functions, one for the rods and one for the cones. When a central area of the retina large enough to contain both rods and cones is used and the area is tested with light from different regions of the spectrum, the data divide into a low-intensity section, identified with rod function, and a high-intensity section, identified with cone function. The transition between the two

sections is marked by an inflection point which is sharp (Fig. 358).[17]

Influence of the region of the retina tested. This subject has been covered in the previous section in which it was shown that the relation between the critical fusion frequency and the intensity of the stimulating light depends entirely on the relative proportion of cones and rods in the region tested. Hecht found the critical fusion frequency to be considerably higher in the fovea than in the peripheral regions of the retina. As shown in Fig. 356, the maximum for the fovea is approximately 45 cycles per second at an illumination of log I = 2 – 2.5 photons, whereas the maximum for 5 degrees off the fovea is 35 cycles per second and for 15 degrees off the fovea it is 18 cycles per second. It is not stated, however, whether the eye is light-adapted or dark-adapted. However, the curve does show that below an illumination of –1.5 log I photons, the critical fusion frequency for the fovea falls below that of the peripheral retina.

Although a number of authors have reported that when the eye is under daylight conditions the critical fusion frequency of the fovea is less than the periphery so that the value rises from the center out to the periphery, it has been claimed that if variations in the size of the entrance pupil are prevented from influencing the amount of retinal illuminance the critical fusion frequency is less in the periphery than in the fovea. Apparently in the earlier work the size of the pupil was not controlled.[18] The critical fusion frequency is highest in midperiphery and then falls off again in the extreme periphery (Fig. 359). On the other hand, when the eye is dark-adapted,

the periphery is lower than the fovea. The difference in the critical fusion frequency of the fovea and the peripheral regions of the retina can be demonstrated nicely by watching the propeller of a plane during flight. If the area of the propeller is looked at directly, using the macular region, no movement is visible since the blades are rotating so rapidly that they are completely fused. On the other hand, if the eye is turned so that the area of the propeller falls on an extramacular region, a distinct pulsation is experienced due to the fact that the critical fusion frequency of this retinal region is high enough to prevent complete fusion, and a sensation of flicker results.

Berger[19] investigated the increase of the critical fusion frequency as a function of the image area with the light-adapted

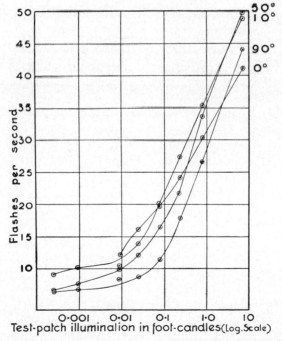

Fig. 359. Relation between the critical frequency of flicker and illumination of the test patch. The curves show the relation at different angles eccentric from the fovea. The surrounds were of equal brightness with the test patch. (After Lythgoe; from Duke-Elder, S.: Textbook of ophthalmology, St. Louis, 1946, The C. V. Mosby Co., vol. 1.)

human fovea. The critical fusion frequency increased with the logarithm of the image area differently with different sizes and with different backgrounds. This suggests that the function of the central fovea as measured by the critical fusion frequency is not uniform. It depends upon the size of the functioning area and the illumination of the directly adjacent surroundings, even when restricted to the rod-free zone. On the basis of experiments on the physiologic resolving power and ability of the human fovea to distinguish forms, Berger and Buchthal[20] introduced the concept of functional units. The functional unit is defined as the number of adjacent cones activating the same ganglion cell and may include single cones or groups of cones. Due to eye movements which spread the image of a point of light over one to four cones in 17 to 80 msec. or less, the practical value to be used is that of the average functional unit with a diameter of about 3 minutes.

Influence of dark adaptation. The effect on the critical fusion frequency of dark-adapting the eye depends entirely on whether the brightness of the flickering test light has an illumination above or below the threshold of the cones (it is assumed that an area containing both rods and cones is being tested). If the test light has an intensity of illumination below the sensitivity of the cones, then as the eye gradually undergoes dark adaptation and the rods adapt, the sensitivity of the retina increases, which is the same as increasing the intensity of the stimulating light. It has been noted previously that this results in shortening the primary image from each flash. Consequently, the frequency will have to be increased before the critical fusion frequency is reached. In other words, if the rod mechanism alone is functioning, the critical fusion frequency will increase with dark adaptation until it reaches a maximum. If, however, the illumination of the flickering light is above the threshold of the cones, so that both cones and rods are functioning, the critical fusion frequency falls with dark adaptation from a normal value of about 40 cycles per second in the light-adapted eye to about 25 cycles per second under complete dark adaptation.

When a region of the retina which is rod-free is selected, the effects of dark adaptation are minimal. Granit has suggested that the rods tend to inhibit the activity of the cones.

Size of pupil. As in all measurements having to do with the amount of light energy reaching the retina, the size of the pupil is of importance and must be controlled by using an artificial pupil when the critical fusion frequency is being measured.

The critical fusion frequency is influenced mainly by the size and intensity of the retinal image. Since the refractive changes of accommodation alter the size and intensity of the retinal image, a study was designed by Berger and Mahneke[21] to determine whether accommodation affects the critical fusion frequency. These authors found that accommodation has no effect upon the critical fusion frequency. This is in agreement with the report of Weekers and Roussell[22] that refraction anomalies have no influence upon the critical fusion frequency. The increase in size of the retinal image due to accommodation, which has been reported by Otero,[23] must be compensated by a corresponding decrease in illumination of the retinal image because the same amount of light is spread over a larger area. Since the critical fusion frequency increases with increasing size of the retinal image, but decreases with decreasing illumination, these two factors, which are inversely proportional, apparently cancel each other out.

Spatial summation and flicker. It will be recalled that in the retina processes initiated in a localized area spread to adjacent or more widely separated areas. The latent period of both the electroretinogram and the discharge of the optic nerve is lessened with an increase in area as well as with an increase in intensity of the stimulus. When the effect of spatial summation is determined, the portions of the retina stimulated need not be exactly adjacent to one another but may be fairly separate. If a single nerve fiber is being tested, they must fall within the receptive field of that fiber (p. 634). Thus, the latent period of the discharge from four separated spots on the retina depends upon whether the stimulus is applied to each of them singly or to all of them together. When they are stimulated simultaneously, the latent period is shortened.

In a similar manner, it has been found that the critical fusion frequency can be changed considerably by spatial summation. The critical fusion frequency of four spots on the retina stimulated simultaneously is higher than that of each spot stimulated singly. This effect of spatial summation on flicker has not been accepted by all authorities, however. It has been suggested[24] that the effect of summation on the fusion frequency is due to the spread of irradiated light throughout the retina and not to real spatial summation.

Monocular and binocular presentations. The critical fusion frequency is usually higher when the observations are made using both eyes than when one eye is exposed alone. Generally these observations have been made with instruments which record revolutions per minute of a revolving sector exposing the light for brief periods, and the lack of information

regarding the ratio of light to dark intervals makes the interpretation of the data less certain.

Age, physique, diurnal variations, and psychologic factors. Changes of this kind are difficult to isolate and control. The factor of the size of the pupil probably plays a considerable part, and the subjective criterion as to what appearance of the test patch is to be designated the critical fusion frequency may enter into many of these reports. Since there is considerable difference among different subjects of the same age, size, and general state of health, any small differences attributed to an isolated factor must be accepted with caution unless statistically valid data are presented.

Oxygen; carbon dioxide. Most persons do not seem to show any change in the critical fusion frequency with anoxia, at least for low degrees of anoxia. If the oxygen lack is marked, a decrease in the critical fusion frequency occurs. On the other hand, inhalation of carbon dioxide has a rapid and marked effect on reducing the critical fusion frequency.[25]

Drugs. Various drugs are reported to influence the critical fusion frequency. A good deal of the work reported lacks data on simultaneous blood concentrations of the drug employed and is difficult to interpret. On the other hand, alcohol has been investigated carefully, and relatively small increases in the concentration of alcohol in the blood cause a drop of 5 to 10 cycles per second in the critical fusion frequency.

Eserine applied topically produces a marked decrement in the critical fusion frequency of the human eye.[26] This does not seem to be true for other autonomic drugs such as pilocarpine, homatropine, and epinephrine. The effect of eserine may be due to a nicotine-like action on the retina that induces inhibition of retinal function similar to the reduction in activity of the ventral horn cells of the spinal cord due to the application of this drug.

Integrity of the visual apparatus. Many studies have been made on the effects of disease processes on the critical fusion frequency. Phillips[27] studied the effects of intracranial tumors on the critical fusion frequency.

Enzer and co-workers[28] found a disturbance in the appearance of flicker in a group of patients with various types of pathologic processes of the brain. This disturbance consisted in the abolition or reduction in intensity of a second or third appearance of flicker in light emitted from an apparatus which used alternating current and a rotator arrangement, increasing the frequency of the light flashes beyond the critical fusion frequency of the first flicker. In normal subjects second and third sensations of flicker appeared, but in patients with cerebral disease these were absent.

Several investigators have studied the critical fusion frequency in amblyopia, with conflicting results. In patients with amblyopia ex anopsia, Miles[29] found the critical fusion frequency of the fovea to be higher than normal; i.e., it performed in the same manner as the periphery of the light-adapted retina. This suggests suppression of the central cones. Feinberg,[30] on the other hand, reports just the reverse.

Alpern and associates[31] find that the different results reported by previous investigators are attributable to their failure to control fluctuations in pupil size and to the fact that the pupillomotor sensitivity of the fovea in the amblyopic eye is reduced compared to that of its fellow eye. These authors report that if fluctuations in pupil diameter are prevented the critical fusion frequency for the fovea is

lower in the amblyopic eye than in the normal eye. The magnitude of the difference depends upon the amount of retinal illumination. At very low levels there is no difference between the critical fusion frequency of the normal eye and the amblyopic eye recorded from the fovea, but as the retinal illumination is increased, this difference becomes more marked. The relation between the critical fusion frequency and the illumination is quite similar to the relation between acuity and illumination. Amblyopia results in an impairment of visual function, both acuity and flicker discrimination, at moderate and high levels of retinal illumination but not at low levels of retinal illumination. These findings suggest that amblyopia is not due to either reduction in the rate of synthesis of the pigments in the foveal cones or tilting of the foveal cones, as has been suggested by Enoch.[32, 33] As Alpern points out, this effect could be due to the fact that in the amblyopic eye fixation is accomplished with a region of the retina just slightly eccentric to the center of the fovea (but still well within the part of the retina stimulated by the central part of the image of the test patch).

Studies of the visual field have been made, using the critical fusion frequency. Mayer and Sherman[34] were able to obtain complete visual fields even to the periphery, using a modified method designed by Riddell.[35] Curves of the critical fusion frequency plotted at various meridians along the horizontal axis agree with the findings of Creed and Ruch,[36] who found that the peak value is in the vicinity of 10 degrees from the fovea in all quadrants. Riddell believes that this peak coincides with the junction of the macular area, with its even number of cones and ganglion cells, and with the periphery, where there are many rods and cones connected to each ganglion cell as well as a profuse intercommunicating synaptic network.

REFERENCES

1. Craik, W.: Origin of visual after-images, Nature, London **145**:512, 1940.
2. Brindley, G.: After-images, Scient. Am., p. 85, Oct., 1963.
3. Brindley, G.: The discrimination of after-images, J. Physiol. **147**:194, 1959.
4. Brindley, G.: Two new properties of foveal after images and a photo-chemical hypothesis to explain them, J. Physiol. **164**:168, 1962.
5. Padgham, C.: Quantitative study of visual after images, Brit. J. Ophth. **37**:165, 1953.
6. Padgham, C.: Further studies of the positive visual after image, Optica acta **4**: 102, 1957.
7. Padgham, C.: The role of the retinal receptors in the formation of the positive visual after image, Vision Res. **3**:45, 1963.
8. Wang, G., and Lu, T.: Action potentials in visual cortex and superior colliculus induced by shadow movement across visual field, Chinese J. Physiol. **10**:149, 1936.
9. Dodt, E., and Wadenstern, L.: The use of flicker electroretinography in the human eye, Acta ophth. **32**:165, 1954.
10. Adrian, E., and Matthews, R.: Action of light on the eye; interaction of retinal neurons, J. Physiol. **65**:273, 1928.
11. Enroth, C.: Spiked frequency and flicker fusion frequency in the nasal visual field, Arch. Ophth. **50**:50, 1953.
12. Hecht, S., Shlaer, S., and Verrijp, C.: Intermittent stimulation by light; the measurement of critical fusion frequency for the human eye, J. Gen. Physiol. **17**: 237, 1933.
13. Hecht, S., and Verrijp, C.: Intermittent stimulation by light; the relation between intensity and critical fusion frequency for different retinal locations, J. Gen. Physiol. **17**:251, 1933.
14. Hecht, S., and Verrijp, C.: Intermittent stimulation by light; a theoretical interpretation of the quantitative data of flicker, J. Gen. Physiol. **17**:269, 1933.
15. Hecht, S., and Verrijp, C.: Influence of intensity, color and retinal location on fusion frequency of intermittent illumination, Proc. Nat. Acad. Sc. **19**:522, 1933.
16. Hecht, S., and Smith, E.: Intermittent stimulation by light; area and relation between critical frequency and intensity, J. Gen. Physiol. **19**:979, 1936.
17. Hecht, S., and Shlaer, S.: Intermittent stimulation by light; the relation between intensity and critical frequency for different parts of the spectrum, J. Gen. Physiol. **19**:965, 1936.
18. Alpern, M., and Spencer, R.: Variation of critical flicker frequency in the nasal visual field, Arch. Ophth. **50**:50, 1953.
19. Berger, C.: Area of retinal image and flicker fusion frequency, Acta physiol. scandinav. **28**:224, 1953.
20. Berger, C., and Buchthal, F.: Der Einfluss von Beleuchtung und Ausdehnung des gereizten Netzhautareals sowie vom Pupillendurchmesser auf das Auslösungsvermögen des emmetropen Auges, Skandinav. Arch. Physiol. **78**:197, 1938.
21. Berger, C., and Mahneke, A.: The influence of accommodation upon the flicker-fusion-frequency of the human eye and its relation to apparent visual size, Acta ophth. **31**:195, 1953.
22. Weekers, R., and Roussell, F.: La mesure de la frequence de fusion en clinique, Docum. ophth. **2**:131, 1948.
23. Otero, A.: J. Optic. Soc. America **41**: 12, 1951.
24. Fry, G., and Bartley, S.: Relations of stray light in the eye to retinal action potential, Am. J. Physiol. **111**:335, 1935.
25. Simonson, E., and Winchell, P.: Effect of high carbon dioxide and low oxygen concentration on fusion frequency of flicker, J. Appl. Physiol. **3**:637, 1951.
26. Alpern, M., and Jampel, R.: The effects of autonomic drugs on human flicker discrimination, Am. J. Ophth. **47**:464, 1959.
27. Phillips, G.: Perception of flicker in lesions of visual pathways, Brain **56**:464, 1933.
28. Enzer, N., Simonson, E., and Blankstein, S.: The reappearance of flicker at high flash frequency in patients with brain pathology and in normal subjects, J. Lab. & Clin. Med. **29**:63, 1944.
29. Miles, P.: Flicker fusion frequency in amblyopia ex anopsia, Am. J. Ophth. **32**: 225, 1949.
30. Feinberg, I.: Critical flicker frequency in amblyopia ex anopsia, Am. J. Ophth. **42**: 473, 1956.
31. Alpern, M., Flitman, D., and Joseph, R.:

Centrally fixed flicker thresholds in amblyopia, Am. J. Ophth. **49**:1194, 1960.

32. Enoch, J.: Amblyopia and the Stiles-Crawford effect; a theoretical treatment, Am. J. Optom. **34**:298, 1957.

33. Enoch, J.: Receptor amblyopia, Am. J. Ophth. **48**:262, 1959.

34. Mayer, L. L., and Sherman, I.: A method

of flicker perimetry, Am. J. Ophth. **21**: 390, 1938.

35. Riddell, L.: The use of flicker phenomenon in an investigation of the field of vision, Brit. J. Ophth. **20**:385, 1936.

36. Creed, R., and Ruch, R.: Regional variations in sensitivity to flicker, J. Physiol. **74**:407, 1932.

CHAPTER 19

VISUAL ACUITY

CLINICAL MEASUREMENTS OF VISUAL ACUITY

The acuity of vision is measured clinically by the use of test type. The letters of this type are so constructed that the letter as a whole subtends an angle of 5 minutes and each part or stroke of the letter subtends an angle of 1 minute. The Snellen visual acuity chart consists of letters of different sizes; at the end of each line of letters the distance at which the letters subtend an angle of 5 minutes is marked on the chart. Thus, if the person to be tested is placed 6 M. from the test chart, he should be able to read the row of letters which subtend an angle of 5 minutes at 6 M. If he does so, his vision is recorded as 6/6. If he fails to read these letters but is able to read those which subtend an angle of 5 minutes at 12 M., his vision is recorded as 6/12. A distance of 6 M. is chosen since rays of light at that distance from a light source for all practical purposes are considered to be parallel. In reality the rays of light are not parallel but divergent. The power of this divergent bundle of rays is 0.17 D. ($\frac{100}{6000 \text{ mm.}}$ = 0.17 D.). Theoretically, therefore, –0.12 D. (the smallest spherical lens in the commonly used trial case and

the smallest fraction to which spectacle lenses are ground) should be added to the findings of trial cases during routine refraction.

By definition, the emmetropic eye is one in which rays of light entering parallel to the principal axis are focused on the retina when the eye is unaccommodated. A person whose vision is 6/6 is said to have normal visual acuity, and one whose acuity is less than 6/6, e.g., 6/12, is said to have subnormal vision. The fractions 6/6, 6/12, etc., are sometimes regarded as fractions which can be reduced. Visual acuity of 6/6 is, therefore, recorded as 1.0. Vision of 6/12 in the same manner would be written as 0.5. Are we correct in thinking that a person whose visual acuity is 6/12 has only one-half normal vision? This is certainly not so. It is an error to reduce the empirical units of visual acuity to fractions and to regard them as signifying the percentage of vision in that form. A person whose visual acuity is 6/12 has considerably more than one-half normal central vision. Visual acuity is measured in strictly empirical units and should be left in this form to avoid misunderstanding.

Why were letters constructed so that each part subtends an angle of 1 minute and the letter as a whole an angle of 5 minutes? What physiologic basis is there for assuming 1 minute to be the smallest visual angle resolvable by the normal human eye and the 5-minute angle to be the normal threshold for the perception and recognition of forms such as letters? The answer to these questions is linked with the historic development of ophthalmology. Like other things in medicine, the practical applications of this test came before the underlying principles were understood. As early as 1738, we find in Robert Smith's *System of Compleat Opticks* the following statement: "Dr. Hook assures us that the sharpest eye cannot well distinguish any distance in the heavens, suppose a spot on the moon's body, or the distance between two stars, which subtends a less angle at the eye than half a minute; and that hardly one of a hundred men can distinguish it when it subtends a minute." It was assumed from statements such as Hook's and from the results of experiments of the early investigators that, since the smallest distance between two points of light which could be discerned (i.e., the minimum separable) was 1 minute of arc, in order for a person to perceive the exact *form* of an object the component parts of the object must subtend an angle of 1 minute. Thus letters constructed on this principle were believed to test adequately the ability of a person to discriminate form. Since this seemed reasonable at the time and was simple and uncomplicated, it was adopted readily for clinical use.

Although this is still probably the best clinical test for measuring defects in the optical system of the eye, its limitations should be appreciated by those using it, and it should be recognized that the values selected as normal are not based on physiologic principles but on experience and utility. It is recognized that most persons with normal eyes have considerably better visual acuity than 6/6, based on a 5-minute letter. As a result, in practice test charts based on a 4-minute test letter are used frequently.

When a person reads letters on a Snellen chart, a number of functions are tested. The power of attention (which in itself is complex), consisting of both the willingness and the ability of the subject to make a conscious effort to read, is demanded of him. The ability to direct the eyes so that an image of each letter falls in turn on the most sensitive part of the retina is required also. There can be little doubt that in most children and in many clinic patients the failure to obtain 6/6 vision is due partly to their lack of cooperation and intelligence; in other words, it is due to a low power of attention. Likewise, the accurate fixation needed to read the smaller letters on the charts is not developed in very young children. The letters on each line of the Snellen test chart are printed in such a way that, as they get smaller, more are crowded on each line. The result is that in order for the subject to read the 6/6 line, accurate fixation of each letter is necessary in order to separate it from its neighbor. Children under 6 or 7 years of age generally do not have the necessary coordination of the ocular muscles to do this. Frequently adults complain that they can read the small letters at the beginning and at the end of a line, but that the ones in the middle get mixed up. This is due to difficulties of fixation. The acuity of vision is better in normal individuals when single letters are presented than when the vision is tested on the usual Snellen chart. The effect of crowding of the letters on the usual chart becomes more apparent in subjects with subnormal vision, and is particularly true in the amblyopia of strabismus (p. 874).[1]

Aside from the various psychologic factors which enter into the test of visual acuity, a number of physiologic factors are concerned in the resolution of complex patterns such as letters.

PHYSIOLOGIC FACTORS INVOLVED IN VISUAL ACUITY

The correct resolution of form such as the letters on a Snellen chart involve a number of different retinal functions such as the threshold of the photoreceptors to light and the change in this threshold which takes place as a result of adaptation, the ability of the photoreceptors to discriminate between different intensities of illumination, the minimum visual angle at which two objects can be recognized, the detection of a gap in a contour, the resolution of gratings, and the resolution of a displacement in a contour, the so-called vernier acuity. Some of the physiologic factors are as yet not understood. It is to be expected that different values of visual acuity would be obtained with different tests. As Pirenne states, "There are in fact as many different 'visual acuities' as there are types of test objects."*

Minimum visible. Reduced to its simplest terms, the function of the retina is the detection of light. This is the discrimination between light and dark. The color sense is a special development of this but is not directly concerned in the present problem. In order for the photoreceptors in the retina to be stimulated, a sufficient quantity of light must enter the eye. It has been shown that under ideal conditions of dark adaptation the rods will respond to practically the minimal amount of light energy which can be emitted, i.e., approximately 5 photons.

*From Pirenne, M.: In Davson, H., editor: The eye, vol. 2, New York, The Blakiston Division, McGraw-Hill Book Co., Inc.

In its passage through the eye, light suffers from the various optical defects of the ocular media and finally reaches the retina in a state somewhat altered from that before it entered the eye due to absorption of certain wavelengths by the ocular media and due to the aberrations of the optical apparatus. This is true even though the eye to be tested is emmetropic. Because of its spherical aberration, chromatic aberration, and diffraction at the edge of the pupil, the image of a point of light entering the eye is not a point on the retina but a somewhat diffuse surface. In the study of optics, the passage of light rays through the eye is generally considered a problem in geometry. Here, it is customary and correct to speak of object points and image points. Even though the rays traced through the emmetropic eye are strictly paraxial, the optical structure of the living eye is so far from the perfection required by geometric optics that the image formed on the retina from a point source of light, e.g., a distant star, is far from being a point.

The distribution on the retina of a bundle of rays after passing through the ocular media is shown in Fig. 360. Let *AB* represent the surface of the retina illuminated by the light from a source, *DC*. Ordinates erected on the retinal plane represent the intensity of light falling on the retinal surface. If there were no optical imperfections in the system, the surface would be evenly illuminated from *A* to *B*. The intensity of the illumination would be measured by the height of *AD* and *BC*. The total illumination of the surface between *A* and *B* would then be equal to the figure *ABCD*. Because of the aberrations present in the eye, however, the light is diffused at the edges of the image. Instead of a sharp demarcation between light and dark at *A* and *B*, the light is diffused and spreads beyond *A*

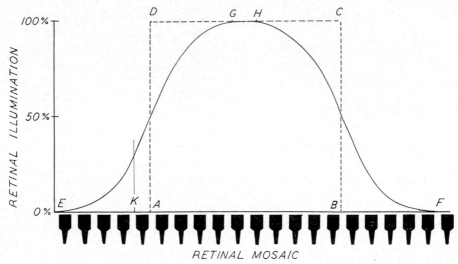

Fig. 360. Distribution of light intensities on the retina from a single light source.

and *B.* As a result of this redistribution of the illumination, the figure *EGHF* is formed. The area of the retina illuminated is larger, therefore, than if the eye were a perfect optical instrument. How much larger the illuminated area will be depends upon the imperfections in the refracting system of the eye and the size of the pupil. If the light is monochromatic and comes, e.g., from the region of the spectrum having a wavelength of 550 mμ and if the pupil measures 3 mm. in diameter, the image of a point source will cover an area of approximately 3.7 μ, i.e., 36 seconds of arc at the nodal point. If the light is not monochromatic but white light, the effects of chromatic aberration must be added to this. Direct measurement of the size of the retinal image in excised steer and cat eyes[3] shows that the blur of the retinal image is even greater than that calculated on theory.

Although spherical aberration is demonstrated easily in the human eye, its exact measurements are difficult. For most eyes the spherical aberration is positive;

i.e., the eye is more myopic for peripheral rays, which is to be expected.

Chromatic aberration. Since the human eye shows considerable chromatic aberration even if diffraction and spherical aberrations are eliminated, the eye could still form a point image only if the object emitted monochromatic light. When white light is used, the rays of short wavelength are refracted more than those of long wavelength. Only one wavelength is focused on the retina at a time. It is evident that the eye is myopic to the blue end of the spectrum and hyperopic to the red end, assuming that it was emmetropic otherwise. The result will be a blue circle having its highest intensity in the center. The normal emmetropic eye is usually focused for yellow rays, which happen to be the most effective in the photopic state. The use of chromatic aberration has been employed in the durochrome test for determining spherical refraction. The subject observes letters on a blue background and compares them with letters on a red background. If both are equally sharp, the

Fig. 361. Diffusion effect. The white square appears larger than the black although both are actually the same size.

focus is on the retina. If the blue are sharp and those on the red background are blurred, the subject is wearing too little plus spherical correction. If the red letters are sharp and the blue are blurred, the subject is wearing too much plus correction. Obviously, the test must be carried out with complete cycloplegia.

Irradiation. The spread of light by irradiation is partly responsible for the apparent difference in size between equally large white and black objects. A small white square on a black background seems larger than an equally large black square on a white background. The white square shown in Fig. 361 spreads out by irradiation on the surrounding cones in the retina and therefore involves a larger area of the retina than its actual visual angle. For the same reason, the white area around the black square causes a similar spread of illumination inward and leaves a smaller area of retina unstimulated than that measured by the visual angle of the black square. Hence, the black square appears to be smaller than the white.

Because of this spread of light, it is impossible to define the threshold of the minimum visible in terms of a visual angle which the retina can just perceive. A good example of this is the visibility of light from stars. The visual angle of light coming from a star is infinitesimal. The rays of light are parallel. Despite this they are visible to us. They do not have the appearance of points because the retinal image of a point of light is not a point but a diffusion circle due to the aberrations of the ocular media, as stated. That they actually appear star-shaped is due to the optical imperfections in the crystalline lens (p. 237). The factor which determines the visibility of a point of light has nothing to do with the visual angle it subtends, therefore, but depends entirely on the amount of light energy falling on the photoreceptors and their sensitivity. The amount of light energy falling on the retina must lie above the threshold of stimulation of one or more photoreceptors. The brighter the star, i.e., the more light energy from it reaching the eye, the larger it appears. This is probably due to irradiation of light so that more photoreceptors are stimulated.

Minimum discriminable (minimum light difference that can be detected). Not only can the eye detect minimal quantities of light, as stated, but it also has the power to discriminate between different intensities of light. As will be pointed out in a later section (p. 770), the essence of this discrimination is the gradient of contrast. If a white paper is looked at with the illumination falling on it from one side, it can be seen that the part of the paper closer to the light is more illuminated than that on the far side. There is no obvious line of demarcation, however, because the gradient of contrast is low; i.e., the decrease in illumination is gradual. If the light illuminating the paper is a desk lamp covered with a shade, there will be a definite shadow on the paper where the shade reduces the illumination, but even here there may be no sharp line of demarcation or boundary line if the gradient of contrast is still low. However, a fine pencil mark on the paper will be sharply demarcated because its gradient of contrast is high.

Directly related to the minimum discriminable is the detection of a black line on a white background or a white line on a black background. These provide us with test objects whose length and diameter can be varied, and the smallest visual angle under which the line becomes visible can be determined. The simplest test object is a single opaque line against a uniformly illuminated background.

A long single opaque black line can be detected when it subtends a visual angle as small as 0.5 second of arc.[4] The detection of such a small object shows how sensitive the cones in the fovea are to small differences in light intensity that fall on them. The resolving power of the eye is dependent on the ability of the cones to detect the smallest difference in light intensity falling on them. If there were no such thing as diffraction, the amount of light falling on the retinal cones covered by a small black line would be nearly zero, whereas the amount of light falling on the adjacent cones would be 100% of the illumination of the background, whatever that might be. In other words, the retinal image would correspond exactly with the geometric image as pictured in optics.

Because of diffraction at the edge of the pupil, however, a point of light produces an image having a finite size on the retina which can be measured. It is not a geometric point but an image consisting of a central bright spot surrounded by successive dark and light rings called diffusion circles. Fig. 362 illustrates diffraction in which light rays strike the edge of an object interposed in their path. At point *A* rays of light from *O* are intercepted by object *AB* and are bent by diffraction. The effect produced on the screen, *XY,* is a series of black and white lines, as shown in *M*. When the rays impinging on the screen are in phase with one another, the light is intensified, and when the rays are out of phase, they nullify one another, producing dark bands. The effect of diffraction at the margins of a circular aperture, with production of light and dark rings is shown in Fig. 363. As previously stated, if the aperture of the pupil is 3 mm. and monochromatic light of 550 mμ is used, the central bright spot will subtend a visual angle of about 36 seconds, and the diffusion circle will cover an area of 3.7 μ on the retina. Since each cone in the fovea is about 1 to 1.5 μ in diameter, such a spot of light must cover several cones.

The distribution of light on the retina produced by a black line on a white background can be determined. Hecht and

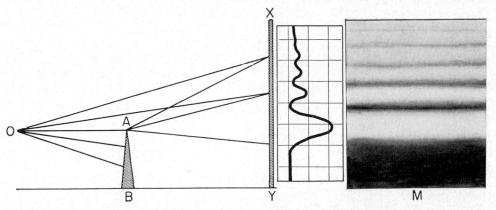

Fig. 362. Diffraction pattern of light produced by a straight edge.

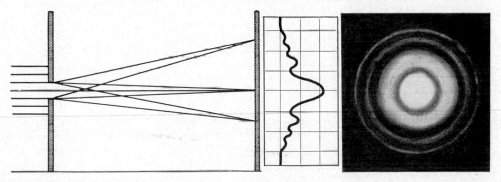

Fig. 363. Diffraction pattern of light produced by a round aperture.

Mintz have calculated the effects of diffraction on such an image in order to describe as nearly as possible the conditions of contrasting illumination between the image and the surrounds on the retina. In Fig. 364 is shown the distribution of the light intensity on the diffracted retinal image produced by a wire whose geometric image is represented to scale by the rectangle in the upper part of the illustration. The size of the pupil for this calculation was 3 mm. The geometric image of the wire was 2.6 μ wide, corresponding to a visual angle of 35.5 minutes. The distribution of light, corresponding to the *smallest* resolvable visual angle just given (0.5 second), is so flat and near the upper edge of the ordinates that it

cannot be shown in a drawing of this scale. However, it has the same form as that shown in Fig. 364, and its vertical dimensions are a constant fraction of that of the larger distribution. This is true of all images, except those which are from very large test objects far above the thresholds of resolution.

The geometric image on the retina of a wire, corresponding to the highest resolution observable at 0.5 second of arc, is hardly 0.04μ wide. This is considerably smaller than the values given by previous workers in this field, but as Hecht points out, this low figure is probably due to the care with which the background was illuminated evenly. The just resolvable angle increases rapidly when the back-

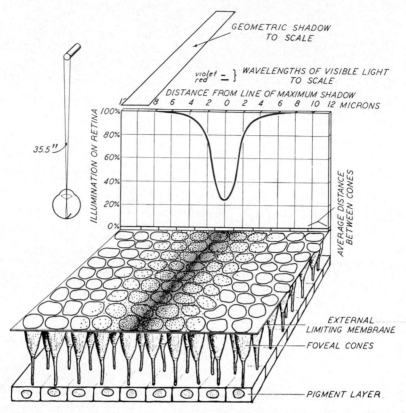

Fig. 364. Distribution of light intensity of diffracted retinal image of a wire.

ground is illuminated irregularly, and for that reason measurements made with the open sky as a background are inadequate. Since the central cones of the fovea are between 1 and 1.5 mµ in diameter, the geometric image is only about one thirtieth of the width of a single cone. As just stated, such comparisons of retinal image and individual diameters of cones are meaningless since the effects of diffraction must spread the shadow, corresponding to the line, over an area of several cones.

To be resolved at this small angle, the test line must have a certain length, many times longer than it is wide, which indicates that the number of retinal elements involved is large. The relation of length of line to width corresponds to

the area yielding the best values for intensity discrimination. This will also be shown to be the case in the determination of displacements of a contour (p. 765).

As I have described on p. 498, the eye is never entirely still but continually undergoes very small movements, called micronystagmus, which do not permit a theoretical point image to remain fixed for an indefinite time on any one spot in the retina. It has been calculated that such a point must be traversing two to four cones in the retina continually. Because of this, any scheme of visual resolution which imagines a fixed pattern of light and shade on the retina and results in stimulation of one cone while adjacent cones on either side remain unstimulated must be modified. The situation as it relates to the resolution of a line measuring 0.5 second of visual angle must be visualized in terms of a constantly moving retina on which the image is projected.

This has been described so well by Hecht and Mintz in their paper that the account is given verbatim. Hecht assumed that the foveal cones are 2.3 μ wide, instead of 1 to 1.5 μ as given by Polyak's latest figures. The principles remain the same, however.

"Assuming the general illumination on the retina to be 100%, then it comes out that a central row of cones 2.3 μ wide is illuminated by 98.83% of the prevailing intensity, while the row to either side has a light intensity of 99.78%. The difference in light intensity between the two rows is 0.95% and is a value near those usually found in measurements of intensity discrimination at high light intensities. It corresponds to a value of $\frac{\triangle I}{I} = 1/105$ and is exceeded only by Aubert's (1865) best value of 1/146 and Helmholtz' (1886) value of 1/167 at the highest illuminations. For more moderate illuminations, like our maximum, the values generally range around 1/100.

"This computation tells us that a fine line is recognized at such small angles because even its fuzzy and extended shadow reduces the light on one long row of cones to a value which is just perceptibly less than the light on the row of cones on either side of it. The line appears sharp because it produces a perceptible shadow on one row of cones only. Note that the row of cones to either side of this critical row has its illumination reduced by only 0.22% compared to the prevailing illumination next to it, and that this small difference in intensity cannot be perceived; it would mean a $\frac{\triangle I}{I}$ of about 1/400 and cannot be achieved by the eye. Thus when a line becomes recognizable, the light distribution which it produces on the retina is such that only one row of cones is just perceptibly shaded by it.

"From Hartridge's original computation it was not clear why a line is perceived as a sharp line instead of as a band of shadow gradually fading at the edges, and it has been necessary to assume some central nervous

mechanism for converting such a gradual distribution into a sharp line. However, in view of our present computation, the line appears sharp simply because its diffracted image on the retina affects only one row of cones differently from the rest. Thus Hartridge's idea that the resolving power of the eye is determined by its capacity for intensity discrimination is even better than originally anticipated.

"We have supposed that in the retina the comparison is made between the row of perceptibly shaded cones and the row immediately next to it. This makes an intensity difference of just 0.95% between the two rows. However, in view of the nature of intensity difference perception (Hecht, 1935) it is even more likely that what is recognized is the intensity difference produced on the central row of cones from the time that it is affected by the general retinal illumination to the time when it is affected by the shaded center of the image, and these successive intensities are achieved by the obvious eye movements made during the effort to resolve the line in the field. Considered this way, the intensity difference is about 1.17% which is also near the minimum perceptible intensity difference. . . ."*

The threshold of visibility of very fine wires varies depending upon the orientation of the wires in space. For example, the threshold has been reported to be lower when the wires are oriented in either the vertical or horizontal meridians than when they are obliquely situated.[5] Another observer has found a lower threshold for the vertical position while the horizontal and oblique positions yielded the same thresholds. The reason for this difference in thresholds is not entirely clear. It might originate from either retinal factors or factors affecting the higher visual pathways.[6, 7] Weymouth believes that it is optical. He calls attention to the characteristic image of a star as seen by individuals with good acuity and emmetropic eyes or eyes made so with correcting glasses. Most such indi-

---

*From Hecht, S., and Mintz, E.: J. Gen. Physiol. **22**:593, 1939.

viduals image a star as a bright central area with eight rays, of which the vertical and horizontal are usually the more prominent. Weymouth believes that with very small linear stimuli such as the ones used in the studies showing orientation preference, the coincidence of image and ray direction might lead to significantly lower thresholds in the vertical and horizontal direction corresponding to the more prominent rays of the star.

Visibility of gratings. We have seen that the threshold of visibility of single black lines depends on the gradient of contrast between the illumination falling on a row of cones (perhaps a row of cone units) and the rest of the retina. If this gradient in illumination is high enough, it will be signaled to the cortex, and the line will be perceived.

This is quite different from the visibility of an illuminated slit on a black background for, as Pirenne points out, "In this case the slit—however thin—always becomes visible when it is sufficiently brightly illuminated." The visibility of a bright slit on a black background depends merely on whether the minimum number of quanta of light reach the retina to activate the minimum number of rods and cones necessary for visual sensation.

In the case of more complicated patterns, such as black gratings on a white background, the same factors which affect the visibility of a black line on a white background are active. The pattern will be resolved on the basis of gradient of contrast. The distribution of the light on the retinal elements from such gratings can be calculated. Shlaer[8] points out that the situation is similar to that of an edge of an extensive dark area adjacent to an extensive light area due to the fact that the bars are very long compared to their width. It is much more difficult to make such computations for test letters, even

simple ones such as the Landolt broken ring because of the shortness of all the dimensions.

From the data shown in Fig. 365, *B* it can be seen that the maximum amount of light to reach the receptors is never above 61% of the total illumination, and the minimum amount of light is only 39% of the total. The limit of the resolving power of the eye for gratings is not set by the difference between the maxima and minima of intensities falling on adjacent rows of receptors. Experiments show that the limit for such resolution is set by the size of the pupil when this is less than 2.3 mm. When the pupil is larger than this, it is the size of the individual cones or functional cone units in the fovea. Assuming the finest resolvable grating to correspond to the spacing of the cones in the fovea and taking the focal length of eye to be 15.5 mm., Shlaer computes the distance between the adjacent rows of foveal cones at be 2.1 μ. The figures of Osterberg correspond well with this (compare Polyak's values of interconal distance in the fovea which equal 1 to 1.5 μ). He gives a distance between adjacent parallel rows of foveal cones as 2.4 μ.

Shlaer proved that the limits for the resolution of a grating were not set by the differences in the intensities of light on the retina by using gratings having the same number of bars per centimeter but with varying widths of each black bar. When a grating whose bars were just half the size of a standard grating and with the same number of bars per centimeter was made, the difference between the intensity maxima and minima of the new grating was half that of the first, but the eye resolved it equally well.

Discrimination of two separate points (minimum separable). As has been pointed out, the early astronomers soon

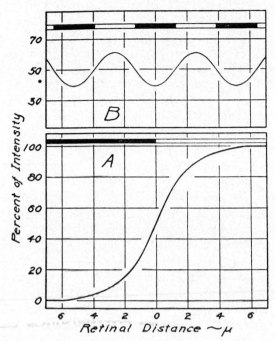

Fig. 365. A, Distribution of the light in an image of an extensive edge on the retina when chromatic aberration and diffraction are taken into account. Values are from Hartridge. **B,** Distribution of light in an image of a grating corresponding to a visual acuity of 1.7 on the retina when chromatic aberration and diffraction are taken into account. (From Shlaer, S.: J. Gen. Physiol. **21:**165, 1937.)

recognized that the eye was able to perceive double stars when their angular separation was at least one minute of arc or more. Stars closer together than this could not be perceived as separate.

The problem of discrimination of two separate images by the retina is similar to that of the discrimination of touch on the surface of the skin. Sensory endings scattered throughout the surface of the skin give rise to the sensation of touch when stimulated (p. 80). In some regions of the body these touch spots are close together, e.g., the tips of the fingers. In other regions they are distributed sparsely, e.g., the skin on the back. When one of these spots is touched with a hair, it gives rise to a sensation of a single contact on the skin. If two hairs are used to touch the skin in two separate regions,

the sensation of two contacts with the skin will occur only when two touch spots are stimulated. If the second hair fails to hit a touch spot, the sensation will still be of one contact only. Since these touch spots are very close together on the tips of the fingers, the hairs do not have to be very far apart before they will both be felt. On the other hand, the touch spots of the skin on the back are very far apart, and the hairs must be widely separated before they will stimulate two separate touch spots so that they can be distinguished as two contacts on the skin. The fineness of perception of touch in discriminating two separate contacts with the skin obviously depends upon the distribution, i.e., the concentration, of touch spots in the skin. Where these are close together, the discrimination will be of a high order, and, where they lie far apart, it will be low.

In the eye, the rods and cones are the sensitive end organs. Except in the fovea, where each cone seems to be connected at least functionally with a single midget ganglion cell, a number of photoreceptors are connected with each ganglion cell. In order that a person can perceive two points of light as separate, the lights must be far enough apart that their images stimulate two separate photoreceptors or two separate functioning units which send their messages to the brain by different paths. At least one unstimulated photoreceptor or unit must lie between these two. If it is assumed that all of the cones in the region tested have the same threshold of stimulation, the amount of light energy from the two point sources must be greater than this threshold value, and the amount of light energy reaching the retina from the surroundings must be below this value.

Instead of two separate points of light, two black dots on a white surface may be used to measure the smallest visual angle under which the eye can discriminate the dots as separate. In the case of the two dots, the principle underlying their detection likewise depends on having unstimulated photoreceptors lying between the two which are stimulated.

The smallest visual angle at which two separate objects can be discriminated is called the minimum separable. The threshold of the minimum separable depends upon the method of measuring it. As stated, early astronomers found that it measured about 60 seconds of arc. Under laboratory conditions the minimum separable has been found to range from 20 to 30 seconds, and Guillery[9] states that it can be as low as 15 seconds.

From what has just been said it is evident that the minimum separable depends upon the number of photoreceptors per unit area in the retina. The smaller each photoreceptor is or, to put it more accurately, the less the distance between each photoreceptor, the smaller will be the visual angle at which two separate stimuli can be discriminated. The fact that the minimum separable, like the visual acuity determined with the Snellen chart, is greatest at the fovea and falls off immediately when extrafoveal regions of the retina are tested strongly suggests that the cones are concerned in this function and that the number of cones per unit area determines its value.

In the center of the human foveola the diameter of the cone according to Polyak is approximately 1 to 1.5 μ. The interconal distance, assuming the cones to be packed tightly together in the fovea, which they apparently are, cannot be less than 1 μ. This corresponds to a visual angle of 12 seconds of arc. In other words the minimum separable could be explained on the known size of the grain of the fovea if the eye were a perfect optical instrument and one did not have to take into consideration the imperfections of the image due to the aberrations and the eye movements described previously. We have seen, however, that these are considerable.

The conclusion that the correspondence between the minimum separable and the size of the foveal cones is not coincidental seems inescapable. It is quite likely that the minimum separable and the acuity of vision, not only the discrimination of test letters, but also the detection of displacements of a contour (sometimes spoken of as the aligning power of the eye), are related intimately to the density of the cone population, but not in such a simple manner as has been depicted. In the case of a photograph the fineness of detail depends entirely on the grain of the film.

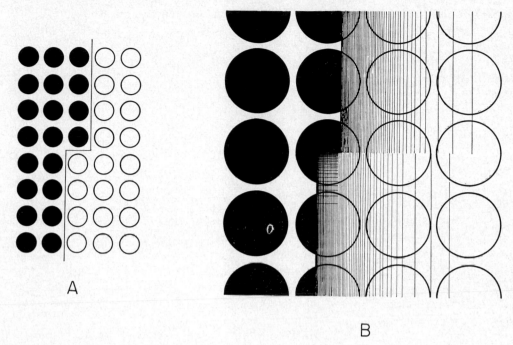

Fig. 366. Diagrammatic explanation of vernier acuity based on the grain of a photographic film in a stationary camera.

It is doubtful that this concept can be transferred directly to the mechanisms of vision.

Aligning power of the eye (vernier acuity). The ability of the eye to detect a displacement of a contour is called the aligning power of the eye. The precision with which we can adjust a mark on a vernier scale depends on the aligning power of the eye. It is found to be extraordinarily fine. A skilled observer can make readings on the scale with an average error of not more than 2 seconds of arc. The aligning power is thus five times as fine as the minimum separable. How is it possible for this threshold to be lower than the diameter of a single foveal cone, i.e., 12 seconds of arc? In the older literature, comparisons were drawn between the eye and a camera in regarding the retina as a light-sensitive film on which an image was formed. The fineness of the retinal image was thought to depend upon the number of photoreceptors per unit area, just as in the camera it depends on the grain of the film. From this point of view it was easy to imagine that the detection of a displacement of a contour consists in part of the image falling on one row of cones and, at the break, the remainder falling entirely on a separate row (Fig. 366, *A* and *B*). The message sent to the brain in this form would be interpreted as a break in contour. Good reasons for abandoning such a concept have already been presented; the retinal image cannot be limited to a row of cones because of the aberrations of the eye, including diffraction at the pupil, and the retina is constantly in motion so that the image cannot stay fixed on any one line.

The difficulty can be resolved, however, by assuming, as Weymouth has done, that what really counts is the difference in threshold of stimulation between individual cones or between cone units. If the difference in light intensity falling upon groups of cones is sufficiently great so that their conducting fibers send different responses to the brain, the displacement of the contour could be interpreted from this response. This would be possible, even though the image was shifting constantly over a large population of receptors due to the movements of the eye or even if the test object itself were in motion. The size of the individual cones would not be the limiting factor to the resolving power of the retina, therefore.

Such a concept requires the ability of the individual cone to signal differences in light intensity, and it has been shown that this can be accomplished by the frequency of the discharge in the nerve fiber. Although each cone and each fiber obeys the all-or-none law, differences in intensity can be signaled by different rates of discharge, more intense illumination producing more rapid discharge in the nerve fiber (p. 707). This mechanism would be aided if large numbers of cones were signaling. It is well known that the aligning power depends to a certain extent on the length of the line, as well as on its width and the extent of the break. This indicates that the number of retinal elements stimulated is a factor in determining the aligning power. It has been suggested that even the constant movements of the eyes may aid in bringing more retinal elements into play.

Anderson and Weymouth[10] point out that every cone in the fovea is connected to a single nerve fiber. It is possible, therefore, to have every cone represented in consciousness. In other words, every cone has its own local sign. The image of a straight line falling on one of two adjacent cones will usually stimulate both simultaneously, and as a consequence these two cones will be linked together in experience, and the local sign of each will partake of the nature of the other. Every group of five or six cones is interrelated likewise with the surrounding groups. The effect of the constant movement of the image across the retina will be to stimulate an entire new series of cones constantly.

It is well known that the accuracy obtained by averaging together a large number of measurements is greater, even though the measurements are done roughly, than if a few measurements are taken with extreme care. In the same manner, the shifted position of a linear image on the retina by stimulating a relatively large number of receptor units, each having its own local sign, results (according to Weymouth and Anderson) in a more accurate localization in consciousness of a line than may be accounted for by a shift in position from one cone to another. The length of the line, according to this theory, will determine materially the accuracy with which a shift in position can be visualized since the longer it is, the more cone groups will be affected. Experiments show this to be so. Within certain limits, the accuracy in the aligning power of the eye is enhanced considerably by increasing the length of the line.

Fig. 367 was constructed by Anderson and Weymouth from a photomicrograph of the human foveal cones made by Fritsch. One half of the field is illuminated, *L-L,* and one half is dark, *D-D,* the line of separation or the geometric margin of the image lying along *g-g.* The physiologic margin of the image will be represented by the line connecting the centers of the last stimulated cones (marked with heavy points). Although this physiologic margin of the image is irregular, if the line is long enough, all

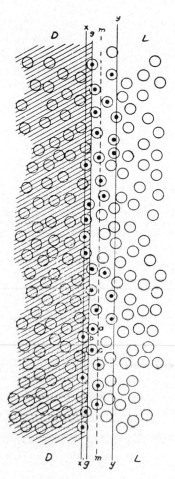

Fig. 367. Diagram of conditions at margin of stimulated area, according to Anderson and Weymouth. (From Anderson, E. E., and Weymouth, F.: Am. J. Physiol. **64**:561, 1923.)

points will lie within a strip having a width equal to the greatest interconal distance and standing always in the same relation to the geometric margin of the image.

Since the eye is moving continually, this physiologic margin of the image will be a succession of such irregular lines, all points of which will lie within the strip between x-x and y-y. This must not be thought of as a fixed area upon the retina, but at the same time it will maintain a

constant relationship to the geometric image.

The center of this strip, m-m, represents the center of gravity, so to speak, of all the points stimulated and hence represents the local sign of the percept to which they give rise. As Anderson and Weymouth state:

"The average, or mean, of these points, which determines the local sign of the straight line, is therefore not restricted to such units as interconal distance or cone diameter but may be accurate to a small fraction of these units just as the mean of a number of measurements made in inches may be accurate to a small fraction of an inch. Such a percept of position we would designate as retinal mean local sign to emphasize its derivation from the averaging of various factors among which we would include not only the many successive stimuli due to motion, but also the mutual effect of adjacent elements and the comparison of the stimuli presented to the two eyes. . . . Since both the straightness and the position of a straight line are complex judgments (even though unconsciously performed), the limits of accuracy are not set wholly by the fineness of the retinal mosaic but by training, and, in general, such neural processes as occur at a much higher level than the retina."*

On this basis, the perception of a slight displacement of one of the segments of a broken line depends upon the difference between the two local signs of the parts of the line. If this difference is great enough, the line will be perceived as discontinuous. How small this difference might be in terms of a cone diameter cannot be stated a priori, and Anderson and Weymouth state the following:

"Since the comparison is between two percepts, it would be chimerical to expect to find in the physical configuration of the retina the final limits of its delicacy. From the present experiments and those of Bourdon, it may be at least as small as one tenth of one cone diameter.

---

*From Anderson, E. E., and Weymouth, F.: Am. J. Physiol. **64**:561, 1923.

The fineness of perception with the two eyes working together depends upon three factors: (1) the mutual effect of adjacent retinal elements in either retina, i.e., the retinal mean local sign; (2) the averaging of successive stimulus patterns on each retinal mosaic caused by the constant slight eye movements; and (3) the combining of the two simultaneous stimulus patterns presented to the two eyes, i.e., fusion. As the result of these three factors, the aligning power of the eye may be so acute that a disparity between images of a fraction of a cone diameter may be clinically perceived."*

In an experimental setup which eliminates length of the lines to be discriminated as a contour and substitutes dots of light instead, Ludvigh[11] found that the discrimination is of such a high order that it cannot be explained on the basis of any existing theory. The accuracy cannot be explained in terms of averaging the mean position of a statistically large number of cones, according to him. Therefore, it seems likely that Anderson and Weymouth's hypothesis cannot account for the accuracy of the aligning power. Even the assumption of neural peaking, that the retinal elements involved are "on-off" elements operating at borders only and calling on the expansion or magnification of the retinal image in the cortex by reason of the divergence of the pathways from the retina to the cortex, still leaves the problem unsolved.

The aligning power of the eye is a much more delicate test for the detection of early damage to the macula than the reading of letters on the Snellen chart. For the purposes of measuring and correcting ametropia, however, no more delicate test than the Snellen chart is required, especially when the letters are constructed on a 4-minute angle and an acuity of better than 6/6 is strived for.

But as Traquair points out, a central acuity of 6/6 does not necessarily mean a normal fovea. Patients whose acuity is 6/6 occasionally show central scotoma to colors. It is possible that the aligning power might also be used clinically as a more delicate measurement of central retinal damage.

Amsler has made an application of some of the principles involved in the vernier test in what is known as the grid test for foveal function. This consists of a lattice of small squares with a fixation point in the middle. Any displacement of the cones in the fovea from edema causes distortion of the lines of the squares around the fixation point and can be detected easily by the patient, even though his acuity may be normal and no scotoma to white or colors is demonstrable (see also discussion of the Haidinger effect as a test for macular edema, p. 830).

It has been shown that visual acuity as tested clinically with Snellen letters involves a number of different retinal functions: minimum visible, minimum discriminable, visibility of gratings, minimum separable, and aligning power of the eye or vernier acuity. In addition, psychologic factors and muscular coordination of the eyes in fixating one letter on the chart at a time come into play. Its very complexity does not allow accurate conclusions to be drawn regarding physiologic mechanisms at the present time, but the recognition of letters is still probably the best method to be used clinically for the determination of refractive errors and the prescription of correcting glasses.

FACTORS INFLUENCING VISUAL ACUITY

Presence of refractive errors in the dioptric system. It would be beyond the scope of this book to discuss the effects of the various forms of ametropia on

---

*From Anderson, E. E., and Weymouth, F.: Am. J. Physiol. **64:**561, 1923.

visual acuity, but it is important to know how blurred images in general affect the function of the eye. Whenever the retinal image is out of focus, it is larger and its outlines are less sharp. Since the image is larger, the intensity of illumination at every point in the image is less than when the image was in focus. The intensity of the light may fall, therefore, below the threshold level of the photoreceptors and fail to stimulate. If it is bright enough to cause stimulation but is still out of focus, the image will seem larger than when it is in focus due to the larger area of the retina illuminated and hence to the increased number of receptors which are active. Patients frequently have difficulty in deciding between a lens which gives a sharp, small image and one which gives a slightly blurred but larger image. They frequently will choose the lens giving a larger image, solely on the basis of size.

The problem that concerns us now is why a person with uncorrected ametropia has low visual acuity. Ludvigh[12] was the first to consider this from the point of view of retinal function, rather than from the point of view of optics.

He points out that, although the obvious answer to the question What is the purpose of correcting ametropia? is to create a clearly focused image of objects on the retina, this answer is incomplete because within certain limits persons can discriminate images which are not focused clearly; yet experience teaches us that these are unsatisfactory. We must define further what the difference between focused and unfocused images on the retina is for a person. How does the retina respond to both types of image? The final answer must be in terms of physiology, rather than in terms of geometric optics.

In the emmetropic eye each point on the retina receives rays of light from only one point of the object (Fig. 368). Therefore, on the test chart each point in the limb of a letter is conjugate with only one point on the retina, and a point just outside the black limb of the letter, coming from the white background, is conjugate likewise with only one point on the retina. If the aberrations from which even emmetropic eyes suffer are excluded, there is a sharp fall in illumination on the retina at the edge of the image of the letter, therefore. If we assume an ideal situation in which we designate the background of the chart as having an intensity of illumination of 100 units, while the letter on the chart has an intensity of zero units in an emmetropic eye, we will obtain 100 units of illumination on the retina until we enter that portion of the retina which corresponds to the limb of the letter when the illumination at once drops to zero. The change of illumination is great, and in terms of distance on the retina the rate of change is high. The gradient of contrast, which is the rate of change of illumination with respect to distance, therefore is high. This permits a sharp boundary line between those retinal receptors which fire off and those which remain silent since there will be a sudden drop in illumination below the threshold of stimulation of the retinal receptors in a line corresponding to the limb of the letter. The pattern of excitation sent up from these receptors to area 17 in the occipital cortex will be sharply defined, and this factor creates the basis for form discrimination by the mind. Nature has provided ingeniously for an enormous expansion of the visual cortex which receives messages from the fovea, whereas there is contraction of those cortical areas which receive messages from the surrounding retina. The area of the cortex which receives the foveal fibers is much larger than that which responds to

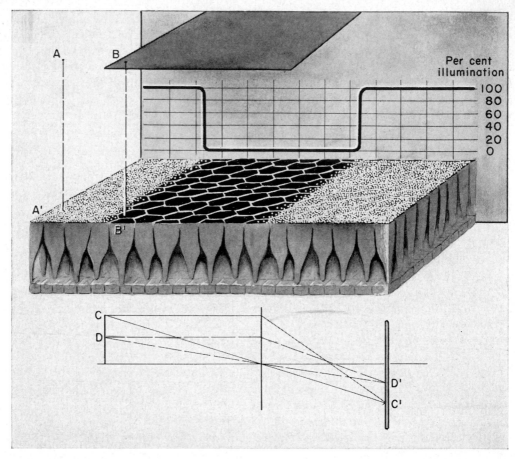

Fig. 368. Stereogram of macular cones in an emmetropic eye with shadow produced on them by a portion of a test letter. The graph at the back portrays the percentage of illumination falling on this retinal area. At the edge of letter **B** the illumination drops from 100% to 0 (for the purpose of this discussion the effects of diffraction have been omitted). The gradient of contrast on the retina is high therefore.

stimulation of the periphery of the retina and shows great magnification of the pattern of response from the fovea. It seems obvious that this is for the purpose of obtaining the benefit of a high gradient of contrast on the retina so that the messages as they come sharply demarcated from the retina do not interfere with one another by peaks and troughs of electrical activity from one set of receptors running into those from an adjoining set.

We can conclude that a high gradient of contrast produces high visual acuity, and this indeed has been found to be true experimentally.

In an ametropic eye each point on the retina receives rays from several points on the chart instead of from one point only (Fig. 369). Each point in the object is conjugate with more than one point on the retina, and the spread of these points increases with the increase in the ametropia. In ametropia there is no sharp boundary line between black and white on the retina, as in the emmetropic eye, and the gradient of contrast is low there-

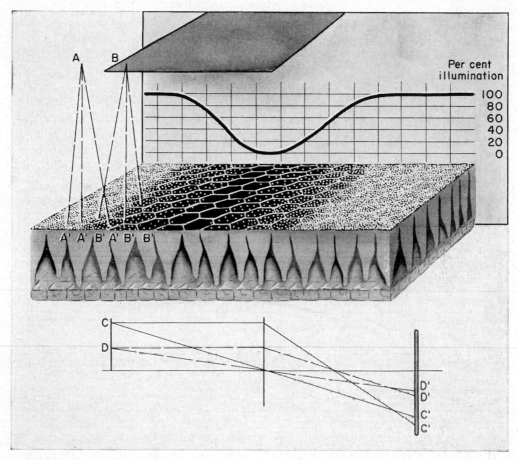

Fig. 369. Stereogram similar to the one shown in Fig. 368, showing the image on the ametropic retina. Note that the gradient of contrast is low.

fore. This means that there is no sharp boundary line between those visual receptors which fire off impulses and those which are silent. Therefore, the contour of excitation in the cortex will be inexact, and the visual discrimination will be correspondingly low.

Thus we see in the uncorrected ametropic eye that the rate of change of illumination with respect to distance on the retina is relatively small, and therefore the contrast value is relatively low. If one considers the change in illumination in a particular direction, it is clear that the gradient of retinal illumination of an ametropic eye will be less than that of an emmetropic eye. Further, the more marked the ametropia, the less will be the gradient of retinal illumination.

From this it is possible to give a specific answer to the question originally proposed: What is the cause of reduced acuity in uncorrected ametropia? The answer is the lower gradient of retinal illumination in ametropia.

When a correcting lens is put in front of the ametropic eye, visual acuity increases because the correcting lens increases the gradient of retinal illumination. Visual acuity is more intimately related to the ratio of the gradient of retinal illumination than to absolute retinal illumination. If we express the gradient of retinal illumination as a fraction of the absolute retinal illumination, we have a concept which gives an immediate qualitative explanation of the loss of acuity with glare and is thus of considerable practical value. Visual acuity is dependent upon many factors besides the gradient of retinal illumination. Among these factors are adaptation, fixation tremor, optical aberrations, spatial induction, etc. In fact the gradient of retinal illumination may be relatively ineffective because of inadequate adaptation. In considering the states of excitation of various retinal elements, we may speak of a gradient of excitation; at the level of the optic nerve and in the occipital lobes we may speak of a gradient of frequency of nerve impulses.

The question may be raised whether a person faced with the necessity of accepting blurred retinal images can learn by a process of trial and error to interpret these better and thus obtain better visual acuity. The answer is Yes. The improvement in visual acuity for persons with uncorrected myopia through so-called visual training is a cerebral process whereby the perceptual processes are trained to better discriminate blurred retinal images. Thus, better visual acuity may be achieved by training, but this in no way creates a higher gradient of contrast on the retina.

Contrast. In the previous sections it was shown that the gradient of contrast is the determining factor in the visibility of contours and that in ametropia the gradient of contrast is low. The correction of ametropia by glasses increases the gradient of contrast. It might be inferred from this that contrast between the object and its surrounds was of equal importance to the gradient, but this is not the case. Ludvigh[13] has found that as the contrast between the letters on the chart and their background is increased from a subliminal value at which no vision is possible the visual acuity mounts very rapidly at first, but more and more slowly thereafter. Thus at low degrees of contrast visual acuity varies markedly with contrast, but at high levels of contrast relatively large changes in the degree of contrast have only slight improvement on visual acuity. A graph showing this is given in Fig. 370. The clinical importance of this is that, if the Snellen chart being used has reasonably high contrast (above 60%), the slight loss of contrast which occurs as a result of use and aging of the chart will have little effect on visual acuity. This is not a recommendation to use dirty charts, however.

Influence of the size of the pupil. Variations in the size of the pupil exercise two effects that are mutually antagonistic upon visual acuity. The larger the pupil, the more light will enter the eye. If the illumination of the test chart is low, this will improve visual acuity. An increase in the size of the pupil, on the other hand, will permit participation of the more peripheral zones of the refracting surfaces in forming the retinal image so that the aberrations are intensified.

If the eye is ametropic, a narrow pupil will increase the visual acuity by cutting down the size of the diffusion circles on the retina because the diameters of these are directly proportionate to the size of the pupil. This is the explanation for the improvement of vision in ametropia by the use of the pinhole disk. The narrow pupil cuts down the amount of light, however, and using an artificial pupil, such as a pinhole disk, markedly reduces the extent of the visual field.

If the pupil is very small, the effect of

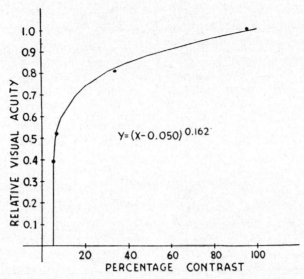

Fig. 370. Average results from tests of visual acuity in three patients. Observations were taken only at the points indicated by solid circles. (From Ludvigh, E.: Arch. Ophth. 25:472, 1941.)

ametropia on visual acuity is less, as shown by the use of the pinhole disk. Although the image is not in focus on the retina, the gradient of contrast is raised by narrowing the spread of the rays on the retina conjugate with each point in the object. Occasionally one finds in doing a manifest refraction, usually on an elderly patient, that a very wide choice of lenses gives the same visual acuity. It may be thought that these patients are mentally obtundant to changes in glass, but it will be found frequently that they have very small pupils which nullify the effects of the ametropia. Weak miotics used to be prescribed by some ophthalmologists for patients who returned after refraction complaining of dissatisfaction with the glasses.

Because of diffraction at the edge of the pupil, a point of light produces an image of measurable size on the emmetropic retina. No matter how small the point source, the image cannot be made smaller than this irreducible size. The image is not a geometric point, but consists of a central bright spot surrounded by successive rings of alternating light and dark. If the aperture of the pupil is 3 mm. and monochromatic light of 550 mμ is used, the central bright spot will subtend a visual angle of 36 seconds. This is equivalent to an area of 3.7 μ in diameter on the retina. Since each foveal cone measures approximately 1.5 μ, such a spot of light must cover several cones. This puts a finite limit to the resolving power of the eye as an optical instrument and therefore limits visual acuity. The smaller the pupil, the greater is the effect of diffraction on the image. For optimal visual acuity it has been calculated that the pupil should be about 3 mm. in diameter. If the pupil is reduced to 2.3 mm., the central light spot will cover an area of 4.9 μ on the retina.

As will be shown, increased illumination improves acuity. Since an increase in illumination generally produces narrower pupils and since chromatic and spherical aberrations are lessened by small pupils and the depth in focus is increased, it might be inquired whether miosis is the sole cause of the increase in visual acuity. It can be shown easily that this is not the case since visual acuity increases with increasing illumination even if pupil size is kept constant by artificial means. In addition, the smaller the pupil, the larger is the effect of diffraction, which of itself not only diminishes acuity, but also actually sets a limit to the final acuity which can be achieved in the case of black lines on a white background. Accordingly, there must be an optimum size of the pupil at which a balance is struck between these two opposing influences. This generally has been set at between 2 and 3 mm. in diameter, as just stated.

The Stiles-Crawford effect. In 1933, Stiles and Crawford[14] showed that light passing through a unit area near the center of the pupil evoked a greater sensation of brightness when compared to light passing through a unit area near the margin of the pupil. If the efficiency of the pupil's center is unity, Stiles and Crawford found that 3 mm. from the center the efficiency or effectiveness had dropped to about one third. This was an astonishing result. It definitely appeared to be a retinal phenomenon and had little or nothing to do with the visual field chosen. It has since been known as the Stiles-Crawford effect or the retinal direction effect. The effect can be tested in a variety of ways by flicker or by simultaneous comparison with a typical photometric field, always with the same results. Later investigation disclosed that the phenomenon did not occur for rod vision, but was very pronounced for cones. These authors suggested that the effect could be caused by absorbing barriers or septa between the cones. Rays from the margin of the pupil entering the retina obliquely

would pass obliquely through such septa and will be absorbed partially and therefore wasted. Rays from the center of the pupil, on the other hand, would enter the retina parallel to the axis of the cones and therefore would not suffer this loss. However, they called attention to the fact that there were no histologic evidences for the existence of such septa. Wright and Nelson[15] suggested that some sort of internal reflection within the cones might occur to trap the light, and that this may not occur for rays from the pupil margin because of their oblique incidence. O'Brien[16] has shown that because of the tapering of the cones the ratio of the diameter of the inner to the outer segment is approximately 3:1. He points out that, if the index of refraction of the cone is sufficient, light entering axially will not escape before the cylindrical outer segment is reached and therefore will be reflected down the outer segment, escaping only at its outer end. If the index is just enough higher than the surrounding medium to accomplish this in the case of a particular cone geometry, then this total reflection for a ray not entering parallel to the axis will not occur, and light will escape into the intercellular fluid and will strike the pigmented epithelium and be lost. Cogan[17] has suggested that the lipid protein layers which presumably exist in the cones orient the molecules of the cone visual pigment or pigments in a way that permits maximal absorption of light energy perpendicular to the laminae. He points out that as yet there is no evidence of such orientation of the molecules of the visual pigment, but that molecular orientation is crucial for the absorption of light energy.

If this is the correct explanation of the Stiles-Crawford effect, most if not all of the light absorption which results in visual sensation must occur in the outer segments of the cones. Although no cone pigment has been isolated as yet, reasoning by analogy with the rods, it seems likely that the cone pigment is concentrated largely in the outer segments of the cones, just as the rod pigment is concentrated largely in the outer segments of the rods. The geometry of the cone, therefore, provides a fortunate mechanism or light funnel that concentrates most of the light incident on the inner segments of the cones into the smaller cross section of the outer segments. O'Brien suggests that the failure of the Stiles-Crawford effect to occur with the rod mechanism is due to the combination of the geometry and refractive index of the rods such that one is unable to observe the phenomenon because of the limitations of the size of the pupil.

The retina of the frog also exhibits a directional effect in the cones chiefly. This is useful in helping to disentangle the contributions of the rods and cones during discharges of the optic nerve.[18] Toraldo di Francia[19] compared the rods and cones to microwave antennae. The most efficient type of receiver for detecting radiation incident along a narrow beam is one constructed with directional sensitivity matched to the angular dimensions of this beam. In the selected direction this type of receiver shows high sensitivity which falls off rapidly outside the receptive angle. When the pattern of sensitivity of the cones with changes of angle of incident light is plotted upon a polar diagram with the radius vector equal to the sensitivity for various angles of incidence upon the retina, the curve resembles the polar sensitivity diagram for a dipole radio antenna. Further, the cones seem to be directional receivers matched to fit the aperture of the pupil under good daylight, i.e., 2 to 3 mm., whereas the rods are matched to fit the

aperture of the pupil under conditions of dark adaptation. Hence, the peripheral rays from a dilated pupil will fall outside the angle of reception for cones but not that for rods, thus limiting the Stiles-Crawford effect to the cones alone.

Intensity of the illumination. Within certain limits increase in the illumination results in better visual acuity. The duplicity theory assumes that the retina is composed of two separate sense organs, one working at low intensities of illumination and the other at high intensities. The increase in visual acuity with increasing illumination supports this theory in general, but there are still relationships between the levels of illumination and changes in visual acuity which cannot be explained on this simple basis.

A number of factors have a profound effect on the relation between visual acuity and illumination, some of which have already been mentioned, such as the size of the pupil and the contrast between the test object and the surrounding field. Since the increase in acuity with illumination is independent of the size of the pupil, the mechanism must reside in the photosensitive pigment, in the number of photoreceptors activated, or in the machinery which transmits the impulses up to the brain.

It has been shown that in the case of rhodopsin the rate of bleaching is proportional to the intensity of the light absorbed, as expressed by the formula

$$\frac{dR}{dt} = k.a.IR$$

in which R is the concentration of rhodopsin, a is the percentage of light absorbed, t is the time, k is a constant, and I is the intensity of light. The amount of visual pigment bleached per unit of time determines the intensity of the stimulus transmitted up the nerve fiber and hence the apparent brightness of the light. Of course, the same argument would apply to any pigment, such as iodopsin, that is associated with cone function. However, this does not answer the question of why this results in greater resolving power for any of the test objects used to measure visual acuity. It merely raises the whole level of illumination on the retina and would not result in any difference in illumination, i.e., contrast between stimulated and unstimulated retinal areas. It must be assumed, therefore, that the mechanism which does this is above the level of the primary breakdown of visual pigments absorbing the light.

The next part of the visual mechanism to be implicated is the sensory receptor, i.e., the rods and cones themselves. Do the visual receptors all have the same threshold of light stimulation? Or do some of them fire off at relatively low intensities and others only at higher intensities? It is known that the sensitivity of both the cones and rods increases in

the dark, but that the amount of increase of sensitivity of the cones is very small compared to that of the rods. The adaptation of the cones begins immediately after the light is turned off and is complete in about 6 minutes. The adaptation of the rods is somewhat delayed and is not complete for nearly an hour. At the maximum of dark adaptation the increase in sensitivity of the rods is so enormously greater than that of the cones that by comparison the fovea (containing only cones) may be said to be a physiologic blind spot. The sensitivity to light, however, is not the function which accounts for increase in visual acuity; despite an increase in sensitivity of both cones and rods as the result of dark adaptation, visual acuity, or the resolution of fine details, is considerably lower than under conditions of light adaptation.

It is evident that the cones simply do not work at low intensities. They have the power to regain a little of their function if they remain in the dark for 6 min-

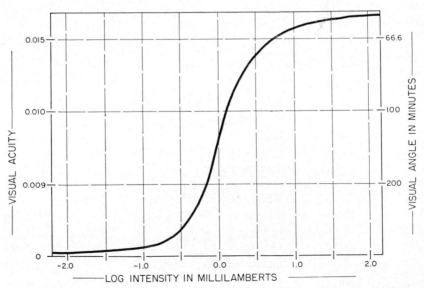

Fig. 371. Relation between visual acuity and illumination in the honeybee. (After Hecht and Wolf; from Pirenne, M.: Vision and the eye, London, 1948, The Pilot Press.)

utes, but this recovery for the resolution of details is so slight that even under these conditions they are practically functionless. Do rods function for detailed vision under conditions of dark adaptation? They must to some extent because the resolution of gratings and of even more complex patterns is considerable in the human eye under conditions of complete dark adaptation, at least when compared to the visual acuity of lower animals. Measurements of the acuity of the honeybee under bright illumination give a value of 0.017 (Fig. 371), which corresponds to a visual angle of 59 minutes. This corresponds to the resolution of a letter, such as that shown in Fig. 372, when held at a distance of 50 cm. Under conditions of complete dark adaptation, the vision of man falls to about that level. The lowest value given by Pirenne is 0.03, which is two and one-half times that of the bee's eye at its best.

As the illumination is increased from a very low level, there is a slight increase in resolving power of the eye which is noticeable about 10^{-4} millilamberts, as shown in Fig. 373. At 10^{-2} millilamberts the acuity begins to increase very rapidly and reaches a maximum at about 10^2 milli-lamberts, beyond which there is no further increase.

The sigmoid curve formed by the graph of visual acuity with increasing illumination strongly suggests that two types of photoreceptors are concerned, one of which functions at very low illuminations and the other coming in only at higher illumination. It is natural to regard this as an expression of activity of the rods and cones. The actual increase in visual acuity ranges from 0.03 to nearly 2.0, which is about a hundredfold.

Because of the fact that the rods and cones have different sensibilities to different regions of the spectrum, it should be possible to prove whether the curve shown in Fig. 373 is actually a combination of rod-and-cone function or due to something else. It would be expected that the short-wave end of the spectrum would give the greatest separation between functions of the rods and cones on this curve, and the intermediate regions of the spectrum would yield intermediate separations. Finally, if the red end of the spectrum were used, it would be expected that cone function alone would show.

This has been tested by Shlaer and co-workers.[20] The relation of visual acuity

Fig. 372. Acuity of the honeybee corresponds approximately to this pattern of black and white seen from a distance of 50 cm. The bee is just able to resolve such a pattern at this distance. It fails to respond to movements of a pattern made of thinner bars.

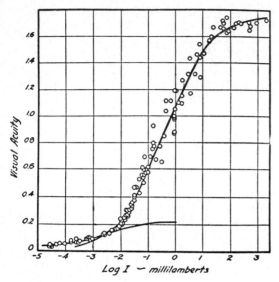

Fig. 373. Curves showing the relation between visual acuity and level of illumination. *Circles,* experimental determinations by Koenig of visual acuity (reciprocal of the minimum separable on the ordinates) for a wide range of intensities of illumination (abscissae). *Upper solid line* (cones) and *lower solid line* (rods), success with which a normal probability integral can be fitted to the data. According to Hecht's theory, the curve represents the number of receptor units whose threshold is attained by a given intensity of illumination, the thresholds of the two receptors being distributed according to the normal probability curve. (After Hecht; from Fulton, J. F., editor: Howell's textbook of physiology, Philadelphia, 1949, W. B. Saunders Co.)

to increase in illumination with red and blue lights is shown in Fig. 374. The value of the greatest acuity at the high intensities of light is the same for both red and blue lights. At a low intensity of illumination the curve for the red light is quite different from that for the blue light. The rods, being more sensitive to blue light than the cones, function alone at low intensities of blue light. On the other hand, with the red light both rods and cones function about equally so that the curve for red is continuous and shows

no isolated rod segment. This is good evidence that the sigmoid form of the curve, showing the relation of visual acuity to increasing intensity of illumination of white light, is due to the function of rods at low intensities and cones at high intensities of illumination.

This explains in a satisfactory manner why visual acuity suddenly increases when the illumination reaches a certain level, but we still must answer the question of why acuity continues to increase from an intensity of 10^{-2} millilamberts up to 10^2 millilamberts, the increase in acuity in this part of the curve ranging from 0.2 (6/30 vision) to 2.0 (6/3 vision) which is roughly a tenfold increase. Various attempts to explain this phenomenon have been made. Helmholtz made the astute suggestion that low visual acuity during dim illumination might be related to poor discrimination of brightness under similar conditions. Broca assumed that the migration of retinal pigment between the cones which occurs in the frog might compress the cones and thus decrease their diameter. This, he supposed, would lead to a greater number of cones per unit area and would result in better acuity on the basis of finer grain. He further supposed that at low illuminations the number of receptor elements connected with a single nerve fiber increased, which would lower the acuity. A modification of this theory has been proposed more recently by Lythgoe who suggested that as the intensity of the light increased inhibitory processes cut the synapses between cones and rods connected to the same ganglion cell, resulting in isolation of individual cones. This would, in effect, increase the grain of the retina physiologically. None of these suggestions has the support of experimental evidence and, in addition, does not fit the data shown in Fig. 373, on a quantitative basis.

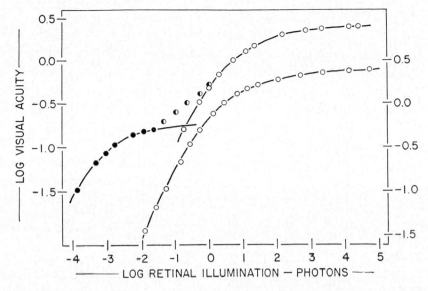

Fig. 374. Human visual acuity in red and blue lights. The test object here is not a grating but a broken ring. The lower data (ordinates at the right) were obtained from the red end of the spectrum, and the upper data (ordinates at the left) were obtained from the blue end of the spectrum. *Filled circles,* measurements made with the retinal periphery in a subjectively colorless field, corresponding to rod vision. *Half-filled circles,* measurements made with the parafovea in a subjectively colored field, which probably represents combined rod and cone vision. *All other circles,* measurements made with the fovea, representing pure cone vision. Photons indicated here are special units of retinal illumination and are not to be confused with the photons of quantum theory. (After Shlaer; from Pirenne, M.: Vision and the eye, London, 1948, The Pilot Press.)

Hecht[21] has offered a theory based on the well-known fact that the resolving power of a photographic plate varies with the grain, i.e., the number of photosensitive particles per unit area. An image of a given size falling on a photographic plate will be recorded either as coarse or fine in its details, depending on whether the plate has a coarse or fine emulsion. Hecht has stated:

"The retina is a surface made up of individual photoreceptors which function as individual units or as groups of units. The way in which visual acuity varies with illumination under comparable conditions of the dioptric mechanism indicates the way in which the resolving power of the retina varies. A low visual acuity means that the average distance between the retinal elements is large, whereas a high visual acuity means that the distance is relatively small. To account for the large variation in visual acuity with illumination, one must suppose that the number of sensitive elements per unit area of retina can and does vary nearly a hundredfold."*

Since the number of rods and cones in the retina is fixed anatomically, it is necessary to assume that the number of elements functioning at any one time can be varied. It can be assumed, for instance, that all the cones are not equally sensitive and that the threshold of some cones is lower than others. On this basis, at low illuminations only a relatively few

*From Hecht, S.: Bulletin No. 4, Howe Laboratory of Ophthalmology, Cambridge, 1931, Harvard University Press.

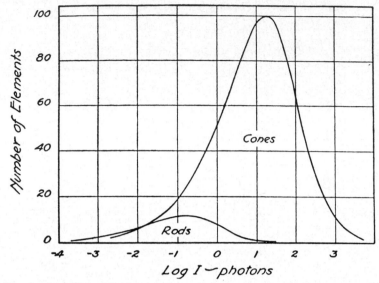

Fig. 375. Distribution of thresholds of rods and cones. The intensities are in photons, a unit introduced by Troland to represent the retinal illumination produced when the eye looks at a brightness of 1 millilambert through a pupil of 1 square millimeter. The two curves are identical in form but different in position and size of ordinates. (From Hecht, S.: J. Gen. Physiol. **10:**781, 1927.)

scattered cones function, whereas more and more cones come into play as illumination is increased until the total number of cones in any area is active. This, in effect, would change the grain of the receptive surface with an increase in illumination.

In order to give quantitative form to this idea, Hecht assumed that the sensitivity of the individual rods and cones is not uniform, but is distributed in relation to the intensity of illumination in the manner of a population curve, which is familiar from the work of statisticians. In Fig. 375 is given the distribution of sensibility which has to be assumed for the cones in the fovea and for the rods in the periphery in order for the data in Fig. 373 to be described. The curves are absolute in their abscissa values but are relative in their ordinate values since these depend on the size of the unit area concerned. The curves of rods and cones are identical

in shape but are different in position and relative height of ordinates. What must be known is not merely the number of elements whose thresholds lie at a specific illumination, but also the total number of elements which are functional at a given illumination. This is given in Fig. 376 and corresponds at any value of I to the area under the curve to the left of that value.

The explanation of the variations in visual acuity that occur with increasing illumination in terms of these two curves is as follows. At the lowest illumination, vision is a function of the rods entirely. The number of rods that are active is small and yields a surface of coarse grain. As the illumination increases, the number of rods activated increases and the grain of the surface is made finer. Finally an illumination in which all the rods are active is reached, but by this time a few of the cone thresholds have been reached. As can be seen in Fig. 373 the rate at

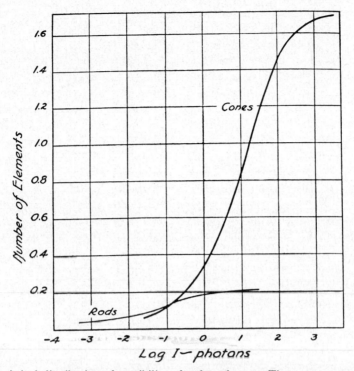

Fig. 376. Statistical distribution of sensibility of rods and cones. These curves are the integrals of those given in Fig. 375 and give the relative number of elements per retinal area functional at any intensity. The curves may be described by the common Gram series of the statisticians. (From Hecht, S.: J. Gen. Physiol. **10:**781, 1927.)

which the cones come into play, from now on with increasing illumination, is nearly ten times as great as the rate of the rods. Therefore, at a certain point the number of cones functioning in the fovea will be equal to the number of rods functioning in the periphery. Beyond this, the number of active foveal cones rapidly outstrips the number of peripheral rods. At this level, therefore, vision will be taken over by the cones. The augmentation of cones with increasing illumination will continue until the threshold of the least sensitive cone has been passed. Visual acuity will increase up to this point, but not beyond it.

In order to compute the data in terms of these curves, Hecht found it was necessary to correct the data for the variation

in size of the pupil with increasing illumination. When this was done, the curve fitted Koenig's data quantitatively. Hecht was careful to point out, however, that this statistical distribution is derived from the photochemical system that he had used previously as the basis for other properties of vision. There is no evidence which proves conclusively that the cones do have different thresholds of sensitivity—i.e., that some cones function at relatively low illumination and others only at higher illumination. On the other hand, it is well established that the signaling of changes in intensity in sensory nerves is brought about by an increased rate of discharge from each single nerve fiber and by an increase in the number of fibers active in the nerve. This latter factor must rest on the supposition that the sensory end organs discharging into the nerve have different thresholds of stimulation. This has been shown to be the case for the optic nerve; therefore we have good reason for assuming the photoreceptors to have different thresholds.

There have been objections to Hecht's proposal on the ground that it is unreasonable to expect such wide variation in threshold among sensory receptors of the same kind. An alternative proposal was made by Pirenne[22] and by Rose[23] which leads to the same result substantially. They suppose that although the cones are all alike and contain similar amounts of absorbing pigment the quantity of pigment present is so small that only a very few quanta of radiation per cone are absorbed at the visual threshold. Under these circumstances the statistical variation in the number of quanta absorbed per cone must necessarily be large, and thus at the lower levels of retinal illumination there will be many cones that fail to absorb the requisite number of quanta for response. If the proper constants are selected, this concept will lead to appropriate coarsening of the cone mosaic at lower levels of illumination, just as will the Hecht theory, and it is not subject to the objection to the Hecht theory just mentioned. We do not know how much of the hypothetical cone pigment is present actually nor how many quanta are absorbed by a cone at the threshold. Thus, we cannot reject the hypothesis of variations in absorption of quanta without further evidence. O'Brien[16] has presented some evidence which would make it appear that both the Hecht and Pirenne hypotheses fail completely to explain the observed change of foveal visual acuity with retinal illumination, and he feels that it is probable that the dominant cause of the phenomenon lies in the central nervous system beyond the retina and probably in the cortex.

The problem of the increase in visual acuity with increasing illumination has been studied extensively by Lythgoe, who controlled not only the illumination of the test object and the surrounds, but also the subject's state of adaptation. The subject was seated in a box whose illumination could be controlled and looked through a window at the test target. When the inside of the box was dark, the subject was dark-adapted although the illumination on the test target was sufficiently high to stimulate the foveal cones. The brightness of the box could be increased so that the subject was light-adapted, and the relationship of the increase in visual acuity with increasing illumination of the test target was studied.

The results of this study (Fig. 377) may be summarized as follows:

1. When the subject is dark-adapted, visual acuity increases up to a maximum at about 15 equivalent footcandles and then falls (curve *A*).

2. If the subject is only partly dark-adapted and the illumination is about the same, but not much greater than the illumination of the test target, the acuity continues to increase to a maximum at approximately 40 equivalent footcandles and then falls (curve *B*).

3. If the subject is light-adapted, visual acuity continues to increase with increase in illumination of the test target (curve *C*).

Even when illumination of the test chart is above that required for cone function, it is apparent that a subject kept at low illumination is still in a state of relative dark adaptation. Some form of retinal interaction seems to be going on in the retina so that the acuity of the

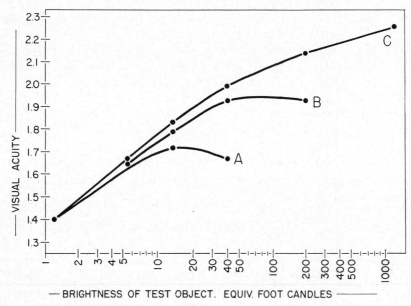

Fig. 377. Illustrating the effects of the brightness of the surround (i.e., state of adaptation of the eye) on visual acuity. **A,** Black surround. Visual acuity increases with increasing brightness of test object only up to a certain point. **B,** Surround brightness 0.011 equivalent foot-candles. **C,** Surround brightness varied continuously so as to be equal to that of test object. (After Lythgoe.)

fovea is influenced by the general illumination of the eye. From a practical point of view, it is important to maintain full light adaptation of the retina during refraction. This can be accomplished only by having the illumination of the refracting booth at the photopic level instead of at the scotopic level, as is often encountered. It is not good practice to refract a patient in a darkened room even though the level of illumination at the test chart is adequate.

Influence of the region of the retina on visual acuity. In several places in this book attention has been called to the fact that visual acuity is not uniform throughout the retina. It is a matter of common experience that foveal acuity is far greater than that of any other region and that the fall in acuity occurs abruptly as one leaves the fovea. If the acuity of the fovea is taken as 1, the acuity at the edge of

the macula (2.5 degrees) has already dropped to 1/2. At 7.5 degrees the acuity had dropped to 1/4, and in the extreme peripheral regions of the retina it is only about 1/40 that of the fovea.

The decrease in acuity cannot be accounted for entirely on the basis of the grain of the retina, however, as is shown from the following illustration from Polyak (Fig. 378).

The factor which seems to be important in affording the fovea such remarkable ability to discriminate details is the number of single lines available to carry a large number of local signs to the cortex. Polyak has given good evidence for the existence of individual lines that connect each foveal cone with a ganglion cell, without the interposition of synapses with either rods or other cones in the same line. These connections act as private lines, so to speak, as compared to those in which

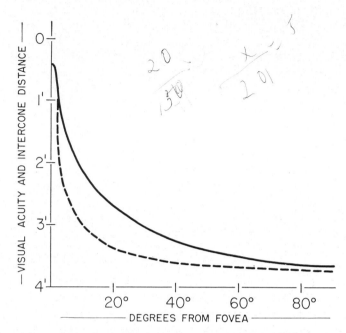

Fig. 378. Comparison of visual acuity and cone density for the central and peripheral portions of the retina. The broken line shows the visual acuity in minutes of visual angle. Note that the lower the curve the larger is the minimum separable. The solid line shows the cone gradient of the retina in terms of intercone distance for the periphery and the cone width for the rod-free areas plotted on the same ordinate as visual acuity. Failure of the curves to correspond proves that factors other than density and diameter of cones determine the minimum separable. (After Polyak; from Fulton, J. F., editor: Howell's textbook of physiology, Philadelphia, 1949, W. B. Saunders Co.)

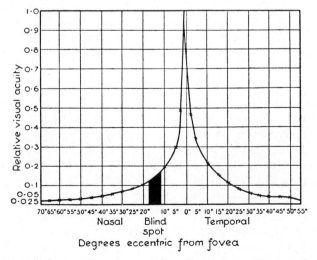

Fig. 379. Regional variations of the visual acuity (Wertheim). (From Duke-Elder, S.: Textbook of ophthalmology, St. Louis, 1932, The C. V. Mosby Co., vol. 1.)

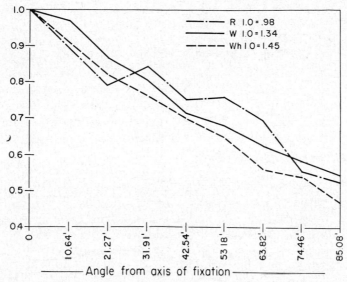

Fig. 380. Average acuity of the three subjects scaled to a fixation acuity of unity for comparison. (After Weymouth and co-workers.)

several receptors are hooked up on the same or party line. The large number of these private lines in the fovea could undoubtedly account for the fineness of detail of foveal vision. This concept necessitates a corresponding fineness of grain of the foveal representation in the cortex, and it has been shown that this is indeed the case (p. 684).

Earlier investigators who studied the changes in visual acuity in different regions of the retina were content to evaluate acuity in steps of 5 degrees from the fovea to the periphery. In Fig. 379 are shown the regional variations obtained from the data of Wertheim, who is the authority most frequently quoted. It can be seen that no determinations were made of acuity from 2.5 degrees to fixation. The curve is extrapolated from 2.5 degrees to fixation, without any experimental data to substantiate it.

Weymouth and co-workers[24] made observations on the acuity within this region and concluded that visual acuity increases in a straight line from 2.5 de-

grees to fixation. In Fig. 380 are given Weymouth's values for acuity from fixation out to a region of the retina at 85 minutes from fixation. At 21 minutes from fixation the value of acuity decreased to 0.8 if it is assumed that the acuity of the fovea equals 1.0. Only one value is given for the acuity within this region, i.e., at 10.64 minutes, and the drop in acuity for this region is so small as to be insignificant.

Adler and Meyer[25] studied the acuity of vision in the central portions of the retina by a method which permitted them to analyze the effect of a number of factors independently. The method consisted of measuring the aligning power of the eye in different regions of the retina with exact control of fixation so that small steps from the fixation point outward could be explored. The effects of changing the width of the test line, its length, and the time of exposure, as well as the eccentricity of the image from the point of fixation, were investigated. It was found that the thresholds depend upon the initial width of the line and are relative, therefore. A subject makes a discrimination successfully only when a certain percentage increase in the width of the original line occurs. It was concluded from this that a correct judgment does not depend upon the stimulation of one visual receptor or one group acting as a unit but probably upon a percentage increase in the number of receptors stimulated. This gives support to the theory that the number of receptors stimulated is of paramount importance in the acuity of details.

In many instances the thresholds obtained were far below the angle subtended by an individual foveal cone. The average threshold for a 42 mm. line, 0.5 mm. in width, with a 4-second exposure was 5 seconds of arc. This corresponds to a linear distance on the retina of 0.41 μ. If we accept Polyak's value of 1 to 1.5 μ for the diameter of the foveal cones, the break in the least detectable contour under these conditions was considerably less than the width of one cone.

When the time of exposure of the test object was shortened below a certain minimum, the thresholds were considerably increased. With exact fixation, which the method used afforded the subject, the thresholds for exposures of 0.44 second were less than half those when the exposure time was reduced to 0.05 second. Exposures of more than 1 second did not improve the threshold materially. This may be due, as Weymouth believes, to the elimination of the effects of micronystagmus which carries the image over more visual receptors. On the other hand, there are additional factors which may account for this. Shortening the time of exposure of the test object increases the latent period of the cortical response considerably, as Bishop has shown. The retina is activated undoubtedly by even the short-

est exposures, and the longer exposures do not cause the receptors to respond any quicker but only more vigorously. As Bishop suggests, the variation in the latent period is due presumably to summation in the nerve synapses rather than in the photoreceptors. This summation may be the cause of the lower thresholds when exposures of longer duration are permitted.

Evidence was obtained that the acuity of vision tested by this method increased as the length of the test line was increased. This occurred when the test line was between 4 and 25 mm. in length. Beyond this length of line, no further lowering of the threshold occurred.

When the region around fixation in the four major directions was explored, the acuity was found to be the same in an area surrounding fixation measuring 250 μ. Beyond this area acuity dropped suddenly. It appears that this area is what might be termed the physiologic fovea and that it acts as a unit. The central rod-free area is about 250 micra in diameter. A visual angle of 1 minute equals 4.85 μ. Therefore, the rod-free area subtends a visual angle of 54 minutes or a little under 1 degree. The number of cones in the rod-free area is estimated to be 147,000 per mm.[8] In this central region where vision is most acute there are, therefore, about 9000 cones. According to this conception the acuity of vision does not increase to a point in the center of the fovea, but there is a plateau, which has measurable extent, throughout which the acuity is at a maximum. This probably acts as a unit. A comparison between this foveal plateau and a finger used to palpate a surface may be drawn for purposes of illustration. The fingertip contains a large number of sensory receptors which can palpate a surface, exploring it and sending informa-

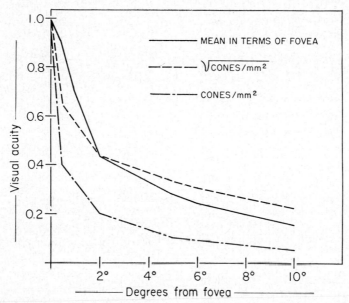

Fig. 381. Graph showing the visual acuity exhibited by retinal regions eccentric from the fovea. (After Ludvigh.)

tion to the brain which is interpreted in terms of the sense of touch. Similarly, the fovea, containing a large number of closely packed receptors, can palpate a surface visually and send information to the brain in terms of the form sense.

Jones and Higgins[26] found a marked falling off of visual acuity at even 10 minutes from the fovea. They could detect a drop of 5% at only 3.5 minutes of arc from the center. According to them there is only a small region of the retina, 7 minutes of arc or 35 μ in diameter within which the highest visual acuity is obtained. In any consideration of resolving power, the number of elements per unit distance across the fovea or the center-to-center spacing is of prime importance. In a number of human eyes,[16] the maximum spread of the center-to-center distance of the most central foveal cones ranged between 2.02 and 2.32 μ. This agrees with the dimensions found by Polyak.

Miles[27] gives the over-all diameter of the fovea from 3 to 5 degrees. Using special filters, the author demonstrated concentric zonation within this foveal area. In normal eyes, he found a central disc area, about 30 minutes in diameter, that in certain ways was functionally distinct from surrounding areas. The subject's fixation point always fell within this area. It comprises a relatively small agglomeration of elongated cones.

Ludvigh[28] has measured the visual acuity of normal subjects for various regions of the retina from the fovea out to the 10-degree periphery, using a Snellen type of test. In Fig. 381 is shown the visual acuity exhibited by retinal regions eccentric from the fovea out to the 10-degree periphery. The foveal acuity of the observer is taken as unity, and the visual acuity with various degrees of eccentric fixation are expressed as a fraction of this.

The variation in visual acuity from the fovea to the periphery was not found to parallel the decrease in either linear or areal density of cones from the center to the periphery.

From the data Ludvigh presents, he concludes that small central scotomas, even if complete, cannot cause the reduction in visual acuity ordinarily attributed to them. A scotoma must be quite large in order to account for any considerable loss of visual acuity. For example, in order to reduce the visual acuity to one fifth of its foveal value, the stimulus must be situated more than 7 degrees from fixation. If one assumes that normal foveal acuity is 20/20, vision of 20/100 can be accounted for by a central scotoma only if the scotoma is 14 degrees in diameter since, if a region of the retina within 7 degrees of the fovea is unaffected, vision of better than 20/100 could be obtained. A central scotoma of over 25 degrees in diameter would be required to account for vision of 20/200 in the absence of other defects. Central scotomas of this size are not common. Ludvigh believes that in patients in whom the visual acuity is markedly reduced and only a small central scotoma is present the scotoma whether real or apparent is not responsible for the reduced acuity, as has generally been assumed.

Weymouth[29] has shown that the minimal angle of resolution or threshold in minutes plotted as a function of the eccentricity is a straight line rising from the lowest threshold in the fovea to high thresholds in the periphery. The minimal angle of resolution is the reciprocal of visual acuity. The linear separation of the ganglion cells is also a straight-line function of the retinal eccentricity, with a slope within the range of the spatial thresholds. Weymouth considers it reasonable to consider the ganglion cells rather than the cones the anatomic basis of the spatial thresholds. Hence there is good correlation between the decrease in acuity from the fovea outward and the diminution in sensory units.

Influence of fixation. The Snellen test chart is undoubtedly the best practical test devised, so far, for the determination of errors of refraction. It affords the subject a test with which he is already perfectly familiar, and the resolution of the letters is an incentive for him to pursue the test with attention and interest. However, we have fallen into an unfortunate situation in the procedure by crowding more and more letters into each line of the test type as we test for better acuity. As the angular size of the letters becomes smaller, the angular distance between each letter likewise is diminished equally. In doing so, we have inadvertently added another hurdle to the test for the patient, in addition to the problem of the resolving power of the eye as an optical instrument. This is the hurdle of fixation. Little is known regarding the exact mechanism by means of which the fovea is able to achieve its maximum resolving power, but we can be sure that the older idea of a fixated pattern of an object on a few retinal cones is not so applicable to the eye as it is to the camera. In other words, there is more in the resolving power of the eye than the fineness of grain of the retinal receptors. The eye is in constant movement so that, even if there were no spherical and chromatic aberration or diffraction at the margins of the pupil, an image of a point of light in the external world could not be localized on one central foveal cone.

It is common experience that the finest detection of form can occur only if the test letters to be resolved are sufficiently separated from each other that the involuntary movements of the eye do not cause interference. The test charts, as they are made today, interfere with the determination of the resolving power and the effect of ametropia on this by introducing this new factor. The charts should be printed with spaces between the letters on the 6/6 line sufficiently wide to ensure that the involuntary movements of the eye do not carry the fovea into the field of attention of an adjoining letter. This is particularly true in the case of children whose voluntary motor mechanism does not allow the small movements of the eyes achieved by an adult. In squint, in which the fixation is even still poorer, this factor is of definite importance. In testing children with amblyopia one will find better acuity for the diminishing visual angle if a single E is presented, instead of asking the child to read the E's on a chart on which more are crowded together as their angular dimensions become smaller.

As the charts are printed now, the visual angles subtended at the eye between the letters of the chart are as shown in Table 53.

In the emmetropic eye 1 minute of arc equals 4.9 μ on the retina. If each foveal cone measures 2 μ, 21 minutes of arc would cover approximately fifty cones. The smallest possible change in fixation must be close to this angle.

Influence of pressure from the eyelids. Most people with myopia soon learn to obtain better visual acuity without glasses by narrowing the fissures of the lids. In a highly astigmatic person this habit is so confirmed that the fissures assume this position, from which the astigmatism may

be predicted. The influence of this on the refraction is exceedingly large. In myopic persons the voluntary narrowing of the fissures during the trial examination of the patient must be constantly watched for and prevented if possible. In astigmatic patients who habitually have narrowed fissures it is sometimes a mistake to insist on opening the fissures and prescribing the correction found since when the glasses are worn the patient is sure to revert to the old habit, and the prescription will be incorrect. Each case in which this factor plays any important part must be judged on its own merits.

A chalazion, if fairly large, by pressure may change the refraction considerably, and no prescription for glasses should be ordered until this has been removed satisfactorily.

Influence of the tear film and winking. The transparency and image-forming ability of the cornea depend partly on the character of tears. One of the most striking chemical features of tears is their relatively high concentration of protein. The total solids amount to 1.8%, and of this protein accounts for over one third. Protein gives tears a much lower surface tension and enables them to wet the epithelial surfaces more perfectly. The optical properties of the eye are improved greatly by this film since microscopic irregularities in the corneal epithelium are abolished thereby, thus producing a perfectly smooth, polished optical surface for the eye (Fig. 382) .

During the trial examination it is important that the patient continue to blink as normal. Many patients fail to do this as they become intent on reading the letters. In elderly people this is especially important, and the examiner will do well to ask the patient to blink at intervals throughout the procedure. Abnormal tears

Table 53

Line on chart	Angular separation of letters
6/30	1° 24′
6/15	0° 42′
6/ 5	0° 21′

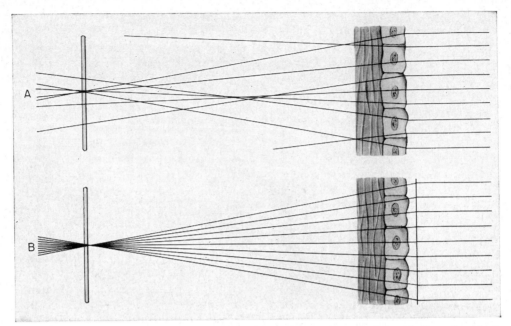

Fig. 382. A, Rays of light strike the relatively uneven surface of the epithelium devoid of tears. The result is some irregular refraction of light. **B,** Tear film covering the epithelial surface forms an ideal optical surface, permitting geometric regular refraction.

and secretions, obviously, may interfere seriously with visual acuity.

Legibility of various letters in the Snellen chart. It is common experience that some of the letters on the Snellen chart are deciphered more easily than others by all subjects. In Table 54 the legibility of these letters as determined by Ludvigh is compared with that determined by the report of a committee appointed to investigate the subject in 1916. The discrep-

Table 54. *Order of legibility of Snellen letters*

	Ludvigh's findings		Committee's report
	Observer 1	Observer 2	Observer 3	

	Observer 1	Observer 2	Observer 3	Committee's report
1	L	L	L	L
2	F	F	C	T
3	E	E	F	C
4	C	C	E	F
5	T	T	T	E

ancies in the findings are not easily explainable, and it is quite likely that many factors which could not be controlled easily account for the observed differences. It is sufficient to point out that a real difference in the legibility of different letters does exist, however. Because of this, attempts have been made to substitute a more standard test object such as the Landolt broken ring, black-and-white gratings (Ives test), etc., but it is not practical to carry out the procedures of office refraction with such tests, and in general they have never become popular. The Snellen charts are sufficient for this purpose undoubtedly, as long as their limitations are appreciated.

Variability of visual acuity. Measurements of visual acuity are fairly constant and change very little in the same person from day to day, without pathologic cause. What variations do occur may be accounted for on the basis of changes in illumination of the test chart and particularly on changes in illumination of the room in which the test is made, which influence the size of the pupil (pp. 772 and 774). Many other factors must come into play; the anterior surface of the cornea probably undergoes constant changes due to variations in composition of the tear

film. Vision ultimately depends on differences in the frequency of discharge of neighboring nerve cells in the retina, and it is known that the cells and their synapses are undergoing constant changes in irritability without any perceptible external cause, just as other nerve cells and synapses do in the central nervous system.[30]

REFERENCES

1. Stuart, A., and Burian, H.: A study of separation difficulty, Am. J. Ophth. **53:** 471, 1962.
2. Davson, H., editor: The eye, vol. II, New York, The Blakiston Division, McGraw-Hill Book Co., Inc., p. 175.
3. Demott, D.: Direct measures of the retinal image, J. Optic Soc. America **49:**571, 1959.
4. Hecht, S., and Mintz, E.: The visibility of single lines at various illuminations and the retinal basis of visual resolution, J. Gen. Physiol. **22:**593, 1939.
5. Ogilvie, J., and Taylor, M.: Effect of orientation on the visibility of fine wires, J. Optic. Soc. America **48:**628, 1958.
6. Leibowitz, H.: Some observations and theory on the variation of visual acuity with the orientation of the test object, J. Optic. Soc. America **43:**902, 1953.
7. Weymouth, F.: Stimulus orientation and threshold and optical analysis, Am. J. Ophth. **48:**6, 1959.
8. Shlaer, S.: The relation between visual acuity and illumination, J. Gen. Physiol. **21:**165, 1937.
9. Guillery, H.: Sehscharfe, Handb. d. Norm. u. Path. Physiol. **12:** 745,
10. Anderson, E., and Weymouth, F.: Visual perception and the retinal mosaic, Am. J. Physiol. **64:**561, 1923.
11. Ludvigh, E.: Direction sense of the eye, Am. J. Ophth. **36:**139, 1953.
12. Ludvigh, E.: A gradient of retinal illumination and its practical significance, Am. J. Ophth. **20:**260, 1937.
13. Ludvigh, E.: Effect of reduced contrast on visual acuity as measured with Snellen letters, Arch. Ophth. **25:**469, 1941.
14. Stiles, W., and Crawford, B.: The luminous efficiency of rays entering the pu-

pil at different points, Proc. Roy. Soc. London s. B **112:**428, 1933.
15. Wright, W., and Nelson, J.: The relation between the apparent intensity of a beam of light and the angle at which the beam strikes the retina, Proc. Phys. Soc., London **48:**401, 1936.
16. O'Brien, B.: Vision and resolution in the central retina, J. Optic. Soc. America **41:** 882, 1951.
17. Cogan, D.: The Stiles-Crawford effect in modern dress, Arch. Ophth. **69:**285, 1963,
18. Donner, D., and Rushton, W.: The Stiles-Crawford effect on the frog's retina, Proc. Phys. Soc., London, 1956; in J. Physiol. **132:** 1956.
19. Toraldo di Francia, T.: The radiation pattern of retinal receptors, Proc. Physiol. Soc. B. **62:**461, 1949.
20. Shlaer, S., Smith, E., and Chase, A.: Visual acuity and illumination in different spectral regions, J. Gen. Physiol. **25:**553, 1942.
21. Hecht, S.: Bull. 4, Laboratory of Ophthalmology, Cambridge, 1931, Harvard University Press.
22. Pirenne, M.: On the variation of visual acuity with light intensity, Proc. Cambridge Philo. Soc. **42:**78, 1945.
23. Rose, A.: The sensitivity performance of the human eye on an absolute scale, J. Optic. Soc. America **38:**196, 1948.
24. Weymouth, F., Hines, D., Acres, L., Raaf, J., and Wheeler, M.: Visual acuity within the area centralis and its relation to eye movements and fixation, Am. J. Ophth. **11:**947, 1928.
25. Adler, F., and Meyer, G.: Mechanism of the fovea, Tr. Am. Ophth. Soc. **33:**266, 1935.
26. Jones, L., and Higgins, G.: On the influence of the region of the retina on the

visual acuity, J. Optic. Soc. America **37:** 217, 1947.

27. Miles, W.: On the central zone of the human fovea, Science **109:**441, 1949.

28. Ludvigh, E.: Extrafoveal visual acuity as measured by Snellen test letters, Am. J. Ophth. **24:**303, 1941.

29. Weymouth, F.: Visual sensory units and the minimal angle of resolution, Am. J. Ophth. **46:** (pt. 2) 102, 1958.

30. Granit, R.: Acta physiol. scandinav. **1:** 316, 1941.

CHAPTER 20

COLOR VISION

In daylight, most objects have colors. They lose this property when the illumination falls below a certain level due to the fact that color depends upon a mechanism in the eye which functions only at high intensities of light. The color of an object also depends upon the property of the object of absorbing certain wavelengths of light and reflecting others back to us. The quality of the light which strikes the object before it is reflected to the eyes naturally is important in producing colors, for if the light contains certain wavelengths but not others, the object cannot reflect the latter back to us. If light falling on a green leaf contains no rays of 500 to 570 mμ (green), it cannot reflect these back; therefore the leaf cannot appear green. Although the sensation of color is a psychologic attribute of vision, it has both physical and physiologic bases.

PHYSICAL BASIS OF COLOR

White light is a mixture of radiant energy of wavelengths of approximately 400 to 700 mμ. When such a mixture of wavelengths in a beam or ray is traveling in free space, its speed is 3×10^{10} cm. per second (186,000 miles per second). If the beam of light now strikes the surface of a transparent medium at any angle other than a right angle, the rays will undergo refraction at the surface, and the angle of refraction will depend upon the angle of incidence of the beam and the optical density of the medium it strikes. The ratio between the sine of the angle of incidence and the sine of the angle of refraction is a constant, called the index of refraction.

$$R = \frac{\text{sine } i}{\text{sine } r}$$

If the light is traveling in air (theoretically a vacuum) before it strikes the second medium, R represents the ratio of the velocity of light in free space to that in the second medium. The beam of light in its passage into the second medium is slowed down, therefore. Not all parts of the beam are slowed down equally, for the rays of shorter wavelength are slowed down more than those of long wavelength.

Bragg[1] has drawn an apt analogy between rays striking the refracting surface and a company of soldiers marching in a straight file across a flat plain and striking soft sand. The line where the soft sand commences is not perpendicular to the line of march but meets this at an acute angle, so that the men at the right-hand end of the column meet the soft sand first. As soon as they enter, their march is slowed up, whereas the rest of the column keeps on at the same speed. This turns the column from its original line of march to parallel the line forming the boundary between hard and soft sand, more or less. As more men in the column reach the soft sand, more are slowed down until finally, when all have entered the soft sand, the file of march will be an unbroken straight line again, but will face in a new direction. It happens, however, that the men's legs are not all the same length in this company of soldiers so that, when the going in the soft sand becomes difficult, those with short legs are held up much more than those with long legs and become separated from them. The column now will be broken up into as many different sections as there are men of different leg lengths, and each section will acquire a new line of march. Eventually, the front rank will contain men with the longest legs and the rear those with the shortest legs and in between they will be graded in orderly sequence.

The analogy with a wave front of light striking an optical surface is obvious. The rays of different wavelengths in the beam are represented by the men of unequal leg lengths. Hence the rays will be divided into separate groups, each containing the same wavelength and pursuing a different line of direction. In this manner, white light is broken up into its component wavelengths by a prism, forming a spectrum. Such a spectrum is said to be formed by dispersion.

White light may also be broken up into its component colors by passing the light through a diffraction grating which consists of a glass plate on which has been ruled a series of very fine parallel scorings. If these are very close together, they succeed in dispersing the light into its spectrum.

The visible spectrum. The spectrum produced by breaking up white light into its component wavelengths is shown in Fig. 383. Although there is a gradual transition of wavelengths from one end of the spectrum to the other, the eye is capable of recognizing only a limited number of steps in this sequence. The human eye can distinguish easily seven or eight different colors in the spectrum, i.e., red, orange, yellow, green, blue-green, blue, indigo, and violet. Each of these regions extends over a small range of wavelengths, and the separation between each is not defined sharply.

In Table 55 are given the wavelength generally chosen to represent each color and the range of wavelengths in millimicrons through which the color is identified by most normal individuals.

Phenomenon of interference. The phenomenon by means of which dispersion takes place is called interference. It is based on the fact that when two or more waves of identical frequency meet one another, they may intensify or nullify each other, depending upon whether they meet in phase or out of phase, i.e., whether both their crests and both their troughs coincide or the crest of one is superimposed on the trough of the other. If the two trains of waves are in phase and

Table 55. *Accepted wavelengths of spectral colors*

Color	Wavelength (mμ)	Range (mμ)
Red	700	650-750
Orange	610	610-640
Yellow	580	560-630
Green	510	500-540
Blue	470	420-500
Violet	420	400-420

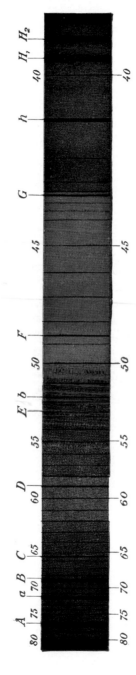

Fig. 383. The photopic spectrum. Calibration in angstrom units × 100. (From Duke-Elder, S.: Text-book of ophthalmology, St. Louis, 1932, The C. V. Mosby Co., vol. 1.)

travel in the same direction over the same path, they will reinforce each other, whereas if they are out of phase, they will nullify each other. In a diffraction grating, a series of waves spreads out from each slit between the scorings on the glass plate, and wherever these new waves intersect, interference phenomena take place. When the light which has passed through such a grating is focused on à screen, the image consists of a series of bright lines where the reinforced waves appear, separated by dark intervals where those waves which have neutralized each other are focused. Now the amount of deflection of the rays depends on their wavelength because rays of short wavelength are deflected more than those of long wavelength. As a result, when white light is passed through a diffraction grating, the light is broken up into its component colors.

In nature, colors are frequently produced by white light passing through natural fine gratings such as the extremely fine ribbings on the wings of some insects, giving rise to a resplendent display of colors. This is the way in which the colors are produced in the wings of some butterflies and in the feathers of peacocks, to mention but two examples.

In a similar fashion, interference phenomena occur when light passes through thin films. Light falling on a soap bubble is partly reflected from the surface and partly transmitted to the inner surface of the membrane. The part that passes inside is reflected back from the inner surface. Both sets of rays then reach our eyes traversing the same path. Since the set which was reflected back from the inner surface of the bubble had to traverse the thickness of the bubble twice, it gets behind the rays which are just reflected from the surface without having to go through the film and out again (Fig. 384). There is a slight lag in time between the two sets of rays, and this lag depends on the thickness of the film and the angle at which the rays traverse the film. We may compute this lag in terms of wavelength. Suppose that monochromatic light, e.g., 500 mμ, strikes the bubble and that the thickness of the bubble and the angle of incidence of the light are just such as to produce a lag between the two sets of reflected rays equal to one, two, or three whole wavelengths, i.e., 500, 1000, or 1500 mμ. Then, as the two sets of waves come back to our eyes, they will be in exact phase with one another—the peaks, and troughs coincide. They will reinforce one another, therefore. The reflection will be strong since the energy will be quadrupled. If, however, the lag was not a whole number of wavelengths, but one and one-half wavelengths, e.g., then the returning waves would be out of phase with each other and would nullify each other. The reflection would be zero since the energy would not get out of the bubble but would go into heat. Now when white light falls on a bubble, it is evident that for any one thickness of bubble some of the wavelengths will be in phase with each other after reflection, as we have described, and others will be out of phase since white light is made up of many different wavelengths. The result will be that the light will be broken up into its component colors, some bright and some dull. If the bubble is very thin so that the lag is reduced to half a wavelength lost by the set of rays reflected from the inner surface, all the reflected rays will be out of step exactly, and there will be an absence of reflection. This happens at the neck of the soap bubble near the pipe, and this area is usually dark. The best display of colors occurs just outside this dark area.

Pigments. Another method by means

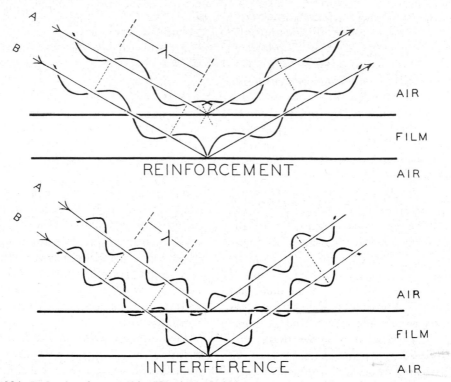

Fig. 384. Reflection from a thin film (soap bubble). Rays labeled **A** are reflected in the air against the film and undergo no change in phase with reflection. Rays labeled **B**, however, are reflected within the film against the air and lose half a wavelength with reflection. Whether or not rays **A** and **B** are reflected in phase (reinforcement) or out of phase (interference) depends upon the wavelength, the angle of reflection, and the thickness of the film.

of which color is produced in nature and the one most commonly met is the selective absorption of wavelengths by a substance. White paper reflects back all the rays of light to our eyes, and if the light striking the paper is white, the surface of the paper will appear white to us. If we now paint the paper with red watercolor, the rays of light pass through the thin film of paint, strike the paper, and are reflected back to us, passing again through the film of paint. The paper is now red due to the fact that the chemical substance of which the paint was composed absorbed almost all of the rays out of the white light, except those having a wavelength from 650 to 750 mμ. The

color of a substance is determined, therefore, by the selective absorption of certain wavelengths by the substance.

The absorption of light of a particular wave length by a pigment is a resonance effect. It is akin to radio reception in that it is an electrical effect and deals with waves in the hypothetical ether, the waves of light as we have seen differing only in wavelength from those used in broadcasting.

The atoms and molecules in the pigment, which act similarly to the receiving set, all are capable of emitting and absorbing light of certain definite wavelengths due to their periods of vibration. Therefore, the color of an object will depend upon whether or not the particular wavelengths it transmits or reflects are present in the light which illuminates it. If we take a bunch of yellow flowers, e.g., and hold them in light of different wavelengths, we find that in yellow light they look natural, in red light they look red, in green light they look green, but in deep blue light they look black. This last color is the only wavelength they do not reflect.

Color is influenced to a considerable degree by psychologic factors. For example, when we look at the snow on a mountain in broad daylight, it may look white, which we know it is; in shadow, especially against the sharp contrast of bright sunlight, the snow looks blue; at sunset it takes on a golden color and then a deep red tint; yet it never occurs to us, as we look at it under these different conditions of lighting, that it is anything but white. We have become accustomed to discount the changing colors due to differences in the quality of light striking such objects as a result of experience. A person who had never seen snow before, if shown a mountaintop at sunset, could easily be made to believe that snow is red.

Hue; brightness; saturation. Thus far color has been considered to consist of one attribute only, i.e., hue. It is evident that at least one other characteristic must be present, namely, brightness. One red light can be brighter than another red light and still have the same hue. A red pigment may be made darker by mixing some black pigment with it. The resulting light which reaches us after reflection from the surface will be less bright than before the black pigment was added. The variations made by mixing black with spectral colors are called shades of the spectral color.

Color possesses another characteristic

Table 56. *Tints produced in spectral colors by addition of white light*

Hue: Pure color plus white light	Tint produced
Red	Pink
Orange	Yellow
Yellow	Green
Green	Yellow
Violet	Salmon pink

called saturation. Nearly all colors in nature are not pure, but are mixed with white light to varying degrees, and are said to be unsaturated. Such unsaturated colors often are called tints of a particular hue. When white light is mixed with monochromatic light in certain proportions, the tint of the monochromatic light is changed.

Yellow-green and blue practically do not change with the addition of any quantities of white light but merely become more unsaturated. As more and more white light is added to any of the spectral colors listed in Table 56, they become more and more unsaturated and eventually will appear to be white. Hue, therefore, is defined as wavelength; however, saturation cannot be measured in terms of physical units but only in terms of the sensation of brightness. This measurement can be made by comparing the sample with a colorless light of known brightness or luminosity. This is the science of heterochromatic photometry. This is a difficult task because it is confusing to compare a colored light with a colorless one. Because of this it is customary to adopt another and much simpler method of determining the luminosity of any colored light—the method of flicker. This subject is discussed more fully in Chapter 18, Sensory Response. This method is based on the fact that the sensation of flicker, produced by the repeated projection of two colored patches on the retina at 6 to 10 cycles per second, disappears when the brightness of one patch has a certain value relative to that of the other patch. When flicker disappears, it is assumed that the two patches are of equal luminosity. The relative luminosity of the different regions of the spectrum has been determined by this means. The luminosity of any one wavelength is usually compared to that of 550 mμ and is known as the luminosity factor or the spectral luminosity. The relative luminosity of the different regions of the visible spectrum when the eye is under conditions of good daylight is given in Fig. 259 (p. 595). The curve shows that the brightness in various portions of the spectrum is considerably different, and the eye under conditions of daylight vision responds most easily to light around the middle of the visible spectrum and least at the two ends. The part of the spectrum which is brightest under daylight vision is at a wavelength of 560 mμ. Hue is not dependent entirely upon wavelength; therefore the correspondence between wavelength and hue is not an entirely constant one. Hue is determined partially by intensity. Most colors upon being brightened shift slightly toward either yellow or blue. This is called the Bezold-Brucke effect. A green of 525 mμ, e.g., must be stepped up 21 mμ when the illumination is reduced from 200 to 100 trolands.

We have said that a normal person can recognize approximately seven distinct hues, but that there are gradual transitions in between these distinct colors. What is the capacity of the human eye to detect small changes in wavelength, λ? It has been found that the size of λ differs in different parts of the spectrum. In some parts λ is as small as 1 mμ and in most parts less than 3 mμ (Fig. 385). It follows that there is a very large number of discriminable hues for a normal person; the figure usually given is 156. If, however, one calculates the actual number of possible discriminable changes of hue, saturation, and brightness, i.e., the total number of just perceptible differences of all kinds within the world of

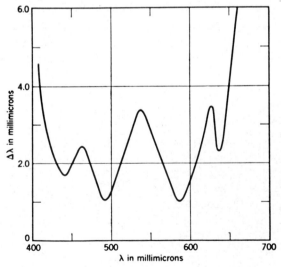

Fig. 385. Discrimination of wavelength by the human eye. The change in wavelength which can be just detected, $\triangle\lambda$, is plotted as a function of wavelength λ. (After Jones; from Geldard, F.: The human senses, New York, 1953, John Wiley & Sons, Inc., p. 42.)

color, the total number is an enormous one—7,500,000.

We have seen that the part of the spectrum which has the greatest luminosity when the eye is light-adapted is in the yellow-green region around 550 mμ. When the eye is completely dark-adapted, the part of the spectrum having the greatest luminosity shifts to the blue-green around 500 mμ. This shift in luminosity from light to dark adaptation was first described by Purkinje in 1825, and since then the phenomenon has been known by his name. It is of theoretic interest since it is one of the fundamental indications of the duplex nature of the retina. It is due to the fact that the cones are only stimulated by light of an intensity equal to that of daylight, whereas rods respond when the illumination is very low, especially after the eye has been exposed to the low illumination for some time, i.e., dark-adapted. The spectral luminosity curve of the eye under photopic and scotopic conditions is shown in Fig. 259. When the eye is light-adapted the various regions of the spectrum tested appear of different hue as well as of different luminosity. When the eye is dark-adapted, on the other hand, all hue disappears, and the different portions of the spectrum appear the same except for differences in luminosity.

The phenomenon is also apparent in that range of illumination known as the mesopic stage, in which the eye is just between light and dark adaptation. Here both rods and cones are operative, the shift in luminosity being due to the superimposition of a rod effect—that stimulates only the light sense—on the cone effect (Davson). When measured at the mesopic level of illumination, the luminosity would lie somewhere between that of the photopic state and that of the scotopic state. Since the phenomenon is due to the ef-fect of rod activity imposed on cone activity, it can only occur in regions of the retina where cones and rods are present together. It cannot be demonstrated in the fovea, therefore.

COLOR MIXTURES

White light, as stated, is composed of all the wavelengths of the spectrum. Not only can it be broken down into its component parts, but it can also be re-formed by combining all the spectral colors. This should not be confused with the combination of pigments forming colored paints. The color of such pigments, it has been shown, is due to resonance phenomena by means of which the atoms and molecules in the pigment hold certain wavelengths of light, let others pass through, and reflect others back to us. When pigments are mixed, the resulting color is due to the sum of the absorptive properties of the substances and bears no relation to the effects produced by mixing spectral lights. The color sensation produced by mixing monochromatic wavelengths in varying proportions is due entirely to the properties of the visual apparatus. Apart from the color effect which mixtures of pigments create, they must always reduce the luminosity of the resulting sensation because their mixture always implies greater absorption of light rays; hence fewer will be reflected back to us. When e.g., blue and yellow pigments are mixed, the result is a green of less luminosity than either the blue or the yellow due to the absorption of both ends of the spectrum. When blue and yellow spectral lights (wavelengths 590 to 610 mμ plus wavelengths 430 to 460 mμ) are mixed, however, the resulting sensation is white. This, as we shall see, is a psychologic effect based on physiologic mechanisms in the retina.

Mixtures of spectral lights. It is pos-

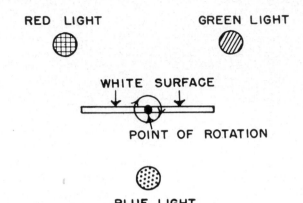

Fig. 386. Effects of mixing monochromatic lights. (Redrawn from Guyton, A.: Textbook of medical physiology, Philadelphia, 1956, W. B. Saunders Co., p. 676.)

sible to mix light from various regions of the spectrum and by varying the proportions of each wavelength chosen to match every other color of the spectrum. Such matchings are made in instruments called colorimeters.[2] The laws governing color mixture have been determined by the use of such instruments.

If three spectral lights, red, green, and blue, are placed equidistant from a white surface which can be rotated around its center (Fig. 386), a subject viewing the surface will see red when the surface is turned perpendicularly to the red light. As the surface is rotated toward the right and therefore further toward the green light, the color of the surface will change. An orange color will be seen when the quantity of light is mainly red but slightly green, and when the amount of the red and green lights are equal, the color yellow will be perceived. Further to the right transitional colors between yellow and green will appear until a pure green is seen. As the surface is turned further clockwise, the color will change from green to blue-green and finally to blue. When the surface is midway between blue and red, a sensation of purple, which is almost the same as violet, will occur. The

experiment may be done for all possible combinations of color, and the resulting sensation will be found to follow definite laws and to be entirely repeatable and predictable. A particular red of λ 671 mμ, when mixed with green of λ 536 mμ, yields a yellow indistinguishable from λ 589 mμ. The more remote in the spectrum are the two colors chosen to be mixed, the less saturated, i.e., the whiter or grayer, the mixture will be. If the second component is chosen as far down the spectrum as 493 mμ, there will be no hue at all, and if the intensities are properly chosen, this mixture will appear white. The two components in this case are said to be complementary colors. A red of 671 mμ combined with a blue-green of 495 mμ, e.g., are complementary colors since their mixture yields white to the normal eye. The selection of two colors from the spectrum which when mixed form white is shown in Fig. 387.

If one selects a portion of the spectrum below 493 mμ as the second component of the mixture, a group of colors that range from nonspectral purple to purplish red appears. This completes the so-called color circle shown in Fig. 388. It can be seen that complementary colors lie at op-

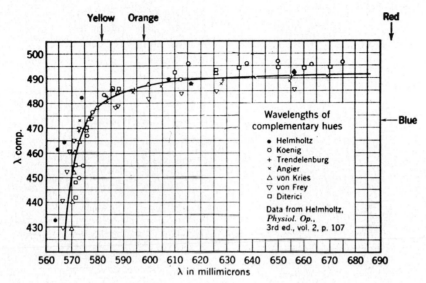

Fig. 387. Complementary color pairs. The data of seven different investigators have been combined in a single plot. The curve, one branch of an equilateral hyperbola, is the locus of a large number of pairs of complementary wavelengths. (From Priest; after Helmholtz. In Geldard, F.: The human senses, New York, 1953, John Wiley & Sons, Inc.)

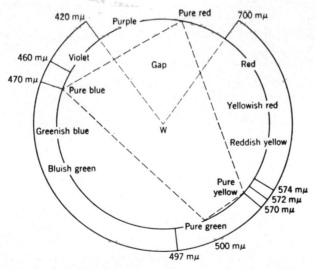

Fig. 388. The hue circle. Spectral stimuli from 420 to 700 mμ are arranged in sequence about the circumference. Complementary colors lie at opposite ends of diagonals. The positions of psychologically pure yellow, green, and blue in the series are noted, as is also that of pure red, which lies in the gap beyond spectral red. (From Gelhard, F.: The human senses, New York, 1953, John Wiley & Sons, Inc., p. 57.)

posite ends of each diameter, whereas psychologically pure red lies between the two ends of the spectrum in the gap at the top of the circle.

Complementary colors. As stated, any two wavelengths of the spectrum which produce white on mixing are called complementary colors. The intensities of the two colors chosen vary within wide limits, depending on the regions of the spectrum selected. For instance, in order for a mixture of yellow and violet to yield white (grayish white), the ratio of luminosities must be nearly 40:1. The following pairs are complementary colors:

Red + greenish blue = white
Orange + cyan blue = white
Yellow + indigo blue = grayish white
Greenish yellow + violet = white

The complementary color for green is purple, which is not a pure spectral color but is formed by mixing the extreme ends of the spectrum together, i.e., red and violet.

Since complementary colors when mixed yield white, it is evident that colors closer together in the spectral series than the complementaries produce a more saturated intermediate color when they are fused; the closer together they are, the more saturated will be the resulting color.

From what has been said one can see that it is possible to produce white light by two different means of retinal stimulation—by a mixture of all the wavelengths in the visible spectrum and by exhibiting two complementary colors simultaneously. This would indicate that the process induced in the retina by these two different stimuli is the same.

Primary colors. In order for one to produce all possible hues in the spectrum, as well as white, it is found that three basic components for the mixture are necessary. If, e.g., one selects rays from the long wave, the short wave, and the middle

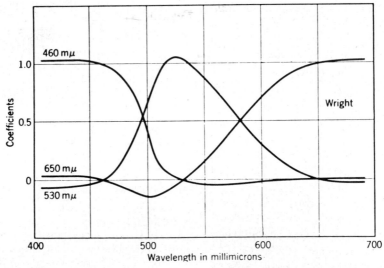

Fig. 389. Reproduction of spectral colors by three primary colors. The curves represent the average readings for ten observers and show the sizes of coefficients necessary to reproduce all spectral points when the primary colors selected are: 650 mμ, red; 530 mμ, green; 460 mμ, violet. (After Wright; from Gelhard, F.: The human senses, New York, 1953, John Wiley & Sons, Inc., p. 58.)

portion of the spectrum, the result is white. Those three portions of the spectrum that yield a sensation of white when mixed are called primary colors. In the example just given they would have been red, green, and violet. Suitable mixtures of these three colors will likewise produce any of the intermediary color shades or purple.

A general color equation can be written as follows

$$C = xR + yG + zV$$

in which x, y, and z are coefficients of varying size for different colors. C is the color produced. The amounts of x, y, and z necessary to produce all the colors of the spectrum are shown in Fig. 389. The primaries selected to be mixed were red, 650 mμ, green, 530 mμ, and violet, 460 mμ.

Different colors of the spectrum may be presented to the two eyes separately, with the result that they are seen either in retinal rivalry or fused. In the latter event they form a new color similar to that which would occur if they had been shown to one eye only. The mixture in this case cannot be by the retina but must be sensed by the brain itself. Not all persons seem to have the ability to do this, however, and even in the same person, this ability varies from time to time and with different colors. Binocular mixtures are notoriously unstable. Suitably chosen red and green portions of the spectrum may be fused mentally when presented simultaneously to the two eyes to form yellow. Mixtures of blue and yellow generally produce the sensation of white under these circumstances.

When one reviews the various portions of the spectrum which combined possess the characteristics of primary colors, as just stated, it is found that any three can be chosen so long as no one of them can

be formed by a mixture of the other two. This being the case, it is a simple matter to arrive at a tristimulus specification of an unknown light if one knows the following factors: (1) the specifications of the spectrum in terms of three suitably selected primaries and (2) the spectral analysis of the unknown light. The exact specifications of the various parts of the spectrum in terms of the three primaries were standardized by the International Commission on Illumination in 1931, and these data were designated the ICI standard observer. They are shown in Fig. 390. The curve labeled $\bar{x}$ represents

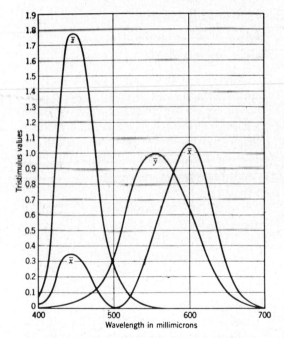

Fig. 390. The standard observer, according to the agreements of the International Commission on Illumination in 1931. The values of $\bar{x}$, $\bar{y}$, and $\bar{z}$ have been so selected as to match for the average observer a unit amount of radiant energy at each wavelength. The $\bar{y}$ curve is of special interest since its values have been chosen to duplicate the photopic luminosity curve for the normal eye. (From Gelhard, F.: The human senses, New York, 1953, John Wiley & Sons, Inc., p. 60.)

a reddish purple primary, y is a green of 520 mμ but more saturated, and $\bar{z}$ is a blue of somewhat greater colorimetric purity than a spectral blue of 477 mμ. At each wavelength the amounts of the three primaries needed to match the spectral band at that wavelength may be found by simply adding the ordinates of all three curves at that spectral position. For example, at 578 mμ approximately equal amounts of reddish purple, $\bar{x}$, and green, $\bar{y}$, are required to match the yellow seen by the normal observer. In the region of 475 mμ a large component of blue, $\bar{z}$, joins with small, about equal amounts of $\bar{x}$ and $\bar{y}$ to match the particular blue seen there.

PHYSIOLOGIC BASIS OF COLOR VISION

The fact that different portions of the spectrum result in different qualities of vision, i.e., color, could be interpreted to indicate that the retina itself responds differently to differences in wavelength and that the message sent up to the brain differs whenever the individual becomes conscious of a change in color. On this basis, the origin of color is in the retina and not in the brain. Evidence has been cited (p. 622) that in the case of a single optic nerve fiber of the eye of *Limulus* the message sent to the brain is independant of the wavelength of the stimulating light. The responses to each portion of the spectrum are identical if the intensities are properly adjusted. One could suppose that in an animal known to respond to differences in wavelength of the stimulating light separate photoreceptors were present in the retina, each capable of being stimulated by one wavelength and one only, and that for every discriminable difference in wavelength there was a corresponding different photoreceptor. It has just been shown, however,

that only three different kinds of photoreceptors are necessary in order to account for normal color vision in man. It is only necessary to postulate three different kinds of retinal messages sent to the brain in order to account for the perception of all the colors of the spectrum and of white.

There is every reason to believe that the messages arise in the cones. Under conditions of dim illumination when the cones are inactive and only rods are responding, vision is achromatic. Color appears only when the illumination is raised to the level at which cones respond. Although it is certain that cones are necessary for color vision, it is not so certain that rods may not play a part, and some investigators take the stand that rods are one of the color receptors.[3] There is no evidence, however, that the entirely rod-free fovea has different color vision from the parafoveal areas containing both rods and cones. It is also unlikely that rods could serve as a mechanism for color vision since as far as is known only one pigment, rhodopsin, has been isolated from the rods, and as we shall see, it is the difference in pigments which probably account for color vision. Since rods contain only one type of pigment, all rods have the same luminosity curve. We would expect to find three different sets of cones, each containing a different visual pigment in individuals with normal color vision.

Attempts have been made to identify three specific receptors having luminosity curves that when summed will reproduce the photopic visibility curve of the spectrum. Abney's construction of a luminosity sensation curve is shown in Fig. 391. The sum of the ordinates at any point in this curve is equal to the ordinate of the photopic luminosity curve. In Fig. 392 is shown another luminosity sensation

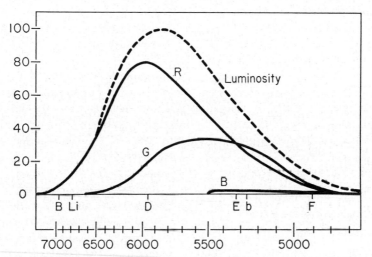

Fig. 391. Abney's luminosity sensation curves. The sum of the ordinates of the three sensation curves, **R, G,** and **B,** at any point is equal to the ordinate of the photopic luminosity curve, see in *dotted line.* (After Watson.)

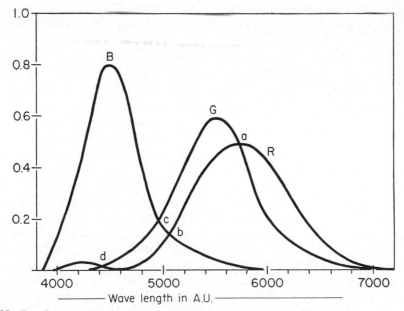

Fig. 392. Equal area sensation curves. Koenig's results corrected by Exner and Ives. (After Duke-Elder.)

curve in which the curves have been altered to conform to coordinates wherein the amounts of the three primaries required to match white are equal.

Another method of identifying different mechanisms having different spectral sensitivities has been developed by Stiles.[4] In effect, he measured the increase in brightness necessary to detect a difference in each portion of the spectrum, presented either to cones or to rods separately. He deduced the existence of five foveal mechanisms, identified as Pi_1 to Pi_5. He concludes, however, that the cone increment thresholds depend upon *three* independent color mechanisms with three spectral sensitivities. Pi_1 is the mechanism for blue, Pi_4 the mechanism for green, and Pi_5 the mechanism for red.

Perhaps one of the most exciting and ingenious experiments in the field of retinal physiology is the recent detection of two visual pigments in the human fovea by Rushton and co-workers. This has been described in detail elsewhere in this book (p. 599). The pigment with greatest sensitivity in the red, erythrolabe, has a λ max. around 590 mμ; that with greatest sensitivity in the green, chlorolabe, has a λ max. around 540 mμ. The blue pigment, which Rushton called cyanolabe but was unable to detect in normal individuals has now been detected in a few subjects whose macular pigmentation was very slight.[5] The three requisites for the theory of trichromacy in human color vision have now been fulfilled, at least qualitatively. It is extremely difficult to determine the absorption spectrum of each of these three pigments. After all, they have not even been isolated from any retina, and their presence and characteristics are only inferred. However, the spectral sensitivities of Stiles' three mechanisms fit the data of Rushton's three foveal pigments suffi-

ciently to justify the conclusion that Stiles' Pi_4 mechanism works by means of chlorolabe, his Pi_5 mechanism by means of erythrolabe, and his Pi_1 mechanism probably by means of cyanolabe (Fig. 393).

Electrophysiology of wavelength discrimination. Mention has been made previously of the responses of individual optic nerve fibers to changes in wavelength of the stimulating light in experimental animals. A considerable advance was made in the optic nerve fiber response to color when Granit found it possible to study the responses from single large ganglion cells in the frog's retina. He found seven different types of response, apparently from seven different types of ganglion cells. However, he felt that the differences between some of these responses were small enough that he could rightfully group the seven into three. These three groups had definitely different responses to different regions of the spectrum. Each group was most sensitive to either the red, green, or blue region. From his data Granit proposed the spectral sensitivity curves for the three different types of receptor as shown in Fig. 394.

According to this, a red of wavelength 600 mμ stimulates the red photoreceptors to an intensity of 91 and stimulates the green receptors to an intensity of 8, and the blue are not stimulated at all. This ratio of 91:8:0, transmitted by these optic nerve fibers to the brain, is translated there into the sensation of red. A blue of wavelength 460 mμ, on the other hand, stimulates the red receptors not at all, but stimulates the green receptors to an intensity of 3 and the blue receptors to an intensity of 5. This ratio of 0:3:5, sent to the brain, yields the sensation of blue. If the red and green receptors are stimulated by an equal amount, it can be seen

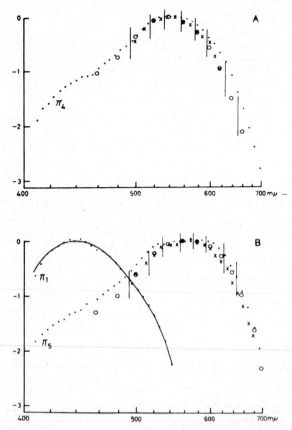

Fig. 393. Log spectral sensitivity curves plotted against wave frequency. *Vertical lines,* action spectral. **A,** Cholorolabe; **B,** erytholabe (Rushton). *Circles,* spectral sensitivity of the fovea, of **A,** of protanopes; **B,** of deuteranopes (Wilmer 1950). *Crosses,* artificial monochromacy. **A,** Green; **B,** red (Brindley 1953). *Dots,* increment threshold mechanisms. **A,** Green mechanism π_4; **B,** red mechanism π_3 and blue mechanisms π_1 and π_2. *Curve,* blue mechanism calculated from color matching (Stiles 1953). (From Rushton, W.: Visual pigments in man, Liverpool, 1962, Liverpool University Press.)

that the blue receptors are not firing, and the ratio of 72:72:0 gives the sensation of approximately 580 mμ, which is yellow. According to this graph, the sensation of yellow could arise even though no yellow lights were thrown into the eye, but merely from the simultaneous stimulation of the same eye with red and green lights or from stimulating one eye with red and the other with green, which we have seen can take place. Further, the simultaneous stimulation of separate red,

green, and blue receptors in the same eye will yield the sensation of white. It is, of course, not known whether there are linkages between these various receptors or whether they send their messages individually to the cortex.

In the dark-adapted eye of the frog Granit[6] found the responses were the same throughout the retina, provided that the stimulus light was of low intensity. The maximal response under these conditions was obtained with wavelengths

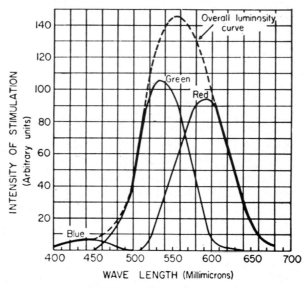

Fig. 394. Theoretical spectral sensitivities of the red, green, and blue cones of the retina as developed in the Granit theory of color vision. Also the total luminosity curve is shown; this represents the sum of stimulation in all of the cones. (After Granit; from Guyton, A.: Textbook of medical physiology, Philadelphia, 1956, W. B. Saunders Co., p. 676.)

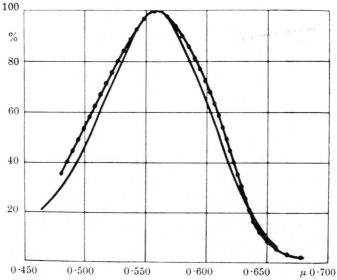

Fig. 395. Distribution of sensitivity of dominator element in the retina of frog (*uninterrupted line*) and snake (*line interrupted by dots*). (From Granit, R.: Nature, London **151**:11, 1943.)

of 500 mμ, showing that the rods containing rhodopsin were the only receptors responding. As soon as the retina was light-adapted, however, the wavelength response curves varied with different spot stimulation. In general the responses fell into two categories which Granit called dominators and modulators. The dominators gave broad sensitivity curves with maximum response around wavelength 550 mμ and were more numerous (Fig. 395). The modulators gave narrow spectral sensitivity curves, largely confined to one region of the spectrum, and as just stated, these could be separated into three groups—one with a maximum around 600 mμ, red-sensitive; one with a maximum around 530 mμ, green-sensitive; one with a maximum around 450 mμ, blue-sensitive (Fig. 396).

The dominator, as shown in Fig. 397, was found in the pure cone eye of the snake, which need not be light-adapted to give this curve. The same dominator has been found in the cat eye, but is lacking in the eyes of guinea pigs and rats. The dominator, Granit suggests, in a sense may be called the carrier of the Purkinje shift. Its curve corresponds to the curve of the human photopic luminosity curve so that the dominator is probably responsible for the sensation of brightness. The sensation of color on the other hand is due to the modulators.

On the basis of these findings Granit proposes that vision in man and all animals possessing both rods and cones is brought about as follows. In the dark only the dominators respond (rods). These contain rhodopsin, and accordingly the scotopic luminosity curve peaks at the λ max. of rhodopsin, namely, 500 mμ. In the light-adapted eye the dominators (cones) continue to respond and by the frequency of their discharge indicate the intensity (but not the color) of the light. These dominators have the maximum sensitivity at 550 mμ and account for the

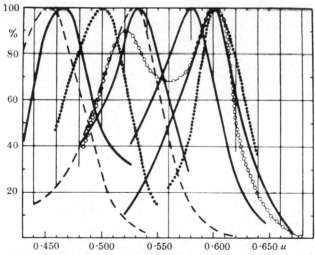

Fig. 396. Distribution of sensitivity of modulator elements from eyes of rat (*dots*), guinea pig (*broken line*), frog (*line in full*), and snake (*line interrupted by circles*). Note that all curves are in percentage of the maximum and that a number of ordinates on either side of 0.560 μ are drawn down to indicate dominator values. All spectrums are of equal quantum intensity in both Figs. 395 and 396. (From Granit, R.: Nature, London **151**:11, 1943.)

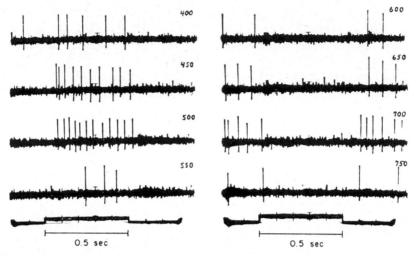

Fig. 397. Variation of response from a single ganglion cell with change in wavelength of stimulus. Wavelength of stimulus in millimicrons at upper right hand of each record. The duration of the stimulus is indicated by the step in the signal trace at the base of each series. Spikes occurring before the onset of the stimulus are off responses from a preceding stimulus. Intensity of stimulus at 600 mμ = 55 μ watts/cm.[2]. (From Wagner, H., MacNichol, E., and Wolbarsht, M.: J. Gen. Physiol. **43:**45, 1960.)

photopic luminosity curve and the Purkinje shift. When the eye is light-adapted, the modulators also come into action, and the spectral composition of the stimulus light determines to what degree each of the three groups shall be stimulated. If green light falls on the retina, the green modulators respond maximally, while the red and blue give small responses.

Granit's findings were made possible by the development of a technique of placing microelectrodes into the retina at different levels so that the responses from isolated structures could be tapped. This work has been carried further by many different workers, with the accumulation of a large literature. At the present time, however, considerable confusion exists as to the actual structures which are being tapped and the interpretation of the changes in potential being recorded (see discussion of electrical phenomena, p. 613). Most of the responses are slow changes in potential (p. 616). These slow

potential changes differ from the spike discharge, which characterizes the message carried by the optic nerve fiber, in that the slow potentials change in size with the stimulus intensity, whereas the spike potentials follow the all-or-none law. The slow potentials are, therefore, often referred to as graded potential responses and consist of a change in the resting potential of either an increase—hyperpolarization—or a decrease—depolarization.

The use of saline-filled ultramicropipet electrodes has permitted the recording of slow electric potentials in highly localized regions of the retina, perhaps even in single cells. This is best done in fishes, whose retinal cells are larger than those of the frog.[20] The responses measure from 10 to 30 mv. superimposed upon a negative resting potential (20 to 50 mv.) and appear to be intracellular since they disappear abruptly as the tip of the electrode is advanced a few microns. The responses consist of an increase in the resting potential, indicating hyperpolarization of the cell membrane. Although at first it was believed that these responses were from the cones themselves, they are now known to be from second-order neurons. They are produced by the cone system however. One type of response having a maximum in the middle of the spectrum (yellow-green) has been called by MacNichol and Svaetichin the L response. They showed that it originates in the outer plexiform layer, presumably in giant horizontal cells. Other responses were picked up from the inner nuclear layer and were tentatively attributed to bipolar cells. These were negative (hyperpolarizing) in the blue-green end of the spectrum and reversed in sign, becoming positive (depolarizing) in the yellow-red end of the spectrum. The three types of response have been referred to by these authors as the luminosity (L), yellow-blue (Y-B) and red-green (R-G) types.

Similar graded potential responses have been found in other species of fish.[8] In the goldfish the changes in the graded potential responses have been correlated with the changes in spike potentials from the retinal ganglion cells. Illumination of the retina with white light evoked a vigorous burst of impulses in "on-off" units, which then subsided quickly. Extinction of the light caused another vigorous burst of impulses which rapidly subsided. However, when various portions of the spectrum were used, a change in the wavelength of the stimulating light converted an essentially pure "on" response to one band of spectral colors into an essentially pure "off" response to illumination in another band of wavelengths. As shown in Fig. 397, light of wavelength 400 to 550 mμ evoked an "on" response only. To illuminations longer than this the response was essentially a pure "off" effect. The short wavelengths of the spectrum gave excitation, whereas the long wavelengths had a strong inhibitory influence during illumination, which was followed by an "off" discharge or postinhibitory rebound. Here again we see that inhibitory processes play an equal part with excitatory processes in the composition of the visual message sent to the brain.

THEORIES OF COLOR VISION

Young-Helmholtz theory. A satisfactory theory is one which not only embraces all known facts, but also points the way to the discovery of new facts. The one fact which emerged during the compilation of the data of color vision is that a combination of three different types of responses from the retina could account for most of the observations. As early as 1807, Thomas Young[9] proposed a theory which has succeeded in maintaining first place among all the various other theories proposed. This is the trichromatic theory. Young proposed that there were three different sets of nerve fibers in the retina—one set sensitive to red, one to green, and the other to violet. Helmholtz expanded this theory and assumed that different degrees of excitation occurred in each of the three kinds of nerve fibers when they were stimulated by light from various parts of the spectrum, as shown in Fig. 398. It can be seen that most of the formulations already given resemble this in general. The peak of the violet curve is in the spectral region that may well be called blue. The designations of blue and violet have been used rather indiscriminately in discussion of the trichromatic theory.

Gradually the idea that there were three different sets of nerve fibers was changed to mean three different photoreceptors, and in general these mean three different types of cones, each with

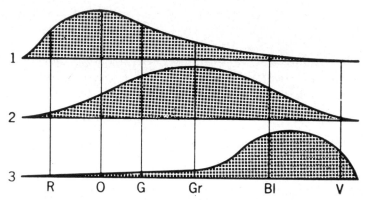

Fig. 398. Original excitation curves of Helmholtz. These three diagrams, entirely imaginary in their construction, indicate something like the degree of excitation of the three kinds of fibres, No. 1 for the red-sensitive fibres, No. 2 for the green-sensitive fibres. (From Gelhard, F.: The human senses, New York, 1953, John Wiley & Sons, Inc., p. 74.)

its own light-sensitive material and absorptive characteristics. A further step is to allocate the differences in the photoreceptors to different pigments, which carries us from an anatomic basis to a chemical basis for color vision.

Newton, who was the principal proponent of the corpuscular theory of light, had supposed that a separate element in the retina vibrated in unison with each of the frequencies of the incident light, but Young had objected to this in his Bakerian lecture before the Royal Society. He suggested that:

"[since] it is almost impossible to conceive each sensitive point on the retina to contain an infinite number of particles each capable of vibrating in perfect unison with every possible undulation, it becomes necessary to suppose the number limited, for instance, to the three principal colors, red, yellow, and blue, of which the undulations are related in magnitude as the numbers 8, 7, and 6; and that each of the particles is capable of being put in motion less or more forcibly by undulations differing less or more from a perfect union; for instance, the undulations of green light will affect equally the particles in unison with yellow and blue and produce the same effect as a light composed of those two species; and each sensitive filament of the nerve may con-

sist of three portions, one for each principal color."*

In making this theory Young was anticipating Müller who laid down the principle of the specific energies of nerves, which was not stated until 1840. He assumed that each fiber could produce only one sensation, no matter how stimulated. In this case the fiber would produce the sensation of red, of green, or of blue, depending only upon itself and not upon the particular wavelength which was used to stimulate it. Whereas Young did not specifically state that the combination of all these nerve fibers, sending impulses to the brain simultaneously, produced the sensation of white, it is an obvious conclusion from his theory.[11]

These ideas lay buried for nearly fifty years when Helmholtz rescued them from oblivion and laid down the theory which has come to us but very slightly modified today. Helmholtz gave the entire credit to Young for this theory, stating:

"The nature of colors with all these marvelous and complicated relations was a riddle which

*From Young, T.: Bakerian lecture, Transactions Philosophical Society, London, 1802.

Goethe in vain attempted to solve, nor were physicists and physiologists more successful. I include myself in the number, for I long worked at the task without getting any nearer my object until I discovered that a wonderfully simple solution had been made at the beginning of this century, and had been in print ever since for anyone to read who chose. This solution was found and published by the same Thomas Young who first showed the correct method of interpreting the Egyptian hieroglyphics. He was one of the most acute men who ever lived, but he had the misfortune to be born far in advance of his contemporaries. They looked on him with astonishment but they could not follow his bold speculations. And so a mass of his most important thoughts remained buried and forgotten in the Philosophical Transactions of the Royal Society until a later generation slowly arrived at the rediscovery of his discoveries, and came to appreciate the force of his argument and the accuracy of his conclusions."

Young's hypothesis both in its original form and after it was modified by Helmholtz has remained unchallenged in the intervening years; no theory has been able to supplant it. Most of the ones which have been given any serious credence, such as those of Aubert,[12] Hering,[13] or Ladd-Franklin,[14] have been founded on psychologic data.

As stated, the Young-Helmholtz theory of color vision assumes the presence of three separate photoreceptors in the retina, each transmitting a different type of message to the visual cortex.

It must be assumed that each of the separate photoreceptors is stimulated to some degree by all of the spectral frequencies, but that each photoreceptor is affected chiefly by light of one wavelength. Since it is impossible to stimulate any one of the three receptors alone, it is not possible to produce a completely saturated color sensation.

This theory explains the phenomenon of negative afterimages satisfactorily. If a green object is fixated for a period of time, the corresponding green receptor is stimulated actively. If later it is exposed to white light, it no longer has the ability to respond to the green wave lengths, but the adjacent photoreceptors, i.e., the red and violet ones, which previously were but little stimulated, now respond to the red and violet frequencies in the white light. The result is an afterimage whose color is a mixture of the red and violet, namely, purple.

Although no anatomic evidence supports the contention that fusion of impulses from the three primary photoreceptors takes place in the brain, the binocular fusion of colors supports the view that cerebral processes play a part. It has been shown that many of the phenomena of monocular color mixtures can be duplicated by exposing each retina to a monochromatic frequency, the cerebral fusion of which results in the same hue as would be produced if the colors were to be exposed to one eye simultaneously. Yellow, e.g., can be obtained by binocular fusion of red and green, showing that it can be produced by cerebral processes. This supports the Young-Helmholtz theory, in opposition to the Hering theory which postulates a yellow receptor in the retina in addition to the other three.

Recent evidence suggests that cone vision, which is generally believed to be largely if not solely concerned with perception of color, is more corticalized than rod vision. In other words, destruction of the cortex plays much more havoc with cone vision than with rod vision. It has been stated by investigators that in rats, cats, and dogs occipital lobectomy does not result in total loss of vision, as judged by the animal's ability to discriminate between light and dark. Even in monkeys,[15] a conditioned response to a change from darkness to light, which is a rod function, can still be elicited after occipital lobectomy; therefore, even at high illuminations it resembles that characteristic of rods, i.e., the scotopic visibility curve.[16] Therefore, it would appear that color vision, a cone function, is dependent largely on the integrity of the cortex and is not entirely a retinal function, even at the physiologic level.

Hering theory. Hering's theory is deserving of mention for comparison with the Young-Helmholtz theory. The Hering theory assumes the existence of three photochemical substances in the retina, but they are of such a nature as to give rise to six different qualities of sensation. Visible light is supposed to break down a substance known as the white-black substance that sets up impulses in the optic nerve and induces the sensation of white. In the absence of light, this substance is resynthesized to its original structure, and this resynthesis sets up impulses that produce the sensation of blackness. In addition to the white-black substance, there are two other substances, red-green and yellow-blue. Like the white-black substance, each of these yields one sensation on breakdown and a different one on resynthesis, as shown in Table 57.

According to this theory complementary colors are really antagonistic to each other so that when they are ex-

Table 57

Photochemical substance	Retinal process	Sensation
White-black	Breakdown	White
	Resynthesis	Black
Red-green	Breakdown	Red
	Resynthesis	Green
Yellow-blue	Breakdown	Yellow
	Resynthesis	Blue

hibited simultaneously to the retina their effects neutralize each other, and only the effects of the white substance remain, which all of the visible wavelengths exert. The theory does not conform to the doctrine of specific nerve energies since it assumes that the same fiber can signal two different sensations to the brain. Further, according to this theory when red and green are thrown on the retina simultaneously, they neutralize each other and yield a sensation of white. Instead, they produce a sensation of yellow unless a blue-green and a blue-red are selected. Some of the recent electrophysiologic findings support the Hering hypothesis, however. We have seen that Wagner, MacNichol, and Wolbarsht found an "on-off" type of discharge from the ganglion cells of the goldfish with white light, but that with monochromatic light the response was either a pure "on" or a pure "off" response, depending upon the wavelength used (Fig. 397, p. 810). This shows that the message from this particular ganglion cell may be inhibitory when the receptors supplying it are excited by red and excitatory when the receptors are excited by blue. Recording from other ganglion cells shows the reverse; i.e., the responses were excitatory from the red end of the spectrum and inhibitory from the blue end. In fact, not only single ganglion cells but also different parts of the receptive field of individual ganglion cells showed this same difference. The center, if excited by red, showed inhibition of the periphery by this wavelength, and if the center was excited by blue, the periphery was inhibited by this wavelength. In other words, we have here messages which are opponent in character. When red light excites, its complementary light, green, inhibits.

Summary. It may well turn out that

both theories are correct. The underlying basis of color vision is probably photochemical, and the evidence at present indicates that only three different pigments are present in the human cones. Human color vision must depend upon at least three different photoreceptor systems, and in all likelihood these must be three or more different photosensitive pigments. Only one pigment would suffice if there were various color selectors interposed between it and the light; however, the experiments of Brindley and Rushton[17] have proved that the color of light is the same whether it is seen coming through the pupil or is seen transsclerally. Since light thrown into the eye transsclerally would not pass first through any color filters, it is obvious that color filters can be ruled out as the basis for trichromatic vision. If subsequent research proves this to be correct, the retinal basis of color vision will be the Young-Helmholtz or three receptor hypothesis. Somewhere higher in the neural pathway the message may be coded in opposite and mutually exclusive responses to certain bands of wavelengths, and to black and white, as Davson[18] suggests, so that the Hering opponent process theory may also be correct. One of the most recent theories proposed is that of Hurvich and Jameson[19] which combines retinal trichromacy with the paired antagonistic systems of Hering. The light falling on the retina is assumed to be absorbed in the receptors by three independent photopigments of differently selective spectral absorptions. These light absorptions excite the visual neural response systems whose properties seem to be such that they can be represented schematically as paired.

"Within each pair, furthermore, the two components are mutually opponent or antagonistic. The three pairs of independent systems are

Neural Responses

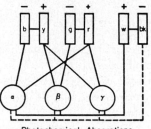

Photochemical Absorptions

Neural Responses

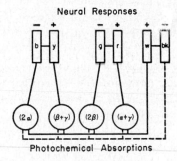

Photochemical Absorptions

$$y-b = k_1(\beta+\gamma-2\alpha)$$
$$r-g = k_2(\alpha+\gamma-2\beta)$$
$$w-bk = k_3(\alpha+\gamma+\beta)-k_4(\alpha+\beta+\gamma)$$

Fig. 399. Schematic representation of opponent colors model. *Upper diagram,* assumes three photochemical substances isolated in individual receptor units. *Lower diagram,* assumes three photochemical substances combined in different receptor units simpler relations to neural response systems. (Hurvich, L., and Jameson, D.: J. Gen. Physiol. **43**(supp.6):63, 1960.)

taken to be directly associated with the color qualities blue or yellow, red or green, and black or white. For the specific set of hypothetical photochemical absorptions that we have taken for the quantitative development of this model, the amounts and qualities of chromatic response excited by the photosensitive light absorptions are specified in the mathematical relations given in Fig. [399]. Different photochemical absorptions from those we have assumed would yield different mathematical relations, but the basic concepts of the theoretical scheme would remain the same. The particular set of absorption functions that we have assumed yield the simplest mathematical relations that are at the same time consistent with a variety of long-duration chromatic and brightness adaptation phenomena."[*]

Svaetichin and MacNichol have called attention to the fact that an analogous situation confronts us in the transmission of color television by the system in use in the United States.

"In this system light from the scene being televised is split into red, green, and blue components which are then imaged on separate camera tubes. The signals from the separate tubes are combined to form a luminosity signal known in the industry as the Y signal. This signal is transmitted directly as video information and can be picked up on black-and-white receivers without modification. In addition, the Y signal is subtracted from the R and B signals to give R-Y and B-Y components, which are transmitted separately. In the receiver, the R-Y, B-Y, and Y components are combined in such a way that the original R, G., and B signals are reconstituted. These are applied to separate electron guns in the picture tube which illuminate separate R, G, and B phosphors. A stranger analyzing the system would conclude that it was a Young-Helmholtz device if he examined the camera tubes and the picture tube and a Hering device if he examined the transmission pathways."[†]

It is, therefore, quite possible that the retina is trichromatic at the receptor level and tetrachromatic at the postsynaptic level and in the visual pathways.

COLOR BLINDNESS

One of the strongest supports for the trichromatic theory of color perception is the defect, relatively common in men, of various degrees of color blindness. Analyses of these persons show that they can be grouped into three main classes,

*From Hurvich, L., and Jameson, D.: J. Gen. Physiol. **43** (**supp. 6**):63, 1960.
† From Svaetichin, G., and MacNichol, E.: Ann. New York Acad. Sc. **74:**402, 1952.

depending upon whether the person affected has lost one, two, or all three of the color processes. These persons are placed in one of the following three classifications: (1) protanopia, in which only one process is defective (*protos,* first), (2) deuteranopia, in which two of the processes are defective (*deuteros,* second), and (3) tritanopia, in which all three of the processes are defective (*tritos,* three).

The classifications of color blindness that are employed generally are given in Table 58.

All three trichromats—normal, protanomalous, and deuteranomalous—require three primary colors with which to match the spectrum, but they use the frequencies from the red and green ends of the spectrum in different proportions to make the same matches. A protanomalous person requires much more of the red end of the spectrum than a normal person, and a deuteranomalous person requires much more of the green end of the spectrum. Many persons with very slight degrees of protanomaly and deuteranomaly are found, but about 4% of the men have severe protanomaly or deuteranomaly.

The second group, dichromats, can match all parts of the spectrum using only two primary colors—blue and green for protanopic persons and blue and red for deuteranopic persons. These persons are supposed to have lost one of the processes as far as function goes, and

Table 58. *Types of color perception*

I *Trichromat*	II *Dichromat*	III *Monochromat*
Normal color vision	Protanopia	Total color blindness
Protanomaly	Deuteranopia	
Deuteranomaly	Tritanopia	

their color perceptions are determined by various combinations of the remaining two, therefore.

The third group, the tritanopes, are very rare. These persons can match the spectrum using one frequency from the end of the spectrum having long wavelengths and one from the middle of the spectrum.

The monochromats can duplicate the whole length of the spectrum using only one wavelength; in other words, they have achromatic vision and may be said to be totally color blind.

Little is known of the pathologic physiology of color blindness. The ability to distinguish colors may be lost as a result of disease of the retina or optic nerve. Such a condition is called acquired color blindness. A person may be born color blind and show no other abnormality of visual functions. Most forms of color blindness are hereditary defects transmitted by females and appear almost entirely in male offspring.

The luminosity of the spectrum is practically normal for persons who belong to the class of deuteranomaly or deuteranopia. Persons in the protanomalous and protanopia groups, on the other hand, see the spectrum considerably shortened. The red end of the spectrum does not even produce the sensation of light, much less of color. The brightest part of the spectrum as seen by persons who are protanomalous and protanopes is at 540 mμ. Protanopes have nothing wrong with their foveas, and their visual acuity may be normal, unless it is measured in red light. Under these conditions they would obviously have poor vision since the red light could not be absorbed due to the absence of erythrolabe. However, Rushton has found that the protanope has twice the amount of chlorolabe in the fovea; hence it is probable that the protanope has the normal complement of cones present and that none of them are empty of pigment, but all are filled with chlorolabe. It is assumed that the deuteranope lacks chlorolabe.

The lack of erythrolabe in the protanope is probably due to the absence of a specific protein. We have seen that all visual pigments are probably built on the same pattern—a specific protein built into the structure of the photoreceptor with the neo-b isomer of vitamin A$_1$ aldehyde. The vitamin is not specific and is used for both rods and cones. As Rushton has picturesquely put it:

"The recipes for making the special materials of our body are genetically handed down encoded in duplicate in the genes of our paired chromosomes. Our parents may mislay one copy without mishap if they give us the other—with one exception—upon the unpaired sex chromosome of the male. Here the loss of the only copy is disastrous. For a boy (whose active sex chromosome is always derived from his mother) is incapable of making the protein of erythrolabe if the chromosome she contributed lacked the recipe. But though condemned to red-blindness he need not lose all vision from half his cones. Chlorolabe he can make, and this he uses to repair his loss. The 'red' cones still function, but it is with chlorolabe that they respond."*

---

*From Rushton, W.: New Scient. **10**:374, 1961.

REFERENCES

1. Bragg, W.: The universe of light, London, 1933, Bell & Sons, Ltd., p. 40.
2. Wright, W. D.: A trichromatic colorimeter with spectral primaries, Tr. Am. Ophth. Soc. **29**:225, 1928.
3. Willmer, E.: Retinal structure and color vision, a restatement and an hypothesis, New York, 1946, Cambridge University Press.
4. Stiles, W.: Colour vision: the approach

through increment threshold sensitivity, Proc. Nat. Acad. Sc. **75:**100, 1959.

5. Rushton, W.: The chemical basis of colour vision, New Scient. **10:**374, 1961.

6. Granit, R.: A physiological theory of color perception, Nature, London **151:**11, 1943.

7. MacNichol, E., and Svaetichin, G.: Electric responses from the isolated retinas of fishes, Am. J. Ophth. **46** (supp.):26, 1958.

8. Wagner, H., MacNichol, E., and Wolbarsht, M.: The response properties of single ganglion cells in the goldfish retina, J. Gen. Physiol. **43:**45, 1960.

9. Young, T.: On the theory of light and colors, Lectures in Natural Philosophy, London **2:**613, 1807.

10. Young, T.: Bakerian lecture, Transactions Philosophical Society, London, 1802.

11. Hecht, S.: The development of Thomas Young's theory of color vision, J. Optic. Soc. America **20:**231, 1930.

12. Aubert, A.: Physiologie der Netzhaut, Breslau, 1865.

13. Hering, E.: Grundzuge der Lehre vom Litchsinn, Berlin, 1920.

14. Ladd-Franklin, C.: Color vision and color theories, New York, 1929, Harcourt, Brace & Co.

15. Marquis, D. G., and Hilgard, E. R.: Conditioned responses to light in monkeys after removal of the occipital lobes, Brain **60:**1, 1937.

16. Malmo, R.: Effect of the removal of the visual cortex on brightness discrimination and spectral brightness discrimination in the rhesus monkey, Psycho. Bull. **37:**497, 1940.

17. Brindley, G., and Rushton, W.: The color of monochromatic light when passed into the human retina from behind, J. Physiol. **147:**204, 1959.

18. Davson, H.: Physiology of the eye, ed. 2, Boston, 1963, Little, Brown, & Co., p. 203.

19. Hurvich, L., and Jameson, D.: Perceived color, induction effects, and opponent-response mechanisms, J. Gen. Physiol. **43** (**supp. 6**):63, 1960.

20. Svaetichin, G., and MacNichol, E.: Ann. New York Acad. Sc. **74:**402, 1958.

CHAPTER 21

ENTOPTIC AND ALLIED PHENOMENA

In the description of entoptic phenomena we are concerned with the visualization of certain structures within the eye through the proper arrangement of incident light. These structures may be normal to the eye, or they may be imperfections such as opacities in the vitreous or lens. The sensations arising from structures normally present in the eye, such as the shadows from the large blood vessels or the movement of blood cells in the capillaries, are generally connected with the retinal circulation. These are usually not visualized by a person, either because his attention has never been called to them or because it takes some special conditions of illumination to make them apparent. Under this heading must be included other phenomena that result from unusual stimulation of the retina by inadequate stimuli, such as phosphenes from digital pressure on the globe and sparks and flashes of light from mechanical stimulation of the retina.

OPACITIES IN THE OCULAR MEDIA

Under ordinary circumstances one is not aware of the imperfections in the ocular media. Most persons have small opacities in the lens, but these do not interfere in any way with vision. None of the ocular media, with the exception of the aqueous humor, are perfectly transparent since they are composed of cells with nuclei; yet under ordinary circumstances one is quite unaware of these imperfections. As a matter of fact, even large opacities in the cornea and lens may not give rise to any imperfections in the retinal image. This is due to the fact, as pointed out by Friedman,[1] that the opacity lies so far in front of the retina that its shadow does not interfere with the formation of the retinal image.

In Fig. 400, if AB is an imperfection or opacity in the lens, it will cast a shadow on the retina. If the eye is in focus, i.e., emmetropic or made so with glasses, this shadow will not interfere with the formation of a retinal image. Since a sufficient number of rays from each point in the object will be focused on the screen, the opacity, AB, will have an effect on this image only in so far as it cuts down the total amount of light. If the eye is ametropic, however, the influence of an

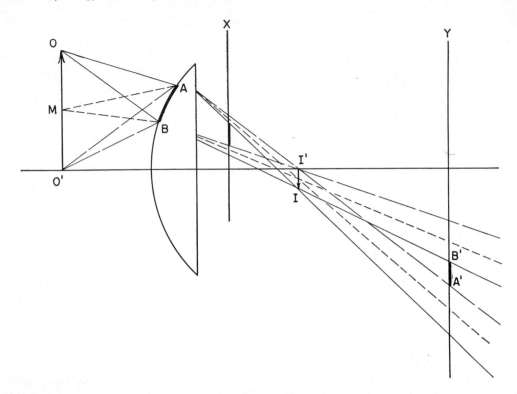

Fig. 400. AB, Paths of the shadows cast by an opacity. The shadows do not interfere with the formation of the image at the focal plane since other rays, such as OL (not drawn), serve to form a complete and shadowless image. The cones of shadow may be intercepted at **X** to form an upright shadow or at **Y** to form an inverted shadow. (After Friedman.)

opacity becomes increasingly important the farther away the retina is from the posterior principal focus of the optical system. For example, if the retina lies at X, in Fig. 400, the image of point O will fall almost entirely within the shadow formed by the lenticular opacity, AB. Similarly, if the retina is at position Y, the image will fall within the shadow of AB after the rays have come to a focus and diverged again. Therefore, any opacity in the cornea or lens will have an influence on the optical image, depending upon whether the eye is emmetropic.

The closer an opacity is to the retina, the more likely is its shadow to interfere with the retinal image, as shown in Fig. 401. LL^1 represents the light passing through the pupillary plane and VO an opacity in the vitreous. V^1O^1 is an opacity of the same size but closer to the retina. Its umbral cone will be larger in direct proportion to its backward displacement. The farther back the location of an opacity in the vitreous, the greater is the probability that its umbra will fall on the retina. The diameter of the conic section falling on the retina will be directly proportionate to the backward displacement of the particular opacity. At a given location, the larger the opacity, the longer and broader will be its umbra. On the other hand, a small opacity close to the retina may cause a larger section of its umbral cone to impinge on the retina than that of an extensive opacity which

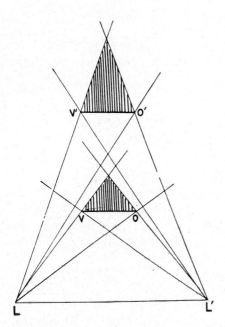

Fig. 401. Lengths of shadows cast by opacities of equal size but unequally distant from the light source. (From Friedman, B.: Arch. Ophth. **28:**285, 1942.)

happens to lie farther forward. An opacity which casts a sharp umbra on the retina may be outlined as a positive scotoma against an evenly white background. Uniformity of the background provides no distracting details which might interfere with the recognition of the shadow.

If the opacity lies well forward in the vitreous, it will have to be relatively large to disturb the retina by its umbra; a small opacity at the same level will cast its umbral cone far in front of the retina and may cause little or no annoyance. The closer the opacity lies to the plane of the retina, the less evident is the penumbra, and the larger and more sharply defined is the umbra. One may readily illustrate this fact by holding a pencil between a light source and a white paper; the closer the pencil is held to the paper, the larger and more clearly defined is the umbra,

and the less evident is the penumbra. There is much greater contrast between the dark shadow and the rest of the receiving surface when the umbra is at its maximum and the penumbra at its minimum.

This statement also applies to the retina, and it explains the extreme annoyance caused by even a very small opacity which lies near the retina and the indifference to a much larger opacity which happens to be situated anteriorly. Patients frequently complain of small specks which can be seen against a bright background on a page of a book. These move about as the eye is moved but tend to sink down in the direction of gravity when the eye is held still. The specks may be single round globules or sometimes chains of little bright spots resembling somewhat a string of pearls. Fine dark lines and amorphous masses are also seen occasionally and may become very annoying when they cross the line of sight. They usually disappear after a few moments, but sometimes they last for days and become a source of discomfort and alarm to the patient. They are called muscae volitantes because they seem to flit about like flies as the line of sight is directed in various directions.

Most of the vitreous opacities seen entopically by patients are entirely harmless, and the patient needs nothing more than reassurance about them. However, vitreous opacities may be of serious import. When a patient complains of vitreous opacities, especially if they are accompanied by flashes of light, they are always suspect of heralding a separation of the retina. One form of vitreous opacity which occurs frequently and patients notice entoptically consists of a large, formed particle which, with the ophthalmoscope, can be seen floating in the anterior part of the vitreous and is large enough to produce a definite shadow on the underlying retina. It may be due to detachment of the posterior part of the vitreous and possibly represents a torn piece of the posterior part of the hyaloid canal.

ENTOPTIC PHENOMENA CONNECTED WITH THE TEAR FILM AND THE CORNEA

A number of interesting entoptic phenomena can be visualized from the cornea and the tear film on its surface. Superficial horizontal bands, due apparently to folds in the corneal epithelium, may be seen in the entoptic field. They run in an unbroken line across the entire width of the pupil and change their positions as the lids are slowly approximated or separated, advancing as the lids advance and receding slightly as the lids recede. When they are straight, they are formed by the pressure of the lower lid, and when they exhibit a slight bowing with the convexity upward, following the curvature of the margin of the upper lid, they are formed by the pressure of the upper lid. They are quite distinct from the entoptic image of the tear film. The lacrimal fluid which adheres to the upper lid margin produces a longitudinal stripe which may be visualized, especially if the palpebral fissure is narrowed and the gaze is directed to a suitably illuminated background.

Droplets of tear fluid and mucus on the cornea likewise can be seen as central bright spots surrounded by a dark ring. These move up and down as the palpebral fissures are widened or narrowed. Various folds and channels may be visualized in the corneal stroma. These consist of vertical lines which are not exactly straight, but present gentle curvatures in some spots; in other regions, the bending is more sharply angular. The individual channels are soon recognized and remembered from the peculiarities of their shape. It will be noted that the same configurations are recognized in successive attempts to visualize the phenomena on different days, which speaks for their definite anatomic structure.

ENTOPTIC PHENOMENA CONNECTED WITH THE LENS

The fact that a star is not visualized as a point of light but as a star figure is due to the structure of the lens which breaks up the rays of light. Probably this phenomenon is related intimately to the suture lines and the isoindical surfaces of the normal lens.

Opacities in the lens are observed against a suitable background very easily and are often the cause of great annoyance to people with incipient cataracts. The radial fibers of the lens may occasionally act as a diffraction grating and produce colored halos around lights.

RETINAL BLOOD VESSELS

The blood vessels of the retina lie in front of the rods and cones; hence they should cast a shadow on these elements and be perceived. That they are not noticed under ordinary conditions of illumination is due to the fact that the visual elements underlying the vessels become adapted to this pattern of illumination. Only when the light is thrown from one side so that the shadow falls on elements unaccustomed to it do they become visible. The vessels are seen easily when the beam of a slit lamp is focused on the sclera as far back from the limbus as possible. Patients will often remark on the picture they see as the beam sweeps over an eye in bringing it to focus on the anterior segment. The interlacing branches of the retinal vessels are seen as black lacework against a red background.

Another method of observing the blood

vessels is to look at a bright background through a pinhole disk which is kept in motion in front of the eye. The blood vessels then appear as dark branching lines on a bright background. If the pinhole is not kept in constant motion, the image disappears; the motion of the disk keeps the shadows falling on different sensitive elements and thus avoids adaptation. When the image falls on one set of sensitive elements for even a short period of time, they rapidly adapt to such an image (p. 77).

If pressure on the eye is made, the vessels can be seen to pulsate. The pulsations of the retinal vessels can sometimes be seen entoptically, especially after physical exercise, according to Friedman.[1] The first change that is observed is a sharp rapid expansion of the part of the arterial tree involved which is synchronous with the cardiac systole. This is followed immediately by a second phase which is a slower contractile movement along the same path. Without physical exercise, the excursions of the vessels are usually too small to effect entoptic visualization although at times their movements are vaguely suggestive. The diameter of a vessel determines the limits of its excursions, and the caliber of the vessels of the arterioles is exceedingly small. Exercise has the effect of dilating the arterioles, thus increasing the vigor and amplitude of their excursions.

The explanation of this phenomenon must be in the retinal circulation and not in the choroidal circulation because the macula is free from the pulsating figures. This fact is in keeping with our knowledge of the avascular structure of the macula. If the choroid were implicated, the pattern would be seen in the macula equally well because the choroidal circulation is essentially the same behind the macula as in the regions adjacent to it.

The pulsating figures are probably caused by the mechanical disturbance of the underlying receptor cells from the exaggerated excursions of the distended blood vessels. The cells are displaced in one direction while the vessel dilates and in the opposite direction when it contracts. Friedman states that there is a marked transition in the physiologic functioning of the retinal arterioles at about the 10-degree zone. Elsewhere in the body the amplitude of pulse waves becomes more restricted the further toward the periphery one goes; in the retina the terminals seem to pulsate more freely than the parent vessels.

The velocity of the pulse wave in the large arteries of the upper part of the body is 6 to 9 M. per second. It must be considerably less in the retinal artery, but, even so, the velocity of the wave front in the wide parts of the artery is too rapid to be caught by the retinal cells except as a blur. It is for this reason that after one has exercised the wide parts of the retinal vessels become evident simultaneously throughout their course from the periphery to the 10-degree zone.

CAPILLARY CIRCULATION

If one looks at a brightly illuminated surface such as a white sheet of paper or at the cloudless sky, small, dancing spots can be seen. These usually appear as bright circles against a somewhat darker background. Occasionally their shape is more oval, and one side is brighter than the other. These spots are highly motile and pursue more or less definite paths which are usually short and somewhat curved. The moving spots are seen best if one looks at a background of monochromatic light in the region from 350 to 450 mμ. This is the region of the spectrum which is absorbed by hemoglobin. Because of this it has been suggested that the moving particles are red blood cells passing through the retinal capillaries. During their passage, the hemoglobin absorbs the blue end of the spectrum; hence a slight shadow is cast on the underlying rods and cones. Naturally, this shadow will be more dense in light which hemoglobin absorbs.

The movement of the corpuscles cannot be seen exactly at the point on which the subject fixates, which is to be expected if the particles are blood corpuscles in the retinal capillaries since the fovea is a blood-free area, so far as retinal circulation is concerned. It has been suggested that the shadows of the blood corpuscles are cast on the underlying rods and cones only when the corpuscles pass down into the deep capillary network (Fig. 94, p. 307). They vanish as they ascend into the inner layers of the retina. This explains why the single points follow each other at such relatively long intervals.

Some authors consider the corpuscles to be white blood cells and not erythrocytes. The chief argument for this point of view is the fact that the number of spots seen in any one field selected for observation are not sufficiently numerous to be red corpuscles. To account for the small number of spots, it has been suggested that the red corpuscles overlap one another in a capillary and therefore cast a continuous shadow on the retina. But when a white cell is present among the red cells, it does not absorb the blue light since it has no hemoglobin and therefore produces a rift in the shadow figure. This rift corresponds to what is seen as a fine bright moving point. Thus, one sees the white corpuscles by contrast with the red corpuscles and sees them best in light which casts the best shadow, i.e., makes the greatest contrast. Since red light passes almost equally well through both erythrocytes and leukocytes, a contrast does not appear.

At the present time it cannot be said which of these theories is correct. There can be scarcely any doubt that the phenomenon is connected intimately with the circulation of the blood. The particles move in more or less definite paths, having the arrangement of capillary loops, and the movement is pulsatile and shows marked acceleration when the heart is speeded up. Finally, the region of the fovea, known to contain no retinal blood vessels, fails to show any of these particles. The relatively few particles seen in the field would incline one to accept the explanation that the spots are white corpuscles, especially since they appear light against a darker background. This explanation, however, would require that a film of closely packed red cells be distributed evenly over the retina at all points except where a white cell occurs. It is known that the spaces between capillaries are relatively wide—much wider than the diameter of a leukocyte, in fact. Where spaces such as these occur, therefore, one should see large stationary bright spots against the darker outlines of the capillaries. Further, the foveal area, free from capillaries, should appear light for the same reason.

Granted that these particles are in the bloodstream, to what exact situation of the retinal circulation should they be assigned? There are two possible locations where the phenomenon may take place. Either the corpuscles are in the precapillary arterioles, or they are in the capillary loops in the deep retinal layers. The patterns made by the particles correspond with the finest branchings of the retinal vessels which can be seen entoptically. These are probably the precapillary arterioles. The phenomenon has served a useful purpose in measuring the

Table 59

Author	Measurement of blood-free area	
Abelsdorff and Nagel	1° 30'	0.410 mm. (author's eye)
Gescher	1° 29'	0.420 mm. (author's eye)
Sperling, Miller, and Adler		0.40-0.50 mm. (38 normal eyes)

blood-free area around the fovea in the living subject.

The measurements of the area devoid of these entoptically seen corpuscles, according to several different authors, are given in Table 59 (compare the values with the area of the functional fovea, pp. 662, 663, and 788).

Although relatively wide variations between subjects exist, the two eyes of the same person are usually identical. The method may be applied clinically to study the effects of drugs or other changes on the fovea, therefore. It has been found that physostigmine and pilocarpine change the entopic appearance of the fovea and that many of the circumfoveal capillaries disappear under the influence of these drugs. Pressure on the eye slows up the movements of the corpuscles until they finally stop. When the pressure is removed, the circulation becomes quicker than before. By the use of the ophthalmodynamometer, it has been determined that the intraocular pressure at which cessation of movement of the particles occurs is about 50 mm. Hg.

Marshall[2] has demonstrated that the corpuscles are not in the retinal circulation of the nerve fiber layer. Their size and velocity are too great for this position, and their course is not that of the main retinal vessels. He determined this by observing the luminous bodies against the reflected mercury light with one eye and produced a map of the main vessels entoptically by eccentric rotation of a pinhole in a piece of black cardboard placed in front of the other eye. It could be seen that the two tracings were on different planes, the luminous points appearing farther away and giving the impression of being more highly magnified. Although the pathways in which the luminous points moved could not be made visible by this method, their jerky movements in what appeared to be a network of channels suggested that the cells were circulating in the capillaries of the inner nuclear layer.

CHORIOCAPILLARY CIRCULATION

Marshall[2] has been able to visualize the choriocapillary circulation in his own eye, but Friedman[1] was unable to confirm his observations. It is difficult on theoretical grounds to see how one could visualize entoptically the choroidal circulation. The spongy character of the choridal network with its superimposed layers of blood vessels would efface any possible shadows of individual vessels. Furthermore, the light would have to be incident to the posterior part of the sclera and not come through the pupil.

BLUE ARCS OF THE RETINA

If the observer in a dark room fixates a point slightly to the temporal side of a small source of light with one eye, he will see two small bands or arcs of light, bright blue in color, radiating from the stimulating light toward the blind spot. These arcs are always in the horizontal plane and appear almost as soon as the stimulating light is turned on. Various authors have observed and described them, but their actual cause is still unknown. The stimulating light may be any color or even white, but red is the best color to use probably because there is less scattering of the rays. The light source may be any shape—usually a rectangular source is employed. When a circular source of light is used and the temporal side of the circle is fixated, both arcs converge toward the blind spot. If the upper edge only is fixated, only the lower arc appears, and similarly when one fixates the lower edge of the bright circle, only the upper arc appears. Fixation on the nasal side of the circle produces a blue haze between the previous regions where the arc appeared which has been referred to as the blue spike.

Blue arcs do not appear if the stimulating light is looked at directly. Amberson[3] has mapped out this central blind area for the production of the arcs. The average measurement for the diameter of this area is 1 degree 58 minutes. This corresponds well with the foveal area free of rods. Because of this, it has been concluded that the phenomenon of the blue arc could be elicited only by a stimulus to the rods, and as far as the primary stimulus goes, this seems justifiable. Friedman[4] has pointed out that a secondary system that is probably related to the cones exists. The blue color of the arcs suggests that they are the result of stimulation of the cones rather than of the rods since the former are concerned principally in the perception of colors. It is possible, however, that the color of the arcs is due to the fact that the receptors for blue are the ones most easily stimulated.

There is evidence for believing that the arcs are due to secondary stimulation of underlying retinal receptors by the action currents in the nerve fibers. The color of the arcs depends to a certain extent upon the strength of the stimulating light.

When this is weak, the resulting color is more gray than blue. There is evidence that the rods are concerned also in color vision; therefore, it is probably unwise to conclude that because the arcs are colored they must be due to stimulation of the cones alone. The characteristic arcing of the blue arcs and their course from near the macula to the blind spot suggest at once that they are associated with the nerve fibers running from the macula into the optic nerve. They follow the pattern of the nerve fibers exactly, and Amberson has reported a patient who had a small scotoma lying between the fovea and the blind spot exactly in the course of the lower arc. When examined for the presence of the blue arc, the patient reported that he could follow the lower arc up to the region of the scotoma where it disappeared. The upper arc was normal. The integrity of the retinal elements in the course of the arcs is necessary, therefore. The blue arcs have been attributed to bioluminescence of the nerve fibers.[5] The most likely explanation, according to Snell,[6] is that of Amberson who believes that it is a secondary stimulation of the underlying receptors by the action currents in the optic nerves. When the rods in the perimacular region are stimulated, the nerve fibers conduct this impulse up the optic nerve. Therefore, an action current travels along the curved fiber, running from the point of stimulation into the optic disc. This action current spreads to the underlying receptors since the insulation in these fibers is not perfect and gives rise to a faint image from these points.

It is not certain which of the retinal elements are stimulated secondarily. The contiguous nerve fibers cannot be responsible because as Friedman points out, "their projective location would depend on the position of their cell receptors, and these would not be in the form of blue arcs."* Either the ganglion cells, the bipolar cells, or the layer of rods and cones must be responsible, therefore. There are no reasons for assuming the bipolar cells to be the intermediaries, and the layer of rods and cones are fairly far back from the layer of nerve fibers to be stimulated by currents as weak as the action currents must be. The intensity of the blue arcs seems to be independent of the intensity of the primary stimulus. The red light used to produce the blue arcs may be of any degree of intensity, provided that it exceeds a certain threshold value, without altering the brightness of the arcs themselves. This further demonstrates that the optic nerve fibers obey the all-or-none law (p. 620).

Boehm[7] carried out experiments with night-blind subjects. Five out of six could see the blue arcs clearly, whereas artificial blue arcs which appeared equally bright to a normal eye were not perceived by these subjects. This constitutes an argument against the theories of luminescence and ultraviolet radiation. Two completely color blind subjects could easily perceive the blue arcs although they saw them as colorless arcs. Consequently, the presence of the cones is not absolutely required to produce this phenomenon. The rods are apparently indispensable, however. Boehm considers the theory of secondary electrical stimulation to be the most likely one, therefore. The ganglion cells are the most likely objects of secondary stimulation. From there, the stimuli are transmitted centrifugally to the rods and cones and thereupon centripetally. Attention is drawn to the considerable degree of anastomosis among the nonmedullated axons in the region where the phenomenon occurs, and the anastomosis may possibly promote synchronization of the stimulus waves. The phenomenon is compared to the phosphene produced by a constant electric current.

SELF-ILLUMINATION OF THE RETINA; PHOSPHENES

When the eyes are kept in the dark and dark adaptation has become complete, a person does not have a sensation of black, but of a definite grayness that is much lighter than the sensation produced by looking at a black velvet surface in the light. This sensation of grayness or of light probably arises from both the retina and the cortex. It is called self-illumination of the retina.

Pressure on the eye produces the impression of a dark circular spot in the field of vision directly opposite the point of pressure on the globe. These visual sensations, produced by inadequate retinal stimuli, are called phosphenes. Prolonged digital pressure over the eye produces a pressure ring in the form of a broad circular band of blue.[1] The pressure has to be strong enough to cause slight discomfort and, according to some authors, must be maintained for 3 minutes. Two spots of blue, one nasally and one temporally, appear, and these slowly expand and assume the form of a broad arc. The figure continues to grow until the arcs coalesce into a blue circle, the center of which is oval and devoid of color. It is sharply demarcated and corresponds approximately to the macular limits. The cause of the phenomenon is not known, but the situation of the pressure oval corresponds roughly to the zone of maximum rod population described by Osterberg.[8]

If gentle pressure is applied to the temporal side of a completely dark-adapted eye, an immediate bright ring of blue appears, seemingly on the temporal side.

---

*From Friedman, B.: Arch. Ophth. 6:663, 1931.

This is almost instantaneous and disappears even though the pressure is continued, This phenomenon is noticed best after a night's sleep if it is elicited while the room is still completely dark, i.e., early in the morning.

PHYSIOLOGIC AND PATHOLOGIC HALOS

Under certain physiologic conditions, colored halos can be seen around small white lights viewed from a distance. These colored rings are due to the breaking up of white light by the various layers of cells of the media through which the light must pass on its way to the retina. The most common site of the halos under normal conditions is the lens. The lens fibers act as a radially arranged diffraction grating. The halos are not very bright as compared to those which can be produced experimentally or are seen in pathologic conditions. They are thought by some to have a smaller angular diameter than pathologic halos. The colors of both physiologic and pathologic halos are the same; i.e., the short waved lights, blue and violet, are next to the stimulating light, with the long waves on the outside and red the outermost ring. The angular diameter of physiologic halos ranges from 7 to 8 degrees, measured to the outer ring. Colored halos are produced easily by steaming a piece of glass or dusting lycopodium powder over a piece of glass and then observing a candle flame through it.

Pathologic halos occur from several conditions. Chronic conjunctivitis with mucous secretion is very likely to produce them, particularly early in the morning after mucus has collected during the night. Patients arising early in the morning and seeing halos around lights may become alarmed. Since this is the time of day when the pressure is elevated in most patients with glaucoma, the condition may alarm the physician also. Halos are complained of frequently by persons who have suffered from too intense exposure to light, such as in snow blindness, and presumably are due to the conjunctivitis caused by the exposure to light.

The chief interest in halos is centered in their occurrence in glaucoma. There can be no doubt that they are due directly to increased pressure in the eye because they come and go as the tension increases and decreases. They probably are caused by the breaking up of light as it passes through the edematous corneal epithelium. When the intraocular pressure is increased, small spaces filled with fluid appear in the cornea just under Bowman's membrane. The fluid from these spaces finds its way through this membrane by following the nerve fibrils as they enter the epithelium. In this manner an edematous condition of the epithelium is produced. Calculations have proved that the pathologic halos of glaucoma are produced in the epithelium. The light is broken up into the spectral colors by droplets of fluid in the epithelium in the same way that light passing through droplets of rain is broken up to form a rainbow.

MOORE'S LIGHTNING STREAKS

In 1935 and again in 1940, Moore[9] described an entoptic phenomenon consisting of flashes of light as follows:

"[they are] most frequently likened to lightning, seen to the temporal side of the eye, never to the nasal side, and vertical in direction. These flashes are accompanied by the simultaneous development of a crop of opacities in the vitreous. They seldom occur before middle age and are more frequent in the female sex. They do not imply any serious disease of the eye, either at the time or subsequently."*

---

*From Moore, R. F.: Brit. J. Ophth. **19:**545, 1935.

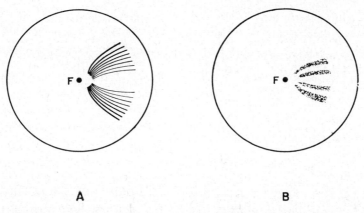

A **B**

Fig. 402. Phosphene of the right eye in a right-to-left flick. **A,** Phosphene pattern in the rested eye. **B,** Pattern after fatigue. **F,** Fovea, as identified by the afterimage of a fixated inducing light. (From Nebel, B.: Arch. Ophth. 58:236, 1957.)

In 1954, Berens and co-workers[10] laid stress on the fact that this syndrome was of more serious import than Moore believed. The question is of some importance to ophthalmologists since a number of people report these streaks and are quite bothered about them. Verhoeff[11] reiterates Moore's belief that these patients should be reassured since he not only has followed such patients for over eighteen years without one of these patients returning with retinal separation, but also has had personal experience with the streaks since 1937. It is obvious, of course, that one must be sure that the streaks patients complain of are those to which Moore first called attention. No evidence is forthcoming as to what could cause these streaks. According to Moore's description, they are seen only in the temporal field, and they are always vertical in direction. This, of course, eliminates the other type of similar entoptic phenomena such as the flashes seen in the eye as the result of detachment of the vitreous[12] and others which completely dark-adapted patients describe as in the form of a horizontal or obliquely horizontal fan of three or four streaks, on movement

of the eye during versions, called the phosphene of quick eye motion.

PHOSPHENE OF QUICK EYE MOTION

A phenomenon which has not been recorded previously is described by Nebel[13] who believes that it is related mechanically to, but definitely distinct from, Moore's lightning flashes. It is described by the term *flick phosphene*. It is observed best by the dark-adapted eye and is seen by most people upon awakening from sleep just before dawn. Then, if one moves the eyes rapidly from one side to the other, one observes in each monocular field a bright pattern having the general shape shown in Fig. 402. Each eye produces its own phosphene which is short-lived and rapidly dies out so that it cannot be repeated as the retina fatigues. The phosphenes are seen in the two eyes simultaneously and are two separate images (Fig. 403). Each has the shape of of a sheaflike pattern, and in most persons the apex is not pointed but truncated. When it is first elicited, the pattern is bright yellow or orange, and details of the sheaves are sharp. With repeated eye

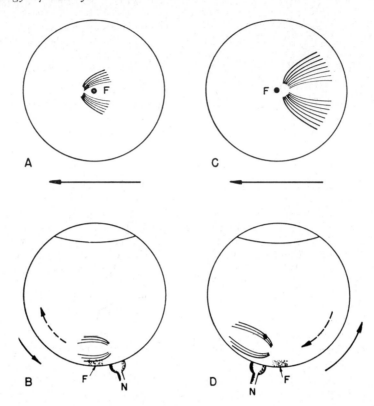

Fig. 403. Phosphenes of a right-and-left flick and an interpretation relating to the topography of their origin. *Upper two drawings,* phosphenes as seen by a person. *Lower two drawings,* Nebel's projection of the phosphenes back to the retina. *Opposing arrows,* shearing forces set up by the acceleration of the wall of the globe and the inertial retardation of the vitreous. **N,** Nerve; **F,** fovea. The projected phosphene is tilted and displaced slightly to make it visible in the drawing. (From Nebel, B.: Arch. Ophth. **58:**237, 1957.)

movements, however, the details become indistinct and blurred. It is ascribed to instantaneous transient deformation of the posterior surface of the vitreous close to the optic disc. When the eye is flicked suddenly, the inertial lag of the vitreous causes the deformation which is transmitted directly to the retina and causes the fibers in this region to fire off. It may be an early senescent sign of normal slight shrinkage of the vitreous.

HAIDINGER'S BRUSHES

If the normal eye observes a surface illuminated by plane-polarized white light, yellow and blue brushes or sheaves radiating from the fixation point are seen. De Vries and co-workers[14] and later Stanworth and Naylor[15] have shown that the brushes are due to variations in absorption by oriented macular pigment in the foveal region.

Since the effect is due to an oriented pigment in front of the layer of photoreceptors, any process which upsets this orientation, even though it does not disturb the photoreceptors themselves, may lead to disappearance of the brushes. Therefore, the test for Haidinger's brushes may show early changes in the macula such as edema before they reach the point of interfering with visual acuity or of being visible ophthalmoscopically. The test

forms a simple, rapid means of demonstrating macular edema in the early stages of macular disease.

REFERENCES

1. Friedman, B.: Observations on entoptic phenomena, Arch. Ophth. **28**:285, 1942.
2. Marshall, C.: Entoptic phenomena associated with the retina, Brit. J. Ophth. **19**: 177, 1935.
3. Amberson, W.: Secondary excitation in the retina, Am. J. Physiol. **69**:354, 1924.
4. Friedman, B.: The blue arcs of the retina, Arch. Ophth. **6**:663, 1931.
5. Ladd-Franklin, C.: Alternative theories to account for the reddish blue arcs and the reddish blue glow of the retina, J. Optic. Soc. America **16**:333, 1928.
6. Snell, P.: The entoptic phenomenon of the blue arc, Arch. Ophth. **1**:475, 1929.
7. Boehm, G. (Basel): The entoptic phenomenon of the "blue arcs" (Observations on subjects affected with night blindness and total color blindness), Ophthalmologica **4-5**:276, 1949; Excerpta Medica, Ophthalmologica **5**:146, 1951.
8. Osterberg G.: Topography of the layer of rods and cones in the human retina, Acta ophth. **6** (supp.):1, 1935.
9. Moore, R. F.: Subjective lightning streaks, Brit. J. Ophth. **19**:545, 1935.
10. Berens, C., Cholst, M., Emmerich, R., and McGrath, H.: Moore's lightning streaks, Tr. Am. Ophth. Soc. **52**:35, 1954.
11. Verhoeff, F.: Are Moore's lightning streaks of serious portent, Am. J. Ophth. **41**:837, 1956.
12. Pischel, D.: Detachment of the vitreous as seen with slitlamp examination, Tr. Am. Ophth. Soc. **50**:329, 1952.
13. Nebel, B.: The phosphene of quick eye motion, Arch. Ophth. **58**:235, 1957.
14. De Vries, H., Spoor, A., and Jielff, R.: Physica. **19**:419, 1953.
15. Stanworth, A., and Naylor, E.: The measurement and clinical significance of the Haidinger effect, Tr. Ophth. Soc. U. Kingdom **75**:67, 1955.

CHAPTER 22

BINOCULAR VISION

BINOCULAR FIELD OF VISION

Binocular vision may be defined as the coordinated use of the two eyes to produce a single visual impression. In its highest development the blending of the two images results in the acquisition of a new quality of vision, stereopsis, i.e., the perception of depth by parallax, which is impossible with either eye alone. There is a fundamental difference between seeing with two eyes alternately and simultaneous binocular vision. An animal whose eyes are situated laterally in the head so that the visual fields of the two eyes never overlap or overlap in only a very small portion can use only one eye at a time. When a bird, e.g., sees a worm on the ground and tilts its head so that it obtains a clear image of the worm with the right eye, the left eye is directed upward. Since the simultaneous image of this eye would detract considerably from the perception of the worm, we have reason to think that one image is suppressed mentally. The bird may direct its attention at will to the image of the left eye and ignore the image of the right eye temporarily. This would surely happen if under these circumstances a hawk were to fly overhead.

Under certain conditions, human beings suppress the image from one eye with both eyes open. Portions of the binocular visual field are constantly suppressed in daily life since, as will be explained, objects situated in certain parts of visual space would otherwise be seen double. Suppression under some conditions has to be learned. When using a microscope, e.g., the novice finds it impossible to look down the tube of the instrument with one eye and keep the other eye open at the same time. With one eye he gets an image of the slide, and with the other he sees the desk in front of him. This results in confusion. With a little practice, however, he soon learns to suppress the image of the eye not in actual use and then finds it much more comfortable to keep both eyes open. This suppression is aided by the fact that when one looks at the slide the microscope is focused for infinity, and accommodation is therefore relaxed. At the same time the table seen with the other eye is almost at the near point; therefore its image would require a considerable amount of accommodation to be in focus. Many novices have difficulty in suppressing the unused eye when doing microscopy because they fail to focus the microscope properly and instead use their own accommodation. This focuses the unused eye on objects on the desk.

Advantages of simultaneous binocular vision. Simultaneous binocular vision has the following advantages.

1. Optical defects present in one eye are made less obvious by the normal image of the opposite eye.

2. Defective vision in any part of one visual field is masked for the same reason since the same defect is not likely to occur in identical parts of the two retinas. The blind spot caused by the entrance of the optic nerve cannot be detected in the binocular visual field since the object whose image falls on the blind area in one eye is perceived by the functioning retina in the other.

3. The binocular visual field is larger than either field alone.

4. Stereoscopic vision or depth perception by parallax is made possible.

There are two stages in the process of simultaneous binocular vision. The image formed on the retina of each eye must give rise to a stimulus pattern, relayed to the visual cortex as an independent sensation. At this point there must be an amalgamation or fusion of the two independent sensations into a unified sensation which may differ not only in quantity but also in quality from the two independent sensations.

Requisites for binocular vision. In order that simultaneous binocular vision be obtained certain conditions must be present.

1. There must be proper fixation with each eye. The muscles controlling the movements of each eye must function normally and turn both eyes in such a manner that the object of regard is fixated

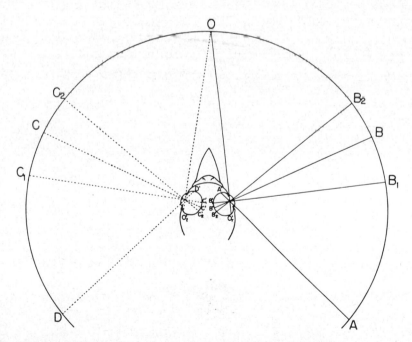

Fig. 404. Horizontal cross section through the visual field of the head and eyes of a bird with panoramic vision. (From Linksz, A.: Physiology of the eye, vol. 2, Vision, New York, 1952, Grune & Stratton, Inc.)

by corresponding retinal areas, e.g., the two foveas.

2. The visual fields of the two eyes must overlap to a large extent.

3. Approximately similar images must be formed on each retina. The images, therefore, must be approximately of the same size, shape, color, and intensity. This necessitates approximate equality in the optical apparatus of each eye. In nature, the object of regard of the two eyes is always the same, provided that both eyes are directed at it. Under experimental conditions, dissimilar images may be presented to the two eyes. If their dissimilarity is such that they cannot be fused readily, antagonism called retinal rivalry will result. When this occurs, first one image and then the other will be presented to consciousness.

4. The retinas must possess physiologically corresponding points, i.e., retinal receptors which are so related that they have a common visual direction.

5. Although it is not a requisite for binocular vision, the semidecussation of fibers in the chiasm is a common attribute of those vertebrates which possess stereoscopic vision. The primitive vertebrate eye is so arranged that almost all the fibers from one retina cross over to the opposite optic tract and end in the visual cortex of the opposite side. In man, each retina is divided by a vertical line through the fovea into a temporal portion (about three fourths of the whole) and a nasal

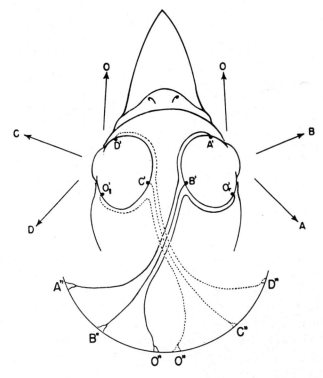

Fig. 405. Horizontal cross section through the eyes and the visual cortex of a bird with panoramic vision showing the transference of retinal spatial organization upon the brain in total crossing of the optic nerves. (From Linksz, A.: Physiology of the eye, vol. 2, Vision, New York, 1952, Grune & Stratton, Inc.)

portion (about one fourth). All the fibers from the nasal side of the retina cross to the opposite side of the brain, whereas the fibers from the temporal side are connected with the ipsilateral half of the brain.

The crossed fibers are the more primitive type, and the diversion of certain fibers to the ipsilateral side of the brain is a secondary adaptation which keeps pace more or less exactly with the overlapping of the fields of vision and, therefore, with the development of binocular vision. The size of the uncrossed tract varies directly with the degree of development of binocular vision in the animal. In the rabbit the uncrossed tract is so small that it was overlooked for a long time; in dogs it is much larger; in monkeys it is larger still; finally, in man it attains its greatest relative proportion.

Linksz[1] calls attention to the fact that in animals whose visual fields are entirely separate, such as the bird, each eye takes in its own part of visual space, the two together encompassing a wide area of the horizon. Each portion of visual space is localized in each retina in such a way that only one point in space, namely, the straight ahead position, is represented in both. As shown in Fig. 404 the point O is imaged at o^r and o'. All other points in space are arranged in each eye individually and probably in such fashion that the spatial order in visual space is preserved in the two retinas. Further, it is likely that spatial organization in the two retinas is transferred to the two halves of the brain. In Fig. 405 is shown the imaginary representation of the two retinas in the visual cortex of a bird that has total crossing of the optic nerve fibers in the chiasm. As can be seen, each eye maintains in its retina a replica of the spatial arrangement of objects seen in its visual field. The straight ahead position,

seen by both eyes, is imaged at o^r and o' in the two retinas, and these are probably linked up with cells in the visual cortex which lie close to each other and hence give rise to the perception of the same locus in space. All other points are arranged in the retinas and the cortex in such a fashion that they, too, mirror the spatial arrangement of their respective loci in space.

This arrangement is quite adequate for animals with panoramic vision. In those

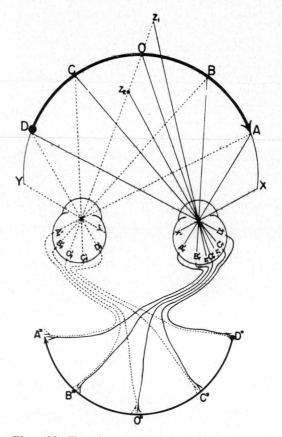

Fig. 406. Transference of retinal spatial organization upon the brain. Horizontal cross section through the field of vision of the eyes and visual cortex of a primate with half-crossing of the optic nerves. (After Ramon y Cajal; from Linksz, A.: Physiology of the eye, vol. 2, New York, 1952, Grune & Stratton, Inc.)

species of animals whose eyes have migrated to the front so that there is considerable overlapping of the visual fields, there must be some other arrangement of the fibers if the advantages of simultaneous binocular vision are to be kept. The answer to this problem was to establish a partial crossing of fibers in the chiasm. Fig. 406 shows how this arrangement of partial crossing of the fibers in man and the higher apes maintains the spatial organization in both the retinas and the two halves of the brain.

6. The reflex activities which produce fusional movements have been described previously. The eyes must be coordinated by this complex mechanism at all times

so that retinal receptors which have a common visual direction will receive the same image at all times.

RETINAL CORRESPONDENCE

In ordinary use we are not conscious of the fact that two eyes are being employed. The image of an object in space seems to come from a single eye, situated in the head about equidistant between the two eyes. This imaginary eye is called the cyclopean eye, from the mythological one-eyed Cyclops (Fig. 407). It is a useful concept, as will be seen, in dealing with our perception of space. Space perception, particularly our sense of position in space, i.e., egocentric localization, is a

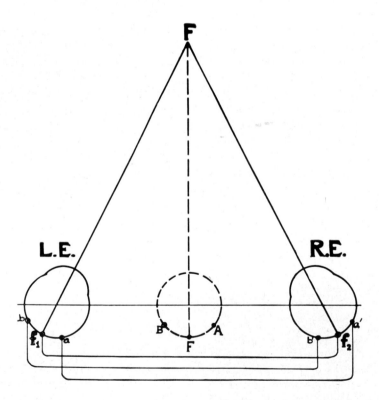

Fig. 407. Normal retinal correspondence. The visual directions of f_1 and f_2 proceed from **F**, the fovea of the imaginary cyclopean eye. **A** and **B** represent the points from which the visual directions belonging to **a** and **a′** and **b** and **b′** would proceed. (From Bielschowsky, A.: Lectures on motor anomalies, Hanover, 1940, Dartmouth College Publications.)

psychologic phenomenon. We regard ourselves as the center of our visual space, and the images of all objects in space falling on our cyclopean retina are mentally projected back into space, usually along the same lines of direction from which they came.

The mental projection of each point on the retina to some particular locus in space was referred to formerly as the local sign of the retinal element. Each retinal point or element had its own local sign or direction in space. The term *visual direction* seems more understandable and simple.

It follows from this that if one could stimulate a point on the retina with a fine electrode the resulting sensation of a flash of light would be mentally projected into space along the line of visual direction of the stimulated photoreceptor. It could not be localized in space beyond being situated on this line, somewhere between the retina itself and infinity. The line of visual direction of the fovea has special importance as it acquires by experience the psychologic attribute of the visual direction of fixation, i.e., the point in space toward which the cyclopean eye is turned.

Retinal elements in the two eyes which have a common visual direction are called corresponding retinal elements or corresponding retinal points. Burian formulates it as follows.

"Corresponding retinal elements are those elements of the two retinas, the stimulation of which—in binocular vision—gives rise to the localization in one and the same visual direction, no matter whether the stimulus reaches the retinal elements in one eye alone, or its corresponding partner in the other eye alone, or both simultaneously."*

---

*From Burian, H.: Tr. Am. Ophth. Soc. **43:** 373, 1945.

The two anatomic regions of the retina which par excellence are corresponding retinal areas and contain corresponding retinal elements are the two foveas. It must be understood, however, that the definition of corresponding retinal elements is not necessarily an anatomic one, but a physiologic one, or perhaps it should be stated, a psychologic one since it is the conscious projection in space of these elements when stimulated which determines whether or not they are corresponding retinal elements. By definition, their conscious projection must be in the same visual direction.

The question as to whether our visual orientation is innate or acquired (i.e., is due to anatomic and physiologic factors with which we are born or acquired by each person through trial and error) has been raised often. This seems to have been answered in favor of the nativistic school of thought which believes that space perception is determined by the anatomic relationships of the visual receptors at birth. The most cogent argument in favor of this point of view are the experiments of Stone[3] in which he showed that the rotation of the eye of a salamander 180 degrees, whether in the original animal or transplanted to another salamander, results in complete reversal of all the visuomotor responses. The animal's head and body movements in response to the stripes on a moving drum are in a direction just opposite those of a normal animal or an animal in which the eye was transplanted but not rotated 180 degrees. The animal snaps in the wrong direction at a moving lure. These abnormal reversed visual responses persist permanently in adult animals with rotated eyes. This would seem to suggest that man's visual orientation is fundamentally innate. On the other hand, it has been shown that the human species can make adaptations to distortions in the visual field and can learn to reorient himself in space in spite of the reversal of the visual field produced experimentally.

Cyclopean eye. As stated, the two eyes of a normal person may be considered a single organ from a subjective sensorial point of view. This single organ or cyclopean eye is shown in Fig. 407. If the two retinas are superimposed so that the foveas as well as the corresponding meridians of each eye cover each other, this double retina then represents the retina of an imaginary cyclopean eye which is situated at the root of the nose. Its nodal point is the center of the subjective visual directions.

More exactly, the visual egocenter in normal individuals is localized in the subjective median plane in the vicinity of the turning point of the head. The exact position differs in different individuals and may even be displaced in subjects with a pronounced master eye toward the position of this master eye. It is also displaced in one-eyed subjects and patients with strabismus.[4]

In order that objects situated in the binocular field of vision shall be seen singly, i.e., produce one mental impression, their images must fall on retinal receptors in the two eyes which have a common visual direction.

Each pair of corresponding points in the two retinas has one and the same visual direction, along which the objects imaged on those points are localized. For instance, as shown in Fig. 407, images lying on f_1 and f_2 are seen in the direction of F, proceeding from that point of the cyclopean eye where f_1 and f_2 are imagined to be superimposed. Between the principle visual direction, as we call the direction in which the objects imaged on the two foveas are localized, and the

visual directions of any other pair of corresponding points is an angle determined by the arc between those points and the fovea. The geometric lines of direction, i.e., the lines connecting retinal points through the nodal points with outlying objects which are imaged on those points, are not coincident with the subjective visual directions in which the objects are located. This difference between the objective and subjective visual spaces is demonstrated easily when one examines the subjective localization in binocular vision. It can easily be shown that the objective position of points in space does not necessarily coincide with the localization which is attributed to them subjectively. As shown in Fig. 408, A, a normal subject fixates the object point, F, binocularly. Two other object points—A_L and A_R—are also situated in the field of view. Suitable screens are arranged so that he sees A_L with the left eye only and A_R with the right eye only. As long as he continues to fixate F, he will see the object points A_L and A_R behind each other in the direction indicated by the symbol ϕ. Analogously, as shown in Fig. 408, B, object points B_L and B_R will appear behind each other in the direction β as long as the subject fixates point F which continues to appear in the direction of the symbol ϕ. Hence, the subjective localization of points A_L, A_R, B_L, and B_R is at variance with their objective position. The pairs of points indicated by the same letter appear to lie in the same direction although they are widely separated in space.

Burian explains this discrepancy as follows.

"The lines which connect in a geometric construction the object points with the retinal elements on which they are imaged are called the lines of direction. Their position is determined by the geometric optic properties of

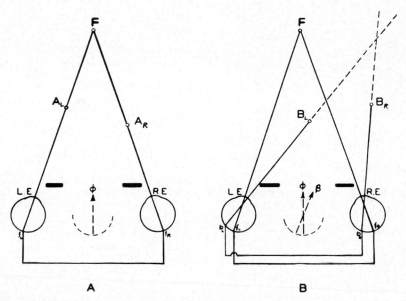

Fig. 408. The lines of direction and the visual directions. Ff_L and Ff_R, lines of direction of the foveas f_L and f_R. B_Lb_L and B_Rb_R, lines of direction of the retinal elements b_L and b_R. ϕ and β, common visual direction of the foveas f_L, f_R and the retinal elements b_L and b_R. In **A** the object points **F**, A_L, and A_R appear to lie behind each other in the direction ϕ. In **B** the points B_L and B_R appear behind each other in the direction β. (From Burian, H.: Tr. Am. Ophth. Soc. **43**:373, 1945.)

the media through which the rays of light emittted or reflected by the object points pass before reaching the sensory epithelium of the retina. The lines of direction belong to the objective sphere and they only determine which retinal element will be stimulated by the object point. The position or localization of the subjective correlative of that point in the subjective space; that is, where it will be seen, is determined by another, a subjective factor, designated as the spatial value of the stimulated retinal element. This spatial value manifests itself in the direction in which the point appears in subjective space; each retinal element possesses a certain visual direction in which the stimulus which reaches the retinal element is localized. The objective lines of direction thus have their subjective correlative in the visual directions. The two are not synonymous and the visual directions as such are independent of the lines of direction. This is evidenced by the fact that localized mechanical or electrical stimulation of retinal elements causes the appearance of a phosphene in the very same direction in which an object causing optical stimulation of the

same retinal elements would be localized. In the case of mechanical or electrical stimulation, there are, of course, no lines of direction."*

As we have stated, the foveas under normal conditions are corresponding retinal areas. The visual direction of the fovea is of particular significance in that it is the principal visual direction, i.e., the visual direction of the object of fixation. The visual directions of all the other retinal elements are relative to this principal visual direction. They change with the position of fixation of the eye but their relation to the principal visual direction remains the same.

Normal retinal correspondence. In defining corresponding retinal elements, we

---

*From Burian, H.: Tr. Am. Ophth. Soc. **43**: 373, 1945.

have at the same time defined normal retinal correspondence. Whenever the retinal elements which should be corresponding, e.g., the two foveas, have common visual directions, a person has normal retinal correspondence.

In adults, one of the methods for demonstrating the sensorial relations between the two eyes is by means of afterimages. An afterimage of a horizontal glowing filament may be produced in one eye and an afterimage of a vertical filament in the other by having the subject fixate with each eye alternately for about 10 seconds at a glowing filament, the center of which is concealed by a black ring with a fixation mark. After the exposure of the two eyes separately in a dark room, the subject will see the positive afterimages which, if he has normal retinal correspondence, will form a cross because the centers of both afterimages are situated on the fovea. It does not make any difference what the position of the eyes relative to each other may be; it cannot influence the position of the afterimages relative to each other if the subject has normal retinal correspondence. One may displace one eye with a finger or with forceps, e.g. The figure of the

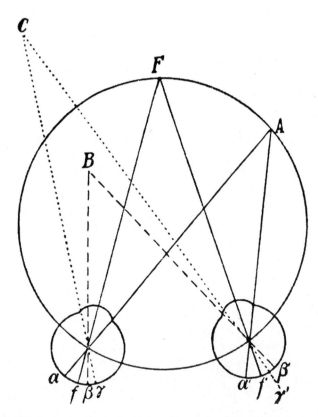

Fig. 409. Vieth-Müller's horopter circle. Points **F** and **A** which lie in the horopter are imaged on corresponding retinal points **f** and **f′** and **a** and **a′**, respectively. **B** and **C**, lying inside and outside the horopter, are imaged on noncorresponding (disparate) points β and $\beta′$ and γ and $\gamma′$. (From Bielchowsky, A.: Lectures on motor anomalies, Hanover, 1940, Dartmouth College Publications.)

cross formed by the afterimages remains unchanged. When a person with normal retinal correspondence fixates the same object with each fovea, the mental projection of that object is to the same point in space and coincides with the actual position of the object. Other objects in the same visual field are projected likewise to their appropriate positions in space relative to the object of regard. As shown in Fig. 409, an object such as *A* situated to the right of the object of regard, *F*, will have its image point fall on the temporal side of the retina in the left eye and on the nasal side of the retina in the right eye. If the object, *A*, is situated in space so that its image falls on corresponding retinal points, it will be seen singly. All other objects similarly situated in space will be seen singly in their appropriate position relative to the object of regard. The sum total of these points forms a geometric figure called the horopter (p. 846).

Another method of determining whether or not a person has normal retinal correspondence is the use of a stereoscope. This instrument invented by Sir David Brewster presents a picture to each eye separately. If the pictures are identical, a person with normal retinal correspondence will fuse them and see them as one image. If the pictures are dissimilar so that they cannot be fused into a single entity, first one and then the other will be seen, but not simultaneously, in a process called retinal rivalry (p. 855). If the pictures are similar but portray the object from slightly different points of view (an object in space seen by both eyes forms a retinal image on the right retina as viewed slightly further around the right and on the left retina slightly around on the left of the object due to the horizontal separation of the two eyes), then the images will be fused. In most normal persons

this fusion will provide a new sensation of depth. This perception of depth, achieved solely by the paralytic displacement of the images on the two retinas, is called stereopsis (p. 865).

A modification of the optical principles underlying the stereoscope and its modern modifications according to Linksz[1] are shown in Fig. 410. Linksz has called attention to the fact that the explanation

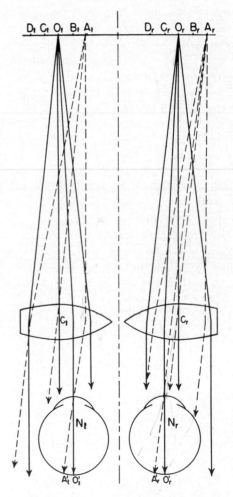

Fig. 410. A more accurate diagram to explain the optics of the so-called prism stereoscope. (From Linksz, A.: Physiology of the eye, vol. 2, Vision, New York, 1952, Grune & Stratton, Inc.)

given in most texts is erroneous and leads to a misunderstanding of the underlying principles of stereoscopy.

Two lenses, C_l and C_r, of plus 5.00 D. are separated by 8.5 cm. O_l and O_r represent the principal focal points of these lenses, situated 20 cm. in front of their respective optical centers. If two pictures of the same object are taken from separate points 8.5 cm. apart and are placed in the instrument at this distance (20 cm.), they will be fused by the observer and will give a mental impression that the objects in the picture have solidity or three-dimensional form, i.e., depth. The continuous lines show the lines of direction from the object through the lenses and into the eyes. Since the distance of the pictures from the lenses is 20 cm. and the lenses are 5.00 D., the lines of direction entering the eyes will be parallel (collimated). No accommodation of the eyes is needed therefore. Since the lines of direction are parallel to each other, the eyes must be directed straight ahead and not converged in order for them to enter each pupil. The rays entering the pupils and falling on each retina will fall on corresponding retinal points only if the two pictures in the stereoscope are identical. If the two pictures are taken from points slightly separated in space (in this case, as stated, 8.5 cm. apart), their images cannot fall on corresponding retinal points, but on disparate retinal points, i.e., photoreceptors which do not have the same visual direction. For most persons the result is a sensation of depth. Therefore, the stereoscope is an instrument devised to present slightly dissimilar images to the two eyes without the use of accommodation or convergence whose images will fall on disparate retinal points. There are limits to this disparity, however. If the pictures are so drawn or photographed that their images fall on *widely* disparate retinal points, double vision and not stereopsis will result. The parameters within which stereopsis instead of diplopia is possible will be discussed in a later section.

So far only the lines of direction which will fall on the two foveas have been considered. In Fig. 410 the broken lines represent lines of direction from parts of the two pictures which will fall on extra-foveal regions. These are drawn as though they would fall on corresponding retinal points. In a stereogram, however, they would actually fall on slightly disparate retinal points, as just explained. It is the simultaneous stimulation of slightly disparate retinal points which causes stereopsis.

EGOCENTRIC LOCALIZATION

In man, the primates, and all those vertebrates who have a specialized region whose visual acuity exceeds that of the rest of the retina, i.e., a fovea, stimulation of this region produces the sensation that the object causing the stimulation is located in the direction toward which the fovea is pointing. If the eye is in the primary position, i.e., looking straight ahead, and the fovea is stimulated, the resulting sensation is that the stimulus object is located somewhere in space on a line directly in front of the individual, i.e., straight ahead (Fig. 411). If the eye is turned to the right, stimulation of the fovea results in a sensation that the stimulus object is to the right of the straight ahead position. Similarly, if the eye is turned to the left, the sensation is that the object is to the left of the straight ahead position (Fig. 412). The same is true when the eye is turned up or down. The position in space where one localizes any stimulus exciting the fovea is determined partly by information sent to the brain from the oculomotor

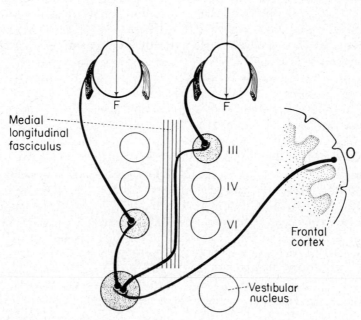

Fig. 411. Stimulation of fovea with the eyes in the primary position. Egocentric localization is in the straight ahead position.

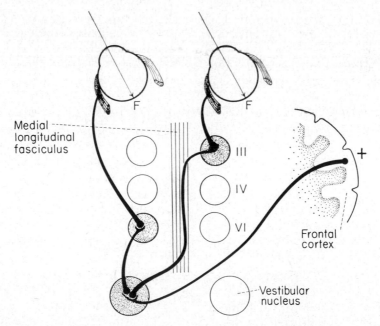

Fig. 412. Stimulation of fovea in eyes to the left. Egocentric localization is to left of the individual.

apparatus. The turning of the eye itself endows the excitation of the foveal photoreceptors with a sense of direction in space in respect to the individual. This is called egocentric localization. This information is probably not derived from the tension of the ocular muscles themselves and is therefore not strictly proprioception in the usual sense of this term but arises from the cortical oculogyric centers where the impulses for turning the eyes are initiated.

This localization in space of the foveal photoreceptors is called the visual direction of the fovea. The resulting sensation is only one of a direction in space, not localization to any one point in space. A small light, such as a muscle light in a dark room or a star in the sky, stimulating the fovea with the eye in the primary position, is localized in space in the direction in front of the individual but gives him no exact idea where in space the light is, i.e., whether 20 feet or 20 million light years away.

It does not matter how the visual cells in the fovea are stimulated, whether in the usual manner by light rays coming into the eye from outside or as the result of artificial stimulation. If one were to place an electrode behind the eyeball, e.g., and stimulate the fovea through the sclera with the eye in the primary position, the sensation experienced by the subject of the experiment would be that of a light situated somewhere in space directly in front of him. Similarly, if the eye were turned to the left, stimulation of the fovea by an electrode behind the eye would result in a sensation of a light situated somewhere in space to the left of the individual.

The visual direction of the fovea is determined therefore by the direction in space toward which the fovea is turned.

As just stated, the visual direction of

the photoreceptors surrounding the fovea is dictated by their anatomic relation to the fovea. Since light rays travel in straight lines and cross at the nodal point in the refracting system of the eye, light coming from the right side of the eye will stimulate photoreceptors on the left of the fovea; those coming from the left side will stimulate receptors on the right side of the fovea; etc. Further, the angular distance of the stimulated receptors from the fovea will determine the angular direction of the light in space from the visual direction of the fovea. If one were to stimulate a group of photoreceptors situated exactly 15 degrees from the fovea in the temporal retina by electrodes placed behind the sclera, the subject of the experiment would have a sensation of a light somewhere in space on a line directed exactly 15 degrees to the nasal side of the visual line, i.e., the point to which the fovea was directed. The visual direction of each photoreceptor outside the fovea is therefore immutably fixed in the normal individual and is determined by the visual direction of the fovea and the distance of the photoreceptor from the fovea. Actually, we can never speak in retinal physiology of what one receptor alone does since we are always working with groups of receptors, but the general principle holds.

To this point we have been speaking of the spatial localization that results from the stimulation of photoreceptors in one eye. When the eyes are used together in the normal subject properly aligned so that the visual lines from each fovea intersect at any one point in space, a light situated at this point will automatically stimulate both foveas simultaneously. The effect will be the same as when one eye only is stimulated. If the eyes are in the primary position, the light will be seen situated somewhere in space straight ahead of the individual—to his right if the eyes are turned to the right, etc. If the light is seen in an otherwise completely dark room so that there are no other spatial clues, the individual will have no conception of how far away from him the light is but only its direction in space.

With the eyes in the primary position a light situated in his binocular field to the right of his point of fixation will stimulate receptors on the left of both foveas and will be seen as a single light in space to the right of his point of fixation—in fact, exactly localized in the direction from which the light rays come. The visual directions of the two foveas correspond, therefore, one with the other. Photoreceptors in the two eyes situated on the same side of each fovea and at the same angular distance in the normal individual have the same visual direction.

Those receptors in the two eyes which have identical visual directions are called corresponding receptors. The term *corresponding points* is commonly used, but since we are dealing as previously pointed out with groups of receptors, a more appropriate term would be *corresponding retinal areas.*

Whenever the image of an object falls on corresponding retinal areas in the two eyes, it will be seen singly and located in space in the visual direction of the photo-

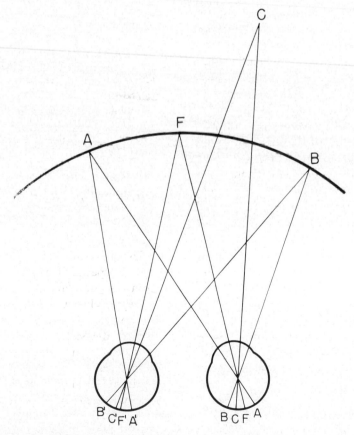

Fig. 413. The horopter **AFB** for convergence of the eyes to **F.**

receptors stimulated. It can be shown by simple geometry that for any degree of convergence of the eyes that portion of space in which one can place a light and have it stimulate corresponding retinal areas is a segment of a circle (Fig. 413). This is called the horopter circle. If the degree of convergence of the eyes changes, the horopter circle changes accordingly. If the eyes maintain a fixed degree of convergence and then move up and down, the horopter circle likewise moves up and down in space, creating a figure in space known as a torus. This part of space then becomes the horopter torus.

As defined, the horopter is that portion of space in which objects will form images on the two retinas on corresponding photoreceptors. As shown in Fig. 409 the horopter forms roughly a portion of a circle. If the eyes are shifted from the position shown in Fig. 409, another portion of space which fulfills the same postulate will be found; therefore a new portion of space becomes the horopter. In Figs. 414 and 415 is shown the geometric figure of the horopter formed by vertical movements of the two eyes maintaining the same degree of convergence. As Linksz has stated:

"Whenever you look while maintaining a certain constant angle of convergence, your fixation point moves along the horopter torus while this torus itself does not change either form or position. As a matter of fact, the whole Vieth-Müller torus can just as well be defined as the sum of all possible fixation points for a given angle of convergence. And since by definition all points of the horopter have the same convergence distance, one can state in general terms that all points in space of equal convergence form a peculiar surface, the torus of Vieth and Müller."*

---

*From Linksz, A.: Physiology of the Eye, Volume 2, Vision, New York, 1952, Grune & Stratton, Inc.

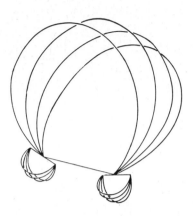

Fig. 414. Geometry of the horopter showing the horopter torus formed by consecutive and simultaneous Vieth-Müller circles. (From Linksz, A.: Physiology of the eye, vol. 2, Vision, New York, 1952, Grune & Stratton, Inc.)

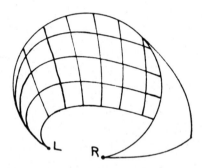

Fig. 415. The horopter forms produced by upward gaze from the horizontal, with the same convergence maintained. (From Linksz, A.: Physiology of the eye, vol. 2, Vision, New York, 1952, Grune & Stratton, Inc.)

Objects lying upon the horopter will always appear single to a person with normal correspondence because they are seen in the same direction by the two eyes. It is apparent that there are two stages in the process of normal binocular vision. The image of each eye must fall on corresponding retinal points, and these two separate images must be relayed to the brain where an amalgamation of these images must take place. This amalgamation is called sensory fusion and will be discussed later. If the images of the two eyes are identical or are nearly similar in size, shape, color, and intensity, then fusion generally takes place. All similar objects which lie on the horopter are fused, therefore.

It might be supposed that fusion is limited strictly to objects which lie on the horopter and that objects not on the horopter cannot be fused. We have seen that this is not so, however, and that within certain limits stimulation of visual disparate retinal points results in stereopsis. It has been found by experiment that an object may be slightly in front of or behind the horopter, and still its images in the two eyes will be fused. This area, as determined experimentally, has been called Panum's fusional space and is shown in Fig. 416. Objects lying in Panum's area will be seen singly and will not produce double vision. The ob-

ject while seen singly will appear to have a slightly different directional value from that which it had when it was lying on the horopter due to the fact that it is being visualized by retinal points which are disparate, i.e., have different visual directions. This is the basis of stereopsis (pp. 865 to 871).

DIPLOPIA

Any object which does not lie in Panum's area in space will necessarily stimulate retinal receptors in the two eyes which do not have the same visual direction. Since the visual directions of the two retinal areas do not correspond, the object will necessarily be seen in two different directions of space. The object will therefore be seen doubly—one in the direction of space that corresponds to the visual direction of the photoreceptors stimulated in the right eye and the second in the direction of space that corresponds to the visual direction of the

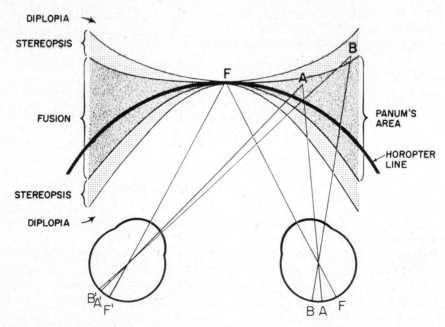

Fig. 416. Panum's area.

receptors stimulated in the left eye. The individual experiences double vision or diplopia.

The term diplopia means double vision, i.e., seeing two images of the same object located in different parts of visual space. This form of diplopia is limited to that of seeing double images of the same object with both eyes, a strictly binocular phenomenon. Monocular diplopia does occur but is of an entirely different nature and is not relevant to this discussion.

Binocular diplopia is both physiologic and pathologic. In order to appreciate how it occurs, one must have an understanding of how each eye normally localizes in space the image of an object falling on its retina.

Physiologic diplopia. The only points in space that can be imaged on corresponding retinal points are those which compose the horopter torus. If the correspondence is normal, each of these points will be seen by the two eyes as single as long as the visual axes are in alignment. Within the area previously described as Panum's area, each of these points will be seen as single and in depth, depending upon the actual location of the points to one another in space, i.e., whether they lie farther away or nearer to the person (stereopsis). If the points lie outside Panum's area, each of these points will be seen double; i.e., each point will be seen in two different positions of space. Surprisingly enough, their images, even though double, may still yield a sensation of depth if they are not located in the same horizontal plane. This fact will be amplified later (p. 865). Each will be seen double; i.e., each will cause diplopia since each is projected mentally to two different directions in space, i.e., along two different lines of visual direction.

It is obvious that in daily life all objects in our surroundings do not lie in the horopter torus. As we fixate one object with both eyes, this object and all other objects lying in a circle having the same radius will be seen singly. Other objects not lying in this horopter torus, but still within Panum's area, will be seen singly and in depth. All objects lying outside Panum's area should be seen double. However, in daily life we are not aware of this doubling of objects in the visual field which lie outside of Panum's area largely because their images are produced by extrafoveal retinal elements with a relatively low visual acuity. This physiologic diplopia is very easy to demonstrate, however. If one looks at an object across the room and at the same time holds the index finger about a foot away from the face in the midline, the finger will appear double. If the right eye is closed while this double image is observed, it will be seen that the left image disappears (Fig. 417, *A*). Similarly, if the left eye is closed, the right image will disappear. The diplopia produced is called crossed diplopia since the left image belongs to the right eye and vice versa. If the subject now looks directly at the finger, the object situated at a distance will be doubled (Fig. 417, *B*). If the right eye is now closed, the right image disappears, and similarly if the left eye is closed, the left image disappears. The diplopia so produced is called uncrossed or homonymous diplopia because the right image comes from the right eye and the left image from the left eye. Physiologic diplopia is usually not bothersome in daily life because, as stated, the images, being perimacular and not foveal, have a much lower valence than those coming from the fovea and hence are easily suppressed. However, it is frequently discovered by patients, especially children, and sometimes causes conster-

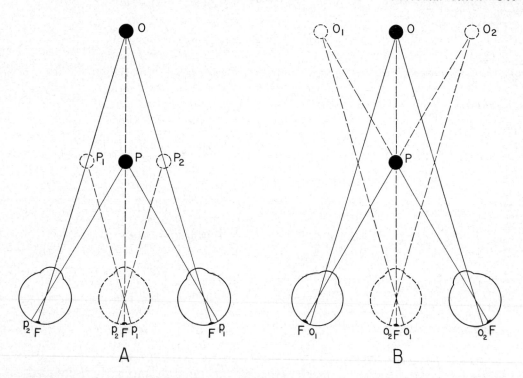

Fig. 417. Diagram illustrating crossed and uncrossed diplopia. A, Distant point O is fixated by both eyes. Its image falls on both foveas, represented in the cyclopean eye by F. The nearer object, P, falls on the temporal side of the fovea in each eye, represented in the cyclopean eye by P_1 and P_2. These are disparate retinal points whose stimulation will result in P being seen in two different visual directions. Therefore, P will be seen double. The image of P_1, that of the right eye, will be seen to the left of O. The image of P_2, that of the left eye, will be seen to the right of O. Therefore, the diplopia will be crossed. B, Point P is fixated by both eyes. Its image falls on the cyclopean fovea at F. The image of the farther object, O, falls on the nasal side of the fovea of each eye, shown in the cyclopean eye at O_1 and O_2. O_2 is the image of the right eye, and O_1 is the image of the left eye. O_2 will be projected to the right of P and O_1 will be projected to the left of P. Therefore, the diplopia will be uncrossed.

nation to them or to the parents and confusion to the unwary ophthalmologist who jumps to the conclusion that the patient must have paralysis of an ocular muscle.

Aside from physiologic diplopia, binocular diplopia never occurs unless the visual lines of the two eyes fail to intersect at the object of regard or the image is displaced on the retina by means of a prism.

Diplopia produced by prisms. Diplopia will be produced whenever the images of

an object fall on disparate retinal elements, provided that the disparateness of these elements be large enough. If the disparateness is small, the object may not be seen doubled, but the two images of the object will still be fused into one. It will then appear to stand out in depth from other objects in the field of view (Fig. 436).

Diplopia may be produced by displacing the image of an object off the fovea of one eye with prisms. The image of an object seen through a prism is shifted on

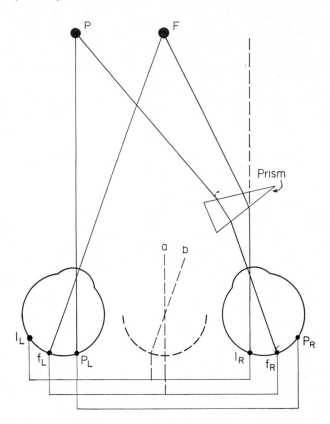

Fig. 418. Effect of a strong prism on the displacement of retinal images.

the retina in the direction of the base of the prism. As shown in Fig. 418, if a strong prism with the base toward the nose is placed in front of the right eye of an observer who is fixating object point F binocularly, the image of F will be shifted to the nasal retinal point I_R. Fixation point F is now imaged on the fovea of the left eye, but on a nasal element of the right eye. These elements are disparate and hence have different visual directions. Point F must be localized, therefore, in two directions in the subjective space simultaneously and will be seen doubled. The photoreceptors at I_R on the nasal side of the fovea of the right eye have a visual direction in space to the right of the object fixated (the

visual direction of the fovea). Hence, the image of F of the right eye will appear in space to the right of the image of the left eye. Hence, homonymous or uncrossed diplopia is produced (Fig. 419). If the prism is placed with its base toward the temple, the image will be shifted to the left of the image of the left eye, and crossed diplopia will be produced.

The relation of the common visual directions of corresponding retinal elements is a quantitative one. Similarly, the disparateness of the retinal elements stimulated simultaneously and the separation of the double images correspond in a quantitative fashion. In other words, the distance of the double images measured in arc degrees or prism diopters is equal

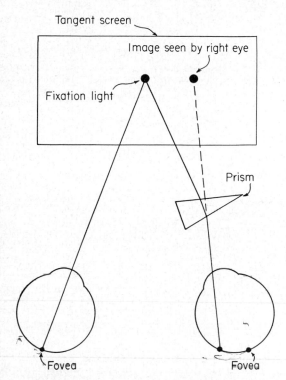

Fig. 419. Homonymous diplopia produced by a base-in prism. (After Burian.)

to the strength of the prism producing the diplopia.

Diplopia due to strabismus. If the visual axes of an individual are not in exact alignment, the image of the object of regard cannot fall on the two foveas. It will fall on disparate retinal elements, therefore. In one, the fixating eye, it will be projected mentally to its correct position in space; from the other eye its image, falling on a retinal element having a different visual direction, will be projected to the part of space which corresponds to the visual direction of that retinal element. A patient with convergent or divergent strabismus whose retinal correspondence is normal reacts in the same way as a normal subject in front of whom a horizontal prism has been placed (Fig. 420, *A*). If the left eye is turned in

10 arc degrees and the right eye fixates the object, its image will fall on an eccentric nasal point of the left retina, of which the distance from the left fovea is 10 arc degrees. The result is that the object will appear in two directions in subjective space, i.e., in the directions of phi and gamma in the cyclopean eye, as shown in Fig. 420, *A*. The angular separation of the double images will be 10 arc degrees, and the image seen with the left eye will be to the left of the one seen by the right eye. Hence, there is uncrossed diplopia. These patients may or may not see double since they often learn to suppress one image.

If the patient has divergent strabismus of 10 arc degrees in the left eye (Fig. 420, *B*), the object point will appear in the subjective visual directions phi and gamma, and the double images again will be separated by 10 arc degrees. This time, the image seen by the left eye is to the right of that seen by the right eye, and the subject will experience crossed diplopia unless he, too, suppresses one image.

Crossed and uncrossed diplopia are the natural consequences of simultaneous stimulation of the fovea of one eye and the photoreceptors of the other eye which have a different visual direction in space. In the same manner if the eyes are not in vertical alignment, vertical diplopia will be produced. If the right eye fixates an object and the left eye is turned upward (left hypertropia), the image of the object will fall above the fovea of the left eye since the fovea is turned down as the front of the eye is rotated upward. The image will fall, therefore, on photoreceptors which have a visual direction below that of the right fovea. Diplopia will ensue, and the image of the left eye will be seen below the image of the right. If one wishes to remember a rule, it is

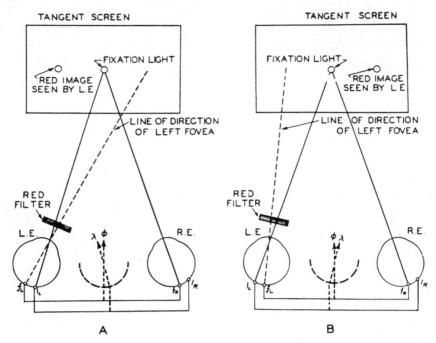

Fig. 420. Diplopia in strabismus with normal correspondence. **A,** Uncrossed diplopia in convergent strabismus. **B,** Crossed diplopia in divergent strabismus. (From Burian, H.: Tr. Am. Ophth. Soc. **43:**373, 1945.)

that the image of the nonfixating eye will be projected in space always in the *opposite* direction to which this eye is turned. In esotropia there is uncrossed diplopia; in exotropia there is crossed diplopia. In right hypertropia the image of the right eye is below that of the left eye, and in left hypertropia the image of the left eye is below that of the right eye.

The two images of the object are alike in all respects except one, i.e., in definition, for the simple reason that one image is derived from the fovea of the fixating eye, whereas the other derives from a perifoveal area of the retina of the other deviated eye. The resolution of details by the fovea is so much better than that of any perifoveal area that its image will be much sharper than the image from the other eye. The less sharp image from the deviated eye has been termed the false

image, but there is nothing false about it. If fixation is taken up by the previously deviated eye and the eye which formerly fixated now deviates, then the so-called false image is transferred to the other eye.

One of the two images obviously disappears as soon as one eye is closed. However, one image may be suppressed by the patient, even with both eyes open, and occasionally it is very difficult to break up this suppression and elicit diplopia in patients in whom the eyes are not in alignment due to ocular muscle paralyses. This is particularly true in congenital ocular muscle paralyses.

Whenever the visual lines of the two eyes do not intersect at the object of regard, diplopia should occur, and since the character of the diplopia depends entirely on the type of deviation of the visual lines, an analysis of the diplopia is an exact means of determining the type of the deviation. In fact, an analysis of the diplopia fields is a much more exact and sensitive index of the deviation of the visual axes than the objective measurement of the squint angle because it is possible for the patient to detect double images which have an angular separation of as little as 1 to 2 $\triangle$, whereas it is almost impossible to measure objectively a deviation of the visual lines of less than 5 to 10 $\triangle$.

Why does the patient see only two objects when one eye is deviated from its fellow? The eye that is deviated still has a fovea, and that is turned, it is true, away from the object of regard which is fixated by the undeviated eye, but nevertheless this deviated fovea has a much greater valency than the area of the retina now yielding the so-called false image. One might suppose that this deviated fovea would register some other object in space whose image falls on it, and in addition the region of the retina of the other eye on which this image fell would register a false image of it. The subject would have quadriplopia, therefore—a double image of the foveally fixated object of one eye and a double image of the foveally fixated object of the other eye. This as we know does not occur. The reason is that the brain never registers in consciousness two dissimilar objects. Similar contours are fused, but dissimilar contours immediately lead to retinal rivalry, with the suppression of one of the images. Which image will be suppressed is largely a matter of the attention value of either object at the moment. This can easily be demonstrated with prisms and with an appropriate experimental setup it can be demonstrated in patients with diplopia due to muscle paralysis. The attention can be changed so that at one moment a

double image of an object falling on the fovea of the sound eye will be registered (the usual response), and in the next moment a double image of the object falling on the fovea of the eye with the paralyzed muscle will be seen. During this shift the eyes will not have moved at all. Under no experimental setup, however, will it be possible to obtain registration of both double images simultaneously (p. 855).

SENSORY FUSION

We have seen that when images of an object fall on corresponding retinal elements in the normal subject they seem to be fused into a single mental impression and to be projected mentally to the same place in space. It naturally follows that the messages which come up the optic nerves from the two retinas go to a common locus in the brain where sensory fusion takes place. No possible locus where this could occur exists in the visual pathways before the lateral geniculate bodies, and here some sort of fusion might occur. There are reasons, however, for believing that the locus must be still higher in the visual pathways and that, if any one area is responsible, it must lie in area 17 of the occipital cortex or even higher. It may well be that this integration is a matter for the brain as a whole, but at least one can postulate with some reason that it is as far from the eyes as the visual cortex. At present there is no anatomic evidence for the existence of any so-called center for sensory fusion. The motor mechanism that controls the eyes during fusional movements has been described previously.

At the present time most authors believe that the binocular percept is the result of true binocular fusion of similar stimuli that originate in corresponding areas of the two eyes. This concept has not gone unchallenged, however. As early as 1760 du Tour claimed that there was no fusion of the two images, but that one of a pair of corresponding points always suppressed the other.[5] Verhoeff in 1935 criticized the theory of fusion and denied that true fusion exists. In place of this he suggested a theory of replacement, which seems to involve the varying suppression of first parts of the image of one eye and then the other, such as occurs in retinal rivalry. Asher[5] has adopted a similar point of view. The experiments on which the replacement theory is based have been criticized by Charnwood[6] and by Roenne.[7]

One of the most satisfying theories of fusion is that of Roenne. This is based on the following assumptions.

1. There is a point-to-point relationship between the retinal functional units and their respective end stations (ganglion cells) in the occipital cortex.

2. Pairs of ganglion cells representing the end station of the visual pathway proper of the right and left eye are physiologically coupled.

3. So-called normal retinal correspondence is the representation and consequence of this physiologic coupling in the visual cortex.

4. This coupling is innate, and potential couplings exist not only between corresponding cortical ganglion cells, but also between disparate cortical ganglion cells.

5. The physiologic significance of the corresponding cortical ganglion cells is to establish and maintain a surface of reference in relation to which, in front or behind, all points

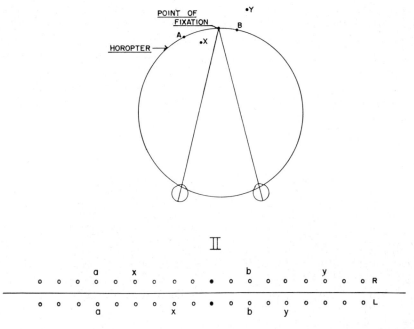

Fig. 421. Roenne's scheme of binocular vision. (From Roenne, G.: Acta Ophth. 34:2, 1956.)

in the subjective visual space are localized.

In Fig. 421, *II*, *R* and *L* represent the cortical ganglionic end stations from the right and left retinas. The solid dots represent the ganglion cells connected with the central foveal cones. The small circles arranged on each side of the horizontal line represent pairs of corresponding cortical ganglion cells. As shown in Fig. 421, *I*, objects lying on the horopter, *A* or *B*, will stimulate corresponding cortical cells, e.g., *a-a* and *b-b* in Fig. 421, *II*. Objects lying outside the horopter, e.g., *X* and *Y* in Fig. 421, *I*, will stimulate disparate or noncorresponding cortical cells *x-x* and *y-y* in Fig. 421, *II*. The distinction between far and near in relation to the horopter follows from simple geometry; near is represented by the disparity *x-x* and far by *y-y* (Fig. 421, *II*). If the objects happen to lie off the horopter, but still inside Panum's area, fusion is still possible (and, as will be explained later, stereopsis will accrue) on the basis that integration of the identical input, *x-x* and *y-y* (Fig. 421, *II*), is possible, i.e., if coupling of disparate cortical cells can be brought into action.

This concept necessitates accepting the belief that retinal correspondence is innate and based on an anatomically condi-tioned structure. It is difficult to reconcile this with the current concept that anomalous retinal correspondence is an adaptation to the angle of squint in comitant strabismus and that it has developed as a learned process in order that the unpleasantness of diplopia be avoided. It negates the emphasis that many workers in the field of sensory derangements in strabismus place on there being no anatomic basis for retinal correspondence and that in a normal infant the association of corresponding points is born out of trial and error. However, accumulating evidence weighs heavily in the direction that anatomic structure, and not trial and error, actually determines these sensory relationships.

RETINAL RIVALRY

If totally dissimilar patterns are presented in a stereoscope to the two eyes, the conscious perception is not a fused image of both patterns, but either one or the other picture dominates the scene. There seems to be a constant struggle in consciousness between the two eyes. This is termed retinal rivalry. It is the dissimilarity of the *contours* which evokes retinal rivalry. For most persons a sort of fusion of dissimilar colors can occur when two colors are presented to the two eyes. Blue and yellow, e.g., can be

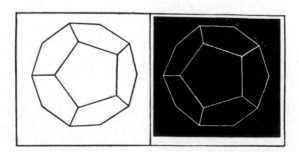

Fig. 422. Figures which show the importance of contours in the perception of stereoscopic depth. (After Helmholtz.)

fused and appear green. Objects such as those shown in Fig. 422 when fused take on an entirely new quality, called luster—the fusion of the black and white creates a quality of sensation which cannot be described except as a quality of shining with reflected light. If the two objects shown in Fig. 422 are viewed in a stereoscope, the body of the fused object appears with this quality of luster; it is neither white, black, nor gray, but has a peculiar sheen or gloss. The white and black contours do not have this and are never fused. They may either be seen side by side or create retinal rivalry, and first one and then the other is seen.

Orthoptists frequently use dissimilar targets, such as a bird and a cage, as a test for simultaneous macular perception and present these to the two foveas simultaneously in a major amblyoscope (a stereoscope in which the targets can be presented to the two eyes at a variable angle). If the patient acknowledges seeing the bird in the cage, he is said to have simultaneous macular perception. The idea that both foveas are fusing the images seems to be implicit in this statement; i.e., the messages from the two foveas are being fused by the brain, and the fused image is seen in one position in space. As Linksz[1] points out, the two images are not fused. The two foveas of a normal person never are able to fuse dissimilar contours, and dissimilar contours are never seen simultaneously in the same position in space. The evidence that we do not see dissimilar foveal images simultaneously is easy to obtain by examining carefully the pictures of the bird and the cage just mentioned in a stereoscope. Whereas one gets the general impression that both the bird and the cage are being seen simultaneously and in the same general direction in space, actually only parts of each picture are seen simultaneously. Those parts which are imaged on the foveas of both eyes are never seen at the same time. First, one sees the bird but not the bars directly overlying the bird, or one sees the bars but not those parts of the bird behind the bars. Further, it can be seen that not only are the parts which underlie those which are seen suppressed, but also a small area on each side of the parts. Suppression extends for some distance on either side of the point of fixation. There is always suppression of one foveal image while the other is seen. There may be retinal rivalry, in which case first one and then the other foveal image takes precedence and asserts itself in consciousness, but there is never fusion of both. What happens is that the foveal image of one eye is seen simultaneously with a perifoveal image of the other eye so that if the bird is considerably smaller than the cage the bird is fixated foveally with one eye, and the cage is seen perifoveally with the other. The parts of the cage which fall on the fovea of this other eye, however, are suppressed. Nature will not allow the foveas to function simultaneously if the contours presented to them are dissimilar.

A rough estimation of the size of the retinal region in which constant retinal rivalry takes place and outside of which fusion of dissimilar contours may occur can be obtained in the following manner. As shown in Fig. 423, *a*, a horizontal line, *AB,* is placed to the left of a large *X*. If the eyes are allowed to diverge while looking at the center of the *X*, the line is seen crossing the *X* at its center, which is now made the center of attention (Fig. 424, *b*). The whole paper is now turned around this point as an axis. When it is turned so that the top of the paper rotates to the right, the straight line appears to pass above the center of the cross and to

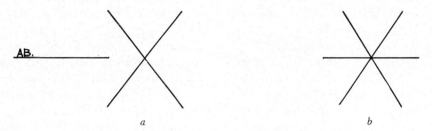

Fig. 423. Diagram to illustrate retinal rivalry (see text).

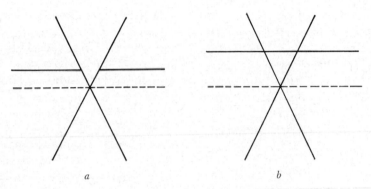

Fig. 424. Diagram to illustrate retinal rivalry (see text).

bisect the top limbs of the *X*. The more the paper is rotated to the right, the further away from the center of the *X* is the line, crossing the upper limbs of the *X*. As the paper is being gradually turned, it will be observed that when the line cuts the upper limbs of the *X* close to the center of the *X* either the line, parts of the line, or parts of the limbs of the *X* disappear, i.e., are suppressed (Fig. 424, *a*). When the line cuts the limbs of the *X* some distance from the center (Fig. 424, *b*), all three lines remain in consciousness, forming a triangle no part of which is suppressed. The paper is then turned to the point at which the whole triangle stays just visible. A pencil point is made where the line cuts either limb of the *X*, and this distance is measured from the center of the *X*. From this, the diameter of the retinal region in the two eyes within which suppression of dissimi-

lar contours must occur can be calculated if one knows the distance of the object from the eyes and uses the figures for a standard eye. Calculations made for the object at various distances from the eyes show good agreement, and the calculated diameter averages 0.4 mm. The rod-free region of the fovea is approximately 0.5 mm. It can be speculated that in the region of the two retinas where there are cones only, dissimilar contours cannot be fused, but where the rods appear, fusion can take place. If one image is confined to the rod-free region, i.e., the fovea, it can be seen simultaneously with a dissimilar image focused on a region of the opposite retina containing rods.

Aside from the difference between rod and cones, these two regions differ from one another in the character of their connections with the brain. In the fovea proper each cone is connected to the cortex by a so-called private wire, whereas in the rod-containing regions the connections of the photoreceptors are those of a party line in which a number of receptors are linked together. It is certain also that many of these photoreceptors are not represented in the cortex. As one follows the visual pathways from the retina to the cortex, there is divergence in the case of the foveal receptors but convergence in the case of the peripheral portions of the retina. The peripheral receptors send their messages up party lines, not private wires, and this may have something to do with fusion. Only party wires, so to speak, can carry dissimilar messages from the two eyes, whereas the private lines are reserved for either similar messages or perhaps only messages from each eye at a time because as yet we really do not know whether both foveas can function together, even when the images are similar. There is no positive evidence that they can do so although most authors, with the exception of Verhoeff and Asher (p. 854), take it for granted. No one has yet made electrical recordings from the cortical foveas showing the simultaneous messages from each fovea, either with dissimilar or similar targets presented to the two foveas. True foveal fusion could be inferred if it could be shown that there is summation when both foveas are used together with similar targets, but Sherrington's classic experiment, which is quoted most often, failed to show any considerable degree of summation.

DEPTH PERCEPTION

The awareness of depth or the third dimension in space is acquired by a number of different mechanisms, many of them psychologic. Previously, we have considered briefly the mechanism of depth perception by parallax, called stereopsis, which is due to the fact that the two eyes are separated laterally from one another by a space, the interpupillary distance; therefore their two images are not identical—one receives a right-slanted view of the object of regard and the other a left-slanted view. Further details of this mechanism will be scrutinized later. It is obvious that even without this mechanism we are quite aware of the fact that objects lie at different distances from us, even when we view them with one eye closed. There are many other clues, therefore, to depth perception besides stereopsis. For descriptive purposes they may be divided into monocular clues and binocular clues.

Monocular clues

The artist uses many monocular clues in order to portray depth in an illustration. These are interposition of one object in front of another, customary size of objects, color and haziness of objects, convergence of lines to the vanishing point, and shadows.

Interposition of one object in front of another, hiding parts of objects behind it. If the objects are made transparent so that we can see through them, the effect of depth is lost entirely unless other clues are afforded us (Fig. 425).

Customary size of objects. The nearer an object is to us, the larger is its retinal image. By experience we learn to associate the distance of objects away from us by the size of their retinal images. Thus, if we have no other clues, we can tell approximately how far away a man is from us merely by the size of his retinal image. If the object is one which has never been seen before, e.g., an airplane seen by an aboriginal savage for the first time, he would have no idea how far away in the sky or how big it was. In order to judge distance by this clue, one must know the actual size of the object.

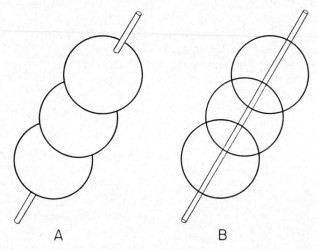

Fig. 425. A, Depth achieved by interposing one object in front of another. **B,** The same forms drawn to avoid a sense of depth.

Its retinal image then gives us the clue to its depth or distance (Fig. 426).

As stated, in ordinary seeing the size of the retinal image enlarges as an object is moved closer to a person. If the object is known to the person from past experience, he should have the impression that the object is getting bigger. Since its apparent size does not change, it is evident that something instructs us to make a mental correction for this increase in the size of the image. The changes in size of the image of objects moving from infinity to within 6 M. are corrected mostly by our previous knowledge of the actual size of the object, and unless this is known, it frequently is impossible to tell, except by parallax against the surrounds, whether an object is getting bigger and not approaching us, not changing its size but approaching us, or both. When an object comes closer to us than 6 M., however, other factors such as accommodation and convergence come into play. The effect of these additional factors on making corrections in the apparent size of objects from their increasing retinal image size will be considered later (p. 862).

Color and haziness of objects. Artists make use of the fact that objects in the distance take on a blue tint and generally become hazed due to the atmosphere. Because of this factor, persons living on the Eastern seaboard of the United States are frequently badly fooled when riding horseback in regions such as Wyoming where the atmosphere is extraordinarily clear. A ranch which looks to an Easterner to be a mile or two distant, because it is seen so clearly, may in reality be 10 miles away. Similarly, on a foggy day objects appear to be very much farther away than they actually are. This frequently necessitates the sudden application of brakes when one is driving an automobile and is one cause of accidents during driving under foggy conditions.

Convergence of lines to the vanishing point. The artist learns to use perspective in order to make objects appear in their proper place in a painting. There is a common vanishing point in every drawing to which all lines of the space pictured must converge. The best example of this is, of course, the converging lines of a road as it goes off into the distance

A

B

Fig. 426. **A,** All objects are drawn to scale, diminishing in size the farther away they are. This creates depth in the picture. **B,** The three cats are drawn the same size, whereas all other objects are drawn to scale. This creates the impression that the cats become larger the farther off they are.

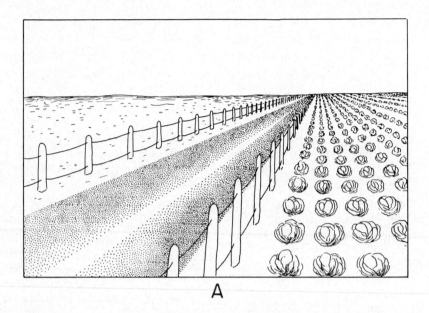

A

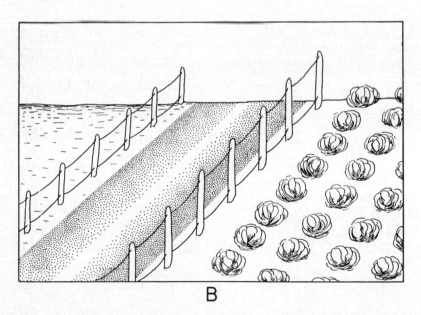

B

Fig. 427. A, All objects are drawn to the scale of the vanishing point, creating perspective. B, All objects are drawn without a vanishing point, i.e., the same size in the background as in the foreground and in parallel rows. This creates the impression of an elevation of the background and a widening of the road as it recedes, i.e., false perspective.

(Fig. 427). If the drawing is made without a vanishing point, the whole perspective and depth perception disappear or are given a false perspective.

Shadows. Shadows make a large contribution to the perception of depth. Since the light comes from above, the length and position of shadows in a picture are helpful in determining their size and depth, particularly if the elevation of the sun above the horizon is indicated in the picture. If this is not known, the shadow is no sure guide to the size of the object unless that is already known. Considerable confusion can arise from shadows which are abnormal in this respect. In Fig. 428 is shown a turret of the Merrimac after it was hit by shells which did not penetrate but made deep dents in it. The rivets are seen plainly as bulges, and the depressions in the surface made by the bullets are likewise clearly indenta-

tions. If the illustration is turned upside down, the rivets immediately become depressions, and the bullet holes assume the shape of blisters protruding out of the structure toward the observer. The perception of depth of both the rivets and the bullet holes shown in the illustration is given by the shadows. Under ordinary circumstances, light coming from above casts a shadow in the upper part of a depression and on the lower part of a bulge. When the illustration is turned upside down, the shadows are reversed. Accordingly, the bulges look like depressions and vice versa.

Binocular clues

Binocular clues to depth perception are convergence, accommodation, and stereoscopic vision.

Convergence. In convergence we have a possible mechanism by means of which

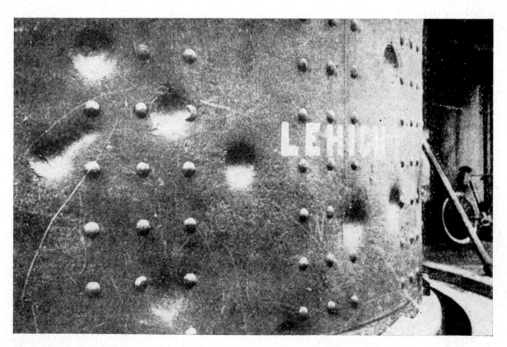

Fig. 428. An example of the contribution shadows make to depth perception (see text).

depth for objects approaching us from within 6 M. can be gauged because as the object approaches within this distance convergence of the visual axes is called on to a greater and greater degree. At the same time a greater degree of accommodation is called on. It is reasonable to assume that these two factors, convergence and accommodation, in addition to all the other factors operative at greater distances, aid us in depth perception for objects close at hand. The influence of convergence is still debated, however. Ogle[8] does not believe that a sense of depth can be derived to any considerable degree from a change in convergence, whereas Ishak and others[9] claim that convergence plays a large role in stereopsis. The following experiment indicates that convergence does play some role in depth perception quite apart from its influence in stereopsis, which is defined as depth perception by parallax. Fig. 429 should be held at the usual reading distance, but the eyes should be allowed to diverge as though the paper were

situated at infinity. It is easier to do if one has exophoria (if this is done properly, the cross will appear inside the square, as shown in Fig. 430). This is simultaneous perception by the two eyes, the foveal image of one eye being seen simultaneously with the perifoveal image of the other. In this sense it represents fusion, but it should be noted that the objects have different contours and therefore cannot be seen singly in the same position in space. Since one is smaller than the other, the two do not overlap, and their images are projected mentally to approximately the same locus in space, one inside the other. When the square containing the cross is seen, notice especially the apparent size of each.

Now, voluntarily cross the eyes as though fixating on an object nearer than the page. Some persons may have to hold a finger momentarily between the page and the eyes in order to converge the eyes to this point successfully. When the right amount of convergence has been exerted, the cross will once again be seen

Fig. 429. Eyes in normal position converged to plane of paper.

Fig. 430. Eyes diverged.

Fig. 431. Eyes converged.

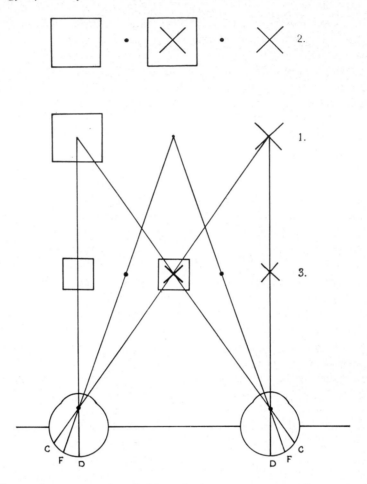

Fig. 432. Change in apparent size of objects due to convergence or divergence of the visual axes.

inside the square. The appearance will be that shown in Fig. 431. It can readily be seen that now the square and the cross are very much smaller than they appeared when the visual axes were diverged.

With a little practice it is possible to change rapidly from the divergent to the convergent position of the visual axes. The change in the apparent size of the cross and square will now be most impressive.

In Fig. 432 are shown the eyes in the position they would be held normally while looking at the picture of the cross

and the square. The eyes would be converged to the plane of the paper and, as shown in the illustration, to a point midway between the cross and the square. *F* represents the fovea in each eye in this position. *D* represents the fovea of each eye when the eyes are diverged, and *C* represents the foveas when the eyes are converged to a point in space nearer the observer than the plane of the paper. The corresponding image as seen by the observer is shown when the eyes are in these various positions—*1, 2,* and *3.*

As stated, when one allows the eyes to

diverge, the image of the cross falls on the right fovea, and the image of the square falls on the perifoveal area of the left eye (Fig. 432, *2*). With normal retinal correspondence, a person will fuse the two images. Since the cross is smaller than the square, no part of its contour will coincide exactly with the contour of the square, and the two will not cause retinal rivalry, therefore. They will be seen simultaneously and in relatively the same position in space, i.e., one inside the other in the same frontoparallel plane.

When the eyes are converged to a point nearer the observer than the plane of the paper (Fig. 432, *3*), the image of the square falls on the right perifoveal area and the image of the cross on the left fovea. The two images are fused under the same conditions as just outlined. There is now marked difference in the apparent size of the square and the cross, however. They are much smaller than they were in the diverged position, and the more the visual axes are overconverged, the smaller does the apparent size of the cross and square become. What has caused this change in apparent size? No change in apparent distance of the fused images from the observer occurs. The only difference between the divergent and convergent positions is one of convergence of the visual axes. The size of the retinal images remains the same, for the object has not moved its position. Only the eyes have moved. Accommodation likewise remains the same for the same reason. Convergence alone, therefore, has created a change in apparent size of an object without change in the size of the retinal image or in accommodation. No other visual clues to apparent size or apparent distance were changed likewise. Why does the fused image look smaller when the eyes are overconverged than when they are con-

verged to the plane of the paper or when they are diverged? Under normal conditions whenever convergence is employed, an object has moved closer to the observer, and its retinal image has increased in size. Convergence then informs the observer that the increased size in the retinal image must be discounted; the object itself has not actually changed in size but merely has come closer. The apparent size of the object, therefore, remains the same. When the eyes converge and the retinal images remain the same size as they were before convergence took place, as in this experiment, the message from convergence is interpreted by the brain as indicating that the object must have gotten smaller, and therefore the apparent size is smaller. This feedback mechanism dictates what the apparent size of objects will be. Without it, objects approaching close to the eyes would increase in apparent size. They would seem to be getting bigger.

From this, it can be concluded that convergence is a factor in our judgment of the size of objects, and since the apparent size of objects is one means of judging distance, convergence must influence our judgment of depth. This does not mean that convergence is concerned in stereopsis because the conditions of this experiment did not produce parallax.

Accommodation. In a certain sense, accommodation is a monocular clue, but accommodation is closely associated with convergence, and under ordinary conditions both eyes are open when it is employed. It has been shown that in binocular vision a change in the vergence of light from an object produces a change in the apparent distance of the object, but that the effect is only about a quarter of that produced by a commensurate change in the convergence necessary to see it.

Stereoscopic vision. If one views two

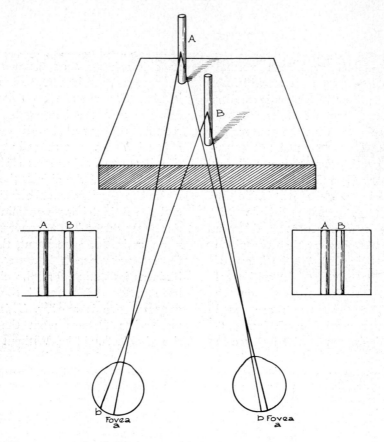

Fig. 433. Disparateness of retinal images, producing stereopsis.

posts, *A* and *B* (Fig. 433), situated at slightly different distances with both eyes open, their separation in depth is readily apparent to a normal person. Even if all monocular clues to depth perception are eliminated, this perception of depth is maintained as long as both eyes are used. If either eye is closed, the effect of depth then vanishes. If the right eye is closed, the appearance of the two posts is that shown on the left-hand side of Fig. 433, and if the left eye is closed, the appearance is that shown on the right side of the illustration. The only difference between these two images is that the posts seem to be farther apart in the fronto-parallel plane when seen with the left eye

than when seen with the right eye. This difference in lateral separation is due to the fact that the receptors stimulated in the left eye are more widely separated from each other than those in the right retina, as shown in Fig. 433, due to the fact that the left eye sees a little farther around on the left of the posts and the right eye sees a little farther around on the right side. If the right-hand post is nearer the person, the lateral separation of their images will be greater in the left eye.

Assuming that the image of post *A* falls on the foveas of each eye, then the image of post *B* will fall on a photoreceptor in the right eye close to the fovea, whereas

Fig. 434. Stereoscopic view showing the dissimilarities between the right and left images. A comparison of the trees in the foreground at the edges of the pictures demonstrates this clearly. (Keystone Stereoscopic Service.)

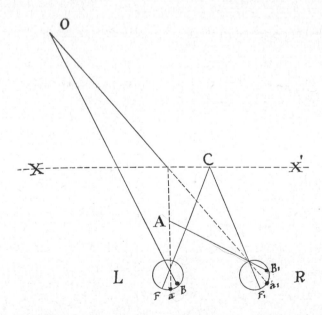

Fig. 435. Scheme showing the effect produced by stimulation of slightly incongruous retinal points. **a—a′,** Corresponding points; **B—B′,** corresponding points; **F—F′,** the foveas.

its image in the left eye will be farther away. The foveas are corresponding points, but the photoreceptors receiving the image of post B are not corresponding points but disparate points. The simultaneous stimulation of these disparate retinal receptors by images which are alike is what produces this sense of depth.

Stereoscopic vision is the judgment of depth by the disparateness of the retinal images. When both eyes are used together, all of the monocular and binocular factors just mentioned operate as usual, but in addition a new factor comes into play; i.e., the two images offered the brain are not exactly identical. The image of the right eye is like that of a photograph taken slightly to the right side of the object, and the image of the left eye is like a photograph taken in a similar fashion slightly to the left (Fig. 434). As a result of this, the images seen by the two eyes are somewhat dissimilar. When these are fused together in the brain, this dissimilarity gives rise to the sense of a third dimension. It can be seen from Fig. 435 that when the images do not fall on exactly corresponding retinal points an impression that the image is in front of or behind a given frontal plane is produced. In Fig. 435 F and F^1 are the foveas fixating a point, C, straight ahead. This point determines the frontal plane, XX^1. An object, A, whose image falls on a in the left eye produces an image at B^1 in the right eye. B^1 is not the corresponding point to a, but lies to the temporal side of this point, which is a^1. Because of this, the impression is that point A lies nearer the eyes than frontal plane XX^1. Similarly, an object, O, whose image falls on B in the left eye produces its image at a^1 in the right eye. The corresponding retinal point of B is B^1. The image of object O lies to the nasal side of this point at a^1 in the right eye. The impression is gained,

therefore, that point O lies beyond frontal plane XX^1.

It can be said, therefore, that in general nasal disparity gives the impression of remoteness of an object, and temporal disparity gives the impression of nearness of an object.

It is stated generally that stereopsis is the third degree of fusion, which implies that it has a physiologic basis in the retina. On the other hand, it has been claimed by some that it does not arise per se from the mere disparity between the images of the right and left eye, but rather from the differences in the subjective content of the images as a whole as perceived separately by the two eyes. As such, the implication is that stereopsis is a purely psychophysical phenomenon. The problem has been investigated, using a modification of the old Hering drop test.[10] These experiments show that there is a limited range of horizontal disparities between the images of the two eyes, within which stereoscopic vision can be experienced. This range is larger than that for Panum's fusional areas. Hence, stereoscopic depth occurs with physiologically double images. Within the central part of this range a very definite sense of depth is experienced, whereas outside the central part there is merely a vague approximation for far or near. Horizontally disparate images can also be made slightly disparate in the vertical plane, and still a definite stereoscopic depth can be appreciated by the subject. Therefore, these limiting horizontal and vertical disparities constitute a sort of stereoscopic area and imply a neuroanatomic association of retinal elements. In other words, for one to obtain a valid sensation of stereopsis, the images must stimulate specifically horizontally associated disparate elements at the same time. These experiments indicate that stereopsis certainly has a defi-

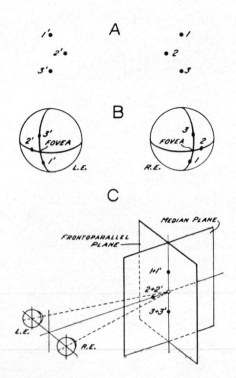

Fig. 436. A, Stereoscopic target. B, Schematic presentation of the images of the dots in A on the retinas (seen from in back). Note that the fovea is not stimulated. C, Appearance of dots to observer. (From Burian, H.: Docum. ophth. 5-6:170, 1951.)

nite physiologic basis and that a purely psychophysical theory can hardly apply since such a theory would not necessitate such limitations. As long as the disparity is not too great, the images of the two eyes will be fused but will appear to have changed position in regard to the established plane of fixation. In addition the fused images will cause a shift in visual direction of the receptors stimulated, as is apparent in the diagram given in Fig. 436.

If Fig. 436, A, is placed in a stereoscope, the dots 1 and 1' and 3 and 3' will be fused by the two eyes and will be seen as two dots lying one above the other but in the same plane, the frontoparallel plane, which now for the observer becomes the plane of reference. Dots 2 and 2' will be fused likewise and will appear as a single dot lying in front of the plane of reference, closer to the observer. But in addition the fused image of dots 2 and 2' is seen also in line with them in the median plane. In Fig. 436, B, are shown the retinal receptors which will be stimulated. It will be seen that 1 and 1' and 3 and 3' will stimulate corresponding retinal receptors, but that 2 and 2' stimulate disparate receptors, each lying on the temporal side of the fovea. In spite of this the visual direction of these receptors is changed, and the fused image of 2 and 2' has assimilated the visual direction of the nonstimulated corresponding retinal receptors which form the center of the Panum area to which the stimulated retinal receptors belong. These centers always dominate the areas by imparting their visual directions to the fused disparate visual impressions which arise in these areas.

Experiments by Burian and others have shown that a sense of depth still occurs under certain conditions even though the disparity of the receptors stimulated is such that they lie outside of Panum's area and therefore are not seen singly but double. In Fig. 437 are shown the regions, as determined by Ogle, in which there is single vision without depth (determined as the horopter), single vision with stereoscopic depth (determined as Panum's area), and, finally, outside of Panum's area a crude sense of depth with diplopia. As Burian points out, it is not strictly correct to call stereopsis third-degree fusion. It is more than that. It is a sense *sui generis*.

Accuracy of stereoscopic vision. Stereoscopic acuity is determined by the smallest discernible difference in binocular parallax. The simplest procedure to de-

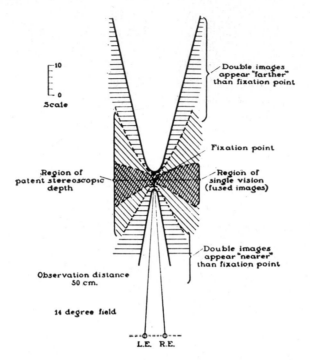

Fig. 437. The regions of obligatory and qualitative stereoscopic perception of depth about the point of fixation. (From Ogle, K.: Arch. Ophth. **60:**770, 1958.)

termine this is by means of the Howard-Dolman apparatus. A short upright rod is mounted 20 feet from the observer in an illuminated box. This rod is stationary, but on a track beside it, running to and away from the observer, is a similar rod which can be moved by a string. The observer is told to bring the two rods into alignment so that they are equidistant from him. No clues of depth perception other than that afforded by binocular parallax are present.

The accuracy of stereoscopic determinations is very great. Anderson and Weymouth found it possible for a trained observer to make correct judgments within 2 seconds of arc.

The majority of normal persons can tell the separation of the two posts in the Howard-Dolman apparatus when their average distance apart is 20 mm. at a distance of 6 M.

A person with one eye has very much less depth perception than a person with stereoscopic vision when tested under such conditions. It is equally true, however, that under natural conditions a one-eyed person can judge depth of objects and speed of movements surprisingly well. This comes as the result of experience and judgment of other factors in addition to stereopsis. Although in the selection of airplane pilots much emphasis has been placed upon the stereoscopic ability of the candidate, it is questionable whether stereopsis itself is a necessary requisite for flying ability. All persons who have good stereopsis must of necessity have well-developed ocular functions, but it is still quite possible that a person without stereopsis may be a safe pilot. Kirschberg[11] found no relationship between depth perception and flying ability, as shown by the successful graduation or failure in the pilot's course of the British Commonwealth Air Training Plan during World War II. Close-formation flying, however, demands stereopsis.

It has already been pointed out that the eye can resolve visual angles which are smaller than the average angular separation of the receptors in the fovea. This has led to the belief that micronystagmus may play a part in the resolution of fine details. Theories of visual acuity which include the effect of involuntary eye movements have been supported by the experiments of Anderson and Weymouth[12] and by Marshall and Talbot.[13] On the other hand, experiments which seem to effectively eliminate eye movements have failed to demonstrate any consistent effects of eye movements upon monocular acuity.[14] In a similar fashion, it has been postulated that involuntary eye movements aid in stereoscopic acuity. The experiments of Anderson and Weymouth show that stereoscopic acuity became better with an increase in the linear dimensions of the test target, provided that the length of the line did not exceed the limits of the fovea. They postulated the existence of a mean retinal local sign built up as the result of micronystagmus, as well as of the static factors resulting from the increased line length. Ogle and Weil[15] have likewise performed experiments which suggest that micronystagmus may play a definite role in stereoscopic acuity. More recently, however, Shortess and Krauskopf[16] found no difference in stereoscopic acuity when the effect of eye movements was eliminated. Although the time of exposure of the test target does considerably change the thresholds arrived at, particularly when the time of exposure is of very short duration, they point out that many other factors besides eye movements may be eliminated by shortening the time of exposure. At the present time, therefore, no clear-cut case can be made for the effect of micronystagmus as an aid to either monocular acuity or stereoscopic acuity produced by the disparity of the two ocular images.

DEVELOPMENT OF BINOCULAR VISION

At birth, the eyes are not associated with each other but act as two independent sense organs. The mechanisms necessary for binocular single vision are not completely developed. The foveas are not formed until the third month of life. As they develop, the stimulus to associate these areas is provided. By trial and error the child learns that when the image of an object is brought onto the two foveas simultaneously the image is most detailed. For this reason alone the visual axes are oriented in such a way that each fovea is directed at the object of regard.

Once this has become an established habit, the relative space perceptions of the child begin to take form. Objects to the right of fixation send images to retinal areas in the two eyes which have a common visual direction, i.e., to the right of fixation. The cross-firing of various sensory phenomena, such as touch with vision, eventually leads to an accurate determination of the child's space. An object seen so many degrees to the right of fixation is eventually interpreted in its correct position, and this is rewarded by checking accurately with the experiences of touch. Hence, by trial and error, the eyes become accurately associated with one another and with tactile sensations until gradually a normal child develops perception of space.

If the eyes are never allowed to become associated, e.g., by failure of development of one fovea or because of paralysis of an ocular muscle so that the two foveas cannot always be focused together on the object of regard, the child never acquires binocular single vision and never learns to fuse the two images into one. Vision under these circumstances is always monocular and generally alternating; first one eye is used and then the other. The image of the eye which is not fixating the object is suppressed.

Is depth perception learned by trial and error, or is it innately determined? Earlier experiments to decide between these two alternatives consisted of preventing young chicks from practicing the sensory-motor coordination involved in pecking by keeping them in dark enclosures or by covering their heads with hoods which masked their eyes but left their beaks free for eating. However, the results of these experiments were questioned when it was suggested that in the absence of stimulation by light the eyes might fail to develop normally. Any inaccuracy in pecking might have been the result of degeneration in the retina or the nerves. To overcome this difficulty Hess developed a technique of fitting chicks' eyes with prismatic lenses which would displace the visual image to the right or left. Twenty-eight Leghorn chicks were hatched in complete darkness and were fitted immediately with thin rubber hoods into which transparent plastic goggles had been inserted.[17] Ten other chicks were fitted with flat pieces of plastic that produced no image displacement. These acted as controls. Twelve of the chicks were fitted with plastic prisms that displaced the whole visual field 7 degrees to the right. Six wore lenses that caused similar displacement of the visual field to the left. The accuracy of their pecking was then determined by embedding small brass nails in modeling clay and photographing the dented clay after a pecking session. These and other experiments led to the con-

clusion that the chicks' visual apparatus for locating objects in space is innate and not learned. The chicks wearing displacement prisms clustered their pecks about the spot where the object was seen. They did not simply peck at random until they struck the target. Further, the chick whose visual field was displaced appeared unable to learn through experience to correct its aim. Its only improvement was to increase the consistency of the distance by which it missed the target. Apparently the innate picture which the chick has of the location of objects in its visual world cannot be modified by learning if what is required is that the chick learn to perform a response which is antagonistic to its instinctive one.

In the human being the anatomic and physiologic factors necessary for depth perception are either present at birth or develop shortly after birth so that, if the eyes are normal and the neuromuscular mechanism for moving the eyes is normal, depth perception will follow automatically. Stereopsis seems to be in a class by itself because it is claimed by some that there are persons with entirely normal eyes and neuromuscular apparatus who do not have depth perception by parallax when all other clues to depth are eliminated. As Ogle[18] has stated.

"Stereopsis is a sensory phenomenon in its own right, with its own physiological mechanisms. [It] seems to be an all-or-none phenomenon, in that in a given person it is either present or not present. Training does not seem to develop stereopsis as such, but training may increase one's ability to discriminate depth differences just as the visual acuity may be slightly improved by training."*

Suppression. Suppression is active inhibition of the vision of one eye. Generally, it is supposed that the whole of

*From Ogle, K.: Arch. Ophth. **60:**770, 1958.

one retinal function is extinguished in consciousness, but this is not usually so, and Burian believes it is not generally the rule. Instead of total extinction, he considers that selective suppression in which only certain regions of one retina are suppressed takes place more often. An example of this is the occurrence of suppression scotoma which can be demonstrated in the foveal area of some children with convergent strabismus. While a target is fixated with the straight or fixating eye of a child with convergent strabismus, another moving target is presented to the deviated eye, and the child is asked to report whether this moving target disappears in any part of the visual field. Frequently, the target disappears when its image falls on the fovea or on the part of the nasal retina which is in line with the fovea of the fixating eye, but is seen throughout the rest of the field. Under these experimental conditions a scotoma in the deviating eye can usually be elicited. This scotoma disappears, however, in this eye when it is made to take up fixation alone, showing that the scotoma was purely a functional one and not due to any organic disease of the retina or visual pathways. The scotoma can be demonstrated in either eye, but only when both eyes are being used, one fixating and the other deviating. The scotoma appears only in the deviating eye, showing that it is conditioned on the relative positions of the eyes to each other. It is in effect a suppression scotoma. Burian believes that suppression may be selective also with regard to a specific retinal function; i.e., the ability to differentiate different parts of the spectrum may be intact, but the ability to resolve contours may be defective momentarily. Some persons who lack stereoscopic vision but have otherwise normal eyes may fuse the identical parts of stereograms but suppress the disparate

elements in the nondominant eye. Suppression may be looked upon as active inhibition brought about because the body is presented with a paradoxical situation which would otherwise be intolerable. When the eyes are crossed, e.g., if the image of one eye were not mentally suppressed, two images would be seen instead of one since the same object would be imaged on the fovea of one eye and on some photoreceptors in the turned-in eye, nasally to its fovea. Since these two regions do not have the same visual direction (in persons with normal correspondence), the image of the object would be projected mentally to two different regions in space. Further, the foveal region of the turned-in eye is inhibited also when an image falls on it while the other fovea is fixating a target because otherwise the two foveas would be seeing two different objects simultaneously. Therefore, since the two foveas have the same visual direction (in persons with normal correspondence), these two objects would be projected mentally to the same point in space—obviously an impossible situation (p. 855).

Since the different parts of the retina vary enormously in their visual acuity, the inhibition of the fovea generally has to be very heavy, whereas that of the periphery need be but light. The effect of retinal inhibition is to flatten the contour of visual acuity sufficiently to allow the other parts of the retina to achieve a requisite degree of dominance.

The suppression which occurs under conditions of strabismus, as just outlined, is facultative, i.e., occurs only under certain conditions. If the strabismus is not alternating, so that first one eye and then the other takes up fixation while the other deviates, but is monocular with one eye remaining the fixating eye and the other constantly deviating, the suppression may become so constant and so deep that it persists. Then when the usually deviating eye is forced to take up fixation, the inhibition of its fovea remains, and the vision in this eye is defective. The suppression under these conditions is no longer facultative but obligatory.[19] This obligatory suppression is called amblyopia.

AMBLYOPIA

Amblyopia, by definition, is defective vision without obvious pathologic cause. The amblyopia which develops in the deviated eye of a child with strabismus has been called amblyopia ex anopsia, i.e., amblyopia from disuse. This connotation is not strictly correct, for it is extremely doubtful if amblyopia could be developed in a child merely by occluding one eye for a long period of time. As just stated, suppression is a process of active inhibition, and at first it is probably always facultative, i.e., occurs only when both eyes whose visual axes are not in alignment are being used simultaneously. It is not merely disuse which brings it about, such as atrophy of muscles in one arm which one would get if the arm were kept in a plaster cast so that the muscles could not be used. However, the degree to which facultative suppression can produce obligatory suppression or amblyopia probably depends upon the age of the child when the facultative suppression begins. The reason for this is obvious when one recalls that an infant is not born with fully developed eyes, anatomically or functionally. If suppression is induced in a very young infant, it probably can become obligatory in a much shorter period of time than if it starts in an older child. The amblyopia is, therefore, deeper and less easily broken up than when it begins later in life. This is in accord with clinical experience. Children whose strabismus begins early in life generally have more deep-seated amblyopia if the strabismus is monocular than those whose squint begins later. Further, it is said that if suppression stops the development of foveal function before it has matured normal vision can never be expected. It will be possible to restore the function of the retina only to the level it had developed before suppression set in.

When test letters on a chart are presented to a normal individual, and dark glasses are worn by the subject, either emmetropic or made so with correcting glasses, visual acuity drops. This is not surprising. It has been found, however, that in children with amblyopia of squint visual acuity is not reduced by the interposition of dark glasses.[20] In some amblyopes acuity may even be improved. In patients whose visual acuity was impaired from disease, on the other hand, reduction in the amount of light reaching the eye caused a much greater drop in visual acuity than in normal subjects.

It is obvious that the amblyopia in strabismus differs from the amblyopia due to disease in that the poor vision in strabismus cannot be due to disease of the central foveal cones or their neural connections. It is difficult to explain why the amblyopia of squint should show no further drop in vision with reduced illumination, unless one assumes that the amblyope is not using his central fovea but is fixating off the fovea where rods as well as cones are found. As the illumination drops, the rods in this area begin to function, thus aiding the amblyope. In a normal person with central foveal fixation no rods are present to function as illumination reaches the mesopic level. Since cone function is diminishing under such illumination, acuity drops more than in the amblyope.

Further studies at the different levels

of illumination have been carried out by von Noorden and Burian,[21] confirming their previous reports and showing that with increasing illumination amblyopic eyes increase in visual acuity at the same or at an even earlier level of illumination than normal eyes. Their maximum resolving power was reached when the normal eyes had not even reached one half of their final visual acuity.

I consider this suggestive evidence that so-called amblyopia ex anopsia is the result of motor disability and not primarily sensory. This would explain the ability of the amblyopic child to better discriminate a single E than those subtending the same visual angle when presented together in a line. It would be easier for such a child with poor fixation to search back and forth, so to speak, over a single E than when a number of E's were close together, which would make it difficult for him to concentrate on any one.

The fact that the fixation pattern of amblyopes is defective in photopic illumination but becomes normal in the scotopic state has been shown by von Noorden and Burian.[22] The light-adapted eyes of persons with strabismic amblyopia showed marked unsteadiness of fixation with jerky movements, while their sound eyes fixated normally. When the patients were dark-adapted, this unsteadiness of fixation of the amblyopic eye disappeared, and the pattern resembled that of normal subjects.

Site of interference. Most of the evidence suggests that the site of interference in amblyopia is a block in the cortex and not a retinal activity. Ludvigh,[23] Wald and Burian,[24] and others have shown that most of the functions of the macula are intact in the presence of amblyopia, e.g., dark adaptation and color vision, but that form vision alone is affected. In patients with amblyopia the absolute light threshold was found to be normal, both foveally and peripherally in cones and rods and in light adaptation and dark adaptation. The entire apparatus of light perception was found to be normal in these patients. The capacity for fixating and localizing illuminated points and areas on the central and peripheral retinas was found to be normal also. The capacity for discrimination of pattern fell as low as 2/200 or 2/400, without any loss of sensitivity to light. This shows that the apparatus for form vision is to some degree distinct from that involved in simple light perception. This is consistent with the results of recent investigations of central structures concerned in vision. It has been shown that in rats (Lashley, 1931), dogs (Marquis, 1934), cats (Smith, 1937), and monkeys (Kluver, 1941 to 1942) complete removal of the occipital lobes results in virtually complete loss of pattern and object vision, with little if any observable loss in the capacity to react to light or to discriminate brightness.[25]

In man complete destruction of the occipital lobes results in complete and permanent blindness. All sensory aspects of vision possess indispensable cortical components. However, functionally, pattern vision is separated completely from light perception and spatial projection and occupies a higher level than light perception. Therefore, strabismic amblyopia is thought by most authors to consist of cortical inhibition of the higher cortical function of pattern vision, without impairment of the lower cortical functions of simple light perception and spatial localization.

Most authors who have studied the electroencephalogram in patients with the amblyopia of strabismus agree that a much higher percentage of abnormalities are found than in normal children of the same age. It has been claimed that these findings support the theory of Keiner known as myelogenesis retardata.

Pathologic cortical rhythms have been found in amblyopic eyes by Dyer and Bierman.[26] However, abnormal rhythms were also found by these authors in 60% of children from 5 to 10 years of age with alternating strabismus, presumably without amblyopia. The abnormal waves seemed to disappear with age, occurring only among members of the younger age group. Parsons-Smith[27] also found abnormal alpha rhythms in amblyopia and in a later study found some patients with amblyopia in whom the effects of driving by flicker were abnormal.[27]

Not all authors are satisfied with the concept that amblyopia is a selective inhibition of the form sense, while all the other functions of the retina remain intact. The flicker fusion threshold of the foveal area of patients with amblyopia has been found to be considerably depressed compared with values obtained from the surrounding retina and with the values obtained from the nonamblyopic eye in the same patients.[28] For the present it can be said that none of the experiments give conclusive proof of the mechanism of amblyopia or of the localization of the inhibition, i.e., whether it is purely retinal, cortical, or perhaps both.

In addition to decreased visual acuity, there is some evidence which points to concomitant weakening of the power of central fixation. It is reported that only 20% of the subjects with amblyopia fixate along the central foveal axis of the poor eye when the good eye is occluded.[29] The shift from the true foveal axis to some outlying area increases with the increased depth of the amblyopia. Von Noorden and Burian[30] have shown that the fixation of light-adapted amblyopic eyes is characterized by unsteadiness and jerky movements, whereas the sound eye fixates

steadily. In the dark-adapted state the fixation of the amblyopic eye resembles that of the normal eye. It was pointed out on p. 783 that the best visual acuity is found in a retinal area measuring approximately 250 μ in each direction from the center of the fovea, and more recently Jones and Higgins[31] reported that the highest visual acuity is confined to a small region of 7 minutes of arc. At 10 minutes of arc there is diminution in visual acuity. Hence, fixation by a region of the retina farther away from the fovea than 10 minutes of arc would reduce visual acuity automatically. I have questioned previously whether the amblyopia that occurs in strabismus might not be due to faulty fixation as the primary factor in the poor acuity. On this basis the recovery of vision might be due to training the subject to use the fovea instead of a more peripheral region of the retina. Kupfer[32] has shown visual improvement in adults with amblyopia by improving fixation.

In discussing the electrical activity of the cortex induced by light stimulation it was pointed out on page 690 that van Balen and Henkes[33] found two separate waves in the recordings which they called c^1 and c^2. The c^1 wave was considered due to the foveal activity and hence was concerned with all of the functions of the fovea, i.e., visual acuity and color vision. The c^2 wave was thought to represent extrafoveal activity. These authors showed that attention had a marked effect on these waves, favoring the development of the c^1 wave at the expense of the c^2 wave. When subjects with the amblyopia of strabismus were examined with the same techniques, it was found that the c^1 wave of the amblyopic eye was generally smaller than that of the normal eye, or the c^2 wave of the normal eye was reduced in comparison to that in the amblyopic eye. They compare the amblyopia of strabismus to the state of vision in the normal eye without attention (p. 490), and they regard amblyopia as due to loss of the activation of the reticular formation, so that in effect it may be regarded as the result of inattentiveness rather than of suppression.

The site at which reticular formation can affect the visual responses on their way to the cortex in the amblyopia of strabismus must be in the part of the visual pathway anterior to the chiasm since amblyopia is confined to one eye. One may speculate that this occurs in the retina itself, in either the ganglion cell layer or at the level of the bipolar cells where horizontal connections mediating a regulating system between the fovea and the extrafoveal regions is thought to occur.

During the attentive state the activity of the fovea may be increased while that of the extrafoveal regions is depressed. In the amblyopia of strabismus this mechanism may be at fault. In support of this we have some evidence that the foveal system is actually depressed—e.g., the rela-

tive central scotoma found in some patients, the decreased pupillary reflex described by Harms, the decreased critical fusion frequency,[28] and the visual acuity of amblyopic eyes at various levels of illumination.[20] The methods of pleoptics which stimulate the fovea and depress the extrafoveal regions are also in line with this hypothesis.

Another suggestion of the origin of amblyopia which incriminates the retina as the primary site of the disturbance is the hypothesis that in strabismus the axes of the cones are not perpendicular to the pigment epithelium but are tilted, so that the light rays as they enter the eye are not funneled down to the cone outer segments. This conception includes as part of its mechanism the Stiles-Crawford effect (p. 774) and was first suggested by Enoch.

Evidence of this possibility is seen by Pugh in the fact that many patients with amblyopia have biased vision as part of their amblyopia. They describe the image of a single letter as asymmetrical in definition and brightness, in that one side of the letter is seen better than the other.[34]

REFERENCES

1. Linksz, A.: Vision. In Daveson, H., editor: Physiology of the eye, vol. 2, New York, 1952, Grune and Stratton, Inc., pp. 317-330.
2. Burian, H.: Sensorial retinal relationship in concomitant strabismus, Tr. Am. Ophth. Soc. **43:**373, 1945.
3. Stone, L.: Normal and reversed vision in transplanted eyes, Arch. Ophth. **42:**28, 1953.
4. Roelofs, C.: Considerations of the visual egocenter, Acta Psychologica **16:**226, 1959.
5. du Tour. Quoted by Asher, H.: Suppression theory of binocular vision, Brit. J. Ophth. **37:**37, 1953.
6. Charnwood, L.: Stereopsis in presence of diplopia, Brit. J. Physiol. Opt. **11:**8, 1954.

7. Roenne, G.: The physiological basis of sensory fusion, Acta ophth. **344:**1, 1956.
8. Ogle, K.: Stereoscopic acuity and the role of convergence, J. Optic. Soc. America **46:**260, 1956.
9. Ishak, I., Hefzalla, I., and Badawy, Y.: Role of convergence in stereoscopic vision, J. Optic. Soc. America **46:**303, 1956.
10. Ogle, K.: Observations on stereoscopic vision, Transactions of the Seventeenth International Congress of Ophthalmology, Toronto, 1955, Toronto Press, p. 1927.
11. Kirschberg, L.: Depth perception and flying ability, Arch. Ophth. **36:**155, 1946.
12. Andersen, E., and Weymouth, F.: Visual perception and retinal mosaic, Am. J. Physiol. **64:**561, 1923.
13. Marshall, W., and Talbot, S.: Recent evi-

dence for neural mechanisms in vision leading to general theory of sensory acuity, Biol. Symposia **7**:117, 1942.

14. Keesey, U.: Effects of involuntary eye movements on visual acuity, J. Optic. Soc. America **50**:769, 1960.

15. Ogle, K., and Weil, M.: Arch. Ophth. **59**:4, 1958.

16. Shortess, G., and Krauskopf, J.: Role of involuntary eye movements in stereoscopic acuity, J. Optic. Soc. America **51**:555, 1961.

17. Hess, E.: Space perception in the chick, Scient. Am., p. 71, July, 1956.

18. Ogle, K.: Present knowledge of stereoscopic vision, Arch. Ophth. **60**:770, 1958.

19. Chavasse, F.: Worth's squint, Philadelphia, 1939, Blakiston Co., p. 341.

20. von Noorden, G., and Burian, H.: Visual acuity in normal and amblyopic patients under reduced illumination, Arch. Ophth. **61**:533, 1959.

21. von Noorden, G., and Burian, H.: Visual acuity in normal and amblyopic patients under reduced illumination. II. The visual acuity at various levels of illumination, Arch. Ophth. **62**:396, 1959.

22. von Noorden, G., and Burian, H.: An electro-ophthalmographic study of the behavior of the fixation of amblyopic eyes in light and dark-adapted state, Am. J. Ophth. **46**:68, 1958.

23. Ludvigh, E.: A hypothesis concerning amblyopia ex anopsia, Transactions of the New England Ophthalmological Society, Arch. Ophth. **43**:397, 1950.

24. Wald, S., and Burian, H.: The dissociation of form vision and light perception in strabismic amblyopia, Am. J. Ophth. **27**: 950, 1944.

25. Fulton, J.: Physiology of the nervous system, London, 1943, Oxford University Press.

26. Dyer, D., and Bierman, E.: Cortical potential changes in suppression amblyopia, Am. J. Ophth. **35**:66, 1952.

27. Parsons-Smith, G.: Activity of the cerebral cortex in amblyopia, Brit. J. Ophth. **37**:359, 1953.

28. Feinberg, I.: Critical flicker frequency in amblyopia ex anopsia, Am. J. Ophth. **42**: 473, 1956.

29. Brock, F., and Givner, I.: Fixation anomalies in amblyopia, Arch. Ophth. **47**:775, 1952.

30. von Noorden, G., and Burian, H.: An electromyographic study of the fixation of amblyopic eyes, Am. J. Ophth. **46**:68, 1958.

31. Jones, L., and Higgins, G.: Some characteristics of the visual system of importance in the evaluation of graininess and granularity, J. Optic. Soc. America **37**:217, 1947.

32. Kupfer, C.: Amblyopia in adults, Am. J. Ophth. **43**:918, 1957.

33. van Balen, A., and Henkes, H.: Attention and amblyopia, Brit. J. Ophth. **46**: 12, 1962.

34. Pugh, M.: Amblyopia and the retina, Brit J. Ophth. **46**:193, 1962.

INDEX